Harper & Row ALGEBRA TWO with Trigonometry

Authors

MAX A. SOBEL

NORBERT LERNER

EVAN M. MALETSKY

LOUIS S. COHEN

1817 **HARPER & ROW, PUBLISHERS, INC.**

New York   Philadelphia   Cambridge   San Francisco   London

Authors

MAX A. SOBEL
Professor of Mathematics and Computer Science
Montclair State College
Montclair, New Jersey

EVAN M. MALETSKY
Professor of Mathematics and Computer Science
Montclair State College
Montclair, New Jersey

NORBERT LERNER
Professor of Mathematics
State University of New York
Cortland, New York

LOUIS S. COHEN
Teacher of Mathematics
Bloomington Jefferson High School
Bloomington, Minnesota

Editorial Advisors

Willie Beatrice Aldridge
Pontiac Schools
Pontiac, Michigan

Donald Hepp
Moon Junior High School
Coraopolis, Pennsylvania

Francis T. Sganga
Volusia County Schools
Daytona Beach, Florida

Winston Bradberry
Jones Valley High School
Birmingham, Alabama

Hilde Howden
Albuquerque Public Schools
Albuquerque, New Mexico

Sister Bette Gould
Diocese of Springfield
Springfield, Massachusetts

Sister Maureen M. Reardon
Diocesan School Office
Hartford, Connecticut

Acknowledgments

For permission to reprint copyrighted material, grateful acknowledgment is made to the *Mathematical Association of America* for problems from the American High School Mathematics Examinations, published by the Mathematical Association of America and reprinted by the M.A.A. Committee on High School Contests.

Page 22   Contest Problem Book IV, 1974 Examination Question 9;
            1973 Examination Question 29
Page 134   Contest Problem Book IV, 1973 Examination Question 2;
            1982 Examination Question 16
Page 295   Contest Problem Book I, 1954 Examination Question 20;
            1960 Examination Question 23
            Contest Problem Book III, 1966 Examination Questions 10, 30;
            1970 Examination Question 11

Cover Photo: Esto Photographics, Inc.: Wolfgang Hoyt
Illustrations by: Vantage Art, Inc.

ISBN 06-544002-1   84858687RRD0987654321

CONTENTS

Chapter 6:   Radical Expressions   **206**

Chapter 7:   Quadratic Equations and Functions   **236**

Chapter 8:   Polynomial Equations and Complex Numbers   **272**

Chapter 9:   Conic Sections   **314**

Chapter 10:   Exponential and Logarithmic Functions   **362**

Chapter 11:   Trigonometric Ratios **410**

Chapter 12:   Trigonometric Equations and Identities **466**

Chapter 13:   Circular Functions

Using the Calculator: *The Area of a Circular Sector*, 508;   Challenge: *Circular Functions on the Unit Circle*, 522;   Strategies for Problem Solving: *Changing the Coordinate System*, 538;   Applications: *Linear and Angular Speeds*, 539;   Computer Activity: *Trigonometric Functions*, 543

Prerequisite Skills Review, 503;   Checkpoint, 525, 533;   Chapter Review, 540;   Chapter Test, 542;   Cumulative Review, Chapters 1–13, 544

Chapter 14:   Sequences and Series

Strategies for Problem Solving: *Using Successive Differences*, 559;   Using the Calculator: *The Fibonacci Sequence*, 563;   Extra Topic: *Mathematical Induction*, 567; Applications: *Astronomy*, 577;   Computer Activity: *Simplifying a Radical*, 581

Prerequisite Skills Review, 547;   Checkpoint, 558, 572;   Chapter Review, 578;   Chapter Test, 580

Chapter 15:   Probability and Statistics

Chapter 16:   Matrices, Determinants, and Linear Systems **620**

Symbols

$=$	is equal to	$\log x$	logarithm of x to the base 10 (common logarithm)
$\neq$	is not equal to		
$<$	is less than	$\overrightarrow{AB}$	ray AB
$\leq$	is less than or equal to	$\angle CAB$	angle CAB
$>$	is greater than	$\overline{AB}$	segment AB
$\geq$	is greater than or equal to	$\triangle PQR$	triangle PQR
		$\circ$	degree(s)
$\approx$	is approximately equal to	$'$	minute(s)
$-r$	opposite or additive inverse of r	ω	omega; angular speed
$\dfrac{1}{x}$	reciprocal or multiplicative inverse of x, where $x \neq 0$	$P(E)$	probability that event E will occur
		$_nP_r$	number of permutations of n different things taken r at a time
$\lvert x \rvert$	absolute value of x		
$\pm$	plus or minus	$_nC_r$	number of combinations of n different things taken r at a time
b^n	nth power of b		
b^0	1, where $b \neq 0$	$!$	factorial
b^{-n}	$\dfrac{1}{b^n}$, where $b \neq 0$	$\overrightarrow{AB}$	vector AB
$b^{\frac{m}{n}}$	nth root of the mth power of b	$\lvert \overrightarrow{AB} \rvert$	magnitude of vector AB
		$\bar{x}$	arithmetic mean
$\sqrt{b}$	principal (positive) square root of b	Σ	sigma; summation symbol
$\sqrt[n]{b}$	nth root of b	s	standard deviation
$\{\ \}$	set	$A = \begin{bmatrix} a & b \\ c & d \end{bmatrix}$	matrix A
$0.\overline{3}$	repeating decimal 0.3333 . . .	$-A$	additive inverse of matrix A
π	pi, approximately 3.14		
i	imaginary unit $(i = \sqrt{-1},\ i^2 = -1)$	A^{-1}	multiplicative inverse of matrix A
$f(x)$	value of the function f at x; f of x	$\det A = \begin{vmatrix} a & b \\ c & d \end{vmatrix}$	determinant of matrix A
$[x]$	greatest integer function	Greek letters:	α (alpha), β (beta), γ (gamma), θ (theta), ϕ (phi)
$\log_b x$	logarithm of x to the base b		

Harper & Row **ALGEBRA TWO** with **Trigonometry**

CHAPTER 1

Numerical data obtained by engineers and technicians are used, with
appropriate equations and formulas, in the monitoring of industrial processes.

REAL NUMBERS, EQUATIONS, AND INEQUALITIES

Prerequisite Skills Review

Write the letter for the correct answer.

1. $1.06 = \underline{\ ?\ }$

    a. $\dfrac{16}{100}$ **b.** $1\dfrac{3}{10}$ **c.** $1\dfrac{6}{100}$ **d.** $1\dfrac{6}{10}$

2. $\dfrac{36}{25} = \underline{\ ?\ }$

    a. 1.44 **b.** 1.4 **c.** $1.\overline{4}$ **d.** none of these

3. $\dfrac{1}{18} = \underline{\ ?\ }$

    a. $0.0\overline{5}$ **b.** 0.08 **c.** $0.\overline{5}$ **d.** none of these

4. $\left(\dfrac{2}{3}\right)^4 = \underline{\ ?\ }$

    a. $\dfrac{8}{81}$ **b.** $\dfrac{16}{81}$ **c.** $\dfrac{16}{3}$ **d.** $\dfrac{8}{12}$

5. $\dfrac{2}{3} + \dfrac{3}{4} = \underline{\ ?\ }$

    a. $\dfrac{5}{7}$ **b.** $\dfrac{5}{12}$ **c.** $\dfrac{17}{24}$ **d.** $\dfrac{17}{12}$

6. $1\dfrac{3}{10} - \dfrac{1}{2} = \underline{\ ?\ }$

    a. $1\dfrac{1}{5}$ **b.** $\dfrac{2}{5}$ **c.** $\dfrac{4}{5}$ **d.** $1\dfrac{1}{2}$

7. $\dfrac{3}{4} \div \dfrac{2}{3} = \underline{\ ?\ }$

    a. $\dfrac{1}{2}$ **b.** $1\dfrac{1}{8}$ **c.** $\dfrac{8}{9}$ **d.** 2

8. $27.8 - 1.05 = \underline{\ ?\ }$

    a. 1.73 **b.** 2.675 **c.** 17.3 **d.** 26.75

9. $0.5 \times 4.8 = \underline{\ ?\ }$

    a. 0.024 **b.** 0.24 **c.** 2.4 **d.** 24

10. $0.4 \div 0.16 = \underline{\ ?\ }$

    a. 2.5 **b.** 0.4 **c.** 0.25 **d.** 4

1-1 Numbers and Expressions

OBJECTIVES _____

To identify whole numbers, integers, rational numbers, and irrational numbers.
To simplify numerical expressions, using the correct order of operations.
To evaluate algebraic expressions for given values of the variables.

_____

Recall these important sets of numbers.

- The **whole numbers** are the *natural*, or *counting*, *numbers and zero*.

$$\{0, 1, 2, 3, 4, \ldots\}$$

- The **integers** are the whole numbers and their *opposites*.

$$\{\ldots, -4, -3, -2, -1, 0, 1, 2, 3, 4, \ldots\}$$

- The **rational numbers** are all numbers that can be represented by a ratio, $\frac{a}{b}$, where a and b are integers and $b \neq 0$.

$$3 = \frac{3}{1} \qquad 2\frac{1}{4} = \frac{9}{4} \qquad -\frac{2}{3} = \frac{-2}{3} = \frac{2}{-3} \qquad 0.5 = \frac{5}{10} = \frac{1}{2}$$

- The **real numbers** are all numbers that have decimal representations. Those with decimals that *terminate* or *repeat* are also rational numbers.

$$\frac{13}{8} = 1.625000 \ldots = 1.625 \qquad \frac{3}{11} = 0.272727 \ldots = 0.\overline{27}$$

- Those with decimals that do not repeat are **irrational numbers.** π and $\sqrt{7}$ are examples of irrational numbers. They have rounded decimal approximations, but they cannot be written exactly as decimals.

$$\pi = 3.1416 \leftarrow \text{rounded to four decimal places} \rightarrow \sqrt{7} = 2.6458$$

A **numerical expression** may be a single number, or it may be two or more numbers combined by mathematical operations. Every numerical expression has a unique value.

$$12 + 2 = 14 \qquad 6 \times 2\frac{1}{2} = 15 \qquad 4 \div 0.25 = 16$$

Some expressions involve exponents. In 5^2, for example, 5 is the **base** and 2 is the **exponent.**

$$5^2 = 5 \times 5 = 25 \qquad \text{The value of 5 \textbf{squared} is 25.}$$
The second **power** of 5 is 25.

$$2^3 = 2 \times 2 \times 2 = 8 \qquad \text{The value of 2 \textbf{cubed} is 8.}$$
The third **power** of 2 is 8.

When an expression includes more than one operation, grouping symbols such as parentheses and brackets can be used. They show the order in which the operations should be done. The following rules will help you find the correct value of a numerical expression, or *simplify* the expression.

1. Simplify within grouping symbols first, when they occur, starting with the innermost grouping.
2. Do the operations in the following order.
   a. Raise numbers to given powers.
   b. Multiply and divide, from left to right.
   c. Add and subtract, from left to right.

EXAMPLE 1   Simplify.

$$\textbf{a. } 10 - [8 - (4 + 1)] = 10 - [8 - 5] \qquad \text{Add within the } \textit{parentheses} \text{ first.}$$
$$= 10 - 3 \qquad\qquad\qquad \text{Then subtract within the } \textit{brackets}.$$
$$= 7$$

$$\textbf{b. } 28 \div 14 + 3^2 - 2 \times 5 = 28 \div 14 + 9 - 2 \times 5 \qquad \text{Square the 3 first.}$$
$$= 2 + 9 - 10 \qquad \text{Multiply and divide, from left to right.}$$
$$= 1 \qquad \text{Add and subtract, from left to right.}$$

The division bar can also be used as a grouping symbol.

EXAMPLE 2   Simplify $\frac{3 \times 4^3}{7 - 1}$.

$$\frac{3 \times 4^3}{7 - 1} = \frac{3 \times 64}{6} = \frac{192}{6} = 32 \qquad \text{First simplify above and below the division bar.}$$

A **variable** is a placeholder for a number. Expressions that contain variables are called **algebraic expressions.** You can *evaluate* an algebraic expression when specific values of the variables are given. First replace each variable with its numerical value and then simplify the resulting numerical expression.

Note that multiplication can be shown in various ways within algebraic expressions. To illustrate, 3 times n may be written in any of these forms.

$$3 \times n \qquad 3 \cdot n \qquad 3n \qquad 3(n) \qquad (3)n \qquad (3)(n)$$

EXAMPLE 3   Evaluate $(2m - 3) \cdot 6$ for $m = 5$.

$$(2m - 3) \cdot 6 = (2 \cdot 5 - 3) \cdot 6 = (10 - 3) \cdot 6 = 7 \cdot 6 = 42$$

REAL NUMBERS, EQUATIONS, AND INEQUALITIES

EXAMPLE 4   Evaluate for x = 18 and y = $\frac{3}{2}$.

$$\textbf{a. } (\textbf{x} \div \textbf{y}) + \textbf{3} = \left(18 \div \frac{3}{2}\right) + 3 = \left(18 \cdot \frac{2}{3}\right) + 3 = 12 + 3 = 15$$

$$\textbf{b. } \textbf{x} \div (\textbf{y} + \textbf{3}) = 18 \div \left(\frac{3}{2} + 3\right) = 18 \div \frac{9}{2} = 18 \cdot \frac{2}{9} = 4$$

CLASS EXERCISES

Simplify.

1. $6 - 3 - 1$ **2.** $4 \cdot 3 + 2$ **3.** $5 + 2 \cdot 4$ **4.** $2 \cdot 3^2$

5. $6 - 2^2$ **6.** $\dfrac{9 + 15}{3}$ **7.** $3(18 - 12)$ **8.** $10 \div (7 - 2)$

*Evaluate for **n** = 3.*

9. $5n + 1$ **10.** n^3 **11.** $15 + 2n$ **12.** $n(n + 1)$

13. $7 - 2n$ **14.** $(n + 1)^2$ **15.** $\dfrac{4n - 2}{5}$ **16.** $6n - (n + 2)$

EXERCISES

A   *Given the real numbers* $\frac{1}{2}$, $\sqrt{2}$, 2, −0.22, 2.$\overline{2}$, *and* −2, *list those that are*

1. whole numbers.   **2.** integers.

3. rational numbers.   **4.** irrational numbers.

*Write **true** or **false**. If the statement is false, give an example where it does not hold.*

5. Every integer is a rational number.

6. Every rational number is an integer.

7. Every real number is either rational or irrational.

8. Every real number can be expressed exactly as a terminating or repeating decimal.

Simplify.

9. $12 - (5 - 2)$ **10.** $12(5 - 2)$ **11.** $12 \div (5 - 2)$

12. $(3 + 4)6$ **13.** $3 + 4 \cdot 6$ **14.** $3 \cdot 4 + 6$

15. $12 \cdot 8 - 4$ **16.** $12(8 - 4)$ **17.** $12 - (8 - 4)$

18. $6[8 - 2 \cdot 3]$ **19.** $6[8(3 - 2)]$ **20.** $6[(8 - 2)3]$

21. $5 \cdot 4^2$

22. $(5 \cdot 4)^2$

23. $5^2 \cdot 4$

24. $2(7 - 3)^2$

25. $2 \cdot 7 - 3^2$

26. $[2(7 - 3)]^2$

27. $\dfrac{10(10 - 3)}{12 - 5}$

28. $\dfrac{10^2 - 2}{(12 - 5)^2}$

29. $\dfrac{20^2 - (200 - 10^2)}{12 \cdot 5^2}$

Evaluate for $n = 5$.

30. $n^2 - 2$

31. $(n - 2)^2$

32. $n - 2^2$

33. $13 - (8 - n)$

34. $(13 - 8) - n$

35. $(13 - 8)n$

36. $n(n^2 + 5)$

37. $n + 5n^2$

38. $5(n^2 + n)$

B *Simplify.*

39. $2 - \left(\dfrac{1}{4} - \dfrac{1}{8}\right)$

40. $\dfrac{1}{2}\left(1 - \dfrac{1}{4}\right)^2$

41. $\dfrac{1}{4} - \left(\dfrac{1}{2}\right)^2$

42. $\dfrac{1}{4} \div \left(\dfrac{1}{2}\right)^2$

43. $\left(\dfrac{1}{4} \div \dfrac{1}{2}\right) \div \dfrac{1}{2}$

44. $\dfrac{1}{4} \div \left(\dfrac{1}{2} \div \dfrac{1}{2}\right)$

45. $4 - \left[1 - \left(\dfrac{1}{2} - \dfrac{1}{4}\right)\right]$

46. $8\left[4\left(\dfrac{1}{2} \div \dfrac{1}{4}\right)\right]$

47. $\left[2\left(4 - \dfrac{1}{4}\right) - \dfrac{1}{2}\right]4$

48. $4 \div \dfrac{1}{2} - \dfrac{1}{8} \cdot 2^2$

49. $8 + \left(\dfrac{1}{4}\right)^2 \div \dfrac{1}{2} - \dfrac{1}{8}$

50. $\dfrac{1}{4}\left(4 \div \dfrac{1}{2}\right)^2 - 8$

Evaluate for $a = 3$ and $b = 4$.

51. $a(b + 2)$

52. $2(a + b)$

53. $a + 2b$

54. $b - a + 2$

55. $b \div 2 + a$

56. $(a + 2)(b + 2)$

57. $a^2 + b$

58. $(a + b)^2$

59. $a + b^2$

60. $a(b \div a)$

61. $b + (a \div b)$

62. $a - (b \div a)$

63. $\dfrac{b + 5}{a^2}$

64. $\dfrac{a^2 + b^2}{5}$

65. $\dfrac{(b + a)^2}{b^2 - a^2}$

C Write an expression that has the given value. Use each of the numbers 2, 3, 4, and 5 exactly once. Also use one or more of the operations symbols $+$, $-$, $\times$, and $\div$, and any necessary grouping symbols.

Sample $12 = 2(3 + 5) - 4$

66. 6

67. 120

68. 4

69. 21

70. 42

71. 5

72. 70

73. 30

74. 13

75. 16

76. 100

77. 23

1-2 Addition and Subtraction

OBJECTIVES _____

To find the sum or difference of two real numbers.
To evaluate algebraic expressions involving addition and subtraction for
   given values of the variables.

_____

Recall that the points to the right of 0 on the number line represent
positive real numbers. The points to the left of 0 represent *negative* real
numbers. Zero is neither positive nor negative.

If two real numbers are positive,
their sum is positive.

$$1.2 + 1.6 = 2.8$$

If two real numbers are negative,
their sum is negative.

$$-3 + \left(-\tfrac{1}{2}\right) = -3\tfrac{1}{2}$$

If one real number is positive
and the other is negative, their
sum may be positive, negative,
or zero. The sign of the sum depends on which number is farther from the origin. If they are
both the same distance from 0,
the sum is 0.

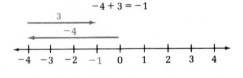

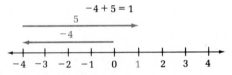

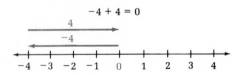

Zero is the **additive identity.** If 0 is added to any real number, r, the
sum is that number, r.

$$8 + 0 = 8 \qquad 0 + (-3) = -3 \qquad 0 + 0 = 0$$

Two numbers located the same distance from 0 on the number line,
but on opposite sides, are **opposites,** or **additive inverses.** The sum of a
real number r, and its opposite, −r, is 0. Zero is its own opposite.

$$7 + (-7) = 0 \qquad -2 + 2 = 0 \qquad 0 + 0 = 0$$

EXAMPLE 1   Add: $-5 + 3 + 2 + (-1)$

Add from left to right.

$$\underbrace{-5 + 3}_{} + 2 + (-1)$$

$$\underbrace{-2 + 2}_{} + (-1) \qquad -2 \text{ and } 2 \text{ are additive inverses.}$$

$$\underbrace{0 + (-1)}_{} \qquad \text{Zero is the additive identity.}$$

$$-1$$

To subtract a number, add its opposite, or additive inverse.

> **For all real numbers r and s**
>
> $$r - s = r + (-s)$$

The difference can be positive, zero, or negative, depending on the numbers.

$$-4 - (-3) = -4 + (+3) = -1$$
$$-4 - (-4) = -4 + (+4) = 0$$
$$-4 - (-5) = -4 + (+5) = 1$$

EXAMPLE 2   Subtract.

a. $3 - 4.5 = 3 + (-4.5) = -1.5$

b. $-1.6 - 5.2 = -1.6 + (-5.2) = -6.8$

c. $-\dfrac{1}{2} - (-8) = -\dfrac{1}{2} + 8 = 7\dfrac{1}{2}$

d. $0 - (-16) = 0 + 16 = 16$

EXAMPLE 3   Evaluate for $a = -2$, $b = -7$, and $c = 4$.

a. $a + b - c = -2 + (-7) - 4 = -9 - 4 = -13$

b. $c - (b - a) = 4 - [-7 - (-2)] = 4 - (-5) = 9$

The **absolute value** of any real number x is the distance between x and 0 on the number line. The symbol $|x|$ means the *absolute value of x*.

$$|-4| = 4 \qquad |3| = 3 \qquad |0| = 0$$

Absolute values can be used to summarize the rules for adding real numbers.

> To add two numbers with the *same sign*, add their absolute values. Give the sum the same sign as the two numbers.
>
> To add two numbers with *different signs*, subtract their absolute values, starting with the greater absolute value. Give the sum the same sign as the number with the greater absolute value. If the numbers are additive inverses, their sum is 0.

EXAMPLE 4   Add, using the absolute value rules.

a. $-4 + 5.5 = (|5.5| - |-4|)$ 5.5 has the greater absolute value.
$\qquad\qquad = (5.5 - 4)$ The sum is positive.
$\qquad\qquad = 1.5$

b. $-6\dfrac{1}{2} + 3 = -(|-6\dfrac{1}{2}| - |3|)$ $-6\dfrac{1}{2}$ has the greater absolute value.
$\qquad\qquad = -(6\dfrac{1}{2} - 3)$ The sum is negative.
$\qquad\qquad = -3\dfrac{1}{2}$

CLASS EXERCISES

Simplify.

1. $6 + (-9)$

2. $-4 + (-17)$

3. $-18 + 25$

4. $-5 - 7$

5. $13 - 21$

6. $-11 - (-10)$

7. $-\dfrac{1}{5} - \dfrac{3}{5}$

8. $-\dfrac{3}{10} - \left(-\dfrac{3}{10}\right)$

9. $\dfrac{1}{8} - \left(-\dfrac{1}{2}\right)$

EXERCISES

A   *Simplify.*

1. $-12 + 5$

2. $-8 + (-18)$

3. $40 + (-54)$

4. $-1 + (-11) + 10$

5. $-3 + 16 + (-5)$

6. $14 + 8 + (-22)$

7. $60 + (-12) + (-72)$

8. $-9 + (-6) + (-23)$

9. $-100 + 35 + 0$

10. $6 - 19$

11. $-8 - 11$

12. $15 - (-5)$

13. $-5 - (-3) - 2$

14. $20 - 16 - 50$

15. $-7 - 4 - 8$

16. $9 + (-9) - (-9)$ **17.** $-18 - (-18) - 4$ **18.** $60 - (-16) - 66$

19. $-6 + 3 - 5$ **20.** $-18 + 6 - 14$ **21.** $-7 + (-4) - 11$

22. $1 - (5 + 3)$ **23.** $1 - (5 - 3)$ **24.** $1 - (3 - 5)$

25. $12 - (8 - 9)$ **26.** $42 - (-5 + 9)$ **27.** $-17 - (3 - 8)$

28. $-30 - (-10 + 12)$ **29.** $-4 - [-14 - (-5)]$ **30.** $45 - [13 - (-84)]$

31. $-4 + 6 + (-17)$ **32.** $-3 - (-9) - 15 - 7$ **33.** $6 - 11 + (-3) - 5$

B

34. $1\frac{1}{2} - \frac{1}{4} + \left(-\frac{3}{4}\right)$ **35.** $-\frac{3}{4} - \left(-\frac{1}{2}\right) + \frac{1}{4}$ **36.** $3\frac{1}{5} - \frac{1}{2} - 4\frac{1}{10}$

37. $\frac{2}{3} - \left(\frac{1}{6} - \frac{1}{3}\right)$ **38.** $-\frac{7}{8} - \left(-\frac{1}{4} + \frac{3}{8}\right)$ **39.** $2\frac{4}{5} - \left[\frac{3}{10} - \left(-1\frac{1}{2}\right)\right]$

Evaluate for $a = 1.2$, $b = -3$, and $c = -1.5$.

40. $a + b + c$ **41.** $b - c - a$ **42.** $c - (b - a)$

43. $a - (c - b)$ **44.** $b - (a - c)$ **45.** $(a - b) - (b - c)$

What can be substituted for n that makes the statement true?

46. $n + y = y$ **47.** $n + y = 0$ **48.** $y - n = 0$

49. $n + y = y - n$ **50.** $n - y = y - n$ **51.** $y - (n - y) = y$

52. What number must be added to -9 to give a sum of 5?

53. What number must be subtracted from -3 to give a difference of 4.5?

54. What number must be added to the sum of -6 and 7.2 to give -8?

55. A newspaper lists a stock as closing at $20\frac{3}{4}$ following a drop of $1\frac{5}{8}$ that day. What was the opening price for the day?

56. A stock opened the week at $39\frac{1}{4}$. The daily changes for the next five days were $+\frac{1}{2}$, $-\frac{1}{4}$, $-\frac{3}{8}$, $-1\frac{1}{2}$, and $\frac{3}{4}$. What was the closing price at the end of the week?

C

Simplify, using the absolute value rules for addition.

57. $-14 + 41$ **58.** $-112 + 16.5$ **59.** $-8.8 + 6.9$

60. $5\frac{1}{2} + \left(-1\frac{3}{4}\right)$ **61.** $5 - 7.8$ **62.** $-3\frac{1}{4} - 2$

63. $\left(-\frac{1}{2} + \frac{1}{4}\right) - \frac{1}{8}$ **64.** $-\frac{3}{4} + \left(-\frac{2}{3} + \frac{1}{2}\right)$ **65.** $-\frac{5}{6} + \frac{1}{3} - \frac{1}{2}$

1-3 Multiplication and Division

OBJECTIVES

To find the product or the quotient of two real numbers.
To evaluate algebraic expressions involving multiplication and division for
   given values of the variables.

If two real numbers are both positive or both negative, their product
and their quotient are positive.

EXAMPLE 1 Simplify.

   a. $(-16)(-6) = 96$ **b.** $\dfrac{-20}{-2.5} = 8$

If one number is positive and the other negative, their product and
their quotient are negative.

EXAMPLE 2 Simplify.

   a. $3(-24) = -72$ **b.** $\dfrac{\frac{1}{2}}{-4} = -\dfrac{1}{8}$

> To multiply or divide two real numbers, multiply or divide their abso-
> lute values. If the two numbers have the *same sign*, their product and
> their quotient are positive. If they have *different signs*, their product
> and their quotient are negative.

When using several operations, be sure to perform them in the correct order.

EXAMPLE 3 Evaluate for $p = -1.2$, $q = -3$, and $r = 0.5$.

   a. $pq - r = -1.2(-3) - 0.5 = 3.6 - 0.5 = 3.1$

   b. $\dfrac{pq + qr}{pr} = \dfrac{-1.2(-3) + (-3)(0.5)}{-1.2(0.5)} = \dfrac{3.6 + (-1.5)}{-0.6} = \dfrac{2.1}{-0.6} = -3.5$

The number 1 is the multiplicative identity. The product of 1 and
any real number r is that number, r. The product of -1 and any real
number r is the opposite of that number, $-r$. The product of 0 and any
real number r is 0.

   $1(-7) = -7$ $-\dfrac{1}{3}(-1) = \dfrac{1}{3}$ $0(9) = 0$

The **multiplicative inverse** of any nonzero real number r is its reciprocal, $\frac{1}{r}$. Zero is the one number that has no reciprocal. The product of any real number and its reciprocal is 1.

$$15\left(\frac{1}{15}\right) = 1 \qquad -\frac{2}{3}\left(-\frac{3}{2}\right) = 1 \qquad \frac{1}{9}(9) = 1$$

EXAMPLE 4   Evaluate for $k = 1$, $m = -1$, and $n = 0$.

a. $3k + (-5m) - 4n = 3(1) + (-5)(-1) - 4(0) = 3 + 5 - 0 = 8$

b. $\dfrac{-2km + 3mn}{km} = \dfrac{-2(1)(-1) + 3(-1)(0)}{1(-1)} = \dfrac{2 + 0}{-1} = -2$

c. $\dfrac{k - m}{k + m} = \dfrac{1 - (-1)}{1 + (-1)} = \dfrac{2}{0}$ The expression cannot be evaluated, since division by zero is not defined.

When a real number is raised to an even power, the product is positive. When such a number is raised to an odd power, the product has the same sign as the base.

EXAMPLE 5   Simplify.

a. $(-2)^6 = -2(-2)(-2)(-2)(-2)(-2) = 64$ The exponent is even, so the product is positive.

b. $(-5)^3 = -5(-5)(-5) = -125$ The exponent is odd and the base is negative, so the product is negative.

c. $\left(\dfrac{1}{3}\right)^5 = \dfrac{1}{3}\left(\dfrac{1}{3}\right)\left(\dfrac{1}{3}\right)\left(\dfrac{1}{3}\right)\left(\dfrac{1}{3}\right) = \dfrac{1}{243}$ When the base is positive the product must be positive.

CLASS EXERCISES

Simplify.

1. $6(-9)$ **2.** $-5(-7)$ **3.** $-1(121)$ **4.** $-15(-12)$

5. $18(-4)$ **6.** $-\dfrac{1}{2}(-38)$ **7.** $\dfrac{0}{-3}$ **8.** $\dfrac{-120}{-24}$

9. $(-2)^3$ **10.** $-(-2)^3$ **11.** -2^3 **12.** $-1(-3 - 2)$

EXERCISES

A   *Simplify.*

1. $7(-8)$ **2.** $-6(-12)$ **3.** $-5(-3)(4)$ **4.** $-2(-11)(-10)$

5. $\dfrac{15}{-3}$ **6.** $\dfrac{-27}{9}$ **7.** $\dfrac{-200}{-5}$ **8.** $\dfrac{-2(-8)}{-4}$

9. $2(6 - 7)$ **10.** $-3(8 - 14)$ **11.** $-2[3 - (-4)]$ **12.** $(-2)^7$

13. $(-5)^4$ **14.** -13^2 **15.** $-(-6)^3$ **16.** $-7(2)^3$

17. $16(-5 + 5)$ **18.** $\dfrac{5 - (-11)}{8(-2)}$ **19.** $\dfrac{-18(-6)}{3(-9)}$ **20.** $\dfrac{-3(-4)(-5)}{-15}$

B

21. $\dfrac{4(-3) - 5(-4)}{2(-5)}$ **22.** $\dfrac{(8 - 7)(9 - 5)}{4 - 11}$ **23.** $\dfrac{-6 - 3 - (-5)}{-8 - 4 - (-9)}$

24. $\dfrac{\dfrac{3(-6)}{-2}}{6 - 3 - 9}$ **25.** $\dfrac{\dfrac{4 - 5}{5 - 6}}{-3(2 - 7)}$ **26.** $\dfrac{\dfrac{2(3 - 4)}{3(2 - 4)}}{4(2 - 3)}$

Evaluate, if possible, for $a = -\frac{1}{2}$, $b = -2$, and $c = 2$.

27. abc **28.** $a(b - c)$ **29.** $ab - ac$

30. $\dfrac{c(a + b)}{b(c - a)}$ **31.** $\dfrac{a - b - c}{a + b + c}$ **32.** $\dfrac{ac + bc}{ab + ac}$

33. $2a - 3b - 4c$ **34.** $3a(b - 4c)$ **35.** $4c + 2(a - 3b)$

36. $b(a + c)$ **37.** $\dfrac{b + c}{b - c}$ **38.** $\dfrac{b - c}{4a + c}$

Evaluate for $x = 0.1$ and $y = -1.5$.

39. $x^2 - y^2$ **40.** $(x + y)(x - y)$ **41.** $(x - y)^2$

42. $\dfrac{x + y}{x - y}$ **43.** $\dfrac{x^2 + y^2}{x^2}$ **44.** $\dfrac{(y + x)^2}{(y - x)}$

45. What number must be multiplied by -2 to give a product of 5?

46. What number must be added to the product of -3 and -4.2 to give -10?

47. A clock loses 25 seconds a day. At this rate, how many days will it take for the clock to lose one hour?

48. What is the sum of the first ten counting numbers and their opposites?

49. What is the product of the first ten counting numbers and their reciprocals?

C

*Tell whether each equation is **true** or **false**.*

50. $15(-5) = -(|\,15\,|\cdot|-5\,|)$ **51.** $-15(-5) = |-15\,|\cdot|-5\,|$

52. $-15(5) = |-15\,|\cdot|\,5\,|$ **53.** $-15 \div 5 = -(|-15\,| \div |\,5\,|)$

54. $15 \div (-5) = |\,15\,| \div |-5\,|$ **55.** $-15 \div (-5) = |-15\,| \div |\,5\,|$

1-4 Properties of Real Numbers

OBJECTIVES

To tell whether two expressions are equal or not equal, using properties of the real numbers.

To compute mentally using the properties.

The basic properties for addition and multiplication of real numbers are summarized below.

For all real numbers r, s, and t

	Addition	Multiplication
Closure Properties	$r + s$ is a unique real number.	rs is a unique real number.
Commutative Properties	$r + s = s + r$	$rs = sr$
Associative Properties	$r + (s + t) = (r + s) + t$	$r(st) = (rs)t$
Identity Properties	$r + 0 = 0 + r = r$	$r \cdot 1 = 1 \cdot r = r$
Inverse Properties	$r + (-r) = -r + r = 0$	$r \cdot \frac{1}{r} = \frac{1}{r} \cdot r = 1$ $(r \neq 0)$

Distributive Property of Multiplication over Addition

$$r(s + t) = rs + rt \quad \text{and} \quad (s + t)r = sr + tr$$

EXAMPLE 1

Tell whether the two expressions are equal or not equal. If they are equal, identify the property illustrated.

a. $-3 + 8$ and $-8 + 3$

Do not mistake this for an illustration of the commutative property for addition. The expressions are *not equal*.

$-3 + 8 = 5$ and $-8 + 3 = -5$. Therefore $-3 + 8 \neq -8 + 3$.

b. $7(2 - 5)$ and $7(2) - 7(5)$

Using the definition of subtraction and the distributive property for multiplication over addition, we see that the expressions are *equal*.

$$7(2 - 5) = 7[2 + (-5)] = 7(2) + 7(-5) = 7(2) - 7(5)$$

This may be verified by simplifying both expressions.

$$7(2 - 5) = 7(-3) = -21 \qquad 7(2) - 7(5) = 14 - 35 = -21$$

Example **1b** illustrates the fact that *multiplication is distributive over subtraction* as well as over addition.

The commutative properties allow the order of *numbers* to be changed in addition or in multiplication. The associative properties allow the order of *operations* to be changed in addition and also in multiplication. These properties are especially useful in mental calculations.

EXAMPLE 2   Simplify.

a. **12 + 18 − 5 + 6 − 25**

Group the positive numbers and the negative numbers separately for easiest computation.

$(12 + 18 + 6) + [(−5) + (−25)] = 36 + (−30) = 6$

b. **4 · 8 · 25 · 7**

Group 4 and 25 to obtain a convenient factor of 100.

$(4 · 25)(8 · 7) = 100(56) = 5600$

CLASS EXERCISES

Identify the property illustrated.

1. $(−8 + 8) + 4 = −8 + (8 + 4)$ **2.** $(−8 + 8) + 4 = [8 + (−8)] + 4$

3. $(−8 + 8) + 4 = 0 + 4$ **4.** $4\left(\dfrac{1}{4}\right) + 0 = \dfrac{1}{4}(4) + 0$ **5.** $4\left(\dfrac{1}{4}\right) + 0 = 1 + 0$

6. $4\left(\dfrac{1}{4}\right) + 0 = 4\left(\dfrac{1}{4}\right)$ **7.** $6(4 + 7) = 6(4) + 6(7)$ **8.** $6(4 + 7) = (4 + 7)6$

EXERCISES

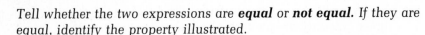

A   *Tell whether the two expressions are **equal** or **not equal**. If they are equal, identify the property illustrated.*

1. $6(−7)$ and $−7(6)$ **2.** $−17 + 0$ and $−17$

3. $18 − 35$ and $35 − 18$ **4.** $7(−3 + 5)$ and $−3(7 + 5)$

5. $\dfrac{1}{5}(5)(37)$ and $0(37)$ **6.** $1\dfrac{1}{2}\left(\dfrac{2}{3}\right)(−6)$ and $−6$

7. $−138 + 138$ and 0 **8.** $−6.1 + (2.8 + 4)$ and $4 + (−6.1 + 2.8)$

9. $8(−8)$ and $0 + 1$ **10.** $1 + (−13)(5)$ and $(−13)(5)$

11. $6(3) + (−9)(3)$ and $[6 + (−9)]3$ **12.** $7(−2)\left(−\dfrac{1}{2}\right)$ and $7(1)$

13. $3(4) + 5(6)$ and $3(5) + 4(6)$ **14.** $5(6 + 7)$ and $5(7 + 6)$

15. $-6[6 + (-19)]$ and $-6(6) + (-19)$ **16.** $15 - 8(2)$ and $15 - 2(8)$

17. Simplify $(13 - 4) - 7$ and $13 - (4 - 7)$.
Does an associative property hold for subtraction?

18. Simplify $48 \div 3$ and $3 \div 48$.
Does a commutative property hold for division?

19. Simplify $(24 \div 4) \div 2$ and $24 \div (4 \div 2)$.
Does an associative property hold for division?

20. Simplify $-3 - (-4)$ and $-4 - (-3)$.
Does a commutative property hold for subtraction?

B   *Simplify mentally.*

21. $6 + 17 + 3 + 4$ **22.** $28 + 5 + 72 + 95$ **23.** $5 \times 13 \times 2$

24. $7 \times 25 \times 4$ **25.** $12 + (-2) + 3 - 13$ **26.** $16 - 18 + 14 - 22$

27. $-\dfrac{5}{3} + \dfrac{1}{2} + \dfrac{2}{3} + \dfrac{5}{2}$ **28.** $-14(18)\left(-\dfrac{1}{7}\right)\left(\dfrac{1}{9}\right)$ **29.** $8(-4)(-25)(-5)$

State which pairs of expressions are equal for all real values of the variables.

30. $(x + y)z$ and $x + yz$ **31.** $m(k + 2)$ and $m(2 + k)$

32. $(-p + p) + q$ and $0 + q$ **33.** $s + tu$ and $t + su$

34. $(jk + 5k) \cdot 1$ and $jk + 5k$ **35.** $y - x$ and $x - y$

36. $(rs) \cdot 0$ and rs **37.** $m + (n + 3)$ and $(m + n) + 3$

38. $x(yz)$ and $(xy)z$ **39.** $x + \dfrac{1}{x}$ and 1

C

40. Give an example to show that addition is not distributive over multiplication.
Hint: Choose values for r, s, and t so that $r + (s \cdot t) \neq (r + s)(r + t)$.

*41. Supply a reason for each step of this proof that $x[(y + z) + w] = (w + y)x + zx$ for all real values of the variables.

$$
\begin{array}{ll}
 & \textbf{Reason} \\
x[(y + z) + w] = x(y + z) + xw & \underline{\quad ? \quad} \\
 = (xy + xz) + xw & \underline{\quad ? \quad} \\
 = xw + (xy + xz) & \underline{\quad ? \quad} \\
 = (xw + xy) + xz & \underline{\quad ? \quad} \\
 = x(w + y) + xz & \underline{\quad ? \quad} \\
 = (w + y)x + zx & \underline{\quad ? \quad}
\end{array}
$$

1-5 Simplifying Algebraic Expressions

OBJECTIVES _____

To identify terms, coefficients, and constants in algebraic expressions.
To simplify expressions by combining like terms.

_____

Special names are given to various parts of an algebraic expression.
Study the following illustrations.

7x $\begin{cases} \end{cases}$ 7x is an algebraic expression with just one *term*, 7x.
A **term** is a single number or variable, or an indicated
product or quotient of numbers and variables. 7 is the
numerical coefficient, or **coefficient,** of 7x.

xy + 6 − 5y $\begin{cases} \end{cases}$ xy + 6 − 5y is an algebraic expression with three
terms, xy, 6, and −5y. The coefficient of xy is 1. The
coefficient of −5y is −5. The **constant term,** or
constant, is 6.

EXAMPLE 1   Write the terms in the expression $3x^2y - x - 8$. Identify the
coefficient of the x-term and identify the constant.

The *terms* are $3x^2y$, −x, and −8.
The *coefficient* of the term −x is −1.
The *constant* is −8.

Like terms are constants, terms that are identical, or terms that differ
only in their numerical coefficients. All others are **unlike terms.**

Pairs of Like Terms	**Pairs of Unlike Terms**
7 and 3	7 and 3x
5x and 5x	5x and 5y
$-x^2y$ and $7x^2y$	$-x^2y$ and $7xy^2$
$6xyz^2$ and xyz^2	$6xyz^2$ and xyz^3

Some algebraic expressions can be simplified by combining like
terms. An algebraic expression of the type considered here is said to be
simplified when the following conditions are met.

• The expression contains no grouping symbols, such as parentheses.

• All like terms containing variables have been combined.

• Constant terms have been combined, if possible.

To combine like terms, we use the distributive property.

EXAMPLE 2   Simplify.

a. $3x + 4 + 5y - 7 - x$ $= (3x - x) + 5y + (4 - 7)$ Regroup.

$= (3 - 1)x + 5y - 3$ Combine like terms.

$= 2x + 5y - 3$

b. $4(x^3 - 2x^2y) + 3x^2y$ $= 4x^3 - 8x^2y + 3x^2y$ Remove the parentheses. Use the distributive property.

$= 4x^3 + (-8 + 3)x^2y$ Combine like terms.

$= 4x^3 - 5x^2y$

When an algebraic expression is simplified, an **equivalent expression** is formed. The expressions have the same value for every possible replacement of each variable.

EXAMPLE 3   Evaluate $4x^2 + 6xy - 5x^2$ for $x = -2$ and $y = 3$

a. by direct substitution.

$4x^2 + 6xy - 5x^2 = 4(-2)^2 + 6(-2)(3) - 5(-2)^2$ Substitute -2 for x and 3 for y.

$= 16 - 36 - 20$

$= -40$

b. by simplifying the expression first.

$4x^2 + 6xy - 5x^2 = (4 - 5)x^2 + 6xy$ Combine like terms.

$= -x^2 + 6xy$

$= -(-2)^2 + 6(-2)(3)$ Substitute -2 for x and 3 for y.

$= -4 - 36$

$= -40$

CLASS EXERCISES

Simplify.

1. $5x + 9 + 8x + 10$

2. $2x^2 - 3x^2 + 5x + 11$

3. $x^2y + 3xy^2 + 7x^2y$

4. $2x^2 + 3x^2 - 9x^2$

5. $3xy + x(3 - y)$

6. $8 - z^2 - 2z^2$

7. $5y + y(3 + y) - 6y^2$

8. $6x(12 - x) - 3x + 2$

EXERCISES

A Write the terms in each expression. Identify the constant, if any, and the coefficient of the **x**-term.

1. $9x + 16y + 8$

2. $-x^2 - 4x + y^2 - 3y - 1$

3. $x - y + z$

4. $\frac{1}{2}x^3 - \frac{1}{4}x^2y + \frac{1}{8}x + \frac{3}{4}$

5. $0.1x^2 - 1.1x - 0.01xy^2$

6. $x^5 - 3x^4 + 5x^3 - x^2 - x - 6$

Simplify, if possible.

7. $4x + 3y + 10x$

8. $5xy + 7xy - 9xy$

9. $3pqr + 5pqr - 8pqr$

10. $2p + 2q + 17p - 4q$

11. $5 + 7a + b - 8$

12. $(s + t) + (2t + 3s)$

13. $(s - 2t) - (3s - t)$

14. $m^2n - mn + 2mn^2$

15. $m^2n^2 + m^2n^2 - mn^2$

16. $5(x + 2) - 4x$

17. $y + 4(x - y)$

18. $(x + y) - (x - y)$

19. $2\pi + 3x - (\pi - x)$

20. $x^2y + x(y^2 + xy + x^2)$

21. $2x(4x + 2) - 3x + 7x^2$

22. $x(x + y) + x(y - x)$

23. $-x(xy - yz) + xyz$

24. $3(4x^2 - \pi) + 5(x^2 + 1)$

B Evaluate each expression for **x** $= -2$ and **y** $= \frac{1}{2}$.

Then simplify each original expression and evaluate again.

25. $x^2y + 3x - x(xy)$

26. $x^2(2 - y) - x^2$

27. $3x + y - 4y + 2x$

28. $8x^3y^6 - x^3y^6$

29. $2(x + y) - (x - y)$

30. $6x^2y - x(4 - 2y) - 2xy$

31. $x(x - y) + y(x - y)$

32. $4(x + y) - (4x - y) - (x - 4y)$

CHECKPOINT

Simplify.

1. $6(12 - 2)$

2. $14 - (5 + 2)$

3. $47 - [15 - (-86)]$

4. $\frac{1}{2}\left(2 \div \frac{1}{4}\right)^2$

5. $\frac{8(12 - 3)}{14 - 8}$

6. $-\frac{5}{8} - \left(-\frac{1}{4}\right) + \frac{3}{8}$

Evaluate for **x** $= -1$, **y** $= -2$, and **z** $= 3$.

7. xyz

8. $x(y - z)$

9. $xy - xz$

10. $\frac{z(x + y)}{y(z - x)}$

Identify the property illustrated.

11. $(-5 + 5) + 1 = -5 + (5 + 1)$

12. $6\left(\frac{1}{6}\right) + 3 = \frac{1}{6}(6) + 3$

1-6 Equations

OBJECTIVES

To solve equations using the properties of equality.
To check solutions to equations.

An **equation** states the equality of two expressions.

3x + 12 = 3(x + 4)	This equation is always true because of the distributive property. It is an **identity.** Every replacement for the variable results in a true statement.
3x + 12 = 13 + 3x	This equation is never true. No replacement for the variable can make it true.
3x + 12 = 2	If a replacement for the variable makes an equation true, that replacement is a **solution,** or **root** of the equation. Can you find a solution for this equation?

Two properties of equality allow you to add or multiply by the same number on each side of an equation. These properties are used to solve equations.

For all real numbers a, b, and c, if $a = b$, then

$$a + c = b + c \qquad \textbf{Addition Property of Equality}$$
$$ac = bc \qquad \textbf{Multiplication Property of Equality}$$

EXAMPLE 1

Solve and check $3x + 12 = 2$.

$$3x + 12 = 2$$
$$3x + 12 + (-12) = 2 + (-12) \qquad \text{Add } -12 \text{ to each side.}$$
$$3x = -10$$
$$\frac{1}{3}(3x) = \frac{1}{3}(-10) \qquad \text{Multiply each side by } \frac{1}{3}.$$
$$x = -3\frac{1}{3}$$

To check, substitute $-3\frac{1}{3}$ in the original equation.

$$3\left(-3\frac{1}{3}\right) + 12 = 3\left(-\frac{10}{3}\right) + 12 = -10 + 12 = 2 \; \blacktriangleright$$

The solution is $-3\frac{1}{3}$.

In Example 1, we could also have subtracted 12 and divided by 3.

$$3x + 12 = 2$$
$$3x + 12 - 12 = 2 - 12 \qquad \text{Subtract 12 from each side.}$$
$$3x = -10 \qquad \text{This is equivalent to adding } -12.$$
$$\frac{3x}{3} = \frac{-10}{3} \qquad \text{Divide each side by 3.}$$
$$\text{This is equivalent to multiplying by } \tfrac{1}{3}.$$
$$x = -3\frac{1}{3}$$

In this book, the *replacement set* of values for the variables will be the set of real numbers, unless otherwise specified. If the replacement set were the whole numbers or integers, there would be no solution to the above equation.

Sometimes intermediate steps in the solution of an equation can be done mentally, as shown in the next example.

EXAMPLE 2   Solve and check $3(2x + 4) = 9x$.

$$3(2x + 4) = 9x$$
$$6x + 12 = 9x$$
$$-3x = -12 \qquad \text{Subtract 12 and } 9x \text{ from each side.}$$
$$x = 4 \qquad \text{Divide each side by } -3.$$

Check to see that 4 is the solution to the equation.

These properties of equality are used in solving and checking equations.

For all real numbers a, b, and c

$a = a$	**Reflexive Property of Equality**
If $a = b$, then $b = a$.	**Symmetric Property of Equality**
If $a = b$ and $b = c$, then $a = c$.	**Transitive Property of Equality**
If $a = b$, then a may be replaced by b, and b by a, in any statement.	**Substitution Property of Equality**

EXAMPLE 3   State the property illustrated by each statement.

    a. If $(x - 5)^2 = 9$ and $9 = (11 - x)^2$, then $(x - 5)^2 = (11 - x)^2$.
    Transitive property of equality

    b. If $70 - 12 = x$, then $x = 70 - 12$.
    Symmetric property of equality

CLASS EXERCISES

Solve.

1. $x + 3 = 11$

2. $x - 6 = 36$

3. $-5 = x + 7$

4. $3x = 18$

5. $\frac{x}{5} = -1$

6. $-4x = 4$

7. $2x + 10 = 30$

8. $6 + 7x = 13$

9. $-2 = 5x - 2$

10. $-3 = 2x - 9$

11. $\frac{x}{2} + 5 = 3$

12. $6 - 2x = 5$

EXERCISES

Solve and check.

1. $x - 3 = 11$

2. $7 + x = -19$

3. $8 - x = -80$

4. $-9 - x = 19$

5. $-x + 16 = 27$

6. $-\frac{1}{2} - x = 1\frac{1}{2}$

7. $3y = -18$

8. $-4y = 6$

9. $-8y = -72$

10. $\frac{3}{4}y = 270$

11. $\frac{1}{8}y = -40$

12. $-\frac{2}{3}y = \frac{4}{3}$

13. $3x + 2 = 17$

14. $5x - 5 = -50$

15. $9x - 6 = 48$

16. $-2x + 3 = 5$

17. $-x - 11 = 11$

18. $6 - 2x = 18$

19. $5 - x = 2.3$

20. $41 - 3x = 2$

21. $3x + 17 = 17$

22. $\frac{x}{2} - 3 = 17$

23. $-6x + 0.5 = -1.9$

24. $4 = 8 - \frac{1}{4}x$

Give a reason for each step.

25. $4(x + 2) = 24$
$\quad 4x + 8 = 24 \quad \underline{\ ?\ }$
$\quad\quad 4x = 16 \quad \underline{\ ?\ }$
$\quad\quad\ x = 4 \quad \underline{\ ?\ }$

26. $2x + 7 - 5x = 16$
$\quad -3x + 7 = 16 \quad \underline{\ ?\ }$
$\quad\quad -3x = 9 \quad \underline{\ ?\ }$
$\quad\quad\ x = -3 \quad \underline{\ ?\ }$

27. $6(x - 5) = 12 - x$
$\quad 6x - 30 = 12 - x \quad \underline{\ ?\ }$
$\quad 7x - 30 = 12 \quad \underline{\ ?\ }$
$\quad\quad 7x = 42 \quad \underline{\ ?\ }$
$\quad\quad\ x = 6 \quad \underline{\ ?\ }$

28. $3(4 + 3x) = 17x + 4$
$\quad 12 + 9x = 17x + 4 \quad \underline{\ ?\ }$
$\quad 12 - 8x = 4 \quad \underline{\ ?\ }$
$\quad\quad -8x = -8 \quad \underline{\ ?\ }$
$\quad\quad\ x = 1 \quad \underline{\ ?\ }$

Tell whether each equation has **one** *solution,* **many** *solutions, or* **none.**

29. $5(4 + x) = 5x + 20$

30. $4x - 5 = 5x - 4$

31. $6x + 7 = 7$

32. $3x + 6 = 6 + 3x$

33. $2x - 2 = 2 + 2x$

34. $8x - 7 = x$

REAL NUMBERS, EQUATIONS, AND INEQUALITIES

State the property illustrated by each statement.

35. If $58 = x$, then $x = 58$.

36. If $p = q^2$ and $q^2 = 3r$, then $p = 3r$.

37. $-3(16) = -3(16)$

38. If $6(3.5) = n$, then $n = 6(3.5)$.

39. If $10 - x = 6$ and $6 = 5x - 14$, then $10 - x = 5x - 14$.

40. If $3x = -2(9) + 6$, then $3x = -18 + 6$.

Solve.

41. $2(x - 5) = 18$

42. $-3(6 - x) = -12$

43. $5(2 - x) = 10$

44. $-12 = 4(3x - 8)$

45. $5(2x - 3) = 15$

46. $7(3 - 5x) = 91$

47. $3(x - 3) = 2(3 - x)$

48. $4(3x + 2) = 3(16 - 6x)$

49. $5x + 6 - 7x = 2x - 10$

50. $3x + 4(x - 3) = 2 + x$

51. $-2.5x - 4(-0.5x + 1) = 6.5$

52. $x - (6.4 + 2x) - 5x = 12.8$

53. $2 - 3(x - 4) - (6 + x) = x$

54. $4(x - 2) + 2(x + 1) = 3(1 - x)$

55. $3(x + 1) + 3 - x = 5(x - 6)$

56. $2x(x - 5) = 3 + x(2x - 1)$

CHALLENGE

Contest Problems

*Can you solve these problems from the American High School Mathematics Examination (**M.A.A. Contest Problem Book**)?*

1. The integers greater than one are arranged in five columns as follows:

	2	3	4	5
9	8	7	6	
	10	11	12	13
17	16	15	14	
	•	•	•	•

In which column will the number 1,000 fall?

(A) first   (B) second   (C) third   (D) fourth   (E) fifth

B

2. Two boys start moving from the same point A on a circular track, but in opposite directions. Their speeds are 5 ft. per sec. and 9 ft. per sec. If they start at the same time and finish when they first meet at the point A again, then the number of times they meet, excluding the start and finish, is

(A) 13   (B) 25   (C) 44   (D) infinity   (E) none of these   *A*

1-7 Formulas

OBJECTIVES _____

To solve a formula for one variable in terms of the other variables.
To find the value of one variable, given the values of the other variables in
   a formula.

_____

An equation that uses variables to express a mathematical rule is called
a **formula.** Generally, variables used in a formula are related to the
quantities they represent or to their units of measurement.

EXAMPLE 1   Use the formula $C = \frac{5}{9}(F - 32)$, where C represents degrees Celsius
and F represents degrees Fahrenheit.

a. Find C when $F = 23$.   **b.** Find F when $C = 15$.

$$C = \frac{5}{9}(F - 32)$$ $$C = \frac{5}{9}(F - 32)$$

$$= \frac{5}{9}(23 - 32)$$ $$15 = \frac{5}{9}(F - 32)$$

$$= \frac{5}{9}(-9)$$ $$27 = F - 32 \quad \text{Multiply each side by } \tfrac{9}{5}.$$

$$C = -5$$ $$59 = F$$

23°F is equivalent to −5°C.   15°C is equivalent to 59°F.

Sometimes it is convenient to solve a formula for one variable in
terms of the other variables before substituting known values.

EXAMPLE 2   Use the formula for the area of a trapezoid, $A = \frac{1}{2}h(b_1 + b_2)$.

a. Solve the formula for h in terms of A, b_1, and b_2.

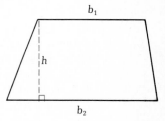

$$A = \frac{1}{2}h(b_1 + b_2)$$

$$2A = h(b_1 + b_2) \quad \text{Multiply each side by 2.}$$

$$\frac{2A}{b_1 + b_2} = h \quad \text{Divide each side by } b_1 + b_2.$$

$$h = \frac{2A}{b_1 + b_2} \quad \begin{array}{l}\text{Symmetric property}\\ \text{of equality}\end{array}$$

b. Find h if $A = 40$, $b_1 = 7$, and $b_2 = 9$.

$$h = \frac{2A}{b_1 + b_2} = \frac{2(40)}{7 + 9} = 5 \quad h \text{ is 5 units in length.}$$

CLASS EXERCISES

Use the formula for the area of a triangle, $A = \frac{1}{2}bh$.

1. Find A when $b = 6$ and $h = 10$.

2. Find h when $A = 16$ and $b = 4$.

Use the formula for the perimeter of a rectangle, $P = 2(l + w)$.

3. Solve the formula for w in terms of P and l.

4. Find w if $P = 46$ and $l = 17$.

EXERCISES

A   Use the formula $C = \frac{5}{9}(F - 32)$.

1. Find C when $F = 59$.   2. Find C when $F = 14$.

3. Find F when $C = 30$.   4. Find F when $C = -5$.

5. Solve $V = lwh$ for w in terms of V, l, and h.

6. Solve $A = \frac{1}{2}bh$ for b in terms of A and h.

7. Solve $A = \frac{1}{2}h(b_1 + b_2)$ for b_2 in terms of A, h, and b_1.

Use the formula for the volume of a pyramid, $V = \frac{1}{3}Bh$.

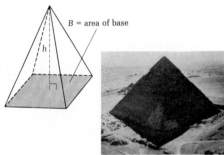

B = area of base

8. Find V when $B = 1.3$ and $h = 39$.

9. Solve the formula for B in terms of V and h.

10. Find B when $V = 50$ and $h = 6$.

11. Solve the formula for h in terms of V and B.

12. Find h when $V = 10.2$ and $B = 8.5$.

B   Temperature is known to have a slight effect on the speed at which sound travels. For each increase of 1 degree Fahrenheit, the speed of sound increases by about 1 foot per second. The relationship is given by the formula $S = 1055 + 1.1F$, where S is the speed of sound in feet per second and F is the temperature in degrees Fahrenheit.

13. What is the speed of sound at 70°F?

14. At what temperature will the speed of sound be 1000 feet per second?

The amount of power used by an appliance is affected both by the electrical current it draws and by the length of time it is in use. The number of kilowatt-hours used is given by $P = \frac{EIt}{1000}$. E is the potential in volts, I is the current in amperes, and t is the number of hours the appliance is in use.

15. In a 110-volt circuit, how much power is used by a color television set drawing a 2.6-ampere current for 8 hours?

16. At a cost of 5.5¢ per kilowatt-hour, what is the total cost of using the television in Exercise 15 for 8 hours? Give your answer to the nearest tenth of a cent.

C

17. The owner of the television set described in Exercise 15 calculates that it uses 26 kilowatt-hours in an average month. About how many hours per day is the set in use? Give your answer to the nearest whole number.

*18. During the spring and early summer, certain species of flowers will blossom earlier at lower altitudes and at lower latitudes. The number of days that blooming is delayed, d, is approximated by the formula $d = 4\left(\frac{A}{500}\right) + 4L$. A is the difference in altitude, in feet, and L is the difference in latitude, in degrees. A certain species of flower blooms on March 9 in Dallas, where the altitude is 481 feet and the latitude is 33°. When can that species be expected to bloom in Denver, where the altitude is 5283 feet and the latitude is 40°?

USING THE CALCULATOR

Repeating Decimals

The decimal for $\frac{9}{17}$ repeats after 16 decimal places. $\frac{9}{17} = 0.\overline{5294117647058823}$

In fact, the digits of the decimals for all seventeenths less than 1 repeat after 16 decimal places. The sequence of digits is the same, but each decimal starts at a different place in that sequence. A calculator will not display all of the digits, but it will show how the sequence starts.

1. Write the decimals displayed on your calculator for $\frac{1}{17}, \frac{2}{17}, \frac{3}{17}, \frac{4}{17}$, and $\frac{5}{17}$. Compare them with the decimal for $\frac{9}{17}$. Then write each decimal to 16 places by using the sequence of digits for $\frac{9}{17}$.

2. What is the repeating decimal for $\frac{16}{17}$? Write down your guess. Then use a calculator to see if it is reasonable. Finally, do the long division to check all 16 digits.

1-8 Problem Solving: Using Equations

To write word sentences as mathematical equations.
To solve problems by first writing and solving equations.

Algebra can be an effective problem-solving tool. You must be able to write word sentences as equations, a skill that requires some practice.

Five minus a number is equal to 16.	$5 - n = 16$
Twice the sum of 9 and some number is 15.	$2(9 + n) = 15$
Eight times a number, divided by 3, equals 20.	$\dfrac{8n}{3} = 20$

EXAMPLE 1   Write an equation.

a. Three more than 4 times a number is 27. $4n + 3 = 27$

b. Twice the difference, n less 5, is 20. $2(n - 5) = 20$

There is no single method that can be used to solve every problem you encounter, but it is possible to present some helpful strategies.

EXAMPLE 2   Two more than 4 times a number is 70. Find the number.

Strategy: Write and solve an equation.

Read the problem to find the key ideas. Ask yourself these questions.

What are the given quantities and conditions?
What am I asked to find?

Use a variable.

Let x be the number.	x
Four times the number	4x
Two more than 4 times the number	4x + 2

Write an equation.

Two more than 4 times the number is 70. $4x + 2 = 70$

Find the solution.

$$4x + 2 = 70$$
$$4x = 68$$
$$x = 17$$

Check the solution with the conditions in the original problem.

Four times 17 is 68.
Two more than 4 times 17 is 68 + 2, or 70. ✔

Answer the question.

The number is 17.

In each of the following examples, first read the problem at least twice to be sure you understand it. Then study the strategy used to solve the problem.

EXAMPLE 3   A cash box contains $4.00 in pennies, nickels, and dimes. How many coins are there if there are the same number of each type?

Use a variable.   Let n be the number of each type of coin.

The value of n pennies, in cents	n
The value of n nickels, in cents	$5n$
The value of n dimes, in cents	$10n$

Write an equation.   The total value is 400 cents. $n + 5n + 10n = 400$

Find the solution.

$$n + 5n + 10n = 400$$
$$16n = 400$$
$$n = 25$$

Check $25(1) = 25$ 25 pennies
$25(5) = 125$ 25 nickels
$25(10) = \underline{250}$ 25 dimes
          400   total value ✔

Answer the question.   There are 25 of each type of coin.

EXAMPLE 4   Two years ago, Camille's father was 3 times as old as she was. If her father is 44 now, how old is Camille?

Let c be Camille's age now.	c
Camille's age 2 years ago	$c - 2$
Three times her age 2 years ago	$3(c - 2)$
Her father's age 2 years ago	42

Three times her age 2 years ago equals her father's age 2 years ago.

$$3(c - 2) = 42$$
$$\frac{3(c - 2)}{3} = \frac{42}{3}$$
$$c - 2 = 14$$
$$c = 16$$

Camille is 16 years old.

Check   If Camille is 16, then 2 years ago she was 14. Three times 14 equals 42, her father's age 2 years ago. ✔

CLASS EXERCISES

Write an equation for each word sentence.

1. Nine more than a number is 20.

2. 6 less than twice a number is 3.

3. Twice a number, plus 2, is 38.

4. Twice the sum of a number and 3 is 8.

5. The quotient of a number divided by -5 equals 12.

6. Three times a number, less 24, is 67.

7. Four times a number is 16 more than that same number.

8. Twice a number, plus 3, is 75 less than that same number.

EXERCISES

A

Write an equation and solve it for n.

1. 4 more than *n* is equal to 17.

2. *n* less than 12 is equal to −15.

3. Three times *n* is equal to 81.

4. Twice *n* is equal to −26.

5. Seven more than 2 times *n* is equal to 3.

6. Twice the sum of −6 and *n* is 16.

7. Sixteen decreased by *n* is equal to *n* increased by 12.

8. Five more than 3 times *n* is equal to 5 times 3 more than *n*.

9. Seven less than the opposite of *n* is equal to 6 times *n*.

10. Three times *n*, less 6, equals 4 times the sum of *n* and 10.

B

*Write an equation and solve it for **x**. Check each answer.*

11. Ten pennies and *x* dimes have a total value of $2.00.

12. *x* nickels and *x* quarters have a total value of $6.00.

13. *x* dimes and twice as many pennies have a total value of $3.60.

14. There are *x* nickels, twice as many dimes as nickels, and 3 times as many quarters as nickels. The total value of the coins is $10.00.

15. The total value of *x* quarters and 3 more than twice as many dimes is $13.80.

Solve each problem.

16. Eight less than 6 times the sum of a number and 5 is 70. Find the number.

17. There are 6 more dimes than nickels. Their total value is $9.00. How many of each are there?

18. One number is 4 greater than another number. Their sum is 10 times the smaller number. Find each number.

19. One number is 12 less than another number. Their sum is 37 less than 3 times the larger number. Find each number.

20. Ted has the same number of nickels, dimes, and quarters, with a total value of $20.00. How many coins are there in all?

21. Increasing a certain number of nickels by 20 would give a value of $15.00. How many nickels are there?

22. Kelly is 3 years older than Neil. If their combined ages total 35, how old is each one?

23. Three years ago Jill was one-half as old as Tony. If Tony is 19 now, how old is Jill?

24. Marty is 35. He is one year more than twice as old as Anna. How old is Anna?

25. In 5 years, Pat's age will be 9 years less than twice Jim's age at that time. Jim is 15 now. How old is Pat?

Searching for Patterns

Here are two number patterns you may have encountered earlier.

The sum of the first n consecutive counting numbers is $\frac{n(n + 1)}{2}$.

$$\underbrace{1 + 2 + 3 + 4 + 5 + \ldots + n}_{n \text{ numbers}} = \frac{n(n + 1)}{2}$$

The sum of the first n consecutive odd numbers is n^2.

$$\underbrace{1 + 3 + 5 + 7 + 9 + \ldots + (2n - 1)}_{n \text{ odd numbers}} = n^2$$

Try to discover another interesting property of consecutive odd numbers first noted by the Greek mathematician Nichomachus in 100 A.D.

Look for a pattern.

$$
\begin{aligned}
1 &= 1 = 1^3 \\
3 + 5 &= 8 = 2^3 \\
7 + 9 + 11 &= 27 = 3^3 \\
13 + 15 + 17 + 19 &= 64 = 4^3
\end{aligned}
$$

Use the pattern to find these sums, without adding.

1. $21 + 23 + 25 + 27 + 29$

2. $31 + 33 + 35 + 37 + 39 + 41$

3. $43 + 45 + 47 + 49 + 51 + 53 + 55$

Apply the pattern.

How many consecutive odd numbers have the given sum?

4. 10^3 **5.** 8000 **6.** k^3

Which consecutive odd numbers have the given sum?

Hint: In Exercise 7, start by using the first number pattern on this page. Find the total number of consecutive odd numbers in the first 8 groups of such numbers, starting with 1. Find the last number in the eighth group, then list the 8 numbers in that group.

7. 8^3 **8.** $1,000,000$ ***9.** k^3

Relate this pattern to others.

***10.** Begin with the first k consecutive counting numbers. Write an expression for the sum of their cubes. Show that it is equal to the square of their sum.

1-9 Inequalities

To graph inequalities in one variable on the number line.
To solve inequalities in one variable.

Expressions of **inequality** can be written in many forms. Several are given here in this example from chemistry.

Mercury is the only metal that exists in liquid form under normal temperature and pressure. Let t be the temperature in degrees Celsius.

When $t = 357$, mercury is at its boiling point. When $t = -39$, mercury is at its freezing point.

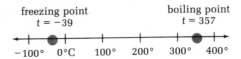

If t is greater than 357, mercury is a gas.

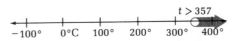

If t is less than -39, mercury is a solid.

If t is between -39 and 357, mercury is a liquid.

For any two real numbers a and b, exactly one of the following three conditions is true. This is called the *Trichotomy Property*.

$$a < b \qquad a = b \qquad a > b$$

Note that if $a < b$, then $b > a$. Also, if $a > b$, then $b < a$.

The *addition property of inequality* allows you to add the same number to each side of an inequality.

Addition Property of Inequality

Let r, s, and t be real numbers. If $r < s$, then

$$r + t < s + t$$

Since $r - t = r + (-t)$, you can also subtract the same number from each side of an inequality.

EXAMPLE 1   Solve and graph $x + 2 > -1$.

$$x + 2 > -1$$
$$x + 2 + (-2) > -1 + (-2)$$ Add -2 to each side, or
$$x > -3$$ subtract 2 from each side.

The solution is the set of all real numbers greater than -3. The point -3 is not included.

When multiplying each side of an inequality by the same number, several different results are possible. Start with the true statement $3 > 2$.

Multiply each side by 4.
$$3 > 2$$
$$4(3) \text{ ? } 4(2)$$
$$12 > 8$$ The direction of the inequality is *unchanged*.

Multiply each side by 0.
$$3 > 2$$
$$0(3) \text{ ? } 0(2)$$
$$0 = 0$$ The inequality becomes an equation.

Multiply each side by -4.
$$3 > 2$$
$$-4(3) \text{ ? } -4(2)$$
$$-12 < -8$$ The direction of the inequality is *reversed*.

When each side of an inequality is multiplied by the same positive number, the direction of the inequality is not changed. Multiplying by a negative number reverses the direction of the inequality.

Multiplication Property of Inequality

Let r, s, and t be real numbers. If $r < s$, then

$$rt < st \text{ when } t \text{ is positive.}$$
$$rt = st \text{ when } t \text{ is 0.}$$
$$rt > st \text{ when } t \text{ is negative.}$$

Since $\frac{r}{t} = r\left(\frac{1}{t}\right)$, the multiplication property also allows you to divide each side of an inequality by the same nonzero number.

The properties of inequality also apply to the inequalities $\leq$ (*is less than or equal to*) and $\geq$ (*is greater than or equal to*).

EXAMPLE 2 Solve.

  a. $2x - 3 \leq 5$

$$2x - 3 + 3 \leq 5 + 3 \qquad \text{Add 3 to each side.}$$
$$2x \leq 8$$
$$\frac{1}{2}(2x) \leq \frac{1}{2}(8) \qquad \text{Multiply each side by the positive number } \frac{1}{2}.$$
$$x \leq 4 \qquad \text{The direction of the inequality is unchanged.}$$

It is impossible to check an inequality by testing every apparent solution. However, testing one or two numbers provides a fairly reliable check.

If $x = 0$: $2(0) - 3 \leq 5$ 　　　　　　　If $x = 4$: $2(4) - 3 \leq 5$
　　　　　　$-3 \leq 5$　　True　　　　　　　　　　　$5 \leq 5$　　True

The solution is the set of all numbers less than or equal to 4.

  b. $-4x > 7 - x$

$$-4x + x > 7 - x + x \qquad \text{Add } x \text{ to each side.}$$
$$-3x > 7$$
$$-\frac{1}{3}(-3x) < -\frac{1}{3}(7) \qquad \text{Multiply each side by the negative number } -\frac{1}{3}.$$
$$\qquad\qquad\qquad\qquad \text{The direction of the inequality is reversed.}$$
$$x < -\frac{7}{3}$$

The solution is the set of all real numbers less than $-\frac{7}{3}$.

CLASS EXERCISES

Graph each inequality on a number line.

1. $x > -2$ 　　**2.** $x \leq 3$ 　　**3.** $x \geq -1$ 　　**4.** $x < -1\frac{1}{2}$

5. $-3 < x < -1$ 　**6.** $-2 \leq x \leq 1$ 　**7.** $0 < x < 4$ 　**8.** $-3 \leq x \leq 0$

Solve.

9. $x + 1 > 2$ 　**10.** $x - 2 < 6$ 　**11.** $3x < -1$ 　**12.** $-2x \geq 6$

EXERCISES

A　*Solve and graph.*

1. $x + 2 < 1$ 　　**2.** $x - 3 > -2$ 　**3.** $2 + x \leq 2$ 　**4.** $3 - x \geq 0$

5. $x - 4 \leq 1$ 　　**6.** $-2 - x > 3$ 　**7.** $6x < 12$ 　　**8.** $4x \geq -16$

9. $3x \leq -3$ 　　**10.** $-5x > 40$ 　**11.** $-2x < -5$ 　**12.** $-4x > 0$

13. $3 < x + 1\frac{1}{2}$ **14.** $0 \le x - 2$ **15.** $-5 < 4 - x$ **16.** $-\frac{1}{2} \ge 2$

Give a reason for each step.   A: Addition property of equality   D: Distributive property
M: Multiplication property of equality

17. $2x - 1 < 7$

$\qquad 2x < 8$ $\underline{?}$

$\qquad x < 4$ $\underline{?}$

18. $-3x + 2 \ge 5$

$\qquad -3x \ge 3$ $\underline{?}$

$\qquad x \le -1$ $\underline{?}$

19. $2(x - 1) > 3$

$\qquad 2x - 2 > 3$ $\underline{?}$

$\qquad 2x > 5$ $\underline{?}$

$\qquad x > \frac{5}{2}$ $\underline{?}$

20. $5(2 - x) \le 40$

$\qquad 10 - 5x \le 40$ $\underline{?}$

$\qquad -5x \le 30$ $\underline{?}$

$\qquad x \ge -6$ $\underline{?}$

Solve.

21. $3x + 2 > 8$ **22.** $4x - 3 \le 7$ **23.** $5x - 4 < -14$

24. $2 - 5x > 12$ **25.** $1 - x \ge 0$ **26.** $3 - x < -2$

B

27. $2(x + 1) > 6$ **28.** $5(4 - x) \ge 20$ **29.** $-3(6 + x) < 60$

30. $-2(2 - x) \le -20$ **31.** $6x - 2 < 3x + 1$ **32.** $7x \ge 4x - 3$

33. $4x + 3x - 2 > 5x + 4$ **34.** $-8x + 5 < 9x - 29$

35. Bart needs $2.25 to pay a highway toll. He has just seven dimes and some quarters. What is the least number of quarters that he needs to pay the toll?

36. Maria has grades of 79, 67, 83, and 90 on four tests. What is the lowest grade she can have on the fifth test if she wants an average of at least 82?

Write an inequality involving **t,** *the temperature in degrees Celsius, when*

37. tungsten is in solid form.

38. mercury is in a gaseous state.

39. tin is in liquid form.

	Melting or Freezing Point	Boiling Point
Mercury	$-39°C$	$357°C$
Tin	$232°C$	$2270°C$
Tungsten	$3380°C$	$5927°C$

C

40. tin and mercury are both in liquid form.

Let **p** $<$ **q.** *Find all values of* **r** *for which*

41. $pr < qr$ **42.** $pr > qr$ **43.** $pr = qr$

44. $p + r < q + r$ **45.** $p + r > q + r$ **46.** $p + r = q + r$

47. $p - r < q - r$ **48.** $\dfrac{p}{r} < \dfrac{q}{r}$ **49.** $\dfrac{p}{r} > \dfrac{q}{r}$

1-10 Compound Inequalities

To graph compound inequalities in one variable on the number line.
To solve compound inequalities in one variable.

Sometimes a variable must satisfy more than one condition of inequality. Here is an illustration of such a **compound inequality.**

Find all positive numbers less than 2.

The numbers must be both positive *and* less than 2.

x is positive.	$x > 0$	
x is less than 2.	$x < 2$	
x is positive *and* x is less than 2.	$x > 0$ *and* $x < 2$	

The word *and* indicates that the solution is the *intersection* of the two inequalities. Thus the graph of $x > 0$ *and* $x < 2$ consists of all points that are in both the graph of $x > 0$ and the graph of $x < 2$. That is, the graph is the set of all points between 0 and 2. This suggests another way to express the same compound inequality.

$0 < x < 2$ *x is greater than 0 and less than 2.*

EXAMPLE 1   Solve and graph $-1 < x + 2 < 3$.

$-1 < x + 2 < 3$ means $-1 < x + 2$ and $x + 2 < 3$.
Solve both inequalities.

$$-1 < x + 2 \qquad\qquad x + 2 < 3$$
$$-1 + (-2) < x + 2 + (-2) \qquad x + 2 + (-2) < 3 + (-2)$$
$$-3 < x \qquad and \qquad x < 1$$

The solution can also be expressed this way.

$-3 < x < 1$ *x is between −3 and 1.*

Note that the solution in the last example can also be found by adding -2 to each expression in $-1 < x + 2 < 3$.

$$-1 < x + 2 < 3$$
$$-1 + (-2) < x + 2 + (-2) < 3 + (-2)$$
$$-3 < x < 1$$

Here is an illustration of another type of compound inequality.

Find all numbers that are more than 2 units from 0 on the number line.

The numbers can be greater than 2 or less than -2.

x is greater than 2.	$x > 2$	
x is less than -2.	$x < -2$	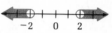
x is greater than 2 or x is less than -2.	$x > 2$ or $x < -2$	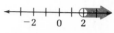

The word *or* indicates that the solution is the *union* of the two inequalities. Thus the graph of $x > 2$ or $x < -2$ consists of all points that are in either the graph of $x > 2$ or the graph of $x < -2$, or in both graphs. In this illustration, there are no points common to both graphs.

EXAMPLE 2   Solve and graph.

a. $x > -2$ or $x > 1$

The solution is every value of x greater than -2 or greater than 1, or both. The solution is $x > -2$.

b. $x > -2$ and $x > 1$

The solution is every value of x that is both greater than -2 and greater than 1. The solution is $x > 1$.

Compound inequalities involving *less than or equal to* and those involving *greater than or equal to* are solved in a similar way.

EXAMPLE 3   Solve and graph.

a. $x - 2 \le -3$ and $2x \ge -8$
$$x \le -1 \text{ and } x \ge -4$$
The solution is $-4 \le x \le -1$.

b. $5x \le -10$ or $4 - x \le 2$
$$5x \le -10 \text{ or } -x \le -2$$
$$x \le -2 \text{ or } x \ge 2$$

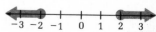

REAL NUMBERS, EQUATIONS, AND INEQUALITIES

CLASS EXERCISES

State whether **x = 6** *is* or *is not* a solution to the compound inequality.

1. x > 1 and 8 < x   **2.** x > 7 or x < 3   **3.** x ≤ 6 and x > −2

4. x > 3 or x > 8   **5.** −5 ≤ x ≤ 7   **6.** −1 < x < 6

Match each inequality with its graph.

7. −1 ≤ x < 2

a.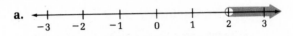

8. 2 > x

b.

9. x > 2 or x ≤ −1

c.

10. −1 ≤ x

d.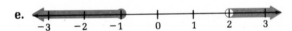

11. x ≥ −1 and x > 2

e.

EXERCISES

A   Write each statement as a compound inequality.

1. x is positive and less than 10.   **2.** x is negative and greater than −5.

3. x is less than 2 and is negative.   **4.** x is positive or greater than 3.

5. x is greater than −5 and less than 2.

6. x is greater than 2 or less than −5.

7. x lies between −1 and 4 on the number line.

Graph each compound inequality.

8. x > 2 and x < 5   **9.** x > 5 or x < 2   **10.** x ≤ 5 or x ≥ 2

11. x ≤ −2 and x ≥ −5   **12.** x ≤ 2 and x > 5   **13.** x < −5 or x ≥ −2

B   Solve and graph.

14. x + 2 < 5 and x − 1 > 1   **15.** 3 + x > 2 and 6 < x + 10

16. x − 4 > −5 or x + 3 < −1   **17.** 4 − x ≥ 7 or −2 ≥ 4 − x

18. 16 > 2x and −6x < −18   **19.** −3x > 18 and 6 − x < 14

20. $-3 < x + 1 < 5$

21. $2 \le 3 + x \le 7$

22. $1 \le 2x + 1 < 17$

23. $-4 < 3x + 2 \le 8$

24. $6 \le -2x \le 10$

25. $-5x \le 10$ or $4x \le -2$

26. $3x < 15$ and $x + 6 > 11$

27. $2x - 3 \ge 5$ or $2x + 3 \le -5$

28. $5x - 8 > 12$ or $6 - 2x < 18$

29. $4x + 3 > 1$ and $4x - 3 < -1$

Write a compound inequality for each graph.

30.  **31.**

32. **33.**

 C *Solve and graph.*

34. All positive numbers x that are greater than -2 and less than 2

35. All negative numbers x that are less than 3 or greater than -3

36. $2x > 5$ and $x + 7 > 6$ and $3x + 2 < 20.$

37. $6 - x < 9$ or $-3x < 18$ or $-2 > x + 6.$

CHECKPOINT

Evaluate for $c = -2$ and $d = -6$.

1. $c(d + 2)$

2. $d \div 2 + c$

3. $c + d^2$

4. $\dfrac{c^2 - d^2}{8}$

Simplify.

5. $9x^2 + 4 - 13x^2 - 7 - 5x^2$

6. $-3x(2xy - 3yz) + 3xyz$

7. $a(5 + 2b) + b(8 + 2a)$

8. $2(m + n) - (n - 2m) + 5m + mn$

Solve.

9. $4(a - 7) = 20$

10. $-5(8 - c) = -15$

11. $5(x + 3) + 5 - x = 7(x + 8)$

12. $4d(d - 7) = 5 + d(4d - 3)$

13. A number n is 4 greater than another number. The sum of the numbers is 24. Write and solve an equation to find the two numbers.

Solve and graph each inequality.

14. $4(x + 3) > 8$

15. $8x - 4 < 5x + 2$

16. $9x \ge 5x + 8$

1-11 Absolute Value Equations and Inequalities

OBJECTIVES _____

To find the absolute values of numerical expressions.
To solve equations and inequalities involving absolute values.

_____

Recall that the *absolute value* of a real number x is the distance between x and 0 on the number line. When x is positive or zero, $|x|$ is equal to x. When x is negative, $|x|$ is the opposite of x. This relationship between a number and its absolute value is summarized in the following definition.

Absolute Value Definition

For any real number *x*,

$$\text{if } x \geq 0, \text{ then } |x| = x.$$
$$\text{if } x < 0, \text{ then } |x| = -x.$$

EXAMPLE 1   Simplify.

a. $|3(-2)^2| = |3(4)| = |12| = 12$

b. $|3 - 2^2| = |3 - 4| = |-1| = 1$

c. $-3|-2^2| = -3|-4| = -3(4) = -12$

EXAMPLE 2   Solve and graph.

a. $|x| = 3$

Both -3 and 3 are solutions. Each number represents a point 3 units from the origin, 0.

$x = -3$ or $x = 3$

b. $|x| > 3$

Every number less than -3 or greater than 3 is a solution. All such numbers are more than 3 units from the origin.

$x < -3$ or $x > 3$

c. $|x| < 3$

Every number greater than -3 and less than 3 is a solution. All such numbers are within 3 units of the origin.

$x > -3$ and $x < 3$ 
$-3 < x < 3$

The preceding examples lead to useful generalizations.

Absolute Value Equality and Inequality Properties

For any real numbers r and k, with $k > 0$,

if $|r| = k$, then $r = k$ or $r = -k$.
if $|r| > k$, then $r > k$ or $r < -k$.
if $|r| < k$, then $r > -k$ and $r < k$. That is, $-k < r < k$.

Similar properties hold for the relationships $\leq$ and $\geq$.

EXAMPLE 3   Solve and graph.

a. $|x - 2| = 5$

This equation is in the form $|r| = k$, where $r = x - 2$ and $k = 5$. Hence, $r = k$ or $r = -k$.

$x - 2 = 5$ or $x - 2 = -5$
     $x = 7$ or $x = -3$

$x = 7$ or $x = -3$ (number line: $-8-7-6-5-4-3-2-1$ 0 1 2 3 4 5 6 7 8 with points at -3 and 7)

Note that $|x - 2| = 5$ means that the distance between x and 2 is 5 units. Both 7 and -3 are 5 units from 2.

b. $|x + 1| \geq 3$

This inequality is in the form $|r| \geq k$, where $r = x + 1$ and $k = 3$. Hence, $r \geq k$ or $r \leq -k$.

$x + 1 \geq 3$ or $x + 1 \leq -3$
     $x \geq 2$ or $x \leq -4$

$x \geq 2$ or $x \leq -4$ 

$|x + 1| \geq 3$, or $|x - (-1)| \geq 3$, means that the distance between x and -1 is greater than or equal to 3 units. Every point in the solution is 3 or more units from -1.

c. $|2x - 1| < 5$

This inequality is in the form $|r| < k$. Thus, $-k < r < k$.

$-5 < 2x - 1 < 5$

$\qquad -4 < 2x < 6 \qquad$ Add 1 to each expression.

$\qquad -2 < \ x < 3 \qquad$ Multiply each expression by $\frac{1}{2}$.

$-2 < x < 3$

That is,

$x > -2$ and $x < 3$

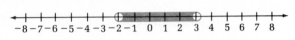

CLASS EXERCISES

Match each equation or inequality with its graph.

1. $|x| < 1$

2. $|x| = 1$

3. $|x| > 1$

4. $|x| \leq 1$

5. $|x| \geq 1$

6. $|x - 1| = 1$

7. $|x - 1| \geq 1$

8. $|x - 1| < 1$

a.

b.

c.

d.

e.

f.

g.

h.

EXERCISES

A

Simplify.

1. $|5 - 12|$ **2.** $|(-2)(-3)|$ **3.** $|-5(4 - 11)|$ **4.** $|7(-4) - 3|$

5. $|6 - 7(1 + 8)|$ **6.** $-5|6(-2)|$ **7.** $-3|-6(3) + 1|$ **8.** $-|2(-2)^2(-3)^3|$

B

Solve and graph.

9. $|2x| = 10$ **10.** $|2x - 1| = 7$ **11.** $|1 - x| = 3$ **12.** $|2x| > 2$

13. $|3x - 1| \leq 2$ **14.** $|4x + 3| > 5$ **15.** $|6x - 3| < 4$ **16.** $|2 - 4x| < 6$

17. $|2(x - 3)| \geq 9$ **18.** $|x| < 2x + 1$ **19.** $|2x - 1| > x$ **20.** $|3(x - 1)| \geq 2x$

21. If $|x - 8| = 4$, how far is x from 8 on the number line?

22. If $|x + 2| = 5$, how far is x from -2 on the number line?

*Describe the location of **x** in terms of its distance from 3 on the number line.*

23. $|x - 3| = 10$ **24.** $|x - 3| > 10$ **25.** $|x - 3| < 10$

Logic Gates in Computers

The circuits in computers are controlled by tiny logic gates. There are AND, OR, and NOT gates. Engineers who design microcircuits need to know how these gates function.

AND gate   OR gate   NOT gate

Current flows out at C only when it flows in at both A and B.

Current flows out at F if it flows in at D or E or at both.

Current flows out at H only when it does not flow in at G.

A	B	C
no	no	no
no	yes	no
yes	no	no
yes	yes	yes

D	E	F
no	no	no
no	yes	yes
yes	no	yes
yes	yes	yes

G	H
no	yes
yes	no

Example   Interpret this automobile circuit.

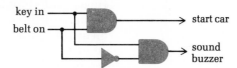

When the key is in the ignition AND the seat belt is on, the car is started but the buzzer is not sounded. When the key is in the ignition AND the seat belt is NOT on, the buzzer is sounded but the car is not started. When the key is NOT in, the car does not start and the buzzer does not sound. It does not matter whether the seat belt is on or not.

*Under what conditions on **A** and **B**, or on **A**, **B**, and **C**, will current flow from **D**?*

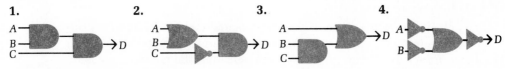

1.   **2.**   **3.**   **4.**

5. Draw a circuit that functions in exactly the same way as the one in Exercise 4, but has just one logic gate.

CHAPTER 1 REVIEW

VOCABULARY

whole numbers (p. 2)
natural numbers (p. 2)
counting numbers (p. 2)
integers (p. 2)
opposites (p. 2)
rational numbers (p. 2)
real numbers (p. 2)
terminating decimal (p. 2)
repeating decimal (p. 2)
irrational numbers (p. 2)
numerical expression (p. 2)
exponent (p. 2)
base (p. 2)
squared (p. 2)
power (p. 2)
cubed (p. 2)
simplify (p. 3)
variable (p. 3)
algebraic expression (p. 3)
evaluate (p. 3)
positive real numbers (p. 6)
negative real numbers (p. 6)
additive identity (p. 6)
additive inverse (p. 6)
absolute value (p. 7)
multiplicative identity (p. 10)
multiplicative inverse (p. 11)
reciprocal (p. 11)
closure properties (p. 13)
commutative properties (p. 13)
associative properties (p. 13)

distributive properties (p. 13)
term (p. 16)
numerical coefficient, or coefficient (p. 16)
constant term, or constant (p. 16)
like terms (p. 16)
unlike terms (p. 16)
equivalent expression (p. 17)
equation (p. 19)
identity (p. 19)
solution, or root (p. 19)
addition property of equality (p. 19)
multiplication property of equality (p. 19)
replacement set (p. 20)
reflexive property of equality (p. 20)
symmetric property of equality (p. 20)
transitive property of equality (p. 20)
substitution property of equality (p. 20)
formula (p. 23)
inequality (p. 30)
addition property of inequality (p. 30)
multiplication property of inequality (p. 31)
compound inequality (p. 34)
intersection (p. 34)
union (p. 35)
absolute value definition (p. 38)
absolute value equality and inequality properties (p. 39)

SUMMARY

This chapter reviews some of the fundamental concepts that you studied in the first year of algebra. Among these topics are operations with signed numbers, properties of real numbers, and the concept of absolute value. Also included is a review of the solution of elementary equations and inequalities. The work with equations is adapted to the solution of verbal problems and problems involving formulas. The basic guidelines established here for problem solving will be used frequently in later work in the course.

REVIEW EXERCISES

1-1 *Simplify.*

1. $24 - (9 - 4)$ **2.** $24(9 - 4)$ **3.** $(5 + 4)(3)^2$ **4.** $5 + [4(3)]^2$

Evaluate for $a = 4$ and $b = 5$.

5. $a(b - 3)$ **6.** $a + b^2$ **7.** $(2a + b)^2$ **8.** $\dfrac{b^2 - a^2}{3}$

1-2 *Simplify.*

9. $7 + (-11)$ **10.** $-7 - 11$ **11.** $-7 - (-11)$ **12.** $\dfrac{5}{6} - \left(\dfrac{4}{9} - \dfrac{1}{3}\right)$

Evaluate for $x = 0.5$, $y = -2.3$, and $z = -1.75$.

13. $x + y + z$ **14.** $y - z - x$ **15.** $z - (y - x)$ **16.** $x - (z - y)$

1-3 *Simplify.*

17. $9(-8)$ **18.** $6(-8)(-2)$ **19.** $(-3)^3$ **20.** $\dfrac{8 - (-12)}{5(-2)}$

Evaluate for $a = -2$, $b = -\frac{1}{2}$, and $c = 3$.

21. $a(b - c)$ **22.** $a^2 - bc$ **23.** $b(ab - c^2)$ **24.** $(ab)^2 - c^2$

1-4 *Identify the property illustrated.*

25. $-8 + 8 = 0$ **26.** $-6(-2 + 7) = -6(-2) + (-6)(7)$

27. $-6(-2 + 7) = -6[7 + (-2)]$ **28.** $(-2)[(-11)(-5)] = [(-2)(-11)](-5)$

1-5 *Simplify by combining like terms.*

29. $4x - 3 + 5x + 2$ **30.** $xy^2 + x^2y - xy(x + y)$

Find the sum of the two expressions.

31. $x(xy - x)$ and $2x^2 - 3x^2y + y^2$ **32.** $3(x + y) - (y - 2x)$ and $x(y - 5) - y$

1-6 *Solve and check.*

33. $6 + x = -18$ **34.** $-4y = 24$ **35.** $-\dfrac{1}{2}y = -60$

36. $7x + 5 = 68$ **37.** $5(x - 5) = 4(5 - x)$ **38.** $7x + 6(x - 5) = 6 + x$

1-7 *Use the formula for the perimeter of a rectangle, $P = 2(l + w)$.*

39. Solve for w in terms of P and l.   **40.** Find w, if $P = 42.6$ and $l = 16.8$.

1-8 *Write an equation and solve it for n.*

41. Four times n, increased by 6, is -2.   **42.** One-half of n, less 12, is equal to 23.

43. Nine times the sum of -3 and n equals 63.

44. Seven more than 6 times n is equal to 3 less than 8 times n.

1-9 *Solve and graph.*

45. $x - 4 > -3$ **46.** $-6x \geq -36$ **47.** $3x - 4 \leq 5$ **48.** $-2(x + 1) < 4$

1-10 *Solve each compound inequality and graph the solution.*

49. $x < 2$ or $x + 5 > 9$ **50.** $-1 \leq x - 2 \leq 3$

1-11 *Evaluate.*

51. $|-5|$ **52.** $|-4(-3)|$ **53.** $|-6(3 - 8)|$ **54.** $|-7| - |9|$

Solve and graph the solution.

55. $|x - 3| = 1$ **56.** $|x| > 2$ **57.** $|x + 1| \leq 3$ **58.** $|x - 2| < 5$

CHAPTER 1 TEST

Simplify.

1. $16 - (7 - 3)$ **2.** $5(13 + 8)$ **3.** $4 + (-5) - (-6)$

4. $5(-3)(-2)$ **5.** $10 - (-4)^3$ **6.** $\dfrac{-6(5 - 12)}{-7(-2)}$

Evaluate for $a = 3$ and $b = -2$.

7. $a(2 + b)$ **8.** $a - b^2$ **9.** $a(b - a)^2$

Identify the property illustrated.

10. $8[6 + (-7)] = 8[(-7) + 6]$ **11.** $8[6 + (-7)] = 8(6) + 8(-7)$

Simplify by combining like terms.

12. $2x^2 - 5x + 6x + x^2 + 3$ **13.** $3x - x(5 - x)$

Solve.

14. $8 - x = -40$ **15.** $2x + 3 = 5$ **16.** $-2(x + 3) = -12$

17. $x - 3 < -4$ **18.** $-4x - 3 > 15$

19. Five less than 9 times some number is 40. Find the number.

20. The total value of q quarters and 3 more than twice as many dimes is $2.55. Find the number of quarters and dimes.

Evaluate.

21. $|-23|$ **22.** $|-3(4 - 7)|$ **23.** $|-3| - |3|$

Solve and graph the solution.

24. $|x + 1| = 2$ **25.** $-4 \leq x - 1 \leq 4$

The Speed of Sound

The speed of an aircraft flying at one and a half times the speed of sound is said to be *Mach* 1.5. This measurement is used because the speed of sound varies, as given by the formula $S = 1055 + 1.1F$, where S is the velocity (ft/sec) and F is the Fahrenheit temperature.

The program below is written in the computer language called BASIC. In BASIC, the order of performing operations is the same as in algebra. The symbol * is used to indicate multiplication and the symbol / indicates division. The variables F and S are the names of memory locations to which values are assigned in the computer memory.

If you have difficulty understanding the program, see the Computer Handbook, starting on page 656.

The Program	What It Does
10 REM SPEED OF SOUND	Gives program a title; does not affect the program itself.
20 PRINT "ENTER TEMPERATURE";	Displays a message, or "prompt."
30 INPUT F	Stops computer and waits for an entry; assigns the entry to memory location F.
40 LET S = 1055 + 1.1 * F	Computes the speed of sound; assigns it to memory location S.
50 PRINT "SPEED OF SOUND IS "	
60 PRINT S; " FEET PER SECOND"	Displays and labels the result, or "output."
90 END	Ends the program.
RUN	Commands computer to run the program.
ENTER TEMPERATURE ? 40	Sample run is for a temperature of 40° F.
SPEED OF SOUND IS	
1099 FEET PER SECOND	Displays the result or output.

Line 40 takes the value in memory location F, performs the computations, and stores the result in memory location S. Line 60 displays the result and the quoted message on the screen.

What will the program above display for these Fahrenheit temperatures?
  1. 80   **2.** 55   **3.** 103   **4.** −16   **5.** −8.5

To display the output in miles per hour, add these lines to the program:
```
70 LET M = S * 15/22
80 PRINT M; " MILES PER HOUR"
```

What will the revised program display for these Fahrenheit temperatures?
  6. 60   **7.** 31   **8.** 98.6   **9.** −54   **10.** 0

11. Write a program in BASIC that asks for the temperature and the Mach number, and displays the speed of the aircraft.

CHAPTER 2

A navigator on a NATO ship is plotting a course through the Mediterranean Sea. The grid he uses is formed by lines of latitude and longitude.

LINEAR EQUATIONS AND FUNCTIONS

Prerequisite Skills Review

Write the letter for the correct answer.

1. The coordinate of point A is ___?___.

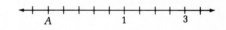

    a. 0   **b.** -1 **c.** $-1\frac{1}{2}$ **d.** -2

2. If $4x - 2y = 1$, then $y =$ ___?___.

    a. $2x + \frac{1}{2}$ **b.** $2x - 1$ **c.** $2x - \frac{1}{2}$ **d.** $-2x - \frac{1}{2}$

3. If $2x + 3y - 5 = 0$ and $x = 0$, then $y =$ ___?___.

    a. $\frac{5}{2}$ **b.** $-\frac{5}{3}$ **c.** $\frac{3}{5}$ **d.** $\frac{5}{3}$

4. If $y = -\frac{1}{2}x - 2$ and $x = -2$, then $y =$ ___?___.

    a. -3 **b.** -1 **c.** 1   **d.** 0

5. If $y = -3x + 5$ and $x = -4$, then $y =$ ___?___.

    a. 17   **b.** -7 **c.** 7   **d.** none of these

6. If $y - 1 = -3(x + 1)$, then $y =$ ___?___.

    a. $-3x - 2$ **b.** $-3x - 4$ **c.** $-3x + 2$ **d.** $-2x - 3$

7. $\dfrac{1 - 4}{-2 - (-3)} = \dfrac{?}{}$

    a. $\frac{3}{5}$ **b.** 3   **c.** -3 **d.** none of these

8. If $pq = -1$ and $p = \frac{2}{3}$, then $q =$ ___?___.

    a. $\frac{2}{3}$ **b.** $\frac{3}{2}$ **c.** $-\frac{2}{3}$ **d.** none of these

9. $(-1, 1)$ is a solution to the inequality ___?___.

    a. $y < 2x + 3$ **b.** $y \le \frac{2}{3}x + \frac{5}{3}$ **c.** $y \ge 1 - x$ **d.** $y > \frac{1}{2}x + 2$

10. $(0, 0)$ is a solution to the inequality ___?___.

    a. $y < 3x - 1$ **b.** $y > 3x - 1$ **c.** $y \le x - 3$ **d.** $y \ge x + 3$

2-1 The Coordinate Plane

To identify points in the coordinate plane by their coordinates.
To graph given ordered pairs of numbers as points in the coordinate plane.

Two reference lines, or *axes*, are used to locate a point in a plane. The **x-axis** is the horizontal reference line. The **y-axis** is the vertical reference line. Together, the axes separate the plane into four **quadrants,** as shown.

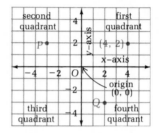

Each point in the plane is represented by an **ordered pair** of real numbers in the form (x, y). The **x-coordinate,** or **abscissa,** is given first. The **y-coordinate,** or **ordinate,** is given second. The x- and y-axes intersect at right angles at the **origin,** the point with coordinates (0, 0).

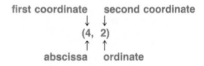

Every point in the **coordinate plane** represents exactly one ordered pair of real numbers. Also, every ordered pair of real numbers represents exactly one point in the coordinate plane. Point P on the graph above has the coordinates (−3, 2), since it is 3 units to the left of the y-axis and 2 units above the x-axis. Point Q has the coordinates (2, −3), since it is 2 units to the right of the y-axis and 3 units below the x-axis.

EXAMPLE 1   Identify each lettered point by its coordinates and by its quadrant or axis.

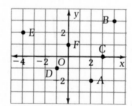

$A(2, -2)$, in fourth quadrant

$B(4, 3)$, in first quadrant

$C(3, 0)$, on x-axis

$D(-1, -1)$, in third quadrant

$E(-4, 2)$, in second quadrant

$F(0, 1)$, on y-axis

EXAMPLE 2

Graph, or *plot*, each ordered pair of numbers.

$G(2, 4)$ $H(0, -2)$

$I(0, 2)$ $J(4, 2)$

$K(-3, 3)$ $L(-4, -1)$

$M(-2, 0)$ $N(0, 0)$

$P(-2, -2)$ $Q(3, -4)$

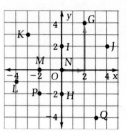

CLASS EXERCISES

Refer to the graph. Name the point described by each statement.

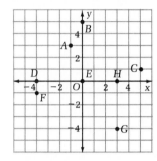

1. The x-coordinate is positive, and the y-coordinate is negative.

2. The abscissa is negative, and the ordinate is zero.

3. The ordinate is positive, and the abscissa is positive.

4. The point lies on the y-axis, but not on the x-axis.

5. Both coordinates are negative.

6. The point lies at the origin.

7. The first coordinate is negative, and the second coordinate is positive.

8. The point lies on the x-axis, and the first coordinate is positive.

EXERCISES

A

Identify each lettered point by its coordinates and by its quadrant or axis.

1. *A*   **2.** *B*

3. *C*   **4.** *D*

5. *E*   **6.** *F*

7. *G*   **8.** *H*

9. *I*   **10.** *J*

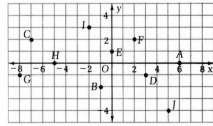

Write the letter for the point with the given coordinates.

11. $(-1, -1)$ **12.** $(-2, 0)$

13. $(-6, -3)$ **14.** $(2, 0)$

15. $(2, -1)$ **16.** $(0, -1)$

17. $(6, 3)$ **18.** $(0, 2)$

19. $\left(\dfrac{1}{2}, -3\right)$ **20.** $\left(-3\dfrac{1}{2}, 3\right)$

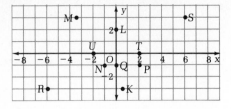

Plot each ordered pair of numbers in the same coordinate plane.

21. $A(5, 7)$ **22.** $B(-6, 1)$ **23.** $C(0, 5)$ **24.** $D(-3, -3)$

25. $E(6, -1)$ **26.** $F(2, -4)$ **27.** $G(0, 0)$ **28.** $H(-3, 0)$

29. $I(0, -1)$ **30.** $J\left(3\dfrac{1}{2}, 1\right)$ **31.** $K\left(-\dfrac{1}{2}, -\dfrac{1}{2}\right)$ **32.** $L(-1.5, 3)$

B

The coordinates of three vertices of a rectangle are given. Graph the three points. Then find the coordinates of the fourth vertex.

33. $(0, 0), (0, 4), (4, 0)$

34. $(-1, 2), (-2, -1), (-2, 2)$

35. $(5, 2), (5, -3), (7, 2)$

36. $(-5, 0), (2, 7), (-6, 1)$

37. $(-2, -2), (0, 0), (3, -3)$

38. $(5, 3), (7, 7), (7, 2)$

Name the quadrant or quadrants containing the points with coordinates (x, y) satisfying the given conditions. Tell if portions of the axes are included.

39. $x > 0$ and $y > 0$ **40.** $x > 0$ and $y < 0$ **41.** $x \leq 0$ and $y \geq 0$

42. $x < 0$ and $y < 0$ **43.** $xy > 0$ **44.** $xy \leq 0$

45. $xy > 0$ and $x < 0$ **46.** $xy > 0$ and $y < 0$ **47.** $xy < 0$ and $x > 0$

C

48. A square has a 4-unit side on each axis. Give the coordinates of the four vertices for each possible location of the square.

49. Two vertices of a square lie at $(1, 2)$ and $(1, -2)$. Find the coordinates of the other two vertices for each possible location of the square. **Hint:** There are three possible locations.

50. The segment with endpoints at $(-3, 3)$ and $(3, -3)$ forms the hypotenuse, or longest side, of each of two right triangles. Find the coordinates of the vertex of the right angle in each triangle, where those coordinates are integers.

*51. Each of three different parallelograms has vertices at $(-3, 0)$, $(3, 0)$, and $(0, 2)$. Find the coordinates of the fourth vertex of each parallelogram. **Hint:** Opposite sides of a parallelogram are parallel and equal in length.

2-2 Linear Equations in Two Variables

OBJECTIVES _____

To graph a linear equation in two variables by first plotting several points
on the line.
To find the *x*- and *y*-intercepts of a line from its equation.

_____

A **linear equation** in two variables is an equation that can be written in
the **standard form** $Ax + By = C$, where A and B are not both zero. A
solution to such an equation is an ordered pair of numbers (x, y) that
makes the equation true.

EXAMPLE 1   Find three solutions for the equation $2x - y = -1$.

Write the equation in the form $y = 2x + 1$. Select three **arbitrary**
values for x. Substitute and find the corresponding values for y.

Let x = 0.	y = 2(0) + 1 = 1	⟶ (0, 1)
Let x = 1.	y = 2(1) + 1 = 3	⟶ (1, 3)
Let x = −1.	y = 2(−1) + 1 = −1	⟶ (−1, −1)

Three solutions are $(0, 1)$, $(1, 3)$, and $(-1, -1)$.

A point is on the graph of an equation if and only if its coordinates
are a solution of the equation. This *if-and-only-if* statement means that
both of the following statements are true.

- If a point is on the graph of an equation, then its coordinates are a
  solution of the equation.
- If the coordinates of a point are a solution of an equation, then the
  point is on the graph of the equation.

All ordered pairs that are solutions of a linear equation identify
points on the same line. That line is the *graph* of the equation. To
graph $2x - y = -1$, we can use the ordered pairs obtained in Example 1.
Only two points are needed to determine the line, but it is useful to
plot a third point as a check.

Plot the three ordered pairs, $(0, 1)$, $(1, 3)$, and
$(-1, -1)$. Draw a straight line through these points.
This line is the graph of $2x - y = -1$.

Note that a point is not on the graph if its coordinates are not a solution to the equation. For example,
$(3, 2)$ is *not* on the line, since $2(3) - 2 \neq -1$.

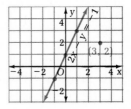

If the variable y is not alone on one side of the given equation, solve the equation for y. Then set up a table of values in order to locate points on the graph.

EXAMPLE 2

Graph $3x + 2y = -4$.

First solve the equation for y in terms of x.

$$3x + 2y = -4$$
$$2y = -3x - 4$$
$$y = -\frac{3}{2}x - 2$$

Then make a table of values. Choose convenient values for x. Do you see why multiples of 2 were chosen in this case? Substitute each value of x in the equation and solve for y.

x	y
-2	1
0	-2
2	-5

$$y = -\frac{3}{2}(-2) - 2$$

$$y = -\frac{3}{2}(0) - 2$$

$$y = -\frac{3}{2}(2) - 2$$

Plot the ordered pairs from the table.

$(-2, 1)$ $(0, -2)$ $(2, -5)$

Draw a straight line through the points.

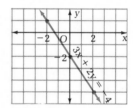

When graphing an equation, it is often convenient to plot the points where the graph crosses the axes. The point at which a line crosses the y-axis has an x-coordinate of 0. The y-coordinate of that point is called the **y-intercept** of the line. The point at which a line crosses the x-axis has a y-coordinate of 0. The x-coordinate of that point is called the **x-intercept** of the line.

EXAMPLE 3

Find the x- and y-intercepts of the line with the equation $2x - 3y = 6$. Use the intercepts to graph the equation.

To find the x-intercept, let $y = 0$. Solve for x.

$$2x - 3(0) = 6$$
$$2x = 6$$
$$x = 3$$

The x-intercept is 3.

To find the y-intercept, let $x = 0$. Solve for y.

$$2(0) - 3y = 6$$
$$-3y = 6$$
$$y = -2$$

The y-intercept is -2.

Plot the points (3, 0) and (0, −2). Draw a straight line through the two points. A third point, such as (6, 2), can be used as a check.

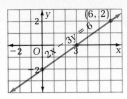

CLASS EXERCISES

Complete the table of values for each equation.

1. $y = x$

x	−3	−2	−1	0
y	?	?	?	?

2. $y = \dfrac{1}{4}x + 1$

x	−8	−4	0	4
y	?	?	?	?

3. $y = -2x - 3$

x	−5	−4	−3	−2
y	?	?	?	?

*Solve for **y** in terms of **x**.*

4. $2x + y = 5$

5. $y - 5x = 0$

6. $-3x + y = 2$

7. $4y = -12x$

8. $-x - y = -1$

9. $x + 5 = y + 2$

*Find three solutions for each equation. Use **x** = −2, **x** = 0, and **x** = 2.*

10. $y = x$

11. $y = \dfrac{1}{2}x$

12. $y = 5x$

13. $y = x - 3$

14. $y = 2x + 6$

15. $x + y = 7$

EXERCISES

A *Find the **y**-value that will make each ordered pair a solution of the equation.*

1. $y = 2x - 5$ (3, _?_) (1, _?_)

2. $5x + y = 15$ (3, _?_) (4, _?_)

3. $4y = x$ (−4, _?_) (1, _?_)

4. $2x + 3y = 6$ (6, _?_) (2, _?_)

5. $x - 6y = 0$ (3, _?_)(−6, _?_)

6. $6x - y = 0$ $(0, \underline{?})\left(\dfrac{1}{2}, \underline{?}\right)$

7. $7x + 3y = -4$ (−4, _?_)(2, _?_)

8. $2x - 3y = 2$ $(1, \underline{?})\left(-\dfrac{1}{2}, \underline{?}\right)$

Complete the table. Then use it to graph the equation.

9. $y = \dfrac{1}{3}x - 2$

x	0	3	9
y	?	?	?

10. $y = 2x + 1$

x	−2	0	2
y	?	?	?

11. $y = \dfrac{x}{4} + 2$

x	−4	0	4
y	?	?	?

Name the **x**- and **y**-intercepts of each line. Assume they are integers.

12.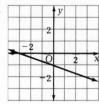

13.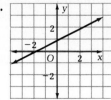

14.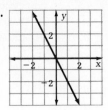

Graph each equation.

15. $y = x + 1$

16. $y = x + 2$

17. $y = x - 2$

18. $y = x - 1$

19. $y = 2x + 2$

20. $y = 3x - 1$

21. $y = -x + 2$

22. $y = -x + 1$

23. $y = -3x + 1$

24. $y = -2x + 3$

25. $y = -2x - 2$

26. $y = -3x - 1$

Find the **x**- and **y**-intercepts of the line with the given equation.

27. $2x - y = 4$

28. $x - 3y = 6$

29. $2x + 3y - 12 = 0$

30. $3x - 2y + 6 = 0$

31. $x - 3y = 5$

32. $2x + y = 3$

33. $3x + 2y = 0$

34. $x + y = -1$

35. $4x - 3y = 4$

36. $5x + 3y = 3$

37. $4x - 3y - 1 = 0$

38. $6x + 8y + 3 = 0$

B

Graph each equation.

39. $y = \dfrac{1}{2}x + 3$

40. $y = \dfrac{1}{4}x - 2$

41. $y = -\dfrac{9}{4}x - 1$

42. $y = -\dfrac{7}{2}x - 1$

43. $y = \dfrac{9}{2}x + \dfrac{1}{4}$

44. $y = \dfrac{13}{4}x + \dfrac{1}{2}$

45. $4x + 2y - 3 = 0$

46. $2x + 3y - 12 = 0$

47. $3x - 3y = 6$

48. $-3x + 2y = 2$

49. $3x - 2y = 6$

50. $-2x - 3y = 1$

51. $x - 3y - 6 = 0$

52. $-x + 2y = 4$

53. $-3x - 2y + 6 = 0$

54. Graph all three of these equations on the same coordinate plane.

$$y = 2x + 3 \qquad y = 2x - 2 \qquad y = 2x + \dfrac{1}{2}$$

What do you notice about all three graphs?
What do all three equations have in common?

55. Repeat Exercise **54** for these three equations.

$$y = -3x + 1 \qquad y = -3x - 1 \qquad y = -3x + 2$$

56. Graph all three of these equations on the same coordinate plane.

$$y = x + 1 \qquad y = 2x + 1 \qquad y = \frac{1}{2}x + 1$$

Note that all three graphs rise to the right. Which of the three graphs is the "steepest?" Which is the least steep? What differences in the equations might account for the differences in the steepness of their graphs?

57. Repeat Exercise **56** for these three equations.

$$y = -x + 1 \qquad y = -2x + 1 \qquad y = -\frac{1}{2}x + 1$$

Note that all three graphs fall to the right.

C *Write a linear equation for the ordered pairs of numbers in each table.*

58.

x	0	1	2	3	4
y	3	4	5	6	7

59.

x	0	1	2	3	4
y	−1	−2	−3	−4	−5

60.

x	−2	−1	0	1	2
y	4	2	0	−2	−4

61.

x	−6	−3	0	3	6
y	−2	−1	0	1	2

62.

x	−2	−1	0	1	2
y	−3	−1	1	3	5

63.

x	−4	−2	0	2	4
y	−3	−2	−1	0	1

USING THE CALCULATOR

Finding Approximate Values of Coordinates

Graph these ordered pairs as accurately as possible. For each irrational number, use your calculator to find a decimal approximation to the nearest tenth.

1. $(2, \sqrt{2})$ **2.** $(\sqrt{3}, 3)$ **3.** $(-1, \sqrt{5})$ **4.** $(-\sqrt{7}, -2)$

5. $(\sqrt{2}, \pi)$ **6.** $\left(\frac{\pi}{4}, -\sqrt{3}\right)$ **7.** $\left(-\frac{\sqrt{3}}{2}, \sqrt{2}\right)$ **8.** $(2\sqrt{2}, -\sqrt{10})$

Complete the table, using decimal approximations to the nearest tenth. Then use the table to obtain an approximation of the graph of the equation.

9. $y = x + \sqrt{2}$

x	−2	0	2
y			

10. $y = \sqrt{3}x$

x	−2	0	2
y			

11. $y = 2x + \sqrt{2}$

x	−2	0	2
y			

12. $y = \sqrt{3}x + \sqrt{3}$

x	−2	0	2
y			

2-3 The Slope of a Line

To find the slope of a line containing two known points.
To find the slope of a line parallel or perpendicular to a line containing two
   known points.
To graph a line, given its slope and a point on the line.

The steepness of a road is defined as the ratio of the vertical *rise* to the
horizontal run. Which of the roads shown below appears to be steeper?

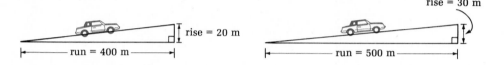

The steepness is $\frac{20}{400}$, or 5%.   The steepness is $\frac{30}{500}$, or 6%

The road on the right is steeper.

The steepness of a line relative to the x-axis is called the **slope** of the
line. To find the slope, choose any two points on the line, say $P(x_1, y_1)$
and $Q(x_2, y_2)$. The slope is given by

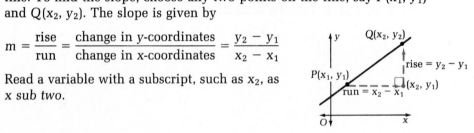

$$m = \frac{\text{rise}}{\text{run}} = \frac{\text{change in y-coordinates}}{\text{change in x-coordinates}} = \frac{y_2 - y_1}{x_2 - x_1}$$

Read a variable with a subscript, such as x_2, as
x sub two.

EXAMPLE 1   Find the slope of the line containing
the points $P(-1, -1)$ and $Q(1, 3)$.

Think of $(-1, -1)$ as (x_1, y_1) and of
$(1, 3)$ as (x_2, y_2).

$$y_2 - y_1 = 3 - (-1) = 4 \qquad \text{rise}$$
$$x_2 - x_1 = 1 - (-1) = 2 \qquad \text{run}$$

Then $m = \frac{y_2 - y_1}{x_2 - x_1} = \frac{4}{2} = 2 \qquad$ slope

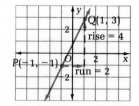

The order in which we take the two points does not matter. Using the last example as an illustration, note that we get the same slope when we interchange *both* y_1 and y_2 and x_1 and x_2.

$$m = \frac{y_1 - y_2}{x_1 - x_2} = \frac{-1 - 3}{-1 - 1} = \frac{-4}{-2} = 2$$

EXAMPLE 2

Find the slope of the line containing the given points.

a. $(-2, 3)$ and $(4, -1)$

$$m = \frac{y_2 - y_1}{x_2 - x_1} = \frac{-1 - 3}{4 - (-2)} = \frac{-4}{6} = -\frac{2}{3}$$

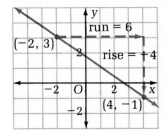

b. $(-4, 2)$ and $(1, 2)$

$$m = \frac{y_2 - y_1}{x_2 - x_1} = \frac{2 - 2}{1 - (-4)} = \frac{0}{5} = 0$$

An equation for this line is $y = 2$. All points on the line are 2 units above the x-axis. Thus, $y_2 - y_1 = 0$ for any two points on the line. In general, the slope of any horizontal line is 0.

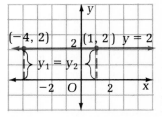

c. $(-3, 3)$ and $(-3, -2)$

$$m = \frac{y_2 - y_1}{x_2 - x_1} = \frac{-2 - 3}{-3 - (-3)} = \frac{-5}{0}$$

Since $\frac{-5}{0}$ is undefined, the slope of the line is undefined. An equation for the line is $x = -3$. All points on the line are 3 units to the left of the y-axis. Thus, $x_2 - x_1 = 0$ for any two points on the line. In general, we say that the slope of any vertical line is undefined.

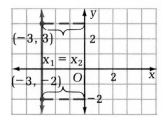

The examples just given illustrate the following general statements.

If a line	*then its slope is*
rises to the right . . .	positive.
falls to the right . . .	negative.
is parallel to the x-axis . . .	zero.
is parallel to the y-axis . . .	undefined.

Recall that lines that lie in a plane and never intersect are called **parallel** lines. Lines that intersect at right angles are called **perpendicular** lines.

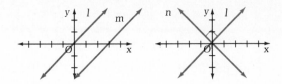

Lines *l* and *m* are parallel. Lines *l* and *n* are perpendicular.

The following statements hold true for lines whose slopes are defined.

Slopes of Parallel Lines and Perpendicular Lines

Lines in the same plane are parallel if and only if they have the same slope.

Two lines are perpendicular if and only if the product of their slopes is −1.

Can you make similar statements about all pairs of lines parallel to the axes?

EXAMPLE 3   Line *l* passes through the points $(-3, 4)$ and $(2, -6)$.

  a. Find the slope of a line parallel to line *l*.

  First, find the slope of line *l*.

  $$m = \frac{-6 - 4}{2 - (-3)} = \frac{-10}{5} = -2$$

  The slope of any line parallel to line *l* is also -2.

  b. Find the slope of a line perpendicular to line *l*.

  The product of the slopes of the two lines is -1.

  From **a**, the slope of line *l* is -2, and

  $$-2\left(\frac{1}{2}\right) = -1$$

  Therefore, the slope of any line perpendicular to *l* is $\frac{1}{2}$.

One method of graphing a linear equation makes use of the slope and the coordinates of a point on the line. There are an infinite number of lines in a plane passing through any given point, but only one of them has a given slope.

EXAMPLE 4   Graph the line containing the point $(-3, 1)$ and having a slope of $\frac{2}{5}$.

Start at $(-3, 1)$. Move 5 units to the right and 2 units up to locate a second point on the line, $(2, 3)$. Draw a line through the two points.

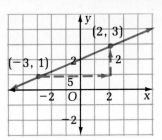

CLASS EXERCISES

Find the slope, if any, of each line.

1. 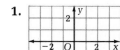   **2.** 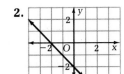   **3.** 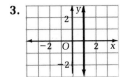   **4.**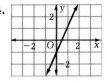

Find the slope of the line containing the given points.

5. $(3, 5)$ and $(5, 7)$ **6.** $(4, 0)$ and $(0, 3)$ **7.** $(-6, -9)$ and $(-3, -8)$

EXERCISES

A   *Find the slope of the line containing the given points.*

1. $(3, 2)$ and $(5, 7)$ **2.** $(-2, -3)$ and $(1, -1)$ **3.** $(-3, 2)$ and $(-1, 1)$

4. $(4, 7)$ and $(2, 3)$ **5.** $(-5, -2)$ and $(-1, -6)$ **6.** $(-3, -1)$ and $(5, -1)$

Find the slope of a line parallel to the line containing

7. $(2, 3)$ and $(-5, 0)$.   **8.** $(-1, 1)$ and $(2, -2)$.   **9.** $(-2, -3)$ and $(-4, -7)$.

Find the slope, if any, of a line perpendicular to the line containing

10. $(0, 0)$ and $(2, 1)$.   **11.** $(-4, 2)$ and $(2, -4)$.   **12.** $(-1, 2)$ and $(3, 2)$.

B   *Graph the line containing the given point and having the given slope.*

13. $(3, 2)$; $m = 2$ **14.** $(-1, -2)$; $m = 1$ **15.** $(-3, -2)$; $m = -2$

16. $(-4, 2)$; $m = \frac{1}{2}$ **17.** $(2, -3)$; $m = 0$ **18.** $(4, -1)$; $m = -\frac{1}{4}$

Plot each set of points and connect them in order. Prove that each figure is a parallelogram by showing that the slopes of the opposite sides are equal.

19. $A(0, 0)$, $B(1, 5)$, $C(4, 7)$, $D(3, 2)$ **20.** $E(0, 0)$, $F(-2, -2)$, $G(-7, -4)$, $H(-5, -2)$

21. $I(3, -2)$, $J(1, -5)$, $K(4, -4)$, $L(6, -1)$ **22.** $P(-3, 1)$, $Q(-1, 4)$, $R(-5, 8)$, $S(-7, 5)$

Plot each set of points and connect them in order to form a square.
Show that the diagonals of each square are perpendicular.

23. $C(0, 0)$, $D(0, 4)$, $E(4, 4)$, $F(4, 0)$ **24.** $G(-2, 2)$, $H(-2, 7)$, $I(-7, 7)$, $J(-7, 2)$

25. $M(4, 2)$, $N(1, 7)$, $P(6, 10)$, $Q(9, 5)$ **26.** $W(0, 0)$, $X(4, 11)$, $Y(-7, 15)$, $Z(-11, 4)$

27. A rectangle is formed when the points $(3, 2)$, $(3, 5)$, $(7, 5)$, and $(7, 2)$ are connected in order. Are the diagonals of the rectangle perpendicular?

28. If a right triangle has vertices at $(3, 1)$, $(3, 5)$, and $(7, 1)$, what is the slope of the hypotenuse?

C

29. The vertices of a quadrilateral are at $P(-4, 1)$, $Q(0, -2)$, $R(6, 6)$, and $S(2, 9)$. Prove that the figure is a parallelogram. Prove that the parallelogram is a rectangle. Are the diagonals of the rectangle perpendicular?

30. A line with slope -3 passes through points $(-4, 5)$ and $(-2, y)$. Find y.

31. A line with slope $\frac{3}{4}$ passes through points $(3, -2)$ and $(x, -5)$. Find x.

32. Do the three points $A(0, 2)$, $B(5, 7)$ and $C(-3, -1)$ lie on one line? Why, or why not?

33. Do the three points $P(-2, -3)$, $Q(0, 0)$, and $R(3, 2)$ lie on one line? Why, or why not?

34. Find the slope of the line with the equation $3x - 2y = 6$.

35. Find the slope of a line perpendicular to the line with the equation $x - 3y + 5 = 0$.

CHECKPOINT

*Graph each equation. Identify the **x**- and **y**-intercepts.*

1. $-4x - 3y + 12 = 0$ **2.** $4y - 5x - 2 = 0$ **3.** $3y = 7x$

4. Find the slope of the line containing the points $(-2, 4)$ and $(6, -3)$.

5. Find the slope of a line parallel to the line containing the points $(-6, -3)$ and $(3, 0)$.

6.. Find the slope of a line perpendicular to the line containing the points $(5, 5)$ and $(5, -3)$.

7. Graph the line with slope $-\frac{3}{4}$ and containing the point $(-1, 5)$.

2-4 The Slope-Intercept Form of a Linear Equation

OBJECTIVES

To find the slope and y-intercept of a line from its equation.
To write an equation for a line, given its slope and either its y-intercept or the coordinates of one point on the line.

If an equation for a line is given, its slope can be calculated from the coordinates of two points on the line. To illustrate, consider the line with the equation $y = 3x + 2$.

First, choose any two values for x and find the corresponding y-values.

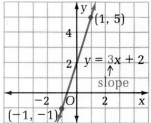

If x = −1, then y = 3(−1) + 2 = −1.
If x = 1, then y = 3(1) + 2 = 5.

Thus, $(-1, -1)$ and $(1, 5)$ are the coordinates of two points on the line. The slope is given by

$$m = \frac{5 - (-1)}{1 - (-1)} = \frac{6}{2} = 3$$

Notice that 3, the slope of the line, is also the coefficient of x in $y = 3x + 2$.

The y-intercept of the line can be found by setting x equal to 0 and solving for y.

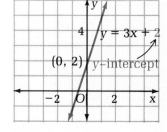

$$y = 3x + 2$$
$$= 3(0) + 2$$
$$= 2$$

The y-intercept is 2. Note that the y-intercept of the line is also the constant term in $y = 3x + 2$.

This discussion leads to the following important generalization.

Slope-Intercept Form of a Linear Equation

When a linear equation is written in the form $y = mx + b$, the slope of the line is m and the y-intercept is b.

$y = mx + b$ is called the *slope-intercept form* of a linear equation.

EXAMPLE 1   Find the slope and y-intercept of the line with the given equation.

a. $-x + 2y = -2$

Write the equation in slope-intercept form.

$$-x + 2y = -2$$
$$2y = x - 2$$
$$y = \frac{1}{2}x - 1 \quad \text{slope-intercept form}$$

slope: $\frac{1}{2}$ y-intercept: -1

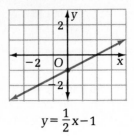

$y = \frac{1}{2}x - 1$

b. $4x + 2(y + 2) - 3 = 1$

$$4x + 2y + 4 - 3 = 1$$
$$4x + 2y = 0$$
$$2x + y = 0$$
$$y = -2x + 0$$

slope: -2 y-intercept: 0

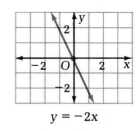

$y = -2x$

c. $x = 3$

The line with the equation $x = 3$ is parallel to the y-axis. The slope of the line is undefined, and there is no y-intercept.

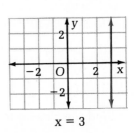

$x = 3$

It is easy to write an equation for a line if the slope and y-intercept are known.

EXAMPLE 2   Write an equation for the line with the given slope m and y-intercept b.

a. $m = 12; b = -5$

$$y = mx + b \qquad \text{Write the general slope-intercept form.}$$
$$y = 12x + (-5) \quad \text{Substitute 12 for } m \text{ and } -5 \text{ for } b.$$
$$y = 12x - 5$$

b. $m = \frac{2}{3}; b = 0$

$$y = mx + b \qquad\qquad\qquad \text{Write the general slope-intercept form.}$$
$$y = \frac{2}{3}x + 0, \text{ or } y = \frac{2}{3}x \quad \text{Substitute } \tfrac{2}{3} \text{ for } m \text{ and } 0 \text{ for } b.$$

If only the slope of the line and the coordinates of one point on the line are known, the y-intercept b can be found as illustrated in the next example.

EXAMPLE 3   Write an equation for the line containing the point $(2, 3)$ and having slope 4.

$y = 4x + b$ Substitute 4 for m in $y = mx + b$.

$3 = 4(2) + b$ $(2, 3)$ is a known point on the line.
                   Substitute 2 for x and 3 for y.

$b = -5$ Solve for b.

$y = 4x - 5$ Substitute 4 for m and -5 for b in $y = mx + b$.

CLASS EXERCISES

*Give the slope and the **y**-intercept of each line, if they exist.*

1. $y = x$ **2.** $y = -x + 3$ **3.** $y = x - 5$ **4.** $y = -x$

5. $y = 3x + 1$ **6.** $y = -\dfrac{1}{2}x - \dfrac{1}{4}$ **7.** $y = 4$ **8.** $x = -\dfrac{1}{4}$

EXERCISES

A   *Find the slope and the **y**-intercept of each line, if they exist.*

1. $y = 6x - 2$ **2.** $y = -7x + 3$ **3.** $y = -5x$ **4.** $y = 13x$

5. $x = 2$ **6.** $y = -9$ **7.** $x + y = 1$ **8.** $3x + 2y = 0$

9. $4y - 8 = 2$ **10.** $6x - 3y = 5$ **11.** $x - 2 = 9$ **12.** $2x + 2y = -6$

*Write an equation for the line with the given slope **m** and **y**-intercept **b**.*

13. $m = 1; b = 2$ **14.** $m = -2; b = 4$ **15.** $m = -3; b = -1$

16. $m = 0.6; b = -0.2$ **17.** $m = \dfrac{1}{2}; b = 1$ **18.** $m = 0; b = -\dfrac{1}{2}$

B   *Find the slope and **y**-intercept of the line with the given equation.*

19. $2y - (3x + 2) = 0$ **20.** $2(3x + y) = 6x - 4$

21. $6x + 2(3 - y) = 0$ **22.** $3(x + 4) + 2(y - 6) = 0$

23. $2(3 - 2x) = 4(2 + y)$ **24.** $3 + 5(2x + y) = 0$

Write the equation of each line in slope-intercept form.

25.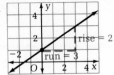

26.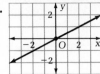

27.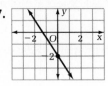

Write an equation for the line containing the given point and having the given slope.

28. (1, 2); m = 1

29. (2, 3); m = −2

30. (5, 2); m = −1

31. (−2, 2); m = $\frac{1}{2}$

32. (6, −3); m = $-\frac{3}{5}$

33. (0, 0); m = $\frac{2}{3}$

34. (−3, −2); m = 0

35. (−3, 0); m = 3

36. (0, −6); m = −6

*Tell whether the two equations represent lines that are **parallel, perpendicular,** or **neither** parallel nor perpendicular.*

37. y = 2x − 3

y = 2x + 5

38. y = 3x + 2

y = −3x − 2

39. y = 3x

y = 3

40. y = −12

x = 1

41. y = −x + 4

y = −x

42. y = $\frac{1}{4}$x

y = −4x − 3

43. y = $-\frac{1}{2}$x + 1

y = −2x + 1

44. y = $\frac{2}{3}$x

2y = −3x

Find the slope of a line perpendicular to the line with the given equation.

45. 2x + 3y = 6

46. −x + 4y = 4

47. 4x = −12

48. 3y = 9x

49. Write an equation for the line with y-intercept 3 that is parallel to the line 3x − 2y + 5 = 0.

50. Write an equation for the line with y-intercept −2 that is perpendicular to the line 2x + 5y − 3 = 0.

C

51. Recall that the standard form of a linear equation is Ax + By = C, where A ≠ 0 or B ≠ 0. Show that if B ≠ 0, then the slope of the line is $-\frac{A}{B}$ and the y-intercept is $\frac{C}{B}$.

52. If possible, find a value of n such that the slope of the line with the equation 2nx − 3y − 8 = 0 is 5.

53. Repeat Exercise **52**, using the equation 2x − 3ny − 8 = 0.

54. If possible, find a value of k such that the y-intercept of the line with the equation 3x + 2ky + 5 = 0 is 4.

55. Repeat Exercise **54** using the equation 3kx + 2y + 5 = 0.

2-5 The Point-Slope Form of a Linear Equation

OBJECTIVE _____

To find an equation of a line, given the coordinates of two points on the line.

_____

You can find an equation for a line if two points on the line are known. The slope can be found using the coordinates of those two points. Then the *slope-intercept form* of a linear equation can be used to find the *y*-intercept.

EXAMPLE 1

Write an equation for the line containing $(1, 4)$ and $(-3, -2)$.

Find the slope, using the coordinates of the given points.

$$m = \frac{y_2 - y_1}{x_2 - x_1} = \frac{-2 - 4}{-3 - 1} = \frac{-6}{-4} = \frac{3}{2}$$

Then find the value of the *y*-intercept *b*.

$$y = \frac{3}{2}x + b \qquad \text{Substitute } \tfrac{3}{2} \text{ for } m \text{ in } y = mx + b.$$

$$4 = \frac{3}{2}(1) + b \qquad \begin{array}{l}\text{Substitute the coordinates of either known point.}\\ \text{We chose } x = 1 \text{ and } y = 4.\end{array}$$

$$b = \frac{5}{2} \qquad \text{Solve for } b.$$

$$y = \frac{3}{2}x + \frac{5}{2} \qquad \begin{array}{l}\text{Substitute } \tfrac{3}{2} \text{ for } m \text{ and } \tfrac{5}{2} \text{ for } b \text{ in } y = mx + b\\ \text{to get an equation for the line.}\end{array}$$

An equation for a line can also be found using the *point-slope form* of a linear equation.

Suppose $(x_1 \ y_1)$ is a point on a line, and (x, y) is any *other* point on the line. Since $x \neq x_1$, the slope of the line is given by

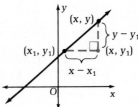

$$\frac{y - y_1}{x - x_1} = m$$

Each side of this equation may be multiplied by $x - x_1$. This gives the **point-slope form of a linear equation:**

$$y - y_1 = m(x - x_1)$$

The next example illustrates the use of the point-slope form to find an equation for a line when the coordinates of two points on the line are known. Compare the procedure with that shown in Example 1.

EXAMPLE 2   Write an equation for the line containing the points $(-2, 9)$ and $(1, -3)$.

Find the slope, using the coordinates of the given points.

$$m = \frac{-3 - 9}{1 - (-2)} = \frac{-12}{3} = -4$$

Then substitute known values for m, x_1, and y_1 in the general point-slope form.

$y - y_1 = m(x - x_1)$

$y - y_1 = -4(x - x_1)$ Substitute -4 for m.

$y - (-3) = -4(x - 1)$ Use either pair of known coordinates as (x_1, y_1).
                             Here we chose $x_1 = 1$ and $y_1 = -3$.

$y + 3 = -4x + 4$

$y = -4x + 1$

You can check this result by substituting the x- and y-coordinates of the other known point in the equation.

$9 = -4(-2) + 1$ Substitute 9 for y and -2 for x.

$9 = 9$ ✔

An equation for the line is $y = -4x + 1$.

Suppose you know an equation for a line parallel to or perpendicular to a second line. An equation for the second line can be found if you know the coordinates of one point on that line.

EXAMPLE 3   Write an equation for the line that is perpendicular to $y = -2x + 6$ and has the x-intercept 6.

The x-intercept is 6, so $(6, 0)$ is one point on the line.

The slope of a line perpendicular to $y = -2x + 6$ is $\frac{1}{2}$, since $-2\left(\frac{1}{2}\right) = -1$.

Either the slope-intercept form or the point-slope form can be used to find the equation. Here we use the point-slope form.

$y - y_1 = m(x - x_1)$

$y - 0 = \frac{1}{2}(x - 6)$ Substitute $\frac{1}{2}$ for m, 6 for x_1, and 0 for y_1.

$y = \frac{1}{2}x - 3$

CLASS EXERCISES

Use the point-slope form to write an equation for the line containing the given point and having the given slope.

1. $(1, 1)$; $m = 1$ **2.** $(3, 2)$; $m = -2$ **3.** $(2, 1)$; $m = 3$

4. $(-2, 3)$; $m = 2$ **5.** $(-3, 2)$; $m = \dfrac{1}{2}$ **6.** $(-2, -3)$; $m = \dfrac{1}{4}$

Use the point-slope form to write an equation for the line containing

7. $(0, 0)$ and $(2, -3)$.   **8.** $(1, -3)$ and $(3, -1)$.   **9.** $(-2, -5)$ and $(2, -4)$.

EXERCISES

A

Use the point-slope form to write an equation for the line containing the given point and having the given slope.

1. $(1, -2)$; $m = 2$ **2.** $(-1, 3)$; $m = -1$ **3.** $(0, 4)$; $m = 1$

4. $(-2, 0)$; $m = \dfrac{1}{2}$ **5.** $(0, 0)$; $m = -\dfrac{3}{4}$ **6.** $(-4, -4)$; $m = -\dfrac{3}{2}$

7. $(3, -1)$; $m = 0$ **8.** $(4, 4)$; $m = 1$ **9.** $(5, -5)$; $m = -5$

Write an equation for the line containing the given points.

10. $(4, 7)$ and $(2, 3)$ **11.** $(-5, -2)$ and $(-1, -6)$ **12.** $(-2, 11)$ and $(1, -4)$

13. $(3, -3)$ and $(0, 0)$ **14.** $(3, 2)$ and $(5, 7)$ **15.** $(-2, -3)$ and $(1, -1)$

16. $(-3, -2)$ and $(-1, -1)$ **17.** $(-1, 1)$ and $(4, 5)$ **18.** $(-3, 2)$ and $(3, -2)$

19. $(0, 0)$ and $(-5, -5)$ **20.** $(2, 7)$ and $(-4, 7)$ **21.** $(3, -4)$ and $(4, -4)$

B

Write an equation for the line that

22. has y-intercept 4 and x-intercept -1.

23. is parallel to $y = x$ and has x-intercept 3.

24. is parallel to the x-axis and passes through $(-3, 4)$.

25. is parallel to the y-axis and passes through $(5, -7)$.

26. is parallel to $3x + y = 2$ and passes through $(4, -3)$.

27. is perpendicular to $y = \dfrac{1}{2}x + 4$ and passes through $(6, 7)$.

28. is parallel to the line through $(4, -3)$ and $(-2, 1)$ and contains $(0, 0)$.

29. is perpendicular to the x-axis and passes through $(1, 4)$.

30. is perpendicular to the y-axis and passes through $(-2, 2)$.

31. is parallel to $2x - 4y = 8$ and passes through $(1, 1)$.

32. Write an equation for the line that is perpendicular to $y = 5x + 2$ and has the same x-intercept as $2x + y = 3$.

C

33. A line contains two points, (x_1, y_1) and (x_2, y_2). Show that if $x_1 \neq x_2$, an equation for the line is

$$y - y_1 = \frac{y_2 - y_1}{x_2 - x_1}(x - x_1)$$

This is called the *two-point form of a linear equation.*

34. Use the *two-point form* presented in Exercise **33** to write an equation for the line through $(3, -2)$ and $(-2, 5)$.

35. One vertex of a triangle is at $(-3, 1)$, and the side opposite that vertex is on the line $x - 2y = 4$. Find an equation for the line containing the altitude of the triangle through the given vertex.

36. The three sides of a triangle are on the lines $2x - y + 5 = 0$, $y + 5 = -3x$, and $x + 2y - 6 = 0$. Prove that the triangle is a right triangle.

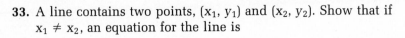

EXTRA TOPIC

The Intercept Form of a Linear Equation

Consider a line with the equation $Ax + By = C$, where A, B, and C are not equal to 0. The intercepts of the line can be expressed in terms of A, B, and C. If $y = 0$, then $Ax = C$ and $x = \frac{C}{A}$; so $\frac{C}{A}$ is the x-intercept. If $x = 0$, then $By = C$ and $y = \frac{C}{B}$; so $\frac{C}{B}$ is the y-intercept.

To obtain the **intercept form** of the equation $Ax + By = C$, each term is divided by C. Then p is substituted for $\frac{C}{A}$ and q for $\frac{C}{B}$.

$$\frac{Ax}{C} + \frac{By}{C} = \frac{C}{C}$$

$$\frac{x}{\frac{C}{A}} + \frac{y}{\frac{C}{B}} = 1$$

Intercept form of a linear equation $\dfrac{x}{p} + \dfrac{y}{q} = 1$ p is the x-intercept. q is the y-intercept.

1. Write the equation $3x - 2y = 6$ in intercept form.

2. Write the intercept form of the equation of the line containing the points $(-4, 0)$ and $(0, 5)$.

2-6   Relations and Functions

OBJECTIVES _____

To identify relations that are functions.
To state the domain and range of a relation or a function.
To evaluate the function value $f(x)$ for given values of x.

_____

The graph at the right shows four points in the plane. The set of ordered pairs of numbers that are the coordinates of these points is called a *relation*.

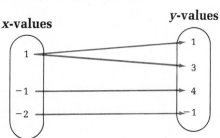

A **relation** is a set of ordered pairs of numbers.

The relation shown in the graph is this set of ordered pairs.

$$\{(1, 1), (1, 3), (-1, 4), (-2, -1)\}$$

We can also show this relation by a **mapping**.

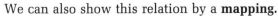

x-values   **y-values**

The set of x-values is called the **domain** of the relation.

The set of y-values is called the **range** of the relation.

EXAMPLE 1   State the domain and the range of the relation
$\{(-1, 3), (0, 2), (0, -3), (1, 5), (2, -2)\}$.

The domain is the set of x-values: $\{-1, 0, 1, 2\}$.

The range is the set of y-values: $\{3, 2, -3, 5, -2\}$.

   In the example above, notice that the x-value 0 is associated with, or mapped into, two different y-values, 2 and -3. Sometimes a set of ordered pairs is given in which there is only one y-value for each x-value. When that is the case, we call the relation a *function*.

   A **function** is a set of ordered pairs of numbers such that
   for each x-value there is exactly one y-value.

A *function can be described by a table of values.*

This function is the set of ordered pairs

$$\{(-2, 1), (-1, 0), (0, 3), (2, -2)\}$$

Domain of the function: $\{-2, -1, 0, 2\}$
Range of the function: $\{1, 0, 3, -2\}$

x	y
−2	1
−1	0
0	3
2	−2

A *function can be described by a graph.*

This is the graph of a function. For each x-value, there is exactly one corresponding y-value.

Domain of the function: all real numbers
Range of the function: all real numbers

A *function can be described by a rule.*

The equation $y = 3x - 2$ is a rule that describes how values of x are to be paired with values of y. For any given value of x, we can use the equation to find the corresponding value of y. We say that *y is a function of x.*

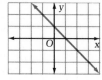

Domain of the function: all real numbers
Range of the function: all real numbers

A **linear function** is a function that can be described by an equation of the form $y = mx + b$, where m and b are real numbers. Therefore, the function described by the equation $y = 3x - 2$ is a linear function. It can be written in *function notation* as

$$f(x) = 3x - 2 \qquad f(x) \text{ is read "} f \text{ of } x.\text{" We speak of } \textit{the}$$
$$\textit{function } f \textit{ defined by } f(x) = 3x - 2 \text{ or,}$$
$$\text{more simply, } \textit{the function } f(x) = 3x - 2.$$

The value of the function when $x = 2$ is given by

$$f(2) = 3(2) - 2 = 4$$

The value of the function when $x = a$ is given by

$$f(a) = 3a - 2$$

Letters other than f are often used in function notation.

EXAMPLE 2   Let $g(x) = x^2 + 5x - 24$.

a. Find $g(0)$. $g(0) = 0^2 + 5(0) - 24 = -24$

b. Find $g(-1)$. $g(-1) = (-1)^2 + 5(-1) - 24 = -28$

c. Find $g(3)$. $g(3) = 3^2 + 5(3) - 24 = 0$

Sometimes it is easy to see that an equation does not define a function.

EXAMPLE 3   Does $y^2 = x$ describe y as a function of x?

No. If $y^2 = x$, then $y = \sqrt{x}$ or $y = -\sqrt{x}$. For instance, if $x = 4$, then $y = 2$ or $y = -2$. There is not a unique value of y for each x.

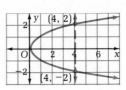

It is also possible to tell whether or not a relation is a function by looking at its graph. The graph of $y^2 = x$ is shown at the right. Note that both $(4, 2)$ and $(4, -2)$ lie on the same vertical line. If any vertical line intersects a graph in more than one point, the graph does not represent a function. It represents a relation that is not a function.

Each of these three graphs represents a function. Consider any line parallel to the y-axis. It will cross the graph in at most one point.

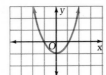 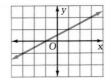 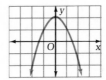

Explain why these three graphs do *not* represent functions.

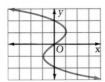 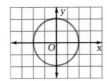 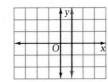

CLASS EXERCISES

*Write the relation shown in the graph. State the domain and the range of the relation. State whether the relation **is** or **is not a function**.*

1. 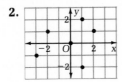   **2.** 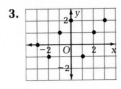   **3.**

Let $g(x) = 2x^2 - 3x + 1$. Find:

4. $g(0)$ **5.** $g(1)$ **6.** $g(-1)$ **7.** $g(-2)$

LINEAR EQUATIONS AND FUNCTIONS

EXERCISES

A Write the domain and the range of each relation. Then state whether the relation **is** or **is not a function.**

1. $\{(2, -1), (3, -2), (4, -3), (5, 0)\}$

2. $\{(1, 3), (2, -2), (3, -2), (-2, 0)\}$

3. $\{(-2, 1), (0, 1), (2, 1), (3, 1)\}$

4. $\{(3, 2), (3, -1), (3, 0), (3, -3)\}$

State whether the relation shown in each graph or mapping **is** or **is not a function.**

5.

6.

7.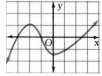

8.

9.

10.

Let $f(x) = 2x + 1$. Find:

11. $f(0)$ **12.** $f(3)$ **13.** $f(5)$ **14.** $f(-2)$

Let $f(x) = \frac{x}{2} - 3$. Find:

15. $f(4)$ **16.** $f(-2)$ **17.** $f(0)$ **18.** $f(3)$

Let $g(x) = 2x^2 - 1$. Find: **21.** $g(-1)$ **22.** $g(-5)$

19. $g(0)$ **20.** $g(2)$

Let $g(x) = x^2 + 5x$. Find: **25.** $g(-3)$ **26.** $g\left(\frac{1}{2}\right)$

23. $g(2)$ **24.** $g(5)$

Let $g(x) = x^2 - 3x + 2$. Find:

27. $g(0)$ **28.** $g(-2)$ **29.** $g(5)$ **30.** $g\left(-\frac{1}{2}\right)$

B Let $f(x) = \frac{5}{x^2 - 1}$. Find:

31. $f(3)$ **32.** $f(0)$ **33.** $f(-4)$ **34.** $f\left(\frac{1}{4}\right)$

Let $g(x) = \frac{1}{2}x^2 - \frac{3}{4}x + 2$. Find:

35. $g(1)$ **36.** $g(4)$ **37.** $g(-4)$ **38.** $g\left(-\frac{1}{2}\right)$

Let $h(x) = x^3 - 2x^2 + 4x - 3$. Find:

39. $h(-1)$ **40.** $h(-4)$ **41.** $h\left(\frac{1}{2}\right)$ **42.** $h\left(-\frac{1}{2}\right)$

43. This is the graph of the function

$$f(x) = \begin{cases} 2, & \text{if } x \le 0 \\ -2, & \text{if } x > 0 \end{cases}$$

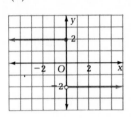

Explain why this relation is a function. Then state the domain and range of the function.

Graph each function.

44. $f(x) = \begin{cases} 1, & \text{if } x \le 0 \\ -3, & \text{if } x > 0 \end{cases}$ **45.** $f(x) = \begin{cases} -2, & \text{if } -2 < x < 0 \\ 1, & \text{if } x \ge 0 \end{cases}$

46. This is the graph of the **absolute value function,** $g(x) = |x|$. The function may be rewritten in this form.

$$f(x) = |x| = \begin{cases} x, & \text{if } x \ge 0 \\ -x, & \text{if } x < 0 \end{cases}$$

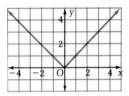

Explain why this relation is a function. Then state its domain and range.

Graph the function given by each equation.

47. $y = |x| + 2$ **48.** $y = |x| - 2$ **49.** $y = |x + 2|$ **50.** $y = |x - 2|$

Consider the function $f(x) = x^2$.

51. Does $f(a) = f(-a)$?   **52.** Does $f(a) = -f(a)$?

Consider the function $g(x) = x^2 + x$.

53. Does $g(a) = g(-a)$?   **54.** Does $g(a) = -g(a)$?

Consider the function $h(x) = x^2 + 3x - 2$.

55. Does $h(2) + h(3) = h(5)$?   **56.** Does $2h(5) = h(10)$?

C

57. Which of the following equations describe functions? Explain your answer.

    a. $y^3 = x$ **b.** $y^4 = x$ **c.** $y^5 = x$

Find the domain for each function.

58. $f(x) = \dfrac{3}{x - 2}$
59. $f(x) = \dfrac{4}{x(x + 1)}$
60. $f(x) = \dfrac{x}{x^2 - 4}$

61. Let $f(x) = x^2 + 3x - 2$ and $g(x) = 2x + 5$. Find $f(-2) + g(3)$.

62. Let $f(x) = 3x - 2$. Simplify $\dfrac{f(x + a) - f(a)}{a}$.

63. Let $f(x) = x^2 + 1$. Simplify $\dfrac{f(a) - f(2a)}{3}$.

Let $\boldsymbol{f(x) = 2x^2 - 3}$ and $\boldsymbol{g(x) = 3x - 5}$.

64. Find $f(g(4))$. **Hint:** First find $g(4)$. **65.** Find $g(f(4))$. **66.** Find $f(f(4))$.

CHECKPOINT

*Use the following directions for Exercises **1–6**.*

Plot the given points and draw a line through them.

Write the slope of the line.

Write the equation of the line in slope-intercept form.

*Identify the **y**-intercept of the line.*

1. (4, 1) and (6, 3)   **2.** (−2, −6) and (1, 3)   **3.** (−2, 1) and (−1, 0)

4. (−2, −2) and (6, 2)   **5.** (−5, −2) and (−1, −2)   **6.** (0, 3) and (−5, 4)

Write the equation of the line parallel to the first line and having the same **y**-intercept as the second line.

7. $y = \dfrac{1}{2}x + 3;\ y = \dfrac{1}{4}x - 2$

8. $y = -\dfrac{7}{2}x - 1;\ y = -\dfrac{9}{4}x + \dfrac{1}{2}$

Write the equation of the line perpendicular to the first line and having the same **y**-intercept as the second line.

9. $-x + 2y = 4;\ -3x - 2y + 6 = 0$ **10.** $x - 3y - 6 = 0;\ -2x - 3y = 1$

Write the **domain** and **range** of each relation. State whether or not the relation is a function.

11. {(3, 1), (3, −1), (3, 2), (3, −2)}   **12.** {(1, 4), (−1, 4), (2, 4), (−2, 4)}

13. {(4, 4), (3, 3), (2, 2), (0, 0)}   **14.** {(a, b), (c, d), (e, f), (a, z)}

Let $\boldsymbol{f(x) = 3x^2 - 4}$. Find:

15. $f(0)$ **16.** $f(-1)$ **17.** $f(1)$ **18.** $f\left(\dfrac{1}{2}\right)$

Discovering a Rule

We are often asked to give a general rule on the basis of a few examples. When this happens, it is important to be careful not to jump to conclusions. To illustrate, what rule, or function, might be defined by the partial listing of ordered pairs in this table?

x	−3	−2	−1	0	1	2	3
y	−3	−2	−1	0	1	2	3

Assuming that the pattern shown in the table holds for all integers, it appears that every integer is mapped onto itself. That is, it seems that the rule is $y = f(x) = x$.

However, it is natural to ask what happens when the x-values are *not* integers. Suppose the table is extended to show additional ordered pairs.

x	−3	−2.2	−2	−1.7	−1	−0.4	0	0.9	1	1.1	2	2.6	3
y	−3	−3	−2	−2	−1	−1	0	0	1	1	2	2	3

Assuming that the pattern holds for real numbers between integers, can you state a general rule? Here is one way to describe this function.

If x is an integer, then y is that same integer.
If x is not an integer, then y is the integer preceding x.

This is known as the **greatest integer function.** It is named and described in abbreviated form as

[x]: the greatest integer not greater than x

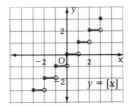

That is, [x] is the greatest integer less than or equal to x. The graph of the function for $-3 \le x \le 3$ is shown at the right. Can you see why $y = f(x) = [x]$ is often called a *step function?*

Try to write a function in terms of [**x**] *that is defined by the ordered pairs in each table. Assume that the pattern shown holds for all real numbers.*

1.

x	−3	−2.1	−2	−1.8	−1	−0.3	0	0.7	1	1.6	2
y	3	3	2	2	1	1	0	0	−1	−1	−2

2.

x	−3	−2.9	−2	−1.5	−1	−0.3	0	0.4	1	1.8	2
y	−6	−6	−4	−4	−2	−2	0	0	2	2	4

3.

x	−3	−2.7	−2	−1.6	−1	−0.5	0	0.2	1	1.9	2
y	−4	−4	−3	−3	−2	−2	−1	−1	0	0	1

2-7 Linear Inequalities in Two Variables

OBJECTIVE _____

To graph a linear inequality in two variables.

_____

Every _linear inequality_ has a related linear equation. For example, the inequality $y < 2x + 1$ has the related equation $y = 2x + 1$. Similarly, the inequality $y \geq 5x - 4$ has the related equation $y = 5x - 4$.

   To graph a linear inequality in two variables, start with the graph of the related equation. This line separates the coordinate plane into three parts: the regions on either side of the line, and the line itself.

   The graph of each inequality above is a region _bounded_ by the line $y = x$. The points on a dashed line are not part of the graph. The points on a solid line are part of the graph. The graph consists of all points (x, y) that satisfy the given inequality.

EXAMPLE 1   Graph $y \leq 2x + 1$.

Graph the related equation
$y = 2x + 1$. This line is the boundary of the graph of the inequality
and is included in the graph.
   To find which region is the graph
of the inequality, test a point not on
the line to see if it is a solution. A
convenient choice here is $(0, 0)$.

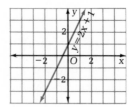

$y \leq 2x + 1$

$0 \leq 2(0) + 1$

$0 \leq 1$

   $(0, 0)$ is a solution, so shade the region that contains the origin. All
points in that region are solutions.

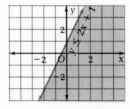

EXAMPLE 2   Graph the inequality $y > \frac{1}{2}x$.

Graph the line $y = \frac{1}{2}x$, using a dashed line to show that it is not part of the graph. The origin lies on this boundary, so test another point, say (1, 0).

For $x = 1$ and $y = 0$: $0 \not> \frac{1}{2}$

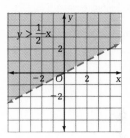

Since (1, 0) is not a solution, shade the region that does *not* contain (1, 0).

In general, the graph of $y > mx + b$ consists of all points *above* the line $y = mx + b$. The graph of $y < mx + b$ consists of all points *below* the line $y = mx + b$.

EXAMPLE 3   Graph $3x - 2y \geq 6$.

First solve the inequality for y.

$$3x - 2y \geq 6$$
$$-2y \geq -3x + 6$$
$$y \leq \frac{3}{2}x - 3$$

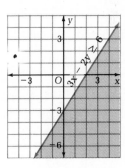

Graph the line $y = \frac{3}{2}x - 3$. Test a point to verify that the graph of the inequality is the region on and below that line.

CLASS EXERCISES

Match the inequality with its graph.

1. $y \leq -x + 1$ **2.** $y < -x + 1$ **3.** $y > -x + 1$ **4.** $y \geq -x + 1$

a.

b.

c.

d.

EXERCISES _____

A *Graph each inequality.*

1. $y > 2x$ **2.** $y < 2x$ **3.** $y < -2x$

4. $y < -x$ **5.** $y \geq 3x$ **6.** $y \geq 4x$

7. $y \leq x + 1$ **8.** $y \leq x - 1$ **9.** $y < 2x - 3$

10. $y < 3x + 2$ **11.** $y > -x - 2$ **12.** $y > -x + 3$

13. $x > 1$ **14.** $x \geq -1$ **15.** $x \leq -2$

16. $y < 4$ **17.** $y > 2$ **18.** $y < -2$

B **19.** $4x + 2y - 3 < 0$ **20.** $2x + 3y > 12$ **21.** $3x + y \geq 8$

22. $y + 3x \leq 0$ **23.** $2x - y > -4$ **24.** $-3x + 2y < 2$

25. $-2x + y \leq -3$ **26.** $3x - 2y \geq 6$ **27.** $3x - 3y \geq 6$

28. $-\dfrac{1}{4}x + y > -2$ **29.** $\dfrac{1}{2}x - y < 2$ **30.** $-2x - 3y \leq 6$

31. Does $y > x$ define a function? Why or why not?

C *Graph each inequality.*

32. $y \geq |x|$ **33.** $y < |x| + 2$ ***34.** $|y| \leq x - 2$

Write an inequality for each graph.

35.   **36.**   **37.**   **38.**

39.   **40.**   **41.**   **42.**

Graph the two inequalities and shade the region that satisfies both.

43. $y < 3$ **44.** $x + y \leq 2$ **45.** $2x + 3y < 9$
$\quad\; x < -1$ $\qquad\; x - y \geq 1$ $\qquad\; y > 3x - 4$

Statistical Data

Statisticians collect and analyze numerical information in many forms. They must be skillful in presenting such data both in tables and in graphs.

Example This table shows how the population of American youth has shifted since 1960. Show the trends in a graph.

Population of Youth in U.S.A. (in millions)

Age	1960	1970	1980	1990*
0-5	24.3	21.0	19.6	23.0
6-11	21.7	24.6	20.7	21.8
12-17	18.2	24.1	23.3	19.5
Totals	64.2	69.7	63.6	64.3

*projected

Line graphs show the population changes visually. In this graph, each age group is represented by a separate line.

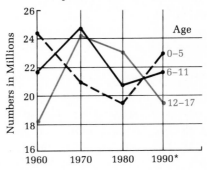

Population of Youth in U.S.A.

Use the table.

1. What is the projected decrease in the 12-17 age group between 1970 and 1990?

2. Approximately what percent of the youth were from 12 through 17 years old in 1980?

3. Approximately 28.4% of the 1980 population of the United States was 17 years old or younger. Estimate the total 1980 population of the United States.

Use the graph.

4. For which age group, and over which ten-year interval, was the population change the greatest?

5. Estimate the year when all three population groups had, or will have, about the same number.

6. Describe trends in the 0–5 age group from 1960 to 1990.

7. In what way does the graph distort the data in the table?

CHAPTER 2 REVIEW

VOCABULARY

x-axis; y-axis (p. 48)
quadrant (p. 48)
ordered pair of real numbers (p. 48)
coordinates (p. 48)
abscissa (p. 48)
ordinate (p. 48)
origin (p. 48)
coordinate plane (p. 48)
linear equation (p. 51)
standard form: $Ax + By = C$ (p. 51)
if-and-only-if statement (p. 51)
x-intercept; y-intercept (p. 52)
rise (p. 56)
run (p. 56)

slope of a line (p. 56)
parallel lines (p. 58)
perpendicular lines (p. 58)
slope-intercept form: $y = mx + b$ (p. 61)
point-slope form: $y - y_1 = m(x - x_1)$ (p. 65)
relation (p. 69)
mapping (p. 69)
domain (p. 69)
range (p. 69)
function (p. 69)
linear function (p. 70)
function notation (p. 70)
linear inequality (p. 76)

SUMMARY

The work in this chapter continues the review and extension of your first-year algebra course. The coordinate plane is reviewed. Then linear equations and their graphs are introduced, with emphasis on the relationships between such equations and the slopes and y-intercepts of their graphs. Different forms of the equation of a line are presented, and the relationships between the slopes of parallel and perpendicular lines are discussed. The chapter ends with an introduction to relations and functions, as well as a lesson on linear inequalities.

REVIEW EXERCISES

2-1 *The coordinates of three vertices of a rectangle are given. Graph the three points. Then find the coordinates of the fourth vertex.*

1. (4, 0), (4, 3), (0, 3)

2. (−1, −2), (2, −2), (2, 2)

2-2 *Complete the table. Then use the ordered pairs to graph the equation.*

3. $y = 3x - 2$

x	0	2	4
y			

4. $y = -\frac{1}{2}x + 3$

x	0	−6	6
y			

Graph each equation.

5. $y = -3x + 1$

6. $y = -x - 2$

7. $3x + 2y = 5$

8. $4y - x = 7$

9. $3y + x - 4 = 0$

10. $2y - x - 2 = 0$

*Find the **x**- and **y**-intercepts of the line with the given equation.*

11. $y = -x + 1$ **12.** $2x - y + 4 = 0$ **13.** $3x - 2y = 12$

2-3   *A line contains the points with coordinates (2, 1) and (5, 2).*

14. Find the slope of the line.

15. Find the slope of any line that is parallel to the given line.

16. Find the slope of any line that is perpendicular to the given line.

*The coordinates of three vertices of a square are **A**(0, 0), **B**(2, 2), and **C**(4, 0).*

17. Find the coordinates of the fourth vertex, D, of the square.

18. Plot the four vertices and connect them in order.

19. Use slopes to show that the opposite sides of the square are parallel.

20. Use the slopes of the sides of the square to show that $\overline{AB} \perp \overline{AD}$ and $\overline{BC} \perp \overline{CD}$.

21. Use the slope to show that the diagonal of the square, $\overline{AC}$, is horizontal.

22. Use the slope to show that the diagonal $\overline{BD}$ is vertical.

23. Graph the line that has a slope of 2 and contains the point (4, 0).

2-4   *Find the slope and **y**-intercept of the line that has the given equation.*

24. $y - 2(5x + 3) = 0$ **25.** $6(x - 2) - 4(y + 2) = 0$ **26.** $7 + 3(4x - y) = 0$

*Write the equation for the line that has the given slope **m** and **y**-intercept **b**.*

27. $m = 2; b = 1$ **28.** $m = -\dfrac{1}{2}; b = -1$ **29.** $m = \dfrac{3}{4}; b = -3$

30. Write the equation for the line with a slope of -3 and containing the point (6, -5).

2-5   *Write an equation for the line that contains the given points.*

31. (4, -4) and (0, 0)   **32.** (2, 3) and (-4, 6)   **33.** (-1, -2) and (5, 0)

2-6   **34.** Write the domain and the range for the relation {(0, 1), (1, 2), (2, 3), (3, 4)}. How do you know that the relation is a function?

35. Let $g(x) = \dfrac{x}{4} - 3$. Find $g(1)$.   **36.** Let $h(x) = \dfrac{3}{x^2 + 5}$. Find $h(0)$.

2-7   *Graph each inequality.*

37. $y < 2x$ **38.** $y > -1$ **39.** $y \leq 2x + 3$

40. $3x - 2y < 4$ **41.** $\dfrac{1}{2}x + \dfrac{1}{4}y \geq -1$ **42.** $x > 0$ and $y > 0$

Identify each lettered point by its coordinates and by its quadrant or axis.

1. A

2. B

3. C

4. D

5. E

6. F

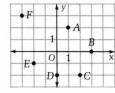

Graph each of the following by using the **x**-intercept and the **y**-intercept. As a check, plot a third point on the line.

7. $2x + 3y = 12$

8. $y - x = 4$

9. Find the slope of the line that contains points with coordinates $(-1, -2)$ and $(6, -4)$.

10. Graph the line that has a slope of 3 and contains the point with coordinates $(5, 3)$.

11. Find the slope and the y-intercept of the line with equation $4y + 3x + 6 = 0$.

12. Find the y-intercept of the line that passes through the point with coordinates $(2, 4)$ and has a slope of 2.

In Exercises 13–16, write the equation of the line that satisfies each given condition.

13. Line with slope $\frac{1}{2}$ and y-intercept -2.

14. Line through the point with coordinates $(1, 2)$ and parallel to the line that has the equation $3x - y - 4 = 0$

15. Line through the point with coordinates $(-2, 3)$ and perpendicular to the line that has the equation $2x - y = 3$

16. Line that contains the points with coordinates $(-2, 3)$ and $(4, -5)$

17. Find the y-intercept of the line that contains the points with coordinates $(-1, 0)$ and $(2, 3)$.

18. Let $g(x) = \frac{2(x - 3)}{4}$. Find $g(1)$.

19. Let $f(x) = 3x^2 - 2$. Find $f(-2)$.

20. Graph the linear inequality: $y > 3x - 4$.

Equation of a Line

The program below asks for the coordinates of one point on a line and for the slope of the line. Then it displays the equation of the line in the form $y = mx + b$. But b can be positive, negative, or zero. When a number is negative, the computer will display its sign. A positive number is displayed without a sign. IF . . . THEN . . . statements are used to do this.

IF b is greater than zero (positive), THEN line 210 instructs the computer to jump to line 250 and display the plus sign. IF b equals zero, THEN line 220 instructs the computer to jump to line 270 and display only mx. When b is less than zero, the computer continues to line 230 for the third type of display. Then GO TO in line 240 sends the computer to line 900.

The Program	What It Does
`100 REM EQUATION OF LINE`	Gives the program a title.
`110 PRINT "ENTER X, Y";`	Prompts you to make an entry.
`120 INPUT X, Y`	Stops the computer. Waits for the two coordinates separated by a comma.
`130 PRINT "ENTER SLOPE";`	
`140 INPUT M`	Waits for slope as an integer or a decimal.
`150 LET B = Y - M * X`	Computes the value of b.
`200 PRINT "EQUATION IS: Y =";`	Labels the output.
`210 IF B > 0 THEN 250`	IF b is positive, jumps to line 250.
`220 IF B = 0 THEN 270`	IF b is zero, jumps to line 270.
`230 PRINT M; "X"; B`	Displays equation when B is negative.
`240 GO TO 900`	
`250 PRINT M; "X + "; B`	Displays equation when B is positive.
`260 GO TO 900`	
`270 PRINT M; "X"`	Displays equation when B is zero.
`900 END`	

`RUN`	The coordinates (5, 2) are entered in order, separated by a comma.
`ENTER X, Y ? 5, 2`	
`ENTER SLOPE ? 3`	A slope of 3 is entered, or *input*.
`EQUATION IS Y = 3X - 13`	The equation is displayed.

The semicolons instruct the computer to display the data that follows on the same line, just next to the previous data.

What does the computer display for each of these entries?

1. (4, 5) Slope 2   **2.** (3, 24) Slope 5   **3.** (−1, 6) Slope −6

4. (2, 5) Slope 1.5   **5.** (3, 4) Slope 0   **6.** (0, 0) Slope −5

7. Write a program in BASIC that asks for the coordinates of two points on a line and displays the slope of the line.

For more information about BASIC, see the Computer Handbook at the back of the book.

A system of equations can be used to determine the amounts of different chemicals needed to obtain a solution with the desired composition.

SYSTEMS OF LINEAR EQUATIONS AND INEQUALITIES

Prerequisite Skills Review

Write the letter for the correct answer.

1. Every solution to the equation $y = 3x - \dfrac{1}{2}$ is also a solution to the equation __?__ .

   a. $3x + y = \dfrac{1}{2}$ **b.** $12x - 4y = -2$ **c.** $6x - 2y = 1$ **d.** $3x - 2y = 1$

2. The value of x nickels, in cents, is __?__ .
   a. $0.05x$ **b.** $0.5x$ **c.** $5x$ **d.** none of these

3. Two-thirds of a number n, less 6, is written mathematically as __?__ .

   a. $\dfrac{2}{3}n - 6$ **b.** $\dfrac{2}{3}(n - 6)$ **c.** $\dfrac{2}{3}(6 - n)$ **d.** none of these

4. If $6 - 2x = 3y$, then $x = $ __?__ .

   a. $-\dfrac{2}{3}y + 2$ **b.** $\dfrac{3}{2}y + 3$ **c.** $3 - 3y$ **d.** none of these

5. If y is 4 less than x, then __?__ .
   a. $x - y = 4$ **b.** $y - x = 4$ **c.** $y = 4 - x$ **d.** none of these

6. If x is 6 less than 5 times y, then __?__ .
   a. $x = 5(y - 6)$ **b.** $x = 6 - 5y$ **c.** $x = 5(6 - y)$ **d.** none of these

7. $3x + (-x) = $ __?__
   a. $4x$ **b.** $2x$ **c.** $-3x^2$ **d.** 3

8. $-4x - (-3x) = $ __?__
   a. x **b.** $-7x$ **c.** $-x^2$ **d.** $-x$

9. Nancy is n years old now. Wendy's age is twice the age that Nancy was 5 years ago. Wendy's age can be expressed as __?__ .
   a. $2n - 5$ **b.** $2(n + 5)$ **c.** $2(n - 5)$ **d.** $2n + 5$

10. There are p pounds of an alloy that is 60% tin. The number of pounds of tin is __?__ .

    a. $0.06p$ **b.** $\dfrac{2}{5}p$ **c.** $6p$ **d.** $\dfrac{3}{5}p$

3-1 Solving Systems of Linear Equations by Graphing

OBJECTIVES _____

To solve systems of linear equations by graphing.
To identify consistent, inconsistent, and dependent systems.

Two nonparallel lines in the same plane intersect in exactly one point. Since this point is on each line, its coordinates are a solution to the equation of each line. The coordinates of this point of intersection are said to be the solution of the **system** of two linear equations.

EXAMPLE 1   Solve the system by graphing: $\begin{array}{l} 2x + y = 9 \\ x = 4y \end{array}$

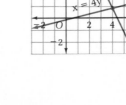

Carefully graph both lines on the same coordinate plane. You may find it convenient to use the slope-intercept form.

$$y = -2x + 9 \text{ and } y = \frac{1}{4}x$$

The point (4, 1) appears to be common to both lines. To check, substitute 4 for x and 1 for y in each equation.

$2(4) + 1 = 8 + 1 = 9$ ✔
$4 = 4(1)$ ✔

The solution to the system is (4, 1).

Certain types of problems can be solved by writing two linear equations and solving them by graphing.

EXAMPLE 2   The sum of a number and twice a smaller number is 10. The difference between the two numbers is 4. What are the numbers?

Strategy: Write a system of equations. Solve by graphing.

Read the problem to find the key ideas.
   Two numbers are to be found. The problem describes a sum and a difference that involve the two numbers.

Use variables.
   Let x be the larger number and y the smaller number.

Write a system of two equations.

The sum of the larger number and twice the smaller number is 10.

$$x + 2y = 10$$

The difference, 4, is positive. That is, the larger number less the smaller number is 4.

$$x - y = 4$$

Find the solution.

Solve the system by graphing both equations on one coordinate plane and finding the point of intersection of the two lines.

This is the only point in the plane with coordinates (x, y) that satisfy $x + 2y = 10$ and $x - y = 4$.

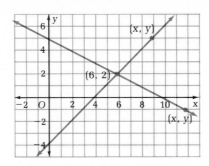

Every point on this line has coordinates (x, y) such that $x - y = 4$.

Every point on this line has coordinates (x, y) such that $x + 2y = 10$.

The solution to the system appears to be (6, 2).

Check the solution with the conditions in the original problem.

The sum of 6 and twice 2 is 10. The difference, 6 less 2, is 4.

Answer the question.

The numbers are 6 and 2.

A system is called **consistent** if it has at least one solution. A system is **independent** if its equations have different graphs. Each of the systems in the first two examples is consistent and independent. That is, the equations in each system have exactly one solution in common.

Another type of consistent system is said to be **dependent.** In a dependent system, every solution of one equation is also a solution of the other equation.

EXAMPLE 3

Solve the system by graphing: $\begin{aligned} x - y &= 3 \\ 3x - 3y &= 9 \end{aligned}$

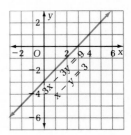

Write each equation in slope-intercept form.

$$x - y = 3 \qquad\qquad 3x - 3y = 9$$
$$y = x - 3 \qquad and \qquad y = x - 3$$

These equations are the same, and their graphs coincide. Every point on this line is a solution of the given system.

Not every system of linear equations has a solution. A system with no solutions is said to be **inconsistent.**

EXAMPLE 4   Solve the system by graphing: $2x + 4y = 12$
$x + 2y = -4$

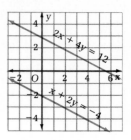

Write each equation in slope-intercept form.

$$y = -\frac{1}{2}x + 3 \ \text{ and } \ y = -\frac{1}{2}x - 2$$

Graph the lines on the same coordinate plane. The lines are parallel, so there is no point of intersection, and no solution to the system.

An inspection of the equations in the last two examples suggests the types of systems represented, without graphing. In Example 3, the equations can be written in identical forms, so the graph of the system is just one line. In Example 4, the equations show that the lines have equal slopes, but different y-intercepts. Therefore, the lines are parallel.

The three types of linear systems are summarized below.

If the graph is   *then the system is*

  two intersecting lines . . .   *consistent* and independent, with exactly one solution.

  two parallel lines . . .   *inconsistent* and independent, with no solutions.

  two lines that coincide . . .   *consistent* and *dependent*, with an infinite number of solutions.

CLASS EXERCISES

*Classify each system as **consistent** or **inconsistent**. Name the solution for each consistent system.*

1.
2.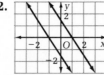
3.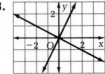

State whether or not the ordered pair (3, −2) is a solution to the system.

4. $x + y = 1$
    $x - y = 6$

5. $x - 2y = 7$
    $2x + 3y = 0$

6. $-x - y = -5$
    $3x - 4y = 17$

EXERCISES

Solve each system by graphing. Use graph paper, and draw the graphs as accurately as possible. Classify each system as **consistent** or **inconsistent**.

1. $x + y = 2$
    $x - y = 0$

2. $x + y = 1$
    $x - y = -3$

3. $2x + y = 2$
    $x - 2y = -4$

4. $2x + 2y = -2$
    $3x - 2y = 12$

5. $x - 4y = 9$
    $2x - 3y = 8$

6. $3x + 9y = 9$
    $2x - 3y = 6$

7. $x + y = 3$
    $x + y = -2$

8. $x - y = 0$
    $2x - y = 0$

9. $x + 2y = 0$
    $x + y = 1$

10. $2x - 4y = -4$
    $3x - 2y = -6$

11. $2x + 3y = 3$
    $4x + 6y = -12$

12. $3x - 2y = -1$
    $2x - 4y = 2$

13. $3x + 3y = 21$
    $3x + 4y = 24$

14. $x - y = 1$
    $y = 2$

15. $y = -1$
    $x = -2$

16. $3x + 2y = 5$
    $9x + 6y = 12$

17. $2x + y = -6$
    $x = -3$

18. $4x + 9y = 13$
    $y = x$

19. Without graphing, identify the *dependent* system or systems.

  a. $6x - 3y = 0$
      $y = 2x$

  b. $x + 2y = 3$
      $y = -x + 3$

  c. $4x + 6y = 8$
      $3y = -2x + 4$

Write a system of two equations for each problem. Then solve by graphing.

20. The sum of two numbers is 13. Their difference is 5. Find the numbers.

21. One number is 7 more than another number. Their sum is 15. Find the numbers.

22. One number is twice another number. The sum of the two numbers is 27. Find the numbers.

23. Three times a number equals 2 times a larger number. The numbers differ by 1. Find the numbers.

24. Ann has 30 coins, each of which is either a nickel or a dime. Their total value is $2.15. How many dimes does she have?

25. A golfer used 79 strokes in 18 holes. He scored either 4 or 5 on each hole. How many holes did he play in 4 strokes?

26. The difference between two numbers is 6, and one number is 3 times the other number. Find two pairs of numbers that meet these conditions.

27. One number is three-fifths of another number. If 4 is added to one of the numbers, the sum will equal the other number. Find two pairs of numbers that meet these conditions.

3-2 Solving Systems of Linear Equations by Substitution

To solve systems of linear equations by the substitution method.
To solve problems by solving such systems.

The graph at the right shows that the system
$3x + 2y = 5$
$\quad x - 3y = 6$ has a single solution, the point
where the two lines intersect. However, the
coordinates of the point of intersection are
not integers, and their values can only be estimated from the graph.

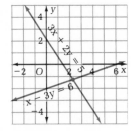

To find the exact solution to the system, we use algebraic methods.
In the **substitution method**, one equation is solved for one variable in
terms of the other. Then that value is substituted for the same variable
in the second equation. This makes sense because at the point of intersection the x- and y-values are the same in both equations.

EXAMPLE 1   Solve the system by substitution: $\begin{array}{l} 3x + 2y = 5 \\ x - 3y = 6 \end{array}$

Notice that the coefficient of x is 1 in the second equation. Start by
solving that equation for x in terms of y.

$$x - 3y = 6$$
$$x = 3y + 6$$

Substitute $3y + 6$ for x in the other equation and solve for y.

$$3x + 2y = 5$$
$$3(3y + 6) + 2y = 5$$
$$9y + 18 + 2y = 5$$
$$11y = -13$$
$$y = -\frac{13}{11}$$

Then substitute $-\dfrac{13}{11}$ for y in $x = 3y + 6$, and solve for x.

$$x = 3\left(-\frac{13}{11}\right) + 6 = -\frac{39}{11} + 6 = \frac{27}{11}$$

Check by substituting $\frac{27}{11}$ for x and $-\frac{13}{11}$ for y in both of the original equations.

$$3\left(\frac{27}{11}\right) + 2\left(-\frac{13}{11}\right) = \frac{81}{11} - \frac{26}{11} = 5 \; ✔ \qquad \frac{27}{11} - 3\left(-\frac{13}{11}\right) = \frac{27}{11} + \frac{39}{11} = 6 \; ✔$$

The solution for the system is $\left(\frac{27}{11},\ -\frac{13}{11}\right)$.

Recall that in a *dependent* system every solution of one of the equations is also a solution of the other. The graphs of the two equations are lines that coincide. When such a system is solved algebraically, both variables are eliminated and the result is a true equation.

EXAMPLE 2 Use substitution to show that the system is dependent: $\begin{array}{l} x - y = 4 \\ 2y = 2x - 8 \end{array}$

Solve the first equation for x.

$$x - y = 4$$
$$x = y + 4$$

Then substitute $y + 4$ for x in the second equation.

$$2y = 2(y + 4) - 8$$
$$2y = 2y + 8 - 8$$
$$0 = 0$$

The variables are eliminated, and $0 = 0$ is a true equation. The system is dependent. Every solution to either equation is a solution of the system.

An *inconsistent* system of two linear equations has no solutions. Its graph is a pair of parallel lines. When an inconsistent system is solved algebraically, both variables are eliminated and the result is a false equation.

EXAMPLE 3 Use substitution to show that the system is inconsistent: $\begin{array}{l} 2x + y = 10 \\ y = 5 - 2x \end{array}$

The second equation gives y in terms of x. Substitute $5 - 2x$ for y in the first equation.

$$2x + (5 - 2x) = 10$$
$$2x + 5 - 2x = 10$$
$$5 = 10$$

The variables are eliminated, and $5 = 10$ is a false equation. The system is inconsistent, so it has no solutions.

EXAMPLE 4   Carlos bought some Bartlett pears at 78¢ per pound and some Bosc pears at 88¢ per pound. In all, he bought 5.5 pounds of pears at a total cost of $4.54. How many pounds of each variety did he buy?

Strategy: Write and solve a system of equations.

Use variables.

Let x be the number of pounds of Bartlett pears.
Let y be the number of pounds of Bosc pears.

The cost of x pounds of Bartlett pears, in dollars, is 0.78x.
The cost of y pounds of Bosc pears, in dollars, is 0.88y.

Write a system of two equations.

The total weight is 5.5 pounds. $x + y = 5.5$

The total cost is $4.54. $0.78x + 0.88y = 4.54$

Find the solution.

$x + y = 5.5$ Solve the first equation for y.
$y = 5.5 - x$

$0.78x + 0.88y = 4.54$
$0.78x + 0.88(5.5 - x) = 4.54$ Substitute $(5.5 - x)$ for y in the second
$0.78x + 4.84 - 0.88x = 4.54$ equation, and solve for x.
$-0.1x = -0.3$
$x = 3$

$y = 5.5 - 3$ Substitute 3 for x in $y = 5.5 - x$.
$y = 2.5$ Solve for y.

Check these results with the conditions in the problem. The total number of pounds is 3 + 2.5, or 5.5. The total cost in dollars is 0.78(3) + 0.88(2.5), or 4.54.

Answer the question.

Carlos bought 3 pounds of Bartlett pears and 2.5 pounds of Bosc pears.

CLASS EXERCISES

Assume that each system is to be solved by substitution. In order to simplify the work, which equation would you solve for one variable in terms of the other? For which variable would you solve that equation?

1. $3x + 2y = 14$
$3y = x - 1$

2. $2x + y = 5$
$3x - 3y = -6$

3. $3x + 4y = -9$
$x - 2y = -3$

4. $2x = y - 10$
$3x - 5y = 7$

5. $5x - 3y = 10$
$6x = 9 - y$

6. $2x = 3y + 8$
$2 = y - 4x$

7. Use the substitution method to solve the systems in Exercises 1–3.

EXERCISES

Use substitution to determine if each system is **inconsistent** or **dependent.** If the system is consistent and independent, find the solution.

1. $x + 2y = 3$
  $3x - 2y = 1$

2. $2x + y = 5$
  $3x - 3y = 3$

3. $2x + 3y = -1$
  $5x - y = 6$

4. $2x + y = -2$
  $8x + 4y = -8$

5. $x + 7y = 9$
  $3x + y = -13$

6. $2x + y = 8$
  $6x + 3y = 24$

7. $x + y = 16$
  $x = 3y$

8. $y = -2x$
  $4x + 2y = 3$

9. $x + 2y = 2$
  $6y = -2x - 2$

10. $x + y = 0$
  $2x - 8y = 5$

11. $5x - 8y = -3$
  $x + 16y = 6$

12. $3x + y = 1$
  $-6x - y = -3$

13. $0.25x + 0.75y = 4$
  $x - y = -4$

14. $0.35x + 0.55y = 3$
  $2x - y = 13$

15. $0.5x + 0.5y = 5$
  $y = -x + 2.5$

16. $x + y = 0$
  $\frac{1}{2}x - \frac{1}{4}y = 6$

17. $x + y = 2$
  $\frac{1}{5}x - \frac{1}{3}y = 2$

18. $2x - 3y = -3$
  $\frac{2}{3}x - y = -1$

Write a system of two equations for each problem. Then solve by substitution.

19. The measures of two angles total 80°. Their difference is 30°. Find the measures of the angles.

20. Ariel's age is twice that of her brother Ben. The sum of their ages is 24. Find their ages.

21. Gail paid $7.50 for 27 pounds of onions. She bought white onions at 26¢ per pound and yellow onions at 30¢ per pound. How many pounds of each variety did she buy?

22. Kay worked a total of 14 hours at two part-time jobs, one paying $4.10 per hour and the other, $3.85 per hour. She earned $55.40. How many hours did she work at each job?

23. Jamil earned $410 one year on two investments. One investment yielded 7% yearly interest, and the other, 8%. If he had $5500 invested, how much was invested at each rate?

24. The receipts from a baseball game were $12,920, paid by 4120 spectators. Bleacher seats sold for $2 each and the other seats for $4. How many of each were sold?

25. A basketball team scored 76 points. The number of field goals scored was 4 less than 3 times the number of free throws. If a field goal is worth 2 points and a free throw, 1 point, how many field goals did the team score?

26. There is a fixed charge to send a telegram, plus an additional charge for each word in the message. If a 32-word telegram costs $4.70 and a 44-word telegram costs $5.90, find the fixed charge and the cost per word.

 **USING THE CALCULATOR**

Starting with a Guess

The symbolism and rules of algebra make the solution of many problems a rather simple matter. But in ancient times—before algebra was invented—people did not know how to write and solve equations.

One method used to solve certain types of number problems was the **rule of double false position.** To use this rule, two different guesses are given for an unknown number. These guesses are recorded, along with the two results obtained when the conditions given in the problem are imposed on the two numbers.

First guess: x_1 First result: r_1
Second guess: x_2 Second result: r_2

The guesses and results are then used to find the correct answer x.

$$x = \frac{r_1 x_2 - r_2 x_1}{r_1 - r_2}$$

EXERCISES

1. Use the rule of double false position to complete the following solution.

Seven less than 4 times a number is 0. Find the number.

Guess that the number is 1. $x_1 = 1$
      The result is -3. $r_1 = -3$ $4(1) - 7 = -3$

Guess that the number is 2. $x_2 = 2$
      The result is 1. $r_2 = 1$ $4(2) - 7 = 1$

Then the solution x is given by

$$x = \frac{r_1 x_2 - r_2 x_1}{r_1 - r_2} = \underline{\ ?\ }$$ Check your answer.

Use a calculator to solve these problems. Use the rule of double false position.

2. If 7837 less than 68 times a number is 0, find the number.
  Use 175 and 45 as the two guesses.

3. If 0.48 less than 12.5 times a number is 0, find the number.
  Use two of your own guesses to find the number.

*4. The rule of double false position only works for problems in which the conditions can be expressed in a linear equation of the form $ax - b = 0$.

The guesses and results form this system of equations: $\begin{aligned} ax_1 - b &= r_1 \\ ax_2 - b &= r_2 \end{aligned}$

Prove algebraically that the rule of double false position works. That is, solve the system shown above for a and b in terms of the other variables. Then substitute those expressions for a and b in the equation $ax - b = 0$ and solve for x.

3-3 Solving Systems of Linear Equations by Addition

OBJECTIVES _____

To solve systems of linear equations using the addition method, preceded
  by multiplication when required.
To solve problems by solving such systems.

_____

Sometimes it is difficult to use the substitution method to solve a linear
system. Another useful procedure is the **addition method,** in which a
simplified equation is formed by adding the given equations.

EXAMPLE 1　　Solve the system by the addition method: $\begin{array}{l} 3y = 6 - 2x \\ 8x = 3y - 1 \end{array}$

First, write each equation in the form $ax \pm by = c$.

$$2x + 3y = 6$$
$$8x - 3y = -1$$

Notice that the y-terms in the two equations are additive inverses. If
the equations are added, the y-terms will be eliminated and the value
of x can be found. Here we add equals to equals, with the understanding that the x- and y-values of the solution are the same in both
equations.

$$\begin{array}{rl} 2x + 3y = & 6 \\ 8x - 3y = & -1 \\ \hline 10x = & 5 \end{array}$$　　Add like terms.

$$x = \frac{5}{10} = \frac{1}{2}$$　　Solve the resulting equation for x.

Now substitute $\frac{1}{2}$ for x in one of the original equations and solve for y.

$$3y = 6 - 2\left(\frac{1}{2}\right)$$
$$3y = 5$$
$$y = \frac{5}{3}$$

Check by substituting $\frac{1}{2}$ for x and $\frac{5}{3}$ for y in each of the original equations.

$$3\left(\frac{5}{3}\right) \stackrel{?}{=} 6 - 2\left(\frac{1}{2}\right) \qquad 8\left(\frac{1}{2}\right) \stackrel{?}{=} 3\left(\frac{5}{3}\right) - 1$$
$$5 = 5 \ ✔ \qquad\qquad 4 = 4 \ ✔$$

The solution is $\left(\frac{1}{2}, \frac{5}{3}\right)$.

To eliminate a variable it may be necessary to multiply one or both of the equations by appropriate numbers before adding.

EXAMPLE 2

Solve the system by the addition method:
$$2x - 3y = -19$$
$$4x + 5y = 17$$

Neither the x-terms nor the y-terms are additive inverses. The easiest way to obtain such inverses here is to multiply by -2 in the first equation. The x-terms are eliminated when the resulting equations are added.

$$2x - 3y = -19 \longrightarrow -4x + 6y = 38$$ Multiply each side of the
$$4x + 5y = 17 \longrightarrow \underline{4x + 5y = 17}$$ first equation by -2.
$$11y = 55$$ Add the equations.
$$y = 5$$ Solve for y.

Substitute 5 for y in either of the original equations and solve for x.

$$2x - 3y = -19$$
$$2x - 3(5) = -19$$
$$2x = -4$$
$$x = -2$$

By substituting -2 for x and 5 for y in each of the original equations, you will find that these results check. The solution to the system is $(-2, 5)$.

Subtracting a number is equivalent to adding its opposite. Therefore, we can use subtraction to eliminate a variable in a system. The procedure is illustrated in the next example.

EXAMPLE 3

A chemist wants to combine two solutions to obtain 80 liters of a mixture containing 28% acid. Solution A is 20% acid, and solution B is 30% acid. How many liters of each must he use?

Use variables.

Let x be the number of liters of A.
Let y be the number of liters of B.

The number of liters of acid in x liters of A is 20% of x, or 0.2x.
The number of liters of acid in y liters of B is 30% of y, or 0.3y.
The number of liters of acid in the mixture is 28% of 80, or 22.4.

Write a system of equations.

$x + y = 80$ There will be 80 liters of the mixture.

$0.2x + 0.3y = 22.4$ The sum of the amounts of acid in x liters of A
                  and in y liters of B is 22.4 liters.

Find the solution.   Solve the system: $0.2x + 0.3y = 22.4$
                                           $x + y = 80$

$0.2x + 0.3y = 22.4 \longrightarrow 2x + 3y = 224$ Multiply by 10 to
                                                         eliminate decimals.

$x + y = 80 \longrightarrow \underline{2x + 2y = 160}$ Multiply by 2.

$y = 64$ Subtract.

$x + 64 = 80$ Substitute 64 for y in one
$x = 16$ of the original equations.

Answer the question.   Check with the conditions in the original problem to show that 16
liters of solution A and 64 liters of solution B are needed.

CLASS EXERCISES

*Assume that each system is to be solved by the addition method and
that you wish to eliminate the **x**-terms. State the number(s) by which
you would multiply one or both of the equations.*

1. $2x + 2y = 1$
$2x + 4y = -5$

2. $8x - 5y = 2$
$4x + 3y = 3$

3. $-6x - 2y = 5$
$2x + 5y = -1$

4. $x + 2y = 8$
$3x - 4y = 10$

5. $3x + 10y = 7$
$-8x - 4y = 17$

6. $-4x + 5y = -6$
$-6x - y = 5$

7. Now assume that you wish to eliminate the y-terms in
Exercises **1–6**. State the number(s) by which you would multiply
one or both of the equations.

EXERCISES

A   *Solve each system by the addition method, and check.*

1. $3x + 4y = -9$
$3x + y = 0$

2. $2x + y = -14$
$3x - y = -6$

3. $2x + 3y = 9$
$-2x - 5y = 1$

4. $-4x + y = -12$
$4x + 2y = 6$

5. $3x + 4y = 0$
$x + 4y = -2$

6. $x + y = 8$
$x - y = 4$

7. $x + 4y = 10$
$3x - 2y = 2$

8. $-2x + 3y = -7$
$3x + y = 16$

9. $3x + 5y = 21$
$-9x + 4y = -6$

10. $3x + 2y = -3$
$2x + 3y = -2$

11. $4x - 3y = 2$
$3x + 5y = 16$

12. $5x + 4y = 12$
$7x - 6y = 40$

B   **13.** $-4x + 7y = 9$
$2y = -5x - 22$

14. $2y = 41 - 5x$
$y = 17 - 2x$

15. $9x = 53 - 4y$
$3y = 26 - 4x$

16. $-4p + 3q = 39$
$-3p + 2q = 36$

17. $-12m + 3n = 4$
$9m = 2n - 3$

18. $8r - 12s = 5$
$10s = -1 - 6r$

19. $0.5x + 0.4y = 6$
$0.4x - 0.1y = 9$

20. $1.5p + 2q = -13$
$2.5p - 9q = 3$

21. $\frac{1}{3}x + \frac{1}{2}y = 6$
$2x - y = 4$

Write a system of two equations for each problem. Then solve.

22. Three times one number added to twice a smaller number equals 4. Twice the larger number less twice the smaller number equals 6. Find the two numbers.

23. Twice the width of a rectangle is 1 inch more than its length. The sum of the width and length is 5 inches. Find the length and width of the rectangle.

24. Joan is 8 years older than Naomi. In 5 years she will be twice as old as Naomi. How old are the girls now?

25. How many ounces each of a 30% alcohol solution and a 50% alcohol solution are needed to get 80 ounces of a 42% solution?

26. An alloy that is 15% copper is combined with an alloy that is 35% copper. If the result is 400 kilograms of 27.5% copper alloy, how much of each alloy was used?

27. An airplane flies 840 miles in 3 hours, with a tail wind. The return trip takes $3\frac{1}{2}$ hours. Find the wind speed and the speed of the plane itself. **Hint:** Add the rates going downwind; subtract them for the return.

C

28. A car averaging 46 miles per hour traveled 3 hours longer and 117 miles farther than a car averaging 52 miles per hour. How many hours did each car travel?

29. A metallurgist has 25 grams of a 64% silver alloy. How much pure silver must she add to obtain a 77.5% silver alloy? How many grams of the 77.5% alloy will she have?

CHECKPOINT

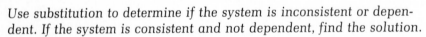

Use substitution to determine if the system is inconsistent or dependent. If the system is consistent and not dependent, find the solution.

1. $2x - 3y = -5$
$y = 3$

2. $6x + 9y = 15$
$5 - 2x = 3y$

3. $x + y = 0$
$-3y + 4 = 5x$

Solve each system by the addition method, and check.

4. $6x + 5y = 8$
$4x + y = 10$

5. $7x - 8y = 3$
$5x - 6y = 2$

6. $\frac{1}{2}x - \frac{1}{4}y = 0$
$\frac{1}{4}x + \frac{1}{2}y = 2\frac{1}{2}$

7. Eight pounds of sugar and 6 pounds of salt cost $4.34 in all. Five pounds of sugar and 10 pounds of salt cost $4.40. Find the cost for each pound of sugar and of salt.

Generalizing from the Specific

1. Start with a three-digit number in which the hundreds digit is at least 2 greater than the units digit.

$$
\begin{array}{rl}
\text{For example, start with 752.} & \mathbf{752} \\
\text{Reverse the digits.} & \mathbf{-\ 257} \\
\text{Find the difference.} & \mathbf{495} \\
\text{Reverse the digits again.} & \mathbf{+\ 594} \\
\text{This time find the sum.} & \mathbf{1089}
\end{array}
$$

2. Follow the same steps with these numbers: 531   844   690

   Then choose three numbers of your own. What result do you get in all cases?

3. You can prove algebraically that this special result always occurs. First, observe that $752 = 100(7) + 10(5) + 2$. In general, a three-digit number may be written in the form $100h + 10t + u$, where h, t, and u are the hundreds, tens, and units digits, respectively. Remember, in this case h is understood to be at least 2 greater than u.

   The first step is to reverse the digits.

   $$100h + 10t + u \qquad \text{original number}$$
   $$\underline{100u + 10t + h} \qquad \text{number with digits reversed}$$

   The next step is to find the difference, one term at a time. But wait! u is less than h, and this will cause trouble in the units place. So, first borrow one 10 from $10t$.

   $$100h + 10(t - 1) + (u + 10) \qquad \text{original number}$$
   $$\underline{100u + 10t \qquad\quad + h} \qquad \text{number with digits reversed}$$

   Now there is a problem subtracting in the tens place, since $10(t - 1)$ is less than $10t$. To handle this, borrow one 100 from $100h$.

   $$100(h - 1) + [10(t - 1) + 100] + (u + 10) \qquad \text{original number}$$
   $$\underline{100u \qquad\ + 10t \qquad\qquad\qquad + h} \qquad \text{number with digits reversed}$$

   Now you can subtract, reverse the digits again, and add. Do you still get that special number 1089?

4. Suppose you were to start with a three-digit number in which the hundreds digit is just 1 greater than the units digit. What is the result when you reverse the digits of such a number and subtract? In order to get 1089 for your final result, what must you do after the subtraction step?

3-4 Solving Systems of Three Linear Equations

To solve systems of three linear equations.
To solve problems by solving such systems.

_____

When solving a system of two equations in two variables, you first eliminate one of the variables. When solving a system of three equations in three variables, you also begin by eliminating a variable. This results in a two-variable system that you can solve using one of the methods you have learned.

EXAMPLE 1 Solve the system:
$$2x + 3y + 2z = 3$$
$$4x - 5y + 5z = -7$$
$$-3x + 7y - 2z = 5$$

Take one pair of equations and eliminate one of the variables. Here we use the first and third equations and eliminate z by the addition method.

$$\begin{array}{l} 2x + 3y + 2z = 3 \\ \underline{-3x + 7y - 2z = 5} \\ -x + 10y \qquad = 8 \qquad \text{Add.} \end{array}$$

Then take another pair of equations and eliminate the *same* variable. Here we use the second and third equations.

$$\begin{array}{lll} 4x - 5y + 5z = -7 & \longrightarrow & 8x - 10y + 10z = -14 & \text{Multiply by 2.} \\ -3x + 7y - 2z = 5 & \longrightarrow & \underline{-15x + 35y - 10z = 25} & \text{Multiply by 5.} \\ & & -7x + 25y \qquad = 11 & \text{Add.} \end{array}$$

We now have a system of two equations in two variables, x and y.

$$-x + 10y = 8$$
$$-7x + 25y = 11$$

We eliminate x by the addition method, solve for y, and then substitute in one of the two equations to find x.

$$\begin{array}{lll} -x + 10y = 8 & \longrightarrow & 7x - 70y = -56 & \text{Multiply by } -7. \\ -7x + 25y = 11 & \longrightarrow & \underline{-7x + 25y = 11} & \\ & & -45y = -45 & \text{Add.} \\ & & y = 1 & \text{Solve for } y. \end{array}$$

$$\begin{array}{lll} -x + 10y = 8 & \longrightarrow & -x + 10(1) = 8 & \text{Substitute 1 for } y \text{ in one} \\ & & & \text{of the two equations.} \\ & & x = 2 & \text{Solve for } x. \end{array}$$

Then substitute 1 for y and 2 for x in one of the original equations and solve for z. Here we use the first of the original equations.

$$2x + 3y + 2z = 3 \longrightarrow 2(2) + 3(1) + 2z = 3$$
$$2z = -4$$
$$z = -2$$

Check by substituting 2 for x, 1 for y, and -2 for z in each equation.

$$
\begin{array}{llll}
2x + 3y + 2z = & 3: & 2(2) + 3(1) + 2(-2) = & 4 + 3 - 4 = & 3 \; ✔ \\
4x - 5y + 5z = & -7: & 4(2) - 5(1) + 5(-2) = & 8 - 5 - 10 = -7 \; ✔ \\
-3x + 7y - 2z = & 5: & -3(2) + 7(1) - 2(-2) = & -6 + 7 + 4 = & 5 \; ✔
\end{array}
$$

Express the solution as an **ordered triple** (x, y, z). The solution is $(2, 1, -2)$.

There is more than one way to solve a system of three linear equations. In the next example we use both the substitution and the addition methods.

EXAMPLE 2 Solve the system:
$$
\begin{array}{l}
3x + 4y = 6z - 2 \\
3y - 3 \;\; = 5x + 10z \\
y - 2z = 0
\end{array}
$$

Solve the third equation for y in terms of z, and substitute in the other two equations.

$y - 2z = 0$, so $y = 2z$.

$$
\begin{array}{ll}
3x + 4y = 6z - 2 & 3y - 3 = 5x + 10z \\
3x + 4(2z) = 6z - 2 & 3(2z) - 3 = 5x + 10z \\
3x + 2z = -2 & 5x + 4z = -3
\end{array}
$$

Now, solve the system $\begin{array}{l} 3x + 2z = -2 \\ 5x + 4z = -3 \end{array}$. It is convenient to use the addition method here.

$$
\begin{array}{lll}
3x + 2z = -2 & \longrightarrow & -6x - 4z = \;\;\; 4 \\
5x + 4z = -3 & \longrightarrow & \underline{\;\;5x + 4z = -3\;} \\
& & -x \;\;\;\;\;\; = \;\;\; 1, \text{ so } x = -1.
\end{array}
$$ Multiply by -2. Add and solve for x.

$$3x + 2z = -2 \longrightarrow 3(-1) + 2z = -2$$
$$z = \frac{1}{2}$$

Substitute -1 for x in one equation and solve for z.

Now, solve for y by substituting in one of the original equations.

$$y - 2z = 0 \longrightarrow y - 2\left(\frac{1}{2}\right) = 0$$
$$y = 1$$

Check by substituting in each of the original equations. The solution is $\left(-1, 1, \frac{1}{2}\right)$.

CLASS EXERCISES

State whether or not the ordered triple $(1, -1, -2)$ is a solution to the equation.

1. $x + y + z = -2$

2. $2x - 3y + z = -3$

3. $3x - 3y - z = 2$

4. $x + 2y - z = 0$

5. $5x - y - 5z = 16$

6. $4x + 5y - 6z = -13$

Find the missing number that will make the resulting ordered triple a solution to the equation $x + 2y - 3z = 8$.

7. $(\underline{\ ?\ }, 0, 1)$

8. $(\underline{\ ?\ }, -2, -2)$

9. $(4, \underline{\ ?\ }, 0)$

10. $(-1, \underline{\ ?\ }, -1)$

11. $(2, 3, \underline{\ ?\ })$

12. $(-3, -2, \underline{\ ?\ })$

EXERCISES

A Solve each system, and check.

1. $x + y + z = 6$
$2x - y + z = 3$
$x + 2y - 3z = -4$

2. $3x + 2y + z = -2$
$2x + y - 3z = -8$
$x - 3y + 2z = 10$

3. $x + 5y + 10z = 47$
$y = z$
$x + y + z = 8$

4. $x + y + z = 1$
$2x + y = 0$
$y + z = -1$

5. $x + y + z = 12$
$x + 2y + 3z = 31$
$9y + z = 1$

6. $x + y - z = 3$
$x - y - 2z = 4$
$x + y + z = 1$

B

7. $x = 3y$
$z = 4x$
$x + y + z = 8$

8. $x + 5y + 10z = 83$
$x = y + z$
$z = 16 - x - y$

9. $x + y + z = 60$
$x - z = y + 6$
$y = 40 - x - 3z$

10. $2x + y + 4z = 3$
$x + 2y = 2z - 3$
$4z + 3y = 0$

11. $x + y + z = 1$
$2x - y + 3z = 4.5$
$4x - 5y - 5z = -0.5$

12. $2(x + z) = 9$
$2(x - y) = 3$
$y - z = -10x$

Write a system of three equations for each problem. Then solve.

13. Adam has 9 coins, each of which is a penny, a nickel, or a dime. There are twice as many dimes as pennies. If the total value of the coins is 57¢, how many of each kind are there?

14. The sum of three numbers is 20. The largest number is equal to twice the smallest, plus the middle number. Three times the smallest number is 5 less than the largest number. Find the numbers.

15. The sum of three numbers is 8. The smallest number is 12 less than the middle number and 20 less than the largest number. Find the numbers.

16. The ordered triples $(-1, 2, 4)$, $(2, -1, 2)$, and $(3, -6, -8)$ are all solutions to the equation $ax + by + cz = -3$. Find the equation by identifying a, b, and c.

17. The perimeter of a triangle is 30 centimeters. Three times the length of the first side equals twice that of the second side, plus 3 times that of the third side. The length of the first side is 4 centimeters less than the sum of the other two sides. Find the length of each side.

18. The greens fee for a member of a golf club is $6. The fee for a nonmember is $14, or $8 if the nonmember is a senior citizen. One day the total receipts for 226 players was $1688. Of the nonmembers that played, the senior citizens outnumbered the others by 16. How many players were there in each category?

19. The treasurer of a junior class invested $6000 of the class savings in three local banks for a year. Part was invested at an annual yield of 9%, part at 8%, and the rest at 7%. The interest for the year earned by the 9% and 7% accounts together was $354, and the 8% and 7% accounts together earned $228. How much was invested at each rate?

20. The sum of the digits of a three-digit number is 13. The hundreds' digit is twice the tens' digit. If the digits are reversed, the resulting number is 297 greater than the original number. Find the number. *Hint:* A three-digit number with hundreds' digit h, tens' digit t, and units' digit u can be written as $100h + 10t + u$.

C

21. Three solutions, each containing the same acid, are to be mixed to form 120 milliliters of a mixture containing 32% acid. The acid concentrations of the three solutions are 25%, 30%, and 52%. How much of each of the three solutions must be used, if the final solution is to contain 3 times as much of the 30% solution as of the 52% solution?

22. A store owner wants to have 40 pounds of mixed nuts to sell at $4 per pound. The mixture is to contain peanuts that sell for $2.40 a pound, pecans that sell for $5.20 a pound, and cashews that sell for $6.80 per pound. If the mixture is to contain 15 more pounds of peanuts than of cashews, how many pounds of each type of nut must be used?

23. The difference between a three-digit number and the number obtained by reversing the digits is 99. The number is 5 more than 57 times the sum of the units' and hundreds' digits. Twice the units' digit is 1 more than the sum of the tens' and hundreds' digits. Find the number.

24. If the digits of a three-digit number are reversed, then the sum of the resulting number and the original number is 665. Their difference is 297. The tens' digit of the original number is twice the hundreds' digit. Find the number.

3-5   Systems of Linear Inequalities

OBJECTIVE _____

To graph systems of linear inequalities.

_____

To graph a *system of inequalities*, we graph each inequality and then identify the region containing the points that satisfy all of the given conditions.

EXAMPLE 1   Graph the system: $\begin{array}{l} x + y > 2 \\ -x + y > 1 \end{array}$

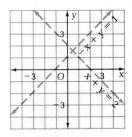

First graph the boundaries. The boundary of $x + y > 2$ is $x + y = 2$. The boundary of $-x + y > 1$ is $-x + y = 1$. Show the boundaries as dashed lines, since the points on the lines are not part of the graph.

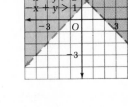

Next, identify the region satisfying each inequality. Shade each region a different color, or use lines drawn in different directions. The graph of the system is the intersection of the two regions. That is, the intersection contains the points with coordinates that satisfy $x + y > 2$ *and* $-x + y > 1$.

As a rough check, choose a point in the solution region and test its coordinates to see that they satisfy each inequality. Here we choose (1, 3).

For $x + y > 2$ we get $1 + 3 > 2$, which is true.
For $-x + y > 1$ we get $-1 + 3 > 1$, which is true.

EXAMPLE 2   Graph the system: $\begin{array}{l} 2x + y \geq 2 \\ x - y \leq 2 \\ y \leq 2 \end{array}$

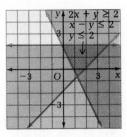

Graph the boundaries, $2x + y = 2$, $x - y = 2$, and $y = 2$. Then graph the three separate inequalities. Check a point to verify that the graph of the system is the triangular region that is the intersection of the three shaded regions. The boundaries of the triangular region are included in the graph of the system.

EXAMPLE 3   Graph $-2 \le x + y < 2$.

This compound inequality may be written as

$-2 \le x + y$ and $x + y < 2$

Graph the boundaries, $-2 = x + y$ and $x + y = 2$, and graph the separate inequalities. The graph of the system

$-2 \le x + y$
$x + y < 2$

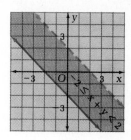

is the intersection of the two regions. Check a point in the intersection of the regions by showing that its coordinates satisfy $-2 \le x + y < 2$.

Note that points on the line $-2 = x + y$ represent solutions to the compound inequality. However, points on the line $x + y = 2$ are *not* solutions to the inequality.

CLASS EXERCISES

Match each system of inequalities with its graph.

1. $y > x$
$y < -x + 1$

2. $y < x$
$y > -x + 1$

3. $y > x$
$y > -x + 1$

4. $y < x$
$y < -x + 1$

a.   **b.**   **c.**   **d.**

State whether or not $(1, -2)$ is a solution to the given system.

5. $y < 3$
$x > y$

6. $x + y < 0$
$x - y < -1$

7. $y \le -2$
$y \le 2x$

8. $3x - y \ge 5$
$-x - 3y < 5$

EXERCISES

A   *Graph each system on the coordinate plane.*

1. $y > 2$
$x < 2$

2. $y \le -1$
$y \ge 3x$

3. $x < 4$
$y < \frac{1}{2}x$

4. $y \le -x$
$x \ge 2y$

5. $x \ge -3y$
$y \ge 3x$

6. $x < 0$
$x + y < 0$

7. $y \ge -x - 1$
$y \le -x + 3$

8. $y < -3x + 4$
$y > -x + 1$

B

9. $y \leq x$
   $y \geq x$

10. $y + 2x \leq 3$
    $y \geq -2x + 5$

11. $x - y < 5$
    $y - x > 3$

12. $y < x$
    $y < 3x$

13. $1 \leq x \leq 3$

14. $-2 < x < 2$

15. $-2 < y \leq 1$

16. $0 \leq y < 2$

17. $x - 4 \leq y \leq x + 2$

18. $-x + 4 < y < x + 2$

19. $-2x < y - 1 < 2x$

20. $2x \leq y + 1 \leq 2x + 2$

21. $y \geq x - 3$
    $-3 \leq y \leq 1$

22. $y \geq 2 - x$
    $-1 \leq x \leq 2$

23. $x + y > 1$
    $y < 3$
    $y - x > -1$

24. $x \geq 2$
    $x + y \leq 3$
    $y \leq -2$

C

Write a system of inequalities for each graph.
Hint: First find the equation of each boundary line.

25.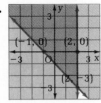

26.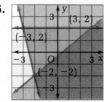

27.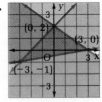

CHECKPOINT

1. Solve the system:
$$2x - 3y - z = 4$$
$$3x + 3y + 2z = 9$$
$$-x + 8y + 6z = 8$$

2. One number plus twice a second number plus 3 times a third number is equal to 20. The sum of the first two numbers equals 5 times the third number. The first number, less the second, equals the third. Find the three numbers.

3. A football team scored 39 points in one game. The number of touchdowns they scored was equal to the number of points-after-touchdown plus the number of field goals they scored. The number of touchdowns was also equal to 1 more than twice the number of field goals. A touchdown scores 6 points, a point-after-touchdown scores 1 point, and a field goal scores 3 points. How many of each did the team score?

Graph each system of inequalities.

4. $y \geq 2x$
   $y \leq -2x$

5. $y < x + 2$
   $-2 < x < 1$

6. $y \leq 6 - x$
   $x - 2y \leq 0$
   $2x - y \geq -3$

3-6 Linear Programming

OBJECTIVE

To solve problems using linear programming methods.

Linear programming is a branch of mathematics developed during World War II to aid the United States Air Force with its logistic problems.

In linear programming, we deal with the graphs of systems of linear inequalities. To illustrate, region **R** is the graph of this system.

$$x \geq 0$$
$$y \geq 0$$
$$x + 2y \leq 16$$
$$2x + y \leq 14$$

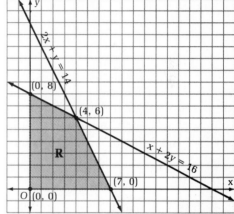

Region **R** is called a **convex region.** That is, no extensions of its boundaries intersect the region.

Which point in **R** has coordinates (x, y) with a sum x + y that is greater than the sum of the coordinates of any other point in **R**? This point is a vertex of **R**, as shown at the right.

The four parallel lines through region **R** have equations x + y = s for s equal to 0, 3, 7, and 10. The "highest" of these parallel lines passes through the vertex with coordinates (4, 6), for which x + y = 4 + 6 = 10. Any line parallel to the others, but "higher" than x + y = 10, will not intersect **R**.

Similarly, the "lowest" of the parallel lines passes through the vertex with coordinates (0, 0), for which x + y = 0 + 0 = 0. Any line parallel to the others, but "lower" than x + y = 0, will not intersect **R**.

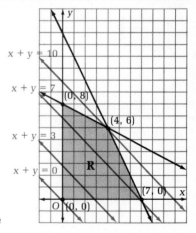

To find the maximum and minimum values of x + y for any point (x, y) in **R**, it is sufficient to list the coordinates of the vertices and their sums.

Vertex	x + y = s	
(0, 0)	0 + 0 = 0	Minimum: s = 0
(7, 0)	7 + 0 = 7	
(4, 6)	4 + 6 = 10	Maximum: s = 10
(0, 8)	0 + 8 = 8	

To summarize, a linear programming problem has **constraints**, which are expressed as inequalities. The graph of that system of inequalities is a convex region **R**. To solve the problem, it is necessary to find the maximum or minimum value of a quantity of the form $ax + by$, where x and y are coordinates of a point in **R**. *If there is such a maximum or minimum value of ax + by, then it occurs when x and y are the coordinates of a vertex of* **R**.

The following example illustrates the use of linear programming to solve a problem in manufacturing.

EXAMPLE   Machine A produces 50 units per hour and costs $10 per hour to operate. Machine B produces 60 units per hour and costs $15 per hour to operate. Production demands are such that at least 580 units must be produced in an 8-hour day. Of all the possible ways to meet production demands, which costs the least?

Step 1   Write the expression to be minimized.

Let C be the total daily cost, in dollars, of operating both machines. Let x be the number of hours machine A is to be operated.
Let y be the number of hours machine B is to be operated.

Then $C = 10x + 15y$ The daily cost, in dollars, of operating both machines.

Step 2   Write the constraints.

$0 \le x \le 8$ Each machine can be operated from 0 through 8 hours.
$0 \le y \le 8$

$50x + 60y \ge 580$ In x hours, A produces $50x$ units. In y hours, B produces $60y$ units. Together, A and B must produce at least 580 units.

Step 3   Graph the region **R**, bounded by the constraints. Find the coordinates of the vertices of **R**.

Vertices of **R**: (2, 8), (8, 8), (8, 3)

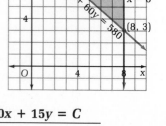

Step 4   Find the minimum value of C by evaluating $10x + 15y = C$ for the x- and y-values at each vertex of **R**.

Vertex	$10x + 15y = C$
(2, 8)	$10(2) + 15(8) = 140$
(8, 8)	$10(8) + 15(8) = 200$
(8, 3)	$10(8) + 15(3) = 125$ Minimum: $C = 125$

The cost is least when machine A is operated for 8 hours and machine B for 3 hours. The minimal cost is $125.

CLASS EXERCISES

1. For the given region **R**, find the coordinates of the vertices A, B, C, and D.

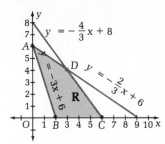

Find the maximim and minimum values of **q** for the region **R** in Exercise 1.

2. $q = x + y$ 　　　　**3.** $q = x + 3y$ 　　　　**4.** $q = 2x + y$

5. $q = 5x + 4y$ 　　　　**6.** $q = 8x + y$ 　　　　**7.** $q = 6x + 7y$

EXERCISES

A

Graph the region **R** given by the system of linear inequalities. Find the maximum and minimum values of **p**, **q**, and **r** under those constraints.

1. $x \geq 0$ 　　　 $p = x + y$ 　　**2.** $x \geq 0$ 　　　 $p = x + 4y$
　　 $y \geq 0$ 　　　 $q = 3x + y$ 　　　　 $y \geq 0$ 　　　 $q = 2x + 13y$
　　 $4x + y \leq 8$ 　 $r = 2x + 3y$ 　　　 $x + 5y \leq 10$ 　 $r = \dfrac{1}{2}x + 6y$

3. $x + y \geq 5$ 　 $p = x + 3y$ 　　**4.** $x \geq 4$ 　　　 $p = x + y$
　　 $y - x \leq 5$ 　 $q = 5x + 2y$ 　　　 $y \geq 4$ 　　　 $q = 3x + y$
　　 $4x + y \leq 20$ 　 $r = 6x + y$ 　　　 $2x + y \leq 20$ 　 $r = 4x + 7y$

B

5. $0 \leq x \leq 9$ 　 $p = x + y$ 　　**6.** $0 \leq y \leq 3$ 　 $p = 5x + y$
　　 $0 \leq y \leq 5$ 　 $q = x + 4y$ 　　　 $x + y \leq 10$ 　 $q = x + 5y$
　　 $x + 2y \geq 12$ 　 $r = 2x + 6y$ 　　　 $3x + 7y \geq 30$ 　 $r = 3x + 4y$

7. $x \geq 0$ 　　　 $p = x + 2y$ 　　**8.** $3x + y \geq 9$ 　 $p = 4x + 2y$
　　 $y \geq 0$ 　　　 $q = 7x + 9y$ 　　　 $3x - 2y \leq 9$ 　 $q = 8x + y$
　　 $x + y \leq 10$ 　 $r = 6x + 5y$ 　　　 $3x - 2y \geq -18$ 　 $r = 12x + 5y$
　　 $3x + 8y \leq 40$ 　　　　　　　　 $3x + y \leq 18$

Use linear programming to solve each problem.

9. A manufacturer of tape recorders makes a $20 profit on each standard model and a $30 profit on each deluxe model. In order to meet the daily demand, the company needs to produce at least 160 of the standard model and at least 130 of the special model each day. The production process limits the total daily output to no more than 500 models. How many of each model should be made in order to obtain the maximum profit?

10. A sporting goods manufacturer produces tricycles and bicycles. Dealer demand requires at least 30 tricycles per week and at least 20 bicycles per week. Production is limited to at most 60 tricycles and 40 bicycles per week. Also, the combined total cannot exceed 90. The profit on each tricycle is $12 and the profit on each bicycle is $18. How many of each should the company produce per week to maximize the profit?

11. Suppose you are to take a test in which items of type A are worth 5 points each and items of type B are worth 8 points each. Assume that it takes 2 minutes to answer an A question and 4 minutes to answer a B question. The total time for the test is 60 minutes, and you may not answer more than 20 questions. Assuming all your answers are correct, and at least 20 questions of each type are given, how many items of each type should you answer to get the best score?

C

12. A ceramics artist makes and sells plates and bowls. The kiln capacity permits her to produce at most 40 of these items combined. It takes her $\frac{1}{2}$ hour to make a plate and 1 hour to make a bowl. The total amount of time spent on these items cannot exceed 26 hours per week. Each plate brings her a $6 profit, and each bowl, a $9 profit. Assuming she sells all the items made, how many of each should she make per week in order to realize a maximum profit?

13. A farmer plans to grow two kinds of crops. The seed for Crop I costs $20 per acre, and the seed for Crop II costs $40 per acre. The most that the farmer plans to spend on seeds is $2000. Labor costs him $50 per acre for Crop I and $30 per acre for Crop II, and he will limit his total labor costs to $2200 or less. If Crop I produces $280 income per acre and Crop II produces $350 income per acre, how many acres of each crop should he plant in order to produce the maximum income?

*14. A dairy farmer wants to make a blend of two kinds of feed. The ounces of corn and oats per pound contained in each type of feed are shown in this table.

	Ounces of Corn per Pound	Ounces of Oats per Pound
Feed I	10	4
Feed II	4	8

He wants the total mixture to contain at least 80 pounds of corn and 64 pounds of oats, but he must buy no less than 40 pounds of each feed. If Feed I costs 8¢ per pound and Feed II costs 10¢ per pound, how much of each kind should he buy to minimize his cost?

Distance from an Earthquake

Seismologists study the frequency, intensity, and distribution of earthquakes. Seismic stations in various places determine the location of a quake by measuring the intervals of time between the different shock waves it sends through the earth. The primary wave travels 5 miles per second. The rate of the secondary wave, which starts at the same time, is 3 miles per second.

Example   If the time between the primary and secondary waves of an earthquake was found to be 14 seconds, how far was the quake from the station?

Use $d = rt$ and let t be the time for the first wave.

$$d = 5t \longleftarrow \text{First wave} \qquad d = 3(t + 14) \longleftarrow \text{Second wave}$$

Set the right sides of the two equations equal to each other, since the distances are the same. Then solve for t.

$$5t = 3(t + 14)$$
$$5t = 3t + 42$$
$$t = 21 \qquad \text{It took the first wave 21 seconds to reach the station.}$$

Substitute 21 for t in $d = 5t$, and solve for d.

$$d = 5 \times 21 = 105$$

The quake occurred 105 miles from the station.

In the above example, there was information from only one station. Hence we can conclude only that the quake was located somewhere on a circle of radius 105 miles, whose center is the station.

Station A measured a time lapse of 2.6 seconds between the primary and secondary shock waves from an earthquake. Station B measured a time lapse of 2.0 seconds.

1. Find the amount of time it took the primary and secondary waves to reach each station, to the nearest tenth.

2. Find the distance from the quake to each station, to the nearest whole number.

3. If stations A and B are 25 miles apart, how many different locations are possible for the quake?

4. If a third station in the vicinity also recorded the time lapse, could a single possible location for the quake be determined? Explain.

CHAPTER 3 REVIEW

VOCABULARY

system of linear equations (p. 86)	substitution method (p. 90)	region (p. 104)
consistent (p. 87)	addition method (p. 95)	linear programming (p. 107)
independent (p. 87)	ordered triple (p. 101)	convex region (p. 107)
dependent (p. 87)	system of linear inequalities (p. 104)	maximum value (p. 107)
inconsistent (p. 88)	boundary (p. 104)	minimum value (p. 107)
		constraints (p. 108)

SUMMARY

This chapter deals with the solution of linear systems of equations and inequalities. Linear systems of two equations in two variables are given geometric interpretations. Then algebraic methods for solving such systems are presented, and these methods are extended to the solution of systems of three linear equations in three variables. Problem situations calling for the solution of linear systems are studied throughout.

Systems of linear inequalities in two variables are solved by graphing. Linear programming, a modern technique that is used in business and industry, is developed as an application of the work with systems of linear inequalities.

REVIEW EXERCISES

3-1 Solve each system by graphing. Classify each system as **consistent** or **inconsistent**.

1. $3x + y = 7$
$x - y = 1$

2. $x - 3y = 5$
$2x - 6y = 1$

3. $y = -5$
$x - 2y = 0$

4. Without graphing, identify the *dependent* system or systems.

a. $5x - 2y = 4$
$2x - 5y = 2$

b. $y = -4x$
$8x + 2y = 0$

c. $4y = 2 - 2x$
$2y = 1 + x$

3-2 Solve each system using the substitution method, and check.

5. $2x + y = 5$
$x - 2y = 5$

6. $x + 2y = 2$
$2x - y = 6\frac{1}{2}$

7. $x + y = 2$
$x - 3y = -4$

Write a linear system for each problem. Then solve.

8. Robert worked a total of 35 hours at two jobs and earned $162.00 in all. One job paid $4.50 per hour, and the other job paid $5.00 per hour. How many hours did he work at each rate?

9. Ahmed's age is 8 years less than one-half his father's age, and Ahmed is also one-third the age of his father. Find Ahmed's age.

3-3   *Solve each system by using the addition method, and check.*

10. $2x - 3y = 1$

$x + 3y = 8$

11. $4x + 2y = 3$

$2x - y = -\dfrac{1}{2}$

12. $2x - 3y = 5$

$3x + 6y = -3$

Write a linear system for each problem. Then solve.

13. The length of a rectangle is 1 foot more than 3 times the width, in feet. Five times the width is 5 feet more than the length. Find the dimensions of the rectangle.

14. Five times a positive number equals 11 times another number. Four times the larger number is 2 less than 9 times the smaller number. Find both numbers.

15. A boat takes 10 minutes to travel 4 miles downstream. The return trip, against the current, takes 15 minutes. Find the speed of the current and the speed of the boat in still water, in miles per hour.

3-4   *Solve each system, and check.*

16. $x + y + z = 2$
$2x - y + z = 7$
$x + 2y - z = -6$

17. $x + 2y + z = 1$
$x + y = 0$
$y + 3z = 5$

18. $4x + y = 0$
$2x - y + 3z = 3$
$8x + 3z = 4$

Write a linear system for each problem. Then solve.

19. Josh has 48 cents in pennies, nickels, and dimes. He has 4 times as many pennies as nickels, and the total number of coins is 13. How many of each type of coin does he have?

20. Part of $8500 is invested at an annual yield of 6%, another part at 7%, and the remainder at 8%. The interest earned in one year by the 6% and 7% accounts together is $330. The interest earned in one year by the 6% and 8% accounts together is $400. How much money is invested at each rate?

3-5   *Graph each system on the coordinate plane.*

21. $y \leq x$
$x \geq 2$

22. $2x - y < 3$
$x > 2y$

23. $x + 2y \geq 4$
$5x + 2y \leq 20$
$2 \leq y \leq 8$

3-6   **24.** Graph the region **R** given by the system of linear inequalities. Find the maximum and minimum values of p and q for the given constraints.

$x \geq 0$
$y \geq 0$
$x + 2y \leq 22$
$3x + 2y \leq 30$

$p = 2x + 5y$
$q = 4x + 3y$

25. A store sells two types of coffee makers, the standard and the deluxe models. There is a $7 profit on each standard model sold and a $9 profit on each deluxe model. Each month, the store manager buys the coffee makers from a wholesaler who requires that the manager buy at least 24 of each model, but a total of no more than 60. Assuming that the store can sell all of the coffee makers, how many of each type should be bought from the wholesaler in order to realize the maximum profit?

CHAPTER 3 TEST

Solve each system algebraically, and check.

1. $x + 3y = 6$

$x - y = 2$

2. $2x - y = 6$

$3x + \dfrac{1}{2}y = 7$

3. $3x + 2y = -4$

$x - 3y = \dfrac{7}{3}$

4. $2x + 3y = -1$
$5x + 4y = 8$

5. $x + y + z = 2$
$x + 2y + 3z = 1$
$2x + y - 2z = 3$

Graph each system on the coordinate plane.

6. $y < 2x$
$2x + y < 5$

7. $y \geq 3$
$2x - y \leq 1$

Solve each problem.

8. One positive number is 2 more than 3 times another positive number. The difference between the two numbers is 7. Find the numbers.

9. Sandra has $1.75 in nickels, dimes, and quarters. She has 13 coins in all. If she has 3 times as many nickels as dimes, how many of each coin does she have?

10. Find the maximum and minimum values of $p = 2x + 9y$ for the region **R**, which is the graph of the following system of constraints.

$x + 3y \leq 21$
$3x - 2y \leq 8$
$4x + y \geq 18$

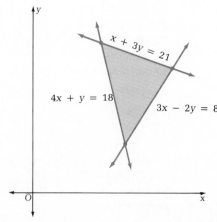

Systems of Equations

The mathematician Gabriel Cramer (1704–1752) developed a procedure for solving a system of equations that is easily programmed.

For the system:
$$\begin{array}{l} Ax + By = C \\ Dx + Ey = F \end{array} \qquad x = \frac{CE - BF}{AE - DB} \quad \text{and} \quad y = \frac{AF - CD}{AE - DB}$$

The program below solves for x and y when the coefficients of the equation are entered. Since x and y are undefined when $AE - DB = 0$, line 210 tests for this possibility. Use parentheses in BASIC whenever a numerator or denominator has more than one term (lines 220 and 230).

The Program	What It Does
`100 REM SYSTEM OF LINEAR EQUATIONS`	
`110 PRINT "ENTER A, B, C"`	Waits for three entries, separated by commas.
`120 INPUT A, B, C`	
`130 PRINT "ENTER D, E, F"`	
`140 INPUT D, E, F`	Waits for second set of entries.
`200 LET M = A * E - D * B`	Computes the denominator.
`210 IF M = 0 THEN 300`	Tests if denominator is zero.
`220 LET X = (C * E - B * F)/M`	Computes value of x.
`230 LET Y = (A * F - C * D)/M`	Computes value of y.
`240 PRINT "X = "; X`	Displays value of x.
`250 PRINT "Y = "; Y`	Displays value of y.
`260 GO TO 400`	
`300 PRINT "EQUATIONS ARE DEPENDENT"`	Displays appropriate message when denominator is zero.
`310 PRINT " OR INCONSISTENT."`	
`400 PRINT "ANOTHER? (1 = YES, 0 = NO)"`	Gives you the option of solving another system immediately.
`410 INPUT Z`	If you enter 1, computer jumps to line 110 and runs the program again.
`420 IF Z = 1 THEN 110`	
`900 END`	

To solve each of these systems, what values should be input in the above program? What solution will be displayed for each?

1. $2x + 5y = 1$
$3x - 2y = 30$

2. $7x - 2y = 4$
$5x + 3y = 25$

3. $9x + 2y = 15$
$2x + 6y = 45$

4. $3x + 15 = -y$
$2x - 7 = 5y$

5. $10x - 6y = 42$
$15x - 63 = 9y$

6. $x = 2y + 1.6$
$5y - 2x = 1$

7. Modify the program so that the solution is displayed as an ordered pair.

8. Write a program in BASIC that will evaluate $y = \frac{x}{5} + 8$ for any value of x that is used as the input.

For more information about BASIC, see the Computer Handbook at the back of the book.

CHAPTER 4

In architecture and interior design, quadratic equations can be useful in solving problems involving perimeter and area.

POLYNOMIALS

Prerequisite Skills Review

Write the letter for the correct answer.

1. $\left(-\dfrac{3}{4}\right)^4 = \underline{\ ?\ }$

   a. $\dfrac{81}{4}$
   b. $-\dfrac{3}{4}$
   c. $-\dfrac{81}{256}$
   d. $\dfrac{81}{256}$

2. Evaluate x^2y^3 for $x = -2$ and $y = -3$.
   a. 108
   b. -108
   c. -72
   d. 36

3. The greatest common factor of 36 and 18 is $\underline{\ ?\ }$.
   a. 9
   b. 18
   c. 36
   d. none of these

4. The greatest common factor of 14, 27, and 48 is $\underline{\ ?\ }$.
   a. 1
   b. 2
   c. 3
   d. none of these

5. $(8 - 5)$ is the opposite of $\underline{\ ?\ }$.
   a. $8 + 5$
   b. $-8 - 5$
   c. $5 - 8$
   d. none of these

6. A solution to the equation $2x^2 - 7x - 15 = 0$ is $\underline{\ ?\ }$.

   a. -5
   b. $\dfrac{3}{2}$
   c. $-\dfrac{3}{2}$
   d. none of these

7. A solution to the equation $3x^2 - 5x - 2 = 0$ is $\underline{\ ?\ }$.

   a. -2
   b. $\dfrac{1}{3}$
   c. 0
   d. none of these

8. If a rectangle is 6 feet long and 8 feet wide, its area is $\underline{\ ?\ }$.
   a. 28 ft
   b. 24 ft^2
   c. 48 ft^2
   d. none of these

9. If the base of a triangle is 12 centimeters and the altitude is 10 centimeters, its area is $\underline{\ ?\ }$.
   a. 120 cm^2
   b. 11 cm^2
   c. 30 cm^2
   d. none of these

10. The length, in inches, of a rectangle is 6 inches less than twice its width, w. The length can be expressed as $\underline{\ ?\ }$.
    a. $2(3 - w)$
    b. $2(w - 6)$
    c. $2(w - 3)$
    d. none of these

4-1 Products of Monomials

OBJECTIVE _____

To find products and powers of monomials using the rules for exponents.

_____

A **monomial** is a number, a variable, or the product of a number and one or more variables. The exponents on the variables must be positive integers. Each of the following expressions is a monomial.

$$y \qquad -\sqrt{3} \qquad 5n \qquad \frac{1}{2}y^2 \qquad -8x^3y^4$$

In a monomial no variable appears in a denominator or under a radical. Expressions such as $\frac{15}{y}, \frac{2y}{x^2}$, and $\sqrt{x}$ are *not* monomials.

Several rules for exponents are useful when finding the products of monomials. The first of these rules applies to the multiplication of *exponential expressions* with the *same base*, such as 2^3 and 2^4.

$$
\begin{aligned}
2^3 \cdot 2^4 &= (2 \cdot 2 \cdot 2)(2 \cdot 2 \cdot 2 \cdot 2) \\
&= 2 \cdot 2 \cdot 2 \cdot 2 \cdot 2 \cdot 2 \cdot 2 \\
&= 2^7
\end{aligned}
$$

We can check this result by simplifying both $2^3 \cdot 2^4$ and 2^7.

$$2^3 \cdot 2^4 = 8 \cdot 16 = 128 \qquad 2^7 = 128$$

This illustration leads to the following general rule.

_____

Product of Powers with the Same Base

If b is a real number and m and n are positive integers, then

$$b^m b^n = b^{m+n}$$

_____

EXAMPLE 1   Write each expression in exponential form with just one exponent.

     a. $(-3)^3(-3)^2 = (-3)^{3+2} = (-3)^5$

     b. $\dfrac{3}{4}\left(\dfrac{3}{4}\right)^6 = \left(\dfrac{3}{4}\right)^{1+6} = \left(\dfrac{3}{4}\right)^7$

The same rule can be applied when finding a product involving more than two monomial factors. Note that when we *simplify* such a product, we show each variable with just one exponent.

EXAMPLE 2   Simplify.

a. $x^4 \cdot x^6 \cdot x^9 = x^{4+6+9} = x^{19}$

b. $(3x^2y^3)(xy^4)(x^5) = 3(x^2 \cdot x \cdot x^5)(y^3 \cdot y^4)$ Group factors with the
same base.

$$= 3x^{2+1+5}y^{3+4}$$ Recall that $x = x^1$.

$$= 3x^8y^7$$

Next, consider taking a power of a power. To illustrate, we square 2^3.

$$(2^3)^2 = 2^3 \cdot 2^3$$
$$= 2^{3+3}$$
$$= 2^6$$

To check this result, observe that $(2^3)^2 = 8^2 = 64$, and $2^6 = 64$. This illustration leads to our second rule for exponents.

Power of a Power

If b is a real number and m and n are positive integers, then
$$(b^m)^n = b^{mn}$$

EXAMPLE 3   Write $(x^7)^3$ in exponential form with just one exponent.

$$(x^7)^3 = x^{7 \cdot 3} = x^{21}$$

Finally, we consider the power of a product, such as $(3 \cdot 2)^3$.

$$(3 \cdot 2)^3 = (3 \cdot 2)(3 \cdot 2)(3 \cdot 2)$$
$$= (3 \cdot 3 \cdot 3)(2 \cdot 2 \cdot 2)$$
$$= 3^3 \cdot 2^3$$

You can check this result by showing that $(3 \cdot 2)^3$ and $3^3 \cdot 2^3$ are each equal to 216.

Power of a Product

If a and b are real numbers and m is a positive integer, then
$$(ab)^m = a^m b^m$$

EXAMPLE 4   Simplify.

$$\textbf{a. } (-2x^3y^2)^4 = (-2)^4(x^3)^4(y^2)^4 = 16x^{3\cdot4}y^{2\cdot4} = 16x^{12}y^8$$

$$\textbf{b. } \left[\left(\frac{1}{2}a\right)^2 b^5\right]^3 = \left[\left(\frac{1}{2}a\right)^2\right]^3(b^5)^3 = \left(\frac{1}{2}a\right)^6 b^{15} = \left(\frac{1}{2}\right)^6 a^6 b^{15} = \frac{1}{64}a^6 b^{15}$$

The power of a product rule can also be written in reversed form as $a^m b^m = (ab)^m$. In this form, the rule is particularly useful in simplifying computations.

EXAMPLE 5   Evaluate x^3y^3 for $x = \frac{1}{4}$ and $y = 12$.

$$x^3y^3 = \left(\frac{1}{4}\right)^3(12)^3 = \left(\frac{1}{4}\cdot12\right)^3 = 3^3 = 27$$

Notice that more difficult computations would have been required in the last example if the rule had *not* been applied, as shown here.

$$x^3y^3 = \left(\frac{1}{4}\right)^3(12)^3 = \left(\frac{1}{64}\right)(1728) = 27$$

CLASS EXERCISES

Express each product or power in exponential form with just one exponent.

1. $9^3 \cdot 9^5$

2. $(-6)^5(-6)^2$

3. $\left(\frac{2}{3}\right)^7\left(\frac{2}{3}\right)^3$

4. $(6^2)^4$

5. $\left[\left(\frac{1}{3}\right)^3\right]^6$

6. $[(-1)^3]^8$

7. $5^6 \cdot 3^6$

8. $\left(\frac{1}{4}\right)^3(8)^3$

9. $(-6)^9\left(\frac{1}{2}\right)^9$

10. $a^8 b^8$

11. $[(xy)^3]^{10}$

12. $2^5 u^5 v^5$

*Classify each statement as **true** or **false**.*

13. $9^2 \cdot 9^3 = 9^6$

14. $(-4)^5(-4)^5 = (-4)^{10}$

15. $[(0.7)^2]^6 = (0.7)^{12}$

16. $(8^3)^5 = 8^8$

17. $(-6)^4(-7)^2 = 42^6$

18. $12^4\left(-\frac{1}{4}\right)^4 = (-3)^4$

19. $(a^4)^3 = a^7$

20. $(-x)^5(-y^5) = (xy)^5$

21. $b^3 b^5 = b^{15}$

22. $(ab^2)^4 = ab^8$

23. $(5y^3)(5y^2) = 10y^5$

24. $(n^2 \cdot n^3)^4 = n^{20}$

25. $(c^2 d^3)^4 = c^6 d^7$

26. $\left[\left(\frac{x}{2}\right)^2\right]^2 = \frac{x^4}{8}$

27. $(-2x)^2(-3x)^3 = -108x^5$

EXERCISES

A

Write each expression in exponential form with just one exponent.

1. $7^6 \cdot 7^3$

2. $(-5)^2(-5)^9$

3. $2 \cdot 2^2 \cdot 2^3$

4. $(0.5)^4(0.5)^8$

5. $(5^3)^4$

6. $[(-10)^4]^7$

7. $4^8 \cdot 2^8$

8. $(-9)^4(-4)^4$

9. $x^2 \cdot x^4 \cdot x^6$

10. $(b^2)^3$

11. $a^{10}b^{10}$

12. $15^2r^2t^2$

13. $\left[\left(\dfrac{2}{5}\right)^6\right]^2$

14. $\left(\dfrac{4}{7}\right)^8(14)^8$

15. $(0.5)^4(6)^4$

16. $\left[\left(\dfrac{1}{2}\right)^3\left(\dfrac{1}{2}\right)^5\right]^2$

Simplify. Show each variable with just one exponent.

17. $(2x^2)^3$

18. $(-2a^3b^2)^2$

19. $\left[\left(\dfrac{2}{3}x\right)^2\right]^2$

20. $(2x^3)(3x^7)$

21. $(ab^2)(a^2b)$

22. $(2x^3)^2x$

23. $(3x^2)(2y^5)(xy)$

24. $(-2x^2y)^3$

B

25. $\left(-\dfrac{5}{9}u^2\right)\left(\dfrac{3}{10}u^4\right)$

26. $\left(-\dfrac{1}{2}xy^2\right)(-8x^3)$

27. $\left(\dfrac{2}{3}x\right)^3\left(\dfrac{3}{2}x\right)^2$

28. $(-5x^2)^3(xy^4)^2$

29. $(x^2y)^4(xy^2)^3$

30. $(2ab)^2(2ab)^3$

31. $(r^2s)^2(4s)^2$

32. $[(2a)^3]^2\left[\left(\dfrac{1}{2}b\right)^3\right]^2$

Evaluate for $x = 24$, $y = \dfrac{1}{2}$, and $z = -4$.

33. $(z^2)^3$

34. y^2y^3

35. x^3y^3

36. y^4z^4

37. $\left(\dfrac{1}{8}\right)^5x^5$

38. $\left(\dfrac{1}{4}\right)^8z^8$

39. $(-2)^7y^7$

40. $(xyz)^2$

Evaluate for $x = 18$ and $y = \dfrac{1}{6}$.

41. x^2y^2

42. $(x^4y^4)^2$

43. $2^3x^3y^3$

44. $\left[\left(\dfrac{1}{2}\right)^2x^2y^2\right]^2$

Evaluate for $x = 2$ and $y = 5$.

45. x^6y^6

46. $(x^3y^3)^3$

47. $10^5x^5y^5$

48. $\left[\left(\dfrac{3}{10}\right)^4x^4y^4\right]^2$

C

Rewrite $(xy^2)^5x^5(y^5)^2$ in exponential form using

49. the base xy^2.

50. the base x^5y^{10}.

51. the base x^2y^4.

Rewrite $(a^2b^3c^2)^2(a^4b^2)^3(b^3c)^4$ in exponential form using

52. the base a^2b^3c.

53. the base $a^8b^{12}c^4$.

54. the base $a^4b^6c^2$.

Simplify. Assume that n represents a positive integer.

55. x^2x^n

56. x^nx^n

57. $x^{2n}x^{3n}$

58. $(x^2)^n$

59. $(x^n)^n$

60. $(x^nx^{2n})^2$

4-2 Combining Polynomials

To classify a polynomial as a monomial, a binomial, or a trinomial, and to give its degree.

To add and subtract polynomials.

A **polynomial** is a monomial or the sum of two or more monomials. Polynomials are named according to the number of terms they contain.

$3xy^2$ is a **monomial.**   It has just one term.

$-5t^4 + 7s^2$ is a **binomial.**   It has exactly two terms.

$10x^5 + (-3x) + 4$ is a **trinomial.**   It has exactly three terms.

The $+$ symbol before the second term in $10x^5 + (-3x) + 4$ would normally be dropped, and the trinomial written as $10x^5 - 3x + 4$.

Polynomials with more than three terms are not given special names.

EXAMPLE 1   Classify each polynomial as a monomial, a binomial, or a trinomial.

    a. $2x^2 + y^3 - z$ A trinomial   The terms are $2x^2$, y^3, and $-z$.

    b. $2x^2y^3z$ A monomial

The **degree** of a monomial is the sum of the exponents on its variables. The degree of any other polynomial is the greatest of the degrees of its terms. The degree of a nonzero constant is 0.

EXAMPLE 2   Give the degree of each polynomial.

    a. x^2y
    Add the exponents: $2 + 1 = 3$.
    The degree of this monomial is 3.

    b. $5x^2 + 2x$
    The degree of $5x^2$ is 2. The degree of $2x$ is 1.
    The degree of the binomial is the greater of these, 2.

Assuming that the replacement set for the variables in a polynomial is the set of real numbers, the polynomials themselves represent real numbers. To add polynomials, we simplify by combining like terms, using the distributive property. Polynomials are usually written with the terms arranged in order of decreasing degree of one variable. Therefore, we group like terms in order, starting with the terms of highest degree.

EXAMPLE 3   Add $7x^4 - 6x^3 + x^2 + x + 1$ and $x^4 - 3x^2 + 5x - 9$.

$$(7x^4 - 6x^3 + x^2 + x + 1) + (x^4 - 3x^2 + 5x - 9)$$
$$= (7x^4 + x^4) - 6x^3 + (x^2 - 3x^2) + (x + 5x) + 1 - 9 \qquad \text{Regroup.}$$
$$= (7 + 1)x^4 - 6x^3 + (1 - 3)x^2 + (1 + 5)x - 8 \qquad \text{Use the}$$
$$= 8x^4 - 6x^3 - 2x^2 + 6x - 8 \qquad\qquad\qquad\quad \text{distributive}$$
property.

When you add more than two polynomials, a vertical format is sometimes helpful.

EXAMPLE 4   Add: $(3x^2y + 2y - xy^2) + (-5x^2y - 4y + 8) + (12xy^2 - 10 - y)$

$$
\begin{array}{l}
3x^2y - xy^2 + 2y \\
-5x^2y   - 4y + 8 \\
\underline{ 12xy^2 - y - 10} \\
-2x^2y + 11xy^2 - 3y - 2 \qquad \text{Align like terms and add by columns.}
\end{array}
$$

When you subtract polynomials, keep in mind that for all real numbers r and s, the following relationships hold.

$$
\begin{array}{lll}
r - s = r + (-s) & \begin{array}{l} -(r + s) = -1(r + s) \\ = (-1)(r) + (-1)(s) \\ = -r - s \end{array} & \begin{array}{l} -(r - s) = -1[r + (-s)] \\ = (-1)(r) + (-1)(-s) \\ = -r + s \end{array}
\end{array}
$$

EXAMPLE 5   Subtract $3x^2 + 8x - 9$ from $7x^2 - x - 15$.

$$(7x^2 - x - 15) - (3x^2 + 8x - 9) = 7x^2 - x - 15 - 3x^2 - 8x + 9$$
$$= (7x^2 - 3x^2) + (-x - 8x) + (-15 + 9)$$
$$= 4x^2 - 9x - 6$$

If the vertical form is used, align like terms.

$$
\begin{array}{l}
7x^2 - x - 15 \\
\underline{3x^2 + 8x - 9} \qquad \text{Subtract by columns.} \\
4x^2 - 9x - 6 \longleftarrow \quad -15 - (-9) = -6 \\
 \qquad -x - 8x = -9x \\
 \qquad 7x^2 - 3x^2 = 4x^2
\end{array}
$$

Subtraction can be checked by addition, as shown below for Example 5.

$$
\begin{array}{l}
7x^2 - x - 15 \\
\underline{3x^2 + 8x - 9} \\
\underline{4x^2 - 9x - 6} \left.\begin{array}{l} \\ \\ \end{array}\right\} \quad \text{Add.} \\
7x^2 - x - 15 \qquad \text{This sum should equal the first polynomial.}
\end{array}
$$

CLASS EXERCISES

Classify each polynomial as a **monomial**, a **binomial**, or a **trinomial**. Then state its degree.

1. $3x^2y^3 + 5$ **2.** $5x^2 + x - 1$ **3.** $-18x^2yz^5$ **4.** $x^3 - 2xy$

Add.

5. $(3x + 8) + (2x - 3)$ **6.** $(x^2 - 2xy + y^2) + (5xy - 3y^2)$

7. $(-7x + 6) + (5x - 9) + (-x + 1)$ **8.** $(x^2 - 4) + (3x - 2) + (4x^2 + x)$

Subtract.

9. $(3x + 8) - (2x - 3)$ **10.** $(2x - 3) - (3x + 8)$

11. $(x^2 + 4x - 1) - (x + 9)$ **12.** $(4x^2 - 6x) - (-x^2 + x + 7)$

13. $(x^2y - 2xy + y^2) - (x^2y - y^2)$ **14.** $(4x^2 - xy) - (4x^2 + xy)$

EXERCISES

A

Classify each polynomial as a **monomial**, a **binomial**, or a **trinomial**. Then give its degree.

1. $-9x^3y^4$ **2.** $-9x^3 - y^4$ **3.** $-9 + x^3 - 4y$ **4.** $-9 + 3x - 4y$

5. $x - 13xy^2$ **6.** $x^3y + x^2y + y^5$ **7.** $3x^3y^3$ **8.** $16x^6 - xy^4$

Add.

9. $(6x - 1) + (2x + 7)$ **10.** $(8x + 3) + (-3x + 8)$

11. $(-5x + 2y) + (3x - 6y)$ **12.** $(xy - z) + (-2xy + z)$

13. $(10x^2 + 7x + 1) + (x^2 - x - 6)$ **14.** $(-x^2y + xy - 3y^2) + (5x^2y - y^2)$

15. $9x + 11$ **16.** $8x^2 - x + 7$ **17.** $-2x^3y^2 + 4x^2y + 9x$

        $x - 4$ $-5x^2 + 4x - 12$ $8x^2y - x$

     $\underline{-3x - 9}$ $\underline{x^2 - 3x + 5}$ $\underline{-3x^3y^2 - x^2y - 9x}$

Subtract.

18. $(4y - 3) - (y + 1)$ **19.** $(8x + 5y) - (-x - y)$

20. $(7z^2 + z) - (2z^2 - 4z)$ **21.** $(4x^2y - xy) - (13x^2y + 9xy)$

22. $(8x^2 - 2x + 1) - (x^2 - 7)$ **23.** $(5x^3 + 4x^2 - x) - (5x^3 - 4x^2 - x)$

Subtract the second polynomial from the first one, and check.

24. $4x - 10$ **25.** $-21xy + 5x + 4$ **26.** $x^2 + 11xy - 18y^2$

     $\underline{3x - 3}$ $\underline{6xy - x - 1}$ $\underline{- 15xy - 23y^2}$

B   *Add or subtract, as indicated.*

27. $(x^2 - 4x + 1) + (-x^2 - 8x - 4) + (8x^2 + x - 12)$

28. $(a^2 + 5ab) + (16a^2 - ab + 10b^2) + (-5a^2 - 9ab - b^2)$

29. $(7x^4 - 3x^3 + x^2 - 5) + (x^3 - 15) + (-x^4 - 8x^2 + 2)$

30. $(-8x^2y + 4xy^2 - 8xy) + (7x^3y^2 - xy^2) + (x^2y - 12xy^2 + 4xy)$

31. $(9x^3 + 5x^2 + x - 1) + (x^3 - 2x + 2) + (-3x^3 - 5) + (4x^2 - 7x)$

32. $(3x^3 + x^2 - 18x + 24) - (-9x^3 - 8x^2 + 30x - 5)$

33. $(-x^5 + 4x^4 - 11x^2 - 45) - (x^5 - 14x^4 - 6x^3 .- 11x^2 + 15)$

34. $(x^3y - 3x^2y^2 + 8) - (5x^3y - x^2y^2 + 18xy^3 - 36)$

35. $(x^3 + 24) - (6x^3 - 18x^2 + 10x - 4)$

36. $(1 + 2y + 8y^2 - y^4) - (8 - y + 5y^3 + y^4)$

Add. Check using $x = 2$ *and* $y = 3$.

> **Sample** $(-8x^2 + x + 7) + (-5x^3 - 4x + 15) + (12x^2 + x - 10)$
>
> $$-8x^2 + x + 7 \longrightarrow -8(2)^2 + 2 + 7 = -23$$
> $$-5x^3 \qquad\quad - 4x + 15 \longrightarrow -5(2)^3 - 4(2) + 15 = -33 \left.\begin{array}{} \\ \\ \end{array}\right\} \text{Add.}$$
> $$\underline{\qquad\quad 12x^2 + x - 10} \longrightarrow \underline{\quad 12(2)^2 + 2 - 10 = \quad 40}$$
> $$-5x^3 + 4x^2 - 2x + 12 \qquad\qquad\qquad\qquad\qquad \mathbf{-16}$$
> $$-5(2)^3 + 4(2)^2 - 2(2) + 12 = \mathbf{-16} \left.\begin{array}{}\end{array}\right] \text{ Check.}$$

37. $(x^2 + x + 1) + (-4x^2 + 3x - 7) + (-x^2 - x + 2)$

38. $(3x^3 - 4x^2 + 6) + (-x^3 + 2x^2 - 12) + (6x^3 + x^2 + 2)$

39. $(x^2 - 2xy + y^2) + (5x^2 + 4xy) + (5xy - 3y^2)$

C   *Simplify.*

40. $(3x - 7) + (4x + 5) - (7x - 6)$ **41.** $(3x - 7) - (4x + 5) - (7x - 6)$

42. $(3x - 7) - (4x + 5) + (7x - 6)$ **43.** $-(3x - 7) - (4x + 5) - (7x - 6)$

44. $(7a - 5) + (-3a - 4) + (a^2 + a + 1) - (a^3 + a^2)$

45. $(8x^3 + 12x^2 + 18x) + (-12x^2 - 18x - 27) - (x^3 - x) - (3x^2 + 15)$

46. $(p^2 - pq + 2q^2) + (2pq - q^2) - (-p^2 + pq) + (5p^2 - 4pq - 9q^2) - 4pq$

47. $6x^2 + 7x - 4 - [x - (2x^2 - x + 7)]$

48. $3a - 2b - [(a - b) - (7a - 4b)]$

49. $[(x^2 - 2x + 1) - (x^2 - 3x)] - [(x^3 + 6x) - (1 + x + x^2)]$

50. $x - [(x^2 + 1) - (x - 1) - (1 - x^2) - (1 - x)]$

51. $x - \{x - [x - (x - 1)]\}$

4-3 Multiplying Polynomials

OBJECTIVE

To find the product of two polynomials.

To multiply polynomials, we use various forms of the distributive property. The resulting polynomial is simplified by combining like terms.

EXAMPLE 1   Multiply.

a. $3x(2x - 5)$ $= 3x(2x) - 3x(5)$
$$= 6x^2 - 15x$$

b. $(3x^2 + 2y)(x^2 + 2y)$ $= 3x^2(x^2 + 2y) + 2y(x^2 + 2y)$
$$= 3x^4 + 6x^2y + 2x^2y + 4y^2$$
$$= 3x^4 + 8x^2y + 4y^2$$

A vertical format is useful when one or both factors have more than two terms. Each term in the upper factor is multiplied by each term in the lower factor, keeping like terms in columns.

EXAMPLE 2   Multiply $(2x - 3)(x^3 - 7x^2 + 8x - 5)$.

$$
\begin{array}{r}
x^3 - 7x^2 + 8x - 5 \\
2x - 3 \\
\hline
-3x^3 + 21x^2 - 24x + 15 \\
2x^4 - 14x^3 + 16x^2 - 10x \\
\hline
2x^4 - 17x^3 + 37x^2 - 34x + 15
\end{array}
$$

Multiply by -3.

Multiply by $2x$.

Add.

You can multiply two binomials using a shortcut.

EXAMPLE 3   Multiply.

a. $(2x + 3)(3x - 4)$

The product of the two binomials is the sum of the products of the *first* terms, the *outer* terms, the *inner* terms, and the *last* terms.

$$(2x + 3)(3x - 4) = 6x^2 - 8x + 9x - 12 = 6x^2 + x - 12$$

b. $(3x^2 - y)(5x - 2y) = 15x^3 - 6x^2y - 5xy + 2y^2$

c. $(x - 6)(x + 6) = x^2 + 6x - 6x - 36 = x^2 - 36$

d. $(2x + 3)^2 = (2x + 3)(2x + 3)$
$$= 4x^2 + 12x + 9$$

A power of a polynomial, written as a sum, is called an **expansion**.

The next example illustrates the simplification of an expression using several operations.

EXAMPLE 4   Simplify $3x(x^2 - 9x + 1) - (x - 2)(4x - 3)$.

$$3x(x^2 - 9x + 1) - (x - 2)(4x - 3) = 3x^3 - 27x^2 + 3x - (4x^2 - 11x + 6)$$
$$= 3x^3 - 27x^2 + 3x - 4x^2 + 11x - 6$$
$$= 3x^3 - 31x^2 + 14x - 6$$

CLASS EXERCISES

Multiply.

1. $2x(3x - 5)$ **2.** $-4x(9 - x)$ **3.** $(-5a + 4b)a^2$

4. $x^2(x^2 - x - 1)$ **5.** $3xy(2x^2 - 7xy - y^2)$ **6.** $(u^2 + 3v^2 - 2uv)u^2v$

7. $(x + 2)(x + 5)$ **8.** $(x + 2)(x - 5)$ **9.** $(x - 2)(x + 5)$

10. $(x - 2)(x - 5)$ **11.** $(2x + 1)^2$ **12.** $(y + 5)(y - 5)$

EXERCISES

A   *Multiply.*

1. $5x(x - 7)$ **2.** $x^2(3x + 1)$ **3.** $(-x + 4)(-3x)$

4. $2a(a^2 - a)$ **5.** $xy(x - y)$ **6.** $-xy(x^2 + y^2)$

7. $6x(1 + x - x^2)$ **8.** $-h(h^3 - 8)$ **9.** $(-3pq + 5)7q^3$

10. $(x - 8)(x + 8)$ **11.** $(x - 8)(x - 5)$ **12.** $(x + 4)^2$

13. $(3x - 1)(3x + 1)$ **14.** $(2x + 3)^2$ **15.** $(4x + 3)(x + 6)$

16. $(1 + 3x)(1 - 3x)$ **17.** $(x + 2y)(x + y)$ **18.** $(1 - h)(3 - 2h)$

19. $(3a + b)(2a - 3b)$ **20.** $(u - 7v)(8u - v)$ **21.** $(3x - 2)^2$

22. $(10x + 3)(2x - 5)$ **23.** $(14x - 1)(x - 2)$ **24.** $(9r + 4s)(2r - 3s)$

25. $x^2 + 8x - 6$ **26.** $x^2 - 8x + 6$ **27.** $x^2 - 2x + 4$
$\underline{x + 5}$ $\underline{2x + 1}$ $\underline{x + 2}$

28. $x^2 + 2x + 4$ **29.** $x^2 + 2x - 3$ **30.** $10x^2 - 6x + 1$
$\underline{x - 2}$ $\underline{-4x - 5}$ $\underline{x^2 + 5x}$

B

31. $(7x - 5)(7 + 6x)$

32. $(4 - 12x)(3x + 5)$

33. $(x^2 - 1)(x^2 + 1)$

34. $(x^2 + 1)^2$

35. $(p^2 - q^2)(p^2 + q^2)$

36. $(x - 1)(x^2 + x)$

37. $(2x + 1)(4x^2 - 2x)$

38. $(x^2 + y)(x - 4y)$

39. $(x - xy)(x + 4)$

40. $(h + 3)(h^2 + 3h + 9)$

41. $(x - 1)(x^2 + x + 1)$

42. $(2x + 1)(4x^2 - 2x + 1)$

43. $(3a - b)(2a^2 + ab - b^2)$

44. $(2x^2 + 3)(4x^2 - 6x + 9)$

45. $(2 - 5t)(7 + 6t - 3t^2)$

46. $(x^2 - 2)(x^4 + 2x^2 + 4)$

47. $(x^2 - 3x + 5)(3x^3 - 2x^2 + x - 1)$

Simplify.

48. $(x + 1)(2x - 3) + (x - 2)^2$

49. $(x + 5)^2 - 4x^2(x^2 - 3x - 6)$

50. $(3x - 8)(4x + 1) - (2x - 1)^2$

51. $-2x(1 - 3x + x^2) + (1 - x)^2$

C

Multiply.

52. $(x + 1)^3$

53. $(x + y + 1)^2$

54. $(2x^2 - 3x + 1)(x^2 + 4x - 3)$

55. $(x + 2)(x^5 - 2x^4 + 4x^3 + x - 1)$

56. $(x - h)(x^3 + hx^2 + h^2x + h^3)$

57. $(x - h)(x^4 + hx^3 + h^2x^2 + h^3x + h^4)$

58. $x[5x - x(2x + 3) + 4]$

59. $-x[(x - y)(x + 2y) - (2x - 5)y]$

*60. $(a^2 + ab + b^2)(a - b)(a + b)(a^2 - ab + b^2)$

CHECKPOINT

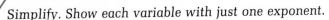

Simplify. *Show each variable with just one exponent.*

1. $x \cdot x \cdot x \cdot x$

2. $x^5(x^4)$

3. $(x^4)^3$

4. $(-x)^5(-y)^5$

Simplify.

5. $(2x - 8) + (3x + 6) - (8x - 7)$

6. $(2x - 8) - (3x + 6) - (8x - 7)$

7. $(2x - 8) - (3x + 6) + (7x - 6)$

8. $-(2x - 8) - (3x + 6) - (8x - 7)$

9. $(9x^3 + 13x^2 + 19x) + (-13x^2 - 19x - 28) - (2x^3 - 2x) - (4x^2 + 16)$

10. $(2m^2 - 2mn + 3n^2) + (3mn - 2n^2) - (-2m^2 + 2mn) + (6m^2 - 5mn - 10n^2)$

11. $7x^2 + 8x - 5 - [2x - (3x^2 - 2x + 8)]$

Multiply.

12. $6x(2x - 8)$

13. $-3a(a^2 - 2a)$

14. $7x(2 + x - 3x^2)$

15. $(x - 7)(x + 7)$

16. $(3x + 2)(3x - 2)$

17. $(3x - 4)(8 + 5x)$

4-4 Common Factors

To find the greatest common factor of two or more monomials.
To factor polynomials with terms containing common factors.

Recall that to find the **greatest common factor (GCF)** of two or more positive integers, we can list the positive integral factors of each number. Then we find the greatest factor that occurs in all of the lists.

EXAMPLE 1   Find the GCF of 24, 60, and 18.

Factors of 24:   1, 2, 3, 4, **6**, 8, 12, 24
Factors of 60:   1, 2, 3, 4, 5, **6**, 10, 12, 15, 20, 30, 60
Factors of 18:   1, 2, 3, **6**, 9, 18

The GCF of 24, 60, and 18 is 6.

The GCF of two or more monomials is found in a similar way. It is the product of the GCF of the coefficients and the lowest power of each of the common variables.

EXAMPLE 2   Find the GCF of $6x^3$, $9x^2y$, and $3x^4y^2$.

3 is the GCF of the coefficients.

Factors of 6: 1, 2, **3**, 6
Factors of 9: 1, **3**, 9
Factors of 3: 1, **3**

x^2 is the GCF of x^3, x^2, and x^4.

x^2 is the lowest power of x in any of the three monomials.

y is not a factor of the first monomial, so y is not a common factor.
The GCF of $6x^3$, $9x^2y$, and $3x^4y^2$ is $3x^2$.

To **factor** a polynomial means to write it as the product of two or more factors. The relationship between multiplication and factoring is illustrated below. The polynomials $6x^2y$ and $2x + 3$ are multiplied on the left, and then the resulting product is factored on the right.

$$6x^2y(2x + 3) = 6x^2y(2x) + 6x^2y(3)$$
$$= 12x^3y + 18x^2y \longleftarrow \text{product}$$

$2x + 3$ has been *multiplied* by $6x^2y$.

$$12x^3y + 18x^2y = 6x^2y(2x) + 6x^2y(3)$$
$$= 6x^2y(2x + 3) \longleftarrow \text{factored form}$$

$6x^2y$ has been *factored out of* the product.

EXAMPLE 3   Factor each polynomial.

a. $6x^2 - 8x = 2x(3x) - 2x(4)$ Factor out $2x$, the GCF of the two terms.

$$= 2x(3x - 4)$$

b. $-5x^3 - 15x^2y = -5x^2(x) - 5x^2(3y)$ Factor out $-5x^2$.

$$= -5x^2(x + 3y)$$ This form is preferred to the equivalent form $5x^2(-x - 3y)$.

c. $30a^4b^2 - 60a^2b^3c - 45a^2bc^2$

First, find the GCF of the coefficients.

Factors of 30:   1, 2, 3, 5, 6, 10, **15**, 30
Factors of 60:   1, 2, 3, 4, 5, 6, 10, 12, **15**, 20, 30, 60
Factors of 45:   1, 3, 5, 9, **15**, 45
The GCF of 30, 60, and 45 is **15**.

The GCF of the three terms in the polynomial is $15a^2b$.

$$30a^4b^2 - 60a^2b^3c - 45a^2bc^2 = 15a^2b(2a^2b - 4b^2c - 3c^2)$$

CLASS EXERCISES

Give the GCF of each set of integers.

1. 4, 8   **2.** 6, 9   **3.** 6, 12   **4.** 9, 12

5. 12, 15   **6.** 14, 25   **7.** 28, 42   **8.** 36, 54

9. 2, 4, 8   **10.** 6, 9, 12   **11.** 12, 18, 42   **12.** 20, 30, 50

Give the GCF of each set of monomials.

13. x^2, x^3 **14.** xy, y^3 **15.** $4x^2y, 8xy^2$ **16.** $6x^4, 8x^6$

17. $3x^2, 9$ **18.** a^2bc^5, a^3c^4 **19.** a^2, ab^2, ab **20.** $6ab^2, 4b^3, 2b$

21. $2x^2, 4x, 8$ **22.** $x^2, xy^2, 3x^2y^2$ **23.** $2r^4s^4, 4r^2s^2, 8rs$ **24.** $2cd^6, 6cd^2, c^2d^6$

EXERCISES

A   *Write the GCF of each set of integers.*

1. 12, 18   **2.** 21, 35   **3.** 8, 20   **4.** 24, 48

5. 6, 12, 16   **6.** 8, 20, 32   **7.** 6, 27, 42   **8.** 26, 39, 52

9. 16, 64, 160   **10.** 18, 36, 90   **11.** 28, 42, 56, 84   **12.** 34, 51, 85, 102

Write the GCF of each set of monomials.

13. y^4, y^6 **14.** x^3y^2, xy^3 **15.** $6xy, 15y^4$ **16.** $10y^3, 8y^6$

17. $18, 12x$ **18.** a^2b, b^2c, ab^2 **19.** $2a^6, 4a, 2a^2$ **20.** $7c^3d, 3cd, 6c^2$

Factor.

21. $4x - 6$

22. $6a - 15$

23. $10 + 15b$

24. $3x^2 - 9$

25. $7x - 42$

26. $6x - 6y$

27. $9x + 9y$

28. $9x^3 - 3x$

29. $12x^2 - 16x^3$

30. $5x^3 - 25x$

31. $9x^2 + 3x$

32. $10a^3b + 100ab$

33. $15a^2b + 12b^3$

34. $66u^2 - 33uv$

35. $8x^2 + 28x$

36. $8ab^2 - 20a^3b$

37. $4x^2 - 8x$

38. $14a^2b - 7ab$

39. $ax + ay$

40. $ax - bx^2$

41. $ax - a^2x$

B

42. $-8h^3 - 12h$

43. $-28x + 21x^3$

44. $9x^3 - 3x^2 + 3x$

45. $6b^6 - 12b^4 - 18b^3$

46. $ax - bx + abx$

47. $ax + ay - az$

48. $3x^3 - 2x^2 + x$

49. $64h^3 - 16h^2 + 14h$

50. $u^3v - u^2v^2 - uv^3$

51. $9a^3b + 21a^2b^2 - 15ab^3$

52. $32h^5 - 16h^4 + 8h^3 - 4h^2 + 2h$

53. $26x^6 - 39x^4 - 52x^3 + 91x^2$

54. $91a^{10}b^4 - 63a^7b^3 - 14a^5b^2 + 21a^2$

Express the perimeter of the shaded region in factored form.

55.

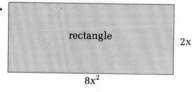

56.

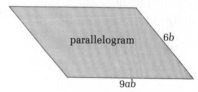

C

57.

58.

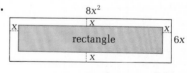

Factor using rational numbers so that the terms of the binomial factor have integral coefficients.

Sample $\frac{1}{2}x + 4 = \frac{1}{2}(x + 8)$

59. $\frac{1}{2}x + 2$

60. $\frac{1}{3}x + 2$

61. $\frac{1}{4}x^2 - 5x$

62. $x^3 - \frac{1}{2}x^2$

63. $3xy + \frac{2}{3}y$

64. $\frac{1}{2}x + \frac{1}{4}$

65. $\frac{1}{3}x - \frac{1}{2}$

66. $\frac{2}{3}x - \frac{1}{4}$

POLYNOMIALS

4-5 Factoring by Grouping

OBJECTIVES

To factor expressions containing common binomial factors.
To group the terms of polynomials in order to find such common factors.

Sometimes the GCF of the terms of an expression is a binomial rather than a monomial.

EXAMPLE 1   Factor.

a. $(x - 4)y - (x - 4)6 = (x - 4)(y - 6)$ Factor out $(x - 4)$, the GCF of the two terms.

b. $s(2r + 6) + 5(r + 3) = 2s(r + 3) + 5(r + 3)$ Factor out 2 in $(2r + 6)$.

$\qquad\qquad\qquad\qquad = (2s + 5)(r + 3)$ Factor out $(r + 3)$.

When a common binomial factor is not shown in an expression, you may be able to group the terms so that such a factor can be identified. To illustrate, it may seem at first glance that $xy^2 + y^2 + 2x + 2$ cannot be factored, since the four terms have no common factor other than 1. However, when the terms are grouped we see that the polynomial can be factored.

$xy^2 + y^2 + 2x + 2 = (xy^2 + y^2) + (2x + 2)$ Group the terms to form two binomials.

$\qquad\qquad\qquad = y^2(x + 1) + 2(x + 1)$ Factor each binomial.

$\qquad\qquad\qquad = (y^2 + 2)(x + 1)$ Factor out $(x + 1)$.

EXAMPLE 2   Factor $rs - 6r + 24 - 4s$.

$rs - 6r + 24 - 4s = (rs - 6r) + (24 - 4s)$ Group the terms to form two binomials.

$\qquad\qquad\qquad = r(s - 6) + 4(6 - s)$ Factor each binomial.

$\qquad\qquad\qquad = r(s - 6) + 4(-1)(s - 6)$ $(s - 6)$ and $(6 - s)$ are opposites. Write $(6 - s)$ as $(-1)(s - 6)$.

$\qquad\qquad\qquad = r(s - 6) - 4(s - 6)$

$\qquad\qquad\qquad = (r - 4)(s - 6)$ Factor out $(s - 6)$.

EXAMPLE 3   Factor $xy^2 + 6 + 2y^2 + 3x$.

$$xy^2 + 6 + 2y^2 + 3x = (xy^2 + 2y^2) + (3x + 6)$$
$$= y^2(x + 2) + 3(x + 2)$$
$$= (y^2 + 3)(x + 2)$$

Rearrange and group the terms.

Do you see other ways the terms could have been grouped in Examples 2 and 3? Will the final factors be the same regardless of how you group the terms?

CLASS EXERCISES

Name the binomial that completes each factorization correctly.

1. $(x + 3)y + (x + 3)6 = (\underline{\ ?\ })(y + 6)$

2. $(x - 2)y + (x - 2) = (x - 2)(\underline{\ ?\ })$

3. $a(2b + 1) - b(2b + 1) = (\underline{\ ?\ })(2b + 1)$

4. $5(a - 3b) - a(a - 3b) = (5 - a)(\underline{\ ?\ })$

Name the missing binomials in each step of the factoring process.

5. $(x^2 + 2x) + (7x + 14) = x(\underline{\ ?\ }) + 7(\underline{\ ?\ }) = (\underline{\ ?\ })(\underline{\ ?\ })$

6. $(5a - 15) - (a^2 - 3a) = 5(\underline{\ ?\ }) - a(\underline{\ ?\ }) = (\underline{\ ?\ })(\underline{\ ?\ })$

7. $ax + ay + 3x + 3y = a(\underline{\ ?\ }) + 3(\underline{\ ?\ }) = (\underline{\ ?\ })(\underline{\ ?\ })$

8. $x^2 - 4x - 12 + 3x = x(\underline{\ ?\ }) - 3(\underline{\ ?\ }) = x(\underline{\ ?\ }) + 3(\underline{\ ?\ }) = (\underline{\ ?\ })(\underline{\ ?\ })$

EXERCISES

 A   *Factor.*

1. $(x + 2)y + (x + 2)5$

2. $a(b - 3) + 5(b - 3)$

3. $5x(x + 4) + 2(x + 4)$

4. $x^2(x - 2) + 3(x - 2)$

5. $(2a + b)b - (2a + b)$

6. $(r - 2s)r - (r - 2s)5$

7. $3v(u^2 - v) - 8(u^2 - v)$

8. $(ab - 2)b - (ab - 2)5$

9. $x(3y + 6) + 2(y + 2)$

10. $8(x^2 - x) - 3(x - 1)$

11. $(ab + 3a) + (5b + 15)$

12. $(3 - 3y) - (4x - 4xy)$

13. $12uv + 2v + 30u + 5$

14. $4xy - 6y + 14x - 21$

15. $xy - y^2 + 6x - 6y$

16. $3ab - 6b - 4a + 8$

17. $5ax - x + 45a - 9$

18. $3x^2 + 6xy + 4x + 8y$

B

19. $20xy - 8y^2 + 5x - 2y$

20. $2u^2 + 3uv - 12u - 18v$

21. $15 + 3y - 5y^2 - y^3$

22. $x^3 - 6x^2 + x - 6$

23. $a^2b - 2b + 3a^2 - 6$

24. $s^3 + 4s^2 + st + 4t$

25. $2x^3 - 5 - x + 10x^2$

26. $3 + a^2b^2 + 3a^2 + b^2$

27. $u^3 - v^3 + uv^2 - u^2v$

28. $3x^2y - 14 - 6x^2 + 7y$

29. $5s + 2r^2 + r^2s + 10r$

30. $8h^2 - 3h - 24 + h^3$

31. $xy - 2 - 2y + x$

32. $10xy - 5y - 2x + 1$

33. $3a - 4b - 4 + 3ab$

34. $6ab^2 - 9b^2 - 15 + 10a$

35. $c^3 - 2d^3 - 2cd + c^2d^2$

36. $5a^3 - a - 5a^2b^2 + b^2$

C

37. $a^2 + ab + ac + 3a + 3b + 3c$

38. $x^5 + x^4 + x^3 + 2x^2 + 2x + 2$

39. $3x^2 + 3y + x^3 + xy + x^2y + y^2$

40. $a^3 + a^2b - 3a^2 + a + b - 3$

Factor out the GCF of the terms in each polynomial. Then factor again by grouping.

Sample $3x^4 - 3x^3 + 6x^2 - 6x = 3x(x^3 - x^2 + 2x - 2) = 3x(x^2 + 2)(x - 1)$

41. $x^2 + x + xy + x^2y$

42. $3a^2b - 6b^2 + 6ab - 3ab^2$

43. $8xy - 4xy^3 + 8x^2y - 4x^2y^3$

44. $3x^3y - 12x^2y^2 - 8xy^2 + 2x^2y$

CHALLENGE

Contest Problems

Here are some more problems from the annual American High School Mathematics Examination (**M.A.A. Contest Problem Book**).

1. One thousand unit cubes are fastened together to form a large cube with edge length 10 units; this is painted and then separated into the original cubes. The number of these unit cubes which have at least one face painted is

(A) 600   (B) 520   (C) 488   (D) 480   (E) 400

2. In the adjoining figure, a wooden cube has edges of length 3 meters. Square holes of side one meter, centered in each face, are cut through to the opposite face. The edges of the holes are parallel to the edges of the cube. The entire surface area including the inside, in square meters, is

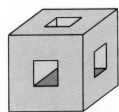

(A) 54   (B) 72   (C) 76   (D) 84   (E) 86

4-6   Factoring Trinomials

OBJECTIVE _____

To factor trinomials of the types $x^2 + bx + c$ and $ax^2 + bx + c$.

_____

Some trinomials can be factored as the product of two binomials. One method that you can use to factor such trinomials involves *analysis* and *trial*. Consider this product.

$$(x + 2)(3x + 4) = 3x^2 + 10x + 8$$

coefficients of x in the binomials →1·3   2·4←constant terms in the binomials

To reverse this process, begin with the form shown on the left below. Since there are two *plus* symbols in the trinomial, plus symbols are shown within each pair of parentheses.

factors of 3   Since 3 = 1·3, try this form.

$$3x^2 + 10x + 8 = (\_x + \_)(\_x + \_) \qquad 3x^2 + 10x + 8 = (1x + \_)(3x + \_)$$

factors of 8   factors of 8

Now, try pairs of factors of 8 in the blank spaces. Test 1 and 8, 8 and 1, 4 and 2, and 2 and 4. The idea is to find a pair that gives a middle term of 10x in the resulting trinomial.

Trial Factors	Middle Term of Trinomial	*Does the middle term equal 10x?*
$(x + 1)(3x + 8)$	$8x + 3x = 11x$	*No*
$(x + 8)(3x + 1)$	$x + 24x = 25x$	*No*
$(x + 4)(3x + 2)$	$2x + 12x = 14x$	*No*
$(x + 2)(3x + 4)$	$4x + 6x = 10x$	**Yes**

The required factors of 8 are 2 and 4. Thus, $3x^2 + 10x + 8 = (x + 2)(3x + 4)$.

EXAMPLE 1   Factor $x^2 - 8x + 15$.

Since the coefficient of x^2 is $1 = 1 \cdot 1$, we begin with the form shown below. Note that *minus* symbols within both pairs of parentheses will produce a negative second term and a positive third term in the trinomial, as required.

$$x^2 - 8x + 15 = (x - \_)(x - \_)$$

factors of 15

Find two factors of 15 whose sum is 8.

$15 = 1 \cdot 15$, and $1 + 15 = 16$ \qquad $15 = 3 \cdot 5$, and $3 + 5 = \mathbf{8}$

The required factors of 15 are 3 and 5, so $x^2 - 8x + 15 = (x - 3)(x - 5)$.

EXAMPLE 2   Factor $4x^2 - 13x + 10$.

Since $4 = 2 \cdot 2$ or $4 \cdot 1$, try these forms.

$(2x - \underline{\quad})(2x - \underline{\quad})$ $(4x - \underline{\quad})(x - \underline{\quad})$

    factors of 10   factors of 10

Since $10 = 1 \cdot 10$ or $2 \cdot 5$, test 1 and 10 in the blank spaces of each expression. Then test 2 and 5 in the blank spaces. Continue testing until you find the combination that gives a middle term of $-13x$ in the trinomial. We find that the required factors of 4 are 4 and 1, and the required factors of 10 are 5 and 2.

$4x^2 - 13x + 10 = (4x - 5)(x - 2)$

Suppose you wish to factor a trinomial in which the constant term is negative. In such cases the constants in the binomial factors must have different signs. It is convenient to begin with a form that does not include the signs.

EXAMPLE 3   Factor $2x^2 - 9x - 18$.

The constant term is negative. Begin with this form.

Omit the signs.

$(2x \quad \underline{\quad})(x \quad \underline{\quad})$

    factors of 18

Try pairs of factors of 18 in the blank spaces and find the difference of the inner and outer products *without regard to sign*. The pairs of factors you can try are 1 and 18, 2 and 9, and 3 and 6. The order of the numbers in each pair may be reversed, of course. You want the difference of the inner and outer products to be $9x$.

Try 2 and 9.   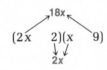   The difference of the inner and outer products, without regard to sign, is $18x - 2x$, or $16x$. Interchanging 2 and 9 gives the difference, $5x$.

Try 3 and 6.   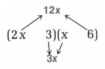   The difference of the inner and outer products, without regard to sign, is $12x - 3x$, or $9x$.

Insert the signs so that the middle term of the trinomial is $-9x$.

$2x^2 - 9x - 18 = (2x + 3)(x - 6)$

EXAMPLE 4

Factor $8x^2 + 11x - 10$.

Begin with forms showing factors of $8x^2$. Omit the signs.

$$(x \quad \underline{\quad})(8x \quad \underline{\quad}) \qquad (2x \quad \underline{\quad})(4x \quad \underline{\quad})$$

factors of 10   factors of 10

Test factors of 10 until $11x$ is obtained for the difference of the inner and outer products, without regard to sign. The required factors are 2 and 5, using the form on the left above.

$$(x \quad 2)(8x \quad 5) \qquad 16x - 5x = 11x$$

Insert the signs so that the middle term of the trinomial is $11x$.

$$8x^2 + 11x - 10 = (x + 2)(8x - 5)$$

Not all trinomials can be factored using integers. This is shown in the next example.

EXAMPLE 5

Factor $5x^2 - 11x - 9$.

Trial Factors	Difference of Inner and Outer Products, without Regard to Sign	Is the difference 11x?
$(5x \quad 1)(x \quad 9)$	$44x$	*No*
$(5x \quad 9)(x \quad 1)$	$4x$	*No*
$(5x \quad 3)(x \quad 3)$	$12x$	*No*

Since all possibilities have been tried and none give the correct middle term, the trinomial is not factorable using integers.

CLASS EXERCISES

Factor.

1. $x^2 + 7x + 12$ **2.** $b^2 - 13b + 12$ **3.** $y^2 - 3y - 10$

4. $a^2 + 4a - 21$ **5.** $n^2 + 7n + 10$ **6.** $k^2 - 8k + 12$

7. $2x^2 + 11x + 5$ **8.** $5t^2 - 16t + 3$ **9.** $7r^2 + 10r + 3$

10. $4x^2 + 8x + 3$ **11.** $6x^2 + x - 1$ **12.** $8y^2 - 9y + 1$

EXERCISES

A *Factor.*

1. $2x^2 + 5x + 3$

2. $5x^2 - 12x + 7$

3. $y^2 + 9y + 8$

4. $25r^2 - 10r + 1$

5. $10b^2 + 11b + 1$

6. $24x^2 - 10x + 1$

7. $a^2 + 2a - 8$

8. $x^2 - 5x - 24$

9. $b^2 - 8b - 20$

10. $24z^2 + 2z - 1$

11. $5t^2 - 36t + 7$

12. $7c^2 + 10c + 3$

13. $8h^2 - 30h + 7$

14. $2k^2 - k - 6$

15. $5x^2 + x - 6$

B *Factor, if possible. If the trinomial cannot be factored using integers, write **not factorable**.*

16. $12x^2 - 17x + 6$

17. $15y^2 + 19y + 6$

18. $20 - 39z + 18z^2$

19. $4x^2 - 12x + 9$

20. $6y^2 + 17y - 3$

21. $2y^2 + 13y + 14$

22. $4b^2 - 25b + 6$

23. $9h^2 + 12h + 4$

24. $6b^2 + 15b - 20$

25. $10a^2 - 31a - 14$

26. $9 - 21n + 8n^2$

27. $4x^2 + 4x - 15$

28. $21y^2 + 11y - 3$

29. $18z^2 - 21z - 4$

30. $3b^2 + 7bc + 4c^2$

31. $10a^2 - 31ab + 15b^2$

32. $3u^2 + 19uv - 14v^2$

33. $6s^2 + 23s - 4t^2$

C **34.** $x^4 + 4x^2 + 3$

35. $6 + 5y^2 - 4y^4$

36. $x^4 - 4x^2 - 21$

37. $4a^4 + 4a^2b - 15b^2$

38. $x^6 + x^3 - 6$

39. $3y^6 - 10y^3 + 8$

*Factor. **n** represents a positive integer.*

40. $x^{2n} + 3x^n + 2$

41. $x^{2n} - 2x^n - 15$

42. $x^{4n} - 5x^{2n} + 6$

43. $6x^{2n} + 19x^n + 10$

44. $4x^{2n} - 9x^n + 2$

45. $9x^{4n} + 9x^{2n} - 4$

Factor out the GCF of the terms in each polynomial. Then factor the trinomial again.

46. $6x^2 - 10x - 4$

47. $45y^2 - 42y - 24$

48. $16a^3 + 8a^2 - 15a$

49. $x^3y + 2x^2y^2 + xy^3$

50. $15 + 5b - 10b^2$

51. $2s^2 - 2s - 112$

Factor out a fraction so that the terms of the trinomial factor have integral coefficients. Then factor the trinomial again.

52. $\frac{1}{3}x^2 + x - 6$

53. $\frac{1}{5}x^2 - x - 10$

54. $x^2 - \frac{1}{12}x - \frac{1}{12}$

55. $x^2 - \frac{1}{6}x - \frac{1}{3}$

56. $\frac{2}{15}x^2 + \frac{1}{3}x - \frac{1}{5}$

57. $\frac{3}{2}x^2 - \frac{1}{4}x - \frac{1}{2}$

*58. Factor $(x^2 - 6xy + 9y^2) + 4(x - 3y) - 21$.

4-7 Special Products and Their Factors

OBJECTIVES

To factor the difference of two squares.
To factor trinomial squares.
To factor the sum or difference of two cubes.

Since factoring is the reverse of multiplying, it is possible to learn some special factoring methods by first observing what happens when *special products* are formed. The special product $(a + b)(a - b) = a^2 - b^2$ gives us a formula for factoring the difference of two squares.

Factoring the Difference of Two Squares

$$a^2 - b^2 = (a + b)(a - b)$$

In order to apply this formula to specific examples, it is necessary to identify the quantities that play the roles of a and b.

EXAMPLE 1   Factor.

a. $x^2 - 4 = x^2 - 2^2$ $a = x$ and $b = 2$
$= (x + 2)(x - 2)$

b. $9x^2 - 25y^2 = (3x)^2 - (5y)^2$ $a = 3x$ and $b = 5y$
$= (3x + 5y)(3x - 5y)$

The square of a binomial also suggests special factoring formulas.

$$(a + b)^2 = (a + b)(a + b) = a^2 + 2ab + b^2$$
$$(a - b)^2 = (a - b)(a - b) = a^2 - 2ab + b^2$$

Factoring Trinomial Squares

$$a^2 + 2ab + b^2 = (a + b)^2$$
$$a^2 - 2ab + b^2 = (a - b)^2$$

EXAMPLE 2   Factor.

$$\textbf{a. } \textbf{x}^2 + \textbf{6x} + \textbf{9} = x^2 + 2(3)(x) + 3^2 \qquad\qquad a = x \text{ and } b = 3$$
$$= (x + 3)^2$$

$$\textbf{b. } \textbf{4x}^2 - \textbf{20xy} + \textbf{25y}^2 = (2x)^2 - 2(2x)(5y) + (5y)^2 \qquad a = 2x \text{ and } b = 5y$$
$$= (2x - 5y)^2$$

Two other special products yield formulas relating to cubes.

$$
\begin{array}{cc}
\begin{array}{r}
a^2 - ab + b^2 \\
a + b \\
\hline
a^2b - ab^2 + b^3 \\
a^3 - a^2b + ab^2 \quad\;\; \\
\hline
a^3 \qquad\qquad + b^3
\end{array}
&
\begin{array}{r}
a^2 + ab + b^2 \\
a - b \\
\hline
-a^2b - ab^2 - b^3 \\
a^3 + a^2b + ab^2 \quad\;\; \\
\hline
a^3 \qquad\qquad - b^3
\end{array}
\end{array}
$$

> **Factoring the Sum and Difference of Two Cubes**
>
> $$a^3 + b^3 = (a + b)(a^2 - ab + b^2)$$
> $$a^3 - b^3 = (a - b)(a^2 + ab + b^2)$$

EXAMPLE 3   Factor.

$$\textbf{a. } \textbf{x}^3 + \textbf{8} = x^3 + 2^3 \qquad\qquad\qquad a = x \text{ and } b = 2$$
$$= (x + 2)(x^2 - x \cdot 2 + 2^2)$$
$$= (x + 2)(x^2 - 2x + 4)$$

$$\textbf{b. } \textbf{27h}^3 - \textbf{1} = (3h)^3 - 1^3 \qquad\qquad a = 3h \text{ and } b = 1$$
$$= (3h - 1)[(3h)^2 + 3h \cdot 1 + 1^2]$$
$$= (3h - 1)(9h^2 + 3h + 1)$$

CLASS EXERCISES

Factor as the difference of two squares.

1. $x^2 - 49$ 　　　　**2.** $1 - 4h^2$ 　　　　**3.** $16s^2 - 81t^2$ 　　　　**4.** $64x^2 - 25y^2$

Factor each trinomial square.

5. $x^2 + 8x + 16$ 　　**6.** $z^2 - 14z + 49$ 　　**7.** $4c^2 - 4c + 1$ 　　**8.** $1 - 8u + 16u^2$

Factor as the sum or difference of two cubes.

9. $x^3 + 27$ 　　　　**10.** $x^3 - 27$ 　　　　**11.** $x^3 + 8y^3$ 　　　　**12.** $1 - 125d^3$

EXERCISES

A

Factor as the difference of two squares.

1. $x^2 - 36$ **2.** $49 - b^2$ **3.** $9x^2 - y^2$ **4.** $4a^2 - 9b^2$

5. $16c^2 - d^2$ **6.** $4x^2 - 121$ **7.** $25u^2 - 9v^2$ **8.** $49 - 144x^2$

Factor each trinomial square.

9. $x^2 - 4x + 4$ **10.** $b^2 + 10b + 25$ **11.** $x^2 - 2xy + y^2$ **12.** $4x^2 + 4x + 1$

13. $9x^2 - 12x + 4$ **14.** $9x^2 + 6x + 1$ **15.** $a^2 + 4ab + 4b^2$ **16.** $9s^2 - 6st + t^2$

Factor as the sum or difference of two cubes.

17. $x^3 + 1$ **18.** $x^3 - 1$ **19.** $x^3 - 125$ **20.** $1 + 64h^3$

21. $64x^3 - 27$ **22.** $27 + 8y^3$ **23.** $216a^3 + 1$ **24.** $s^3 - 216t^3$

B

Factor.

25. $8x^3 + 343y^3$ **26.** $9x^2 + 30x + 25$ **27.** $81x^2 - 169$

28. $x^2 + 30xy + 225y^2$ **29.** $a^3b^3 - 216$ **30.** $196r^2 - 140rs + 25s^2$

31. $512a^3 + 729b^3$ **32.** $1000x^3 - y^3z^3$ **33.** $10,000 - 9c^2d^2$

34. $1 - 1728u^3$ **35.** $289 - 400p^2$ **36.** $18x^2 - 36xyz + 4y^2z^2$

Find each product mentally, using the formula $(a + b)(a - b) = a^2 - b^2$.

     Sample $(33)(27) = (30 + 3)(30 - 3) = 900 - 9 = 891$

37. $(22)(18)$ **38.** $(51)(49)$ **39.** $(52)(48)$ **40.** $(64)(56)$

41. $(85)(75)$ **42.** $(93)(87)$ **43.** $(99)(101)$ **44.** $(206)(194)$

C

Factor using rational numbers.

45. $y^2 - 0.01$ **46.** $y^3 - 0.001$ **47.** $x^2 + x + 0.25$ **48.** $0.125 - z^3$

49. Illustrate a factoring formula by expressing the area of the shaded region two ways. Write it as the sum of the areas of the smaller regions. Then write it as the square of one side of the shaded region.

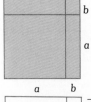

50. Illustrate another factoring formula by expressing the area of this shaded region two ways.

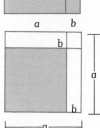

4-8 Factoring Completely

OBJECTIVE _____

To factor polynomials completely, using integral coefficients.

_____

When you factor a polynomial, look first to see if the terms have a common factor. Then look for other methods that can be applied. Here is a brief list of factoring methods, with examples.

Method	Example
greatest common factor	$2x^2 + 4xy = 2x(x + 2y)$
grouping	$xy + 2y + x^2 + 2x = y(x + 2) + x(x + 2)$ $= (y + x)(x + 2)$
trinomial	$4x^2 - 13x + 10 = (4x - 5)(x - 2)$
difference of two squares	$x^2 - 9y^2 = (x + 3y)(x - 3y)$
trinomial square	$x^2 - 6x + 9 = (x - 3)^2$
sum of two cubes	$27 + y^3 = (3 + y)(9 - 3y + y^2)$
difference of two cubes	$8x^3 - 1 = (2x - 1)(4x^2 + 2x + 1)$

When you are asked to factor a polynomial, you should factor it *completely.* You may have to factor more than once. When none of the individual factors can be factored again, the polynomial is **completely factored.** Remember that all factoring is done using integral coefficients, unless otherwise stated.

EXAMPLE 1   Factor.

a. $x^3 - 13x^2 + 36x = x(x^2 - 13x + 36)$ First factor out the GCF of the three terms.

$= x(x - 4)(x - 9)$ Then factor the resulting trinomial.

No other factoring can be done, so the result is the completely factored form of the polynomial.

b. $6x^4y - 48xy = 6xy(x^3 - 8)$ First factor out the GCF of the two terms.

$= 6xy(x - 2)(x^2 + 2x + 4)$ Then factor $x^3 - 8$ as the difference of two cubes.

When the terms of the polynomial have no common monomial factor except 1, see if another factoring method can be used.

EXAMPLE 2 Factor.

a. $t^4 - 16 = (t^2)^2 - 4^2$ The terms have no common factor.

$\qquad\qquad = (t^2 + 4)(t^2 - 4)$ Factor as the difference of two squares

$\qquad\qquad = (t^2 + 4)(t + 2)(t - 2)$ Factor $t^2 - 4$ as the difference of two squares.

b. $x^3 - 9x + x^2 - 9 = (x^3 - 9x) + (x^2 - 9)$ The four terms have no common factor. Group into binomials.

$\qquad\qquad = x(x^2 - 9) + (x^2 - 9)$ Factor out the x in the first binomial.

$\qquad\qquad = (x + 1)(x^2 - 9)$ Factor out the common binomial factor, $x^2 - 9$.

$\qquad\qquad = (x + 1)(x + 3)(x - 3)$ Factor $x^2 - 9$ as the difference of two squares.

CLASS EXERCISES

*Tell which factoring method you would use **first** in order to factor each polynomial.*

1. $8x^2 - 2$

2. $18x^2 + 3xy - 3y^2$

3. $x - 3 - xy^2 + 3y^2$

4. $x^4 - 3x^2 - 4$

5. $x^4 + x^2 - 2$

6. $4x^2 - 4$

7. $7x^2 + 14x - 21$

8. $x^4 - 81$

9. $x^5 - x^3$

10. $3 + 24y^3$

11. $x^2y - 4y + 2x^2 - 8$

12. $a^4 - 2a^2b^2 + b^4$

EXERCISES

A   *Factor.*

1. $2x^3 - 18x$

2. $x^3y - xy^3$

3. $3a^2b - 48b$

4. $x^3 + 6x^2 + 5x$

5. $8x^3 - 8x^2 - 6x$

6. $5a^3b + 19a^2b^2 + 12ab^3$

7. $2h^4 - 24h^3 + 72h^2$

8. $x^4 + x$

9. $a^4 - 81$

10. $54h - 2h^4$

11. $b^5 - 64b$

12. $20x^2 - 40x + 15$

13. $3x^3 + 15x^2 - 18x$

14. $16x^5 - 2x^2$

15. $3a^3b - 12ab^3$

16. $15x^4 - 14x^3 - 8x^2$

17. $36x - 48x^2 + 16x^3$

18. $x^2y^2 + 12xy^2 + 36y^2$

19. $(x + 1)a^2 - (x + 1)$

20. $(x - 1) - (x - 1)b^3$

21. $x^3(x + y) - y^3(x + y)$

B   **22.** $x^3 - x - 3x^2 + 3$

23. $x^4 - 8x + 5x^3 - 40$

24. $y^4 + 27y - y^3 - 27$

25. $2a^5 - 162a$

26. $x^4 - 10x^2 + 9$

27. $16x^4 - 8x^2 + 1$

28. $5a^4 - 40ab^3$ **29.** $3x^5 + 6x^3 + 3x$ **30.** $x^6 - 64$

31. $(a - 1)x^3 - (a - 1)xy^2$ **32.** $49x^2y - 21xy + 9x - 21x^2$

33. $x^5 - 16x^3 + 8x^2 - 128$ **34.** $3x^4 - 15x^2 + 12$

C

35. $10x^9 - 1{,}000{,}000{,}000x$ **36.** $z^5 - 64z^2 + z^4 - 64z$

37. $a^5 - 16ab^4 - 2a^4b + 32b^5$ **38.** $x^4 + 4x^3 + 4x^2 + x$

Factor using rational numbers. Factor out a fraction first so that the remaining polynomial factor has integral coefficients.

> **Sample** $\dfrac{1}{4}x^2 + \dfrac{3}{2}x + 2 = \dfrac{1}{4}(x^2 + 6x + 8) = \dfrac{1}{4}(x + 2)(x + 4)$

39. $x^4 - \dfrac{1}{16}$ **40.** $\dfrac{1}{8}x^3 - 1$ **41.** $\dfrac{1}{6}x^2 - \dfrac{4}{3}x + 2$

42. $\dfrac{1}{2}x^4 - \dfrac{13}{2}x^2 + 18$ **43.** $3x^2 + 3x + \dfrac{3}{4}$ **44.** $\dfrac{1}{2}xy + \dfrac{1}{3}y + \dfrac{1}{2}x + \dfrac{1}{3}$

45. $\dfrac{1}{2}xy - \dfrac{3}{4}y - \dfrac{5}{2}x + \dfrac{15}{4}$ **46.** $\dfrac{1}{10}x^3 + \dfrac{1}{2}x - \dfrac{1}{5}x^2 - 1$ **47.** $\dfrac{1}{8}x^5 - \dfrac{1}{2}x^3 - x^2 + 4$

*48. Factor $a^3 + 3a^2b + 3ab^2 + b^3$.
     Hint: Regroup as $(a^3 + b^3) + (3a^2b + 3ab^2)$.

*49. Factor $a^3 - 3a^2b + 3ab^2 - b^3$.

CHALLENGE

Another Factoring Method

The polynomial $x^4 - 11x^2 + 25$ does not appear to be factorable. However, if $-11x^2$ is written as $-10x^2 - x^2$, the expression can be factored.

$$\begin{aligned} x^4 - 11x^2 + 25 &= (x^4 - 10x^2 + 25) - x^2 \\ &= (x^2 - 5)^2 - x^2 \\ &= (x^2 + x - 5)(x^2 - x - 5) \end{aligned}$$

Factor the following polynomials.

  1. $x^4 - 3x^2 + 1$ **2.** $x^4 + x^2 + 1$ **3.** $4x^4 + 3x^2 + 9$

  4. $x^4 + 3x^2y^2 + 4y^4$ **5.** $x^4 + 4$ **Hint:** $x^4 + 4 = (x^4 + 4x^2 + 4) - 4x^2$

  6. $x^4 + 64$ **7.** $4x^4 + 1$ **8.** $4x^4 + 625y^4$

  9. $a^8 - 31a^4 + 81$ **10.** $a^2 + b^2 + c^2 + 2ab + 2ac + 2bc$

4-9 Solving Equations by Factoring

OBJECTIVE

To solve quadratic and cubic equations by factoring.

An equation that can be written in the form $ax^2 + bx + c = 0$, where $a \neq 0$, is called a **quadratic equation.** If the left side of an equation in that form can be factored, then the equation can be solved using the following property of zero. This property tells us that if the product of two factors is zero, then at least one of the factors must be zero.

> If a and b are real numbers and $ab = 0$, then
> $a = 0$ *or* $b = 0$, or both a and b equal 0.

EXAMPLE 1   Solve $x^2 + 5x - 24 = 0$.

$$x^2 + 5x - 24 = 0$$
$$(x + 8)(x - 3) = 0 \qquad \text{Factor the trinomial.}$$
$$x + 8 = 0 \quad \text{or} \quad x - 3 = 0 \qquad \text{Set each factor equal to 0.}$$
$$x = -8 \qquad\qquad x = 3 \qquad \text{Solve each equation.}$$

Check $(-8)^2 + 5(-8) - 24 = 64 - 40 - 24 = 0 \checkmark$
$3^2 + 5(3) - 24 = 9 + 15 - 24 = 0 \checkmark$

The solutions are -8 and 3.

To use this property of zero, one side of the equation must be 0. If the equation is not in that form, begin by rewriting it.

EXAMPLE 2   Solve $4x^2 + 3 = 4x + 2$.

$$4x^2 + 3 = 4x + 2$$
$$4x^2 - 4x + 1 = 0 \qquad \text{Write the equation with 0 on the right side.}$$
$$(2x - 1)^2 = 0 \qquad \text{Factor. Notice that the factors are equal.}$$
$$2x - 1 = 0 \qquad \text{Set the factor equal to 0 and solve for } x.$$
$$x = \frac{1}{2}$$

Check in the original equation. The only solution to this equation is $\frac{1}{2}$. This is called a **double root** of the equation.

The property of zero used in the preceding examples can be extended. Thus, if the product of more than two factors is zero, at least one of the factors must be zero. This is illustrated in the next example in which a *cubic equation* has three real solutions. A **cubic equation** can be written in a form showing a third degree polynomial equal to zero.

EXAMPLE 3

Solve $x^3 - 25x = 0$.

$$x^3 - 25x = 0$$

$$x(x^2 - 25) = 0 \qquad \text{Factor out } x.$$

$$x(x + 5)(x - 5) = 0 \qquad \text{Factor } x^2 - 25.$$

$$x = 0 \text{ or } x + 5 = 0 \quad \text{or } x - 5 = 0 \qquad \text{Set each factor equal to 0 and}$$

$$x = 0 \qquad\qquad x = -5 \qquad\qquad x = 5 \qquad \text{solve the three equations.}$$

Check

$$0^3 - 25(0) = 0 - 0 = 0 \text{✔}$$
$$(-5)^3 - 25(-5) = -125 + 125 = 0 \text{✔}$$
$$5^3 - 25(5) = 125 - 125 = 0 \text{✔}$$

The solutions are 0, −5, and 5.

Do *not* try to simplify an equation by first dividing through by a variable. We illustrate by showing what happens if we first divide through by x in the equation given in Example 3.

$$x^3 - 25x = 0$$

$$x^2 - 25 = 0 \qquad \text{Each term is divided by } x.$$

$$(x + 5)(x - 5) = 0$$

$$x + 5 = 0 \quad \text{or } x - 5 = 0$$

$$x = -5 \qquad\qquad x = 5$$

Only two roots, −5 and 5, are found using this method. The third root, 0, has been lost. This results from dividing the terms of the original equation by x, when one possible value for x is 0.

EXAMPLE 4

Solve $x^3 - 4x + 5x^2 - 20 = 0$.

$$x^3 - 4x + 5x^2 - 20 = 0$$

$$(x^3 - 4x) + (5x^2 - 20) = 0 \qquad \text{Group the terms.}$$

$$x(x^2 - 4) + 5(x^2 - 4) = 0 \qquad \text{Factor the binomials.}$$

$$(x + 5)(x^2 - 4) = 0 \qquad \text{Factor out the common binomial } x^2 - 4.$$

$$(x + 5)(x + 2)(x - 2) = 0 \qquad \text{Factor } x^2 - 4.$$

$$x + 5 = 0 \quad \text{or } \quad x + 2 = 0 \quad \text{or } x - 2 = 0 \qquad \text{Set each factor equal to 0.}$$

$$x = -5 \qquad\qquad x = -2 \qquad\qquad x = 2$$

Check each result in the original equation. The solutions are −5, −2, and 2.

CLASS EXERCISES

Solve.

1. $(x - 3)(x - 7) = 0$
2. $(x + 4)(x + 6) = 0$
3. $(x - 1)(x + 8) = 0$
4. $x(x - 5) = 0$
5. $8x(x + 1) = 0$
6. $(x + 4)(x + 4) = 0$
7. $(x + 2)(x - 4)(x - 6) = 0$
8. $x(x + 3)(3x + 4) = 0$
9. $x^2 - 2x = 0$
10. $x^2 + x - 2 = 0$

EXERCISES

A   Solve and check.

1. $2x(x - 5) = 0$
2. $x(4x + 1) = 0$
3. $5x(x + 4) = 0$
4. $-3x(4x - 3) = 0$
5. $(x - 2)(x - 3) = 0$
6. $(x + 2)(x + 3) = 0$
7. $(x + 7)(x - 9) = 0$
8. $(2x - 1)(x + 1) = 0$
9. $(3x + 2)(2x - 3) = 0$
10. $x^2 - 3x = 0$
11. $3x^2 - x = 0$
12. $x^3 - 16x = 0$
13. $-8x^2 - 4x = 0$
14. $x^2 - 5x + 6 = 0$
15. $x^2 - x - 6 = 0$
16. $x^2 + 7x + 10 = 0$
17. $x^2 + 3x - 10 = 0$
18. $x^2 - 2x = 24$
19. $3x^2 - 5x = -2$
20. $2x^2 = 10 - x$
21. $x^3 = 9x$

B   22. $3x^2 + 13x - 10 = 0$
23. $4x^2 + 31x - 8 = 0$
24. $4x^2 + 9 = -12x$
25. $-20x - 3 = 25x^2$
26. $x(x^2 - 4x + 4) = 0$
27. $-x(4x^2 - 4x + 1) = 0$
28. $x^3 - 5x^2 - 14x = 0$
29. $x^3 + 25x = 10x^2$
30. $3x^3 = 2x - 5x^2$
31. $(x^2 - 4)x + (x^2 - 4) = 0$
32. $3x(x^2 - 1) - 5(x^2 - 1) = 0$
33. $x^3 - x + 2x^2 - 2 = 0$
34. $2x^3 - x^2 = 18x - 9$

C   35. $x^4 - 5x^2 = -4$
36. $4x^4 - x^2 = 36x^2 - 9$
37. $3x(x + 1) = 17x + 5$
38. $4x(x^2 - 1) = 12 - 3x^2(1 - x)$
39. $x(2x + 1)(x - 1) = 17x - 9$
40. $(2x^2 - 1)^2 = 24(4x^2 - 1) + x^2$

Solve by first factoring out a fraction, so that the remaining polynomial factor has integral coefficients.

41. $\frac{1}{2}x^2 - 2 = 0$
42. $x^2 + \frac{1}{6}x - \frac{1}{3} = 0$
43. $3x^2 - \frac{1}{4}x - 5 = 0$

44. $\frac{3}{2}x^2 + 5x - 4 = 0$
45. $x^2 - \frac{1}{3}x - \frac{2}{3} = 0$
46. $\frac{5}{4}x^2 - x + \frac{1}{5} = 0$

47. $\frac{2}{3}x^2 + \frac{5}{6}x - 1 = 0$
48. $\frac{1}{10}x^2 + \frac{5}{6}x - \frac{5}{3} = 0$
49. $\frac{1}{3}x^3 - x^2 - \frac{1}{3}x + 1 = 0$

STRATEGIES for PROBLEM SOLVING

Draw a Diagram

A simple diagram, or sketch, can often supply the clues needed to set up and solve a problem.

A square is cut into two rectangles. Can the larger rectangle have twice the area of the smaller one? Can it have twice the perimeter?

Draw a Diagram

1. Draw and label a sketch, using variables.

   Let s represent the length of a side of the square.
   Let x be less than $\frac{1}{2}s$.

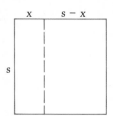

Use the Diagram

2. Use the sketch to set up an equation relating the areas of the two rectangles.

the area of the smaller rectangle	sx
the area of the larger rectangle	$s(s - x)$
The larger area is twice the smaller area.	$s(s - x) = 2(sx)$

   Now, solve for x in terms of s, and answer the first question above. If the larger area is twice the smaller area, what is the ratio of x to s?

3. Express the perimeters of the two rectangles in terms of s and x. Write an equation showing that the larger perimeter is twice the smaller perimeter. Do you get a meaningful result when you try to solve the equation? How would you answer the second question above?

Now try these.

4. A rectangle is cut once to form two pieces, one a square. Suppose you want the smaller piece to have one-half the area of the larger piece. Find two different ratios of length to width for the original rectangle that will make this possible.

5. A rectangle is cut as in Exercise 4. Suppose you want the smaller piece to have one-half the perimeter of the larger piece. How many different ratios of length to width for the original rectangle will make this possible? Name all such ratios.

4-10 Problem Solving: Using Quadratic Equations

OBJECTIVE _____

To solve problems using quadratic equations that can be solved by
factoring.

_____

Can you solve this puzzle?

> 55 added to the square of a number is equal to
> 16 times that number. Find all such numbers.

To solve this by guessing might take some time. However, we can solve
it systematically using algebraic methods.

EXAMPLE 1 Solve the puzzle given above.

Strategy: Write and **Use a variable.**
solve an equation.

Let x represent the number.

55 added to the square of the number	$x^2 + 55$
16 times the number	$16x$

Write an equation.

55 added to the square of the number is equal to 16 times the number.	$x^2 + 55 = 16x$

Solve the equation.

$$x^2 + 55 = 16x$$
$$x^2 - 16x + 55 = 0 \qquad \text{Write the equation with 0 on one side.}$$
$$(x - 5)(x - 11) = 0 \qquad \text{Factor.}$$
$$x - 5 = 0 \quad \text{or} \quad x - 11 = 0$$
$$x = 5 \qquad\qquad x = 11$$

Check in the original problem.

The square of 5 is 25. 55 added to 25 is 80,
and 80 is equal to 16 × 5. ✔
The square of 11 is 121. 55 added to 121 is 176,
and 176 is equal to 16 × 11. ✔

Answer the question.

The numbers are 5 and 11.

Sometimes it is helpful to draw a diagram in order to see the relationships among the various quantities or measurements in a problem. First assign a variable. Then label parts of the figure using given
values and expressions involving the variable.

EXAMPLE 2

One leg of a right triangle is 4 centimeters less than 3 times the length of the other leg. The area of the triangle is 42 square centimeters. Find the lengths of the two legs.

Strategy: Draw a diagram. Write and solve an equation.

Use a variable.

Draw a diagram. Let x represent the length of one leg, or the base of the triangle, in centimeters. Then $3x - 4$ represents the length of the other leg, or the altitude, also in centimeters.

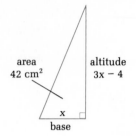

area
42 cm²

altitude
3x − 4

x
base

Write an equation.

$$\frac{1}{2}(\text{base})(\text{altitude}) = \text{area}$$
$$\frac{1}{2}x(3x - 4) = 42$$

Solve the equation.

$$\frac{1}{2}x(3x - 4) = 42$$
$$x(3x - 4) = 84 \qquad \text{Multiply each side by 2.}$$
$$3x^2 - 4x = 84$$
$$3x^2 - 4x - 84 = 0$$
$$(3x + 14)(x - 6) = 0$$

$$3x + 14 = 0 \qquad \text{or} \quad x - 6 = 0$$
$$x = -\frac{14}{3} \qquad\qquad x = 6$$

$-\frac{14}{3}$ is a solution to the equation, but it is not an answer to the problem, since dimensions cannot be negative. If the other solution, 6, is the answer, then the base is 6 centimeters long and the altitude is $3(6) - 4$, or 14 centimeters. These results check, since the area of such a triangle is $\frac{1}{2}(6)(14)$, or 42 square centimeters.

Answer the question.

One leg of the triangle measures 6 centimeters, and the other leg measures 14 centimeters.

EXAMPLE 3

A rectangular cement patio has an area of 187 square feet. It is to be enlarged by a brick border of uniform width. The length of the enlarged patio will be 21 feet, and the width, 15 feet. What are the dimensions of the original cement patio?

Draw a diagram.

Use a variable.

Let x be the width of the border, in feet. Then $21 - 2x$ represents the length of the original patio, and $15 - 2x$ represents its width, in feet.

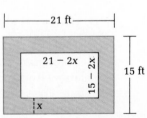

21 ft

21 − 2x

15 − 2x

15 ft

x

Write an equation.

Solve the equation.

$$(length)(width) = area$$
$$(21 - 2x)(15 - 2x) = 187$$
$$315 - 72x + 4x^2 = 187$$
$$4x^2 - 72x + 128 = 0$$
$$x^2 - 18x + 32 = 0 \qquad \text{Divide each side by 4.}$$
$$(x - 16)(x - 2) = 0$$
$$x - 16 = 0 \quad or \quad x - 2 = 0$$
$$x = 16 \qquad\qquad x = 2$$

The width of the border cannot be 16 feet. Why?
If the border is 2 feet wide, then the original dimensions of the patio are found as follows:

$$21 - 2x = 21 - 2(2) = 17 \qquad \text{length}$$
$$15 - 2x = 15 - 2(2) = 11 \qquad \text{width}$$

Answer the question.

Check these dimensions with the conditions in the original problem. The original patio is 17 feet long and 11 feet wide.

CLASS EXERCISES

*Write an algebraic expression in terms of **x** for each expression given in words.*

1. Six times a number x, added to the square of the number

2. The square of three more than twice a number x

3. The sum of the squares of two consecutive integers, the smaller of which is x

4. The product of two consecutive even integers, the smaller of which is x

5. The area of a rectangle whose length is five units more than its width, x

6. The area of a rectangle whose length is two units less than three times its width, x

EXERCISES

A   *Solve each problem.*

1. The sum of two numbers is 18, and their product is 65. Find the numbers.

2. The difference between two positive numbers is 6, and their product is 55. Find the numbers.

3. The larger of two positive numbers is 5 more than the smaller. Their product is 36. Find the numbers.

4. The product of a positive number and 1 more than twice itself is 78. Find the number.

5. When 10 times a positive number is subtracted from the square of the number, the result is 24. Find the number.

6. Twice the square of an integer is equal to 21 less than 13 times the integer. Find the integer.

7. The sum of the square of a negative number and 5 times the number is 84. Find the number.

8. The base and the altitude of a right triangle are the same length. The area of the triangle is 72 square inches. Find the length of the base and the altitude.

9. The length of a rectangle is 3 centimeters greater than twice its width. If the area is 65 square centimeters, find the length and width.

B

10. The product of a number and 3 times that same number is 507. Find all such numbers.

11. The product of two consecutive positive integers is 23 more than 7 times their sum. Find the integers.

12. The product of two consecutive even integers, added to the next consecutive even integer, totals 134. Find the three integers.

13. The sum of the squares of two consecutive positive odd integers is 290. Find the integers.

14. The base of a right triangle measures 5 inches more than twice the altitude. The area of the triangle is 125 square inches. Find the altitude and base of the triangle.

15. The length of a rectangle is 7 meters greater than the width. If the width is doubled and the length is diminished by 6 meters, the new rectangle will be 36 square meters larger than the original rectangle. Find the dimensions of the original rectangle.

16. A rectangular piece of paper is 18 inches by 22 inches. Strips of equal width are cut off each of the four sides, leaving a rectangle with an area of 192 square inches. How wide is each strip?

17. A picture measuring 8 inches long and 6 inches wide is in a frame of uniform width. The area of the frame is $1\frac{1}{2}$ times the area of the picture. How wide is the frame?

18. Each side of a square piece of cardboard measures 21 centimeters. Small squares of equal size are cut from each of the four corners. If the resulting figure has an area of 377 square centimeters, what is the length of a side of each small square?

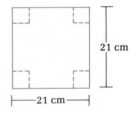

21 cm

21 cm

C

19. The area of a square piece of tin is 625 square inches. Squares of equal size are cut out of the two top corners. Larger squares, each 4 times the area of a top corner square, are cut out of the two bottom corners. The resulting figure has an area of 535 square inches. What is the length of each side of the smaller corner squares? of the larger corner squares?

20. A rectangular piece of cardboard is 6 centimeters longer than it is wide. Squares measuring 2 centimeters on each side are cut out of the four corners, and the extending parts are folded up to form a box. If the volume of the box is 320 cubic centimeters, find the dimensions of the original piece of cardboard.

21. A ball is thrown straight up from the ground. In t seconds the number of feet h that the ball will rise is given by $h = 96t - 16t^2$. How long does it take the ball to rise 144 feet?

22. Refer to Exercise 21. How long will it take the ball to rise to a height of 128 feet? How many seconds after it is tossed will it be back at 128 feet, on its way down?

23. The units' digit of a two-digit number is 3 more than the tens' digit. The square of the units' digit is 2 more than the number. Find all such numbers.

24. The units' digit of a two-digit number is 2 more than the tens' digit. The product of the number and its tens' digit is 6 more than the number obtained by reversing the digits of the original number. Find the number.

25. The length of a rectangular-shaped box is 5 times as great as the width, and the height is twice the width. The total area of the six faces of the box is 306 square centimeters. Find the dimensions of the box.

26. The area of this letter **F** is 128 square units. What is the value of x?

CHECKPOINT

Simplify.

1. $5m - 4n - (3m - 2n) - (9m - 6n)$ 2. $(5x - 2)(3x + 4) - (2x - 3)^2$

Factor.

3. $21x^2y - 7xy$

4. $12xy - 9x - 8y + 6$

5. $x^2 - 11x + 24$

6. $8x^2 - 14x - 15$

7. $27x^3 - 1000y^3$

8. $18x^2 + 24xy + 8y^2$

Solve and check.

9. $x^2 = x + 6$

10. $3x^2 - 3 = 9$

11. $x^3 - x = 0$

12. The sum of the squares of two consecutive positive even integers is 452. Find the integers.

POLYNOMIALS

4-11 Solving Inequalities by Factoring

OBJECTIVES

To solve quadratic and cubic inequalities by factoring.
To graph the solutions to such inequalities on the number line.

Factoring can be used to solve certain types of inequalities. To solve an inequality, we start with the solution to the related equation. Study the following illustrations.

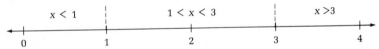

$x^2 = 1$
Solution:
   $x = -1$ or $x = 1$

$x^2 < 1$
Solution:
   $x > -1$ and $x < 1$
   That is, $-1 < x < 1$

$x^2 > 1$
Solution:
   $x < -1$ or $x > 1$

EXAMPLE 1   Solve and graph $x^2 - 4x + 3 < 0$.

First solve the related equation.
$$x^2 - 4x + 3 = 0$$
$$(x - 1)(x - 3) = 0$$
$$x = 1 \quad \text{or} \quad x = 3$$

The points 1 and 3 separate the number line into three parts, all x to the left of 1, all x between 1 and 3, and all x to the right of 3.

It turns out that in any one of these parts, $x^2 - 4x + 3$ is either positive for all values of x or negative for all values of x. Therefore, we can solve the given inequality by selecting a single test value from each part.

Part	Test Value	Value of $x^2 - 4x + 3$	Sign of $x^2 - 4x + 3$
$x < 1$	$x = 0$	$0^2 - 4(0) + 3 = 3$	positive
$1 < x < 3$	$x = 2$	$2^2 - 4(2) + 3 = -1$	negative
$x > 3$	$x = 4$	$4^2 - 4(4) + 3 = 3$	positive

From the table we see that the solution is $1 < x < 3$, since $x^2 - 4x + 3$ is less than 0 for all such values of x.

graph of $x^2 - 4x + 3 < 0$

CHAPTER 4

EXAMPLE 2   Solve and graph $x^2 - 2x \geq 15$.

Solve the related equation.

$$x^2 - 2x = 15$$
$$x^2 - 2x - 15 = 0$$
$$(x + 3)(x - 5) = 0$$
$$x = -3 \text{ or } x = 5$$

Use the points -3 and 5 to separate the number line into three parts.

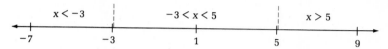

Then test a value from each part to find the sign of the expression $x^2 - 2x - 15$. Here we use the factored form, $(x + 3)(x - 5)$, to determine the sign.

Part	Test Value	Value of $x^2 - 2x - 15 =$ $(x + 3)(x - 5)$	Sign of $x^2 - 2x - 15$
$x < -3$	$x = -4$	$(-4 + 3)(-4 - 5) = 9$	positive
$-3 < x < 5$	$x = 0$	$(0 + 3)(0 - 5) = -15$	negative
$x > 5$	$x = 6$	$(6 + 3)(6 - 5) = 9$	positive

From the table we see that $x^2 - 2x - 15 > 0$, or $x^2 - 2x > 15$, is true for $x < -3$ or $x > 5$. Since it is also true that $x^2 - 2x - 15 = 0$ for $x = -3$ and for $x = 5$, the solution of $x^2 - 2x \geq 15$ is $x \leq -3$ or $x \geq 5$.

graph of $x^2 - 2x \geq 15$

When an inequality has a related equation with three different solutions, those three points separate the number line into four parts. Again, we test a point from each to find the parts that represent solutions to the inequality.

EXAMPLE 3   Solve and graph $x^3 - 3x < 2x^2$.

The related equation is $x^3 - 2x^2 - 3x = 0$, which can be factored as $x(x - 3)(x + 1) = 0$. The solutions to the equation are $x = 0$, $x = 3$, and $x = -1$. These points separate the number line into four parts. Testing a point in each part, we find that the solution is $x < -1$ or $0 < x < 3$.

graph of $x^3 - 3x < 2x^2$

CLASS EXERCISES

*Tell if the statement is **true** or **false**.*

1. If $x = 1$, then $x(x - 2) > 0$.

2. If $x = 2$, then $(x + 2)(x - 3) < 0$.

3. If $x = \dfrac{1}{2}$, then $x(2x - 1) \geq 0$.

4. If $x = -5$, then $(x - 2)(x + 7) > 0$.

5. If $x < 0$, then $x(x - 1) > 0$.

6. If $x > \dfrac{1}{3}$, then $x(3x - 1) \geq 0$.

7. If $3 < x < 5$, then $(x - 3)(x - 5) < 0$.

8. If $-3 < x < 0$, then $x(x - 4)(x + 3) \leq 0$.

EXERCISES

A   *Solve and graph.*

1. $x(x + 2) > 0$

2. $3x(x - 5) < 0$

3. $(x - 2)(x - 4) \leq 0$

4. $(x + 1)(x - 7) \geq 0$

5. $(x + 3)(x + 4) > 0$

6. $(2x - 1)(x - 5) < 0$

7. $(3x + 1)(x - 2) \leq 0$

8. $(2x - 3)(x + 1) > 0$

9. $x^2 - 1 \geq 0$

10. $x^2 - 1 < 0$

11. $x^2 - 4x - 12 > 0$

12. $x^2 - 9x + 20 \leq 0$

13. $x^2 + 9x + 8 \geq 0$

14. $x^2 < 9$

15. $x^2 > 4$

16. $x^2 - 4x > -3$

17. $x^2 < 3x + 10$

18. $10x + 21 \geq -x^2$

B   19. $-x^2 + 9 \geq 0$

20. $-x^2 + 4x < 0$

21. $-x^2 - 7x > 0$

22. $-2x < 15 - x^2$

23. $15x^2 + 7x - 2 > 0$

24. $8x^2 - 14x - 15 \leq 0$

25. $x(x - 2)(x - 4) > 0$

26. $x(x - 1)(x + 3) < 0$

27. $x^3 - 6x^2 - 7x \geq 0$

28. $x^3 < 24x - 2x^2$

29. $x^3 - 9x > 0$

30. $x^3 \leq 3x^2 + 4x$

C   31. $(x^2 - 1)(x + 3) > 0$

32. $x^3 - 4x - 5x^2 + 20 < 0$

33. $2x^3 - x^2 \geq 18x - 9$

34. $x^4 - 10x^2 + 9 > 0$

35. **a.** Verify that $x^2 - 2x + 4 = (x - 1)^2 + 3$ is true.
    b. Use **a** to explain why $x^2 - 2x + 4 > 0$ for all real values of x.
    c. Use **b** to solve $x^3 + 8 > 0$.

36. Solve $x^4 - 16 < 0$.

37. Show that $a^2 + b^2 > 2ab$ is true for all unequal real numbers a and b.
    Hint: Start with the true inequality $(a - b)^2 > 0$ for $a \neq b$.

*38. Show that the sum of any positive number and its reciprocal is greater than or equal to 2.

Present Value

Suppose you will need $1000 in five years. You can deposit enough money in the bank now so that the required amount will be available at that time. The amount you should deposit now is called the *present value* of the $1000. This value depends on the rate of interest and on the frequency with which the interest is compounded. The present value can be calculated by using the *compound interest formula*.

$$A = P(1 + i)^n$$

P is the amount deposited, in dollars.
i is the interest rate per period, in decimal form.
n is the number of periods.
A is the amount, in dollars, at the end of the time.

Example   Find the present value of $1000, assuming the money is to be deposited for 5 years at 8% interest, compounded quarterly.

$$P = \frac{A}{(1 + i)^n}$$ Solve the compound interest formula for *P*, which is the amount deposited or the *present value*.

Substitute: $A = 1000$

$$P = \frac{1000}{1.02^{20}}$$ $$i = \frac{8\%}{4} = 2\% = 0.02$$

$$n = 5 \times 4 = 20$$

$$P = \frac{1000}{1.486}$$ Use a scientific calculator to evaluate 1.02^{20}, or use an appropriate value from the table below.

$$1.02^{20} = (1.02^{10})^2 \approx 1.219^2 \approx 1.486$$

$$P = 672.95$$

To the nearest dollar, the present value of the $1000 is $673.

Find the present value of $10,000 if the money is deposited for 5 years under the given conditions.
Use a calculator or the table.
Round answers to the nearest dollar.

$1.02^{10} \approx 1.219$	$1.04^{10} \approx 1.480$
$1.03^{10} \approx 1.344$	$1.05^{10} \approx 1.629$

1. 10% interest, compounded twice a year

2. 16% interest, compounded quarterly

3. 12% interest, compounded quarterly

4. 12% interest, compounded every 2 months

CHAPTER 4 REVIEW

VOCABULARY

monomial (p. 118)
exponential expression
  (p. 118)
base (p. 118)
simplify (p. 118)
polynomial (p. 122)
binomial (p. 122)
trinomial (p. 122)

degree (p. 122)
expansion (p. 127)
greatest common factor,
  GCF (p. 129)
factor (p. 129)
difference of two squares
  (p. 139)
trinomial square (p. 139)

sum of two cubes (p. 140)
difference of two cubes
  (p. 140)
completely factored (p. 142)
quadratic equation (p. 145)
double root (p. 145)
cubic equation (p. 146)

SUMMARY

This chapter develops three major interrelated topics. The first involves the properties of exponents as used in multiplication. These concepts and skills should be learned thoroughly before proceding to the second topic, operations with polynomials. Addition, subtraction, and multiplication of polynomials are covered here. The third major topic is the factoring of polynomials. All of the major factoring methods are presented, including common monomial factors, factoring by grouping, factoring trinomials, and factoring special products. The chapter concludes with the application of factoring to the solution of equations and inequalities and to problem solving.

REVIEW EXERCISES

4-1   *Simplify. Show each variable with just one exponent.*

1. $(3x^3)^2$ **2.** $(-2c^2d^4)^3$ **3.** $\left[\left(\frac{1}{2}yz^2\right)^3\right]^2$ **4.** $(-6x^3)^3(y^5)^2$

Evaluate for $x = \frac{1}{2}$, $y = \frac{3}{4}$, *and* $z = -4$.

5. $(y^2)^3$ **6.** xy^2z^3 **7.** $(xy)^2z^4$ **8.** $[(x^2z)^2]^2$

4-2   *Add or subtract, as indicated.*

9. $(3x - 5) + (-7x + 5)$ **10.** $(3ab^2 - 5b) - (ab^2 + 4b)$

11. $(5x^2 + 3x - 4) + (3x^2 - x)$ **12.** $(4x^2y - xy + y^2) - (x^2y - 2y^2)$

13. $(3x^2 - 5x) - (-6x^2 + 7) - 8x$ **14.** $(6r^2s - 34s^2 + 3s^3) - (8r^2s + 6s^3)$

4-3   *Multiply.*

15. $(2x - 3)(8x + 5)$ **16.** $(3x - y)(4x - 7y)$ **17.** $4x^2(3x^2 - x + 5)$

18. $(a + 4b)(a - 4b)$ **19.** $(5x - 2y)^2$ **20.** $(a - 2)(2a^3 - 4a^2 + 7)$

21. $(x + y)(x^2 - xy + y^2)$ **22.** $(x^2 + 4x - 8)(2x^2 - x + 3)$

Simplify.

23. $(3x - y)(4x - y) - 2x(x + y)$

24. $(x - 1)(2x + 1) - (x + 3)^2$

25. $(x + 1)(x + 2) + (x + 3)(x + 4)$

26. $(5x + 6)^2 - (6x + 5)^2$

4-4   *Write the GCF of each set of integers or monomials.*

27. 8, 24, 40

28. 12, 42, 48

29. 26, 52, 65

30. x^6, x^8

31. $9x^2y$, $15xy^2$

32. $5a^3b^2$, $10a^4$, $12a^2b$

Factor.

33. $8x - 10$

34. $x^2 - 3x$

35. $7a - 7b$

36. $8x^4 + 2x$

37. $15ab - 45ab^3$

38. $6c^3 - 3c^2 + 3c$

39. $6xy^2 - 4x^2y^3 + 12xy^4$

40. $27p^4 - 9p^2 + 18p - 6p^3$

4-5   **41.** $(x - 1)y + (x - 1)3$

42. $2y(y + 4) - 5(y + 4)$

43. $xy - 2y^2 + 6x - 12y$

44. $(4 - 8y) + (x - 2xy)$

45. $6t^3 - t - 6t^2w^2 + w^2$

46. $x^3 - 4y^3 - 4xy + x^2y^2$

4-6   **47.** $x^2 - 11x + 18$

48. $15x^2 + 13x - 6$

49. $x^2 + 2x - 3$

50. $6x^2 + x - 12$

51. $4x^2 - 5x + 1$

52. $3y^2 - 4y - 4$

53. $8x^2 + 10x + 3$

54. $10y^2 - 13y - 3$

55. $10w^2 - 11w - 18$

4-7   **56.** $4a^2 - 9b^2$

57. $4x^2 + 12x + 9$

58. $h^3 - 27$

59. $8a^3 + 125y^3$

60. $16x^2 - 8x + 1$

61. $x^3y^3 - 1$

62. $x^2y^2 - 144$

63. $9x^2 - 30xy + 25y^2$

64. $s^3 + 64y^3$

4-8   **65.** $2x^2 - 2y^2$

66. $x^3 - 4x + 5x^2 - 20$

67. $x^4 - 81$

68. $2y^4 + 16y$

69. $x^3 - x^2 - 6x$

70. $y^3 - 16y + y^2 - 16$

4-9   *Solve and check.*

71. $3x(x + 2) = 0$

72. $(x + 1)(x - 5) = 0$

73. $(x + 3)(2x - 1) = 0$

74. $6x^2 - 2x = 0$

75. $x^2 - 4x + 4 = 0$

76. $x^2 - 2x - 15 = 0$

77. $6x^2 + 15 = 19x$

78. $4x^2 + 4x + 1 = 0$

79. $4x^2 - 2x = 12$

80. $x^3 - 2x^2 + x = 0$

81. $16x^3 - 8x^2 + x = 0$

82. $2x^3 - 3x = -x^2$

4-10   **83.** Eighteen times a number is equal to the square of the number, increased by 81. Find the number.

84. Twice the sum of the square of a number and 6 times the number is 6 more than the number. Find all such numbers.

85. The perimeter of a rectangle is 50 centimeters and the area is 126 square centimeters. Find the dimensions of the rectangle.

86. The length of a rectangle is 7 times its width. If the width is increased by 3 inches and the length is increased by 4 inches, the area will be doubled. Find the dimensions of the original rectangle.

4-11   *Solve and graph.*

87. $x^2 - 4x < 0$ **88.** $x^2 + 3x - 40 \geq 0$ **89.** $x^2 - 1 \leq 8$

90. $2x^2 + x > 1$ **91.** $x^2 - 4 < 5$ **92.** $2x^2 - 3x - 9 \geq 0$

93. $x^3 - 16x \leq 0$ **94.** $x^3 > x$ **95.** $x^3 - x^2 < 6x$

CHAPTER 4 TEST

Simplify. Show each variable with just one exponent.

1. $x^3 \cdot x^4 \cdot x^5$ **2.** $[(xy^3)^4]^2$

Add or subtract, as indicated.

3. $(6x + 11) + (3x - 4) + (-2x - 7)$ **4.** $(5x^4 - 6x^2 + x) - (x^3 - 6x^2 - 2x)$

Multiply.

5. $-3ab^2(a^2b - 5ab^2 - 4)$ **6.** $(7x - 6)(3x + 4)$

Factor.

7. $8x^2y^3 - 12xy^2$ **8.** $15x + 10x^2 - 5x^4$

9. $xy - 5y - 2x + 10$ **10.** $3x^2 - 2y + 6x - xy$

11. $x^2 - 17x + 72$ **12.** $8x^2 - 10x + 3$

13. $9x^2 - 100y^2$ **14.** $9x^2 + 12x + 4$

15. $6x^3 + 48$ **16.** $81 - b^4$

Solve and check.

17. $35x^2 - 20x = 0$ **18.** $5x^3 = 45x$

19. A picture 50 centimeters long and 40 centimeters wide is placed into a frame of uniform width. The area of the frame is one-half the area of the picture. How wide is the frame?

20. Solve and graph $x^2 - 3x - 18 \leq 0$.

Greatest Common Factor

To factor $548a^2 - 1233b^2$ completely, first find the greatest common factor of 548 and 1233. The program below does this by starting with the smaller of the two numbers, S. It uses FOR . . . NEXT . . . statements to work back to 1, testing each value to determine if it is a factor of the two numbers.

Line 200 instructs the computer to place the value of S in D, and decrease it by one each step. The next value for D is computed each time NEXT D is reached. When D = 1, the computer continues to the line after NEXT D.

To find if one number is a factor of another, we use the *greatest integer function*, INT(X). If the divisor is a factor, there is an equality. But if the divisor is not a factor, there is an inequality.

The Program

What It Does

```
100 REM GREATEST COMMON FACTOR
110 PRINT "ENTER SMALLER NUMBER";
120 INPUT S
130 PRINT "ENTER GREATER NUMBER";
140 INPUT G
200 FOR D = S TO 1 STEP -1

210 IF INT(S/D) < > S/D THEN 230

220 IF INT(G/D) = G/D THEN 300

230 NEXT D

300 PRINT "THEIR GCF IS "; D
900 END
```

- **200** Assigns S to D; decreases it by one in each step, until D = 1.
- **210** Tests if D is factor of S; if not, goes to line 230. If it is, continues.
- **220** Tests if D is factor of G. If it is, D is the GCF; jumps to line 300.
- **230** Sends computer back to line 200 for the next value of D.
- **300** Displays the GCF.

What will the program display as the GCF of each of these pairs?

1. 36, 60   **2.** 15, 16   **3.** 407, 566   **4.** 548, 1233

5. Run the program to find the GCF of 1337 and 4202. Time the computer. Is this program practical for large numbers? Why?

6. Run the program, entering the greater number first. Does the computer display the correct GCF? What happens?

7. What number is displayed as the GCF of each pair of entries if line 200 is changed to FOR D = 1 TO S STEP 1?

8. Use the statement FOR N = 0 TO 40 STEP 2 to write a program that displays the even numbers 0 through 40.

9. Write a program to display all the factors of a number entered.

For more information about BASIC, see the Computer Handbook at the back of the book.

PART I

Write the letter for the correct answer.

1. Evaluate $y(xy - z^2)$ for $x = -3$, $y = -\frac{1}{3}$, and $z = 3$.

   a. $-\dfrac{8}{3}$ **b.** $-\dfrac{5}{3}$ **c.** -1 **d.** $\dfrac{5}{3}$ **e.** $\dfrac{8}{3}$

2. $5x^2 - 7x^2 + 5x - 13 + 3x$ is equivalent to $\underline{\ ?\ }$.

   a. $6x^2 - 13$ **b.** $2x^2 + 8x - 13$ **c.** $-2x^2 + 5x - 10$

   d. $-2x^2 + 8x - 13$ **e.** $-35x^2 + 8x - 13$

3. The graph of which inequality is shown here?

   a. $|x + 3| \le 5$ **b.** $|x - 3| \le 5$

   c. $|x - 3| \ge 5$ **d.** $|x + 5| \le 3$ **e.** $|3 + x| \ge 5$

4. The equation of the line with slope -3, passing through $(-3, 3)$ is $\underline{\ ?\ }$.

   a. $3x + y = -3$ **b.** $x + y = -3$ **c.** $3x + y = -6$

   d. $3x - y = 6$ **e.** $x - 3y = -6$

5. If $f(x) = 3x^2 - x - 4$, then $f(-1) = \underline{\ ?\ }$.

   a. $f(1)$ **b.** $f\left(\dfrac{4}{3}\right)$ **c.** $f\left(-\dfrac{4}{3}\right)$ **d.** $f(0)$ **e.** $f(2)$

6. Find the y-value of the solution for this system: $\begin{array}{l} -5x + 3y = 9 \\ x - 2y = 1 \end{array}$

   a. 6 **b.** 3 **c.** -3 **d.** 2 **e.** -2

7. Which ordered pair satisfies the system $x \le y$ and $y > -1$?

   a. $(1, -3)$ **b.** $(-2, 3)$ **c.** $(3, -1)$ **d.** $(2, 1)$ **e.** $(-3, -2)$

8. Which line is perpendicular to $x + y = -3$ and has the same y-intercept?

   a. $x + y = 3$ **b.** $x - y = -3$ **c.** $x + y = \dfrac{1}{3}$ **d.** $x - y = \dfrac{1}{3}$ **e.** $x - y = 3$

9. $(2x - 3)(8x + 5) = \underline{\ ?\ }$.

   a. $16x^2 - 15$ **b.** $16x^2 - 24x - 15$ **c.** $16x^2 + 10x - 15$

   d. $16x^2 - 14x - 15$ **e.** $16x^2 + 15$

10. One factor of $x^3 + 3x^2 - 9x - 27$ is $\underline{\ ?\ }$.

   a. $x^2 + 9$ **b.** $(x - 3)^2$ **c.** $x + 9$ **d.** $x + 3$ **e.** $x^2 - 3$

11. The solutions for $x = 3x^2 - 10$ are $\underline{\ ?\ }$.

   a. $-\dfrac{5}{3}$ and 2 **b.** -5 and 2 **c.** 3 and 1 **d.** $\dfrac{3}{5}$ and 5 **e.** 5 and -2

PART II

12. Write $\frac{8}{9}$ as a repeating decimal.

13. Solve: $6x - 24 = 3x + 15$ **14.** Solve: $3x - 2 = 2(x - 5)$

15. Write the following as a mathematical equation, and solve for n:
Fifteen less than eight times a number n is 22.

16. $(x + 2)$ dimes and 7 less than 4 times as many quarters have a total value of $8.15. Find the number of dimes and quarters.

Graph each compound inequality.

17. $x > 5$ or $x + 8 < 12$ **18.** $-4 < x + 5 < 7$

19. Given $s = a + (n - 1)d$, solve for d in terms of the other variables.

20. In 4 years, Robert's age will be 8 years greater than one-half of Tony's age at that time. If Tony is 16 now, how old is Robert?

21. Find the slope of the line containing the points $(-4, 7)$ and $(7, -4)$.

22. Write the domain and range of the relation $\{(-1, 0), (2, 4), (4, 4), (-2, 1)\}$, and state whether or not it is a function.

23. If $g(x) = -3x^2 - 4x + 1$, find $g(-2)$.

24. Are the lines with the equations $2y = x - 6$ and $x - 2y - 10 = 0$ parallel, perpendicular, or neither?

25. Find the slope and the y-intercept of the line $2x - 3y = 6$.

26. Graph the line that has the y-intercept 2, and is parallel to $y = 3x - 1$.

Solve each system.

27. $x + 2y = 5$
    $2x - y = 0$

28. $3x - 2y = 4$
    $2x + 5y = -1$

29. $x + 2y - z = -6$
    $3x + y - z = -1$
    $x - y + 2z = 15$

30. Graph the system: $\begin{array}{l} x > 1 + 3y \\ 5y < x + 5 \end{array}$

31. Two investments totaling $2600 earn interest at 8% and 7.5% annually. If the total interest for one year is $201, how much was invested at each rate?

Simplify.

32. $(x^2y^3)^4(x^5y^2)^3$ **33.** $(5x^2y^3 - 2y^2) - (6x^2y^3 + y^2)$

Factor completely.

34. $9x^2 - 49$ **35.** $2xy - 4y^2 + 12x - 24y$

CHAPTER 5

The average rate of each race car can be expressed as a ratio. Problems involving such rates can often be solved by writing and solving proportions.

RATIONAL EXPRESSIONS

Prerequisite Skills Review

Write the letter for the correct answer.

1. Which of the following fractions is not defined?

a. $\dfrac{6}{(-2)^2 + 2}$ **b.** $\dfrac{6}{(-2)^2 - 2}$ **c.** $\dfrac{6}{(-2)^2 + 4}$ **d.** $\dfrac{6}{(-2)^2 - 4}$

2. If $b \neq c$, then $\dfrac{-a}{b - c} = \underline{\ ?\ }$.

a. $-\dfrac{a}{c - b}$ **b.** $\dfrac{a}{c - b}$ **c.** $\dfrac{a}{b + c}$ **d.** none of these

3. The reciprocal of 8 is $\underline{\ ?\ }$.

a. -8 **b.** $-\dfrac{1}{8}$ **c.** $\dfrac{1}{8}$ **d.** none of these

4. The least common multiple of 16 and 6 is $\underline{\ ?\ }$.

a. 2   **b.** 16   **c.** 48   **d.** 96

5. The least common denominator of $\dfrac{5}{12}$ and $\dfrac{3}{4}$ is $\underline{\ ?\ }$.

a. 48   **b.** 24   **c.** 12   **d.** 4

6. If each side of the equation $\dfrac{x}{2} + \dfrac{3}{8} = \dfrac{3}{4}$ is multiplied by 8, the result is $\underline{\ ?\ }$.

a. $8x + 3 = 6$ **b.** $4x + 3 = 24$ **c.** $7x = 6$ **d.** none of these

7. If $(2x + 1)(x - 1) = 0$, then the possible values for x are $\underline{\ ?\ }$.

a. $-\dfrac{1}{2}$ and -1 **b.** 1 and -1 **c.** $\dfrac{1}{2}$ and 1   **d.** $-\dfrac{1}{2}$ and 1

8. The denominator of a fraction is 3 more than twice the numerator. If x represents the numerator, then the denominator is represented by $\underline{\ ?\ }$.

a. $2x + 3$ **b.** $3x + 2$ **c.** $\dfrac{x}{2x + 3}$ **d.** $2(x + 3)$

9. If 8 of the 60 passengers on a bus are standing, then the ratio of the number of passengers standing to the number *not* standing is $\underline{\ ?\ }$.

a. $\dfrac{2}{15}$ **b.** $\dfrac{2}{13}$ **c.** $\dfrac{13}{2}$ **d.** $\dfrac{2}{17}$

10. Two hours 40 minutes is equivalent to $\underline{\ ?\ }$.

a. $2\dfrac{2}{3}$ hr   **b.** 140 min   **c.** 2.4 hr   **d.** none of these

5-1   Simplifying Rational Expressions

OBJECTIVES _____

To simplify rational expressions by dividing the numerator and denominator by their greatest common factor.
To evaluate rational expressions for given values of the variables.

_____

Fractions such as $\frac{2}{3}$ and $-\frac{15}{7}$ are called *rational numbers*, since their numerators are integers and their denominators are nonzero integers. In a **rational expression,** the numerator and denominator are polynomials. Since integers are monomials, fractions such as $\frac{2}{3}$ and $-\frac{15}{7}$ are special types of rational expressions. The following are also rational expressions.

$$\frac{x+2}{5} \qquad \frac{13}{8ab} \qquad \frac{h-1}{h^2-1}$$

Rational expressions are not defined for values of the variables that result in zero denominators. For example, $\frac{13}{8ab}$ is not defined for $a = 0$ or for $b = 0$. For what values of h is $\frac{h-1}{h^2-1}$ undefined? When working with rational expressions in this text, we make the assumption that no variable may have a value that results in a denominator of zero.

A fraction is *simplified* by dividing both the numerator and the denominator by their greatest common factor.

Cancellation Rule

If **p, q,** and **r** are real numbers, with **q ≠ 0** and **r ≠ 0,** then

$$\frac{p \cdot r}{q \cdot r} = \frac{p}{q}$$

Since the numerator and denominator of a rational expression represent real numbers, this rule applies to all rational expressions.

EXAMPLE 1   Simplify.

a. $\dfrac{80}{48} = \dfrac{5 \cdot 16}{3 \cdot 16}$ Factor the numerator and the denominator. Use their GCF, 16.

$\quad\ \ = \dfrac{5}{3}$ Divide the numerator and the denominator by 16. That is, use the cancellation rule.

b. $\dfrac{12xy^2}{78x^3y} = \dfrac{6xy(2y)}{6xy(13x^2)}$ Factor the numerator and the denominator. Use their GCF, $6xy$.

$= \dfrac{2y}{13x^2}$ Divide the numerator and the denominator by $6xy$.

c. $\dfrac{2x - 4}{x^2 + 2x - 8} = \dfrac{2(x - 2)}{(x + 4)(x - 2)}$ Factor.

$= \dfrac{2}{x + 4}$ Divide the numerator and the denominator by $x - 2$.

Recall that the expressions $(y - x)$ and $(x - y)$ are opposites. That is, $(y - x)$ is equal to $-1(x - y)$. We use this fact when simplifying a rational expression in which factors in the forms $y - x$ and $x - y$ appear, one in the numerator and the other in the denominator.

EXAMPLE 2   Simplify $\dfrac{9 - x^2}{3x^2 - 4x - 15}$.

$\dfrac{9 - x^2}{3x^2 - 4x - 15} = \dfrac{(3 - x)(3 + x)}{(x - 3)(3x + 5)}$

$= \dfrac{-1(x - 3)(3 + x)}{(x - 3)(3x + 5)}$ $3 - x = -1(x - 3)$

$= \dfrac{-1(3 + x)}{3x + 5}$ Divide the numerator and the denominator by $x - 3$.

$= -\dfrac{3 + x}{3x + 5}$ $\dfrac{-p}{q} = -\dfrac{p}{q}$

Rational expressions may be evaluated in the same manner as other algebraic expressions.

EXAMPLE 3   Evaluate $\dfrac{2x - 7}{x^2 - 1}$, if possible, for

a. $x = 0$ **b.** $x = 1$

$\dfrac{2(0) - 7}{0^2 - 1} = \dfrac{-7}{-1} = 7$ $\dfrac{2(1) - 7}{1^2 - 1} = \dfrac{-5}{0}$ Undefined

CLASS EXERCISES

Simplify.

1. $\dfrac{21}{35}$ **2.** $\dfrac{4}{14}$ **3.** $\dfrac{x - 3}{(x + 1)(x - 3)}$ **4.** $\dfrac{(x + 5)x}{(x - 5)x}$

5. $\dfrac{24x}{14x^2}$ **6.** $\dfrac{m^2n}{mn^2p}$ **7.** $\dfrac{-32x^2y^3}{24xy^5}$ **8.** $\dfrac{5x}{10 + 15x}$

9. $\dfrac{x^2 - 4}{x + 2}$ **10.** $\dfrac{y^2 - y}{2y}$ **11.** $-\dfrac{3 - c}{c - 3}$ **12.** $\dfrac{x^2 - 2x + 1}{x^2 - 1}$

EXERCISES

A *Simplify.*

1. $\dfrac{70}{25}$

2. $\dfrac{18}{96}$

3. $-\dfrac{46}{92}$

4. $-\dfrac{225a^2b}{75ab^2}$

5. $\dfrac{4x}{12x^2}$

6. $\dfrac{20m^2n}{6m^3n^3}$

7. $\dfrac{5x-5}{(x-1)^2}$

8. $\dfrac{h^2+2h}{4+2h}$

9. $\dfrac{x^3y^4}{x^2y}$

10. $\dfrac{2x}{x^2}$

11. $\dfrac{x-3}{2x-6}$

12. $\dfrac{x^2+2x+1}{x+1}$

13. $\dfrac{2x^2+x-3}{4x+6}$

14. $\dfrac{r-s}{s-r}$

15. $\dfrac{3-x^2}{2x^2-6}$

16. $\dfrac{x^2-25}{6x^2+29x-5}$

Evaluate $\dfrac{2x}{x^2-9}$ *for the given values of* ***x***.

17. $x=-2$

18. $x=0$

19. $x=4$

20. $x=-4$

Evaluate $\dfrac{x^2-9}{x+3}$ *for the given values of* ***x***.

21. $x=-1$

22. $x=0$

23. $x=5$

24. $x=-5$

B *Evaluate* $\dfrac{4x^2}{3x-2}$, *if possible, for the given values of* ***x***.

25. $x=3$

26. $x=0$

27. $x=\dfrac{1}{3}$

28. $x=\dfrac{2}{3}$

Evaluate $\dfrac{x+4}{x^2-16}$, *if possible, for the given values of* ***x***.

29. $x=0$

30. $x=4$

31. $x=16$

32. $x=-4$

Simplify.

33. $\dfrac{5x-10}{8-2x-x^2}$

34. $\dfrac{6h^2-4h}{9h^2-12h+4}$

35. $\dfrac{15y^2-2y-8}{12y-15y^2}$

36. $\dfrac{x-3}{x^2-6x+9}$

37. $\dfrac{16-x^2}{4x-16}$

38. $\dfrac{4x^2+4x+1}{2x^2-5x-3}$

39. $\dfrac{x-1}{x^3-1}$

40. $\dfrac{a^3+b^3}{a^2b-ab^2+b^3}$

41. $\dfrac{xy-2y+3x-6}{xy+3x+4y+12}$

42. $\dfrac{m^4-16}{m^4+m^2-12}$

43. $\dfrac{9p+3p^2+p^3}{p^3-27}$

44. $\dfrac{x^2-2x+xy-2y}{x^3-8}$

C **45.** $\dfrac{(y-2)^{n+3}x^{3m}}{x^{5m+1}(y-2)^n}$

46. $\dfrac{x^{2n}-1}{x^{2n}+2x^n+1}$

*47. $\dfrac{2^{n+1}-(-2)^{n+1}}{4}$, where n is an even integer

Writing Repeating Decimals as Fractions

Any infinite repeating decimal can be written in fraction form.

Example 1 Express 0.777. . . in the form $\frac{p}{q}$, where p and q are integers.

The digit 7 repeats endlessly. The first 7 is called the *first cycle* of the repeating decimal 0.777. . .

Let $x = 0.777. . .$

Step 1 $10x = 7.777. . .$ Multiply x by 10 to get the decimal point to the *right* of the first cycle.

Step 2 $-\ \ x = 0.777. . .$ The decimal point in $x = 0.777. . .$ is to the *left* of
$\ \ \ \ \ \ \ \ 9x = 7.000. . .$ the first cycle. Subtract x from $10x$, and solve for x.

$$x = \frac{7}{9}$$

You can check this result by dividing 9 into 7.
The repeating decimal 0.777. . . is equal to $\frac{7}{9}$.

The procedure is similar when the repeating decimal is written in abbreviated form, with a bar over the first cycle.

Example 2 Express $1.2\overline{34}$ in the form $\frac{p}{q}$, where p and q are integers.

$1.2\overline{34} = 1.2343434. . . .$ The first cycle is 34.

Let $x = 1.2\overline{34}$.

Step 1 $1000x = 1234.\overline{34}$ Multiply x by 1000 to get the decimal point to
the *right* of the first cycle.

Step 2 $-\ 10x = \ \ \ \ \ 12.\overline{34}$ Multiply x by 10 to get the decimal point to the *left*
of the first cycle. Subtract $10x$ from $1000x$, and solve for x.

$990x = 1222.\overline{00}$

$$x = \frac{1222}{990} = \frac{611}{495}$$

Check by division to show that $0.2\overline{34}$ is equal to $\frac{611}{495}$.

Now you try it! Express each infinite repeating decimal in the form $\frac{p}{q}$, where
p and q are integers and $\frac{p}{q}$ is in simplest form.

1. 0.555. . .   **2.** 0.0555. . .   **3.** 2.6444. . .   **4.** 0.818181. . .

5. $0.00\overline{3}$ **6.** $1.\overline{20}$ **7.** $4.0\overline{16}$ **8.** $0.4\overline{63}$

9. $0.0\overline{306}$ **10.** $0.\overline{0306}$ **11.** $2.4\overline{321}$ **12.** $0.\overline{9}$

5-2 Multiplying and Dividing Rational Expressions

OBJECTIVE

To find the product or quotient of two rational expressions.

To find the product of two fractions, multiply the numerators to find the numerator of the product. Then multiply the denominators to find the denominator of the product. The result is simplified, when possible.

Rule for Multiplying Fractions

If p, q, r, and s are real numbers, with $q \neq 0$ and $s \neq 0$, then

$$\frac{p}{q} \cdot \frac{r}{s} = \frac{pr}{qs}$$

The same rule applies to the multiplication of rational expressions, since such expressions represent rational numbers.

EXAMPLE 1   Multiply.

a. $\dfrac{3}{7} \cdot \dfrac{5}{2} = \dfrac{3 \cdot 5}{7 \cdot 2} = \dfrac{15}{14}$ Multiply the numerators.
    Multiply the denominators.

b. $\dfrac{2x}{5y} \cdot \dfrac{9}{7y} = \dfrac{2x \cdot 9}{5y \cdot 7y} = \dfrac{18x}{35y^2}$

c. $\dfrac{n}{n-1} \cdot \dfrac{n-1}{n+1} = \dfrac{n(n-1)}{(n-1)(n+1)} = \dfrac{n}{n+1}$

The work can often be simplified by using a shortcut. In this procedure we divide numerators and denominators by common factors *before* multiplying.

EXAMPLE 2   Multiply.

a. $\dfrac{4x^3}{x^2 - 5x} \cdot \dfrac{x-5}{12} = \dfrac{4x^3}{x(x-5)} \cdot \dfrac{x-5}{12}$ Factor $x^2 - 5x$.

$= \dfrac{\overset{1}{\cancel{4x^3}}^{x^2}}{\underset{1}{x}\underset{1}{(\cancel{x-5})}} \cdot \dfrac{\cancel{x-5}}{\underset{3}{\cancel{12}}}$ 4, x, and $x - 5$ are each factors of both a numerator and a denominator.

$= \dfrac{x^2}{3}$ Multiply.

b. $\dfrac{x^2 - 4}{x^2 - 5x + 6} \cdot \dfrac{2x + 1}{6x + 3} = \dfrac{(x + 2)\overset{1}{\cancel{(x - 2)}}}{(x - 3)\underset{1}{\cancel{(x - 2)}}} \cdot \dfrac{\overset{1}{\cancel{2x + 1}}}{3\underset{1}{\cancel{(2x + 1)}}}$

$$= \dfrac{x + 2}{3(x - 3)}$$

Recall that when we divide by a fraction, we write the reciprocal of the divisor and then multiply. The procedure can be justified using examples of the following type:

There are 3 halves in $\dfrac{3}{2}$. $\qquad\qquad\qquad \dfrac{3}{2} \div \dfrac{1}{2} = 3$

The same result is obtained if $\dfrac{3}{2}$ is multiplied
by the reciprocal of $\dfrac{1}{2}$, which is 2. $\qquad \dfrac{3}{2} \cdot 2 = 3$

The rule is stated formally below. Note that it applies to rational expressions as well as to rational numbers in fraction form.

Rule for Dividing Fractions

If p, q, r, and s are real numbers, with $q \neq 0$, $r \neq 0$, and $s \neq 0$, then

$$\dfrac{p}{q} \div \dfrac{r}{s} = \dfrac{p}{q} \cdot \dfrac{s}{r} = \dfrac{ps}{qr}$$

EXAMPLE 3   Divide.

a. $-\dfrac{5}{9} \div \dfrac{4}{15} = -\dfrac{5}{9} \cdot \dfrac{15}{4}$ Write the related multiplication example.
    Use the reciprocal of the divisor.

$$= -\dfrac{75}{36}$$

$$= -\dfrac{25}{12}$$

b. $\dfrac{1}{x - 1} \div 4 = \dfrac{1}{x - 1} \cdot \dfrac{1}{4} = \dfrac{1}{4(x - 1)}$

c. $\dfrac{h + 5}{h^2 + 5h} \div \dfrac{2h^2 - h - 1}{5h} = \dfrac{h + 5}{h^2 + 5h} \cdot \dfrac{5h}{2h^2 - h - 1}$

$$= \dfrac{\overset{1}{\cancel{h + 5}}}{\cancel{h}(\underset{1}{\cancel{h + 5}})} \cdot \dfrac{5\overset{1}{\cancel{h}}}{(2h + 1)(h - 1)}$$

$$= \dfrac{5}{(2h + 1)(h - 1)}$$

CLASS EXERCISES

Multiply or divide, and simplify.

1. $\dfrac{1}{2} \cdot \dfrac{2}{1}$

2. $\dfrac{x}{2} \div \dfrac{1}{x}$

3. $\dfrac{3}{4} \div \dfrac{4}{3}$

4. $\dfrac{5}{6} \div \left(-\dfrac{10}{3}\right)$

5. $\dfrac{m}{2n} \cdot \dfrac{n^2}{m}$

6. $\dfrac{2-x}{x+3} \div \dfrac{15x^3}{x+3}$

7. $\dfrac{x+3}{3y} \cdot \dfrac{6xy^2}{x^2-9}$

8. $\dfrac{6r}{s^3} \div \dfrac{3r^2}{5s}$

EXERCISES

A

Multiply or divide, and simplify.

1. $\dfrac{3}{8} \cdot \dfrac{12}{15}$

2. $-\dfrac{72}{17} \cdot \dfrac{34}{27}$

3. $\dfrac{1}{4} \div \dfrac{1}{2}$

4. $\dfrac{1}{4} \div \dfrac{1}{4}$

5. $\dfrac{2a}{b} \div 6b^2$

6. $\dfrac{16x^2}{45y} \div \dfrac{48x}{75y^2}$

7. $\dfrac{5x}{6y^2} \cdot \dfrac{8y}{10x^3}$

8. $\dfrac{9rs^2}{t} \cdot \dfrac{2t^2}{27r^2s}$

9. $\dfrac{3x^3}{y} \div \dfrac{3x^2}{2y^2}$

10. $\dfrac{x-4}{3y} \cdot \dfrac{9xy}{x^2-16}$

11. $\dfrac{5m+n}{m-2} \div \dfrac{5m}{m-2}$

12. $\dfrac{x^2+3x}{x-5} \div \dfrac{x}{5-x}$

13. $\dfrac{x^2+2x+1}{x-1} \cdot \dfrac{2x^2-2x}{x^2-1}$

14. $\dfrac{x^2-5x+6}{x+5} \cdot \dfrac{3x+15}{x^2-4x+4}$

B

15. $\dfrac{4z}{3z^2-2z-8} \div \dfrac{12z^3}{9z^2-16}$

16. $\dfrac{x^2-3x-18}{x^2+6x+9} \div \dfrac{2x^2-11x-6}{2x^3+6x^2}$

17. $\dfrac{3p}{4q^2} \cdot \dfrac{12q}{5p^2} \cdot \dfrac{15p^3}{8q}$

18. $\dfrac{r-1}{r+1} \cdot \dfrac{2r+2}{3r-3} \cdot \dfrac{9}{4}$

19. $\dfrac{t^2+5t}{5+t} \div \dfrac{t^2-25}{t+1}$

20. $\dfrac{h+2}{h^2-4h+4} \div \dfrac{2h+4}{h^2-2h}$

21. $\dfrac{10x^3+13x^2-3x}{3x-15x^2} \div (4x^2+12x+9)$

22. $\dfrac{2h^2+7h+3}{3h^2+7h-6} \cdot \dfrac{3h^2+h-2}{h^2+2h+1}$

Perform the indicated operations, and simplify.

23. $\left(\dfrac{n^2+1}{n^2-1} \cdot \dfrac{n+1}{5n}\right) \div \dfrac{n-1}{10n^2}$

24. $\dfrac{7x^2}{5-3x} \div \left(\dfrac{21}{2x+4} \cdot \dfrac{2x^3}{3x-5}\right)$

25. $\left(\dfrac{x^2-1}{3x} \cdot \dfrac{x^2}{x+1}\right) \div \dfrac{x^2-2x+1}{6x}$

26. $\left(\dfrac{x^2+x-2}{6x^2-11x+3} \div \dfrac{x^2-1}{6x-2}\right) \cdot \dfrac{2x-3}{2x+4}$

27. $\left(\dfrac{a}{b} \cdot \dfrac{c}{d}\right) \div \dfrac{e}{f}$

28. $\dfrac{a}{b} \cdot \left(\dfrac{c}{d} \div \dfrac{e}{f}\right)$

29. $\left(\dfrac{a}{b} \div \dfrac{c}{d}\right) \div \dfrac{e}{f}$

30. $\dfrac{a}{b} \div \left(\dfrac{c}{d} \div \dfrac{e}{f}\right)$

C

31. $\left(\dfrac{u^3+v^3}{u^3-u^2v+uv^2} \cdot \dfrac{u^2+uv}{u^2+2uv+v^2}\right) \div \dfrac{u^2-9}{u^3-27}$

*32. $\left(\dfrac{mn-3n-2m+6}{n^2+n} \div \dfrac{n^3-2n^2-n+2}{n^3+1}\right) \div \dfrac{n^2-n+1}{n^2-n}$

5-3 Adding and Subtracting Rational Expressions

OBJECTIVE

To find the sum or difference of two rational expressions.

Fractions with the same denominator are easy to add or subtract. We simply add or subtract the numerators and use the common denominator.

$$\frac{4}{5} + \frac{7}{5} = \frac{11}{5} \qquad \frac{11}{5} - \frac{7}{5} = \frac{4}{5}$$

Rule for Adding and Subtracting Fractions With the Same Denominator

If p, q, and r are real numbers, with $r \neq 0$, then

$$\frac{p}{r} + \frac{q}{r} = \frac{p + q}{r} \quad \text{and} \quad \frac{p}{r} - \frac{q}{r} = \frac{p - q}{r}$$

The same rule applies to the addition and subtraction of rational expressions. Where possible, the answers are simplified.

EXAMPLE 1   Add $\frac{3}{2x} + \frac{7}{2x}$.

$$\frac{3}{2x} + \frac{7}{2x} = \frac{3 + 7}{2x} \qquad \text{Add the numerators.}$$
$$\text{Use the common denominator.}$$

$$= \frac{10}{2x}$$

$$= \frac{5}{x} \qquad \text{Simplify.}$$

In order to simplify the result, it is sometimes necessary to factor the numerator or denominator, or both.

EXAMPLE 2   Add $\frac{x}{x^2 - 9} + \frac{3}{x^2 - 9}$.

$$\frac{x}{x^2 - 9} + \frac{3}{x^2 - 9} = \frac{x + 3}{x^2 - 9}$$

$$= \frac{x + 3}{(x + 3)(x - 3)} \qquad \text{Factor the denominator.}$$

$$= \frac{1}{x - 3} \qquad \text{Simplify.}$$

RATIONAL EXPRESSIONS

EXAMPLE 3   Subtract $\dfrac{4h^2}{h^2 + h - 6} - \dfrac{2h^2 + 4h}{h^2 + h - 6}$.

$$\dfrac{4h^2}{h^2 + h - 6} - \dfrac{2h^2 + 4h}{h^2 + h - 6} = \dfrac{4h^2 - (2h^2 + 4h)}{h^2 + h - 6}$$

$$= \dfrac{2h^2 - 4h}{h^2 + h - 6}$$

$$= \dfrac{2h(h - 2)}{(h + 3)(h - 2)} \qquad \text{Factor the numerator}$$
$$\text{and the denominator.}$$

$$= \dfrac{2h}{h + 3} \qquad \text{Simplify.}$$

When adding or subtracting fractions with different denominators, we write them first as equivalent fractions having a common denominator. Recall that the **least common denominator (LCD)** of two or more fractions is the *least common multiple* of their denominators. One way to find the LCD is to write each denominator as a product of prime factors. The LCD of the denominators is the product of these factors, each taken the greatest number of times it appears in any one denominator.

EXAMPLE 4   Add $\frac{5}{18} + \frac{7}{24}$.

First find the LCD of the two fractions.

$$18 = 2 \cdot 3 \cdot 3 \qquad\qquad 24 = 2 \cdot 2 \cdot 2 \cdot 3$$

The LCD of $\frac{5}{18}$ and $\frac{7}{24}$ is $2 \cdot 2 \cdot 2 \cdot 3 \cdot 3 = 72$.

Then use the property $\dfrac{p}{q} = \dfrac{p \cdot r}{q \cdot r}$ to write equivalent fractions with denominator 72, and add.

$$\dfrac{5}{18} = \dfrac{5 \cdot 4}{18 \cdot 4} = \dfrac{20}{72} \qquad\qquad \dfrac{7}{24} = \dfrac{7 \cdot 3}{24 \cdot 3} = \dfrac{21}{72}$$

$$\dfrac{5}{18} + \dfrac{7}{24} = \dfrac{20}{72} + \dfrac{21}{72} = \dfrac{41}{72} \qquad \text{Add the numerators.}$$
$$\text{Use the common denominator.}$$

The procedure is similar when combining rational expressions containing variables. We factor the denominators, write equivalent expressions using the LCD, add or subtract, and simplify the result, if possible.

EXAMPLE 5   Add $\dfrac{x}{3y^2} + \dfrac{4}{15x^2y}$.

First find the LCD.

$$3y^2 = 3 \cdot y \cdot y \qquad\qquad 15x^2y = 3 \cdot 5 \cdot x \cdot x \cdot y$$

The LCD is $3 \cdot 5 \cdot x \cdot x \cdot y \cdot y$, or $15x^2y^2$.

Now write equivalent expressions using the LCD, and add.

$$\dfrac{x}{3y^2} + \dfrac{4}{15x^2y} = \dfrac{x(5x^2)}{3y^2(5x^2)} + \dfrac{4(y)}{15x^2y(y)} = \dfrac{5x^3}{15x^2y^2} + \dfrac{4y}{15x^2y^2} = \dfrac{5x^3 + 4y}{15x^2y^2}$$

EXAMPLE 6   Subtract $\dfrac{x+5}{x^2-9} - \dfrac{1}{x^2+3x}$.

$$\frac{x+5}{x^2-9} - \frac{1}{x^2+3x} = \frac{x+5}{(x+3)(x-3)} - \frac{1}{x(x+3)} \qquad \text{Factor. The LCD is } x(x+3)(x-3).$$

$$= \frac{x(x+5)}{x(x+3)(x-3)} - \frac{x-3}{x(x+3)(x-3)}$$

$$= \frac{x(x+5) - (x-3)}{x(x+3)(x-3)} \qquad \text{Subtract.}$$

$$= \frac{x^2+4x+3}{x(x+3)(x-3)} \qquad \text{Simplify the numerator.}$$

$$= \frac{(x+3)(x+1)}{x(x+3)(x-3)} \qquad \text{Factor the numerator.}$$

$$= \frac{x+1}{x(x-3)} \qquad \text{Simplify the expression.}$$

CLASS EXERCISES

Add or subtract, and simplify.

1. $\dfrac{5}{12} + \dfrac{3}{12}$ **2.** $\dfrac{15}{4} - \dfrac{7}{4}$ **3.** $\dfrac{2}{3} + \dfrac{7}{6}$ **4.** $\dfrac{11}{15} - \dfrac{2}{5}$

5. $\dfrac{2x}{5} + \dfrac{8x}{5}$ **6.** $\dfrac{3a}{b} - \dfrac{7a}{b}$ **7.** $\dfrac{2}{x+1} - \dfrac{3}{x+1}$ **8.** $\dfrac{x}{y} - \dfrac{y}{y}$

9. $\dfrac{h}{h+1} + \dfrac{1}{h+1}$ **10.** $\dfrac{a}{a-3} - 1$ **11.** $y + \dfrac{5}{2y}$ **12.** $\dfrac{x}{x^2-4} - \dfrac{2}{x^2-4}$

EXERCISES

A   *Add or subtract, and simplify.*

1. $\dfrac{4}{9} + \dfrac{2}{9}$ **2.** $\dfrac{18}{7} - \dfrac{4}{7}$ **3.** $\dfrac{3}{8} + \dfrac{1}{2}$ **4.** $\dfrac{17}{12} - \dfrac{1}{3}$

5. $\dfrac{5}{3x} + \dfrac{2}{3x}$ **6.** $\dfrac{a}{3b} + \dfrac{2a}{3b}$ **7.** $\dfrac{5}{x+y} - \dfrac{7}{x+y}$ **8.** $\dfrac{c-1}{3} - \dfrac{c-2}{3}$

9. $\dfrac{5c}{b} + \dfrac{1-5c}{b}$ **10.** $\dfrac{3r}{r+1} - \dfrac{2r-1}{r+1}$ **11.** $\dfrac{13}{3r^2} + \dfrac{2}{3r^2}$ **12.** $\dfrac{x}{x^2-4} + \dfrac{2}{x^2-4}$

13. $2 + \dfrac{x}{3}$ **14.** $y - \dfrac{3}{y}$ **15.** $\dfrac{1}{x+1} + x$ **16.** $\dfrac{y}{y-3} - 3$

17. $\dfrac{2r}{3s} - \dfrac{3}{r}$ **18.** $\dfrac{x}{3} + \dfrac{x}{2}$ **19.** $\dfrac{2}{a} + \dfrac{7}{5a}$ **20.** $\dfrac{2}{3} - \dfrac{4b}{a}$

21. $\dfrac{x}{3} - \dfrac{3}{x}$ **22.** $\dfrac{m}{n} - \dfrac{2}{3}$ **23.** $\dfrac{1}{2x} + \dfrac{3}{5x}$ **24.** $\dfrac{1}{2} + \dfrac{x}{x+2}$

25. $\dfrac{3}{x^2y} + \dfrac{5}{2x^2y^3}$

26. $\dfrac{x}{3y^2} - \dfrac{y}{12x^2}$

27. $\dfrac{5}{a^2bc} + \dfrac{1}{ab^2c^3}$

28. $\dfrac{1}{p-1} + \dfrac{1}{p+1}$

29. $\dfrac{x}{x^2+1} - \dfrac{2}{x+2}$

30. $\dfrac{r}{2(r+s)} - \dfrac{s}{3(r+s)^2}$

31. $\dfrac{z}{z-3} + \dfrac{z+5}{z+2}$

32. $\dfrac{t+7}{t} + \dfrac{t-3}{t+1}$

33. $\dfrac{2x}{x-1} - \dfrac{x+3}{x}$

B

34. $\dfrac{2}{x} - \dfrac{3}{x^2-4x}$

35. $3p + \dfrac{p^2}{7p+1}$

36. $5m + \dfrac{m^2-1}{m}$

37. $\dfrac{a}{b} + \dfrac{c}{d}$

38. $\dfrac{a}{b} - \dfrac{c}{d}$

39. $\dfrac{h}{h-2} + \dfrac{4h}{h^2-4h+4}$

40. $\dfrac{5x}{2} + \dfrac{5x}{4x-2}$

41. $\dfrac{2x}{x-1} - \dfrac{16x}{x^2+6x-7}$

42. $\dfrac{2x}{2x-1} + \dfrac{5x}{2x^2-7x+3}$

43. $\dfrac{x}{x-2} - \dfrac{x^2+3x}{2x^2-3x-2}$

44. $\dfrac{2n}{n^2-1} - \dfrac{n}{n-1}$

45. $\dfrac{y^2+3y}{y^2+3y+2} + \dfrac{y}{y+2}$

46. $\dfrac{5}{x^2-4} - \dfrac{3-x}{4-x^2}$

47. $\dfrac{1}{x^3+x^2} + \dfrac{2}{x^2+x}$

48. $\dfrac{n}{n^2+n-6} - \dfrac{n}{n^2-9}$

Evaluate $\dfrac{12}{x+5} + \dfrac{3x-2}{x+5}$ *for each value of* **x.**

49. x = 5

50. x = 15

51. x = −4

Evaluate $\dfrac{2}{2-y} + \dfrac{4+y^2}{4-y^2} + \dfrac{y}{2+y}$ *for each value of* **y.**

52. y = 8

53. y = 10

54. y = −14

C   *Perform the indicated operations, and simplify.*

55. $\dfrac{1}{a} - \dfrac{2}{a^2} - \dfrac{3}{a^3}$

56. $\dfrac{h}{h-1} + \dfrac{1}{h} - \dfrac{1}{h^2-h}$

57. $\dfrac{7x}{x^2-25} - \dfrac{2}{x-5} + \dfrac{15}{25-x^2}$

58. $\dfrac{2x}{x+1} + \dfrac{4}{x-1} - \dfrac{4}{x^2-1}$

59. $\dfrac{x}{x-2} + \dfrac{1}{x} + \dfrac{2}{x^2-2x}$

60. $\dfrac{24}{x^2+4x-5} + \dfrac{x}{x+5} - \dfrac{4}{x-1}$

61. $\dfrac{x}{x+1} - \dfrac{4}{x+4} + \dfrac{3}{x^2+5x+4}$

62. $\dfrac{5x}{2x^2-x-3} + \dfrac{x}{x+1} - \dfrac{x}{2x-3}$

63. $\dfrac{2a}{a-b} + \dfrac{b}{a+b} - \dfrac{2ab}{a^2-b^2}$

64. $\dfrac{x-2}{xy+x-2y-2} - \dfrac{x}{x-2} + \dfrac{y}{y+1}$

*65. $\dfrac{1}{a+b-1} - \dfrac{2}{a^2+2ab+b^2-1}$

5-4   Complex Fractions

OBJECTIVE

To simplify complex fractions.

What is the average of $\frac{1}{3}$ and $\frac{1}{2}$? The average of any two numbers is their sum divided by 2. Thus, to find the average of $\frac{1}{3}$ and $\frac{1}{2}$ we need to simplify this *complex fraction*:

$$\frac{\frac{1}{3} + \frac{1}{2}}{2}$$

A **complex fraction** is a fraction in which the numerator, the denominator, or both contain one or more fractions. When we *simplify* a complex fraction, we write it as a single fraction in simplest form, with no fractions in the numerator or the denominator. One way to simplify a complex fraction is to multiply both the numerator and the denominator by the LCD of all of the fractions shown.

EXAMPLE 1   Find the average of $\frac{1}{3}$ and $\frac{1}{2}$.

$$\frac{\frac{1}{3} + \frac{1}{2}}{2} = \frac{\left(\frac{1}{3} + \frac{1}{2}\right) \cdot 6}{2 \cdot 6}$$ Multiply the numerator and denominator by 6, the LCD of $\frac{1}{3}$ and $\frac{1}{2}$.

$$= \frac{2 + 3}{12}$$

$$= \frac{5}{12}$$

Another way to simplify a complex fraction is to divide the numerator by the denominator.

EXAMPLE 2   Simplify.

a. $\dfrac{\frac{3}{8}}{\frac{5}{6}} = \dfrac{3}{8} \div \dfrac{5}{6} = \dfrac{3}{8} \cdot \dfrac{6}{5} = \dfrac{18}{40} = \dfrac{9}{20}$

b. $\dfrac{\frac{2}{a}}{\frac{4}{ab^2}} = \dfrac{2}{a} \div \dfrac{4}{ab^2} = \dfrac{2}{a} \cdot \dfrac{ab^2}{4} = \dfrac{b^2}{2}$

In the next example, both methods are used to simplify the same complex fraction. Study the steps involved, and use the method you find easier when you do the exercises for this lesson.

EXAMPLE 3   Simplify $\dfrac{\dfrac{1}{x} + \dfrac{1}{y}}{\dfrac{1}{x^2} - \dfrac{1}{y^2}}$.

Method I   Multiply both the numerator and the denominator by the LCD of the four fractions.

$$\frac{\dfrac{1}{x} + \dfrac{1}{y}}{\dfrac{1}{x^2} - \dfrac{1}{y^2}} = \frac{\left(\dfrac{1}{x} + \dfrac{1}{y}\right) \cdot x^2 y^2}{\left(\dfrac{1}{x^2} - \dfrac{1}{y^2}\right) \cdot x^2 y^2}$$ x^2y^2 is the LCD of $\dfrac{1}{x}$, $\dfrac{1}{y}$, $\dfrac{1}{x^2}$, and $\dfrac{1}{y^2}$.

$$= \frac{xy^2 + x^2y}{y^2 - x^2}$$

$$= \frac{xy(y + x)}{(y + x)(y - x)}$$

$$= \frac{xy}{y - x}$$

Method II   First express the numerator and the denominator each as a single fraction. Then divide.

$$\frac{\dfrac{1}{x} + \dfrac{1}{y}}{\dfrac{1}{x^2} - \dfrac{1}{y^2}} = \frac{\dfrac{y + x}{xy}}{\dfrac{y^2 - x^2}{x^2 y^2}}$$ xy is the LCD of $\dfrac{1}{x}$ and $\dfrac{1}{y}$.

          x^2y^2 is the LCD of $\dfrac{1}{x^2}$ and $\dfrac{1}{y^2}$.

$$= \frac{y + x}{xy} \div \frac{y^2 - x^2}{x^2 y^2}$$

$$= \frac{y + x}{xy} \cdot \frac{x^2 y^2}{y^2 - x^2}$$

$$= \frac{y + x}{xy} \cdot \frac{x^2 y^2}{(y + x)(y - x)}$$

$$= \frac{xy}{y - x}$$

CLASS EXERCISES

Simplify each complex fraction, using both methods.

1. $\dfrac{1 + \dfrac{1}{4}}{\dfrac{1}{2} + 2}$ **2.** $\dfrac{1 - \dfrac{2}{5}}{\dfrac{4}{5} - 2}$ **3.** $\dfrac{3}{\dfrac{1}{m} + \dfrac{1}{n}}$ **4.** $\dfrac{\dfrac{1}{xy}}{\dfrac{2}{x} + \dfrac{3}{y}}$

EXERCISES

A   Find the average of the two fractions.

1. $\frac{2}{3}$ and $\frac{1}{2}$

2. $\frac{5}{4}$ and $\frac{9}{8}$

3. $-\frac{3}{4}$ and $\frac{2}{5}$

4. $\frac{1}{8}$ and $\frac{5}{12}$

Simplify.

5. $\dfrac{\frac{1}{2}}{\frac{5}{3}}$

6. $\dfrac{\frac{3}{5} - 4}{\frac{1}{10} - 2}$

7. $\dfrac{8}{\frac{3}{4} - \frac{5}{6}}$

8. $\dfrac{\frac{r}{s}}{t}$

9. $\dfrac{r}{\frac{s}{t}}$

10. $\dfrac{1}{\frac{1}{r - s}}$

11. $\dfrac{\frac{1}{x - 1}}{4}$

12. $\dfrac{4}{\frac{1}{x - 1}}$

13. $\dfrac{\frac{2}{x} - \frac{2}{5}}{\frac{7}{15} - \frac{3}{x^2}}$

14. $\dfrac{1 + \frac{1}{x}}{x^3}$

15. $\dfrac{\frac{1}{3} - \frac{5}{9}}{\frac{5}{12} - \frac{1}{6}}$

16. $\dfrac{\frac{2rx}{y}}{\frac{r^2 x^2}{3y}}$

17. $\dfrac{\frac{2}{x} - xy}{\frac{2}{xy^2}}$

18. $\dfrac{2 - \frac{1}{x}}{2 + \frac{1}{x}}$

19. $\dfrac{\frac{1}{x + 1} - 1}{\frac{1}{x + 1}}$

20. $\dfrac{\frac{n}{m^2 - 25}}{\frac{n}{m + 5}}$

21. $\dfrac{\frac{3x + 9}{5}}{\frac{x + 3}{15}}$

22. $\dfrac{\frac{1}{n + 4}}{1 - \frac{1}{n + 4}}$

23. $\dfrac{\frac{1}{x} - \frac{1}{y}}{\frac{1}{xy}}$

24. $\dfrac{\frac{1}{x^2} + \frac{1}{y^2}}{\frac{2}{xy}}$

B   Evaluate $\dfrac{\frac{1}{x} - \frac{1}{y}}{\frac{1}{x} + \frac{1}{y}}$ for the given values of **x** and **y**.

25. x = 1, y = 1

26. x = 2, y = 3

27. x = −2, y = 4

28. x = −1, y = −4

Simplify.

29. $\dfrac{\frac{1}{k - 1} - \frac{1}{k + 1}}{\frac{2}{k^2 - 1}}$

30. $\dfrac{\frac{1}{y^2 - 4}}{\frac{1}{y + 2} + \frac{1}{y - 2}}$

31. $\dfrac{\frac{x}{x^2 + 10x + 25}}{1 - \frac{1}{x + 5}}$

32. $\dfrac{1 - \frac{2xy}{x^2 + y^2}}{\frac{2x^2}{x^2 + y^2} - 1}$

33. $\dfrac{\frac{1}{n + 2} - \frac{1}{n - 3}}{1 + \frac{1}{n^2 - n - 6}}$

34. $\dfrac{2 - \frac{7}{y^2 - 1}}{\frac{2}{y - 1} - \frac{1}{y + 1}}$

35. $\dfrac{\dfrac{1}{2x^2 - 5x - 3} - \dfrac{1}{x - 3}}{2 - \dfrac{1}{2x + 1}}$

36. $\dfrac{x^2 + x + 1 - \dfrac{7}{x - 1}}{\dfrac{1}{x - 1} - 1}$

37. $\dfrac{\dfrac{2x}{x - 1} - \dfrac{2y}{y + 3}}{\dfrac{3x + y}{xy - y + 3x - 3}}$

C

38. $1 + \dfrac{1}{1 + \dfrac{1}{1 + \dfrac{1}{2}}}$

39. $1 + \dfrac{1}{1 + \dfrac{1}{1 + \dfrac{1}{y}}}$

40. $2 + \dfrac{2}{2 - \dfrac{2}{2 + \dfrac{2}{n}}}$

Evaluate $1 - \dfrac{1}{1 - \dfrac{1}{1 - \dfrac{1}{x}}}$ for the given values of **x**.

41. $x = 2$ **42.** $x = 3$ **43.** $x = -1$ **44.** $x = -4$

*45. In computing the course average for a certain class, the average of three tests counts as much as the final exam. If t_1, t_2, and t_3 are the three test scores, and f is the final exam grade, show that the course average is given by $\dfrac{t_1 + t_2 + t_3 + 3f}{6}$.

CHECKPOINT

Simplify.

1. $\dfrac{36}{81}$

2. $\dfrac{16x^2 y}{64xy}$

3. $\dfrac{x - 4}{3x - 12}$

4. $\dfrac{x^2 - 36}{x^2 - x - 42}$

Evaluate $\dfrac{x - 5}{x^2 - 25}$, if possible, for the given values of **x**.

5. $x = 0$ **6.** $x = 5$ **7.** $x = -5$ **8.** $x = 25$

Perform the indicated operation, and simplify.

9. $\dfrac{5}{8} \cdot \dfrac{6}{25}$

10. $\dfrac{3}{4} \div \dfrac{5}{6}$

11. $\dfrac{5}{8} + \dfrac{3}{8}$

12. $\dfrac{3}{4} - \dfrac{5}{6}$

13. $\dfrac{14a^2}{15b^3} \cdot \dfrac{3b^5}{2a^6}$

14. $\dfrac{9xy}{11a^2 b} \div \dfrac{4x^3}{33b^2}$

15. $\dfrac{5}{4x} + \dfrac{3}{4x}$

16. $\dfrac{3}{x + 2} - \dfrac{5}{x - 3}$

17. $\dfrac{3}{x} + \dfrac{5}{y}$

18. $\dfrac{4x}{x^2 - 1} \cdot \dfrac{x + 1}{12}$

19. $\dfrac{x^2}{x^2 - x} \div \dfrac{3x}{4}$

20. $\dfrac{x - 2}{x + 3} - \dfrac{x + 2}{x - 3}$

Simplify.

21. $\dfrac{6}{\dfrac{5}{8} - \dfrac{7}{12}}$

22. $\dfrac{3 + \dfrac{2}{x}}{x^4}$

23. $\dfrac{a^{\frac{1}{2}} - b^{\frac{1}{2}}}{\dfrac{3}{a} - \dfrac{3}{b}}$

24. $\dfrac{\dfrac{4}{x^2 - 4}}{\dfrac{3}{x^2 + x - 2}}$

5-5 Fractional Equations

OBJECTIVES

To solve equations containing one or more rational expressions.
To solve problems involving such equations.

A **fractional equation** contains one or more rational expressions. To solve such an equation, we begin by multiplying each side by the least common denominator of all rational expressions shown.

EXAMPLE 1 Solve $\dfrac{2}{x + 1} - \dfrac{3}{2x} = \dfrac{1}{10x}$.

$$\frac{2}{x + 1} - \frac{3}{2x} = \frac{1}{10x}$$

$$10x(x + 1)\left(\frac{2}{x + 1}\right) - 10x(x + 1)\left(\frac{3}{2x}\right) = 10x(x + 1)\left(\frac{1}{10x}\right)$$

$$10x(2) - 5(x + 1)(3) = (x + 1)(1)$$

$$20x - 15x - 15 = x + 1$$

$$4x = 16$$

$$x = 4$$

Check

$$\frac{2}{4 + 1} - \frac{3}{2(4)} \stackrel{?}{=} \frac{1}{10(4)}$$

$$\frac{2}{5} - \frac{3}{8} \stackrel{?}{=} \frac{1}{40}$$

$$\frac{1}{40} = \frac{1}{40} \quad ✔$$

Sometimes one or more of the denominators must be factored in order to find the LCD.

EXAMPLE 2 Solve $\dfrac{x - 3}{3x} = \dfrac{1}{x + 3} + \dfrac{1}{3x^2 + 9x}$.

$$\frac{x - 3}{3x} = \frac{1}{x + 3} + \frac{1}{3x^2 + 9x}$$

$$\frac{x - 3}{3x} = \frac{1}{x + 3} + \frac{1}{3x(x + 3)} \qquad \begin{array}{l}\text{Factor } 3x^2 + 9x.\\ \quad\text{The LCD is } 3x(x + 3).\end{array}$$

$$3x(x + 3)\left(\frac{x - 3}{3x}\right) = 3x(x + 3)\left(\frac{1}{x + 3}\right) + 3x(x + 3)\left(\frac{1}{3x(x + 3)}\right)$$

$$(x + 3)(x - 3) = 3x + 1$$

$$x^2 - 3x - 10 = 0$$

$$(x + 2)(x - 5) = 0$$

$$x + 2 = 0 \quad \text{or} \quad x - 5 = 0$$

$$x = -2 \qquad\qquad x = 5$$

Check to show that both -2 and 5 are solutions.

Sometimes multiplication by the LCD produces an equation with more roots than the original equation. Therefore, it is essential to check each solution *in the original equation*.

EXAMPLE 3 Solve $\dfrac{x-1}{x-5} - \dfrac{3}{x+1} = \dfrac{4}{x-5}$.

$$\frac{x-1}{x-5} - \frac{3}{x+1} = \frac{4}{x-5}$$

$$(x-5)(x+1)\left(\frac{x-1}{x-5}\right) - (x-5)(x+1)\left(\frac{3}{x+1}\right) = (x-5)(x+1)\left(\frac{4}{x-5}\right)$$

$$(x+1)(x-1) - 3(x-5) = 4(x+1)$$
$$x^2 - 1 - 3x + 15 = 4x + 4$$
$$x^2 - 7x + 10 = 0$$
$$(x-5)(x-2) = 0$$
$$x - 5 = 0 \quad \text{or} \quad x - 2 = 0$$
$$x = 5 \qquad\qquad x = 2$$

When you check the two possible roots, one of them fails to satisfy the original equation.

Check   When $x = 5$:

$$\frac{5-1}{5-5} - \frac{3}{5+1} \overset{?}{=} \frac{4}{5-5}$$

$$\frac{4}{0} - \frac{3}{6} \overset{?}{=} \frac{4}{0}$$

$\dfrac{4}{0}$ is not defined, so

5 is not a solution.
The only solution to the equation is 2.

When $x = 2$:

$$\frac{2-1}{2-5} - \frac{3}{2+1} \overset{?}{=} \frac{4}{2-5}$$

$$-\frac{1}{3} - \frac{3}{3} \overset{?}{=} -\frac{4}{3}$$

$$-\frac{4}{3} = -\frac{4}{3} \checkmark$$

EXAMPLE 4   The denominator of a fraction is 5 more than the numerator. If the numerator is decreased by 1, the resulting fraction is equal to $\frac{1}{2}$. Find the fraction.

Strategy: Write and solve an equation.

Use a variable.

Let n represent the numerator. $\qquad n$

The denominator is 5 more than the numerator. $\qquad n + 5$

Write the original fraction. $\qquad \dfrac{n}{n+5}$

Write the fraction with the numerator decreased by 1. $\qquad \dfrac{n-1}{n+5}$

Write an equation.

If the numerator is decreased by 1, the resulting fraction is equal to $\frac{1}{2}$. $\qquad \dfrac{n-1}{n+5} = \dfrac{1}{2}$

Find the solution.

$$\frac{n - 1}{n + 5} = \frac{1}{2}$$

$$2(n + 5)\left(\frac{n - 1}{n + 5}\right) = 2(n + 5)\left(\frac{1}{2}\right) \qquad \text{Multiply each side by the LCD, } 2(n + 5).$$

$$2n - 2 = n + 5$$

$$n = 7$$

If the numerator is 7, then the denominator must be 5 more than 7, or 12. To check, note that if the numerator 7 is decreased by 1, the resulting fraction is $\frac{7 - 1}{12} = \frac{6}{12} = \frac{1}{2}$. ✔

Answer the question.

The fraction is $\frac{7}{12}$.

CLASS EXERCISES

Name the LCD by which you would multiply each side of the equation.
Do not solve.

1. $\frac{3}{4}x = \frac{1}{4}$

2. $\frac{5}{9} - \frac{z}{3} = 1$

3. $\frac{5n}{12} - \frac{1}{6} = \frac{2}{3}$

4. $\frac{2}{p} = \frac{4}{7}$

5. $\frac{3}{4t} = \frac{5}{12}$

6. $\frac{5}{x - 1} = \frac{1}{2}$

7. $\frac{1}{s} - \frac{3}{5s} = \frac{2}{15}$

8. $\frac{1}{x + 3} = 3 - \frac{2}{x - 1}$

9. $\frac{3}{x} = \frac{x}{6} + \frac{1 - x}{3x(x + 2)}$

10. $\frac{1}{x^2 - 1} = \frac{3}{x + 1}$

11. $\frac{1}{x} - \frac{1}{x^2 + x} = \frac{1}{x + 1}$

12. $\frac{4}{x^2 - x - 6} = \frac{1}{x - 3}$

EXERCISES

A   *Solve and check. Write **no solution** where appropriate.*

1. $\frac{x - 2}{x} = \frac{3}{4}$

2. $\frac{y - 1}{5} + 2 = \frac{2y - 3}{3}$

3. $\frac{x + 1}{x - 3} = \frac{3}{5}$

4. $\frac{8}{x + 1} = \frac{12}{3}$

5. $\frac{n - 1}{2} + 2 = \frac{1 - 2n}{3}$

6. $\frac{3}{x - 8} + 2 = \frac{5}{x}$

7. $\frac{1}{x + 1} + \frac{1}{x} = \frac{x + 2}{2x}$

8. $\frac{1}{x} + \frac{1}{x^2} = \frac{3}{4}$

9. $\frac{x - 1}{2x + 1} = \frac{5x + 3}{6x^2 + 3x}$

10. $\frac{5 - x}{2x} + \frac{4}{x - 5} = \frac{2x - 1}{x}$

11. $\frac{3}{y + 1} + \frac{15}{y^2 - 1} = \frac{4}{y - 1}$

12. $\frac{5}{x^2 - 9} = \frac{3}{x + 3} - \frac{2}{x - 3}$

13. $\frac{t}{9} - \frac{4}{2t + 3} = 1$

14. $\dfrac{1}{x-2} = \dfrac{3}{x} + \dfrac{2}{x^2-2x}$

15. $\dfrac{2}{2s+1} + \dfrac{1}{2s^2+s} = -\dfrac{1}{s}$

B

16. $\dfrac{2n}{4n-1} + \dfrac{n}{4n+1} = \dfrac{1}{16n^2-1} + \dfrac{1}{2}$

17. $\dfrac{3}{2y} - \dfrac{6}{2y+y^2} = \dfrac{1}{y+2}$

18. $\dfrac{2}{x+2} - \dfrac{6}{x^2+5x+6} = \dfrac{5}{(x+2)^2}$

19. $\dfrac{1}{n-5} - \dfrac{2n}{n^2-8n+15} = \dfrac{n}{n-3}$

20. $\dfrac{2}{y+4} = \dfrac{1}{y-2} - \dfrac{2y-1}{y^2+2y-8}$

21. $\dfrac{3}{x-2} - \dfrac{4}{x-3} + \dfrac{6}{x^2-5x+6} = 0$

22. $\dfrac{4n-3}{n-1} - n = \dfrac{n}{n-1}$

23. $\dfrac{x+3}{3-x} = \dfrac{1-5x}{x+3} - \dfrac{3x+1}{x^2-9}$

24. $\dfrac{x^2}{x^2-1} + \dfrac{1}{x+1} = \dfrac{1}{x-1} + \dfrac{2x^2-3}{x^2-1}$

25. $\dfrac{x}{x+5} + \dfrac{5x-10}{6} = \dfrac{2x^2-4x}{x+5}$

26. The numerator of a fraction is 4 less than twice the denominator. If 5 is added to the denominator, the resulting fraction is equal to 1. Find the original fraction.

27. Two positive integers differ by 9, and their reciprocals differ by $\frac{1}{4}$. Find the integers.

28. A student had grades of 79, 83, and 92 on three tests. What grade must she get on the fourth test in order to achieve an average of 87?

29. A 44-foot rope is cut into two pieces. The longer piece is $4\frac{1}{4}$ times the length of the shorter piece. Find the length of each piece.

C

Solve and check.

30. $\dfrac{6}{x^3+2x^2-x-2} + \dfrac{3}{x^2-1} = \dfrac{6}{x+2}$

31. $\dfrac{3}{x^4-16} + \dfrac{1}{x^2+4} = \dfrac{1}{3} + \dfrac{1}{x^2-4}$

32. For what value of a does the equation $\frac{1}{x} + \frac{1}{a} = \frac{2}{x}$ have the solution $x = \frac{1}{2}$?

33. For what value of b does the equation $2x + 1 = \frac{3+x}{b}$ have the solution $x = \frac{2}{3}$?

34. For what value of c does the equation $\frac{3}{x+1} + \frac{3}{x-1} = c$ have the solution $x = -\frac{1}{2}$? Find another solution for that equation.

*35. Use the following epitaph to find the final age of Diophantus, a Greek mathematician who lived in the third century A.D. "Diophantus passed one sixth of his life in childhood, one twelfth in youth, and one seventh more as a bachelor. Five years after his marriage was born a son who died four years before his father at half his father's final age."

5-6　Problem Solving: Ratio and Proportion

OBJECTIVES

To solve proportions.
To solve problems using proportions.

A manufacturer of a lawn mower with a two-cycle engine specifies that the fuel mixture should be 1 ounce of oil to every 32 ounces of gasoline. That is, the **ratio** of oil to gasoline is 1 ounce to 32 ounces, which may be written 1 : 32, or $\frac{1}{32}$.

Since the ratio of oil to gas is $\frac{1}{32}$, 2 ounces of oil are needed for 64 ounces of gas. This may be written as the *proportion* $\frac{2}{64} = \frac{1}{32}$, which is read *2 is to 64 as 1 is to 32.*

A **proportion** is an equation stating that two ratios are equal. In general, if both sides of a proportion $\frac{a}{b} = \frac{c}{d}$ are multiplied by bd, we obtain $ad = bc$.

Proportion Rule

For any real numbers a, b, c, and d, with $b \neq 0$ and $d \neq 0$,

$$\text{if } \frac{a}{b} = \frac{c}{d}, \text{ then } ad = bc.$$

EXAMPLE 1　How much oil must be mixed with 80 ounces of gasoline for the two-cycle engine described above?

Strategy:
Write and solve a proportion.

Use a variable.
　Let x represent the number of ounces of oil needed.

Write a proportion.

$$\begin{array}{c} \text{oil} \\ \text{gas} \end{array} \quad \frac{x}{80} = \frac{1}{32}$$

Find the solution.

$$32x = 80(1) \qquad \frac{x}{80} \bowtie \frac{1}{32}$$
$$x = 2\frac{1}{2}$$

Check to see that the ratio of $2\frac{1}{2}$ ounces of oil to 80 ounces of gas is equal to $\frac{1}{32}$.

$$\frac{2\frac{1}{2}}{80} = \frac{\frac{5}{2}}{80} = \frac{5}{160} = \frac{1}{32} ✔$$

Answer the question.
　$2\frac{1}{2}$ ounces of oil are needed.

EXAMPLE 2   The ratio of girls to boys in a mathematics class is 4 : 3. If there are 35 students, how many girls are there?

Use a variable.   Let x represent the number of girls.
Then $35 - x$ represents the number of boys.

Write a proportion.
girls $\dfrac{x}{35 - x} = \dfrac{4}{3}$
boys

Find the solution.
$$3x = 4(35 - x)$$
$$7x = 140$$
$$x = 20$$

Check to see that the ratio of 20 girls to $(35 - 20)$ boys equals $\frac{4}{3}$. $\dfrac{20}{35 - 20} = \dfrac{20}{15} = \dfrac{4}{3}$ ✔

Answer the question.   There are 20 girls in the class.

CLASS EXERCISES

Complete the proportion.

1. $\dfrac{5}{15} = \dfrac{?}{3}$ **2.** $\dfrac{2}{5} = \dfrac{8}{?}$ **3.** $\dfrac{?}{8} = \dfrac{3}{4}$ **4.** $\dfrac{24}{?} = \dfrac{8}{9}$

Use the proportion rule to solve for **x**.

5. $\dfrac{2}{3x} = \dfrac{4}{9}$ **6.** $\dfrac{4}{6} = \dfrac{7x}{21}$ **7.** $\dfrac{9}{\frac{1}{3}x} = \dfrac{6}{2}$ **8.** $\dfrac{2}{x} = \dfrac{x}{2}$

EXERCISES

A   Solve the proportion.

1. $\dfrac{x}{60} = \dfrac{5}{12}$ **2.** $\dfrac{5}{4} = \dfrac{20}{x}$ **3.** $\dfrac{t + 2}{4} = \dfrac{3}{2}$

4. $\dfrac{2}{3x - 2} = \dfrac{3}{x + 11}$ **5.** $\dfrac{3}{r} = \dfrac{6 - r}{3}$ **6.** $\dfrac{2p + 5}{4} = \dfrac{4p + 3}{3}$

7. $\dfrac{2y}{3} = \dfrac{6}{y}$ **8.** $\dfrac{3}{2y + 1} = \dfrac{y}{2 - y}$ **9.** $\dfrac{m - 4}{1} = \dfrac{2}{m - 3}$

10. $\dfrac{4}{\frac{1}{2}x} = \dfrac{3}{x - 5}$ **11.** $\dfrac{\frac{2}{3}x}{4} = \dfrac{2 - x}{7}$ **12.** $\dfrac{\frac{1}{4}x - 2}{4} = \dfrac{\frac{2}{3}x - 7}{9}$

13. $\dfrac{1}{\frac{1}{2}x} = \dfrac{x + 2}{x^2}$ **14.** $\dfrac{\frac{3}{4}x}{x - 6} = \dfrac{x}{x - 4}$ **15.** $\dfrac{\frac{2}{3}x}{2x + 3} = \dfrac{\frac{1}{3}x + 1}{3x}$

16. The sum of two numbers is 22. The ratio of the larger to the smaller is 7 : 4. Find the numbers.

17. An 18-meter board is to be cut into two parts so that the ratio of the lengths of the parts is 4 : 5. How long is each part?

B

18. A gear setting on Ellen's bicycle produces 4 revolutions of the rear wheel for every $2\frac{1}{2}$ turns of the pedals. How many times must she turn the pedals so that the rear wheel makes 1000 revolutions?

19. The scale on the blueprints of a house indicates that 2 centimeters represent 5 meters. If the width of the house on the blueprint is 9.2 centimeters, how wide is the house?

20. A high school has 3685 students. The ratio of the number of freshmen to the number of students in the upper classes is 3 : 8. How many students are there in the upper classes?

21. The ratio of the area of a square (in square meters) to its perimeter (in meters) is 3 : 8. Find the length of a side of the square.

22. The ratio of the volume V of a sphere to its radius r is $4A : 3$, where A is the area of a circle of radius r. Find the volume of a sphere of radius 5 centimeters. Leave the answer in terms of π.

Assume that the proportion $\frac{a}{b} = \frac{c}{d}$ is true, and no variable equals zero. Which of the following proportions must also be true?

23. $\dfrac{a}{c} = \dfrac{b}{d}$ **24.** $\dfrac{b}{a} = \dfrac{c}{a}$ **25.** $\dfrac{a + c}{c} = \dfrac{b + d}{d}$

26. $\dfrac{a}{c - a} = \dfrac{b}{d - b}$ **27.** $\dfrac{2a}{c} = \dfrac{b}{2d}$ **28.** $\dfrac{c - 2a}{a} = \dfrac{d - 2b}{b}$

C

*If $\frac{a}{x} = \frac{x}{b}$, we say that x is the **mean proportional** between a and b. In the figure below, a right triangle is inscribed in a semicircle, and h is the mean proportional between a and b.*

29. If $a = 2$ and the radius of the semicircle is 4, find h. Leave the answer in radical form.

30. Show that c is the mean proportional between a and $a + b$. **Hint:** Recall facts about similar triangles, or use the Pythagorean theorem.

31. Show that d is the mean proportional between b and $a + b$.

*32. The ratio of the width to the length of a rectangular piece of cardboard is $\frac{3}{5}$. The cardboard is cut into two pieces, one square and the other rectangular. If the area of the square piece is 12 square inches greater than that of the smaller rectangular piece, find the dimensions of the original rectangular piece of cardboard.

Mark leaves at 7:00 A.M. driving at a constant speed of 40 miles per hour. Fran leaves from the same place at 7:30 A.M. and drives down the same road at a constant speed of 55 miles per hour. When and where will Fran pass Mark?

Try some values.

Find how far each person has traveled at each of these times.

| 8:00 A.M. | 8:30 A.M. | 9:00 A.M. |

Use your results to make reasonable estimates of the answers.

Draw a graph.

Try to improve your estimate by drawing two lines. Draw one through the points for Mark and draw the other through the points for Fran.

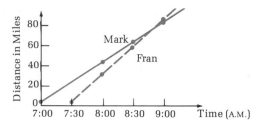

Estimate the answers from the graph.

Use the lines to estimate the time Fran and Mark meet and the distance they have traveled at that time.

Consider alternative solutions.

Use the formula $d = rt$.

distance = rate × time

For Mark: $d_1 = 40t$

For Fran: $d_2 = 55\left(t - \dfrac{1}{2}\right)$

The distances traveled are the same when they meet, so $d_1 = d_2$. Find the time they meet and the distance they have traveled at that time. Compare the answers with your estimates from the graph.

Now try these.

Use a graph to estimate the answers. Assume the same starting point, same path, and constant speeds. Then solve each problem, using an equation.

1. Kris starts out on her bicycle at 10:00 A.M. Kerry starts out at 11:00 A.M. If Kris rides at 8 miles per hour and Kerry at 10 miles per hour, when and where will they meet?

2. Janine leaves at 6:00 A.M. and jogs at a rate of 4 miles per hour. Jim jogs at a rate of 6 miles per hour and meets Janine at 6:30 A.M. When did he leave the starting point?

5-7 Problem Solving: Rate Problems

OBJECTIVE

To solve a variety of rate problems and work problems using proportions and other fractional equations.

A jogger running at an average rate of 7 miles per hour can cover 14 miles in 2 hours.

$14 = 7 \times 2$

$d = r \times t$ distance = rate × time
In this formula, *rate* means average rate.

EXAMPLE 1

One jogger ran 16 miles in the same time that another jogger ran 12 miles. If the rate of the faster jogger was 2 miles per hour greater than that of the slower one, find the rate of each.

Strategy: Make a table. Write and solve a proportion.

Use a variable.

Let x represent the rate of the slower jogger, in miles per hour.
Then x + 2 represents the rate of the faster jogger.
It is helpful to arrange the facts in a table.

	distance *d*	rate *r*	time $t = \dfrac{d}{r}$
Faster jogger	16	x + 2	$\dfrac{16}{x + 2}$
Slower jogger	12	x	$\dfrac{12}{x}$

Write a proportion.

Each jogger ran the same amount of time, so set the expressions in the right hand column equal.

$$\frac{16}{x + 2} = \frac{12}{x}$$

Find the solution.

$$16x = 12(x + 2)$$
$$4x = 24$$
$$x = 6$$
$$x + 2 = 8$$

Check

At 6 miles per hour, the slower jogger runs 12 miles in 2 hours $\left(t = \dfrac{d}{r} = \dfrac{12}{6} = 2\right)$. At 8 miles per hour, the faster jogger runs 16 miles in the same amount of time $(d = rt = 8 \times 2 = 16)$.

Answer the question.

The rates are 6 miles per hour and 8 miles per hour.

Fractional equations can be used to solve certain types of work problems. Suppose it takes you 6 hours to complete a job while working at a constant rate. Then you will do $\frac{1}{6}$ of the job in 1 hour, $\frac{2}{6}$ of the job in 2 hours, and so forth. Fractions are used to represent *parts of a job done in a given length of time.*

EXAMPLE 2

When Earl and his younger brother Roy work together, they can clean and polish the family car in 2 hours. Working alone, Earl can do the job in 3 hours. How long would it take Roy to do the job alone?

Use a variable.

Let t be the time it takes Roy to do the job alone.

Then he can do $\frac{1}{t}$ of the job in 1 hour.

Earl can do the job in 3 hours, so he can do $\frac{1}{3}$ of the job in 1 hour.

They can do the job together in 2 hours, so they can do $\frac{1}{2}$ of the job in 1 hour.

Write an equation.

$$\frac{1}{t} + \frac{1}{3} = \frac{1}{2}$$

The sum of the parts they can do alone in 1 hour equals the part they can do together in 1 hour.

$$6t\left(\frac{1}{t}\right) + 6t\left(\frac{1}{3}\right) = 6t\left(\frac{1}{2}\right)$$

Multiply each side by the LCD, $6t$.

$$6 + 2t = 3t$$
$$6 = t$$

Check to see that if it takes Roy 6 hours to do the job alone, he can do $\frac{2}{6} = \frac{1}{3}$ in 2 hours. Earl can do $\frac{2}{3}$ of the job in 2 hours. Since $\frac{1}{3} + \frac{2}{3} = 1$, the entire job can be completed in 2 hours.

Answer the question. It would take Roy 6 hours to do the job, working alone.

CLASS EXERCISES

1. A car travels 200 miles in 4 hours. What is the average rate in miles per hour?

2. A car travels 900 miles at an average rate of 45 miles per hour. How long does it take?

3. A car travels 3 hours at an average rate of 40 miles per hour. How far does it go?

4. It takes a machine 4 hours to produce 1000 items. How many can it produce in 1 hour?

EXERCISES

A

1. A train travels 234 miles at an average rate of 72 miles per hour. How long does it take to make this trip?

2. It takes an airplane 2 hours 30 minutes to travel 600 miles. What is its average rate?

3. If it takes a machine 7 hours to produce 560 items, how many items are produced in 1 hour?

4. It takes Robert 6 hours to complete a job. If David works twice as fast, what part of the job can he do alone in 1 hour?

5. Maria rides her bicycle 10 miles in the same amount of time that Tina walks 3 miles. If Maria travels 7 miles per hour faster than Tina, what is the rate of each?

6. An airplane flies 1050 miles in the same amount of time that a car goes 150 miles. If the plane is going 50 miles per hour more than 6 times the speed of the car, find the rate of each.

7. Jim walks 1 kilometer to the bus stop. He then rides the bus for 5 kilometers, at 10 times the rate at which he walks. If the total trip takes 15 minutes, how fast does he walk? What is the rate of the bus?

8. The older of two brothers can clean the attic in 3 hours; the younger brother needs 6 hours to do the job. How long does it take them to clean the attic if they work together?

B

9. Two trains leave the same station at the same time and travel in opposite directions. The faster train goes 80 miles per hour, and the slower train travels $\frac{4}{5}$ as fast. When will the trains be 504 miles apart?

10. A boat can travel 34 kilometers downstream in the same amount of time that it takes it to go 26 kilometers upstream. If the rate of the current is 8 kilometers per hour, what is the speed of the boat in still water?

    Hint: Let $r + 8$ represent the downstream rate of the boat, and $r - 8$ the upstream rate, relative to the shore.

11. One gardener can mow a lawn twice as fast as another. Working together they can get the job done in 1 hour 20 minutes. How long would it take each gardener to do the job working alone?

12. Three water pipes of the same diameter can fill a tank in 2 hours. How long would it take one pipe to fill the tank, if the other two pipes were closed?

C

13. A pipe can fill a water tank in 8 hours. There is a leak in the tank that would empty the full tank in 2 days. If the tank is empty and the pipe is open, how long will it take to fill the tank?

14. Working together, a teacher, a junior, and a sophomore need 3 hours to solve a set of mathematics problems. The teacher, working alone, can do the job 3 times as fast as the sophomore and $1\frac{1}{2}$ times as fast as the junior. How long does it take each of them to do the work alone?

RATIONAL EXPRESSIONS

5-8 Variation

OBJECTIVES

OBJECTIVES _____

To write equations showing direct and inverse variation.
To solve problems involving variation.

Suppose cheddar cheese is selling for $3 per pound. Then x pounds of the cheese will cost y dollars, where $y = 3x$. The cost varies with the amount of cheese you buy. In fact, y increases 3 times as fast as x. We say that **y varies directly as x**, and that 3 is the **constant of variation**.

> **Direct Variation**
>
> **y varies directly as x if $y = kx$, with $k \neq 0$.**

When y is equal to kx, we also say that y is **directly proportional to x**, and k is the **constant of proportionality**. To justify this terminology, note that $y = kx$ is equivalent to $\frac{y}{x} = k$. Therefore, if the ordered pairs (x_1, y_1) and (x_2, y_2) satisfy $y = kx$, then $\frac{y_1}{x_1} = k$ and $\frac{y_2}{x_2} = k$. This results in the proportion

$$\frac{y_1}{x_1} = \frac{y_2}{x_2}$$

EXAMPLE 1   y varies directly as x, and $y = 6$ when $x = 5$. Find y when $x = 15$.

Method I   First find the constant of variation, using an equation of the form $y = kx$.

$6 = k(5)$ $y = 6$ when $x = 5$.

$\dfrac{6}{5} = k$

The equation relating x and y is $y = \frac{6}{5}x$.
Substitute 15 for x and solve for y.

$y = \dfrac{6}{5}(15) = 18$

Method II   Since it is not necessary here to find the value of k, a proportion can be used.

$\dfrac{y}{15} = \dfrac{6}{5}$ Let $y_1 = y$, $x_1 = 15$, $y_2 = 6$, $x_2 = 5$.

$5y = 90$

$y = 18$

An equation of the form $y = \frac{k}{x}$ expresses another type of variation. In this case, we say that x and y **vary inversely,** and k is the *constant of variation.*

Inverse Variation

y varies inversely as x if $y = \dfrac{k}{x}$, with $k \neq 0$.

We also say that y is **inversely proportional to** x, and k is the *constant of proportionality.* If the ordered pairs (x_1, y_1) and (x_2, y_2) satisfy $y = \frac{k}{x}$, then $x_1 y_1 = k$ and $x_2 y_2 = k$, so that

$$x_1 y_1 = x_2 y_2$$

EXAMPLE 2   x and y vary inversely, and $y = 7\frac{1}{2}$ when $x = 4$. Find y when $x = 12$.

Method I   First find the constant of variation, using an equation of the form $y = \frac{k}{x}$.

$$7\frac{1}{2} = \frac{k}{4} \qquad y = 7\frac{1}{2} \text{ when } x = 4.$$

$$30 = k$$

The equation relating x and y is $y = \frac{30}{x}$.
Substitute 12 for x and solve for y.

$$y = \frac{30}{12} = 2\frac{1}{2}$$

Method II   Use an equation of the form $x_1 y_1 = x_2 y_2$.

$$12y = 4\left(7\frac{1}{2}\right) \qquad \text{Let } x_1 = 12,\ y_1 = y,\ x_2 = 4,\ y_2 = 7\frac{1}{2}.$$

$$12y = 30$$

$$y = 2\frac{1}{2}$$

Many problems in mathematics and science involve direct or inverse variation. Two such problems are illustrated in the following examples.

EXAMPLE 3   According to *Hooke's law,* the force F required to stretch a spring x units beyond its natural length varies directly as x. A force of 30 pounds stretches a certain spring 5 inches. Find how far the spring is stretched by a 50-pound weight.

Strategy: Substitute the three known values in a proportion. Solve for the fourth value.

$$\frac{F_1}{x_1} = \frac{F_2}{x_2}$$

$$\frac{30}{5} = \frac{50}{x}$$

$$30x = 250$$

$$x = 8\frac{1}{3}$$ The spring is stretched $8\frac{1}{3}$ inches.

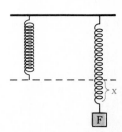

EXAMPLE 4

The pressure P of a compressed gas is inversely proportional to its volume V, according to *Boyle's law*. A pressure of 40 pounds per square inch is created by 600 cubic inches of a certain gas. Find an equation that relates P and V. Then find the pressure when the gas is compressed to 200 cubic inches.

Strategy: Use $P = \dfrac{k}{V}$ to find the constant of variation. Use $V = 200$ to find P.

$$P = \frac{k}{V}$$

$$40 = \frac{k}{600} \qquad P = 40 \text{ when } V = 600.$$

$$24{,}000 = k$$

An equation relating P and V is $P = \dfrac{24{,}000}{V}$.

Then, for $V = 200$: $P = \dfrac{k}{V} = \dfrac{24{,}000}{200} = 120$

The pressure is 120 pounds per square inch.

CLASS EXERCISES

y varies directly as x. Write an equation that relates x and y

1. if y = 8 when x = 4.

2. if y = 5 when x = 20.

3. if y = 5 when x = 2.

4. if y = 6 when x = 10.

x and y vary inversely. Write an equation that relates x and y

5. if y = 8 when x = 4.

6. if y = 5 when x = 20.

7. if y = 5 when x = 2.

8. if y = 6 when x = 10.

9. Assume y is directly proportional to x, and y = 4 when x = 8. Use a proportion to find the value of y when x = 30.

10. Assume y is inversely proportional to x, and y = 6 when x = 4. Use an equation of the form $x_1 y_1 = x_2 y_2$ to find y when x = 3.

EXERCISES

A *y varies directly as x. Write an equation that relates x and y*

1. if y = 18 when x = 3.

2. if y = 4 when x = 10.

3. if y = 4 when x = 3.

4. if y = 4 when $x = \dfrac{1}{2}$.

x and y vary inversely. Write an equation that relates x and y

5. if y = 1 when x = 2.

6. if y = 4 when x = 4.

7. if y = 27 when $x = \dfrac{1}{3}$.

8. if $y = \dfrac{9}{2}$ when $x = \dfrac{4}{3}$.

If y varies directly as x, and y = 24 when x = 3, find

9. the constant of variation.

10. y, when x = 2.

*If **y** is directly proportional to **x**, and **y** = 7 when **x** = $\frac{1}{2}$, find*

11. the constant of proportionality. **12.** x, when y = 21.

*If **x** and **y** vary inversely, and **y** = 5 when **x** = 2, find*

13. the constant of variation. **14.** y, when x = 5.

*If **y** is inversely proportional to **x**, and **y** = 45 when **x** = $\frac{1}{3}$, find*

15. the constant of proportionality. **16.** x, when y = 30.

17. y is directly proportional to x, and y = 4 when x = 18. Use a proportion to find y when x = 3.

18. y varies directly as x, and y = 1 when x = 4. Use a proportion to find y when x = 18.

19. x and y vary inversely, and y = 4 when x = 7. Use an equation of the form $x_1y_1 = x_2y_2$ to find x when y = 2.

20. x and y are inversely proportional, and y = $\frac{4}{3}$ when x = 48. Use an equation of the form $x_1y_1 = x_2y_2$. Find x when y = $\frac{1}{2}$.

B

21. The circumference C of a circle varies directly as the radius r. If C = 4π when r = 2, find C when r = 8. Give the answer in terms of π.

22. In a rectangle of constant area, the length l is inversely proportional to the width w. If l = 6 when w = 4, find the length when w = $1\frac{1}{2}$.

23. Use Hooke's law to find the force required to stretch a spring 10 inches beyond its natural length if a force of 2.4 pounds is required to stretch it 8 inches.

24. Use Hooke's law to find how many pounds of force are needed to stretch a spring 15 inches if it takes 18 pounds to stretch it $13\frac{1}{2}$ inches.

25. A pressure of 20 pounds per square inch is exerted by 400 cubic inches of a certain gas. Use Boyle's law to find the pressure of the gas when it is compressed to a volume of 100 cubic inches.

26. For the gas described in Exercise 25, what is the volume when the pressure is 4 pounds per square inch?

*If **z** = $\frac{kx}{y}$, where k ≠ 0, we say that **z** **varies directly as x and inversely as y.***

27. z varies directly as x and inversely as y. If z = $\frac{2}{3}$ when x = 4 and y = 3, find z when x = 18 and y = 6. **Hint:** First find k.

28. z varies directly as x and inversely as y. If z = 6 when x = 1 and y = 3, find x when y = 2 and z = 9.

If $z = kxy$, where $k \neq 0$, we say that z varies jointly as x and y.

29. z varies jointly as x and y. If $z = 36$ when $x = 2$ and $y = 3$, find z when $x = 1$ and $y = \frac{1}{2}$.

30. z varies jointly as x and y. If $z = 45$ when $x = 9$ and $y = 15$, find y when $z = 60$ and $x = 40$.

C

31. z varies directly as x and inversely as the square of y. If $z = \frac{1}{3}$ when $x = 3$ and $y = 6$, find z when $x = 18$ and $y = 3$.

32. If w varies jointly as x and the square of y, and inversely as z, how does x vary with respect to y, w, and z?

Each of the equations $y = kx$ and $y = \frac{k}{x}$ defines y as a function of x.

33. Graph the function defined by $y = 3x$ for $-3 \leq x \leq 3$.

34. Graph the function defined by $y = \frac{12}{x}$ for $0 < x < 12$ and $-12 < x < 0$.

35. The volume V of a right circular cone varies jointly as the height h and the square of the radius r of the base. The volume is 120π cubic units when $h = 10$ and $r = 6$. Find V when $h = 6$ and $r = 8$. Give the answer in terms of π.

36. Neglecting air resistance, the distance S that an object falls from a height near the earth's surface is directly proportional to the square of the time t it has fallen. If the object falls 64 feet in 2 seconds, how far will it fall in 3 seconds?

37. If the object in Exercise 36 is dropped from a height of 1296 feet, how long will it take to hit the ground?

38. The illumination I from a light source varies inversely as the square of the distance d from the light source. If the illumination $I = 20$ foot-candles when $d = 4$ feet, find the illumination at a distance of 8 feet.

39. The volume V of a sphere varies directly as the cube of its radius r. If $V = 36\pi$ cubic inches when $r = 3$ inches, find the formula for V in terms of r.

CHECKPOINT

Solve and check.

1. $\dfrac{x + 3}{x} = \dfrac{5}{6}$

2. $\dfrac{2x - 1}{x + 1} - \dfrac{3}{x^2 + x} = 0$

3. $\dfrac{2}{x + 1} - \dfrac{3}{x - 1} = \dfrac{5}{x^2 - 1}$

4. The width w of a rectangle is inversely proportional to its length l. If $w = 6$ when $l = 4$, find the width when $l = 36$.

5-9 Zero and Negative Integral Exponents

OBJECTIVE

To combine and simplify expressions involving integral exponents.

In the work with exponents in Chapter 4, x^n was defined only for positive integers n. Now we extend the exponential concept to cases where n is zero or a negative integer. This is done in such a way that the basic rules for exponents are preserved.

First we show that if the rule $b^m b^n = b^{m+n}$ is to remain valid when $m = 0$, then b^0 must equal 1.

$$b^0 b^n = b^{0+n}$$
$$b^0 b^n = b^n$$
$$b^0 = \frac{b^n}{b^n} \qquad \text{Divide by } b^n. \text{ Assume } b \neq 0.$$
$$b^0 = 1$$

Similarly, if the rule is to remain valid when n is any positive or negative integer, then b^{-n} must be the reciprocal of b^n.

$$b^{-n} b^n = b^{-n+n}$$
$$b^{-n} b^n = b^0$$
$$b^{-n} b^n = 1$$
$$b^{-n} = \frac{1}{b^n} \qquad \text{Divide by } b^n. \text{ Assume } b \neq 0.$$

The definitions are stated formally below.

For any nonzero real number b and any integer n

$$b^0 = 1 \text{ and } b^{-n} = \frac{1}{b^n}$$

Expressions of the form 0^n, where n is not a positive number, are not defined. We will assume that when the base of a power is a variable, and the exponent is not positive, then the variable does not represent 0.

EXAMPLE 1   Simplify.

　　a. $(-3)^0 = 1$　　　**b.** $2^{-3} = \frac{1}{2^3} = \frac{1}{8}$　　　**c.** $\frac{1}{3^{-2}} = 3^2 = 9$

The product and power rules for exponents stated earlier are valid for any integral powers defined.

Product and Power Rules for Integral Exponents

If a and b are nonzero real numbers and m and n are integers, then

$$b^m b^n = b^{m+n} \qquad (b^m)^n = b^{mn} \qquad (ab)^m = a^m b^m$$

When a monomial is *simplifed*, it is written using a single positive exponent on each variable.

EXAMPLE 2 Simplify.

a. $x^{-3}(x^{-2})^2 = x^{-3}x^{-2\cdot2} = x^{-3}x^{-4} = x^{-3+(-4)} = x^{-7} = \dfrac{1}{x^7}$

b. $x^2(x^{-1}y^4)^2 = x^2(x^{-1})^2(y^4)^2 = x^2 x^{-2}y^8 = x^{2+(-2)}y^8 = x^0 y^8 = 1\cdot y^8 = y^8$

Two additional rules are useful when finding the quotient of powers or the power of a quotient. These rules are illustrated below, and then stated formally. The rules are valid for all integral exponents.

$$\frac{2^5}{2^2} = \frac{2\cdot2\cdot2\cdot2\cdot2}{2\cdot2} \qquad\qquad \left(\frac{3}{2}\right)^4 = \frac{3}{2}\cdot\frac{3}{2}\cdot\frac{3}{2}\cdot\frac{3}{2}$$

$$= \frac{2\cdot2\cdot2}{1} \qquad\qquad = \frac{3\cdot3\cdot3\cdot3}{2\cdot2\cdot2\cdot2}$$

$$= 2^3 \quad \text{Note that } \frac{2^5}{2^2} = 2^{5-2}. \qquad = \frac{3^4}{2^4} \quad \text{Note that } \left(\frac{3}{2}\right)^4 = \frac{3^4}{2^4}.$$

Quotient Rules for Integral Exponents

If a and b are nonzero real numbers and m and n are integers, then

$$\frac{b^m}{b^n} = b^{m-n} \qquad \left(\frac{a}{b}\right)^m = \frac{a^m}{b^m}$$

EXAMPLE 3 Simplify.

a. $\dfrac{x^{-3}}{x^{-2}} = x^{-3-(-2)} = x^{-1} = \dfrac{1}{x}$ **b.** $\left(\dfrac{x^{-2}}{2}\right)^{-3} = \dfrac{(x^{-2})^{-3}}{2^{-3}} = 2^3 x^6 = 8x^6$

Notice that an expression of the form $\dfrac{b^m}{b^n}$ may be rewritten as follows:

$$\frac{b^m}{b^n} = b^{m-n} = \frac{1}{b^{-(m-n)}} = \frac{1}{b^{n-m}}$$

This gives an alternate method of simplifying the expression in Example 3a.

$$\frac{x^{-3}}{x^{-2}} = \frac{1}{x^{-2-(-3)}} = \frac{1}{x}$$

Negative exponents are sometimes shown on polynomials of two or more terms. Factored forms may be used when such expressions are simplified.

EXAMPLE 4   Subtract $3x(x + 1)^{-2}$ from $(2x + 1)(x + 1)^{-1}$.

$$(2x + 1)(x + 1)^{-1} - 3x(x + 1)^{-2} = \frac{2x + 1}{x + 1} - \frac{3x}{(x + 1)^2}$$

$$= \frac{(2x + 1)(x + 1)}{(x + 1)^2} - \frac{3x}{(x + 1)^2}$$

$$= \frac{2x^2 + 3x + 1 - 3x}{(x + 1)^2}$$

$$= \frac{2x^2 + 1}{(x + 1)^2} \qquad \text{The denominator may be left in factored form.}$$

CLASS EXERCISES

Simplify.

1. $x^3 x^{-5}$ **2.** $\dfrac{m^2}{m^{-3}}$ **3.** $(x^{-1})^2$ **4.** $(y^3)^{-1}$

5. $3x^0$ **6.** $(3x)^0$ **7.** $\dfrac{3a^{-1}}{b^{-1}}$ **8.** $\left(\dfrac{a}{b}\right)^{-1}$

EXERCISES

Simplify.

1. 3^{-4} **2.** $(-4)^{-3}$ **3.** $(-5)^0 6^{-2}$ **4.** $5^4 5^{-4}$

5. $(x^{-3})^4$ **6.** $x^4 y^{-3}$ **7.** $(x^2 y^2)^{-2}$ **8.** $\left(\dfrac{x}{y^2}\right)^{-3}$

9. $x^3\left(\dfrac{y^{-2}}{x^{-1}}\right)^{-3}$ **10.** $y^{-4}(y^3)^{-2}$ **11.** $(ab^2 c^3)^{-1}$ **12.** $a^{-2}(b^{-1})^3$

13. $\dfrac{1}{x^{-4} x^3}$ **14.** $\dfrac{-12r^{-9}}{20r^{-7}}$ **15.** $\dfrac{72xy^{-2}}{36x^{-1}y}$ **16.** $\dfrac{a^2 b^{-1}}{a^{-2}b}$

17. $\dfrac{(xy)^{-2}}{x^4 y^5}$ **18.** $\dfrac{(-x)^{-1}}{x^2}$ **19.** $\dfrac{(a + b)^{-1}}{(a + b)^{-3}}$ **20.** $\dfrac{5x^2 y^{-3}}{10x^{-3}}$

21. $(2x - 1)^2 (2x - 1)^{-1}$ **22.** $(x - 5)(x^2 - 25)^{-1}$ **23.** $(x + 5)^{-1}(x^2 - 25)$

24. $(x - y)(y - x)^{-1}$ **25.** $(2x + 6)(x + 3)^{-3}$ **26.** $3x^{-2}(x^2 + 3x)$

27. $4y(y^2 - y)^{-1}$ **28.** $6(3x + 6)^{-1}$ **29.** $(h - 3)^2 (h^2 - 9)^{-1}$

30. $(x^2)^{-1}(x^{-4})^{-2}$ **31.** $(k - 8)(8 - k)^{-2}$ **32.** $(x^2 + 2x)^{-1}(x + 2)$

33. $\dfrac{(x^2 - x - 6)^{-1}}{(x + 2)^{-1}}$ **34.** $\dfrac{(x - 4)^{-2}}{(x^2 - 7x + 12)^{-1}}$ **35.** $\dfrac{7x^{-3}(x + 3)}{49^0 (x + 3)^{-1}}$

B *Combine and simplify.*

36. $x + y^{-1}$

37. $x^{-1} - y$

38. $x^{-1} + y^{-1}$

39. $\dfrac{x}{y} \div \left(\dfrac{y}{x}\right)^{-1}$

40. $x - x^{-1}$

41. $\dfrac{4x}{9} \div \left(\dfrac{7x^2}{6}\right)^{-1}$

42. $\dfrac{x^2 + x}{3}\left(\dfrac{x + 1}{9}\right)^{-1}$

43. $\dfrac{x^2 - 9}{x + 4}\left(\dfrac{x - 3}{2x + 8}\right)^{-1}$

44. $\dfrac{3}{x^2 + x} \div \left(\dfrac{x + 1}{2}\right)^{-1}$

45. $\left(\dfrac{25y^2}{-8x^2}\right)^{-1} \div \dfrac{16x}{15y}$

46. $x^{-2} + 2x^{-3}$

47. $(x + 1)^{-1} + (x - 1)^{-1}$

48. $\dfrac{x^2 - 6x + 9}{x^2 - 9}\left(\dfrac{x^2 - 3x}{x^2 + 4x + 3}\right)^{-1}$

49. $(2x + y)x^{-1} - (2y + x)y^{-1}$

50. $\dfrac{6x + 9}{x^2 + 3x} + x(x + 3)^{-1}$

51. $(x + 3)^{-1} - (x + 2)(x + 3)^{-2}$

52. $x(x + 1)^{-2} - (x + 1)^{-1}$

53. $2x(x^2 + 1)^{-1} - 2x(x^2 - 1)(x^2 + 1)^{-2}$

C **54.** $\dfrac{x^{-1} + y^{-1}}{x^{-2}y^{-2}}$ **Hint:** Multiply the numerator and the denominator by x^2y^2.

55. $\dfrac{x^{-1} - 1}{x^{-1} + 1}$

56. $\dfrac{x^{-2} - y^{-2}}{x^{-1} + y^{-1}}$

57. $\dfrac{x^{-2} - y^{-2}}{x^{-1}y^{-1}}$

58. $(x + y)(x^{-1} + y^{-1})$

59. $(x + y)^{-1}(x^{-1} - y^{-1})$

60. $(x - y)^{-1}(x^{-1} - y^{-1})$

CHALLENGE

Prove Your Conjecture

I Write any whole number with three different nonzero digits.

II Write all possible two-digit numbers, using these three digits.

III Add these six numbers.

IV Add the three digits in the original number.

V Divide the sum in Step III by the sum in Step IV.

Example: 437

$$43$$
$$34$$
$$37$$
$$73$$
$$47$$
$$\underline{74}$$
$$308$$

$4 + 3 + 7 = 14$

$$\begin{array}{r} 22 \\ 14\overline{)308} \end{array}$$

1. Try this for another number. What is the quotient in Step V? What do you think the quotient will be whenever this procedure is followed?

2. Prove your conjecture.

Equivalent Resistances

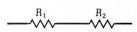

Electricians use mathematics in work with electrical circuits.

When two resistances, R_1 and R_2, are wired *in series*, the equivalent resistance R is equal to their sum.

$$R = R_1 + R_2 \longleftarrow \text{series}$$

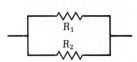

When wired *in parallel*, the equivalent resistance R can be found using this reciprocal relationship.

$$\frac{1}{R} = \frac{1}{R_1} + \frac{1}{R_2} \longleftarrow \text{parallel}$$

Each of these equations can be extended for more than two resistances.

Example   Two resistances measure 2000 ohms and 3000 ohms, respectively.

   a. Find the single equivalent resistance when they are wired in series.

   $2000 + 3000 = 5000$ The equivalent resistance is 5000 ohms.

   b. Find the single equivalent resistance when they are wired in parallel.

   $\dfrac{1}{2000} + \dfrac{1}{3000} = \dfrac{3 + 2}{6000} = \dfrac{1}{1200}$ The equivalent resistance is 1200 ohms.

Let $R_1 = 1000$ *ohms,* $R_2 = 5000$ *ohms, and* $R_3 = 1500$ *ohms.*
Find a single equivalent resistance for each circuit.

1. R_1 and R_2 are wired in series.   **2.** R_1 and R_3 are wired in parallel.

3. 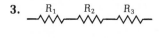   **4.** 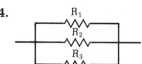   **5.**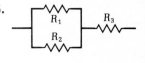

6. What resistance, wired in parallel with a 20,000-ohm resistance, will give an equivalent resistance of 4000 ohms?

7. Because of its low resistance, copper is widely used in electrical wiring. However, the resistance of copper wire does increase as its length increases. The relationship is given by the following formula.

$R = \dfrac{10.4l}{d^2}$ R is the resistance of copper wire, in ohms.
l is the length of the wire, in feet.
d is its diameter, in thousandths of an inch.

What is the resistance of 5 miles of copper wire if its diameter is $\frac{1}{2}$ inch?

CHAPTER 5 REVIEW

VOCABULARY

rational number (p. 166)
rational expression (p. 166)
cancellation rule (p. 166)
reciprocal (p. 171)
least common denominator (p. 174)
least common multiple (p. 174)
complex fraction (p. 177)
fractional equation (p. 181)
ratio (p. 185)

proportion (p. 185)
rate (p. 189)
direct variation (p. 192)
constant of variation (p. 192)
directly proportional (p. 192)
constant of proportionality (p. 192)
inverse variation (p. 193)
inversely proportional (p. 193)
joint variation (p. 196)

SUMMARY

The basic algebra of rational expressions is emphasized in the first half of this chapter. Methods of simplifying, multiplying, dividing, adding, and subtracting such expressions are presented. These procedures are then used to simplify complex fractions and to solve fractional equations.

Three major problem-solving areas are examined. These deal with applications using ratios and proportions, constant or average rates of change, and direct and inverse variation. The chapter concludes with an introduction to zero and negative exponents, which provide other useful ways of writing rational expressions.

REVIEW EXERCISES

5-1   *Simplify.*

1. $\dfrac{48}{80}$

2. $\dfrac{36xy^3}{54x^3y^2}$

3. $\dfrac{x - 5}{x^2 - 10x + 25}$

4. $\dfrac{3x - 9}{15 + x - 2x^2}$

5. $\dfrac{4x^2 - 9}{2x + 3}$

6. $\dfrac{x^2 - 16}{4 - x}$

7. $\dfrac{x^2 - 7x + 12}{x^2 - 6x + 8}$

8. $\dfrac{4x^2 - 9}{2xy - 3y + 4x - 6}$

Evaluate $\dfrac{x + 1}{x^2 - 1}$, *if possible, for the given values of* ***x.***

9. $x = 0$

10. $x = 3$

11. $x = -1$

12. $x = -3$

Perform the indicated operations, and simplify.

5-2   13. $\dfrac{2ab^2}{a^2 + 7a} \cdot \dfrac{a + 7}{8b^3}$

14. $\dfrac{-5a^4b}{8a^3} \div \dfrac{25a^3b}{24ab^2}$

15. $\dfrac{x^2 - 9}{5x^2 + 15x} \div \dfrac{4x^2 - 7x - 15}{2x^2}$

16. $\dfrac{xy - 2y + 3x - 6}{2xy^2 - x^2y}\left(\dfrac{3x^2 - 10x + 8}{x^3 - 8} \div \dfrac{y^2 + 6y + 9}{x^3 + 2x^2 + 4x}\right)$

5-3   17. $\dfrac{5}{3x} - \dfrac{20}{3x}$

18. $\dfrac{2a - b}{a^2 - 4b^2} + \dfrac{3b - a}{a^2 - 4b^2}$

19. $\dfrac{3y}{xy^3} - \dfrac{1}{x^2y}$

20. $\dfrac{x}{x^2 + 7x + 12} + \dfrac{3}{x + 3}$

21. $\dfrac{x + 2}{2x^2 - 3x} + \dfrac{2}{x^2 + 2x} - \dfrac{7}{2x^2 + x - 6}$

5-4 *Simplify.*

22. $\dfrac{1 - \dfrac{2}{5}}{\dfrac{4}{5} - 2}$

23. $\dfrac{\dfrac{1}{xy}}{\dfrac{2}{x} + \dfrac{3}{y}}$

24. $\dfrac{\dfrac{1}{x + 1} - \dfrac{1}{x^2 + 4x + 3}}{\dfrac{x}{x + 3} - \dfrac{2}{x + 1}}$

5-5 *Solve and check. Write **no solution,** where appropriate.*

25. $\dfrac{5x}{3x - 2} = \dfrac{15}{7}$

26. $\dfrac{8}{x} - \dfrac{4}{3x} = \dfrac{x + 4}{9}$

27. $\dfrac{4}{x + 3} - \dfrac{5}{x - 3} = \dfrac{2x}{x^2 - 9}$

28. $\dfrac{x}{x - 5} - 2 = \dfrac{5}{x - 5}$

29. $\dfrac{1}{x^2 - 1} + \dfrac{x + 1}{x - 1} = \dfrac{x - 1}{x + 1}$

5-6 **30.** If 30 pounds of apples sell for $8.00, what is the price of 75 pounds?

31. An 18-foot pipe is cut into two parts. The ratio of the shorter part to the longer part is $\frac{2}{7}$. How long is each part?

32. The sum of two numbers is 32, and the ratio of the larger to the smaller number is $5:3$. Find the numbers.

5-7 **33.** A car leaves town at noon and travels at a rate of 40 miles per hour. One hour later, a second car leaves the same town and travels at 48 miles per hour along the same route. At what time will the second car overtake the first one?

34. It takes Sue 2 hours to clean her apartment. Her roommate needs 3 hours to do the same job. How long would it take them if they worked together?

35. When both the hot- and the cold-water faucets are open, a tub can be filled in 5 minutes. It takes twice as long for the hot-water faucet to fill the tub as it takes the cold-water faucet. How long does it take each to fill the tub alone?

5-8 **36.** If y varies directly as x, and $y = 2$ when $x = 9$, find y when $x = 36$.

37. x and y are inversely proportional, and $y = \frac{1}{3}$ when $x = 45$. Find x when $y = \frac{1}{4}$.

38. If a varies jointly as x and y, and $a = 5$ when $x = 3$ and $y = 2$, find a when $x = 4$ and $y = 4$.

39. The surface area S of a sphere varies directly as the square of its radius r. If $S = 100\pi$ square centimeters when $r = 5$ centimeters, find the formula for S in terms of r.

Simplify. Use positive exponents to express the results.

40. $5^0 x^{-6} x^2$

41. $\dfrac{6a^3 b^{-4}}{4a^{-4} b^2}$

42. $\dfrac{x^{-1} + y^{-1}}{(x + y)^{-1}}$

43. $(x^2)^{-3} \left(\dfrac{x^4}{2}\right)^{-1}$

44. $2x(x - 4)^{-1}$

45. $\left(\dfrac{5}{4x^2 - 2x}\right)\left(\dfrac{10}{2x - 1}\right)^{-1}$

CHAPTER 5
TEST

Simplify.

1. $\dfrac{15a^3 b^2 c}{12ab^2 c^3}$

2. $\dfrac{3x^2 - 13x - 10}{9x + 6}$

3. $\dfrac{(x + 2)^2}{x^2 + 4x + 4}$

Perform the indicated operations, and simplify.

4. $\dfrac{5y}{x^2} \cdot \dfrac{x^3}{20y^2}$

5. $\dfrac{4ab}{3c} \div \dfrac{2a^3}{9c}$

6. $\dfrac{3x^2 - 12x}{x^2 - 16} \div \dfrac{9x^2}{x + 4}$

7. $\dfrac{2}{x} - \dfrac{3}{2x}$

8. $\dfrac{1}{x - 3} + \dfrac{1}{x + 3}$

9. $\dfrac{x}{x^2 - x - 2} - \dfrac{1}{x + 1}$

10. $\dfrac{\dfrac{4}{x}}{\dfrac{4}{3x^2}}$

11. $\dfrac{\dfrac{1}{n} - n}{\dfrac{2}{n} + 2}$

12. $\dfrac{\dfrac{5}{x - 7} - \dfrac{5}{x + 7}}{\dfrac{7}{x^2 - 49}}$

Solve and check.

13. $\dfrac{12}{x} - \dfrac{1}{2} = \dfrac{27}{2x}$

14. $\dfrac{3x}{x^2 - 2x - 15} = \dfrac{2x}{x - 5} + \dfrac{x}{x + 3}$

15. x and y are directly proportional. If $y = 24$ when $x = 6$, find y when $x = 2$.

16. y varies inversely as x, and $y = \frac{3}{4}$ when $x = 12$. Find y when $x = 18$.

Simplify. Use positive exponents to express the results.

17. $x^{-6}(x^5)^{-2}$

18. $(x^{-3} + y^{-2})^{-1}$

Solve each problem.

19. A 50-foot tree casts a 16-foot shadow. How tall is another tree that casts a 20-foot shadow at the same time of day?

20. Two trains leave the same station and travel in opposite directions. The first train leaves at 12 noon and travels 58 miles per hour. The second train leaves at 12:30 P.M. and travels 62 miles per hour. When will the trains be 329 miles apart?

Inflation

During a period of economic inflation, the value of currency decreases, and most prices increase. Although the rate of inflation varies from year to year and from item to item, it is convenient to assume a constant rate and a uniform effect upon prices.

If the price of an article is $10 at the beginning of a year, and the annual inflation rate is 5%, the price at the end of the year is $10 + 0.05 \times 10$. For the second year, the increase in price will be $0.05(10 + 0.05 \times 10)$. By the end of the second year, the price will be $(10 + 0.05 \times 10) + 0.05(10 + 0.05 \times 10)$. Factoring gives $10(1 + 0.05)^2$. This suggests the formula $F = S(1 + R)^N$ where S is the starting price, and F the final price, after N years inflation at annual rate R, where R is expressed as a decimal.

The program below predicts a future price. Before entering it, check to see which symbol your computer uses for exponentiation.

Line 210 rounds to the nearest cent. To see how this line works, substitute several values for F and evaluate. For more information, see the Appendix, Section XII: Using Rounding.

The Program	What It Does
``` 100 REM INFLATION ```	
``` 110 PRINT "ORIGINAL PRICE"; ```	Waits for entry, which should have no dollar sign.
``` 120 INPUT S ```	
``` 130 PRINT "INFLATION RATE AS DECIMAL"; ```	Will reject an entry that has a percent sign.
``` 140 INPUT R ```	
``` 150 PRINT "NUMBER OF YEARS"; ```	Waits for entry.
``` 160 INPUT N ```	
``` 200 LET F = S * (1 + R) ↑ N ```	Evaluates the formula.
``` 210 LET F = INT(F * 100 + .5)/100 ```	Rounds to the nearest cent.
``` 220 PRINT "INFLATED PRICE MAY BE $"; F ```	
``` 900 END ```	You may insert lines that instruct the computer to run the program again. See p. 115.

What will the computer display for each of these items?

1. $100 camera   5% annual inflation   2 years

2. $6000 auto   8% annual inflation   5 years

3. $400 VCR   6% annual inflation   7 years

4. $40 game   9.5% annual inflation   15 years

5. After N years of inflation at annual rate R, the value of a given amount of currency, A, is $A(1 - R)^N$. Write a program to display the value of a given amount of currency.

For more information about BASIC, see the Computer Handbook at the back of the book.

CHAPTER 6

The volume of these oil refinery storage tanks in Los Angeles can be calculated from their dimensions. Or, if the volume of a spherical tank is known, its radius can be calculated using an equation involving a radical.

RADICAL EXPRESSIONS

Prerequisite Skills Review

Write the letter for the correct answer.

1. If $x < 0$, then $|x|$ is equal to ___ .

    a. x **b.** 0 **c.** $-x$ **d.** none of these

2. Which of the following numbers is a perfect square and *also* a factor of 294?

    a. 6   **b.** 16   **c.** 42   **d.** 49

3. Which of the following numbers is the greatest perfect square that is *also* a factor of 80?

    a. 4   **b.** 9   **c.** 16   **d.** 20

4. Which of the following numbers is the greatest perfect square that is *also* a factor of 128?

    a. 4   **b.** 16   **c.** 36   **d.** 64

5. $m - 3(3n - m) =$ ___

    a. $4m - 9n$ **b.** $-5m$ **c.** $-2m - 9n$ **d.** none of these

6. $(2p + q)(p - 3q) =$ ___

    a. $2p^2 + 7pq - 3q^2$ **b.** $2p^2 - 7pq + 3q^2$

    c. $2p^2 - 5pq - 2q^2$ **d.** none of these

7. Which of the following expressions is equivalent to $a^2 - b^2$?

    a. $(a + b)^2$ **b.** $(a + b)(a - b)$ **c.** $(a - b)(a - b)$ **d.** $a(a - b^2)$

8. Which of the following expressions is always equal to -1 if $a \neq \pm b$?

    a. $\dfrac{a - b}{a + b}$ **b.** $\dfrac{a + b}{a - b}$ **c.** $\dfrac{a - b}{b - a}$ **d.** $\dfrac{a - b}{a - b}$

9. Which of the following expressions is always equal to -1 if $a \neq \pm b$?

    a. $\dfrac{a^2 - b^2}{b^2 - a^2}$ **b.** $\dfrac{a^2 - b^2}{a + b}$ **c.** $\dfrac{a^2 - b^2}{a^2 - b^2}$ **d.** $\dfrac{(a - b)^2}{(b - a)^2}$

10. $(x^4 \cdot x^2)^3 =$ ___

    a. x^9 **b.** x^{11} **c.** x^{18} **d.** x^{24}

6-1 Roots and Radicals

OBJECTIVES

To solve equations of the form $x^2 = k$ and $x^3 = k$.
To find the principal nth root of a perfect nth power.
To estimate roots using a table.

The equation $x^2 = 4$ has two solutions, $x = 2$ and $x = -2$, since

$$(2)^2 = 4 \quad \text{and} \quad (-2)^2 = 4$$

The solutions 2 and -2 are said to be the **square roots** of 4.
Similarly, the equation $x^3 = 125$ has one real solution, $x = 5$.

$$(5)^3 = 125$$

The solution 5 is the **cube root** of 125.

EXAMPLE 1   Solve.

a. $x^2 = \dfrac{36}{25}$

$x = \dfrac{6}{5}$ or $x = -\dfrac{6}{5}$

b. $2x^3 = -16$
$x^3 = -8$
$x = -2$

Check $\left(\dfrac{6}{5}\right)^2 = \dfrac{36}{25}$ ✔ $\left(-\dfrac{6}{5}\right)^2 = \dfrac{36}{25}$ ✔

$2(-2)^3 = 2(-8) = -16$ ✔

The solutions are $\dfrac{6}{5}$ and $-\dfrac{6}{5}$.

The solution is -2.

The **radical symbol** $\sqrt{}$ indicates the *positive* square root, or **principal square root,** of a number. The *negative* square root of a number is indicated by $-\sqrt{}$. For example, $\sqrt{4} = 2$, and $-\sqrt{4} = -2$. Note that the square root of a negative number is *not* a real number. For example, $\sqrt{-4}$ is not a real number because there is no real number whose square is -4. Such numbers as $\sqrt{-4}$ and $\sqrt{-15}$ will be studied in Chapter 8.

The radical symbol $\sqrt[3]{}$ indicates the **principal cube root** of a number. Every real number has one principal cube root, which has the same sign as the number itself. For the principal cube roots of 64 and -64, we write

$$\sqrt[3]{64} = 4, \text{ since } 4^3 = 64 \qquad \sqrt[3]{-64} = -4, \text{ since } (-4)^3 = -64$$

Similarly, $x = \sqrt[n]{b}$ means $x^n = b$, provided $\sqrt[n]{b}$ is a real number. The number b is called the **radicand.** n, a positive integer greater than 1, is called the **index.** Note that an even root of a negative number, such as $\sqrt[4]{-16}$, is *not* a real number.

The principal nth root is positive, except in the case where n is odd and the radicand is negative. Since a variable may or may not represent a positive number, we use absolute value symbols when working with an expression such as $\sqrt{x^2}$.

Suppose $x = -4$. Then $\sqrt{x^2} = \sqrt{(-4)^2} = \sqrt{16} = 4 = |-4|$.
Suppose $x = 4$. Then $\sqrt{x^2} = \sqrt{4^2} = \sqrt{16} = 4 = |4|$.

In each of the cases just shown, $\sqrt{x^2} = |x|$.
Here are some additional illustrations.

$$\sqrt[4]{y^4} = |y| \qquad \sqrt{n^6} = |n^3| \qquad \sqrt{x^4} = x^2$$

Do you see why absolute value symbols are not necessary in the third case shown above?

EXAMPLE 2   Find each root.

   a. $\sqrt[3]{\dfrac{1}{64}} = \dfrac{1}{4}$ $\qquad$ $\left(\dfrac{1}{4}\right)^3 = \dfrac{1}{64}$

   b. $\sqrt[5]{-32} = -2$ $\qquad$ $(-2)^5 = -32$

   c. $\sqrt{81x^2} = 9|x|$ $\qquad$ $(9|x|)^2 = 81x^2$

   d. $\sqrt{100y^4} = 10y^2$ $\qquad$ $(10y^2)^2 = 100y^4$

Recall that $\sqrt{7}$ is not a rational number, since it cannot be written as the ratio of two integers. The value of an irrational number can be approximated in decimal form. You can use a calculator or the table on page 668 to find a decimal approximation for $\sqrt{7}$.

$\sqrt{7} \approx 2.646$ The symbol $\approx$ is read "is approximately equal to."

It is helpful to know some perfect squares and perfect cubes when finding roots. This table gives the squares and cubes of the first 12 counting numbers.

n	1	2	3	4	5	6	7	8	9	10	11	12
n^2	1	4	9	16	25	36	49	64	81	100	121	144
n^3	1	8	27	64	125	216	343	512	729	1000	1331	1728

If you know, for example, that 6^3 is equal to 216, then you know that $\sqrt[3]{216}$ is equal to 6. The tables on pages 668 and 669 allow you to find other roots, as shown in the next example.

EXAMPLE 3   Find each root correct to three decimal places. Use the tables.

   a. $-\sqrt{5} = -2.236$ $\sqrt{5}$ is positive, so $-\sqrt{5}$ is negative.

   b. $\sqrt[3]{-4.5} = -1.651$ The cube root of a negative number is negative.

The tables in the back of the book can be used to find the square roots of numbers 10 times the listed values of n and cube roots of numbers 10 or 100 times the value of n. Study the following example.

EXAMPLE 4   Find $\sqrt{24}$ correct to three decimal places. Use the table.

Think of $\sqrt{24}$ as $\sqrt{10 \times 2.4}$. Find 2.4 in the column headed **n**. In that row, find the entry under the heading $\sqrt{10n}$.

n	n²	√n	√10n
2.4	5.76	1.549	4.899

$\sqrt{24} = 4.899$, correct to three decimal places.

CLASS EXERCISES

Find each root, if it is a real number.

1. $\sqrt{64}$
2. $-\sqrt{100}$
3. $\sqrt{-49}$
4. $\sqrt{0}$
5. $\sqrt[3]{1000}$

6. $\sqrt[3]{-125}$
7. $\sqrt{\dfrac{9}{16}}$
8. $\sqrt{-\dfrac{25}{49}}$
9. $-\sqrt[3]{\dfrac{8}{27}}$
10. $\sqrt[3]{-\dfrac{64}{343}}$

11. $\sqrt{n^2}$
12. $-\sqrt{n^2}$
13. $\sqrt{n^4}$
14. $\sqrt[3]{n^3}$
15. $-\sqrt[3]{8n^3}$

Solve.

16. $x^2 = 64$
17. $2x^2 = 72$
18. $x^3 = -64$
19. $2x^3 = -250$

EXERCISES

A   *Find each root, if it is a real number.*

1. $\sqrt{81}$
2. $\sqrt{-36}$
3. $-\sqrt{36}$
4. $\sqrt[3]{512}$
5. $\sqrt[3]{-27}$

6. $-\sqrt[3]{1000}$
7. $\sqrt{\dfrac{1}{4}}$
8. $-\sqrt{\dfrac{25}{144}}$
9. $\sqrt{-\dfrac{81}{25}}$
10. $-\sqrt[3]{\dfrac{125}{216}}$

11. $\sqrt{a^2}$
12. $-\sqrt{a^2}$
13. $\sqrt{121a^2}$
14. $\sqrt[3]{a^3}$
15. $\sqrt[3]{512a^3}$

16. $\sqrt{0.09}$
17. $-\sqrt{0.25}$
18. $\sqrt{1.44}$
19. $\sqrt[3]{-0.001}$
20. $\sqrt[3]{0.027}$

Solve.

21. $x^2 = 9$
22. $2x^2 = 98$
23. $3x^2 = 75$
24. $5x^2 = 125$

25. $x^2 = \dfrac{4}{9}$
26. $x^2 = \dfrac{81}{64}$
27. $x^2 = \dfrac{9}{225}$
28. $x^2 = \dfrac{100}{49}$

29. $2x^3 = 250$
30. $3x^3 = 81$
31. $3x^3 = -24$
32. $-2x^3 = 1024$

B *Find each root, correct to three decimal places. Use the tables.*

33. $\sqrt{7.5}$ **34.** $\sqrt{9.8}$ **35.** $\sqrt{28}$ **36.** $\sqrt{47}$ **37.** $\sqrt[3]{5.3}$

38. $\sqrt[3]{8.7}$ **39.** $\sqrt[3]{87}$ **40.** $\sqrt[3]{870}$ **41.** $-\sqrt{65}$ **42.** $\sqrt[3]{-72}$

Find $\sqrt{2}$, $\sqrt{3}$, $\sqrt{5}$, and $\sqrt{6}$, correct to three decimal places.

43. Does it appear that $\sqrt{2} + \sqrt{3} = \sqrt{5}$? **44.** Does it appear that $\sqrt{2} \cdot \sqrt{3} = \sqrt{6}$?

Find $\sqrt{7}$, $\sqrt{8}$, and $\sqrt{56}$, correct to three decimal places.

45. Does it appear that $\sqrt{56} \div \sqrt{8} = \sqrt{7}$? **46.** Does it appear that $\sqrt{56} \div 8 = \sqrt{7}$?

C *Find each root, if it is a real number.*

47. $\sqrt[4]{81}$ **48.** $-\sqrt[5]{32}$ **49.** $\sqrt[6]{-64}$ **50.** $-\sqrt[6]{64}$ **51.** $\sqrt{625x^2}$

52. $\sqrt[4]{81x^4}$ **53.** $-\sqrt[5]{243x^5}$ **54.** $\sqrt[3]{-1728x^3}$ **55.** $\sqrt{169x^4}$ **56.** $\sqrt[3]{729x^6}$

57. List the solutions for $x^2 \le 9$, where x is an integer.

58. List the solutions for $4 \le x^2 \le 25$, where x is an integer.

USING THE CALCULATOR

Estimating Square Roots

You can estimate the square root of a number mentally. Study the example below. After estimating, we find the percent error using a calculator.

Example Estimate the square root of 770.

Estimate first.

We know that $20^2 = 400$ and $30^2 = 900$, so $\sqrt{400} = 20$ and $\sqrt{900} = 30$. Therefore, a reasonable estimate of $\sqrt{770}$ might be 27.

Evaluate $\sqrt{770}$ on a calculator.

$\sqrt{770} = 27.749$, correct to three decimal places.

Compute the percent error on the calculator to the nearest tenth of a percent.

First find the error. $27.749 - 27 = 0.749$

Then express the error as a percent of the correct root. $\dfrac{0.749}{27.749} \approx 0.027 = 2.7\%$

Now you try it! Estimate the square root of each number mentally. Then use a calculator to find the square root directly, and compute the percent error.

1. 131   1310   13,100   **2.** 247   2470   24,700

3. 9.67   96.7   967   **4.** 18.4   184   1840

6-2 Multiplying and Simplifying Radicals

OBJECTIVE

To simplify radical expressions and products of radical expressions.

Compare the answers in these two examples involving square roots.

$$\sqrt{4} \cdot \sqrt{9} = 2 \cdot 3 = 6 \atop \sqrt{4 \cdot 9} = \sqrt{36} = 6 \Bigg\}$$
The answers are the same. That is,

$$\sqrt{4} \cdot \sqrt{9} = \sqrt{4 \cdot 9}$$

Now compare the answers in these two examples involving cube roots.

$$\sqrt[3]{8} \cdot \sqrt[3]{125} = 2 \cdot 5 = 10 \atop \sqrt[3]{8 \cdot 125} = \sqrt[3]{1000} = 10 \Bigg\}$$
The answers are the same. That is,

$$\sqrt[3]{8} \cdot \sqrt[3]{125} = \sqrt[3]{8 \cdot 125}$$

These illustrations lead to the following general rule.

Product of Roots

If $\sqrt[n]{a}$ and $\sqrt[n]{b}$ are real numbers, then $\sqrt[n]{a} \cdot \sqrt[n]{b} = \sqrt[n]{ab}$.

EXAMPLE 1   Simplify $\sqrt{6} \cdot \sqrt{24}$.

$$\sqrt{6} \cdot \sqrt{24} = \sqrt{6 \cdot 24} \qquad \sqrt{a} \cdot \sqrt{b} = \sqrt{ab}$$
$$= \sqrt{144}$$
$$= 12$$

The rule for finding the product of roots is often used in the reversed order, $\sqrt[n]{ab} = \sqrt[n]{a} \cdot \sqrt[n]{b}$, as shown in the next example.

EXAMPLE 2   Simplify $\sqrt[3]{512}$.

$$\sqrt[3]{512} = \sqrt[3]{8 \cdot 64} \qquad \text{8 and 64 are perfect cubes.}$$
$$= \sqrt[3]{8} \cdot \sqrt[3]{64} \qquad \sqrt[3]{ab} = \sqrt[3]{a} \cdot \sqrt[3]{b}$$
$$= 2 \cdot 4$$
$$= 8$$

In general, the radicand of a *simplified* radical expression with index n contains no factor, other than 1, that is an nth power. If the radicand is not a perfect nth power, the expression can be simplified if it has a factor that is such a power.

EXAMPLE 3   Simplify.

a. $\sqrt{28} = \sqrt{4 \cdot 7}$ 4 is a perfect square.

$\quad\quad\quad = \sqrt{4} \cdot \sqrt{7}$

$\quad\quad\quad = 2\sqrt{7}$

b. $\sqrt[4]{48x^4} = \sqrt[4]{16x^4 \cdot 3}$ $16x^4$ is a perfect fourth power.

$\quad\quad\quad\quad = \sqrt[4]{16x^4} \cdot \sqrt[4]{3}$

$\quad\quad\quad\quad = 2\,|x|\,\sqrt[4]{3}$ $\sqrt[4]{x^4}$ must be positive, so we
$\quad\quad\quad\quad\quad\quad\quad\quad\quad\quad$ write absolute value symbols.

c. $\sqrt[3]{40x^6} = \sqrt[3]{8x^6 \cdot 5}$ $8x^6$ is a perfect cube.

$\quad\quad\quad\quad = \sqrt[3]{8x^6} \cdot \sqrt[3]{5}$

$\quad\quad\quad\quad = 2x^2\sqrt[3]{5}$

Your work will be simpler if you find the factor that is the greatest possible perfect power. For example, here are two ways to simplify $\sqrt{72}$.

$$\sqrt{72} = \sqrt{9} \cdot \sqrt{8} = 3\sqrt{8} = 3(\sqrt{4} \cdot \sqrt{2}) = 3 \cdot 2\sqrt{2} = 6\sqrt{2}$$
$$\sqrt{72} = \sqrt{36} \cdot \sqrt{2} = 6\sqrt{2} \quad \text{This way is shorter.}$$

When finding a product, it is sometimes easier to simplify each radical expression first, and then multiply.

EXAMPLE 4   Simplify. Assume all variables represent positive numbers.

a. $\sqrt{18x^2y^3} \cdot \sqrt{48xy^2} = \sqrt{9x^2y^2 \cdot 2y} \cdot \sqrt{16y^2 \cdot 3x}$

$\quad\quad\quad\quad\quad\quad\quad\quad = 3xy\sqrt{2y} \cdot 4y\sqrt{3x}$ Since we assume x and y

$\quad\quad\quad\quad\quad\quad\quad\quad = (3xy \cdot 4y)(\sqrt{2y} \cdot \sqrt{3x})$ are positive, absolute
$\quad\quad\quad\quad\quad\quad\quad\quad\quad\quad\quad\quad\quad\quad\quad\quad\quad\quad\quad\quad$ value symbols are
$\quad\quad\quad\quad\quad\quad\quad\quad = 12xy^2\sqrt{6xy}$ not needed.

b. $(-5\sqrt[3]{16})(2\sqrt[3]{27x^4}) = (-5\sqrt[3]{8 \cdot 2})(2\sqrt[3]{27x^3 \cdot x})$

$\quad\quad\quad\quad\quad\quad\quad\quad\quad\quad = (-5 \cdot 2\sqrt[3]{2})(2 \cdot 3x\sqrt[3]{x})$

$\quad\quad\quad\quad\quad\quad\quad\quad\quad\quad = (-10\sqrt[3]{2})(6x\sqrt[3]{x})$

$\quad\quad\quad\quad\quad\quad\quad\quad\quad\quad = (-10 \cdot 6x)(\sqrt[3]{2} \cdot \sqrt[3]{x})$

$\quad\quad\quad\quad\quad\quad\quad\quad\quad\quad = -60x\sqrt[3]{2x}$

CLASS EXERCISES

Simplify.

1. $\sqrt{2} \cdot \sqrt{8}$ **2.** $\sqrt{2} \cdot \sqrt{32}$ **3.** $\sqrt{3} \cdot \sqrt{6}$ **4.** $\sqrt{5} \cdot \sqrt{8}$

5. $(\sqrt{7})^2$ **6.** $(\sqrt[3]{13})^3$ **7.** $\sqrt{4m} \cdot \sqrt{4n}$ **8.** $\sqrt{6} \cdot \sqrt{12}$

9. $\sqrt{80}$ **10.** $\sqrt{63}$ **11.** $\sqrt[3]{250}$ **12.** $\sqrt[3]{2000}$

EXERCISES

A *Simplify.*

1. $\sqrt{5} \cdot \sqrt{5}$　　　2. $\sqrt{4} \cdot \sqrt{36}$　　　3. $\sqrt{2} \cdot \sqrt{72}$　　　4. $\sqrt{45} \cdot \sqrt{5}$

5. $\sqrt{6} \cdot \sqrt{8}$　　　6. $\sqrt{11} \cdot \sqrt{11}$　　　7. $\sqrt{7} \cdot \sqrt{14}$　　　8. $\sqrt{12} \cdot \sqrt{6}$

9. $\sqrt[3]{4} \cdot \sqrt[3]{16}$　　　10. $\sqrt[3]{7} \cdot \sqrt[3]{8}$　　　11. $\sqrt[3]{2} \cdot \sqrt[3]{-11}$　　　12. $\sqrt[3]{5} \cdot \sqrt[3]{25}$

13. $\sqrt{12} \cdot \sqrt{10}$　　　14. $\sqrt{20} \cdot \sqrt{6}$　　　15. $\sqrt[3]{9} \cdot \sqrt[3]{9}$　　　16. $\sqrt[3]{24} \cdot \sqrt[3]{9}$

17. $\sqrt{2} \cdot \sqrt{2x^2}$　　　18. $\sqrt{4x^2} \cdot \sqrt{3}$　　　19. $\sqrt{6x^2} \cdot \sqrt{3}$　　　20. $\sqrt{5} \cdot \sqrt{5x^2}$

B *Simplify, if possible. Assume all variables represent positive numbers.*

21. $\sqrt{44}$　　　22. $\sqrt{108}$　　　23. $\sqrt{243}$　　　24. $\sqrt{245}$

25. $\sqrt{2.88}$　　　26. $\sqrt{6.76}$　　　27. $\sqrt[3]{432}$　　　28. $\sqrt{257}$

29. $\sqrt{16x^6}$　　　30. $\sqrt{36n^8}$　　　31. $\sqrt{144t^{10}}$　　　32. $\sqrt[3]{-16p^3q}$

33. $\sqrt{12k^8}$　　　34. $\sqrt{40x^{12}}$　　　35. $\sqrt{50v^2w^4}$　　　36. $\sqrt[3]{54x^4y^5}$

37. $\sqrt[3]{-8} \cdot \sqrt[3]{27}$　　　38. $2\sqrt[3]{125} \cdot 3\sqrt[3]{8}$　　　39. $5\sqrt[3]{5} \cdot \sqrt[3]{y}$

40. $\sqrt[4]{\dfrac{3}{16}} \cdot \sqrt[4]{\dfrac{1}{3}}$　　　41. $\sqrt[4]{81} \cdot \sqrt[4]{3}$　　　42. $2\sqrt[4]{5} \cdot 3\sqrt[4]{5}$

43. $\sqrt{3s} \cdot \sqrt{5t}$　　　44. $\sqrt{4x} \cdot \sqrt{9y}$　　　45. $\sqrt{8m} \cdot \sqrt{8n}$

46. $\sqrt{2x^2} \cdot \sqrt{8y}$　　　47. $\sqrt{6p} \cdot \sqrt{8pq}$　　　48. $\sqrt{10xy^2} \cdot \sqrt{6xy}$

49. $2\sqrt[3]{4x} \cdot 3\sqrt[3]{2x^2}$　　　50. $4\sqrt{8x} \cdot \sqrt{2x^2}$　　　51. $\sqrt{6w} \cdot 3\sqrt{8w^2}$

52. $-3\sqrt{6r^3s} \cdot 2\sqrt{3rs^5}$　　　53. $2\sqrt{2x^3y^2} \cdot 5\sqrt{22x}$　　　54. $4\sqrt{8xyz^2} \cdot 3\sqrt{10x^2yz^2}$

55. $(3\sqrt{5})^2$　　　56. $(-2\sqrt[3]{7})^3$　　　57. $(-5x\sqrt[3]{2x})^3$

58. $(2m\sqrt{3n})^2$　　　59. $(3\sqrt{2x+1})^2$　　　60. $(-4\sqrt[3]{x-1})^3$

61. $3(3\sqrt[3]{16x})(2\sqrt[3]{5x^2})$　　　62. $(2\sqrt[3]{4x})(-3\sqrt[3]{16x})$　　　63. $(2\sqrt[4]{8x^5})(3\sqrt[4]{8x^2})$

C *Simplify. Assume x and y represent positive numbers and n a positive integer.*

64. $\sqrt{x^{2n}}$　　　65. $\sqrt{x^{2n+1}}$　　　66. $x^n\sqrt{x^{4n}y^{6n}}$

67. $\sqrt[3]{x^{3n}}$　　　68. $\sqrt[3]{x^{3n+2}}$　　　69. $x^n\sqrt[4]{x^{8n}y^{4n}}$

Simplify. Assume that x and y represent positive numbers.

Sample　$\sqrt{x^3 - 4x^2 + 4x} = \sqrt{(x-2)^2x} = \sqrt{(x-2)^2} \cdot \sqrt{x} = |x-2|\sqrt{x}$

70. $\sqrt{x^2 + 4x + 4}$　　　71. $\sqrt{4x^2 - 12xy + 9y^2}$　　　72. $\sqrt{x^3 + 6x^2 + 9x}$

73. $\sqrt{12x^3 + 12x^2 + 3x}$　　　*74. $\sqrt{1 + \left(\dfrac{x^2}{2} - \dfrac{1}{2x^2}\right)^2}$　　　*75. $\sqrt[3]{(x^3+1) + 3x^2 + 3x}$

Trial and Error

Very often a problem can be solved by trial and error. However, it is usually possible to avoid making blind guesses. Rather, we begin with an educated guess, or estimate, and then try to refine this initial value or reduce the range of possible values.

As an example of this strategy, let us find the cube root of 2584, to the nearest tenth. Here are some steps that might be followed.

Step 1   Make a rough estimate mentally.

$10^3 = 10 \times 10 \times 10 = 1000$ too small

$20^3 = 20 \times 20 \times 20 = 8000$ too large

$\sqrt[3]{2584}$ lies between 10 and 20.

Step 2   Try a few values between 10 and 20. Since 2584 is closer to 10^3 than to 20^3, you might start with 12^3. Use a calculator, if one is available, but do not use the cube-root key.

$12^3 = 12 \times 12 \times 12 = 1728$ too small

$13^3 = 13 \times 13 \times 13 = 2197$ too small

$14^3 = 14 \times 14 \times 14 = 2744$ too large

$\sqrt[3]{2584}$ lies between 13 and 14.

Step 3   Repeat the same process for decimals between 13 and 14.

$13.6^3 = 2515.456$

$13.7^3 = 2571.353$ 2571.353 is closer to 2584 than is 2628.072.

$13.8^3 = 2628.072$ To the nearest tenth, $\sqrt[3]{2584} = 13.7$.

This strategy can be used to find the fourth root of 331,776. First, estimate.

$10^4 = 10{,}000$

$20^4 = 160{,}000$

$30^4 = 810{,}000$

$\sqrt[4]{331{,}776}$ lies between 20 and 30.

Then test some values between 20 and 30.

$22^4 = 234{,}256$

$23^4 = 279{,}841$

$24^4 = 331{,}776$ $\sqrt[4]{331{,}776} = 24$

Use the method illustrated above to find each root. If the root is not a whole number, find it to the nearest tenth.

1. $\sqrt{9216}$ **2.** $\sqrt[3]{17{,}576}$ **3.** $\sqrt[3]{29{,}600}$ **4.** $\sqrt[3]{170{,}954}$

5. $\sqrt[4]{3{,}200{,}000}$ **6.** $\sqrt[4]{1{,}874{,}161}$ **7.** $\sqrt[5]{248{,}832}$ **8.** $\sqrt[5]{5{,}000{,}000}$

6-3 Combining Radicals by Addition and Subtraction

OBJECTIVE

To simplify radical expressions by combining terms with the same index and radicand.

Sums and differences of radicals with the same index and radicand can be simplified using the distributive property. The procedure is much like combining *like terms*.

Simplify $4x + 2x$.

$4x$ and $2x$ are like terms, so

$$4x + 2x = (4 + 2)x = 6x$$

Simplify $4\sqrt{5} + 2\sqrt{5}$.

The indices and radicands are the same, so

$$4\sqrt{5} + 2\sqrt{5} = (4 + 2)\sqrt{5} = 6\sqrt{5}$$

We often simplify one or more radicals before combining terms.

EXAMPLE 1   Simplify $\sqrt{8} + \sqrt{72} - \sqrt{18}$.

$$
\begin{aligned}
\sqrt{8} + \sqrt{72} - \sqrt{18} &= \sqrt{4 \cdot 2} + \sqrt{36 \cdot 2} - \sqrt{9 \cdot 2} \\
&= (\sqrt{4} \cdot \sqrt{2}) + (\sqrt{36} \cdot \sqrt{2}) - (\sqrt{9} \cdot \sqrt{2}) \\
&= 2\sqrt{2} + 6\sqrt{2} - 3\sqrt{2} \\
&= (2 + 6 - 3)\sqrt{2} \qquad \text{Use the distributive property.} \\
&= 5\sqrt{2}
\end{aligned}
$$

EXAMPLE 2   Simplify $\sqrt[3]{16x} + \sqrt[3]{54x^4}$.

$$
\begin{aligned}
\sqrt[3]{16x} + \sqrt[3]{54x^4} &= \sqrt[3]{8 \cdot 2x} + \sqrt[3]{27x^3 \cdot 2x} \\
&= (\sqrt[3]{8} \cdot \sqrt[3]{2x}) + (\sqrt[3]{27x^3} \cdot \sqrt[3]{2x}) \\
&= 2\sqrt[3]{2x} + 3x\sqrt[3]{2x} \\
&= (2 + 3x)\sqrt[3]{2x} \qquad \text{Use the distributive property.} \\
&\phantom{= (2 + 3x)\sqrt[3]{2x}} \qquad \text{The expression is now in} \\
&\phantom{= (2 + 3x)\sqrt[3]{2x}} \qquad \text{simplest form.}
\end{aligned}
$$

Note how the distributive property is used to find the product in the next example.

EXAMPLE 3   Multiply $2\sqrt{3}(\sqrt{6} + 3\sqrt{8})$.

$$
\begin{aligned}
2\sqrt{3}(\sqrt{6} + 3\sqrt{8}) &= 2\sqrt{3}(\sqrt{6}) + 2\sqrt{3}(3\sqrt{8}) \\
&= 2\sqrt{18} + 6\sqrt{24} \\
&= 2(3\sqrt{2}) + 6(2\sqrt{6}) \\
&= 6\sqrt{2} + 12\sqrt{6}
\end{aligned}
$$

$$\sqrt{18} = \sqrt{9} \cdot \sqrt{2} = 3\sqrt{2}$$
$$\sqrt{24} = \sqrt{4} \cdot \sqrt{6} = 2\sqrt{6}$$

To multiply two expressions such as $3\sqrt{2} + \sqrt{3}$ and $5\sqrt{3} - \sqrt{2}$, we use the procedure for multiplying two binomials. The diagram in the next example reviews the process, but you should learn to complete some of the steps mentally.

EXAMPLE 4   Multiply and simplify $(3\sqrt{2} + \sqrt{3})(5\sqrt{3} - \sqrt{2})$.

The product is the sum of the products of the *first* terms, the *outer* terms, the *inner* terms, and the *last* terms.

$$(3\sqrt{2} + \sqrt{3})(5\sqrt{3} - \sqrt{2}) = 15\sqrt{6} - 6 + 15 - \sqrt{6} = 14\sqrt{6} + 9$$

EXAMPLE 5   Expand and simplify $(3\sqrt{5} + 2\sqrt{3})^2$.

Recall the special product $(r + s)^2 = r^2 + 2rs + s^2$.
Let $r = 3\sqrt{5}$ and $s = 2\sqrt{3}$.

$$(3\sqrt{5} + 2\sqrt{3})^2 = (3\sqrt{5})^2 + 2(3\sqrt{5})(2\sqrt{3}) + (2\sqrt{3})^2.$$
$$= 9(5) + 12\sqrt{15} + 4(3)$$
$$= 45 + 12\sqrt{15} + 12$$
$$= 57 + 12\sqrt{15}$$

CLASS EXERCISES

Simplify.

1. $5\sqrt{3} + 3\sqrt{3}$ **2.** $8\sqrt{7} - 5\sqrt{7}$ **3.** $10\sqrt[3]{5} - \sqrt[3]{5}$

4. $\sqrt{8} + \sqrt{2}$ **5.** $2\sqrt{12} + \sqrt{27}$ **6.** $\sqrt[3]{40} - \sqrt[3]{27}$

Multiply or expand, and simplify.

7. $3\sqrt{2}(5\sqrt{2} + 3\sqrt{4})$ **8.** $(5\sqrt{2} - 3\sqrt{5})^2$ **9.** $(2\sqrt{5} + \sqrt{3})(3\sqrt{5} - \sqrt{3})$

EXERCISES

A   *Simplify.*

1. $7\sqrt{2} + 5\sqrt{2}$ **2.** $9\sqrt{3} - 2\sqrt{3}$ **3.** $8\sqrt{7} - \sqrt{7}$

4. $5\sqrt[3]{6} - 3\sqrt[3]{6}$ **5.** $4\sqrt[4]{9} + 5\sqrt[4]{9}$ **6.** $\sqrt[3]{-27} - \sqrt[3]{-8}$

7. $\sqrt{64} + 2\sqrt{25}$ **8.** $\sqrt{12} + \sqrt{3}$ **9.** $\sqrt{12} - \sqrt{3}$

10. $\sqrt{20} - \sqrt{5}$ **11.** $\sqrt{27} + \sqrt{3}$ **12.** $\sqrt{20} + \sqrt{45}$

13. $\sqrt{28} - \sqrt{63} + \sqrt{7}$ **14.** $\sqrt{11} + \sqrt{24} + \sqrt{44}$ **15.** $\sqrt{8} - \sqrt{28} + \sqrt{50}$

16. $2\sqrt{18} + 3\sqrt{8} + \sqrt{4}$ **17.** $7\sqrt{50} - 2\sqrt{72} + \sqrt{98}$ **18.** $2\sqrt{20} - 5\sqrt{45} + 3\sqrt{80}$

19. $\sqrt[3]{32} + \sqrt[3]{40}$ **20.** $\sqrt[3]{-16} + \sqrt[3]{-250}$ **21.** $\sqrt[3]{128} - \sqrt[3]{54}$

22. $3\sqrt{27x} + \sqrt{48x}$ **23.** $5\sqrt{24x^2} + 3\sqrt{54x^2}$ **24.** $8\sqrt{200x^2} - 2\sqrt{20}$

Multiply or expand, and simplify.

25. $2\sqrt{3}(3\sqrt{2} + 3)$ **26.** $3\sqrt{2}(\sqrt{4} + \sqrt{6})$ **27.** $4\sqrt{5}(\sqrt{5} - \sqrt{20})$

28. $(\sqrt{2} + \sqrt{5})(\sqrt{2} - \sqrt{5})$ **29.** $(\sqrt{2} + \sqrt{5})(\sqrt{2} + \sqrt{5})$ **30.** $(\sqrt[3]{2} - 7)(\sqrt[3]{4} - 7)$

31. $(2\sqrt{3} - 5)^2$ **32.** $(3\sqrt{5} + \sqrt{2})^2$ **33.** $(6 + \sqrt{5})^2$

B

*Multiply or expand, and simplify. Assume **x** and **y** represent positive numbers.*

34. $(3\sqrt{x} - 2\sqrt{y})(2\sqrt{x} + 3\sqrt{y})$ **35.** $(5\sqrt{x} - 3\sqrt{y})(5\sqrt{x} + 3\sqrt{y})$

36. $3(\sqrt{x} + \sqrt{y})(\sqrt{x} + \sqrt{y})$ **37.** $\sqrt{2}(\sqrt{2x} - y)(\sqrt{2x} + y)$

38. $-5(\sqrt{x + y})(\sqrt{x + y})$ **39.** $\sqrt{3x}(\sqrt{2x} + \sqrt{3x} - \sqrt{8x})$

40. $2(\sqrt{3x} - \sqrt{2y})^2$ **41.** $5(\sqrt{2x} + \sqrt{3y})^2$

42. $(\sqrt[3]{x} + \sqrt[3]{y})(\sqrt[3]{x} - \sqrt[3]{y})$ **43.** $(\sqrt[4]{x^2} + \sqrt[4]{y^2})(\sqrt[4]{x^2} - \sqrt[4]{y^2})$

*Simplify. Assume **x** and **y** represent positive numbers.*

44. $-2\sqrt[3]{56} + 5\sqrt[3]{189} - 3\sqrt[3]{7}$ **45.** $\sqrt[3]{625} - 2\sqrt[3]{1080} + 3\sqrt[3]{40}$

46. $5\sqrt[4]{32} - 2\sqrt[4]{162} + \sqrt[4]{1250}$ **47.** $5\sqrt{32xy^3} + 3\sqrt{50xy^3} - 2y\sqrt{18xy}$

48. $\sqrt[3]{24x^3y} + \sqrt[3]{81x^3y} - x\sqrt[3]{3y}$ **49.** $\sqrt[3]{250x^3y^6} + x\sqrt[3]{2000y^6} - y^2\sqrt[3]{2x^3}$

C

*Multiply or expand, and simplify. Assume **x** represents a positive number.*

50. $(x - \sqrt[3]{2})(x^2 + x\sqrt[3]{2} + \sqrt[3]{4})$ **51.** $(x + \sqrt[3]{2})(x^2 - x\sqrt[3]{2} + \sqrt[3]{4})$

52. $(\sqrt[3]{x} + 1)^3$ **53.** $(x + \sqrt{x} + \sqrt[3]{x})(x - \sqrt{x} + \sqrt[3]{x})$

CHECKPOINT

Find each root, if it is a real number.

1. $\sqrt{49}$ **2.** $\sqrt{-49}$ **3.** $-\sqrt{49}$ **4.** $\sqrt{64x^2}$ **5.** $\sqrt[3]{-64x^3}$

Simplify. Assume all variables represent positive numbers.

6. $\sqrt{6} \cdot \sqrt{6}$ **7.** $\sqrt{9} \cdot \sqrt{81}$ **8.** $\sqrt[3]{3} \cdot \sqrt[3]{9}$ **9.** $\sqrt{99}$ **10.** $\sqrt{162}$

11. $\sqrt[3]{1728}$ **12.** $5\sqrt{2} + 3\sqrt{2}$ **13.** $7\sqrt{7x^2} - 8\sqrt{7x^2}$ **14.** $3\sqrt[3]{6y} - \sqrt[3]{6y}$

6-4 Dividing and Simplifying Radicals

OBJECTIVES

To simplify quotients of radical expressions.
To simplify radical expressions by rationalizing the denominators.

Compare these two computations.

$$\left.\begin{array}{l} \dfrac{\sqrt{9}}{\sqrt{25}} = \dfrac{\sqrt{3 \cdot 3}}{\sqrt{5 \cdot 5}} = \dfrac{3}{5} \\[4mm] \sqrt{\dfrac{9}{25}} = \sqrt{\dfrac{3}{5} \cdot \dfrac{3}{5}} = \dfrac{3}{5} \end{array}\right\}$$ The results are the same. Therefore, $\dfrac{\sqrt{9}}{\sqrt{25}} = \sqrt{\dfrac{9}{25}}$

This illustrates the following general rule.

Quotient of Roots

If $\sqrt[n]{a}$ and $\sqrt[n]{b}$ are real numbers, with $\sqrt[n]{b} \neq 0$, then

$$\frac{\sqrt[n]{a}}{\sqrt[n]{b}} = \sqrt[n]{\frac{a}{b}}$$

This rule can be used in the order given or in the reversed order:

$$\sqrt[n]{\frac{a}{b}} = \frac{\sqrt[n]{a}}{\sqrt[n]{b}}$$

EXAMPLE 1   Simplify.

a. $\dfrac{\sqrt{72}}{\sqrt{8}} = \sqrt{\dfrac{72}{8}}$ b. $\sqrt[3]{\dfrac{5}{27}} = \dfrac{\sqrt[3]{5}}{\sqrt[3]{27}}$

$\qquad\qquad = \sqrt{9}$ $\qquad\qquad\qquad = \dfrac{\sqrt[3]{5}}{3}$

$\qquad\qquad = 3$

c. $\sqrt{\dfrac{8x^2}{49}} = \dfrac{\sqrt{(4x^2)(2)}}{\sqrt{49}}$

$\qquad\quad = \dfrac{2|x|\sqrt{2}}{7}$, or $\dfrac{2\sqrt{2}}{7}|x|$

When simplifying a radical expression, we write the expression in such a way that there is no radical in the denominator. Sometimes this can be done by division, as in Example 1a. However, this method cannot always be applied. A more general method is to multiply the numerator and denominator by a number that will give a rational denominator. This is equivalent to multiplying the fraction by 1, so its value is unchanged. The procedure is called **rationalizing the denominator.**

EXAMPLE 2   Simplify $\dfrac{2}{\sqrt{3}}$.

$$\dfrac{2}{\sqrt{3}} = \dfrac{2}{\sqrt{3}} \cdot \dfrac{\sqrt{3}}{\sqrt{3}} \qquad \text{Multiply by } \dfrac{\sqrt{3}}{\sqrt{3}} = 1.$$

$$= \dfrac{2\sqrt{3}}{\sqrt{9}}$$

$$= \dfrac{2\sqrt{3}}{3}$$

Let us summarize what you have learned about simplified radicals.

Assume an expression contains one or more radicals.
If the expression is in *simplest form*, then

• for any radical with index n, the radicand has no factor, other than 1, that is an nth power.

• no radicand contains a fraction.

• no denominator contains a radical.

• terms with the same index and radicand are combined.

Compare the two methods used to simplify the expression in Example 3. There are fewer steps if you multiply by the smallest possible number to obtain a perfect square, as shown in the second method.

EXAMPLE 3   Simplify $\dfrac{5}{\sqrt{12}}$.

Method I	**Method II**
$\dfrac{5}{\sqrt{12}} = \dfrac{5}{\sqrt{12}} \cdot \dfrac{\sqrt{12}}{\sqrt{12}}$	$\dfrac{5}{\sqrt{12}} = \dfrac{5}{\sqrt{12}} \cdot \dfrac{\sqrt{3}}{\sqrt{3}}$
$= \dfrac{5\sqrt{12}}{12}$	$= \dfrac{5\sqrt{3}}{\sqrt{36}}$
$= \dfrac{5\sqrt{4 \cdot 3}}{12}$	$= \dfrac{5\sqrt{3}}{6}$
$= \dfrac{10\sqrt{3}}{12}$	
$= \dfrac{5\sqrt{3}}{6}$	

The next example illustrates the rationalization of a denominator in which the radicand contains a variable.

EXAMPLE 4   Simplify $\dfrac{\sqrt[3]{2}}{\sqrt[3]{3x}}$. Assume x does not represent 0.

$$\frac{\sqrt[3]{2}}{\sqrt[3]{3x}} = \frac{\sqrt[3]{2}}{\sqrt[3]{3x}} \cdot \frac{\sqrt[3]{9x^2}}{\sqrt[3]{9x^2}} \qquad 3x \cdot 9x^2 = 27x^3, \text{ a perfect cube.}$$

$$= \frac{\sqrt[3]{18x^2}}{\sqrt[3]{27x^3}}$$

$$= \frac{\sqrt[3]{18x^2}}{3x}$$

Now, suppose you wish to rationalize the denominator of the fraction $\dfrac{6}{\sqrt{5} + \sqrt{2}}$. First, recall that

$$(r + s)(r - s) = r^2 - s^2$$

Then use this result, with $r = \sqrt{5}$ and $s = \sqrt{2}$.

$$(\sqrt{5} + \sqrt{2})(\sqrt{5} - \sqrt{2}) = (\sqrt{5})^2 - (\sqrt{2})^2 = 5 - 2 = 3$$

Each of the expressions $\sqrt{5} + \sqrt{2}$ and $\sqrt{5} - \sqrt{2}$ is the **conjugate** of the other. The product of two such conjugates is a rational number. Therefore, to rationalize the denominator of $\dfrac{6}{\sqrt{5} + \sqrt{2}}$, we multiply by 1 in the form $\dfrac{\sqrt{5} - \sqrt{2}}{\sqrt{5} - \sqrt{2}}$.

$$\frac{6}{\sqrt{5} + \sqrt{2}} = \frac{6}{\sqrt{5} + \sqrt{2}} \cdot \frac{\sqrt{5} - \sqrt{2}}{\sqrt{5} - \sqrt{2}} = \frac{6(\sqrt{5} - \sqrt{2})}{3} = 2(\sqrt{5} - \sqrt{2})$$

EXAMPLE 5   Simplify $\dfrac{\sqrt{3} + 3}{5 - \sqrt{3}}$.

$$\frac{\sqrt{3} + 3}{5 - \sqrt{3}} = \frac{\sqrt{3} + 3}{5 - \sqrt{3}} \cdot \frac{5 + \sqrt{3}}{5 + \sqrt{3}} \qquad \text{The conjugate of } 5 - \sqrt{3} \text{ is } 5 + \sqrt{3}.$$

$$= \frac{5\sqrt{3} + 3 + 15 + 3\sqrt{3}}{25 - 3}$$

$$= \frac{18 + 8\sqrt{3}}{22} = \frac{9 + 4\sqrt{3}}{11}$$

CLASS EXERCISES

Explain why each expression is not in simplified form. Then simplify.

1. $\dfrac{\sqrt[3]{16}}{5}$ **2.** $\dfrac{5}{\sqrt{5}}$ **3.** $\sqrt{\dfrac{16}{5}}$ **4.** $\dfrac{\sqrt{5} + 3\sqrt{5}}{16}$ **5.** $\dfrac{16}{5\sqrt{3}}$

EXERCISES

A

Simplify.

1. $\sqrt{\dfrac{4}{9}}$ 2. $\sqrt{\dfrac{16}{81}}$ 3. $\sqrt{\dfrac{1}{49}}$ 4. $\sqrt{\dfrac{25}{36}}$ 5. $-\sqrt{\dfrac{25}{121}}$

6. $\sqrt{\dfrac{11}{225}}$ 7. $\sqrt{\dfrac{8}{144}}$ 8. $\sqrt{\dfrac{8}{49}}$ 9. $\sqrt{\dfrac{27}{100}}$ 10. $\sqrt{\dfrac{12}{81}}$

11. $\sqrt{\dfrac{18}{121}}$ 12. $-\sqrt{\dfrac{50}{121}}$ 13. $\sqrt{\dfrac{18}{196}}$ 14. $\dfrac{\sqrt{75}}{\sqrt{3}}$ 15. $\dfrac{\sqrt{81}}{\sqrt{3}}$

16. $\dfrac{3\sqrt{125}}{\sqrt{5}}$ 17. $\dfrac{\sqrt{128}}{4\sqrt{2}}$ 18. $\dfrac{\sqrt{256}}{\sqrt{8}}$ 19. $\dfrac{\sqrt{3}+2\sqrt{3}}{\sqrt{3}}$ 20. $\dfrac{\sqrt{2}+5\sqrt{2}}{6}$

21. $\dfrac{\sqrt{24x^2}}{\sqrt{16}}$ 22. $\dfrac{\sqrt{12x^2}}{\sqrt{64}}$ 23. $\dfrac{\sqrt{12x^2}}{\sqrt{16}}$ 24. $\dfrac{\sqrt{32x^2}}{2\sqrt{8}}$ 25. $\dfrac{6}{\sqrt{6}}$

26. $\dfrac{10}{2\sqrt{5}}$ 27. $\dfrac{3}{\sqrt{8}}$ 28. $\dfrac{\sqrt{80}}{\sqrt{2}}$ 29. $\dfrac{9}{\sqrt{3}}$ 30. $\dfrac{20}{\sqrt{5}}$

31. $\dfrac{8}{\sqrt{8}}$ 32. $\sqrt[3]{\dfrac{81}{3}}$ 33. $\dfrac{\sqrt[3]{-8x}}{8}$ 34. $\dfrac{\sqrt[3]{32}}{\sqrt[3]{4}}$ 35. $\dfrac{\sqrt[3]{54}}{\sqrt[3]{2}}$

36. $\dfrac{3\sqrt{10}}{\sqrt{6}}$ 37. $\dfrac{27}{3\sqrt{9}}$ 38. $\dfrac{\sqrt[3]{2}}{\sqrt[3]{27}}$ 39. $\sqrt{\dfrac{8}{3}}$ 40. $\sqrt{\dfrac{7}{2}}$

B

Simplify. Assume all variables represent positive numbers.

41. $\dfrac{\sqrt{3x}}{\sqrt{2}}$ 42. $\dfrac{\sqrt{2}}{\sqrt{3x}}$ 43. $\dfrac{\sqrt{5y}}{-\sqrt{8}}$ 44. $\dfrac{5\sqrt{10}}{\sqrt{5x^3}}$ 45. $\sqrt{\dfrac{5}{6x}}$

46. $\sqrt{\dfrac{8}{72x^5}}$ 47. $\sqrt{\dfrac{7x^2}{50}}$ 48. $\dfrac{\sqrt[3]{-256}}{\sqrt[3]{-2}}$ 49. $\dfrac{\sqrt[3]{81x^3}}{\sqrt[3]{3}}$ 50. $\dfrac{\sqrt[4]{80}}{\sqrt[4]{5x^4}}$

51. $\dfrac{\sqrt[3]{2x^3}}{\sqrt[3]{y^2}}$ 52. $\sqrt[3]{\dfrac{5}{2x}}$ 53. $\sqrt[3]{\dfrac{y^3}{25x^3}}$ 54. $\sqrt[3]{\dfrac{81}{4x^2}}$ 55. $\sqrt[4]{\dfrac{16}{x^3}}$

56. $\dfrac{9}{\sqrt{3}-\sqrt{2}}$ 57. $\dfrac{10}{\sqrt{5}+\sqrt{3}}$ 58. $\dfrac{\sqrt{3}+\sqrt{2}}{\sqrt{3}-\sqrt{2}}$ 59. $\dfrac{\sqrt{5}-\sqrt{3}}{\sqrt{5}+\sqrt{3}}$

60. $\dfrac{\sqrt{x}+\sqrt{y}}{\sqrt{x}-\sqrt{y}}$ 61. $\dfrac{5-\sqrt{3}}{5+\sqrt{3}}$ 62. $\dfrac{2-\sqrt{6}}{\sqrt{6}-3}$ 63. $\dfrac{x-\sqrt{y}}{x+\sqrt{y}}$

C

64. $\dfrac{\sqrt{3}}{3\sqrt{2}}+\dfrac{\sqrt{2}}{2\sqrt{3}}$ 65. $\dfrac{\sqrt{5}}{\sqrt{3x}}-\dfrac{\sqrt{3}}{\sqrt{5x}}$ 66. $\dfrac{\sqrt{b}}{\sqrt{a}}+\dfrac{\sqrt{a}}{\sqrt{b}}$ 67. $\dfrac{6}{\sqrt{3}}+\dfrac{8}{\sqrt{2}}$

68. $\dfrac{\sqrt{x+y}}{3+\sqrt{x+y}}$ 69. $\dfrac{\sqrt{x+y}+\sqrt{x-y}}{\sqrt{x+y}-\sqrt{x-y}}$ *70. $\dfrac{1}{\sqrt[3]{x}+\sqrt[3]{y}}$

6-5 Fractional Exponents

OBJECTIVES

To write expressions involving fractional exponents as radicals, and the reverse.
To evaluate expressions with fractional exponents.
To use fractional exponents to simplify radical expressions.

Fractional powers such as $9^{\frac{1}{2}}$ have not yet been defined. To arrive at definitions for such powers, we will assume that the rules for integral exponents apply to fractional exponents as well. Then we can use our knowledge of roots to give meaning to such exponents, as illustrated below.

$$(9^{\frac{1}{2}})^2 = 9^{\frac{1}{2} \cdot 2} = 9^1 = 9$$

$$\text{Also, } (\sqrt{9})^2 = 9$$
$$\text{Now we define: } 9^{\frac{1}{2}} = \sqrt{9}$$
$$\text{In general, } b^{\frac{1}{2}} = \sqrt{b} \text{ for } b \geq 0$$

We can give meaning to the exponent $\frac{1}{3}$ in a similar way.

$$(8^{\frac{1}{3}})^3 = 8^{\frac{1}{3} \cdot 3} = 8^1 = 8$$
$$\text{Also, } (\sqrt[3]{8})^3 = 8$$
$$\text{Therefore, } 8^{\frac{1}{3}} = \sqrt[3]{8}$$
$$\text{In general, } b^{\frac{1}{3}} = \sqrt[3]{b}$$

These illustrations lead to the following general definition.

For a real number b and an integer n, with $n > 1$,
$$b^{\frac{1}{n}} = \sqrt[n]{b}$$
provided that $\sqrt[n]{b}$ is a real number.

EXAMPLE 1   Evaluate.

a. $9^{\frac{1}{2}} = \sqrt{9} = 3$ **b.** $8^{\frac{1}{3}} = \sqrt[3]{8} = 2$

c. $256^{\frac{1}{4}} = \sqrt[4]{256} = 4$ **d.** $(-125)^{\frac{1}{3}} = \sqrt[3]{-125} = -5$

We are now ready to extend the definition of fractional exponents, as in the following illustration.

$$8^{\frac{2}{3}} = (8^2)^{\frac{1}{3}}$$
$$= \sqrt[3]{8^2}$$

Also, $8^{\frac{2}{3}} = \left(8^{\frac{1}{3}}\right)^2$
$$= (\sqrt[3]{8})^2$$

Therefore, $8^{\frac{2}{3}} = \sqrt[3]{8^2} = (\sqrt[3]{8})^2$

This leads to the following general definition.

For a nonzero real number b and for integers m and n, where $n > 1$,
$$b^{\frac{m}{n}} = \sqrt[n]{b^m} = (\sqrt[n]{b})^m$$
provided that $\sqrt[n]{b}$ is a real number.

EXAMPLE 2   Write each expression in radical form.

a. $5^{\frac{3}{4}} = \sqrt[4]{5^3} = \sqrt[4]{125}$ **b.** $x^{\frac{4}{5}} = \sqrt[5]{x^4}$

EXAMPLE 3   Write each expression in exponential form.

a. $\sqrt[3]{7^2} = 7^{\frac{2}{3}}$ **b.** $\sqrt{x^3} = x^{\frac{3}{2}}$

You can often evaluate an expression with a fractional exponent in more than one way. For example, here are two ways to evaluate $8^{\frac{2}{3}}$.

Method I   **Method II**

$$8^{\frac{2}{3}} = (\sqrt[3]{8})^2 = 2^2 = 4 \qquad 8^{\frac{2}{3}} = \sqrt[3]{8^2} = \sqrt[3]{64} = 4$$

Usually it is easier to take the root first, then raise to a power, as shown in Method I. To see why this is true, try evaluating the first expression in Example 4 by first cubing the number and then taking the indicated root.

EXAMPLE 4   Evaluate.

a. $32^{\frac{3}{5}} = (\sqrt[5]{32})^3 = 2^3 = 8$

b. $25^{-\frac{3}{2}} = \dfrac{1}{25^{\frac{3}{2}}} = \dfrac{1}{(\sqrt{25})^3} = \dfrac{1}{5^3} = \dfrac{1}{125}$

c. $(-0.001)^{\frac{5}{3}} = (\sqrt[3]{-0.001})^5 = (-0.1)^5 = -0.00001$

It is often helpful to use fractional exponents when simplifying radicals, as shown in this final example.

EXAMPLE 5   Simplify. Express the answers in radical form.

a. $\sqrt[6]{9} \cdot \sqrt[6]{3} = \sqrt[6]{3^2} \cdot \sqrt[6]{3} = 3^{\frac{2}{6}} \cdot 3^{\frac{1}{6}} = 3^{\frac{2}{6}+\frac{1}{6}} = 3^{\frac{1}{2}} = \sqrt{3}$

b. $\dfrac{\sqrt[3]{9}}{\sqrt{3}} = \dfrac{\sqrt[3]{3^2}}{\sqrt{3}} = \dfrac{3^{\frac{2}{3}}}{3^{\frac{1}{2}}} = 3^{\frac{2}{3}-\frac{1}{2}} = 3^{\frac{1}{6}} = \sqrt[6]{3}$

CLASS EXERCISES

Write each expression in radical form.

1. $7^{\frac{1}{2}}$　　　**2.** $9^{\frac{1}{3}}$　　　**3.** $2^{\frac{2}{3}}$　　　**4.** $x^{\frac{3}{4}}$　　　**5.** $(3x)^{\frac{2}{3}}$

Write each expression in exponential form.

6. $\sqrt[3]{11}$　　　**7.** $\sqrt[4]{13}$　　　**8.** $\sqrt[3]{x^2}$　　　**9.** $\sqrt[5]{x^4}$　　　**10.** $\sqrt[4]{(2x)^3}$

Evaluate.

11. $64^{\frac{1}{3}}$　　　**12.** $36^{\frac{1}{2}}$　　　**13.** $36^{\frac{3}{2}}$　　　**14.** $8^{-\frac{2}{3}}$　　　**15.** $16^{\frac{3}{4}}$

EXERCISES

A

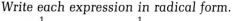

Write each expression in radical form.

1. $19^{\frac{1}{2}}$　　　**2.** $7^{\frac{1}{3}}$　　　**3.** $6^{\frac{1}{4}}$　　　**4.** $(3x)^{\frac{1}{2}}$　　　**5.** $(2a)^{\frac{1}{3}}$

6. $7^{\frac{2}{3}}$　　　**7.** $3^{\frac{3}{4}}$　　　**8.** $3^{\frac{4}{3}}$　　　**9.** $2x^{\frac{2}{3}}$　　　**10.** $(2x)^{\frac{2}{3}}$

11. $5x^{-\frac{1}{2}}$　　　**12.** $19^{-\frac{1}{3}}$　　　**13.** $7^{-\frac{2}{3}}$　　　**14.** $(2a)^{-\frac{1}{2}}$　　　**15.** $(3b)^{-\frac{3}{4}}$

Write each expression in exponential form.

16. $\sqrt{23}$　　　**17.** $\sqrt{35}$　　　**18.** $\sqrt[3]{17}$　　　**19.** $\sqrt[3]{-25}$　　　**20.** $\sqrt[3]{89}$

21. $-\sqrt{31}$　　　**22.** $-\sqrt[3]{11}$　　　**23.** $\sqrt[3]{9^2}$　　　**24.** $(\sqrt[3]{9})^2$　　　**25.** $\sqrt[4]{8^3}$

26. $\sqrt[3]{x}$　　　**27.** $\sqrt[3]{x^2}$　　　**28.** $\sqrt[3]{2x^2}$　　　**29.** $\sqrt[3]{(2x)^2}$　　　**30.** $\sqrt[4]{x^3}$

Evaluate.

31. $81^{\frac{1}{2}}$　　　**32.** $125^{\frac{1}{3}}$　　　**33.** $27^{\frac{1}{3}}$　　　**34.** $(-125)^{\frac{1}{3}}$　　　**35.** $27^{-\frac{1}{3}}$

36. $49^{\frac{3}{2}}$　　　**37.** $49^{-\frac{3}{2}}$　　　**38.** $27^{\frac{2}{3}}$　　　**39.** $27^{-\frac{2}{3}}$　　　**40.** $32^{\frac{2}{5}}$

B

41. $\left(\dfrac{1}{27}\right)^{\frac{1}{3}}$　　　**42.** $\left(\dfrac{1}{27}\right)^{-\frac{1}{3}}$　　　**43.** $\left(\dfrac{8}{27}\right)^{\frac{2}{3}}$　　　**44.** $\left(\dfrac{8}{27}\right)^{-\frac{2}{3}}$　　　**45.** $\left(\dfrac{1}{16}\right)^{\frac{3}{4}}$

46. $\dfrac{9^{\frac{1}{2}}}{27^{\frac{1}{3}}}$ **47.** $\dfrac{25^{-\frac{1}{2}}}{36^{\frac{1}{2}}}$ **48.** $\dfrac{16^{\frac{1}{2}}}{16^{\frac{1}{4}}}$ **49.** $\dfrac{(-125)^{\frac{2}{3}}}{4^{\frac{3}{2}}}$ **50.** $\dfrac{9^{-\frac{3}{2}}}{8^{-\frac{2}{3}}}$

Use fractional exponents to simplify. Express answers in radical form.

51. $\sqrt{5} \div \sqrt[6]{5}$ **52.** $\sqrt{7} \cdot \sqrt[6]{7}$ **53.** $\sqrt[4]{9} \div \sqrt[3]{3}$ **54.** $\sqrt[3]{4} \div \sqrt[6]{2}$

55. $\sqrt{8} \div \sqrt[4]{4}$ **56.** $\sqrt[4]{8} \cdot \sqrt[8]{4}$ **57.** $\sqrt[3]{\sqrt{2}}$ **58.** $\sqrt{\sqrt{5}}$

59. Evaluate and compare the answers in **a** and **b**.

   a. $\left(\dfrac{1}{8}\right)^{\frac{1}{3}} + \left(\dfrac{1}{27}\right)^{\frac{1}{3}}$ **b.** $\left(\dfrac{1}{8} + \dfrac{1}{27}\right)^{\frac{1}{3}}$

Evaluate.

60. $\left(64^{\frac{1}{2}}\right)^{\frac{1}{3}}$ **61.** $\left(64^{-\frac{1}{2}}\right)^{\frac{2}{3}}$ **62.** $\left(27^{\frac{2}{3}}\right)^{\frac{1}{2}}$ **63.** $\left(125^{\frac{2}{3}}\right)^{-\frac{1}{2}}$

C

Simplify. Assume all variables represent positive numbers.

64. $\left(16x^4y^8\right)^{-\frac{3}{2}}$ **65.** $\left(-8a^3b^6\right)^{\frac{1}{3}}$ **66.** $\left(64a^2b^4\right)^{\frac{3}{2}}$ **67.** $\left(16a^8b^4\right)^{\frac{3}{4}}$

68. $\left(\dfrac{8x^6}{y^{-6}}\right)^{\frac{1}{3}}$ **69.** $\left(\dfrac{125a^3}{b^{12}}\right)^{-\frac{1}{3}}$ **70.** $\left(\dfrac{27x^5y}{-8x^2y^4}\right)^{\frac{2}{3}}$ **71.** $\left(\dfrac{-64a^7b^{-1}}{a^{-2}b^8}\right)^{-\frac{2}{3}}$

72. $\left(\dfrac{x^a}{x^{a-2}}\right)^{\frac{1}{2}}$ **73.** $\left(\dfrac{x^n}{x^{n-3}}\right)^{-\frac{1}{3}}$ **74.** $\left(\dfrac{x^ny^{n-1}}{x^{3n}y^{n+1}}\right)^{-\frac{1}{2}}$ **75.** $\left(\dfrac{x^{2n-1}y^{7n}}{x^{2n+2}y^n}\right)^{\frac{2}{3}}$

*76. Here is a "proof" that $2 = -2$. Can you find the error?

$$\sqrt[3]{-8} = (-8)^{\frac{1}{3}} = (-8)^{\frac{2}{6}} = \sqrt[6]{(-8)^2} = \sqrt[6]{64} = 2$$

But we also know that $\sqrt[3]{-8} = -2$. Therefore $2 = -2$.

CHECKPOINT

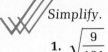

Simplify.

  1. $\sqrt{\dfrac{9}{121}}$ **2.** $\dfrac{2\sqrt{10x^2}}{\sqrt{5}}$ **3.** $\dfrac{2}{\sqrt{5} - \sqrt{3}}$ **4.** $\dfrac{3 + \sqrt{5}}{3 - \sqrt{5}}$

Multiply or expand, and simplify. Assume all variables represent positive numbers.

  5. $(5\sqrt{x} - 4\sqrt{y})(4\sqrt{x} + 5\sqrt{y})$ **6.** $(2\sqrt{x} - \sqrt{y})(3\sqrt{x} + \sqrt{y})$

  7. $-3(\sqrt{2x + y})(\sqrt{2x + y})$ **8.** $4(\sqrt{3x} + \sqrt{2y})^2$

Write each expression in exponential form.

  9. $\sqrt{21}$ **10.** $\sqrt[3]{37}$ **11.** $\sqrt[3]{5^2}$ **12.** $(\sqrt[3]{5})^2$ **13.** $\sqrt[3]{8x}$

6-6 Radical Equations

OBJECTIVES _____

To solve radical equations.
To solve problems involving such equations.

_____

A **radical equation** is one in which one or more radicands contain variables. Such an equation is solved by raising both sides to an appropriate power in order to eliminate the radicals. Study the following examples.

EXAMPLE 1   Solve and check.

a. $\sqrt{x + 1} = 5$

$(\sqrt{x + 1})^2 = 5^2$ Square each side of the equation.

$x + 1 = 25$

$x = 24$

Check $\sqrt{24 + 1} = \sqrt{25} = 5$ ✔

The solution is 24.

b. $\sqrt[3]{x - 2} = 2$

$(\sqrt[3]{x - 2})^3 = 2^3$ Cube each side of the equation.

$x - 2 = 8$

$x = 10$

Check $\sqrt[3]{10 - 2} = \sqrt[3]{8} = 2$ ✔

The solution is 10.

The following general property was used to solve the equations above.

Suppose r and s are real numbers, and n is a positive integer.

If $r = s$, then $r^n = s^n$.

After each side of an equation has been raised to a power, a new equation is formed. It may be possible to obtain solutions to this new equation that are _not_ solutions to the original equation, as is the case in the next example. This points out the fact that it is essential to check all results in order to identify such _apparent solutions_, or _extraneous roots_.

EXAMPLE 2   Solve and check: $\sqrt{x + 4} + 1 = x - 1$.

$$\sqrt{x + 4} + 1 = x - 1$$
$$\sqrt{x + 4} = x - 2 \qquad \text{"Isolate" the radical on one side of the}$$
$$\text{equation.}$$
$$(\sqrt{x + 4})^2 = (x - 2)^2 \qquad \text{If } r = s, \text{ then } r^2 = s^2.$$
$$x + 4 = x^2 - 4x + 4$$
$$x^2 - 5x = 0$$
$$x(x - 5) = 0$$
$$x = 0 \quad \text{or} \quad x - 5 = 0 \qquad \text{If } ab = 0, \text{ then } a = 0 \text{ or } b = 0.$$
$$x = 5$$

Check   For $x = 0$: $\sqrt{0 + 4} + 1 \overset{?}{=} 0 - 1$
$$2 + 1 \overset{?}{=} -1$$
$$3 = -1 \qquad \text{False}$$

0 is an extraneous root. It is *not* a solution to the original equation.

For $x = 5$: $\sqrt{5 + 4} + 1 \overset{?}{=} 5 - 1$
$$3 + 1 \overset{?}{=} 4$$
$$4 = 4 \qquad \text{True}$$

5 is the solution to the original equation.

At times you may need to square twice, as in the next example.

EXAMPLE 3   Solve and check: $\sqrt{x} - \sqrt{x - 5} = 1$.

$$\sqrt{x} - \sqrt{x - 5} = 1$$
$$\sqrt{x} - 1 = \sqrt{x - 5} \qquad \text{"Isolate" one of the radicals.}$$
$$x - 2\sqrt{x} + 1 = x - 5 \qquad \text{Square each side.}$$
$$-2\sqrt{x} = -6$$
$$\sqrt{x} = 3$$
$$x = 9 \qquad \text{Square each side again.}$$

Show that 9 is the solution by checking in the original equation.

CLASS EXERCISES

Solve and check. State **no solution,** if applicable.

1. $\sqrt{x - 2} = 3$

2. $\sqrt{x + 10} = 5$

3. $\sqrt{2x} = 3$

4. $1 + \sqrt{x} = 7$

5. $\sqrt{x + 3} = 5$

6. $\sqrt{x + 5} = 2$

7. $\sqrt[3]{x + 1} = 2$

8. $\sqrt[3]{x + 2} = 5$

9. $\sqrt[3]{x - 4} = -2$

10. $\sqrt{x - 1} = x - 1$

11. $\sqrt{x + 2} = x$

12. $\sqrt{x} = x - 6$

EXERCISES

Solve and check. Write **no solution,** if applicable.

1. $\sqrt{x + 2} = 3$
2. $\sqrt{x - 1} = 4$
3. $\sqrt{2x + 3} = 7$
4. $\sqrt{3x - 2} = 8$
5. $\sqrt{x + 5} = 12$
6. $\sqrt{x - 3} = 11$
7. $\sqrt{2x - 3} = 7$
8. $5 + \sqrt{3x} = 12$
9. $\sqrt[3]{x + 2} = 1$
10. $\sqrt[3]{x - 2} = 3$
11. $\sqrt[3]{x} - 3 = 5$
12. $2 + \sqrt[3]{x} = 7$
13. $\dfrac{1}{\sqrt{x}} = 4$
14. $\dfrac{\sqrt{x}}{\sqrt{2}} = \sqrt{3}$
15. $\dfrac{1}{\sqrt[3]{x + 1}} = 2$
16. $\dfrac{1}{\sqrt[3]{x - 1}} = 2$
17. $3\sqrt{x + 2} = 0$
18. $5\sqrt{x} = 3\sqrt{2}$
19. $\sqrt{x^2 + 5} = 3$
20. $\sqrt{3 - x^2} = 2$
21. $\sqrt{x + 6} = x + 6$
22. $\sqrt{3x - 4} = 3$
23. $\sqrt{2x + 4} = x - 2$
24. $1 + \sqrt{3x + 1} = x$
25. $\sqrt{2x - 1} + 2 = x$
26. $\sqrt{x + 4} + 2 = x$
27. $\sqrt{x - 4} = x - 4$

B
28. $\sqrt{x + 7} = 1 + \sqrt{x}$
29. $\sqrt{x + 5} + \sqrt{x} = 5$
30. $\sqrt{x - 7} - \sqrt{x} = 1$
31. $3\sqrt{x - 5} = 2\sqrt{x - 5} + 2$
32. $\sqrt{2x + 3} = 5 - \sqrt{x + 1}$
33. $\sqrt{3x + 1} + \sqrt{x + 1} = 8$
34. $\sqrt{2x + 1} - \sqrt{x - 3} = 2$

Write an equation for each problem, and solve.

35. If 3 is added to twice a certain number, the square root of the sum is 3. Find the number.

36. The square root of the sum of 3 times a certain number and 1 is equal to 1 less than the number. Find the number.

37. The cube root of the sum of 2 and the square of a positive number is 3. Find the number.

38. The square root of the sum of a certain number and 3 equals $\frac{1}{2}$ the number. Find the number.

39. The sum of the square root of a number and the square root of 5 less than the number is 7. Find the number.

40. The product of a number and $1\frac{1}{5}$ is equal to the sum of the square root of the number and $1\frac{1}{5}$. Find the number.

C Solve and check.

41. $\sqrt[4]{x + 2} = 1$
42. $\sqrt[5]{3x - 5} = -2$
43. $\sqrt[4]{x^2 + 4} = 2$
44. $\sqrt[5]{3x^2 + 5} = 2$
45. $\sqrt[4]{5x + 1} = \sqrt{3x - 5}$
46. $\sqrt{3x - 5} = \sqrt{2\sqrt{x + 1}}$

47. The radius of a circle whose area is A is given by the formula $r = \sqrt{\dfrac{A}{\pi}}$. Find a formula for A in terms of r and π.

RADICAL EXPRESSIONS   **229**

48. The formula $r = \frac{1}{2}\sqrt{\frac{A}{\pi}}$ gives the radius of a sphere with surface area A. Use the formula to find A in terms of π and r.

49. The formula $r = \sqrt{\frac{3V}{\pi h}}$ gives the radius of a right circular cone with height h and volume V. Use the formula to find V in terms of π, r, and h.

50. Find a formula for the volume V of a sphere if the radius is given by the formula $r = \sqrt[3]{\frac{3V}{4\pi}}$.

51. The formula for the area of the curved surface of a right circular cone with radius r and height h is given by the formula $S = \pi r\sqrt{r^2 + h^2}$. Solve this formula for h in terms of S, r, and π.

CHALLENGE

Indirect Proof

In an **indirect proof**, we assume the opposite of the statement to be proved. Then we show that this assumption leads to a contradiction. Here is an indirect proof that $\sqrt{2}$ is an irrational number.

$\sqrt{2}$ is either rational or irrational. There are no other possibilities. Assume $\sqrt{2}$ is rational. Then $\sqrt{2}$ can be expressed in the form $\frac{p}{q}$, where p and q are integers, q is not 0, and the fraction is in simplified form. If $\sqrt{2} = \frac{p}{q}$, then $2 = \frac{p^2}{q^2}$, and $2q^2 = p^2$. Since $2q^2$ has a factor of 2, $2q^2$ is an even number. Therefore p^2 is even. If p^2 is even, then p is even.

If p is even, we can let $p = 2k$, where k is an integer. Then $p^2 = 4k^2$. But $p^2 = 2q^2$, so $2q^2 = 4k^2$, and $q^2 = 2k^2$. Since $2k^2$ is an even number, q^2 is also even. Since q^2 is even, q is even.

Thus the assumption that $\sqrt{2}$ is rational leads to the conclusion that p and q are both even numbers. But this contradicts the assumption that $\frac{p}{q}$ is in simplified form. Therefore, the assumption that $\sqrt{2}$ is rational is incorrect, and $\sqrt{2}$ must be irrational.

1. In the indirect proof above, we assumed that if p^2 is an even integer, then p is even. Prove this indirectly by assuming that p is odd and showing that this leads to a contradiction.

2. Show that if p^2 is a multiple of 5, then p is a multiple of 5.
   Hint: If p is not a multiple of 5, p can be written in the form $5k + 1$, $5k + 2$, $5k + 3$, or $5k + 4$, where k is an integer.

3. Write an indirect proof that $\sqrt{5}$ is an irrational number.

Relating Skid Marks to Speed

Police frequently estimate the speed of a car based on the length of the skid marks it leaves when braking. On a dry concrete surface the speed s, in miles per hour, can be approximated using the formula

$$s = \sqrt{24d}$$

where d is the length of the skid marks in feet.

Example A car coming to a sudden stop on a dry concrete road leaves skid marks 85 feet long. Estimate the speed of the car before braking.

$$s = \sqrt{24 \times 85} = \sqrt{2040} \approx 45$$

The car was traveling at about 45 miles per hour before braking.

Estimate the speed of a car on dry concrete for skid marks of the given length.

1. 70 feet   **2.** 30 feet   **3.** 100 feet   **4.** 200 feet

Estimate the length of the skid expected for emergency braking on dry concrete at each speed.

5. 25 miles per hour   **6.** 75 miles per hour

The nomograph shown below can be used to estimate speeds on various types of roads and under wet or dry conditions. The line used to find the speed on dry concrete for 85-foot skid marks is shown in color. Use the nomograph to estimate the speed for 85-foot skid marks on each surface.

7. gravel   **8.** wet concrete   **9.** dry brick   **10.** wet brick

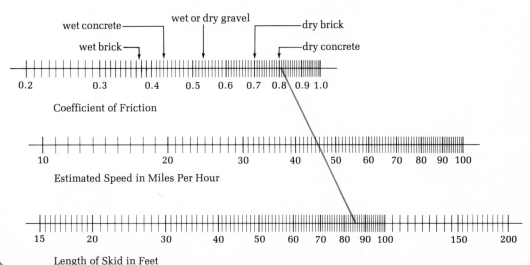

RADICAL EXPRESSIONS

CHAPTER 6 REVIEW

VOCABULARY

square root; cube root (p. 208)
radical symbol $\sqrt{}$ (p. 208)
positive; negative square root (p. 208)
principal square root (p. 208)
principal cube root (p. 208)
radicand (p. 208)
index (p. 208)

principal nth root (p. 209)
simplified radical expression (p. 212)
rationalize the denominator (p. 220)
conjugate (p. 221)
fractional exponent (p. 223)
radical equation (p. 227)
extraneous root (p. 227)

SUMMARY

Several lessons in this chapter deal with simplifying radical expressions and finding sums, differences, products, and quotients of such expressions. The concept of exponents is extended to include fractional exponents that are defined by using radicals. Techniques for solving radical equations are developed, and these methods are used in work with formulas and in the solution of verbal problems.

REVIEW EXERCISES

6-1   *Find each root, if it is a real number.*

1. $-\sqrt[4]{81}$ **2.** $\sqrt{\dfrac{9}{16}}$ **3.** $\sqrt{-\dfrac{64}{121}}$ **4.** $\sqrt[3]{8}$ **5.** $\sqrt[3]{b^3}$

6. $\sqrt[5]{32x^5}$ **7.** $\sqrt[6]{64}$ **8.** $-\sqrt{x^4}$ **9.** $\sqrt[4]{16x^4}$ **10.** $\sqrt[3]{-125x^6}$

Solve.

11. $x^2 = 49$ **12.** $3x^2 = 27$ **13.** $5x^2 = 320$ **14.** $7x^2 = 343$

15. $x^2 = \dfrac{16}{25}$ **16.** $3x^2 = \dfrac{12}{121}$ **17.** $x^3 = 64$ **18.** $-2x^3 = 250$

Find each root, correct to three decimal places. Use the tables on pages 668–669.

19. $\sqrt{5.8}$ **20.** $\sqrt{1.6}$ **21.** $\sqrt{88}$ **22.** $\sqrt{39}$ **23.** $-\sqrt{9.3}$

24. $-\sqrt{44}$ **25.** $\sqrt[3]{3.7}$ **26.** $-\sqrt[3]{8.1}$ **27.** $\sqrt[3]{-5.5}$ **28.** $\sqrt[3]{38}$

29. $-\sqrt[3]{73}$ **30.** $\sqrt[3]{-18}$ **31.** $\sqrt[3]{200}$ **32.** $-\sqrt[3]{420}$ **33.** $\sqrt[3]{-990}$

34. List the solutions for $1 \le x^2 \le 49$, where x is an integer.

6-2   *Simplify.*

35. $\sqrt{13} \cdot \sqrt{13}$ **36.** $\sqrt{9} \cdot \sqrt{25}$ **37.** $\sqrt{2} \cdot \sqrt{50}$ **38.** $\sqrt{5} \cdot \sqrt{125}$

39. $\sqrt{8} \cdot \sqrt{5}$ **40.** $\sqrt{18} \cdot \sqrt{6}$ **41.** $\sqrt{12} \cdot \sqrt{8}$ **42.** $\sqrt[3]{16} \cdot \sqrt[3]{16}$

43. $\sqrt[3]{48} \cdot \sqrt[3]{4}$ **44.** $\sqrt{3} \cdot \sqrt{3x^2}$ **45.** $\sqrt{7} \cdot \sqrt{7y^3}$ **46.** $\sqrt{x^2} \cdot \sqrt{x^2}$

Simplify, if possible. Assume all variables represent positive numbers.

47. $\sqrt{75}$ **48.** $\sqrt{128x^2}$ **49.** $\sqrt{153}$ **50.** $\sqrt{97y}$

51. $\sqrt[3]{24x^3y^4}$ **52.** $\sqrt{6x^2}\cdot\sqrt{8}$ **53.** $\sqrt[3]{4}\cdot\sqrt[3]{16y}$ **54.** $3\sqrt[3]{6x}\cdot\sqrt[3]{4x^2}$

6-3   *Simplify.*

55. $8\sqrt{3}-4\sqrt{3}$ **56.** $5\sqrt{11}+\sqrt{11}$ **57.** $3\sqrt[3]{10}+3\sqrt[3]{10}$

58. $2\sqrt[5]{8}-\sqrt[5]{8}$ **59.** $\sqrt{45}-\sqrt{5}$ **60.** $\sqrt{24}+\sqrt{54}$

61. $2\sqrt{63}-\sqrt{7}$ **62.** $8\sqrt{24x^2}+7\sqrt{6x^2}$ **63.** $2\sqrt{12}-\sqrt{27}+4\sqrt{48}$

Multiply or expand, and simplify. Assume all variables represent positive numbers.

64. $3\sqrt{5}(6\sqrt{5}+\sqrt{20})$ **65.** $2\sqrt{3}(\sqrt{6}+\sqrt{12})$ **66.** $(\sqrt{3}+\sqrt{5})(\sqrt{3}+\sqrt{5})$

67. $(\sqrt[3]{5}-1)(\sqrt[3]{5}+1)$ **68.** $(8-2\sqrt{3})^2$ **69.** $(\sqrt{2}-\sqrt{5})(\sqrt{8}+\sqrt{5})$

70. $5(\sqrt{x}-\sqrt{y})(\sqrt{x}+\sqrt{y})$ **71.** $3(\sqrt{3x}-y)(\sqrt{3x}+y)$

72. $-3(\sqrt{2x}+y)(\sqrt{2x}+y)$ **73.** $\sqrt{5x}(\sqrt{3x}+\sqrt{5x}-\sqrt{12x})$

6-4   *Simplify. Assume all variables represent positive numbers.*

74. $\sqrt{\dfrac{36}{81}}$ **75.** $-\sqrt{\dfrac{144}{9}}$ **76.** $\sqrt{\dfrac{50}{2}}$ **77.** $\dfrac{\sqrt{5}+3\sqrt{5}}{\sqrt{5}}$ **78.** $\dfrac{\sqrt[3]{56}}{\sqrt[3]{7}}$

79. $\dfrac{17}{\sqrt{17}}$ **80.** $\dfrac{28}{3\sqrt{8}}$ **81.** $\dfrac{64}{\sqrt{8}}$ **82.** $\dfrac{\sqrt{8x^2}}{\sqrt{24}}$ **83.** $\dfrac{\sqrt[3]{81x^3}}{\sqrt[3]{3}}$

84. $-\sqrt{\dfrac{12}{25}}$ **85.** $\sqrt{\dfrac{18}{289}}$ **86.** $\dfrac{-3\sqrt{12}}{\sqrt{3}}$ **87.** $\dfrac{\sqrt{5}}{\sqrt{75}}$ **88.** $\dfrac{\sqrt[3]{128x^3}}{\sqrt[3]{2}}$

89. $\dfrac{\sqrt{2}+\sqrt{5}}{\sqrt{2}-\sqrt{5}}$ **90.** $\dfrac{4}{\sqrt{3}+\sqrt{7}}$ **91.** $\dfrac{\sqrt{10}}{\sqrt{5}+\sqrt{10}}$ **92.** $\dfrac{-3}{2+\sqrt{5}}$

93. $\dfrac{x-y}{\sqrt{x}+\sqrt{y}}$ **94.** $\dfrac{x-\sqrt{x}}{x+\sqrt{x}}$ **95.** $\dfrac{1-\sqrt{x}}{1+\sqrt{x}}$ **96.** $\dfrac{x-1}{\sqrt{x}-1}$

6-5   *Write each expression in radical form.*

97. $13^{\frac{1}{2}}$ **98.** $7^{\frac{1}{3}}$ **99.** $3^{\frac{2}{3}}$ **100.** $5^{-\frac{1}{2}}$ **101.** $(-2)^{\frac{1}{3}}$

102. $3x^{\frac{3}{4}}$ **103.** $(3x)^{\frac{3}{4}}$ **104.** $(2b)^{-\frac{3}{2}}$ **105.** $(-3c)^{\frac{1}{5}}$ **106.** $7c^{-\frac{3}{2}}$

Write each expression in exponential form.

107. $\sqrt{37}$ **108.** $\sqrt[3]{26}$ **109.** $\sqrt[4]{71}$ **110.** $\sqrt{5^3}$ **111.** $\sqrt[3]{7^2}$

112. $\dfrac{1}{\sqrt[3]{19}}$ **113.** $\dfrac{1}{\sqrt[3]{7^2}}$ **114.** $\dfrac{1}{\sqrt{2x}}$ **115.** $\sqrt[3]{(3x)^2}$ **116.** $\sqrt[3]{3x^2}$

Evaluate.

117. $144^{\frac{1}{2}}$ **118.** $8^{\frac{1}{3}}$ **119.** $-(125)^{-\frac{1}{3}}$ **120.** $8^{-\frac{2}{3}}$ **121.** $64^{-\frac{3}{2}}$

122. $\left(\dfrac{1}{64}\right)^{\frac{1}{3}}$ **123.** $\dfrac{27^{\frac{1}{3}}}{9^{\frac{1}{2}}}$ **124.** $\dfrac{16^{\frac{1}{4}}}{16^{\frac{1}{2}}}$ **125.** $\dfrac{4^{-\frac{3}{2}}}{125^{\frac{2}{3}}}$ **126.** $\dfrac{8^{-\frac{2}{3}}}{9^{-\frac{3}{2}}}$

127. $\left(16^{\frac{1}{3}}\right)^{\frac{3}{4}}$ **128.** $\left(16^{\frac{3}{2}}\right)^{\frac{1}{3}}$ **129.** $\left(125^{\frac{1}{2}}\right)^{-\frac{4}{3}}$ **130.** $(81^{-2})^{-\frac{3}{4}}$

6-6   *Solve and check. Write **no solution,** if applicable.*

131. $\sqrt{x+4}=5$ **132.** $\sqrt{x-3}=6$ **133.** $\sqrt{3x+5}=9$

134. $\sqrt{3x}-6=9$ **135.** $7+\sqrt{5x}=14$ **136.** $\sqrt{2x-1}=2\sqrt{x}-1$

137. $\sqrt{x+4}=x-2$ **138.** $\sqrt[3]{x+4}=3$ **139.** $\sqrt{x+3}=x+3$

140. $\sqrt{x+5}=2+\sqrt{x}$ **141.** $\sqrt{x}-\sqrt{x+11}=2$ **142.** $3\sqrt{x-5}=2\sqrt{2x+3}$

143. The square root of the sum of twice a certain number and 1 is equal to 7 less than the number. Find the number.

144. The product of a certain negative number and 4 is equal to the cube root of the number. Find the original number.

CHAPTER 6 TEST

Simplify. Assume all variables represent positive numbers.

1. $\sqrt{45}$ **2.** $\sqrt[3]{-16}$ **3.** $\sqrt{9x^2}$ **4.** $\sqrt[3]{125a^3}$

5. $\sqrt{\dfrac{12}{5}}$ **6.** $\dfrac{\sqrt[3]{32x}}{\sqrt[3]{2}}$ **7.** $\sqrt{12}\cdot\sqrt{6}$ **8.** $\sqrt[4]{10}\cdot\sqrt[4]{8}$

9. $\sqrt{8xy^2}\cdot\sqrt{5xy^2}$ **10.** $\sqrt[3]{4}\cdot\sqrt[3]{10x^4}$ **11.** $8\sqrt{50}+2\sqrt{18}$

12. $\dfrac{10}{\sqrt{5}}+\sqrt{20}$ **13.** $\sqrt[3]{40}+\sqrt[3]{-250}$ **14.** $(3\sqrt{2}+\sqrt{5})(3\sqrt{2}-\sqrt{5})$

15. $\dfrac{8}{2+\sqrt{3}}$ **16.** $(5\sqrt{2}+2\sqrt{3})^2$ **17.** $\dfrac{9-x}{3+\sqrt{x}}$

Evaluate.

18. $9^{\frac{1}{2}}$ **19.** $8^{-\frac{2}{3}}$ **20.** $\dfrac{36^{\frac{1}{2}}}{25^{-\frac{1}{2}}}$ **21.** $\left(81^{\frac{3}{2}}\right)^{\frac{1}{2}}$

Solve and check.

22. $\sqrt{5-x}=4$ **23.** $\sqrt{4x+5}=x-4$

24. $\sqrt{2x+4}=\sqrt{3x+1}$ **25.** $\sqrt{x-7}+\sqrt{x}=7$

Square Root

Many scientific laws are expressed as formulas involving square roots. For example, the distance in miles you can see on a clear day is given by $M = \sqrt{1.5H}$, where H is the height of your eyes above the earth's surface, in feet. The program below computes and displays the distance you can see to the nearest tenth of a mile.

In BASIC, SQR(N) computes the *square root* of N.

The Program	**What It Does**
| ```
100 REM HOW FAR?
110 PRINT "FEET ABOVE GROUND";
120 INPUT H
200 LET M = SQR(1.5 * H)
210 LET M = INT(M * 10 + .5)/10
220 PRINT "CAN SEE "; M; " MILES"
900 END
``` | Computes the distance you can see.<br>Rounds to nearest tenth of a mile. |

On many computers, LET may be omitted in lines 200 and 210.

What will the program HOW FAR? display for each length in feet?
   1. 6   **2.** 12   **3.** 20   **4.** 60   **5.** 96   **6.** 600   **7.** 1200   **8.** 60,000

9. Approximately what height is needed to see a distance of 1000 miles?

10. If you have access to more than one type of computer, display SQR(2) on each. Determine the number of significant digits displayed by each machine. If possible, determine whether the values displayed have been rounded or merely truncated.

P is the number of seconds that it takes for a pendulum L feet long to swing back and forth. Then $P = 2\pi\sqrt{\frac{L}{32}}$. Write a program that displays P (to the nearest hundredth) when the length of the pendulum is entered. *Tell what the program will display for each length in feet.*

   11. 0.5   **12.** 1   **13.** 2   **14.** 3

15. Approximately how far will the pendulum swing in two seconds?

A formula that relates the rate of flow of water near the bottom, b, of some rivers to the rate of flow near the surface, s, is $\sqrt{b} = \sqrt{s} - 1$. Write a program to display the rate of flow near the bottom of a river when the rate of flow near the surface is entered. Have the result rounded to the nearest tenth. *What does the program display for each of the following surface rates of flow?*

   16. 3   **17.** 4   **18.** 9   **19.** 2

For more information about BASIC, see the Computer Handbook at the back of the book.
```

The parabolic arches of the McCullough Memorial Bridge in Oregon are both functional and pleasing to the eye.

QUADRATIC EQUATIONS AND FUNCTIONS

Prerequisite Skills Review

Write the letter for the correct answer.

1. $(3\sqrt{5})^2 = \underline{\ ?\ }$

   a. $9\sqrt{5}$ **b.** 15 **c.** 45 **d.** none of these

2. $\sqrt{32} = \underline{\ ?\ }$

   a. $16\sqrt{2}$ **b.** $4\sqrt{2}$ **c.** 8 **d.** $5\sqrt{7}$

3. $y^2 - 6y + 9 = \underline{\ ?\ }$

   a. $(y + 3)^2$ **b.** $(y - 3)^2$ **c.** $(y - 6)^2$ **d.** $(y + 3)(y - 3)$

4. Which of the following is a trinomial square?

   a. $4x^2 - 4x + 1$ **b.** $4x^2 + 4x + 4$ **c.** $x^2 + 4x - 4$ **d.** $4x^2 - 4x - 1$

5. $(3 - 2\sqrt{3})^2 = \underline{\ ?\ }$

   a. $21 - 6\sqrt{3}$ **b.** 21 **c.** $45 - 12\sqrt{3}$ **d.** $21 - 12\sqrt{3}$

6. $\sqrt{(-8)^2 - 4(3)(-3)} = \underline{\ ?\ }$

   a. $2\sqrt{13}$ **b.** $2\sqrt{7}$ **c.** $\sqrt{10}$ **d.** 10

7. $\dfrac{-2 \pm \sqrt{36}}{4} = \underline{\ ?\ }$

   a. 1 or -2 **b.** 1 or -1 **c.** -1 or -2 **d.** 1 or 2

8. $\dfrac{6 \pm \sqrt{112}}{2} = \underline{\ ?\ }$

   a. $\dfrac{17}{2}$ or $-\dfrac{5}{2}$ **b.** $3 + 2\sqrt{7}$ or $3 - 2\sqrt{7}$

   c. $3 + 4\sqrt{7}$ or $3 - 4\sqrt{7}$ **d.** none of these

9. Which of the following points lies on the graph of $y = (x - 4)^2 - 3$?

   a. $(0, -3)$ **b.** $(2, -7)$ **c.** $(3, -2)$ **d.** $(-2, 3)$

10. The point $(-1, 4)$ lies on the graph of which equation?

    a. $y = x^2$ **b.** $y = (x + 2)^2$

    c. $y = (x + 2)^2 + 2$ **d.** $y = 2(x + 2)^2 + 2$

7-1 Solving Quadratic Equations by Completing the Square

OBJECTIVE ─────────────────────────────────

To solve quadratic equations by completing the square of a binomial.

───

Quadratic equations can be written in the following form.

$$ax^2 + bx + c = 0 \qquad (a \neq 0)$$

You have already learned how to solve such equations under special conditions. For example, it was shown in Chapter 4 that some quadratic equations can be solved by factoring. Then, in Chapter 6, you learned that an equation such as $x^2 = 12$ can be solved by taking a square root.

$$x^2 = 12$$
$$x = \pm\sqrt{12} \qquad \text{If } x^2 = k, \text{ then } x = \pm\sqrt{k}.$$
$$x = \pm 2\sqrt{3} \qquad \text{Simplify the radical.}$$

$$\text{Check} \qquad (2\sqrt{3})^2 = 4 \cdot 3 = 12 \ ✔$$
$$(-2\sqrt{3})^2 = 4 \cdot 3 = 12 \ ✔$$

The solutions are $2\sqrt{3}$ and $-2\sqrt{3}$.

You can also use this method when the square of a binomial is equal to a constant. Study the example that follows.

EXAMPLE 1   Solve $x^2 + 2x + 1 = 5$.

$$x^2 + 2x + 1 = 5 \qquad \text{The left side is a perfect square.}$$
$$(x + 1)^2 = 5 \qquad \text{Factor the left side.}$$
$$x + 1 = \pm\sqrt{5} \qquad \text{Take the square root of each side.}$$

$$x + 1 = \sqrt{5} \quad \text{or} \quad x + 1 = -\sqrt{5}$$
$$x = \sqrt{5} - 1 \qquad x = -\sqrt{5} - 1$$

Check $(\sqrt{5} - 1)^2 + 2(\sqrt{5} - 1) + 1 = 5 - 2\sqrt{5} + 1 + 2\sqrt{5} - 2 + 1$
$$= 5 \ ✔$$

$(-\sqrt{5} - 1)^2 + 2(-\sqrt{5} - 1) + 1 = 5 + 2\sqrt{5} + 1 - 2\sqrt{5} - 2 + 1$
$$= 5 \ ✔$$

The solutions are $\sqrt{5} - 1$ and $-\sqrt{5} - 1$.

When the equation does not show a trinomial square equal to a constant, you can write it that way by a process called **completing the square.**

This procedure is easy if you recall how a binomial is squared.

$$(x + b)^2 = x^2 + 2bx + b^2$$

Note that the constant term b^2 is the square of $\frac{1}{2}$ of the coefficient of x. That is, $(\frac{1}{2} \cdot 2b)^2 = b^2$.

Now, let us work in the reverse direction. Suppose you wish to write a trinomial square whose first two terms are $x^2 + 10x$. What constant term must be added?

$$x^2 + 10x + \underline{\ ?\ } \qquad (\tfrac{1}{2} \cdot 10)^2 = 5^2 = \mathbf{25}$$

The constant to be added is 25, and the trinomial square is $x^2 + 10x + \mathbf{25}$. Show that $x^2 + 10x + 25$ is equal to $(x + 5)^2$.

EXAMPLE 2   Supply the missing term to form a trinomial square. Then factor the trinomial.

a. $\mathbf{x^2 - 6x +}$ $\underline{\ ?\ }$

The constant must be $(\frac{1}{2} \cdot 6)^2 = 3^2 = \mathbf{9}$.

Then $x^2 - 6x + \mathbf{9} = (x - 3)^2$.

b. $\mathbf{x^2 + x +}$ $\underline{\ ?\ }$

The constant must be $(\frac{1}{2} \cdot 1)^2 = (\frac{1}{2})^2 = \frac{1}{4}$

Then $x^2 + x + \frac{1}{4} = (x + \frac{1}{2})^2$.

Now you are ready to solve a quadratic equation by completing the square.

EXAMPLE 3   Solve $x^2 - 8x - 2 = 0$.

$x^2 - 8x - 2 = 0$	The left side cannot be factored.
$x^2 - 8x = 2$	Write the equation with the constant term on the right.
$x^2 - 8x + \mathbf{16} = 2 + \mathbf{16}$	Complete the square. Add 16 to each side. $(\frac{1}{2} \cdot 8)^2 = 4^2 = 16$

$$(x - 4)^2 = 18$$

$$x - 4 = \pm\sqrt{18}$$
$$x - 4 = \pm 3\sqrt{2}$$
$$x = 4 \pm 3\sqrt{2}$$

Check $(4 + 3\sqrt{2})^2 - 8(4 + 3\sqrt{2}) - 2 = 16 + 24\sqrt{2} + 18 - 32 - 24\sqrt{2} - 2$
$$= 0 \ ✔$$
$(4 - 3\sqrt{2})^2 - 8(4 - 3\sqrt{2}) - 2 = 16 - 24\sqrt{2} + 18 - 32 + 24\sqrt{2} - 2$
$$= 0 \ ✔$$

The solutions are $4 + 3\sqrt{2}$ and $4 - 3\sqrt{2}$.

If the coefficient of the x^2 term is not 1, both sides of the equation should be divided by that coefficient before completing the square.

EXAMPLE 4   Solve $2x^2 - 5x + 3 = 0$.

$$2x^2 - 5x + 3 = 0$$

$$x^2 - \frac{5}{2}x + \frac{3}{2} = 0$$ Divide each term by 2 so that the x^2 term has the coefficient 1.

$$x^2 - \frac{5}{2}x = -\frac{3}{2}$$ Write the equation with the constant term on the right.

$$x^2 - \frac{5}{2}x + \frac{25}{16} = -\frac{3}{2} + \frac{25}{16}$$ Complete the square. Add $\frac{25}{16}$ to each side.

$$\left(x - \frac{5}{4}\right)^2 = \frac{1}{16}$$ Factor the left side. Simplify the right side.

$$x - \frac{5}{4} = \pm\frac{1}{4}$$

$$x = \frac{5}{4} \pm \frac{1}{4}$$

$$x = \frac{5}{4} + \frac{1}{4} = \frac{3}{2} \quad \text{or} \quad x = \frac{5}{4} - \frac{1}{4} = 1$$

Check $2\left(\frac{3}{2}\right)^2 - 5\left(\frac{3}{2}\right) + 3 = \frac{9}{2} - \frac{15}{2} + 3 = 0$ ✔

$$2(1)^2 - 5(1) + 3 = 2 - 5 + 3 = 0 ✔$$

The solutions are $\frac{3}{2}$ and 1.

CLASS EXERCISES

Supply the missing term to form a trinomial square.
Then factor the trinomial.

1. $x^2 + 4x + \underline{\ ?\ }$ **2.** $x^2 - 4x + \underline{\ ?\ }$ **3.** $x^2 + 8x + \underline{\ ?\ }$

4. $x^2 - 8x + \underline{\ ?\ }$ **5.** $x^2 + 10x + \underline{\ ?\ }$ **6.** $x^2 - 10x + \underline{\ ?\ }$

7. $x^2 + 5x + \underline{\ ?\ }$ **8.** $x^2 - 3x + \underline{\ ?\ }$ **9.** $x^2 - x + \underline{\ ?\ }$

10. $x^2 - 2x + \underline{\ ?\ }$ **11.** $x^2 + 9x + \underline{\ ?\ }$ **12.** $x^2 - 11x + \underline{\ ?\ }$

EXERCISES

A
Supply the missing term to form a trinomial square.
Then factor the trinomial.

1. $x^2 - 6x + \underline{\ ?\ }$ **2.** $x^2 + 12x + \underline{\ ?\ }$ **3.** $x^2 + 2x + \underline{\ ?\ }$

4. $x^2 + x + \underline{\ ?\ }$ **5.** $x^2 - 5x + \underline{\ ?\ }$ **6.** $x^2 + 7x + \underline{\ ?\ }$

Solve by taking the square root of each side.

7. $(x + 2)^2 = 4$ **8.** $(x - 1)^2 = 9$ **9.** $(x + 3)^2 = 16$

10. $(x - 1)^2 = 5$ **11.** $(x + 1)^2 = 7$ **12.** $(x - 2)^2 = 3$

13. $x^2 + 4x + 4 = 3$ **14.** $x^2 - 4x + 4 = 5$ **15.** $x^2 - 6x + 9 = 4$

Solve by completing the square.

16. $x^2 + 6x + 8 = 0$ **17.** $x^2 - 8x + 15 = 0$ **18.** $x^2 + 2x - 6 = 0$

19. $x^2 + 4x - 5 = 0$ **20.** $x^2 - 4x + 1 = 0$ **21.** $x^2 - 6x - 11 = 0$

B

22. $2x^2 - 3x + 1 = 0$ **23.** $2x^2 - 5x - 3 = 0$ **24.** $2x^2 - 6x + 2 = 0$

25. $3t^2 - 4t - 2 = 0$ **26.** $2n^2 - 3n - 3 = 0$ **27.** $2s^2 + 3s - 5 = 0$

28. $x^2 - 6 + 5x = 0$ **29.** $5x^2 - 2 + x = 0$ **30.** $3 - 2x - x^2 = 0$

31. $19 - 2x^2 + 2x = 0$ **32.** $3s^2 + 1 = 5s$ **33.** $2r^2 + 5r = 1$

34. $\dfrac{x^2}{2} + \dfrac{x}{3} - \dfrac{1}{6} = 0$ **35.** $\dfrac{x^2}{8} - \dfrac{x}{4} - \dfrac{1}{2} = 0$ **36.** $\dfrac{x^2}{2} - \dfrac{3x}{10} = \dfrac{1}{5}$

C

37. $\dfrac{x^2 - 4}{3} = 2x$ **38.** $\dfrac{x^2 - x}{8} = \dfrac{3}{4}$ **39.** $\dfrac{1}{x - 2} + \dfrac{2}{x + 1} = 1$

40. $n^2 + (4\sqrt{2})n - 5 = 0$ **41.** $y^2 - (6\sqrt{3})y = 1$ **42.** $4x^2 = (8\sqrt{2})x + 2$

*43. Solve by completing the square: $ax^2 + bx + c = 0$.

USING THE CALCULATOR

Solving Quadratic Equations

Can you solve the quadratic equation $x^2 + 572x = 368{,}445$ by completing the square? It would be a difficult task without the help of a scientific calculator, but the steps are the same as those you've been using in this lesson.

$$x^2 + 572x = 368{,}445$$

Use a calculator.

$$x^2 + 572x + \mathbf{81{,}796} = 368{,}445 + \mathbf{81{,}\ 796}$$
$$\left(\tfrac{572}{2}\right)^2 = (286)^2 = 81{,}796$$

$$(x + \mathbf{286})^2 = 450{,}241$$

$$x + 286 = \pm\, \mathbf{671}$$
$$\pm\, \sqrt{450{,}241} = \pm\, 671$$

$$x = -286 \pm 671$$

Solutions: $x = 385$ or $x = -957$

Now you try it! Use a calculator to help solve and check each equation.

1. $x^2 + 158x = 308{,}480$ **2.** $x^2 - 204x = 445{,}221$ **3.** $x^2 + 4.482x = 7.403544$

7-2 The Quadratic Formula

OBJECTIVES

To solve quadratic equations using the quadratic formula.
To solve equations that can be written in quadratic form.

Rather than completing the square for every individual quadratic equation, we may solve the *general quadratic equation*. This will give us a formula that may be used to solve all such equations.

$$ax^2 + bx + c = 0$$ — Begin with the general quadratic equation.

$$x^2 + \frac{b}{a}x + \frac{c}{a} = 0$$ — Divide each term by a. ($a \neq 0$)

$$x^2 + \frac{b}{a}x = -\frac{c}{a}$$ — Write the equation with the constant term on the right.

$$x^2 + \frac{b}{a}x + \frac{b^2}{4a^2} = -\frac{c}{a} + \frac{b^2}{4a^2}$$ — Complete the square. Add $\frac{b^2}{4a^2}$ to each side.

$$\left(x + \frac{b}{2a}\right)^2 = \frac{b^2}{4a^2} - \frac{c}{a}$$ — Factor the left side.

$$\left(x + \frac{b}{2a}\right)^2 = \frac{b^2 - 4ac}{4a^2}$$ — Combine terms on the right side.

$$x + \frac{b}{2a} = \pm \frac{\sqrt{b^2 - 4ac}}{2a}$$ — Take the square root of each side.

$$x = -\frac{b}{2a} \pm \frac{\sqrt{b^2 - 4ac}}{2a}$$ — Solve for x.

$$x = \frac{-b \pm \sqrt{b^2 - 4ac}}{2a}$$ — Combine terms.

Quadratic Formula

If $ax^2 + bx + c = 0$ ($a \neq 0$), then

$$x = \frac{-b \pm \sqrt{b^2 - 4ac}}{2a}$$

EXAMPLE 1   Solve $x^2 - x - 6 = 0$.

Apply the quadratic formula, using $a = 1$, $b = -1$, and $c = -6$.

$$x = \frac{-(-1) \pm \sqrt{(-1)^2 - 4(1)(-6)}}{2(1)} = \frac{1 \pm \sqrt{1 + 24}}{2} = \frac{1 \pm 5}{2}$$

$$x = \frac{1 + 5}{2} = 3 \text{ or } x = \frac{1 - 5}{2} = -2$$

Check $(3)^2 - 3 - 6 = 9 - 3 - 6 = 0$ ✔

$(-2)^2 - (-2) - 6 = 4 + 2 - 6 = 0$ ✔

The solutions are 3 and -2.

EXAMPLE 2 Solve $5x = x^2 + 2$. Approximate the solutions to two decimal places.

$x^2 - 5x + 2 = 0$ Write the equation in general form.

$x = \frac{-(-5) \pm \sqrt{(-5)^2 - 4(1)(2)}}{2(1)}$ Apply the quadratic formula using $a = 1$, $b = -5$, $c = 2$.

$= \frac{5 \pm \sqrt{25 - 8}}{2} = \frac{5 \pm \sqrt{17}}{2}$

Check by substituting in the original equation.

The solutions are $\frac{5 + \sqrt{17}}{2}$ and $\frac{5 - \sqrt{17}}{2}$. Using a calculator or a table of square roots, we find that the value of $\sqrt{17}$, correct to two decimal places, is 4.12. Thus the solutions may be approximated as

$$\frac{5 + 4.12}{2} = 4.56 \quad \text{and} \quad \frac{5 - 4.12}{2} = 0.44$$

Sometimes equations of different types can be written in *quadratic form* and solved using the quadratic formula. In the next example, a fourth-degree equation is solved by expressing it as a quadratic in terms of x^2.

EXAMPLE 3 Solve $x^4 - 10x^2 + 24 = 0$.

$(x^2)^2 - 10(x^2) + 24 = 0$ Write the equation as a quadratic in x^2.

$x^2 = \frac{-(-10) \pm \sqrt{(-10)^2 - 4(1)(24)}}{2(1)}$ Apply the quadratic formula using $a = 1$, $b = -10$, $c = 24$.

$x^2 = \frac{10 \pm \sqrt{100 - 96}}{2}$

$x^2 = \frac{10 \pm 2}{2}$

$x^2 = \frac{10 + 2}{2} = 6 \quad \text{or} \quad x^2 = \frac{10 - 2}{2} = 4$

Note that we have solved for x^2, but not for x. However, if $x^2 = 6$, then $x = \pm\sqrt{6}$. If $x^2 = 4$, then $x = \pm 2$.

Check by substituting all four of these values in the original equation. The solutions are $\sqrt{6}$, $-\sqrt{6}$, 2, and -2.

CLASS EXERCISES

Give the values of **a**, **b**, and **c** in the quadratic formula. Solve Exercises 1–3.

1. $x^2 + 5x + 6 = 0$ 2. $x^2 - 2x - 15 = 0$ 3. $x^2 - 10x + 25 = 0$

4. $2x^2 - 3x + 6 = 0$ 5. $-2x^2 + 3x + 2 = 0$ 6. $3x^2 - 5x + 2 = 0$

7. $x^2 + 3x + 5 = 10$ 8. $x^2 = 5x + 7$ 9. $x^2 = x + 4$

EXERCISES

A   Solve, using the quadratic formula. Check your solutions.

1. $x^2 + 7x + 12 = 0$ 2. $x^2 - x - 12 = 0$ 3. $-x^2 - x + 12 = 0$

4. $x^2 + 4x + 4 = 0$ 5. $x^2 + 6x + 5 = 0$ 6. $x^2 - 6x + 8 = 0$

7. $2x^2 + 3x + 1 = 0$ 8. $4x^2 + 4x + 1 = 0$ 9. $2x^2 - 3x - 2 = 0$

10. $9x^2 - 30x + 25 = 0$ 11. $8x^2 + 18x - 5 = 0$ 12. $-12x^2 + 5x + 2 = 0$

13. $2x^2 - 3 = 0$ 14. $2x^2 = 3x$ 15. $3x^2 = 5$

B   Solve, using the quadratic formula.

16. $x^2 + 3x - 3 = 0$ 17. $2x^2 - 4x + 1 = 0$ 18. $3x^2 + x - 3 = 0$

19. $x^2 + 3x - 4 = 2$ 20. $x^2 + 4x + 3 = 4$ 21. $2x^2 - 2 = 2x - 1$

22. $\frac{1}{4}x^2 + \frac{1}{4}x - 1 = 0$ 23. $\frac{1}{5}x^2 - 2x = -5$ 24. $x^2 - \frac{1}{8} = \frac{3}{4}x$

25. $\frac{1}{2}x - \frac{2}{x} = 2$ 26. $\frac{x-2}{3} = \frac{4-x}{2x}$ 27. $x^4 - 5x^2 + 4 = 0$

Approximate each solution to two decimal places.

28. $x^2 - 5x + 2 = 0$ 29. $2x^2 + x - 4 = 0$ 30. $x^2 + 1 = 3x$

31. $x^2 + 8 = 6x + 2$ 32. $2(x^2 - x) = 5$ 33. $3(x^2 - 2x) = 5 - 2x$

C   Solve.

34. $n^2 + 2\sqrt{2}n + 1 = 0$ 35. $2n^2 - n - \sqrt{2} = 0$ 36. $3y^2 - 2\sqrt{5}y - 2 = 0$

37. $3y^2 - y - 2\sqrt{3} = 0$ 38. $4x^4 - 17x^2 + 18 = 0$ 39. $9x^4 + 17x^2 - 2 = 0$

40. $(t + 2)^2 - 3(t + 2) - 5 = 0$ 41. $x + 2\sqrt{x} - 3 = 0$
   Hint: Let $n = t + 2$. Solve for n. Then find t.   **Hint:** Write x as $(\sqrt{x})^2$.

Find the values of **k** such that the equation will have real numbers as solutions.

42. $3x^2 + kx + 3 = 0$ 43. $kx^2 - 2x + 1 = 0$

7-3 The Discriminant

OBJECTIVE

To describe the real roots of a quadratic equation, using the discriminant.

As you learned in the preceding section, the solutions, or roots, of the quadratic equation $ax^2 + bx + c = 0$ can be written in this way:

$$x = \frac{-b + \sqrt{b^2 - 4ac}}{2a} \quad \text{and} \quad x = \frac{-b - \sqrt{b^2 - 4ac}}{2a}$$

The expression under the radical symbol, $b^2 - 4ac$, is called the **discriminant**. The value of the discriminant determines the number of roots of the equation. The three different cases that can arise are illustrated below.

Case 1 When $b^2 - 4ac > 0$, the equation has *two real roots*.

For example, suppose $x^2 + x - 6 = 0$.
Then $b^2 - 4ac = 1 + 24 = 25$, and $25 > 0$.

Solving for x: $x = \dfrac{-1 \pm \sqrt{25}}{2} = \dfrac{-1 \pm 5}{2}$

$$x = 2 \text{ or } x = -3$$

The two roots are 2 and -3.

Case 2 When $b^2 - 4ac = 0$, the equation has *one real root*.

For example, suppose $x^2 - 4x + 4 = 0$.
Then $b^2 - 4ac = 16 - 16 = 0$.

Solving for x: $x = \dfrac{4 \pm \sqrt{16 - 16}}{2} = \dfrac{4 \pm 0}{2}$

$$x = 2$$

The root 2 is called a *double root*.

Case 3 When $b^2 - 4ac < 0$, the equation has *no real roots*.

For example, suppose $x^2 - 4x + 6 = 0$.
Then $b^2 - 4ac = 16 - 24 = -8$, and $-8 < 0$.

Solving for x: $x = \dfrac{4 \pm \sqrt{16 - 24}}{2} = \dfrac{4 \pm \sqrt{-8}}{2}$

Since $\sqrt{-8}$ is not a real number, the equation has no real roots.

These results are summarized in the table at the top of the next page.

QUADRATIC EQUATIONS AND FUNCTIONS

$ax^2 + bx + c = 0$ $(a \neq 0)$	
Discriminant	**Number of Distinct Real Roots**
$b^2 - 4ac > 0$	two
$b^2 - 4ac = 0$	one
$b^2 - 4ac < 0$	none

EXAMPLE 1   Tell whether the equation $2x^2 - 3x - 5 = 0$ has two real roots, exactly one real root, or none.

$$b^2 - 4ac = (-3)^2 - 4(2)(-5) \qquad a = 2, b = -3, c = -5$$
$$= 9 + 40$$
$$= 49$$

Since $49 > 0$, the equation has two real roots.

The value of the discriminant of $2x^2 - 3x - 5 = 0$ is 49, a perfect square. When such is the case, and a, b, and c are rational, the roots of the equation are distinct *rational* numbers. To illustrate this, show that the roots of $2x^2 - 3x - 5 = 0$ are -1 and $\frac{5}{2}$. If the value of the discriminant is a positive number that is *not* a perfect square, the roots are two *irrational* numbers.

EXAMPLE 2   Find a value for k so that the equation $kx^2 + x - 1 = 0$ has only one real root.

$$b^2 - 4ac = (1)^2 - 4(k)(-1) \qquad a = k, b = 1, c = -1$$
$$= 1 + 4k$$

There is only one real root when the value of the discriminant is 0. Therefore, we set $1 + 4k$ equal to 0 and solve for k.

$$1 + 4k = 0$$
$$4k = -1$$
$$k = -\frac{1}{4}$$

Check to show that $-\frac{1}{4}x^2 + x - 1 = 0$ has just one root, 2.
$kx^2 + x - 1 = 0$ has only one real root when $k = -\frac{1}{4}$.

CLASS EXERCISES

Find the value of the discriminant for each equation.

1. $x^2 - 4x + 7 = 0$ **2.** $x^2 - 6x + 9 = 0$ **3.** $x^2 - 2x + 5 = 0$

*Tell whether the equation has **two** real roots, exactly **one**, or **none**.*

4. $x^2 + 10x + 25 = 0$ **5.** $-x^2 + 3x - 1 = 0$ **6.** $x^2 + 3x + 10 = 0$

EXERCISES

A *Tell whether the equation has **two** real roots, exactly **one**, or **none**.*

1. $x^2 - 6x + 9 = 0$ **2.** $x^2 + 2x - 3 = 0$ **3.** $x^2 - 4 = 0$

4. $2x^2 + x - 1 = 0$ **5.** $-4x^2 + 12x - 9 = 0$ **6.** $x^2 - 3x + 4 = 0$

7. $x^2 + 2x + 1 = 0$ **8.** $2x^2 - x - 3 = 0$ **9.** $2x^2 + 2x + 1 = 0$

10. $x^2 - 5x = 5$ **11.** $2x^2 + 3 = 2x$ **12.** $4x^2 = 20x - 25$

B **13.** $2x^2 - 3x - \sqrt{2} = 0$ **14.** $x^2 - 5\sqrt{3}x + 1 = 0$ **15.** $\sqrt{3}x^2 - 2\sqrt{2}x - \sqrt{3} = 0$

16. $-\frac{1}{4}x^2 + x - 1 = 0$ **17.** $\frac{1}{2}x^2 + x + 2 = 0$ **18.** $\frac{1}{4}x^2 - \frac{1}{2}x - 2 = 0$

*Find a value for **k** so that the equation has only one real root.*

19. $x^2 - kx + 9 = 0$ **20.** $4x^2 - kx + 1 = 0$ **21.** $6x^2 - 12x + k = 0$

22. $kx^2 - 12x + 9 = 0$ **23.** $kx^2 - x + 1 = 0$ **24.** $x^2 - x + k = 0$

C **25.** Find the values for k such that $2x^2 - kx + 3 = 0$ has no real roots.

*26. For any integer k, show that the roots of $2x^2 + kx + (k - 2) = 0$ are rational. For what value of k is there just one rational root?

CHALLENGE

Investigating the Discriminant

*Assume that **b** is an even integer.*

1. Is b^2 an even integer?   **2.** Is b^2 a multiple of 4?

3. Show why the discriminant $b^2 - 4ac$ is a multiple of 4.
Hint: To represent b as an even integer, let $b = 2n$, where n is some integer.

*Assume that **b** is an odd integer.*

4. Is b^2 an odd integer?   **5.** Is b^2 a multiple of 4?

6. Is b^2 one more than a multiple of 4?

7. Show why the discriminant is one more than a multiple of 4.
Hint: Let $b = 2n + 1$, where n is some integer.

*Now, put this information to use! State which numbers in each group can be the value of the discriminant, when **a**, **b**, and **c** are integers.*

8. 20   21   22   23   24   **9.** 255   256   257   258   259

7-4 The Sum and the Product of the Roots of a Quadratic Equation

OBJECTIVES _____

To find the sum and the product of the roots of a quadratic equation from the coefficients of the equation.
To write a quadratic equation with given roots.
_____

There are interesting relationships between the roots and the coefficients of a quadratic equation. To discover them, begin by letting x_1 and x_2 be the roots of the general quadratic equation $ax^2 + bx + c = 0$ $(a \neq 0)$.

$$x_1 = \frac{-b + \sqrt{b^2 - 4ac}}{2a} \qquad x_2 = \frac{-b - \sqrt{b^2 - 4ac}}{2a}$$

By adding these roots, we have the following:

$$
\begin{aligned}
x_1 + x_2 &= \frac{-b + \sqrt{b^2 - 4ac}}{2a} + \frac{-b - \sqrt{b^2 - 4ac}}{2a} \\
&= \frac{-b + \sqrt{b^2 - 4ac} - b - \sqrt{b^2 - 4ac}}{2a} \\
&= \frac{-2b}{2a} \\
&= -\frac{b}{a}
\end{aligned}
$$

The sum of the roots of a quadratic equation

$$ax^2 + bx + c = 0 \text{ is } -\frac{b}{a}. \qquad (a \neq 0)$$

EXAMPLE 1

Find the sum of the roots of $x^2 + 5x + 6 = 0$.

$$-\frac{b}{a} = -\frac{5}{1} = -5 \qquad a = 1, b = 5$$

The sum of the roots is -5.
We can check by solving the equation and adding the roots.

$$x^2 + 5x + 6 = 0$$
$$(x + 2)(x + 3) = 0$$

$$x + 2 = 0 \quad \text{or} \quad x + 3 = 0$$
$$x = -2 \qquad\qquad x = -3 \qquad -2 + (-3) = -5 \; ✔$$

Next, consider the product of the roots of $ax^2 + bx + c = 0$ $(a \neq 0)$.

$$x_1 \cdot x_2 = \left(\frac{-b + \sqrt{b^2 - 4ac}}{2a}\right)\left(\frac{-b - \sqrt{b^2 - 4ac}}{2a}\right)$$

$$= \frac{(-b)^2 - (\sqrt{b^2 - 4ac})^2}{4a^2}$$

$$= \frac{4ac}{4a^2} = \frac{c}{a}$$

The product of the roots of a quadratic equation

$ax^2 + bx + c = 0$ **is** $\dfrac{c}{a}$. $\quad (a \neq 0)$

EXAMPLE 2   Find the product of the roots of $x^2 + 5x + 6 = 0$.

$\dfrac{c}{a} = \dfrac{6}{1} = 6 \qquad a = 1;\ c = 6$

The product of the roots is 6. To check, note that the roots of the equation were found to be -2 and -3 in Example 1. $\qquad (-2)(-3) = 6$ ✔

If the roots of a quadratic equation are known, it is possible to use the ideas of this section to write the equation that has the given roots.

EXAMPLE 3   Write a quadratic equation with the roots $\dfrac{1 + \sqrt{3}}{2}$ and $\dfrac{1 - \sqrt{3}}{2}$.

$-\dfrac{b}{a} = \dfrac{1 + \sqrt{3}}{2} + \dfrac{1 - \sqrt{3}}{2} = \dfrac{2}{2} = 1$ $\qquad$ Find the sum of the roots.

$\dfrac{b}{a} = -1$ $\qquad$ Find the opposite of the sum.

$\dfrac{c}{a} = \left(\dfrac{1 + \sqrt{3}}{2}\right)\left(\dfrac{1 - \sqrt{3}}{2}\right) = \dfrac{1 - 3}{4} = -\dfrac{1}{2}$ $\qquad$ Find the product of the roots.

Substitute these values in the general quadratic equation, after dividing each term by a.

$ax^2 + bx + c = 0$

$x^2 + \dfrac{b}{a}x + \dfrac{c}{a} = 0$ $\qquad$ Divide each side by a.

$x^2 + (-1)x + \left(-\dfrac{1}{2}\right) = 0$ $\qquad$ Substitute: $\dfrac{b}{a} = -1;\ \dfrac{c}{a} = -\dfrac{1}{2}$.

$2x^2 - 2x - 1 = 0$ $\qquad$ Multiply each side by 2.

Check by solving $2x^2 - 2x - 1 = 0$.

CLASS EXERCISES

Find the sum and the product of the roots for each equation.

1. $x^2 + 4x + 4 = 0$ **2.** $x^2 + 3x + 1 = 0$ **3.** $x^2 - 9 = 0$

4. $-x^2 + 3x + 10 = 0$ **5.** $6x^2 - x - 2 = 0$ **6.** $4x^2 + 6x - 5 = 0$

7. $2x^2 + \frac{1}{2}x = 0$ **8.** $-x^2 + \frac{2}{3}x + \frac{1}{3} = 0$ **9.** $\frac{1}{2}x^2 - 2x - 4 = 0$

EXERCISES

A

Find the sum and the product of the roots for each equation. Check by solving the equation, then adding the roots and multiplying them.

1. $x^2 + 2x - 3 = 0$ **2.** $9x^2 - 1 = 0$ **3.** $-2x^2 - 5x + 3 = 0$

4. $x^2 + 3x - 2 = 0$ **5.** $x^2 + x - 3 = 0$ **6.** $2x^2 - x - 10 = 0$

7. $\frac{1}{2}x^2 + 2x + 2 = 0$ **8.** $-\frac{1}{4}x^2 + x - 1 = 0$ **9.** $\frac{1}{4}x^2 - 1 = 0$

Write a quadratic equation with the given roots x_1 and x_2. Write the equation in the form $ax^2 + bx + c = 0$, where a, b, and c are integers.

10. $x_1 = 2, x_2 = 3$ **11.** $x_1 = 2, x_2 = -3$ **12.** $x_1 = -2, x_2 = -3$

13. $x_1 = -10, x_2 = -5$ **14.** $x_1 = -5, x_2 = 10$ **15.** $x_1 = 5, x_2 = -10$

B

16. $x_1 = \frac{1}{2}, x_2 = \frac{1}{4}$ **17.** $x_1 = -2, x_2 = \frac{1}{2}$ **18.** $x_1 = -\frac{1}{2}, x_2 = -\frac{1}{2}$

19. $x_1 = 1 + \sqrt{2}, x_2 = 1 - \sqrt{2}$ **20.** $x_1 = 2 - \sqrt{3}, x_2 = 2 + \sqrt{3}$

21. $x_1 = \dfrac{1 + \sqrt{2}}{2}, x_2 = \dfrac{1 - \sqrt{2}}{2}$ **22.** $x_1 = \dfrac{4 + \sqrt{5}}{3}, x_2 = \dfrac{4 - \sqrt{5}}{3}$

23. Write a quadratic equation with the roots $\dfrac{3 \pm \sqrt{5}}{2}$.

C

24. Find values for k such that the sum of the roots of $(k - 1)x^2 + k^2x + 21 = 0$ is $-\frac{16}{3}$.

25. Find values for k such that the product of the roots of $(k - 1)x^2 + 3x - k^2 = 0$ is $-\frac{9}{2}$.

26. Find the equation whose roots are the opposites of those for $6x^2 + 7x - 20 = 0$.

27. Find the equation whose roots are the opposites of those for $x^2 - 2x - 1 = 0$.

*28. One root of $kx^2 - kx = 3kx - 10$ is twice the reciprocal of the other. Find the value of k. Then find the roots and verify that one root is twice the reciprocal of the other.

7-5   Problem Solving: Using Quadratic Equations

OBJECTIVE

To solve problems that give rise to quadratic equations.

Many problems can be solved using quadratic equations. We will review some basic steps in problem solving as we find the solution to the following problem.

> The width of a rug is 1 meter less than the length. The area of the rug is 8.75 square meters. Find the dimensions of the rug.

Express the unknown dimensions using a variable.

In this case, it is helpful to draw and label a diagram.

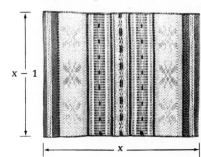

Let x represent the length, in meters.
Then x − 1 represents the width.

Write and solve an appropriate equation.

We know that the area is 8.75 square meters and that the area of a rectangle is the product of its length l and width w.

$$lw = 8.75$$
$$x(x - 1) = 8.75$$
$$x^2 - x - 8.75 = 0$$

Substitute $l = x$ and $w = x - 1$.

$$x = \frac{-(-1) \pm \sqrt{(-1)^2 - 4(1)(-8.75)}}{2(1)}$$

Use the quadratic formula.

$$x = \frac{1 \pm 6}{2}$$

$$x = \frac{7}{2} = 3.5 \text{ or } x = -\frac{5}{2} = -2.5$$

Interpret and check the solutions. Then state the answer to the problem.

The dimensions must be positive numbers, so the solution −2.5 is rejected. If the rug is 3.5 meters long, then it is 3.5 − 1, or 2.5 meters wide.

Check   2.5 meters is 1 meter less than 3.5 meters.
The area of a rug 3.5 meters by 2.5 meters is 8.75 square meters.

$$3.5 \times 2.5 = 8.75 \; \text{✓}$$

The rug is 3.5 meters long and 2.5 meters wide.

EXAMPLE 1

A rectangular garden is 15 meters wide and 20 meters long. It is surrounded by a walk of uniform width with an area of 74 square meters. How wide is the walk?

Strategy:
Write an equation that expresses the area of the walk in two ways.

Use a variable.

Draw a diagram and label it. Let x be the width of the walk, in meters. The area of the garden is $15 \times 20 = 300$ square meters. The area of the garden *plus the walk* is $(15 + 2x)(20 + 2x)$ square meters.

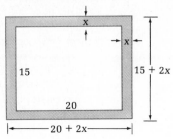

Write an equation.

The difference of the two areas is the area of the walk, 74 square meters.

$$(15 + 2x)(20 + 2x) - 300 = 74$$

Find the solution.

$$300 + 70x + 4x^2 - 300 = 74$$
$$2x^2 + 35x - 37 = 0$$
$$(2x + 37)(x - 1) = 0$$
$$2x + 37 = 0 \quad or \quad x - 1 = 0$$
$$x = -\frac{37}{2} \qquad x = 1$$

A negative answer makes no sense in this problem, so the first solution is rejected. Now check the other solution. If the walk is 1 meter wide, then the width of the garden plus walk is 17 meters and the length is 22 meters. Then the area of the walk, in square meters, is $(17 \times 22) - (15 \times 20) = 374 - 300 = 74.$ ✔

Answer the question.

The width of the walk is 1 meter.

EXAMPLE 2

The sum of a number and its reciprocal is 5. What is the number?

Use a variable.

If x represents the number, then $\frac{1}{x}$ represents its reciprocal.

Write an equation.

$$x + \frac{1}{x} = 5 \qquad \text{The sum of the number and its reciprocal is 5.}$$

Find the solution

$$x\left(x + \frac{1}{x}\right) = x(5) \qquad \text{Multiply each side by } x.$$

$$x^2 - 5x + 1 = 0$$

$$x = \frac{-(-5) \pm \sqrt{(-5)^2 - 4(1)(1)}}{2(1)} = \frac{5 \pm \sqrt{21}}{2} \qquad \text{Use the quadratic formula.}$$

To check, show that both roots of the equation are solutions to the problem.

Answer the question. The number is either $\frac{5 + \sqrt{21}}{2}$ or $\frac{5 - \sqrt{21}}{2}$.

CLASS EXERCISES

*State a mathematical expression in **n** to represent each phrase.*

1. The sum of two consecutive integers

2. The product of two consecutive integers

3. The sum of a number and its reciprocal

4. Four less than three times a number

5. Five more than one-half of a number

6. The sum of a number and the square of that number

7. The sum of the squares of two consecutive integers

8. The square of the sum of two consecutive integers

9. The square of a number diminished by the number

10. The sum of a number and twice the square of that number

EXERCISES

A 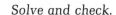 *Solve and check.*

1. Find two consecutive positive integers whose product is 240.

2. The sum of a negative integer and its square is 90. Find the integer.

3. Find two consecutive positive integers such that the sum of their squares is 265.

4. One positive integer is 5 less than another. The sum of their squares is 193. What are the integers?

5. The sum of a number and its reciprocal is $2\frac{1}{6}$. Find two values for the number.

6. Find two consecutive positive *even* integers whose product is 168.

7. The sum of an integer and twice its square is 55. Find the integer.

8. One number is 3 greater than another. If 3 is subtracted from the smaller number, and 8 is added to the larger number, the product of the resulting numbers is 95. Find all possible values of the numbers.

9. The length of a rectangle is 1 centimeter greater than twice the width. The area is 55 square centimeters. What are the dimensions of the rectangle?

B
10. The perimeter of a rectangle is 60 centimeters, and the area is 216 square centimeters. Find the length and the width of the rectangle.

11. In a right triangle, one leg is 2 centimeters more than twice the length of the other leg. The area of the triangle is 30 square centimeters. What is the length of the hypotenuse?
Hint: Recall the Pythagorean theorem: In a right triangle with legs of lengths a and b, and hypotenuse of length c, $a^2 + b^2 = c^2$.

12. In a parallelogram, the base is 1 centimeter less than three times the altitude. The area of the parallelogram is 24 square centimeters. Find the length of the base.

13. In a right triangle, one leg is twice the length of the other. The length of the hypotenuse is 12 centimeters. Find the length of each leg. Leave your answers in radical form.

14. A rectangular pool is 8 meters wide and 16 meters long. The pool is surrounded by a path of uniform width with an area of 48 square meters. Find the width of the walk in meters, correct to the nearest hundredth.

C

15. The length of each of two opposite sides of a square is increased by 4 inches. The length of each of the other two sides is decreased by 2 inches. The area of the rectangle formed is 2 square inches greater than that of the original square. Find the length of a side of the square.

16. To form a box without a top, a 2-inch square is cut from each corner of a square piece of tin. The sides are then folded up to form a box with a volume of 128 cubic inches. What was the length of each side of the original square?

*17. Two cars each travel 72 miles at constant rates. One car travels 6 miles per hour faster than the other and arrives 10 minutes before the other arrives. Find the rates of speed of the two cars.

CHECKPOINT

1. Solve $x^2 + 2x = 15$ by completing the square.

Solve, using the quadratic formula.

2. $16x^2 = 9$ **3.** $25 - 30x = -9x^2$ **4.** $x^2 + 46 - 14x = 0$

*State whether the equation has **two** real roots, exactly **one**, or **none**. Use the discriminant.*

5. $16x^2 = 8x - 1$ **6.** $2x^2 - 3x = -7$ **7.** $3x^2 - 4x + 5 = 0$

8. Write a quadratic equation with the roots $7 + 3\sqrt{3}$ and $7 - 3\sqrt{3}$.

9. Three times the square of a positive number, added to 5 times the same number, is equal to 12. Find the number.

Organizing and Interpreting Data

One dial on this camera adjusts the shutter speed. Another dial adjusts the lens opening, or f-stop.

Here are some different settings that can be used for the same exposure. The first number in each pair is the f-stop reading f, and the second number is the shutter speed s, in seconds.

$$\left(8.0, \frac{1}{60}\right) \qquad \left(5.6, \frac{1}{125}\right) \qquad \left(11.0, \frac{1}{30}\right) \qquad \left(4.0, \frac{1}{250}\right)$$

1. **Is the relationship between f and s linear?**
   To find out, copy and complete Table 1. Write the f-values from least to greatest. Write the corresponding s-values as decimals, correct to the nearest thousandth.

   Table 1

f	4.0	5.6	8.0	11.0
s	0.004			

   $\dfrac{1}{250} = 0.004$

   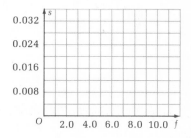

   Now, graph the data in the table. Do the points you plotted lie in a straight line? Is the relationship linear?

2. **Which of the following equations best represents the relationship between f and s?**

   $$s = \frac{1}{f^2} \qquad s = \frac{f}{1000} \qquad s = \frac{f^2}{4000}$$

   To find out, copy and complete Table 2. Compare the last three rows in Table 2 with the last row in Table 1. Which equation best describes the relationship between f and s?

   Table 2

f	4.0	5.6	8.0	11.0
$s = \dfrac{1}{f^2}$				
$s = \dfrac{f}{1000}$				
$s = \dfrac{f^2}{4000}$				

7-6 Graphing Quadratic Functions

OBJECTIVE _____

To graph functions of the form $f(x) = ax^2 + c$.

The *general quadratic function* defined by the equation $y = ax^2 + bx + c$ can be written as

$$y = f(x) = ax^2 + bx + c \qquad (a \neq 0)$$

Such functions can be graphed by plotting a number of points and then connecting them with a smooth curve. A table of values is helpful in listing ordered pairs of numbers. Consider the following table for the function given by the equation $y = x^2$, and written as $f(x) = x^2$.

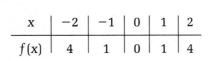

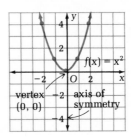

The graph of $f(x) = x^2$ is called a **parabola.** Both the graph and the table of values show that the parabola is *symmetric* about the line with the equation $x = 0$. This line, the y-axis, is called the **axis of symmetry.**

The parabola turns, or changes direction, at $(0, 0)$. This turning point is called the **vertex** of the parabola. It is the lowest point on the curve and gives the **minimum value** of the function, $f(0) = 0$.

The *domain* of the function $f(x) = x^2$ is the set of all real numbers. That is, x may be any real number. The *range* of the function is the set of all positive real numbers and zero. That is, $y \geq 0$.

EXAMPLE 1 Graph $f(x) = -x^2$. Give the coordinates of the vertex, the equation of the axis of symmetry, and the minimum or maximum value of the function. Then state its domain and range.

A table of values could be used here. However, note that for each x-value, the value of the function is the opposite of that for $f(x) = x^2$. For example, when $x = 2$, $x^2 = 4$, whereas $-x^2 = -4$. Thus the graph is the same size and shape as—or *congruent* to—the graph of $f(x) = x^2$, but it is *reflected* through the x-axis.

Notice that the vertex of the graph of $f(x) = -x^2$ is at (0, 0), the highest point on the curve. The equation of the axis of symmetry is $x = 0$, and the **maximum value** of the function is $f(0) = 0$. The domain of the function $f(x) = -x^2$ is the set of real numbers. The range is the set of negative real numbers and zero. That is, $y \leq 0$.

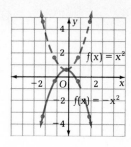

The graphs of functions with equations of the form $f(x) = x^2 + c$ or $f(x) = -x^2 + c$ are also congruent to the graphs of $f(x) = x^2$ or $f(x) = -x^2$, as is shown in the next example. However, the graphs are shifted, or **translated** c units up or down.

EXAMPLE 2

Graph each function. Write the coordinates of the vertex, the equation of the axis of symmetry, and the minimum or maximum value of the function. State the domain and the range.

a. $f(x) = x^2 + 2$

The graph is congruent to that of $f(x) = x^2$, but translated 2 units up.

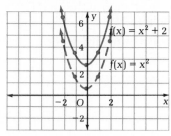

Vertex: (0, 2)
Axis of symmetry: $x = 0$
Minimum value: $f(0) = 2$
Domain: All real numbers
Range: All real numbers
    greater than or
    equal to 2

b. $f(x) = -x^2 - 4$

The graph is congruent to that of $f(x) = -x^2$, but translated 4 units down.

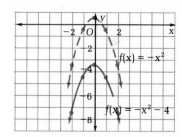

Vertex: (0, −4)
Axis of symmetry: $x = 0$
Maximum value: $f(0) = -4$
Domain: All real numbers
Range: All real numbers
    less than or equal
    to −4

If the coefficient of x^2 is not 1 or −1, the shape of the parabola is not the same as those just shown. When the coefficient of x^2 is greater than 1 or less than −1, the parabola is narrower than that of $y = x^2$ or $y = -x^2$. When the coefficient of x^2 is between −1 and 1, the parabola is wider. Compare the graphs of the functions in Example 3 with the graphs of $y = x^2$ and $y = -x^2$, which are shown as dashed curves.

EXAMPLE 3   Graph the function given by each equation.

a. $y = 2x^2$

x	−2	−1	0	1	2
y	8	2	0	2	8

b. $y = -\dfrac{1}{2}x^2$

x	−2	−1	0	1	2
y	−2	$-\dfrac{1}{2}$	0	$-\dfrac{1}{2}$	−2

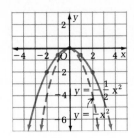

The following table summarizes the information in this lesson.

$$f(x) = ax^2 + c \qquad (a \neq 0)$$

Graph: a parabola

Vertex: $(0, c)$

Equation of axis of symmetry: $x = 0$

If $a > 0$, the parabola opens upward and has a minimum value $f(0) = c$.

If $a < 0$, the parabola opens downward and has a maximum value $f(0) = c$.

CLASS EXERCISES

Match each equation with a graph below.

1. $y = x^2$ **2.** $y = -x^2 + 1$ **3.** $y = x^2 - 1$

4. $y = -x^2 - 1$ **5.** $y = -x^2$ **6.** $y = x^2 + 1$

a. **b.** 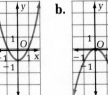 **c.** 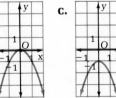 **d.** 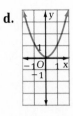 **e.** 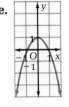 **f.**

CHAPTER 7

EXERCISES

Graph each quadratic equation. First make a table of values.

1. $y = 4x^2$

2. $y = \dfrac{1}{4}x^2$

3. $y = -4x^2$

4. $y = -\dfrac{1}{4}x^2$

5. $y = x^2 - 2$

6. $y = -x^2 + 2$

7. $y = 2x^2 - 2$

8. $y = 2x^2 + 2$

9. $y = -\dfrac{1}{2}x^2 - 2$

Graph each function by translating the graph of $f(x) = x^2$ or $f(x) = -x^2$.

10. $f(x) = x^2 + 3$

11. $f(x) = x^2 - 3$

12. $f(x) = -x^2 - 3$

13. $f(x) = x^2 + 4$

14. $f(x) = -x^2 + 4$

15. $f(x) = x^2 - 1$

B

Without graphing, give the coordinates of the vertex of the parabola, the equation of its axis of symmetry, and the **minimum** or **maximum** value of the function.

16. $f(x) = x^2 + 5$

17. $f(x) = x^2 - 5$

18. $f(x) = -x^2 + 8$

19. $f(x) = -x^2 - 8$

20. $f(x) = 8x^2$

21. $f(x) = -6x^2 + 2$

Find the value of **a** if the graph of $y = ax^2 + 3$ passes through the given point. **Hint:** Substitute the x- and y-values in the equation and solve for a.

22. $(1, 2)$

23. $(-1, 4)$

24. $(4, -5)$

The parabola with the equation $y = ax^2 + c$ passes through the given points. Find the values of **a** and **c**.

25. $(2, 2)$ and $(0, -2)$

26. $(0, 2)$ and $(2, -2)$

27. $(1, 1)$ and $(2, 3)$

State the domain and range for each function.

28. $f(x) = x^2 + 3$

29. $f(x) = (x + 3)^2$

30. $f(x) = x^2 - 3$

31. $f(x) = -x^2 + 3$

C

32. Draw the graph of $y^2 = x$. Explain why this equation does not define y to be a function of x.

33. Use a table of values to help you draw the graphs of $y = x^2 - 2$ and $y = (x - 2)^2$. Draw the graph of each equation on the same set of axes. Are the graphs congruent?

34. The roots of $ax^2 + c = 0$ are the x-intercepts of $f(x) = ax^2 + c$. Find the x-intercepts of $f(x) = 2x^2 - 8$.

7-7 The Quadratic Function in h, k Form

To write the equation of a quadratic function in h, k form.
To graph a quadratic function using the h, k form.
To find the minimum or maximum value of a quadratic function.

The **h, k form** of a quadratic function is

$$f(x) = a(x - h)^2 + k \qquad (a \neq 0)$$

This form is particularly useful in sketching the graphs of such functions. In general, the graph of $f(x) = a(x - h)^2 + k$ is congruent to that of $f(x) = ax^2$, which has its vertex at $(0, 0)$. But it is translated h units horizontally and k units vertically, so that the new vertex has the coordinates (h, k). The figures below show how the graph of $f(x) = (x - 2)^2 + 1$ is obtained by translating the graph of $f(x) = x^2$.

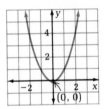

$f(x) = x^2$

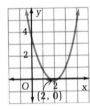

$f(x) = (x - 2)^2$

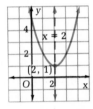

$f(x) = (x - 2)^2 + 1$

The graph of $f(x) = (x - 2)^2 + 1$ is congruent to that of $f(x) = x^2$, but it is translated 2 units to the right and 1 unit up. The new vertex is at $(2, 1)$, and the equation of the axis of symmetry is $x = 2$. The minimum value of the function is $f(2) = 1$. The domain of the function is the set of all real numbers, and the range is the set of real numbers greater than or equal to 1. These facts are summarized below for any quadratic function in h, k form.

$$f(x) = a(x - h)^2 + k \qquad (a \neq 0)$$

Graph: a parabola

Vertex: (h, k)

Equation of axis of symmetry: $x = h$

**If $a > 0$, the parabola opens upward and has a minimum value
$f(h) = k$.**

**If $a < 0$, the parabola opens downward and has a maximum value
$f(h) = k$.**

EXAMPLE 1   Graph the function given by the equation $y = -(x + 1)^2 + 4$. Write the coordinates of the vertex, the equation of the axis of symmetry, and the minimum or maximum value of the function.

We can think of the graph of $y = -(x + 1)^2 + 4$ as a translation of the graph of $y = -x^2$. Since $h = -1$ and $k = 4$, the vertex is translated from $(0, 0)$ to $(-1, 4)$. Every other point on the graph of $y = -x^2$ is also translated one unit to the left and four units up.

It is helpful to make a brief table of values in order to locate a few points.

x	-3	-2	-1	0	1
$y = -(x + 1)^2 + 4$	0	3	4	3	0

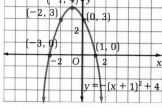

Coordinates of vertex: $(-1, 4)$ (h, k)

Axis of symmetry: $x = -1$ $x = h$

Maximum value: $f(-1) = 4$ $f(h) = k$

To see why the function in the example above has a maximum value of 4, note that when x has *any* value other than -1, $-(x + 1)^2$ is negative, and $-(x + 1)^2 + 4$ must be less than 4. However, for $x = -1$, $-(x + 1)^2 = 0$, and $f(x) = -(x + 1)^2 + 4$ has its greatest possible value, 4.

When a quadratic function is not given in h, k form, you can write it in that form by *completing the square*. The procedure is similar to that used in Section 7–1, where we solved quadratic equations by completing the square.

EXAMPLE 2   Write the function $f(x) = 2x^2 - 4x - 5$ in h, k form. Find the minimum or maximum value of the function.

$$f(x) = 2x^2 - 4x - 5$$
$$= 2(x^2 - 2x) - 5 \qquad \text{Factor 2 from the first two terms.}$$
$$= 2(x^2 - 2x + 1) - 5 - 2 \qquad \begin{array}{l}\text{Complete the square. Since 2(1) is added,} \\ \text{2 is subtracted on the same side.}\end{array}$$
$$= 2(x - 1)^2 - 7 \qquad \begin{array}{l}\text{Factor } x^2 - 2x + 1 \text{ and simplify to obtain} \\ \text{the } h, k \text{ form.}\end{array}$$

Compare $f(x) = 2(x - 1)^2 - 7$ to the general h, k form, $f(x) = a(x - h)^2 + k$. Since a equals 2, which is greater than 0, the function has a *minimum value*, $f(h) = k$. Since $f(1) = -7$, that minimum value is -7. Sketch the graph of $f(x) = 2x^2 - 4x - 5$ to verify this.

CLASS EXERCISES

Match each graph with one of the given equations.

1. **2.** **3.** **4.** **5.** **6.**

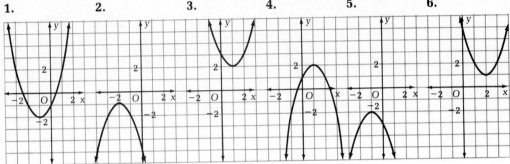

a. $y = (x - 1)^2 + 2$ **b.** $y = (x + 1)^2 - 2$ **c.** $y = (x - 2)^2 + 1$

d. $y = -(x + 1)^2 - 2$ **e.** $y = -(x + 2)^2 - 1$ **f.** $y = -(x - 1)^2 + 2$

EXERCISES

A *Write each function in **h**, **k** form.*

1. $f(x) = x^2 + 8x - 5$ **2.** $f(x) = x^2 - 6x + 1$ **3.** $f(x) = x^2 - 2x + 3$

4. $f(x) = x^2 + 4x + 1$ **5.** $f(x) = x^2 + 4x + 4$ **6.** $f(x) = x^2 - 12x + 8$

7. $f(x) = x^2 - x + 2$ **8.** $f(x) = 2x^2 - 12x - 5$ **9.** $f(x) = 3x^2 + 6x - 1$

Graph the function given by each equation.

10. $y = (x - 2)^2 + 3$ **11.** $y = (x + 1)^2 - 3$ **12.** $y = -(x + 2)^2 - 1$

B *Write each equation in **h**, **k** form. Write the coordinates of the vertex and the equation of the axis of symmetry of the parabola. Then graph the parabola. State the domain and the range.*

13. $y = x^2 + 6x + 9$ **14.** $y = x^2 - 4x + 5$ **15.** $y = x^2 - 2x + 3$

16. $y = x^2 - 8x + 13$ **17.** $y = -x^2 - 2x + 5$ **18.** $y = -x^2 + 4x - 4$

19. $y = -x^2 - 2x + 3$ **20.** $y = 2x^2 - 4x + 3$ **21.** $y = -2x^2 + 4x$

*Find the **minimum** or **maximum** value for each function.*

22. $f(x) = x^2 - 8x + 2$ **23.** $f(x) = x^2 + 6x - 2$ **24.** $f(x) = -x^2 - 6x + 3$

25. $f(x) = -x^2 + 4x + 1$ **26.** $f(x) = \frac{1}{2}x^2 - 2x + 3$ **27.** $f(x) = -\frac{1}{2}x^2 + x - 1$

28. $f(x) = 2x^2 + 2x + 5$ **29.** $f(x) = -2x^2 + x - 1$ **30.** $f(x) = 3x^2 - 6x + 4$

Graph each inequality.

Sample $y > (x - 1)^2 - 2$

Graph the related equation $y = (x - 1)^2 - 2$. The parabola borders the graph of the inequality. Test a point not on the parabola, such as $(0, 0)$.

$$0 > (0 - 1)^2 - 2$$
$$0 > -1 \quad \text{True}$$

$(0, 0)$ is a solution. Shade the region containing the origin. Points *on* the dashed curve are not part of the graph of $y > (x - 1)^2 - 2$.

31. $y < x^2$

32. $y \geq (x + 1)^2 + 3$

33. $y \leq -x^2 + 2x - 4$

C

Graph the function given by each equation. For each equation, let $y = 0$ and find the x-intercepts. Also find the value of the discriminant and state how this value relates to the x-intercepts of the graph.

34. $y = 4x^2 - 12x + 9$

35. $y = x^2 + 2x - 3$

36. $y = x^2 + 2x + 2$

Give the domain and range for each function. Also find all of the x- and y-intercepts for the graph of the function.

37. $f(x) = 2x^2 - 4x + 3$

38. $f(x) = -x^2 + 6x - 8$

39. $f(x) = -2x^2 - 4x - 3$

*40. Write the function $f(x) = ax^2 + bx + c$ in h, k form. Find the equation of the axis of symmetry and the coordinates of the vertex of its graph.

CHECKPOINT

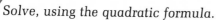

Solve, using the quadratic formula.

1. $5x^2 - 2x - 7 = 0$

2. $3x^2 + 4x - 8 = 0$

3. $-x^2 + \dfrac{5}{6}x + 1 = 0$

*Find a value for **p** so that the given equation has exactly one real root.*

4. $px^2 - 6x + 7 = 0$

5. $2x^2 + 5x - p = 0$

6. $4x^2 + px + 3 = 0$

7. Find two consecutive positive odd numbers whose product is 143.

8. The parabola with the equation $y = ax^2 - c$ passes through the points $(0, 1)$ and $(-3, 4)$. Find the values of a and c.

9. Write the equation $y = -2x^2 + 4x + 3$ in h, k form. Write the coordinates of the vertex and the equation of the axis of symmetry of the parabola. Then graph the parabola.

10. Find the minimum or maximum value for the function $f(x) = 3x^2 - 6x + 5$.

7-8 Minimum and Maximum Values of Quadratic Functions

OBJECTIVES

To find the minimum or maximum value of a quadratic function in general form.

To solve problems that involve finding minimum and maximum values.

Often a quadratic function is given in the form $f(x) = ax^2 + bx + c$. We can find the minimum or maximum value of such a function without having to rewrite it in h, k form. Recall that a minimum or maximum value is the value of the function at the vertex of its graph. Note that $f(x) = 0$ at any point where the graph crosses the x-axis. The x-values of such points are the real roots of the equation $ax^2 + bx + c = 0$. We will call these roots x_1 and x_2.

The axis of symmetry is perpendicular to the x-axis and intersects it at a point midway between the x-intercepts. Therefore, the x-coordinate of the vertex may be found by taking the average of the roots. Recall that the sum of the roots of a quadratic equation is $-\frac{b}{a}$. Therefore, the average of the roots is

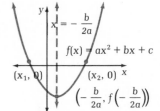

$$\frac{1}{2}(x_1 + x_2) = \frac{1}{2}\left(-\frac{b}{a}\right) = -\frac{b}{2a}$$

Since the x-coordinate of the vertex is $-\frac{b}{2a}$, we have the following:

The equation of the axis of symmetry is $x = -\frac{b}{2a}$.

The minimum or maximum value of the function is $f\left(-\frac{b}{2a}\right)$.

EXAMPLE 1

Find the minimum or maximum value of the function $f(x) = -2x^2 + x + 6$.

$$-\frac{b}{2a} = -\frac{1}{2(-2)} = \frac{1}{4}$$

$$f\left(-\frac{b}{2a}\right) = f\left(\frac{1}{4}\right) = -2\left(\frac{1}{4}\right)^2 + \frac{1}{4} + 6 = \frac{49}{8}$$

Since a is negative, the graph of the function opens downward. Therefore, $\frac{49}{8}$ is the *maximum* value of the function.

We can check the above answer by graphing or by writing the given function in h, k form, as follows.

$$f(x) = -2x^2 + x + 6$$

$$= -2\left(x^2 - \frac{1}{2}x\right) + 6$$

Factor -2 from the first two terms only.

$$= -2\left(x^2 - \frac{1}{2}x + \frac{1}{16}\right) + 6 + \frac{2}{16}$$

Complete the square. Since $2\left(\frac{1}{16}\right)$ is subtracted, add the same quantity.

$$= -2\left(x - \frac{1}{4}\right)^2 + \frac{49}{8}$$

Factor and simplify to obtain the h, k form.

From the h, k form, we see that a maximum occurs at $x = \frac{1}{4}$, and that the maximum value is $f\left(\frac{1}{4}\right)$, or $\frac{49}{8}$.

EXAMPLE 2

An object is thrown straight upward with an initial velocity of 32 feet per second. Its height in feet, y, after t seconds, is given by this formula:

$$y = -16t^2 + 32t$$

In how many seconds does the object reach its maximum height? What is the maximum height?

The maximum height occurs when t equals $-\frac{b}{2a}$.

$$-\frac{b}{2a} = -\frac{32}{2(-16)} = 1 \qquad a = -16, \ b = 32$$

The maximum height occurs 1 second after the object is thrown.

For $t = 1$: $y = -16(1)^2 + 32(1) = 16$.

The maximum height is 16 feet.

CLASS EXERCISES

Write the equation of the axis of symmetry. Then find the **minimum** or **maximum** value of the function.

1. $f(x) = x^2 - 4x + 5$

2. $f(x) = x^2 + 2x - 3$

3. $f(x) = -x^2 - 6x + 1$

4. $f(x) = -x^2 - 2x + 2$

5. $f(x) = 2x^2 + 4x - 3$

6. $f(x) = -3x^2 + 5x$

EXERCISES

A

Write the equation of the axis of symmetry. Then find the **minimum** or **maximum** value of the function.

1. $f(x) = -x^2 - 2x + 1$

2. $f(x) = -x^2 + 2x + 2$

3. $f(x) = 3x^2 - 6x + 5$

4. $f(x) = 2x^2 + 4x - 7$

5. $f(x) = x^2 + 3x - 2$

6. $f(x) = x^2 - 3x + 5$

7. $f(x) = -2x^2 + 10x$

8. $f(x) = -3x^2 - 3x + 4$

9. $f(x) = \frac{1}{2}x^2 + 4x - 3$

10. $f(x) = -\frac{1}{3}x^2 - 3x + 5$

11. The sum of two numbers is 10. Find the two numbers if their product is to be a maximum. **Hint:** Find the maximum value for $y = x(10 - x)$.

B

12. The sum of two numbers is $\frac{1}{2}$. Find the numbers, if their product is to be maximum. Also find the maximum product.

13. The difference of two numbers is 20. Find the numbers, if their product is to be a minimum. Also, find the minimum product.

14. A rectangular garden is to be enclosed by 400 feet of fencing. Find the dimensions that will produce the maximum area.

15. The sum of two numbers is n. Find the numbers, if their product is to be a maximum. Are there two numbers with the given sum n that will give a minimum product?

C

16. One side of a rectangular garden is to be against a house. There are 80 meters of fencing available to enclose the other three sides of the garden. Find the dimensions that will give the maximum area.

17. The sum of the lengths of the two legs of a right triangle is 40 inches. Find the lengths of the legs if the square of the hypotenuse is a minimum.

18. An object is thrown straight upward. Its height in feet, y, after t seconds, is given by the formula $y = -16t^2 + 128t$. What is the maximum height reached by the object? How long does it take to reach that height?

19. In Exercise 18, how many seconds pass from the time the object is thrown until it returns to its starting position?

20. In Exercise 18, how many seconds pass from the time the object is thrown until it first reaches a height of 192 feet?

*21. It is expected that 1200 people will attend a concert if the admission price is $6. For each dollar added to the price of admission, attendance is expected to decrease by 100. What should the admission price be in order to yield the greatest gross receipts?

22. A piece of wire 80 centimeters long is cut into two smaller pieces. Each piece is bent to form a square. What is the length of each piece, if the sum of the areas of the two squares is a minimum?

*23. Suppose that the piece of wire in Exercise 22 is to be cut into two pieces, one of which is bent to form a square and the other to form a circle. What is the length of each piece, if the sum of the areas of the two figures is a minimum?

Approximating Areas Under Curves

Many problems in science have solutions that can be represented by areas under curves. For example, the area under the *normal curve* is important in actuarial work. The ancient Greek mathematician Archimedes was the first to approximate such areas with great accuracy. This example illustrates the method he used.

Example Find the area bounded by the parabola $y = x^2$, the line $x = 2$, and the x-axis.

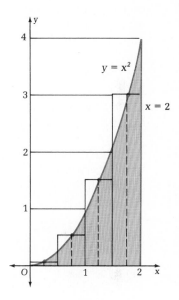

Divide the interval between 0 and 2 on the x-axis into four equal intervals. Use the lengths of these intervals as the widths of four rectangles. For the heights of the rectangles, use the y-values of the curve at the midpoints of the intervals. The sum of the areas of the rectangles is an approximation of the area bounded by the curve and the two lines.

$$A = \frac{1}{2}\left(\frac{1}{4}\right)^2 + \frac{1}{2}\left(\frac{3}{4}\right)^2 + \frac{1}{2}\left(\frac{5}{4}\right)^2 + \frac{1}{2}\left(\frac{7}{4}\right)^2$$

$$= \frac{1}{32} + \frac{9}{32} + \frac{25}{32} + \frac{49}{32}$$

$$= \frac{84}{32} = 2\frac{5}{8}$$

An approximation of the area is $2\frac{5}{8}$ square units. For a more accurate approximation by this method, increase the number of intervals on the x-axis between 0 and 2.

Newton and Leibniz invented the calculus in the seventeenth century. With their new discovery, the area in the problem above can be found to be exactly $2\frac{2}{3}$ square units.

1. Approximate the area bounded by the parabola $y = x^2$, the line $x = 2$, and the x-axis. Use eight $\frac{1}{4}$-unit intervals on the x-axis. Compare your results with those in the example above and with the exact area, $2\frac{2}{3}$ square units.

2. Approximate the area bounded by the parabola $y = x^2 + 2$, the lines $x = 1$ and $x = 4$, and the x-axis. Use six $\frac{1}{2}$-unit intervals on the x-axis.

CHAPTER 7 REVIEW

VOCABULARY

completing the square (p. 238)
general quadratic equation (p. 242)
quadratic formula (p. 242)
discriminant (p. 245)
double root (p. 245)
general quadratic function (p. 256)
parabola (p. 256)
axis of symmetry (p. 256)

vertex (p. 256)
minimum value (p. 256)
congruent (p. 256)
reflected (p. 256)
maximum value (p. 257)
translated (p. 257)
h, k form (p. 260)

SUMMARY

In this chapter, quadratic equations in one variable are solved by completing the square and by using the quadratic formula. Other topics are the analysis of roots using the discriminant, formulas for the sum and product of the roots, and problem solving. Then quadratic functions of the form $y = ax^2 + bx + c$, whose graphs are parabolas, are introduced. The h, k form is used to simplify the graphing of the functions. The chapter concludes with a lesson about finding maximum and minimum values of quadratic functions and solving problems involving such values.

REVIEW EXERCISES

7-1 *Supply the missing term to form a trinomial square. Then factor the trinomial.*

1. $x^2 + 16x + \underline{\ ?\ }$ **2.** $x^2 - 9x + \underline{\ ?\ }$ **3.** $x^2 + 3x + \underline{\ ?\ }$

Solve by taking the square root of each side.

4. $(x + 3)^2 = 25$ **5.** $(x - 2)^2 = 16$ **6.** $x^2 - 16x + 64 = 81$

Solve by completing the square.

7. $x^2 - 4x = -3$ **8.** $x^2 + 3x = 7$ **9.** $2x^2 - 4 = 7x$

7-2 *Solve, using the quadratic formula.*

10. $x^2 + 5x + 3 = 0$ **11.** $x^2 - 8 = 3x$ **12.** $x + 7 = x^2$

13. $7x^2 = 3$ **14.** $2x^2 - 5x + 3 = 0$ **15.** $\frac{3}{4}x^2 - \frac{5}{8}x - \frac{1}{2} = 0$

16. Find the solutions to $x^2 + 3x - 1 = 0$ to two decimal places.

7-3 *Use the discriminant to determine the number of real roots.*

17. $2x^2 + 3x - 5 = 0$ **18.** $4x^2 + 4x + 1 = 0$ **19.** $x^2 + x + 1 = 0$

*Find a value for **k** so that the equation has exactly one real root.*

20. $kx^2 + 6x - 1 = 0$ **21.** $3x^2 - kx + 2 = 0$ **22.** $\frac{1}{4}x^2 + 3x = -k$

7-4 Find the sum and the product of the roots for each equation. Check by solving the equation, then adding the roots and multiplying them.

23. $2x^2 - 5x + 1 = 0$ **24.** $\frac{1}{2}x^2 - \frac{1}{4}x - 6 = 0$ **25.** $x^2 - 3x - 5 = 0$

26. $3x^2 - 1 = 0$ **27.** $5x^2 + 4x = 0$ **28.** $\frac{1}{3}x^2 - x - 1 = 0$

Write a quadratic equation with the given roots x_1 and x_2. Write the equation in the form $ax^2 + bx + c = 0$.

29. $x_1 = -8$, $x_2 = 3$ **30.** $x_1 = \frac{6}{7}$, $x_2 = 5$

31. $x_1 = 3 + \sqrt{2}$, $x_2 = 3 - \sqrt{2}$ **32.** $x_1 = \dfrac{-1 + \sqrt{3}}{5}$, $x_2 = \dfrac{-1 - \sqrt{3}}{5}$

7-5 Solve and check.

33. Find two positive numbers such that one is 6 less than the other and their product is 72.

34. The length of a rectangle is 3 inches greater than twice the width. The area is 77 square inches. What are the dimensions of the rectangle?

35. In a right triangle, one leg is one-half the length of the other leg. The length of the hypotenuse is 25 centimeters. Find the length of each leg. Leave your answers in radical form.

7-6 Graph each function by translating the graph of $f(x) = x^2$ or $f(x) = -x^2$.

36. $f(x) = x^2 + 1$ **37.** $f(x) = -x^2 - 2$

Without graphing, give the coordinates of the vertex of the parabola, the equation of its axis of symmetry, and the **minimum** or **maximum** value of the function.

38. $f(x) = x^2 + 6$ **39.** $f(x) = -x^2 - 7$ **40.** $f(x) = 3x^2$

41. Find the value of a if the graph of $y = ax^2 - 3$ contains the point $(-2, 5)$.

7-7 Write each equation in h, k form. Write the coordinates of the vertex and the equation of the axis of symmetry of the parabola. Then graph the parabola.

42. $y = x^2 - 6x + 3$ **43.** $y = 2x^2 + 6x + 3$ **44.** $y = -3x^2 + 6x - 5$

7-8 Write the equation of the axis of symmetry. Then find the **minimum** or **maximum** value of the function.

45. $f(x) = x^2 + 6x - 4$ **46.** $f(x) = -2x^2 + 3x - 2$

47. One hundred feet of fencing is available to enclose a rectangular garden lot. If the area is to be a maximum, what will be the dimensions of the garden?

Solve by taking the square root of each side.

1. $(x - 3)^2 = 16$

2. $x^2 + 8x + 16 = 19$

Solve by completing the square.

3. $x^2 - 4x - 12 = 0$

4. $2x^2 - x - 1 = 0$

Solve, using the quadratic formula.

5. $3x^2 + 5x - 2 = 0$

6. $2x^2 - x - 4 = 0$

Use the discriminant to determine the number of real roots.

7. $x^2 - 8x = 5$

8. $9x^2 - 12x = -4$

Find the sum and product of the roots for each equation.

9. $x^2 + 5x - 10 = 0$

10. $-2x^2 + 3x + 7 = 0$

Write a quadratic equation with the given roots x_1 and x_2. Write the equation in the form $ax^2 + bx + c = 0$.

11. $x_1 = -\frac{1}{2}, x_2 = \frac{3}{2}$

12. $x_1 = \sqrt{5}, x_2 = -\sqrt{5}$

13. $x_1 = 1 + \sqrt{7}, x_2 = 1 - \sqrt{7}$

14. One positive integer is 6 more than another, and the sum of the squares of the two integers is 68. Find the two integers.

15. Graph the function $f(x) = x^2 - 5$ by translating the graph of $f(x) = x^2$.

16. Write the equation $y = \frac{1}{4}x^2 - 2x + 3$ in h, k form. Identify the coordinates of the vertex and the equation of the axis of symmetry of the parabola.

Find the **minimum** or **maximum** value of each function.

17. $f(x) = x^2 - 8x + 3$ **18.** $f(x) = -3x^2 + 5x - 2$ **19.** $f(x) = 4x^2 - 5$

20. The sum of two numbers is 50. Find the numbers if their product is to be a maximum.

Profit or Loss

Here are two different methods of computing the rate of profit.

When rate is based on cost:

$$\text{rate of profit} = \frac{\text{profit}}{\text{cost}}$$

When rate is based on selling price:

$$\text{rate of profit} = \frac{\text{profit}}{\text{selling price}}$$

Consider a computer that costs \$175 and sells for \$280. Based on cost, the rate of profit is $\frac{105}{175}$, or 60%. Based on selling price, the rate of profit is only $\frac{105}{280}$, or $37\frac{1}{2}$%.

When C is the rate based on the cost, and S is the rate based on the selling price, $C = \frac{S}{1 - S}$ and $S = \frac{C}{1 + C}$. The program below can evaluate both formulas. If you enter the rate based on the cost, the rate based on the selling price is displayed. To determine the rate based on cost, first enter 0. The computer recognizes this signal, jumps to line 300 and asks for the input.

The Program	What It Does
`100 REM RATE OF PROFIT OR LOSS`	Gives instructions about
`110 PRINT "ENTER RATES AS DECIMALS."`	use of the program.
`120 PRINT "RATE BASED ON COST?"`	
`130 PRINT "IF UNKNOWN, ENTER ZERO."`	
`140 INPUT C`	If C is to be computed,
`150 IF C = 0 THEN 300`	jumps to line 300.
`200 LET R = C/(1 + C)`	Finds rate based on selling price.
`210 PRINT "BASED ON SELLING PRICE"`	Labels result.
`220 GO TO 400`	
`300 PRINT "RATE BASED ON SELLING PRICE";`	
`310 INPUT S`	
`320 LET R = S/(1 - S)`	Finds rate based on cost.
`330 PRINT "BASED ON COST"`	Labels result.
`400 PRINT "RATE IS "; R`	
`900 END`	

When the above program is run, what is displayed for each of these entries? What percent does each entry and display represent?

Rate based on the cost: **1.** 0.25　　**2.** 0.5　　**3.** 2

Rate based on the selling price: **4.** 0.5　　**5.** 0.75　　**6.** 0.95

Modify the program so it will accept the input as an integer (enter 75% as 75) and display the result to the nearest whole percent. *What will this modified program display for these entries?*

Rate based on the cost: **7.** 20%　　**8.** 150%　　**9.** −50%

Rate based on the selling price: **10.** 37.5%　　**11.** 90%　　**12.** −50%

For more information about BASIC, see the Computer Handbook at the back of the book.

COMPUTER ACTIVITY　　271

CHAPTER 8

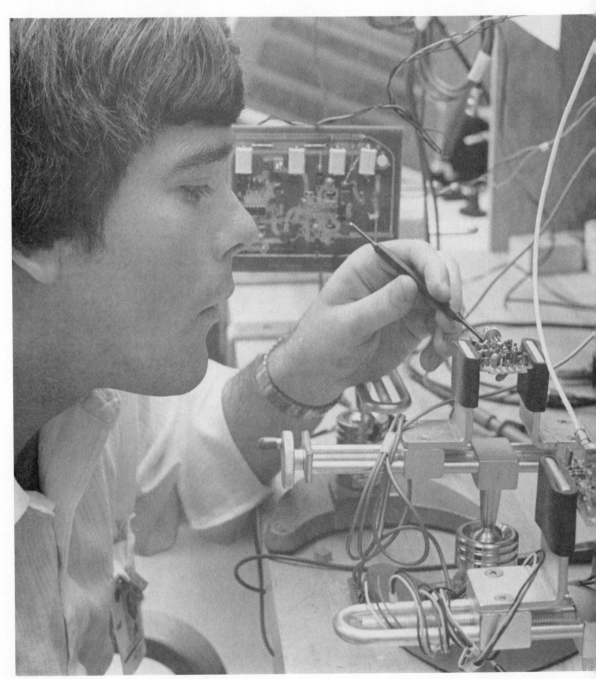

Electrical engineers use complex numbers in the analysis of circuits.

POLYNOMIAL EQUATIONS AND COMPLEX NUMBERS

Prerequisite Skills Review

Write the letter for the correct answer.

1. $12x^2 \div 4x = \underline{\ ?\ }$

    a. $3x$ **b.** 3 **c.** $3x^2$ **d.** none of these

2. $8x^2 \div x^2 = \underline{\ ?\ }$

    a. $4x$ **b.** $3x$ **c.** 4 **d.** none of these

3. If $2x^2 - 4x + 3$ is subtracted from $2x^2 - 2x - 5$, the result is $\underline{\ ?\ }$.

    a. $4x^2 - 6x - 2$ **b.** $2x - 8$ **c.** $-2x + 8$ **d.** $-6x - 8$

4. $(2x + 1)(5x - 2) + 3 = \underline{\ ?\ }$

    a. $10x^2 + 3x + 1$ **b.** $10x^2 + x + 1$

    c. $10x^2 + x + 5$ **d.** $10x^2 + 5x + 1$

5. $x(3x - 1)(x + 2) - 4 = \underline{\ ?\ }$

    a. $3x^2 + 5x - 6$ **b.** $3x^3 + 5x^2 - 2x - 4$

    c. $3x^3 + 5x^2 - 6x$ **d.** $3x^4 + 5x^3 - 2x^2 - 4$

6. The degree of the polynomial $2x^2 - 7x + 8$ is one less than the degree of $\underline{\ ?\ }$.

    a. $3x^2 - 2x + 4$ **b.** $x^3 - 6$

    c. $3x^4 + 2x + 9$ **d.** $x^4 - 8$

7. If $p(x) = x^3 + 2x^2 - x + 6$, then $p(-2) = \underline{\ ?\ }$.

    a. 8 **b.** 24 **c.** -8 **d.** 4

8. If $p(x) = x^3 - x^2 - 8x + 5$, then $p\left(\frac{1}{2}\right) = \underline{\ ?\ }$.

    a. $\frac{7}{8}$ **b.** $1\frac{1}{8}$ **c.** $1\frac{3}{8}$ **d.** $1\frac{1}{4}$

9. Which of the following is *not* a real number?

    a. $-\sqrt{64}$ **b.** $\sqrt[3]{-64}$ **c.** $\sqrt{-64}$ **d.** $-\sqrt[3]{64}$

10. Which of the following names a real number?

    a. $\sqrt{8^2 - 2(5)(6)}$ **b.** $\sqrt{9^2 - 2(6)(7)}$ **c.** $\sqrt{10^2 - 2(7)(8)}$ **d.** $\sqrt{11^2 - 2(8)(9)}$

8-1 Dividing Polynomials

OBJECTIVES

To divide polynomials, expressing each answer in terms of the quotient and remainder.
To check the answers to such division examples.

Can you divide $12x^2 - 7x - 10$ by $4x - 5$? One way to find this quotient is to simplify the following rational expression.

dividend
$$\frac{12x^2 - 7x - 10}{4x - 5} = \frac{(3x + 2)(4x - 5)}{4x - 5} = 3x + 2$$
divisor   quotient

The quotient can also be found using a method similar to long division in arithmetic. This procedure is particularly useful when it is not obvious that the dividend can be factored, or when the divisor is not a factor of the dividend.

Step 1
$$\begin{array}{r} 3x \\ 4x - 5{\overline{\smash{\big)}\,12x^2 - 7x - 10}} \end{array}$$
Divide $12x^2$, the first term in the dividend, by $4x$, the first term of the divisor. Write the result, $3x$, above the line.

Step 2
$$\begin{array}{r} 3x \\ 4x - 5{\overline{\smash{\big)}\,12x^2 - 7x - 10}} \\ 12x^2 - 15x \end{array}$$
Multiply $4x - 5$ by $3x$ and write the product below the dividend. Write like terms in the same columns.

Step 3
$$\begin{array}{r} 3x \\ 4x - 5{\overline{\smash{\big)}\,12x^2 - 7x - 10}} \\ \underline{12x^2 - 15x} \\ 8x - 10 \end{array}$$
Subtract and bring down the next term, -10.

Now repeat the steps, but this time divide $8x$ by $4x$. Write $+2$ above, multiply the divisor by 2, write the product below, and subtract.

$$\begin{array}{r} 3x\ +\ 2 \longleftarrow \text{quotient} \\ \text{divisor} \longrightarrow 4x - 5{\overline{\smash{\big)}\,12x^2 - 7x - 10}} \longleftarrow \text{dividend} \\ \underline{12x^2 - 15x} \\ 8x - 10 \\ \underline{8x - 10} \\ 0 \longleftarrow \text{remainder} \end{array}$$

Check: divisor × quotient = dividend

$$(4x - 5)(3x + 2) = 12x^2 - 7x - 10 \ \text{✔}$$

In the division just illustrated, the remainder is zero because the divisor is a factor of the dividend. In the next example, the divisor is not a factor of the dividend.

EXAMPLE 1   Divide $5x^3 - 3x^2 + 7x - 1$ by $x^2 - x + 2$, and check.

$$
\begin{array}{r}
5x + 2 \\
x^2 - x + 2 \overline{)5x^3 - 3x^2 + 7x - 1} \\
\underline{5x^3 - 5x^2 + 10x} \\
2x^2 - 3x - 1 \\
\underline{2x^2 - 2x + 4} \\
-x - 5
\end{array}
$$

Divide $5x^3$ by x^2.

Multiply $x^2 - x + 2$ by $5x$.

Subtract, and bring down the -1. Then divide $2x^2$ by x^2.

Multiply $x^2 - x + 2$ by 2.

Subtract to find the remainder. Stop, since the degree of the remainder is less than that of the divisor.

Check

$$
\begin{array}{r}
x^2 - x + 2 \\
5x + 2 \\
\hline
2x^2 - 2x + 4 \\
5x^3 - 5x^2 + 10x \\
\hline
5x^3 - 3x^2 + 8x + 4 \\
-x - 5 \\
\hline
5x^3 - 3x^2 + 7x - 1 \ \text{✔}
\end{array}
$$

Multiply the quotient and the divisor.

Add the remainder.

The result should equal the dividend.

Show the answer in this form: quotient $+ \dfrac{\text{remainder}}{\text{divisor}}$.

$$\frac{5x^3 - 3x^2 + 7x - 1}{x^2 - x + 2} = 5x + 2 + \frac{-x - 5}{x^2 - x + 2}$$

The preceding illustrations demonstrate that the division process continues until the remainder is zero or the degree of the remainder is lower than that of the divisor. Recall that the degree of a polynomial in one variable is the highest power of that variable. A constant such as 2 has degree zero, because $2 = 2 \cdot 1 = 2x^0$.

The division process is easiest when the terms of each polynomial are arranged in order of decreasing powers of the variable. If terms involving one or more of the consecutive powers of the variable are missing, insert appropriate terms with zero coefficients.

EXAMPLE 2   Divide $30x + 2x^4 - 9x^3 - 2$ by $-3x + x^2$.

$$
\begin{array}{r}
2x^2 - 3x \quad - 9 \\
x^2 - 3x\overline{)2x^4 - 9x^3 + 0x^2 + 30x - 2} \\
\underline{2x^4 - 6x^3} \\
-3x^3 + 0x^2 \\
\underline{-3x^3 + 9x^2} \\
-9x^2 + 30x \\
\underline{-9x^2 + 27x} \\
3x - 2
\end{array}
$$

Write the terms of each polynomial in order of decreasing powers of x. Insert $0x^2$ for the missing second degree term.

You should check this result by multiplying the quotient by the divisor and then adding the remainder.

$$\frac{2x^4 - 9x^3 + 30x - 2}{x^2 - 3x} = 2x^2 - 3x - 9 + \frac{3x - 2}{x^2 - 3x}$$

CLASS EXERCISES

Find each quotient by simplifying the rational expression.

1. $\dfrac{x^2 + 3x}{x}$

2. $\dfrac{8 - 12x}{4}$

3. $\dfrac{5a^3 - 15a^2}{5a^2}$

4. $\dfrac{4x^2 - 6x}{-2x}$

5. $\dfrac{8x^3 - 6x^2 + 4x}{2x}$

6. $\dfrac{2a^2 - a}{1 - 2a}$

7. $\dfrac{x^2 - 4}{x - 2}$

8. $\dfrac{(x + 3)^2}{x + 3}$

9. $\dfrac{2a^2 - ab}{b - 2a}$

Divide. Express the answer in the form **quotient** $+ \dfrac{\textbf{remainder}}{\textbf{divisor}}$.

Sample $\dfrac{2x^2 + 3}{x^2} = \dfrac{2x^2}{x^2} + \dfrac{3}{x^2} = 2 + \dfrac{3}{x^2}$

10. $\dfrac{x^2 + 2}{x}$

11. $\dfrac{5b - 1}{b}$

12. $\dfrac{4x^2y - 6xy^2 + 5}{2xy}$

13. $\dfrac{4x - 1}{2x}$

14. $\dfrac{y^2 + 4y + 1}{y}$

15. $\dfrac{x^2 + 2x - 3}{x^2}$

EXERCISES

A

Find each quotient by simplifying the rational expression.

1. $\dfrac{x^3 - 4x^2}{x^2}$

2. $\dfrac{x^3 + x^2 - x}{x}$

3. $\dfrac{2h^3 - 4h^2 + 6h}{h}$

4. $\dfrac{x - 3}{3 - x}$

5. $\dfrac{a^2 - 2a}{2 - a}$

6. $\dfrac{(x + 6)^3}{(x + 6)^2}$

7. $\dfrac{x^2 - 9}{x - 3}$ **8.** $\dfrac{x^2 - 6x + 9}{x - 3}$ **9.** $\dfrac{4y^2 + 4y + 1}{2y + 1}$

10. $\dfrac{x^2 - y^2}{y - x}$ **11.** $\dfrac{x^2 + xy - 2y^2}{x - y}$ **12.** $\dfrac{9a^2 + 6ab + b^2}{3a + b}$

Divide and check. Express the answer in the form **quotient** $+ \dfrac{\textbf{remainder}}{\textbf{divisor}}$.

13. $\dfrac{4x + 7}{2}$ **14.** $\dfrac{3xy^2 + 6xy + 7}{3y}$ **15.** $\dfrac{10x^2 - 5x + 7}{5x}$

16. $x + 2 \overline{)x^2 + 7x + 12}$ **17.** $x - 3 \overline{)x^2 - 10x + 18}$

18. $x - 3 \overline{)x^2 - 6x + 9}$ **19.** $x + 5 \overline{)2x^2 + 9x - 3}$

20. $3x - 1 \overline{)6x^2 + 7x + 5}$ **21.** $2x + 5 \overline{)8x^2 + 6x - 25}$

B

22. $x - 1 \overline{)4x^2 - 11x + 5}$ **23.** $x + 6 \overline{)5x^2 + 21x - 50}$

24. $2x + 7 \overline{)2x^2 - x - 25}$ **25.** $2x + 3 \overline{)8x^2 + 2x - 13}$

26. $x + 9 \overline{)3x^2 + 26x - 11}$ **27.** $x^2 + 2x \overline{)x^4 - 2x^2 + 5}$

28. $(x^3 + 3x^2 - 3x + 2) \div (x^2 + x - 1)$ **29.** $(4 - x + 3x^2) \div (1 + x)$

30. $(5x + x^4 - 2x^2) \div (x^2 + 2x)$ **31.** $(-x^2 + 3 - 11x + x^3) \div (x + 2)$

32. $(2x^3 + 16x - 7 - x^2) \div (2x - 1)$ **33.** $(x^3 - 2x - 1) \div (x^2 - x - 1)$

34. $(x^3 - 1) \div (x - 1)$ **35.** $(x^3 - 1) \div (x + 1)$

36. $(x^5 - 32) \div (x - 2)$ **37.** $(x^5 - 32) \div (x + 2)$

38. $(x^5 + 32) \div (x + 2)$ **39.** $(x^5 + 32) \div (x - 2)$

C

40. $(x^4 - x^3 - 2x^2 - x - 5) \div (x^2 + 1)$

41. $(x^4 + 6x^3 - 5x^2 + 4x) \div (x^2 - 1)$

State whether the second polynomial **is a factor** or **is not a factor** of the first polynomial.

42. $(x^4 - x^3 - 2x^2 - x - 5); (x^2 + 1)$

43. $(x^5 - 3x^4 + 13x^2 - 10x); (x^2 - 2x)$

44. $(y^3 - y^2 - y + 10); (y^2 - 3y + 5)$

45. $(8x - 4x^3 + 6x^5 + 15); (2x^2 - 4x)$

46. $(3 + 11x^3 - 10x^4 - 15x + 6x^6); (2x^3 + 3)$

*47. Divide $x^5 - a^5$ by $x - a$.

POLYNOMIAL EQUATIONS AND COMPLEX NUMBERS

8-2 Synthetic Division

OBJECTIVE

To divide a polynomial in x by a binomial of the form $x - c$, using synthetic division.

There is a convenient shortcut, called **synthetic division,** by which a polynomial can be divided by a binomial of the form $x - c$. Only the constant term c in the divisor and the coefficients (including any constant term) in the dividend are used. To illustrate, the division shown at the right is repeated below using this shortcut.

$$
\begin{array}{r}
2x^2 - 7x + 8 \quad \longleftarrow \text{ quotient} \\
x - 3\overline{)2x^3 - 13x^2 + 29x - 20} \\
\underline{2x^3 - 6x^2} \\
-7x^2 + 29x \\
\underline{-7x^2 + 21x} \\
8x - 20 \\
\underline{8x - 24} \\
\text{remainder} \longrightarrow 4
\end{array}
$$

Write the value of c. Compare $x - c$ to $x - 3$: $c = 3$.

$$
\begin{array}{r|rrrr}
3 & 2 & -13 & 29 & -20 \\
& & & & \\
\hline
\end{array}
$$

Write the coefficients of the terms of the dividend in order of decreasing degree.

$$
\begin{array}{r|rrrr}
3 & 2 & -13 & 29 & -20 \\
& & 6 & & \\
\hline
& 2 & -7 & & \\
\end{array}
$$

Bring down the 2 and multiply it by 3. Record 6 under -13 and add.

$$
\begin{array}{r|rrrr}
3 & 2 & -13 & 29 & -20 \\
& & 6 & -21 & \\
\hline
& 2 & -7 & 8 & \\
\end{array}
$$

Multiply -7 by 3. Record -21 under 29 and add.

$$
\begin{array}{r|rrrr}
3 & 2 & -13 & 29 & -20 \\
& & 6 & -21 & 24 \\
\hline
& 2 & -7 & 8 & 4 \\
\end{array}
$$

Multiply 8 by 3. Record 24 under -20 and add.

This last sum, 4, is the remainder.

The first three numbers are the coefficients of the terms of the quotient.

$$
\underbrace{2x^2 - 7x + 8}_{\text{quotient}}
$$

Check: $(x - 3)(2x^2 - 7x + 8) + 4 = (2x^3 - 13x^2 + 29x - 24) + 4$

$$
= 2x^3 - 13x^2 + 29x - 20 \ ✔
$$

The quotient is $2x^2 - 7x + 8$, and the remainder is 4.

In synthetic division, it is essential that missing terms in the dividend be replaced by zeros.

EXAMPLE

Divide $x^4 - 15x^2 - 2x - 24$ by $x + 4$, using synthetic division.

Compare $x - c$ to $x + 4$, or $x - (-4)$: $c = -4$.

Write 0 for the coefficient of the missing x^3 term.

$$
\begin{array}{r|rrrrr}
-4 & 1 & 0 & -15 & -2 & -24 \\
   &   & -4 & 16 & -4 & 24 \\
\hline
   & 1 & -4 & 1 & -6 & \boxed{0} \leftarrow \text{remainder}
\end{array}
$$

quotient $\longrightarrow x^3 - 4x^2 + x - 6$

Check this solution to verify that the quotient is $x^3 - 4x^2 + x - 6$ and the remainder is 0.

CLASS EXERCISES

*Assume that synthetic division is to be used in each exercise. Give the value of **c** for the divisor in the form **x − c**. Then give the coefficients of the terms in the dividend in the order of decreasing degree.*

1. $(x^3 - 6x^2 + 9x + 7) \div (x - 3)$ **2.** $(2x^4 + 7x^3 - 4x^2 + 4x - 1) \div (x + 4)$

3. $(-3x^5 + 8x^4 + x^2 + 12) \div (x - 5)$ **4.** $(x^2 + 2x - 5x^3 + 7) \div (x + 1)$

5. $(9x - 4x^2 + 15x^3 - 6) \div (x - 8)$ **6.** $(2 + 6x^4 - 9x) \div (x + 2)$

7. $(x^3 - 64) \div (x - 4)$ **8.** $(x^3 + 64) \div (x + 4)$

EXERCISES

A

*Complete each synthetic division example, and show your answer in the form **quotient; remainder**. Use the longer division method to check.*

1. $(x^3 - 8x^2 + 17x - 10) \div (x - 5)$

$$
\begin{array}{r|rrrr}
5 & 1 & -8 & 17 & -10 \\
  &   & 5 & & \\
\hline
  & 1 & -3 & &
\end{array}
$$

2. $(2x^3 + x^2 - 16x + 7) \div (x - 3)$

$$
\begin{array}{r|rrrr}
3 & 2 & 1 & -16 & 7 \\
  &   & 6 & & \\
\hline
  & 2 & 7 & &
\end{array}
$$

3. $(x^4 - 3x^3 + x^2 - x + 1) \div (x - 1)$

$$
\begin{array}{r|rrrrr}
1 & 1 & -3 & 1 & -1 & 1 \\
  &   & 1 & & & \\
\hline
  & 1 & & & &
\end{array}
$$

4. $(3x^3 - 5x + 14) \div (x + 2)$

$$
\begin{array}{r|rrrr}
-2 & 3 & 0 & -5 & 14 \\
   &   & -6 & & \\
\hline
   & 3 & & &
\end{array}
$$

Divide using synthetic division, and check. Show your answers in the form **quotient; remainder.**

5. $(-2x^3 + 3x^2 - 3x + 5) \div (x + 1)$

6. $(5x^2 + 12x - 13) \div (x - 2)$

7. $(x^3 - 5x^2 + 5x - 5) \div (x - 1)$

8. $(2x^3 + 3x^2 - 8x - 10) \div (x + 2)$

9. $(3x^3 - 2x^2 - x + 1) \div (x - 1)$

10. $(x^3 - 5x^2 + 7x - 8) \div (x - 2)$

11. $(x^3 + 2x^2 - 2x + 3) \div (x + 3)$

12. $(x^3 - 2x^2 - 4x + 5) \div (x - 3)$

13. $(2x^3 - 7x^2 + x - 20) \div (x - 4)$

14. $(x^3 + 5x^2 - 7x - 1) \div (x + 6)$

15. $(4x^3 + 23x^2 - 13x + 10) \div (x + 6)$

16. $(3x^3 + 18x^2 + 21x + 10) \div (x + 4)$

B

17. $(x^3 - 12x + 6) \div (x - 4)$

18. $(5x^2 - 7x) \div (x - 3)$

19. $(9x + 2x^3 - 20) \div (x + 2)$

20. $(3x - 15x^3 + 4x^4 + 20) \div (x - 3)$

21. $(x^4 - 6x^3 + 3x - 18) \div (x - 6)$

22. $(x^4 - x^3 - 2x^2 + 2x) \div (x - 1)$

23. $(x^4 + 2x^3 + 2x + 6) \div (x + 2)$

24. $(10x - 3x^4 + x^5 - 4x^2) \div (x - 3)$

25. $(x^3 - 8) \div (x - 2)$

26. $(x^3 - 8) \div (x + 2)$

27. $(x^3 - 27) \div (x - 3)$

28. $(x^3 - 64) \div (x - 4)$

29. $(x^4 - 16) \div (x + 2)$

30. $(x^4 - 16) \div (x - 2)$

31. $(x^5 - 32) \div (x - 2)$

32. $(x^5 - 32) \div (x + 2)$

C

33. $\left(x^3 - \dfrac{1}{8}\right) \div \left(x - \dfrac{1}{2}\right)$

34. $\left(x^3 - \dfrac{1}{2}x^2 + \dfrac{1}{4}\right) \div (x - 1)$

35. $\left(2x^4 + 6x^2 - \dfrac{1}{4} - 3x^3 - \dfrac{1}{2}x\right) \div \left(x + \dfrac{1}{2}\right)$

36. $\left(\dfrac{3}{4} - \dfrac{1}{2}x^2 + x^3 - \dfrac{1}{3}x\right) \div \left(x - \dfrac{3}{2}\right)$

37. $\left(x^5 + \dfrac{3}{2}x^4 + 3x^3 + 6x^2 + 12x - 8\right) \div \left(x - \dfrac{1}{2}\right)$

Use synthetic division to find the value of **n** if

38. $x - 1$ is a factor of $x^3 + x^2 - 4x + n$.

39. $x + 1$ is a factor of $x^4 + x^3 - 2x - n$.

40. $x - 2$ is a factor of $x^4 - 8x^3 + 15x^2 + nx - 18$.

41. $x + 4$ is a factor of $x^3 + nx^2 - 25x + 28$.

42. $x - 3$ is a factor of $nx^3 - 13x^2 + 2x + 3$.

43. $x - n$ is a factor of $x^2 + x + (n + 1)$.

Write each rational expression in the form **quotient** + $\dfrac{\textit{remainder}}{\textit{divisor}}$.

Sample $\dfrac{2x^3 - 15x^2 + 22x - 2}{2x - 3} = \dfrac{2x^3 - 15x^2 + 22x - 2}{2\left(x - \frac{3}{2}\right)}$ Factor out the coefficient of x.

$= \dfrac{1}{2}\left(\dfrac{2x^3 - 15x^2 + 22x - 2}{x - \frac{3}{2}}\right)$ Obtain a divisor in the form $x - c$.

$= \dfrac{1}{2}\left(2x^2 - 12x + 4 + \dfrac{4}{x - \frac{3}{2}}\right)$ Use synthetic division.

$= x^2 - 6x + 2 + \dfrac{4}{2x - 3}$ Multiply by $\dfrac{1}{2}$.

44. $\dfrac{2x^3 - x^2 - 4x + 7}{2x - 1}$ **45.** $\dfrac{2x^3 - x^2 - 4x + 2}{2x - 1}$

46. $\dfrac{3x^4 + x^3 - 9x^2 + 6}{3x + 1}$ **47.** $\dfrac{3x^4 - 8x^3 + 13x^2 + 6}{3x - 2}$

48. $\dfrac{4x^4 + x^3 - 3x^2 + 20x - 15}{4x - 3}$ **49.** $\dfrac{2x^4 + 3x^3 - 4x - 6}{2x + 3}$

*50. Use synthetic division to divide $p(x) = x^4 - 4x^3 + x^2 + 12x - 12$ by $(x - 2)^2$.

Hint: $p(x) \div (x - 2)^2 = \dfrac{p(x)}{x - 2} \div (x - 2)$

CHECKPOINT

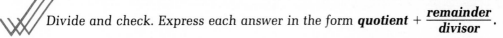

Divide and check. Express each answer in the form **quotient** + $\dfrac{\textit{remainder}}{\textit{divisor}}$.

1. $x - 2 \overline{)x^2 + 5x - 2}$ **2.** $2x - 1 \overline{)6x^3 - 5x^2 + 7x + 9}$

3. $(2x^2 - 3x + 5) \div (2x + 1)$ **4.** $(3x + x^4 - 8) \div (x^2 - 3)$

Divide by using synthetic division, and check. Show your answers in the form **quotient; remainder.**

5. $(3x^2 - 2x + 5) \div (x - 2)$

6. $(-5x^3 - 12x^2 + 10x - 6) \div (x + 3)$

7. $(4x^4 + 4) \div (x + 1)$

8. $\left(x^5 - \dfrac{32}{243}\right) \div \left(x - \dfrac{2}{3}\right)$

8-3 The Remainder Theorem and the Factor Theorem

OBJECTIVES _____

To evaluate $p(c)$ in order to find the remainder when a polynomial $p(x)$ is divided by $x - c$.
To determine if $x - c$ is a factor of $p(x)$ by evaluating $p(c)$.

It is possible to find the remainder in some division examples without actually going through the division process. The function notation $p(x)$ will be useful in explaining this. First, divide $p(x) = x^3 - 2x^2 + 5x + 6$ by $x - 2$.

$$
\begin{array}{r|rrrr}
2 & 1 & -2 & 5 & 6 \\
  &   & 2 & 0 & 10 \\
\hline
  & 1 & 0 & 5 & \boxed{16}
\end{array}
$$

quotient: $q(x) = x^2 + 5$ remainder: $r = 16$

Then use the quotient and remainder form used for checking division and write

$$x^3 - 2x^2 + 5x + 6 = (x - 2)(x^2 + 5) + 16$$

or $\quad p(x) = (x - 2)q(x) + \mathbf{16}$

The important thing to note here is that the remainder is equal to $p(2)$.

$$p(x) = x^3 - 2x^2 + 5x + 6$$

Substitute: $x = 2$ $p(2) = 2^3 - 2(2)^2 + 5(2) + 6 = \mathbf{16}$

Using the quotient and remainder form, the result is the same.

$$p(x) = (x - 2)q(x) + 16$$

Substitute: $x = 2$ $p(2) = (2 - 2)q(x) + 16$
$$= 0 \cdot q(x) + 16 = \mathbf{16}$$

In general, if a polynomial $p(x)$ is divided by $x - c$, there will be a quotient $q(x)$ and a remainder r such that

$$p(x) = (x - c)q(x) + r$$

Let $x = c$. $p(c) = (c - c)q(c) + r$
$$= 0 \cdot q(c) + r$$
$$= 0 + r$$
$$= r$$

This result is called the **remainder theorem.**

Remainder Theorem

When a polynomial $p(x)$ is divided by $x - c$, the remainder r is equal to the value of the polynomial when x is replaced by c. That is, $r = p(c)$.

EXAMPLE 1 Use the remainder theorem to find the remainder when $f(x) = x^3 - 6x^2 + 4x + 7$ is divided by $x - 3$. Check by synthetic division.

$$r = f(3) = 3^3 - 6(3)^2 + 4(3) + 7 = -8 \qquad \text{Use the remainder theorem.}$$

Check

$$
\begin{array}{r|rrrr}
3 & 1 & -6 & 4 & 7 \\
  &   & 3 & -9 & -15 \\
\hline
  & 1 & -3 & -5 & -8 = r \ \checkmark
\end{array}
$$

When $f(x) = x^3 - 7x + 6$ is divided by $x - 2$, the remainder is 0. This can be shown by synthetic division or by applying the remainder theorem.

Using Synthetic Division

$$
\begin{array}{r|rrrr}
2 & 1 & 0 & -7 & 6 \\
  &   & 2 & 4 & -6 \\
\hline
  & 1 & 2 & -3 & 0 = r = f(2)
\end{array}
$$

Using the Remainder Theorem

$$f(2) = (2)^3 - 7(2) + 6$$
$$= 8 - 14 + 6$$
$$= 0$$

Since the remainder is 0, $x - 2$ must be a factor of $f(x) = x^3 - 7x + 6$. The results of the synthetic division provide the coefficients of the second factor, and we have

$$f(x) = x^3 - 7x + 6 = (x - 2)(x^2 + 2x - 3)$$

This illustrates the **factor theorem.**

Factor Theorem

$x - c$ is a factor of a polynomial $p(x)$ if and only if $p(c) = 0$.

To prove the factor theorem, begin with the general equation

$$p(x) = (x - c)q(x) + r$$

Using the remainder theorem, r is replaced by $p(c)$.

$$p(x) = (x - c)q(x) + p(c)$$

Note that when $p(c) = 0$, then $x - c$ is a factor of $p(x)$. Conversely, when $x - c$ is a factor of $p(x)$, then $p(c)$ equals 0. Thus, $x - c$ is a factor of $p(x)$ if and only if $p(c) = 0$.

EXAMPLE 2   Determine whether $x - 2$ is a factor of $f(x) = x^3 + 2x^2 - 2x + 5$. Use the factor theorem.

$$f(2) = 2^3 + 2(2)^2 - 2(2) + 5 = 17 \qquad \text{Evaluate } f(2).$$

Since $f(2) \neq 0$, $x - 2$ is *not* a factor of $f(x)$.

Synthetic division may sometimes be used when you factor a polynomial completely.

EXAMPLE 3   **a. Show that $x + 3$ is a factor of $f(x) = x^3 - x^2 - 8x + 12$.**

$$
\begin{array}{r|rrrr}
-3 & 1 & -1 & -8 & 12 \\
   &   & -3 & 12 & -12 \\
\hline
   & 1 & -4 & 4 & 0
\end{array}
$$

$\qquad$ Use synthetic division.

$0 \leftarrow$ remainder

Since $r = f(-3) = 0$, $x + 3$ is a factor of $f(x)$.

b. Factor $f(x) = x^3 - x^2 - 8x + 12$ completely.

From the results of the synthetic division in **a,** you know that $x + 3$ and $x^2 - 4x + 4$ are factors of $f(x) = x^3 - x^2 - 8x + 12$.

$$
\begin{aligned}
f(x) = x^3 - x^2 - 8x + 12 &= (x + 3)(x^2 - 4x + 4) \\
&= (x + 3)(x - 2)^2 \qquad \text{Factor } x^2 - 4x + 4.
\end{aligned}
$$

Check by multiplying to show that $(x + 3)(x - 2)^2 = f(x)$.

CLASS EXERCISES

Complete the following statements for $p(x) = x^2 - 10x + 25$.

1. $p(5) = 0$. Therefore, by the $\underline{\ ?\ }$ theorem, when $p(x)$ is divided by $x - 5$, the remainder is $\underline{\ ?\ }$.

2. By the $\underline{\ ?\ }$ theorem, $\underline{\ ?\ }$ is a factor of $p(x)$.

3. Since $p(-5) = 100$, the remainder is $\underline{\ ?\ }$ when $p(x)$ is divided by $x + 5$.

4. Since $p(-5) = 100$, we know by the factor theorem that $\underline{\ ?\ }$ is *not* a factor of $p(x)$.

5. For $f(x) = x^3 - 8$, $f(2) = \underline{\ ?\ }$. Therefore, $\underline{\ ?\ }$ is a factor of $f(x)$.

EXERCISES

A   *Find the remainder using the remainder theorem. Check by synthetic division.*

1. $(6x^2 + 3x - 9) \div (x - 1)$ $\qquad$ 2. $(6x^2 + 3x - 9) \div (x + 1)$

3. $(2x^3 + 4x^2 - 5x + 9) \div (x + 3)$ $\qquad$ 4. $(-x^3 + 6x^2 - 10x + 3) \div (x - 4)$

5. $(2x^4 - 9x^3 + 14x^2 - 8) \div (x - 2)$ **6.** $(2x^2 - 9x^3 + 14x^2 - 8) \div (x + 2)$

7. $(x^4 - 81) \div (x + 3)$ **8.** $(x^4 - 81) \div (x - 3)$

9. $(x^3 + 125) \div (x + 5)$ **10.** $(x^3 + 125) \div (x - 5)$

Determine whether **x − 2 is a factor** or **is not a factor** of $f(x)$, using the factor theorem.

11. $f(x) = x^3 - 2x^2 - 9x + 18$ **12.** $f(x) = x^3 - 3x^2 + 14x - 20$

13. $f(x) = x^4 + x^3 - 8x - 9$ **14.** $f(x) = x^5 - x^4 - 16x + 16$

Determine whether **x + 2 is a factor** or **is not a factor** of $p(x)$, using the factor theorem.

15. $p(x) = x^3 + 3x^2 + 3x + 4$ **16.** $p(x) = x^3 - 5x^2 + 8x - 4$

17. $p(x) = x^4 + x^3 + 3x^2 + x - 6$ **18.** $p(x) = x^4 + 10x + 4$

B   Show that the given binomial is a factor of the polynomial $p(x)$, using synthetic division. Then factor $p(x)$ completely.

19. $p(x) = x^3 + 4x^2 + x - 6; x - 1$ **20.** $p(x) = x^3 + 3x^2 - 6x - 8; x - 2$

21. $p(x) = x^3 - 4x^2 - 3x + 18; x + 2$ **22.** $p(x) = x^3 + 6x^2 - 7x - 60; x + 5$

23. $p(x) = 6x^3 - 17x^2 - 16x + 7; x + 1$ **24.** $p(x) = x^3 + 3x^2 - 16x - 48; x + 3$

25. $p(x) = 2x^3 - 13x^2 + 17x + 12; x - 3$

26. $p(x) = 25x^3 + 50x^2 - 9x - 18; x + 2$

C   **27.** $p(x) = x^4 - 4x^3 + 4x^2 - 4x + 3; x - 1$

28. $p(x) = x^4 - x^3 - 2x - 4; x - 2$

29. $p(x) = 2x^4 - 4x^3 - 15x^2 - 2x - 8; x + 2$

30. $p(x) = x^4 + 3x^3 - x - 3; x + 3$

31. $p(x) = x^4 - 4x^3 + 8x - 32; x - 4$

32. $p(x) = x^4 + 7x^3 + 9x^2 - 7x - 10; x + 5$

33. $p(x) = x^4 - 3x^3 - 22x^2 + 12x + 72; x - 6$

34. $p(x) = x^5 - x^4 - 10x^3 + 10x^2 + 9x - 9; x - 1$

For Exercises 35 and 36, use the remainder theorem or the factor theorem.

35. Find the value of d if $x + 1$ is a factor of $x^3 + 3x^2 + dx + 1$.

36. Find all possible values of c if the remainder is 18 when $x^2 - 3x - 10$ is divided by $x - c$.

STRATEGIES for PROBLEM SOLVING

Estimating Roots Graphically

When it is difficult to find the exact answer to a problem, we sometimes look for a good estimate instead. Suppose you were asked to find a number whose cube is 3 less than 3 times the square of the number. Most likely, you would write the equation $x^3 = 3x^2 - 3$ and then try to find the roots of $x^3 - 3x^2 + 3 = 0$.

The roots of this equation are irrational, and the equation cannot be solved using the methods studied in this chapter. However, the irrational roots can be estimated by graphing.

First let $y = f(x) = x^3 - 3x^2 + 3$. Make a table of values, plot the points, and carefully connect them with a smooth curve.

x	f(x)
−1	−1
−0.5	2.1
0	3
0.5	2.4
1	1
1.5	−0.4
2	−1
2.5	−0.1
3	3

It is helpful to use a calculator to find $f(x)$ for decimal values of x.

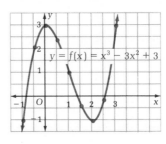

The roots of $y = f(x)$ $= x^3 - 3x^2 + 3 = 0$ are the x-intercepts of the curve.

From the graph, the three roots can be estimated as −0.8, 1.3, and 2.6. To get estimates accurate to one decimal place, use a calculator. Evaluate $f(x)$ for the first estimates of x and for one-place decimals close to these values.

x	−1.0	−0.9	−0.8	1.2	1.3	1.4	2.4	2.5	2.6
f(x)	−1.0	−0.159	0.568	0.408	0.127	−0.136	−0.456	−0.125	0.296

$f(-0.9) = -0.159$ is closer to 0 than is $f(-0.8) = 0.568$ or $f(-1.0) = -1.0$. Therefore the first root is −0.9, correct to one decimal place. Also, 1.3 and 2.5 are approximations of the other two roots, to one decimal place.

Now you try it! Find the irrational roots of each equation to the nearest tenth.

1. $x^3 - 3x + 4 = 0$
   (one real root, irrational)

2. $2x^3 + 3x^2 + 6x - 3 = 0$
   (one real root, irrational)

3. $x^4 - 3x^2 - 5 = 0$
   (two real roots, both irrational)

4. $x^3 + x^2 - 6x - 2 = 0$
   (three real roots, all irrational)

8-4 The Rational Root Theorem

To find the rational roots of a polynomial equation $p(x) = 0$.
To factor a polynomial $p(x)$ completely.

Study the solution of the following polynomial equation.

$$p(x) = 15x^2 - 22x + 8 = 0$$
$$(3x - 2)(5x - 4) = 0$$

$$3x - 2 = 0 \text{ or } 5x - 4 = 0 \qquad \text{If } ab = 0, \text{ then } a = 0 \text{ or } b = 0.$$

$$x = \frac{2}{3} \qquad\qquad x = \frac{4}{5}$$

The roots of the equation are $\frac{2}{3}$ and $\frac{4}{5}$. Observe that the numerators of the roots are factors of 8, the constant term of $p(x)$. Also, the denominators of the roots are factors of 15, which is the *leading coefficient,* or the coefficient of the term of highest degree. In general, we have the following useful theorem.

Rational Root Theorem

Let a rational number $\frac{r}{s}$, in lowest terms, be a root of a polynomial equation with integral coefficients, $p(x) = 0$. Then the numerator r is a factor of the constant term of $p(x)$ and the denominator s is a factor of the leading coefficient of $p(x)$.

EXAMPLE 1   Find all possible rational roots of $f(x) = 2x^3 - 3x^2 - 11x + 6 = 0$.

Possible numerators: $\pm1, \pm2, \pm3, \pm6$ Factors of 6, the constant term

Possible denominators: $\pm1, \pm2$ Factors of 2, the leading coefficient

Possible rational roots:

$$\pm1, \pm\frac{1}{2}, \pm2, \pm3, \pm\frac{3}{2}, \pm6 \qquad \text{Each factor of 6 is divided by each factor of 2.}$$

Recall that a number c is a root of an equation $p(x) = 0$ when $p(c) = 0$. Therefore, we can decide if a number c is a root of $p(x) = 0$ by evaluating $p(c)$. This can be done either by substituting c for x in $p(x)$ or by synthetic division, in which the remainder is the value $p(c)$. In the examples that follow, it is advantageous to use synthetic division.

EXAMPLE 2　　Find the rational roots of $f(x) = 2x^3 - 3x^2 - 11x + 6 = 0$.

The possible rational roots are: ± 1, $\pm \frac{1}{2}$, ± 2, ± 3, $\pm \frac{3}{2}$, ± 6.
Use synthetic division to test the possibilities.

Try $c = 1$:

$$
\begin{array}{r|rrrr}
1 & 2 & -3 & -11 & 6 \\
  &   & 2 & -1 & -12 \\
\hline
  & 2 & -1 & -12 & -6 = f(1)
\end{array}
$$

$f(1) \neq 0$, so 1 is *not* a root.

Try $c = -1$:

$$
\begin{array}{r|rrrr}
-1 & 2 & -3 & -11 & 6 \\
   &   & -2 & 5   & 6 \\
\hline
   & 2 & -5 & -6 & 12 = f(-1)
\end{array}
$$

$f(-1) \neq 0$, so -1 is *not* a root.

Try $c = \frac{1}{2}$:

$$
\begin{array}{r|rrrr}
\frac{1}{2} & 2 & -3 & -11 & 6 \\
            &   & 1 & -1 & -6 \\
\hline
            & 2 & -2 & -12 & 0 = f\!\left(\frac{1}{2}\right)
\end{array}
$$

$f(\frac{1}{2}) = 0$, so $\frac{1}{2}$ is a root.

Then, by the factor theorem, $x - \frac{1}{2}$ is a factor of $f(x)$. Coefficients of the other factor are obtained from the results of the last synthetic division. The other factor is $2x^2 - 2x - 12$, so we have

$$f(x) = 2x^3 - 3x^2 - 11x + 6 = \left(x - \frac{1}{2}\right)(2x^2 - 2x - 12)$$

Instead of testing the remaining possible rational roots, we can factor $2x^2 - 2x - 12$.

$$\left(x - \frac{1}{2}\right)(2)(x^2 - x - 6) = 0$$
$$\left(x - \frac{1}{2}\right)(2)(x + 2)(x - 3) = 0$$

$$x - \frac{1}{2} = 0 \quad \text{or} \quad x + 2 = 0 \quad \text{or} \quad x - 3 = 0 \qquad \text{Set each factor containing } x \text{ equal to 0.}$$

$$x = \frac{1}{2} \qquad\qquad x = -2 \qquad\qquad x = 3$$

Check to show that the roots of $f(x) = 2x^3 - 3x^2 - 11x + 6 = 0$ are $\frac{1}{2}$, -2, and 3.

Since $x - c$ is a factor of a polynomial $p(x)$ when $p(c) = 0$, the factors of $p(x)$ can be found by finding the roots of $p(x) = 0$.

EXAMPLE 3　　Factor $p(x) = x^3 + 3x^2 - 6x - 8$ completely.

The leading coefficient is 1, and its only factors are ± 1. Thus, the possible rational roots of $p(x) = 0$ are the factors of 8: ± 1, ± 2, ± 4, and ± 8.

$$\text{Try } c = 1: \quad 1 \ \begin{array}{|rrrr} 1 & 3 & -6 & -8 \\ & 1 & 4 & -2 \\ \hline 1 & 4 & -2 & \boxed{-10} = p(1) \end{array}$$

$p(1) \neq 0$, so $x - 1$ is *not a factor.*

$$\text{Try } c = -1: \quad -1 \ \begin{array}{|rrrr} 1 & 3 & -6 & -8 \\ & -1 & -2 & 8 \\ \hline 1 & 2 & -8 & \boxed{0} = p(-1) \end{array}$$

$p(-1) = 0$, so $x - (-1)$, or $x + 1$, *is* a factor.

We have found that $x + 1$ is one factor of $x^3 + 3x^2 - 6x - 8$. From the results of the synthetic division, we know that the other factor is $x^2 + 2x - 8$. Thus

$$\begin{aligned} p(x) = x^3 + 3x^2 - 6x - 8 &= (x + 1)(x^2 + 2x - 8) \\ &= (x + 1)(x + 4)(x - 2) \end{aligned}$$

Check by multiplying to show that $p(x) = (x + 1)(x + 4)(x - 2)$, in factored form.

CLASS EXERCISES

Why is it impossible for

1. $\dfrac{2}{3}$ to be a root of $8x^3 - 5x + 6x + 4 = 0$?

2. $-\dfrac{3}{5}$ to be a root of $5x^4 + x^3 - 7x^2 + 2x - 4 = 0$?

3. 6 to be a root of $x^5 - 2x^3 + 16x^2 + 15 = 0$?

4. $-\dfrac{1}{4}$ to be a root of $6x^4 - 8x^2 - 3x + 8 = 0$?

5. $\dfrac{3}{8}$ to be a root of $4x^3 - 3x^2 + 5x^4 + 2x - 9 = 0$?

6. What should you do to the equation $2x^3 - \dfrac{1}{4}x^2 + 5x - 3 = 0$ before applying the rational root theorem?

EXERCISES

A

In Exercises 1–6, list

    a. the numerators **r** of possible rational roots of the equation.

    b. the denominators **s** of possible rational roots.

    c. the possible rational roots $\dfrac{r}{s}$.

1. $x^2 - 4x - 12 = 0$ 2. $x^2 - 4x + 12 = 0$ 3. $3x^2 - 7x + 6 = 0$

4. $x^3 - 3x^2 + 4 = 0$ 5. $9x^3 - 10x + 4 = 0$ 6. $4x^3 + 5x^2 + 6x - 9 = 0$

Find the rational roots of each equation.

7. $p(x) = x^3 - 6x^2 + 11x - 6 = 0$ **8.** $p(x) = x^3 - 3x^2 + 4 = 0$

9. $p(x) = 6x^3 + x^2 - 4x + 1 = 0$ **10.** $p(x) = 8x^3 - 14x^2 + 7x - 1 = 0$

11. $p(x) = 2x^3 + 3x^2 - 23x - 12 = 0$ **12.** $p(x) = 3x^3 - 10x^2 - 27x + 10 = 0$

13. $p(x) = 4x^3 - 12x^2 - 15x - 4 = 0$ **14.** $p(x) = 4x^3 + 20x^2 - x - 5 = 0$

B

15. $p(x) = 7x + 12x^3 - 1 - 16x^2 = 0$ **16.** $p(x) = 12 - 27x^2 - 8x + 18x^3 = 0$

Factor completely.

17. $x^3 - 6x^2 + 12x - 8$ **18.** $x^3 - 6x^2 - x + 30$ **19.** $x^3 + 3x^2 - 33x - 35$

20. $6x^3 + 17x^2 - 26x + 8$ **21.** $12x^3 - 28x^2 - 7x + 5$ **22.** $6x^3 - 11x^2 + 6x - 1$

23. A box is in the shape of a rectangular prism. Its length is 4 inches greater than its width, and its height is 2 inches greater than its width. If its volume is 105 cubic inches, find the dimensions of the box. Use $V = lwh$.

24. A pyramid has a rectangular base. The width of the base is 2 centimeters less than the height, and the length is 2 centimeters more than the height. If the volume of the pyramid is 64 cubic centimeters, what is its height? Use $V = \frac{1}{3}lwh$.

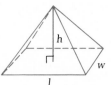

C

25. A tank in the shape of a rectangular prism has a volume of 27 cubic yards. The width of the tank is $1\frac{1}{2}$ times its height, and the length is $\frac{1}{2}$ yard more than twice the height. Find the dimensions of the tank.

26. The volume of a cube (in cubic inches) is 800 more than 3 times its surface area (in square inches). Find the volume of the cube.

Find all of the real roots of each equation. Use the rational root and factor theorems to find one rational root. Then use the quadratic formula to find two more real roots.

27. $x^3 - x^2 - 3x + 2 = 0$ **28.** $x^3 + x^2 - 7x - 3 = 0$

29. $4x^3 - 8x^2 + x + 1 = 0$ **30.** $x^3 - 15x + 22 = 0$

Show that the given equations have no rational roots.

31. $x^4 + x^3 + x^2 + x + 1 = 0$ **32.** $2x^3 + 5x^2 - x + 7 = 0$

Factor completely.

*33. $f(x) = x^4 + x^3 - 7x^2 - x + 6$ ***34.** $f(x) = 2x^4 + x^3 - 19x^2 - 9x + 9$

Proving That Certain Real Numbers Are Irrational

The rational root theorem can be used to prove that certain real numbers are irrational. For example, to prove that $\sqrt{5}$ is irrational, begin with a polynomial equation with integral coefficients and the root $\sqrt{5}$.

$\sqrt{5}$ is a root of $x^2 - 5 = 0$, since $(\sqrt{5})^2 - 5 = 0$.

Next, check all the possible rational roots of $x^2 - 5 = 0$. By the rational root theorem, the possible roots are ± 1 and ± 5.

$(\pm 1)^2 - 5 = 1 - 5 = -4$ $-4 \neq 0$, so neither 1 nor -1 is a root.

$(\pm 5)^2 - 5 = 25 - 5 = 20$ $20 \neq 0$, so neither 5 nor -5 is a root.

Since none of these four rational numbers is a root, and since $\sqrt{5}$ is a root, it follows that $\sqrt{5}$ cannot be rational. Furthermore, since all real numbers are either rational or irrational, $\sqrt{5}$ must be irrational.

Example   Prove that $\sqrt{\frac{3}{2}}$ is irrational.

Consider the equation $x^2 - \frac{3}{2} = 0$.

First, write the equation with integral coefficients:

$2x^2 - 3 = 0$

We know that $\sqrt{\frac{3}{2}}$ is a root of this equation, since

$2\left(\sqrt{\frac{3}{2}}\right)^2 - 3 = 3 - 3 = 0$.

By the rational root theorem, we know that the only possible rational roots are ± 1, $\pm \frac{1}{2}$, ± 3, and $\pm \frac{3}{2}$. Substitute each possible root for x in the equation $2x^2 - 3 = 0$.

$2(\pm 1)^2 - 3 = 2 - 3 = -1 \neq 0$ $2(\pm 3)^2 - 3 = 18 - 3 = 15 \neq 0$

$2\left(\pm \frac{1}{2}\right)^2 - 3 = \frac{1}{2} - 3 = -\frac{5}{2} \neq 0$ $2\left(\pm \frac{3}{2}\right)^2 - 3 = \frac{9}{2} - 3 = \frac{3}{2} \neq 0$

None of the eight rational numbers is a root. Therefore, since $\sqrt{\frac{3}{2}}$ is a root, it is irrational.

Now, you try it! Prove that each of these real numbers is irrational.

1. $\sqrt{2}$ **2.** $\sqrt{3}$ **3.** $\sqrt{\frac{2}{5}}$ **4.** $\sqrt{\frac{8}{3}}$ **5.** $\sqrt[3]{2}$ **6.** $2\sqrt[3]{3}$

7. $9 + \sqrt{6}$ **Hint:** Consider $x^2 - 18x + 75 = 0$.

8-5   Imaginary Numbers

OBJECTIVES _____

To express square roots of negative numbers in terms of the imaginary
  unit *i*.
To perform basic operations with imaginary numbers.

_____

The equation $x^2 = -1$ has no real solutions, since the square of a real
number cannot be negative. However, taking square roots gives the
result $x = \pm\sqrt{-1}$. Thus $x = \sqrt{-1}$ and $x = -\sqrt{-1}$ may be regarded as
nonreal solutions of $x^2 = -1$. Rather than refer to $\sqrt{-1}$ as a nonreal
number, we define $i = \sqrt{-1}$ as the **imaginary unit**.

$$i = \sqrt{-1} \text{ and } i^2 = -1$$

This new number *i* is used to express other imaginary numbers such
as 5*i*. Any expression of the form *bi*, where *b* is a real number, is called
a **pure imaginary number**, or more simply, an **imaginary number.**
  Within this set of new numbers are the square roots of negative real
numbers. For example, here is a way to express $\sqrt{-4}$ using *i*.

$$\sqrt{-4} = \sqrt{4(-1)} = \sqrt{4i^2} = \sqrt{(2i)(2i)} = 2i$$

This suggests the following definition.

If x is a positive real number, then

$$\sqrt{-x} = i\sqrt{x}$$

For example, $\sqrt{-7}$ can be written as $i\sqrt{7}$ or $\sqrt{7}i$. However, to avoid
accidentally showing the *i* under the radical, it is frequently clearer to
write $i\sqrt{7}$.
  When operating with square roots of negative numbers, first write each
number using *i*. Then follow the usual algebraic procedures to simplify.

EXAMPLE 1   Add: $\sqrt{-9} + \sqrt{-25}$. Simplify the answer.

$$\sqrt{-9} + \sqrt{-25} = i\sqrt{9} + i\sqrt{25} \qquad \sqrt{-x} = i\sqrt{x}$$
$$= 3i + 5i$$
$$= (3 + 5)i$$
$$= 8i \qquad\qquad \text{The sum is an imaginary number.}$$

It is important that radical expressions such as $\sqrt{-9}$ and $\sqrt{-25}$ are rewritten using i *before* they are multiplied. The rule $\sqrt{r} \cdot \sqrt{s} = \sqrt{rs}$ is *not* true when r and s are both negative.

EXAMPLE 2   Multiply: $\sqrt{-9} \cdot \sqrt{-25}$. Simplify the answer.

$$\sqrt{-9} \cdot \sqrt{-25} = i\sqrt{9} \cdot i\sqrt{25}$$
$$= 3i \cdot 5i$$
$$= 15i^2$$
$$= -15 \qquad \text{The product is a real number.}$$

EXAMPLE 3   Simplify $\sqrt{-\dfrac{27}{50}}$, and rationalize the denominator.

$$\sqrt{-\frac{27}{50}} = i\sqrt{\frac{27}{50}}$$
$$= \frac{i\sqrt{27}}{\sqrt{50}}$$
$$= \frac{3i\sqrt{3}}{5\sqrt{2}}$$
$$= \frac{3i\sqrt{3}}{5\sqrt{2}} \cdot \frac{\sqrt{2}}{\sqrt{2}} \qquad \text{Rationalize the denominator.}$$
$$= \frac{3i\sqrt{6}}{10}, \text{ or } \frac{3\sqrt{6}}{10}i$$

The rules for integral exponents apply to pure imaginary numbers. This allows us to simplify powers of i according to the pattern shown at the right.

$$\sqrt{-1} = i$$
$$i^2 = -1$$
$$i^3 = i^2 \cdot i = -1 \cdot i = -i$$
$$i^4 = i^2 \cdot i^2 = (-1)(-1) = 1$$

For powers greater than 4, this sequence repeats over and over: $i, -1, -i, 1$. When simplifying powers of i, it is convenient to use the fact that i^4 is equal to 1.

EXAMPLE 4   Simplify by expressing each power of i as i, -1, $-i$, or 1.

a. $i^{12} = (i^4)^3$ 12 is a multiple of 4, so write i^{12} as $(i^4)^3$.
$$= 1^3 = 1$$

b. $i^{23} = (i^{20})(i^3)$ 20 is the greatest multiple of 4 that is less than 23.
$$= (i^4)^5(i^3)$$
$$= 1^5 i^3$$
$$= i^3 = -i$$

CLASS EXERCISES

Simplify.

1. $\sqrt{-49}$ **2.** $-3\sqrt{-9}$ **3.** $-8\sqrt{-64}$ **4.** $5\sqrt{-\dfrac{16}{25}}$ **5.** $\sqrt{-5}$

6. $2\sqrt{-12}$ **7.** $-3\sqrt{-\dfrac{18}{25}}$ **8.** i^5 **9.** i^6 **10.** i^8

EXERCISES

A

Simplify.

1. $\sqrt{-2}$ **2.** $3\sqrt{-7}$ **3.** $\sqrt{-25}$ **4.** $7\sqrt{-\dfrac{2}{9}}$ **5.** $\sqrt{-8}$

6. $5\sqrt{-12}$ **7.** $-\sqrt{-50}$ **8.** $-3\sqrt{-200}$ **9.** $6\sqrt{-\dfrac{9}{4}}$ **10.** $2\sqrt{-\dfrac{27}{25}}$

Simplify and rationalize the denominators.

11. $\sqrt{-\dfrac{1}{3}}$ **12.** $\sqrt{-\dfrac{9}{5}}$ **13.** $\sqrt{-\dfrac{1}{8}}$ **14.** $\sqrt{-\dfrac{4}{27}}$ **15.** $\sqrt{-\dfrac{12}{7}}$

16. $4\sqrt{-\dfrac{3}{2}}$ **17.** $-3\sqrt{-\dfrac{2}{27}}$ **18.** $10\sqrt{-\dfrac{24}{75}}$ **19.** $-2\sqrt{-\dfrac{81}{32}}$ **20.** $\dfrac{2}{3}\sqrt{-\dfrac{27}{128}}$

Simplify by expressing each power of i as i, -1, $-i$, or 1.

21. i^9 **22.** i^{10} **23.** i^{11} **24.** i^{12} **25.** i^{13}

26. i^{29} **27.** i^{30} **28.** i^{50} **29.** i^{75} **30.** i^{96}

B

Write the numbers using i. Then perform the indicated operation and simplify the answer.

31. $\sqrt{-4} + \sqrt{-16}$ **32.** $\sqrt{-25} - \sqrt{-9}$ **33.** $2\sqrt{-8} + 3\sqrt{-50}$

34. $i\sqrt{-36} - i^2$ **35.** $\sqrt{-\dfrac{4}{9}} + 10\sqrt{-\dfrac{1}{25}}$ **36.** $\sqrt{-16} \cdot \sqrt{-100}$

37. $3\sqrt{-9} \cdot 2\sqrt{-49}$ **38.** $\sqrt{-\dfrac{4}{9}} \cdot \sqrt{\dfrac{49}{81}}$ **39.** $\sqrt{-12} \cdot \sqrt{-36}$

40. $\sqrt{-48} \cdot \sqrt{72}$ **41.** $3\sqrt{-\dfrac{1}{32}} \cdot \sqrt{-\dfrac{20}{27}}$ **42.** $14\sqrt{-80} \cdot \sqrt{\dfrac{1}{98}}$

43. $(i^2)(i^6)$ **44.** $(3i^7)(-5i^{12})$ **45.** $(i^5)\sqrt{-36}$

46. $(-5i^7)(-2i^7)$

C

47. $i^3\sqrt{-50}\sqrt{-\dfrac{1}{2}}$ **48.** $\dfrac{15}{4}(i^6)\sqrt{-\dfrac{48}{175}}$ **49.** $-8i^{10}\sqrt{-\dfrac{3}{32}}$ **50.** $(i^2)(i^3)(i^6)$

51. Find the fallacy in this "proof" that $6 = -6$.

$$6 = \sqrt{36} = \sqrt{(-4)(-9)} = \sqrt{-4}\sqrt{-9} = (2i)(3i) = 6i^2 = -6$$

*Write each number in the form **bi**, where **b** is a real number.*

Sample $\quad 2i^{-1} = \dfrac{2}{i} = \dfrac{2}{i} \cdot \dfrac{i}{i} = \dfrac{2i}{i^2} = \dfrac{2i}{-1} = -2i$

52. $-\dfrac{3}{i}$ **53.** $\dfrac{7}{i^3}$ **54.** $\dfrac{2}{3}i^{-7}$ **55.** $\dfrac{1}{4}i^{-5}$

56. $4i^{-9}$ **57.** $\dfrac{1}{2}i^{-15}$ **58.** $(3i)^{-1}$ **59.** $(2i)^{-3}$

*60. Prove that $\dfrac{i^{4n} - i^{2n}}{2}$ equals 0 or 1 for all positive integers n.

CHALLENGE

Contest Problems

*Here are some more problems from the annual American High School Mathematics Examination (**M.A.A. Contest Problem Book**). As you look for solutions, try to identify relationships that will help to simplify your work!*

1. The equation $x^3 + 6x^2 + 11x + 6 = 0$ has
 (A) no negative real roots   (B) no positive real roots
 (C) no real roots   (D) 1 positive and 2 negative roots
 (E) 1 negative and 2 positive roots

2. The radius R of a cylindrical box is 8 inches, the height H is 3 inches. The volume $V = \pi R^2 H$ is to be increased by the same fixed positive amount when R is increased by x inches as when H is increased by x inches. This condition is satisfied by
 (A) no real value of x   (B) one integral value of x
 (C) one rational, but not integral, value of x
 (D) one irrational value of x   (E) two real values of x

3. If the sum of two numbers is 1 and their product is 1, then the sum of their cubes is
 (A) 2   (B) $-2 - \dfrac{3\sqrt{3}i}{4}$ (C) 0   (D) $-\dfrac{3\sqrt{3}i}{4}$ (E) -2 [i denotes $\sqrt{-1}$.]

4. If three of the roots of $x^4 + ax^2 + bx + c = 0$ are 1, 2, and 3, then the value of $a + c$ is
 (A) 35   (B) 24   (C) -12 (D) -61 (E) -63

5. If two factors of $2x^3 - hx + k$ are $x + 2$ and $x - 1$, the value of $|2h - 3k|$ is
 (A) 4   (B) 3   (C) 2   (D) 1   (E) 0

8-6 Complex Numbers

OBJECTIVE

To perform basic operations with complex numbers.

The sum of a real number and a pure imaginary number is called a **complex number.**

> A complex number is any number that may be written in *rectangular form* as $a + bi$, where a and b are real numbers and $i = \sqrt{-1}$.

Real numbers and pure imaginary numbers are special kinds of complex numbers and can be written in the $a + bi$ form. For example, $\sqrt{7}$ may be written as $\sqrt{7} + 0i$. Similarly, $-3i$ may be written as $0 + (-3)i$, or $0 - 3i$.

> Two complex numbers $a + bi$ and $c + di$ are equal if and only if $a = c$ and $b = d$.

EXAMPLE 1

Find values of x and y so that $\frac{1}{2}x - 3yi$ and $4 - 6i$ are equal.

The real parts must be equal.

$$\frac{1}{2}x = 4 \qquad \text{Set } \tfrac{1}{2}x \text{ equal to 4, and solve for } x.$$
$$x = 8$$

The coefficients of i must also be equal.

$$-3y = -6 \qquad \text{Set } -3y \text{ equal to } -6, \text{ and solve for } y.$$
$$y = 2$$

Check $\quad \frac{1}{2}(8) - 3(2)i = 4 - 6i$ ✔ The value of x is 8, and the value of y is 2.

The sum and difference of two complex numbers are defined as follows.

> **The Sum and Difference of Two Complex Numbers**
>
> If $a + bi$ and $c + di$ are complex numbers, then
> $$(a + bi) + (c + di) = (a + c) + (b + d)i$$
> $$(a + bi) - (c + di) = (a - c) + (b - d)i$$

EXAMPLE 2   Add: $(7 - 3i) + (-4 + 2i)$

$$(7 - 3i) + (-4 + 2i) = [7 + (-4)] + (-3 + 2)i$$
$$= 3 + (-1)i$$
$$= 3 - i$$

EXAMPLE 3   Subtract: $(4 - 3i) - (4 + 5i)$

$$(4 - 3i) - (4 + 5i) = (4 - 4) + (-3 - 5)i$$
$$= 0 + (-8)i$$
$$= 0 - 8i, \text{ or } -8i$$

Answers are to be expressed in the form $a + bi$, unless you are directed to express them differently. Answers that are pure imaginary numbers or real numbers, however, need not be expressed in $a + bi$ form. For example, $0 - 2i$ may be written as $-2i$, and $3 + 0i$ may be written as 3.

The definition of the product of two complex numbers is based on the procedure for multiplying two binomials.

$$(a + bi)(c + di) = ac + adi + bci + bdi^2$$
$$= ac + (ad + bc)i + bd(-1)$$
$$= (ac - bd) + (ad + bc)i$$

The formal definition is given below.

The Product of Two Complex Numbers

If $a + bi$ and $c + di$ are complex numbers, then

$$(a + bi)(c + di) = (ac - bd) + (ad + bc)i$$

Rather than memorize the above definition, you will probably find it easier to simply multiply two complex numbers just as you would two binomials.

EXAMPLE 4   Multiply: $(8 + 7i)(5 + 2i)$

$$(8 + 7i)(5 + 2i) = (8 \cdot 5) + (8 \cdot 2i) + (7i \cdot 5) + (7i \cdot 2i)$$
$$= 40 + 16i + 35i + 14i^2$$
$$= 40 + (16 + 35)i + 14(-1)$$
$$= 26 + 51i$$

Finally, let us examine the quotient of two complex numbers. Such a quotient can be found by a procedure similar to that of rationalizing a denominator to eliminate a radical. If the denominator is $c + di$, multiply by its **conjugate**, $c - di$, in order to make the new denominator a real number.

$$(c + di)(c - di) = c^2 - d^2i^2 = c^2 + d^2 \qquad \text{A real number}$$

EXAMPLE 5   Divide: $\dfrac{5 + 4i}{2 - 3i}$

$$\frac{5 + 4i}{2 - 3i} = \frac{5 + 4i}{2 - 3i} \cdot \frac{2 + 3i}{2 + 3i} \qquad 2 + 3i \text{ is the conjugate of } 2 - 3i.$$

$$= \frac{10 + 15i + 8i + 12i^2}{4 - 9i^2}$$

$$= \frac{(10 - 12) + (15 + 8)i}{4 + 9}$$

$$= \frac{-2 + 23i}{13}$$

$$= -\frac{2}{13} + \frac{23}{13}i \qquad a + bi \text{ form}$$

When $\dfrac{a + bi}{c + di}$ is multiplied by $\dfrac{c - di}{c - di} = 1$, we get the general result shown below.

The Quotient of Two Complex Numbers

If $a + bi$ and $c + di$ are complex numbers, then

$$\frac{a + bi}{c + di} = \frac{ac + bd}{c^2 + d^2} + \frac{bc - ad}{c^2 + d^2}i \qquad (c + di \neq 0)$$

It is usually easier to multiply by the conjugate of the denominator, as in Example 5, than it is to memorize this definition.

CLASS EXERCISES

To show that each number is a complex number and may be written in the form $a + bi$, identify the values of a and b.

1. $3i$ **2.** 5 **3.** 0 **4.** i^2 **5.** i^3

6. $\dfrac{4 - 8i}{2}$ **7.** $9 + \sqrt{-4}$ **8.** $-7i^4 + \sqrt{-2}$ **9.** $i^5 - i^4$ **10.** $\dfrac{6 + 3i}{2}$

*State whether the two complex numbers are **equal** or **not equal**, and give a reason for your answer.*

11. $3 - 5i;\ 5 - 3i$ **12.** $4 - 9i;\ 4 + (-9i)$

13. $\dfrac{1}{2}(4 + 6i);\ 2 + 3i$ **14.** $\dfrac{2}{3} + \dfrac{1}{2}i;\ -\dfrac{2}{3}i^2 + \dfrac{1}{2}\sqrt{-1}$

EXERCISES

A   *Find the values of* **x** *and* **y** *so that the two complex numbers are equal.*

1. $2x + 3i; \dfrac{1}{2} - \dfrac{y}{3}i$ **2.** $6xi; y + 4i$ **3.** $6 + \dfrac{3}{2}i; \dfrac{3y}{4} - \dfrac{x}{4}i$

Perform the indicated operations.

4. $(2 + 7i) + (6 - 3i)$ **5.** $(-5 + i) + (5 + 10i)$ **6.** $(8 + 6i) + (2 + i)$

7. $-9 + (4 - 2i)$ **8.** $(-2 + 7i) + (6 + 3i)$ **9.** $(5 - i) + (-5 - 10i)$

10. $(1 + i) - (-1 - i)$ **11.** $(1 + i) - (-1 + i)$ **12.** $(1 + i) - (1 - i)$

13. $(1 + i) - (1 + i)$ **14.** $3i - (4 + 15i)$ **15.** $(4 - 3i) - (7 + 2i)$

16. $(4 + 5i)(4 - 5i)$ **17.** $(-2 + 3i)(-2 - 3i)$ **18.** $(2 + 5i)(6 + 3i)$

19. $(10 - i)(7 + 5i)$ **20.** $(6 + 7i)(6 + 7i)$ **21.** $(-2 - 5i)(-2 - i)$

22. $(5 - 4i)(4 - 5i)$ **23.** $(-4 - 10i)(-4 + 10i)$ **24.** $(8 + 9i)(10 + 11i)$

25. $\dfrac{2 + i}{2 - i}$ **26.** $\dfrac{2 - i}{2 + i}$ **27.** $\dfrac{3 - 4i}{1 + 2i}$

28. $\dfrac{-5 + i}{3 - i}$ **29.** $\dfrac{1 + 2i}{2 + 2i}$ **30.** $\dfrac{1 + 2i}{1 + 3i}$

B   **31.** $(7 - 9i) - 3(4i)$ **32.** $8 - (-4 - 8i)$ **33.** $(4 - \sqrt{-2}) + (6 + \sqrt{-2})$

34. $(1 + \sqrt{-1}) - (1 - \sqrt{-1})$ **35.** $\left(-\dfrac{2}{3} + \dfrac{1}{3}i\right) + \left(\dfrac{1}{6} - \dfrac{5}{6}i\right)$

36. $\left(\dfrac{1}{2} + i\right) + \left(-1 + \dfrac{1}{2}i\right)$ **37.** $(\sqrt{2} + 3i)(\sqrt{2} - 3i)$

38. $(\sqrt{27} - 3i)(\sqrt{3} + i)$ **39.** $(\sqrt{2} - i\sqrt{3})(\sqrt{2} + i\sqrt{3})$

40. $2i(3i - 2)$ **41.** $(2 + 5i)^2$ **42.** $(3 - 6i)^2$

43. $\sqrt{-1}(10 - 6\sqrt{-1})$ **44.** $\left(\dfrac{1}{2} - \dfrac{1}{2}i\right)(2 + 6i)$ **45.** $\left(\dfrac{1}{4} - i\right)\left(1 - \dfrac{3}{4}i\right)$

46. $\dfrac{1 + i\sqrt{3}}{1 - i\sqrt{3}}$ **47.** $\dfrac{\sqrt{2} + i}{\sqrt{2} - i}$ **48.** $\dfrac{1 + i\sqrt{3}}{2 - i\sqrt{3}}$

49. $\dfrac{7}{2 + 2i}$ **50.** $\dfrac{5 - 3i}{i}$ **51.** $\dfrac{2\sqrt{-50}}{-3i}$

52. $2(4 - i) - i(1 + i)$ **53.** $2i(3 - 3i) + 4i$ **54.** $\dfrac{1}{1 - i} - \dfrac{4 + i}{1 - i}$

55. Multiply $\dfrac{a + bi}{c + di}$ by $\dfrac{c - di}{c - di}$ and derive the formula for the quotient of two complex numbers.

C   *Perform the indicated operations.*

56. $(2 + i)(2 - i)(1 - i)$ **57.** $\left(-\dfrac{1}{2} + \dfrac{3}{2}i\right)^3$ **58.** $\dfrac{3 + 4i}{5 + i} - \dfrac{1 + 2i}{5 - i}$

59. $\dfrac{1}{(1 + i)^2}$ **60.** $\left(\dfrac{1}{1 - i}\right)^2$ **61.** $(5 + i)^{-1}$

62. $(2 - i)^{-1}$ **63.** $(3 - i)^{-2}$ **64.** $(2 + 3i)^{-2}$

65. Express the reciprocal of the complex number $c + di \neq 0$ in the form $a + bi$.

66. Use the result in Exercise 65 to verify that the product of $(a + bi)$ and the reciprocal of $(c + di)$ gives the general result for the quotient of two complex numbers.

In Exercises 67–69, find the value of $x^2 + 2x + 2$ *for each value of* x.

67. $x = -1 + i$ **68.** $x = -1 + 2i$ **69.** $x = 2 - i$

70. What is the additive inverse of $a + bi$?

*71. Prove that the distributive property $u(v + w) = uv + uw$ holds for complex numbers $u = a + bi$, $v = c + di$, and $w = e + fi$.

The polynomials in the following exercises are not factorable if you use real numbers. Factor each polynomial by using complex numbers.

> **Samples** $x^2 + 1 = x^2 - (-1) = x^2 - i^2 = (x - i)(x + i)$
> $x^2 + ix + 6 = x^2 + ix - 6i^2 = (x + 3i)(x - 2i)$

72. $x^2 + 9$ **73.** $3x^2 + 12$ **74.** $x^3 + 4x$

75. $x^2 - 2ix + 15$ **76.** $4x^2 - 5ix + 6$ **77.** $x^2 - 4ix - 4$

CHECKPOINT

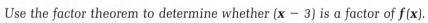

Use the factor theorem to determine whether $(x - 3)$ *is a factor of* $f(x)$.

1. $f(x) = 3x^2 - 2x - 21$ **2.** $f(x) = x^4 + x^3 - 35x$

Find all the real roots. Use the rational root and factor theorems to find one rational root. Use the quadratic formula to find two more real roots.

3. $9x^3 - 15x^2 - 5x + 3 = 0$ **4.** $x^3 - 20x - 5x^2 = -100$

5. Add $1 - i$ and its reciprocal.   **6.** Subtract $1 - i$ from its reciprocal.

7. Multiply $-1 - i$ by its conjugate.   **8.** Divide $-1 - i$ by its conjugate.

The Complex Plane

A complex number $x + yi$ can be represented by the ordered pair of real numbers (x, y). This makes it possible to match the complex numbers with the points in the **complex plane.**

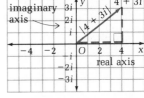

The horizontal axis is called the **real axis.** All real numbers x are represented by points on this line.

The vertical axis is called the **imaginary axis.** All pure imaginary numbers yi are represented by points on this line.

The point for a complex number $x + yi$ is located in the same way as an ordered pair of real numbers (x, y) is located in the more familiar coordinate system. An arrow is drawn from the origin to that point. The distance between a point for a complex number such as $4 + 3i$ and the origin is called the **modulus** and is denoted by $|4 + 3i|$. Using the Pythagorean theorem, we see that $|4 + 3i| = \sqrt{4^2 + 3^2} = \sqrt{25} = 5$. In general,

$$|x + yi| = \sqrt{x^2 + y^2} \qquad \text{the modulus of } x + yi$$

To add complex numbers geometrically, use the **parallelogram law.**

Example   Find $(3 + 2i) + (-5 + 3i)$ geometrically.

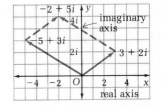

Step 1   Locate points for $3 + 2i$ and $-5 + 2i$. Draw an arrow from the origin to each point.

Step 2   Complete the parallelogram, as shown. The sum is the complex number represented by the fourth vertex of the parallelogram: $-2 + 5i$.

Step 3   Check algebraically: $(3 + 2i) + (-5 + 3i) = -2 + 5i$.

Now, you try it! Graph each complex number on one complex plane and find the modulus of each.

  1. $3 + 4i$ **2.** $-7 + 2i$ **3.** $-8 - 6i$ **4.** $5 - 4i$

Find the sum or difference geometrically. Check algebraically. Recall that
$a - b = a + (-b)$.

  5. $(1 + 4i) + (4 + i)$ **6.** $(-4 + 4i) + (-6 - 5i)$ **7.** $(8 + 6i) + (8 - 6i)$

  8. $(8 - 5i) - (2 + 3i)$ **9.** $(-6 + i) - (-2 - 3i)$ **10.** $(3 + 3i) - (-3 + 3i)$

11. $(3 + i) + (-2 + 2i) + (8 - 2i)$

8-7 Solving Equations for Real and Complex Roots

OBJECTIVES

To determine the number of complex roots of a given polynomial equation.
To solve quadratic equations for complex roots, using the quadratic formula.
To find the real and imaginary roots of equations of the third and fourth
  degree.

Before the complex numbers were introduced, we found only real solutions of quadratic equations. Now it is possible to find complex solutions that are not real. For example, $x^2 + 1 = 0$ has no real roots, but it does have the two imaginary roots i and $-i$, since $(\pm i)^2 + 1 = 0$. When you are trying to solve a polynomial equation it is helpful to know, at the outset, just how many roots there are. The following theorems provide this information.

The Fundamental Theorem of Algebra

Every polynomial equation with degree greater than zero has at least one complex root.

The next theorem is based on the fundamental theorem.

Theorem

Every polynomial equation of positive degree n has exactly n complex roots.

The above theorem tells us that every quadratic equation has exactly two roots, every cubic equation has exactly three roots, and so forth. Some of the roots may not be distinct. For example, the equation

$$x^2 + 2x + 1 = 0, \text{ or } (x + 1)^2 = 0$$

has a *double root*, -1. The root occurs twice, since the two factors of $x^2 + 2x + 1$ are the same.

In other cases, a *multiple root* may appear more than twice. To illustrate, the equation $x^4 - x^3 = 0$ has degree 4 and therefore has four roots. If we factor the left side to obtain $x^3(x - 1) = 0$, we see that 0 is a multiple root, occurring three times. The fourth root, of course, is 1.

In general, the complex roots of a quadratic equation are found using the quadratic formula.

EXAMPLE 1

Solve $2x^2 - x + 1 = 0$.

Use the quadratic formula.

$$x = \frac{-(-1) \pm \sqrt{(-1)^2 - 4(2)(1)}}{2(2)}$$

$$= \frac{1 \pm \sqrt{-7}}{4}$$

$$= \frac{1 \pm i\sqrt{7}}{4}$$

$$= \frac{1}{4} \pm \frac{\sqrt{7}}{4}i$$

The check for $x = \frac{1}{4} + \frac{\sqrt{7}}{4}i$ is shown below.

$$2\left(\frac{1}{4} + \frac{\sqrt{7}}{4}i\right)^2 - \left(\frac{1}{4} + \frac{\sqrt{7}}{4}i\right) + 1 = 2\left(\frac{1}{16} + \frac{\sqrt{7}}{8}i - \frac{7}{16}\right) - \frac{1}{4} - \frac{\sqrt{7}}{4}i + 1$$

$$= 2\left(\frac{\sqrt{7}}{8}i - \frac{3}{8}\right) + \frac{3}{4} - \frac{\sqrt{7}}{4}i$$

$$= \frac{2\sqrt{7}}{8}i - \frac{6}{8} + \frac{3}{4} - \frac{\sqrt{7}}{4}i$$

$$= \frac{\sqrt{7}}{4}i - \frac{3}{4} + \frac{3}{4} - \frac{\sqrt{7}}{4}i$$

$$= 0$$

The check for $x = \frac{1}{4} - \frac{\sqrt{7}}{4}i$ is similar.

The solutions are $\frac{1}{4} + \frac{\sqrt{7}}{4}i$ and $\frac{1}{4} - \frac{\sqrt{7}}{4}i$.

Notice that the roots in the above example are conjugates. In general, imaginary roots occur in **conjugate pairs,** as stated in the following theorem.

Conjugate Root Theorem

Let a and b be real numbers with $b \neq 0$. If $a + bi$ is a root of a polynomial equation with real coefficients, then $a - bi$ is also a root of the equation.

EXAMPLE 2   One root of $p(x) = x^4 - 2x^3 + 4x^2 + 2x - 5 = 0$ is $1 + 2i$. Find the remaining roots.

The second theorem on page 302 tells us that this equation has four roots. Since imaginary roots occur as conjugate pairs, both $1 + 2i$ and $1 - 2i$ are roots. Consequently, $x - (1 + 2i)$ and $x - (1 - 2i)$ are factors of $p(x)$. Then

$$[x - (1 + 2i)][x - (1 - 2i)] = x^2 - 2x + 5$$

is a factor of $p(x)$. We divide $p(x)$ by $x^2 - 2x + 5$ to find another factor.

$$
\begin{array}{r}
x^2 - 1 \\
x^2 - 2x + 5 \overline{)x^4 - 2x^3 + 4x^2 + 2x - 5} \\
\underline{x^4 - 2x^3 + 5x^2} \\
-x^2 + 2x - 5 \\
\underline{-x^2 + 2x - 5} \\
0
\end{array}
$$

Now we have

$$p(x) = (x^2 - 2x + 5)(x^2 - 1)$$
$$= (x^2 - 2x + 5)(x + 1)(x - 1)$$

Setting each of the last two factors of $p(x)$ equal to zero produces the additional roots 1 and -1. You should verify that all four solutions check when substituted in the original equation. Thus the four roots of $p(x) = x^4 - 2x^3 + 4x^2 + 2x - 5 = 0$ are $1 + 2i$, $1 - 2i$, 1, and -1.

In Example 2, the last two roots of $p(x)$ were found by factoring $x^2 - 1$. In other words, two of the roots of $p(x) = 0$ are the roots of $x^2 - 1 = 0$. By the factor theorem, if r is a root of the polynomial equation $p(x) = 0$, then $x - r$ is a factor of $p(x)$ and

$$p(x) = q(x)(x - r)$$

where $q(x)$ is a polynomial. The remaining roots of $p(x) = 0$ are the roots of the **depressed equation** $q(x) = 0$.

When solving for the roots of a polynomial equation of degree three or greater, it is often best to start by testing for possible rational roots. After finding one or more rational roots, it may be possible to find additional roots if you solve the depressed equation by factoring or by using the quadratic formula.

EXAMPLE 3   Solve: $p(x) = 3x^3 - 7x^2 + 8x - 2 = 0$

There are three roots. By the rational root theorem, the possible rational roots are: ± 1, $\pm \frac{1}{3}$, ± 2, and $\pm \frac{2}{3}$. Synthetic division shows that $\frac{1}{3}$ is a root.

$$\begin{array}{r|rrrr}
\frac{1}{3} & 3 & -7 & 8 & -2 \\
 & & 1 & -2 & 2 \\
\hline
 & 3 & -6 & 6 & \boxed{0} = f\left(\frac{1}{3}\right)
\end{array}$$

Then $x - \frac{1}{3}$ is a factor of $p(x)$, and the other factor is $3x^2 - 6x + 6$.

$$\begin{aligned}
p(x) &= \left(x - \frac{1}{3}\right)(3x^2 - 6x + 6) \\
&= \left(x - \frac{1}{3}\right)(3)(x^2 - 2x + 2) \\
&= (3x - 1)(x^2 - 2x + 2)
\end{aligned}$$

The remaining roots of $p(x) = 0$ are the roots of the depressed equation $q(x) = x^2 - 2x + 2 = 0$. Verify that the quadratic formula gives $x = 1 \pm i$, and check the three solutions in the original equation. The roots of $p(x) = 0$ are $\frac{1}{3}$, $1 + i$, and $1 - i$.

CLASS EXERCISES

Give the number of complex roots of each equation. (Assume that a double root counts as two roots, and so forth.)

1. $x^4 - 2x^3 + x^2 - 4x + 1 = 0$

2. $x^7 + 1 = 0$

3. $-5x^3 + 6x = 100x^5 - 2$

4. $x^3(1 + x - x^3) = 0$

5. One root of $2x^3 - x^2 + 8x - 4 = 0$ is $2i$. Name another root. How many real roots are there?

6. Two roots of $x^4 - 2x^3 + 6x^2 + 8x - 40 = 0$ are 2 and $1 - 3i$. Name another root. How many real roots are there?

7. $2 + i$ and $-i\sqrt{3}$ are roots of $x^4 - 4x^3 + 8x^2 - 12x + 15 = 0$. Name the remaining roots.

8. The equation $x^4 - 3x^2 - 4 = 0$ can be written in the form $(x^2 + 1)(x^2 - 4) = 0$. Name the roots of the equation.

9. The equation $x^4 - x^3 - 2x - 4 = 0$ can be written in the form $(x + 1)(x - 2)(x^2 + 2) = 0$. Name the roots of the equation.

EXERCISES

Solve each equation using the quadratic formula.

1. $x^2 + 16 = 0$

2. $x^2 + 49 = 0$

3. $x^2 + 2 = 0$

4. $x^2 + 8 = 0$

5. $x^2 - 4x + 13 = 0$

6. $x^2 - 6x + 4 = 0$

7. $x^2 + 2x + 3 = 0$

8. $x^2 + 4x + 6 = 0$

9. $x^2 + 5x + 8 = 0$

B

10. $4x^2 + 1 = 0$

11. $25x^2 + 9 = 0$

12. $2x^2 - x + 2 = 0$

13. $x^2 - x + 1 = 0$

14. $x^2 - 3x + 4 = 0$

15. $2x^2 - 3x = -3$

16. $4x + 7 = -3x^2$

17. $2x^2 - x + 1 = x - x^2$

18. $x(x - 4) = 4(x + 5)$

19. $3x(x + 1) = x - 5$

Solve. Begin by factoring.

20. $x^3 + x^2 = 0$

21. $x^4 + 4x^2 = 0$

22. $2x^3 + 6x = 0$

23. $3x^4 + 15x^2 = 0$

24. $x^3 + 6x^2 + 10x = 0$

25. $6x^3 - 2x^2 + 3x = 0$

One root of each equation is given. Find the remaining roots.

26. $x^3 + 2x^2 + 4x + 8 = 0$; $2i$

27. $3x^3 + 3x + 2x^2 + 2 = 0$; $-i$

28. $x^3 - 3x^2 + 4x - 2 = 0$; $1 + i$

29. $2x^3 - 17x^2 + 42x - 17 = 0$; $4 - i$

30. $x^4 + 5x^3 + 3x^2 + 45x - 54 = 0$; $3i$

31. $16x^4 + 7x^2 - 9 = 0$; i

32. $x^4 - 7x^3 + 13x^2 + x - 20 = 0$; $2 + i$

33. $x^4 + 19x^2 + 48 = 0$; $-i\sqrt{3}$

34. $x^4 - 3x^3 + 18x^2 - 22x + 60 = 0$; $1 + 3i$

C

Solve. Begin by factoring or by using the rational root theorem.

35. $p(x) = x^3 - x^2 + x - 1 = 0$

36. $p(x) = x^3 + 2x^2 + 3x + 6 = 0$

37. $p(x) = x^3 - 3x^2 + 4x - 2 = 0$

38. $p(x) = 2x^3 - x^2 + 18x - 9 = 0$

39. $p(x) = 3x^3 + 2x^2 + 15x + 10 = 0$

40. $p(x) = x^3 - 6x^2 + 15x - 18 = 0$

41. $p(x) = x^4 - 16 = 0$

42. $p(x) = x^3 - 8 = 0$

43. $p(x) = x^4 + x = 0$

44. $p(x) = x^4 - 4x^3 + 7x^2 - 6x = 0$

45. $p(x) = 2x^4 + x^3 - 22x^2 + 29x + 20 = 0$

*A polynomial equation in **x** has real coefficients. Write the equation, given that*

46. the term of highest degree is x^3, and two roots of the equation are $2i$ and -3.

47. the term of highest degree is x^4, and two roots of the equation are i and $1 + i$.

48. the term of highest degree is x^5, and three roots of the equation are -1, i, and $2 - i$.

*49. Let $p(x) = 0$ be a polynomial equation of odd degree, with real coefficients. Prove that $p(x) = 0$ must have at least one real root.

Descartes' Rule of Signs

Recall that the imaginary roots of a polynomial equation with real co-efficients occur in conjugate pairs. Thus, if such an equation has any imaginary roots at all, then there must be an even number of such roots. There is also a useful rule that tells us something about the number of real roots. It is based on the number of variations in sign in the polynomial on the left side of the equation $p(x) = 0$.

Consider a polynomial with its terms arranged in order of decreasing powers of the variable, and ignore any missing terms. A variation in sign occurs when there is a change in sign between terms. For example:

$$p(x) = x^5 - 3x^4 + 7x^2 + 5x - 8$$

The polynomial $p(x)$ has *three* variations in sign.

The following rule was first stated by René Descartes, a famous French mathematician of the seventeenth century.

Descartes' Rule of Signs

Let $p(x) = 0$ be a polynomial equation with real coefficients and with its terms arranged in descending powers of x.

1. **The number of positive real roots of $p(x) = 0$ is either equal to the number of variations in sign in $p(x)$, or it is less than that number by an even positive integer.**

2. **The number of negative real roots is either equal to the number of variations in sign in $p(-x)$, or it is less than that number by an even positive integer.**

Example Use Descartes' rule to determine the possibilities for the number of positive and negative real roots and the number of imaginary roots of

$$p(x) = x^5 - 3x^4 + 7x^2 + 5x - 8 = 0$$

We have already determined that $p(x)$ has three variations in sign. Then the first part of the rule tells us that $p(x) = 0$ has either three positive real roots, or just one.

To use the second part of the rule, first write

$$p(-x) = (-x)^5 \quad - \quad 3(-x)^4 \quad + \quad 7(-x)^2 \quad + \quad 5(-x) \quad - \quad 8$$
$$= \quad -x^5 \quad - \quad 3x^4 \quad + \quad 7x^2 \quad - \quad 5x \quad - \quad 8$$

− to + ⟋ + to −

Since $p(-x)$ has two variations in sign, $p(x) = 0$ has either two negative real roots, or none.

The table below summarizes the possibilities for the roots of $p(x) = 0$. Keep in mind that every polynomial equation of positive degree n has exactly n complex roots, and that imaginary roots appear in conjugate pairs.

$p(x) = x^5 - 3x^4 + 7x^2 + 5x - 8 = 0$		
Number of Positive Real Roots	Number of Negative Real Roots	Number of Imaginary Roots
3	2	0
3	0	2
1	2	2
1	0	4

EXERCISES

Determine the possibilities for the number of positive and negative real roots, and the number of imaginary roots, of each equation. Use Descartes' rule.

1. $2x^3 + x - 5 = 0$ **2.** $x^3 + x + 1 = 0$

3. $x^4 - x^2 - 1 = 0$ **4.** $x^4 + x^2 + 1 = 0$

5. $3x^4 + x^2 - 5x + 3 = 0$ **6.** $x^3 + 8 = 0$

7. $x^5 + 7x^3 - 3x^2 - x + 4 = 0$ **8.** $x^6 - x^5 + x^3 + x^2 - 1 = 0$

9. Prove that $x^4 - x^2 - 1 = 0$ has exactly two real roots.

10. Find the possibilities for the types of roots of $x^4 - 3x^3 + 6x^2 - 12x + 8 = 0$.

11. Solve the equation in Exercise 10. Begin by using the rational root theorem.

*12. Prove that $x^7 - 6x^6 - x^5 + 30x^4 + x^3 - 6x^2 - x + 30 = 0$ has exactly three real roots and four imaginary roots.

*13. Prove that $x^7 + 2x^5 + 3x^3 + 4x = 0$ has exactly one real root.

*14. Prove that $x^{10} - 1 = 0$ has exactly two real roots.

Gear Speeds

Machinists who work with gears need to know their directions and speeds. The speed of a driven gear is determined by the number of teeth it has and by the speed and number of teeth in the driving gear.

Example In the gear train shown, gear A drives gear B, which then drives gear C. Gear A turns at a rate of 20 revolutions per minute (rpm) and has 54 teeth. Gear C has 36 teeth. Find the speed and direction of gear C.

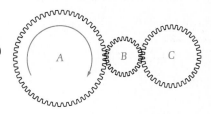

A: 54 teeth   C: 36 teeth

Gear C has $\frac{2}{3}$ as many teeth as gear A. Thus gear C turns $1\frac{1}{2}$ times while gear A makes 1 full turn. That is, gear C turns $\frac{3}{2}$ as fast as gear A.

$$\frac{3}{2} \times 20 = 30$$

Idler gear B turns in the reverse direction from gear A. Hence gear C turns in the same direction as gear A. Note that the idler gear affects only the direction of the driven gear, not its speed. Thus gear C turns clockwise at 30 rpm.

1. Gear A drives gear B, which is locked to gear C. Gear C drives gear D. If gear A is turning counterclockwise at 60 rpm, how fast and in what direction is gear D turning?

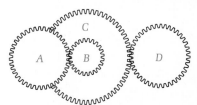

A: 40 teeth   C: 60 teeth
B: 24 teeth   D: 40 teeth

Gears F and G are locked together, as are gears H and I. The driving gear E is turning at 240 rpm.

2. How fast is the driven gear J turning?

3. Is gear J turning in the same direction as gear E, or in the opposite direction?

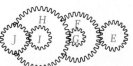

E: 20 teeth   H: 40 teeth
F: 32 teeth   I: 16 teeth
G: 12 teeth   J: 20 teeth

CHAPTER 8 REVIEW

VOCABULARY

synthetic division (p. 278)
remainder theorem (p. 282)
factor theorem (p. 283)
leading coefficient (p. 287)
rational root theorem (p. 287)
imaginary unit, i (p. 292)
(pure) imaginary number (p. 292)

complex number (p. 296)
conjugate (p. 297)
fundamental theorem of algebra (p. 302)
multiple root (p. 302)
conjugate pair (p. 303)
conjugate root theorem (p. 303)
depressed equation (p. 304)

SUMMARY

In this chapter some new methods for factoring polynomials and solving polynomial equations are presented. These methods make it possible to solve equations that we could not solve before. Central to this work are the factor, remainder, and rational root theorems. These theorems are applied with the aid of synthetic division, which is a short-cut based on the long division process for dividing a polynomial in x by an expression of the form $x - c$.

Imaginary and complex numbers, and operations with these numbers, are introduced. This background, along with the fundamental theorem of algebra, the conjugate root theorem, and the theorems previously mentioned, now make it possible to find all of the complex roots of many polynomial equations of various degrees.

REVIEW EXERCISES

8-1   *Divide and check. Express the answer in the form* **quotient** $+ \dfrac{\textbf{remainder}}{\textbf{divisor}}$.

1. $\dfrac{10x - 12x^2}{5x}$ **2.** $\dfrac{12x - 18y}{2x - 3y}$ **3.** $\dfrac{8x^3 - 4x^2y + 6xy^2}{2x}$

4. $(4x^3 - 10x^2 - 2x + 9) \div (2x + 1)$

5. $(x^5 - 7x^4 + 25x^2 + 30x + 4) \div (x^2 - 3x)$

6. $(2x^3 - 3x^2y - 2xy^2 + 3y^2) \div (2x - 3y)$

7. $(x^6 - 3x^4 + 5x^2 + 75) \div (x^2 - 5)$

8-2   *Divide by using synthetic division, and check. Show your answers in the form* **quotient; remainder.**

8. $(x^3 - 5x^2 + 8x + 1) \div (x - 2)$ **9.** $(x^4 + 7x + 2) \div (x + 2)$

10. $(2x^4 + 9x^3 + 5x^2 - 16x - 10) \div (x + 3)$

11. $\left(4x^4 - 8x^3 - 5x^2 + x + \dfrac{1}{2}\right) \div \left(x - \dfrac{1}{2}\right)$

8-3 Find the remainder by using the remainder theorem. Check by synthetic division.

12. $(x^3 - 7x^2 + 6x - 8) \div (x - 3)$　　　　**13.** $(3x^4 + 5x^3 - 8x - 4) \div (x + 2)$

14. Determine whether $(x - 5)$ is or is not a factor of
$f(x) = x^3 - 10x^2 + 32x - 35$ by using the factor theorem.

15. Determine whether $(x + 1)$ is or is not a factor of
$p(x) = x^4 - 6x^2 + 10x + 7$ by using the factor theorem.

16. Show that $(x - 4)$ is a factor of $p(x) = 6x^3 - 25x^2 - 11x + 60$ by
using synthetic division. Then factor $p(x)$ completely.

8-4 Find the rational roots of each equation.

17. $2x^3 + x^2 - 2x - 6 = 0$　　　　**18.** $x^3 - 7x^2 + 17x - 15 = 0$

19. $9x^3 - 18x^2 - 25x = 6$　　　　**20.** $x^3 + 4x^2 - 7x - 10 = 0$

21. $2x^3 - 3x^2 - 23x + 12 = 0$　　　　**22.** $x^4 - x^3 - 7x^2 + x + 6 = 0$

23. $3x^4 + 2x^3 - 28x^2 - 18x + 9 = 0$　　　　**24.** $4x^4 - 8x^3 - 105x^2 + 200x = -125$

8-5 Simplify. Rationalize all denominators.

25. $\sqrt{-16}$　　　　**26.** $4\sqrt{-11}$　　　　**27.** $7\sqrt{-12}$　　　　**28.** $2\sqrt{-10}$　　　　**29.** $-2\sqrt{-300}$

30. $6\sqrt{-\dfrac{8}{9}}$　　　　**31.** $5\sqrt{-\dfrac{5}{2}}$　　　　**32.** $\dfrac{1}{2}\sqrt{-\dfrac{64}{81}}$　　　　**33.** $\dfrac{3}{4}\sqrt{-\dfrac{12}{25}}$　　　　**34.** $-\dfrac{2}{3}\sqrt{-\dfrac{3}{2}}$

Simplify by expressing each power of *i* as *i*, *−1*, *−i*, or *1*.

35. i^{15}　　　　**36.** i^{25}　　　　**37.** i^{80}　　　　**38.** i^{90}　　　　**39.** i^{95}

Write the numbers using *i*. Then perform the indicated operation and simplify.

40. $(\sqrt{-36})(\sqrt{-64})$　　　　**41.** $3\sqrt{-9} + 2\sqrt{-25}$　　　　**42.** $\dfrac{1}{4}\sqrt{-12} \cdot \sqrt{20}$　　　　**43.** $2\sqrt{-\dfrac{1}{4}} \cdot \sqrt{-\dfrac{8}{9}}$

8-6 Perform the indicated operations.

44. $(-3 + i) - (5 - 7i)$　　　　**45.** $(2 - 3i)(5 + 7i)$　　　　**46.** $4i(-6 - i)$

47. $\dfrac{4 + 3i}{1 - 2i}$　　　　**48.** $2(5 - 3i) - 4i(6 + 5i)$　　　　**49.** $\left(\dfrac{3 + i}{1 + 2i}\right)\left(\dfrac{1 - 4i}{2 + 3i}\right)$

8-7 Solve each equation using the quadratic formula.

50. $x^2 - 3x - 5 = 0$　　　　**51.** $9x^2 + 1 = 0$　　　　**52.** $3x^2 - x + 1 = 0$

One root of each of the following equations is *i*. Find the remaining roots.

53. $x^3 + x^2 + x + 1 = 0$　　　　**54.** $x^4 - x^3 + 2x^2 - x + 1 = 0$

One root of each of the following equations is $1 + 2i$. Find the remaining roots.

55. $x^3 - 3x^2 + 7x - 5 = 0$ **56.** $x^4 - 2x^3 + x^2 + 8x - 20 = 0$

Solve. Begin by factoring or by using the rational root theorem.

57. $p(x) = x^4 - 81 = 0$ **58.** $p(x) = x^3 - 2x^2 + 4x - 8 = 0$

CHAPTER 8 TEST

Divide. Express the answer in the form $\textbf{quotient} + \dfrac{\textbf{\textit{remainder}}}{\textbf{\textit{divisor}}}$.

  1. $(6x^4 - x^3 - 11x^2 + 3x + 8) \div (3x - 2)$ **2.** $(x^4 - 6x^2 + 9) \div (x^2 - 2)$

Divide by using synthetic division. Express the answer in the form **quotient; remainder.**

  3. $(3x^4 + 8x^3 - x^2 - 14x - 8) \div (x - 1)$ **4.** $(36x^4 - 13x^2 + 1) \div \left(x + \dfrac{1}{2}\right)$

Find the remainder by using the remainder theorem.

  5. $(3x^3 + x^2 - 3x - 2) \div \left(x + \dfrac{1}{3}\right)$ **6.** $(-2x^4 + 5x^2 - 7x - 9) \div (x - 2)$

  7. Show that $(x + 2)$ is a factor of $p(x) = x^3 - 5x^2 - 8x + 12$ by using the factor theorem. Then factor $p(x)$ completely.

  8. List all of the possible rational roots of $2x^5 - 7x^3 + x^2 - 4x + 9 = 0$. Do not solve the equation.

Find all of the **rational** roots of each equation.

  9. $4x^3 - 4x^2 + x - 1 = 0$ **10.** $x^3 + 3x^2 - 4 = 0$

Simplify. Rationalize all denominators.

  11. $\sqrt{-9} \cdot \sqrt{-25}$ **12.** $\dfrac{1}{2}\sqrt{-\dfrac{8}{45}}$ **13.** $i^{16} + i^{10}$

Perform the indicated operations, and simplify the answers.

  14. $(5 - 6i)(4 + 7i)$ **15.** $\dfrac{-2 + i}{3 - 4i}$ **16.** $\left(\dfrac{1}{2} - 3i\right) - \left(\dfrac{1}{4} + 8i\right)$

Solve each equation by using the quadratic formula.

17. $x^2 + 2x + 3 = 0$ **18.** $3x^2 = 4x - 5$

19. One root of $2x^3 + x^2 + 2x + 1 = 0$ is i. Find the remaining roots.

20. One root of $x^4 - 2x^3 + 28x^2 - 50x + 75 = 0$ is $-5i$. Find the remaining roots.

Zeros of a Cubic Function

The zeros of a function $f(x)$ are those values of x for which $f(x) = 0$. The real zeros can be found by examining the values of $f(x)$ for a change in sign. The program below searches for the zeros between x = −5 and x = 5 for a cubic function of the form $f(x) = ax^3 + bx^2 + cx + d$.

The coefficients a, b, c, and d are entered via the DATA statement in line 300. The instruction READ A, B, C, D in line 120 causes the computer to read four values, left to right, from the DATA statement. It assigns them to memory locations A, B, C, and D respectively. The values in line 300 are the coefficients of the function $f(x) = 4x^3 − 13x^2 − 22x + 40$. For a different function, we simply change the values in the DATA statement.

The Program	What It Does
`100 REM CUBIC FUNCTION`	
`110 LET T = 0`	Starting value for T
	Reads values from
`120 READ A, B, C, D`	line 300.
`130 FOR X = -5 TO 5`	Values of X to evaluate
`140 LET Y = A * X ↑ 3 + B * X ↑ 2 + C * X + D`	Evaluates $f(x)$.
`150 LET Y = INT(Y * 1000 + .5)/1000`	Rounds to nearest 0.001.
`160 PRINT "X = "; X; " F(X) = "; Y`	Displays pair of values.
`200 IF Y = 0 THEN 220`	Tests for a zero.
`210 IF Y * T > = 0 THEN 230`	Tests for a change
`220 PRINT "ZERO LOCATED"`	in sign.
`230 LET T = Y`	Stores value of $f(x)$ in T.
`240 NEXT X`	
`300 DATA 4, -13, -22, 40`	Supplies coefficients for
`900 END`	the READ statement.

The display   `X = 1 F(X) =    9`
                 `X = 2 F(X) = -24`
                 `ZERO LOCATED`

indicates that at least one zero of the function lies between x = 1 and x = 2. To obtain a closer approximation, or to locate additional zeros, line 130 may be changed to: `130 FOR X = -10 TO 10 STEP .25`

1. What will the computer display when the above program is run?

How should line 300 be written for each of the following?

2. $f(x) = 2x^3 + 18x^2 + 52x + 48$ 3. $f(x) = x^3 − 2x^2 − 4x + 8$

4. $f(x) = x^3 − 3x^2 + x + 1$ 5. $f(x) = x^3 + 2x^2 − 4x − 5$

6. Where are the zeros located for Exercises 2 through 5?

For more information about BASIC, see the Computer Handbook at the back of the book.

CHAPTER 9

The computer display shows two ellipses centered at the origin. The ellipses are the graphs of the equations $\frac{x^2}{9} + \frac{y^2}{25} = 1$ and $\frac{x^2}{25} + \frac{y^2}{9} = 1$.

Prerequisite Skills Review

Write the letter for the correct answer.

1. $|-8 - (-6)| = \underline{\ ?\ }$

    a. 14   **b.** 2   **c.** -2 **d.** none of these

2. If the legs of a right triangle measure 5 and 12, then the hypotenuse measures $\underline{\ ?\ }$.

    a. 17   **b.** $\sqrt{119}$ **c.** 7   **d.** none of these

3. If the hypotenuse of a right triangle measures 2 and one leg measures 1, then the measure of the other leg is $\underline{\ ?\ }$.

    a. 1   **b.** $\sqrt{3}$ **c.** 3   **d.** none of these

4. If $x^2 + 6x = 1$, then $(x + 3)^2 = \underline{\ ?\ }$.

    a. 1   **b.** 8   **c.** 9   **d.** 10

5. The axis of symmetry of the parabola $y = (x - 2)^2 - 3$ has the equation $\underline{\ ?\ }$.

    a. $x = -2$ **b.** $x = 2$ **c.** $x = 3$ **d.** $x = -3$

6. The vertex of a parabola with the equation $y = (x + 3)^2 - 4$ is the point with the coordinates $\underline{\ ?\ }$.

    a. $(-3, 4)$ **b.** $(-3, -4)$ **c.** $(3, -4)$ **d.** $(3, 4)$

7. The x-intercepts of the graph of $x^2 + \dfrac{y^2}{4} = 1$ occur at the points $\underline{\ ?\ }$.

    a. $(1, 0), (-1, 0)$ **b.** $(0, 2), (0, -2)$

    c. $(4, 0). (-4, 0)$ **d.** $(2, 0), (-2, 0)$

8. The graph of $xy = 9$ has $\underline{\ ?\ }$.

    a. both x- and y-intercepts   **b.** x-intercepts, but no y-intercepts

    c. neither x- nor y-intercepts   **d.** y-intercepts, but no x-intercepts

9. A line and a circle can intersect in at most $\underline{\ ?\ }$.

    a. 1 point   **b.** 2 points   **c.** 3 points   **d.** 4 points

10. A circle and a parabola can intersect in at most $\underline{\ ?\ }$.

    a. 2 points   **b.** 3 points   **c.** 4 points   **d.** 6 points

9-1 Distance and Midpoint Formulas

Points are located on a coordinate plane by ordered pairs of real numbers.

When two points are on a line parallel to the x- or y-axis, the distance between them is easy to find. For example, points A and B are on a line parallel to the y-axis. To find the distance between them, take the absolute value of the difference of their y-coordinates. The points can be taken in either order.

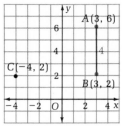

$$|6 - 2| = |4| = 4 \text{ or } |2 - 6| = |-4| = 4$$

The distance between points A and B is 4 units. This is the same as saying that the length of segment AB, or BA, is 4 units, or simply 4. Distance or length is always a positive number or zero, never a negative number.

EXAMPLE 1 Find the distance between points $B(3, 2)$ and $C(-4, 2)$.

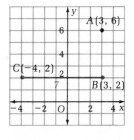

Points B and C are on a line parallel to the x-axis. Therefore, take the absolute value of the difference of their x-coordinates.

$$|3 - (-4)| = |7| = 7 \text{ or } |(-4) - 3| = |-7| = 7$$

The distance between points B and C is 7.

EXAMPLE 2 Find the distance between points $A(3, 6)$ and $C(-4, 2)$.

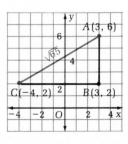

Draw segment AC on the coordinate plane. The figure should immediately suggest the use of the *Pythagorean theorem*. Triangle ABC is a right triangle with legs measuring 4 and 7. The longest side, AC, is called the *hypotenuse*.

$$AC^2 = AB^2 + BC^2$$
$$AC^2 = 4^2 + 7^2$$
$$AC = \sqrt{4^2 + 7^2}$$ Use the positive square root, since
$$AC = \sqrt{16 + 49}$$ distance cannot be negative.
$$AC = \sqrt{65}$$

The distance between points A and C is $\sqrt{65}$.

The example just shown suggests a way of finding the distance between any two points $P(x_1, y_1)$ and $Q(x_2, y_2)$. First, complete right triangle PQR with hypotenuse PQ and right angle at R.

R has the same x-value as P and the same y-value as Q. The Pythagorean theorem is used to find the distance between P and Q.

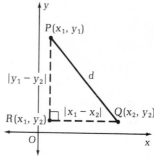

$$PQ^2 = d^2 = QR^2 + PR^2$$
$$d^2 = |x_1 - x_2|^2 + |y_1 - y_2|^2$$
$$d^2 = (x_1 - x_2)^2 + (y_1 - y_2)^2$$
$$d = \sqrt{(x_1 - x_2)^2 + (y_1 - y_2)^2}$$

Distance Formula

The distance between two points with coordinates (x_1, y_1) and (x_2, y_2) is
$$d = \sqrt{(x_1 - x_2)^2 + (y_1 - y_2)^2}$$

If the points are on a line parallel to the x-axis, then $y_1 = y_2$ and the distance between the points is $|x_1 - x_2|$. If the points are on a line parallel to the y-axis, then $x_1 = x_2$ and the distance between the points is $|y_1 - y_2|$.

EXAMPLE 3

Find the distance between the points with coordinates $(-3, -1)$ and $(9, -6)$.

$$d = \sqrt{(-3 - 9)^2 + [-1 - (-6)]^2}$$
$$= \sqrt{(-12)^2 + (5)^2}$$
$$= \sqrt{169}$$
$$= 13$$

The **midpoint** of a segment separates the segment into two parts of equal length. What are the coordinates of the midpoint of the segment connecting the points with coordinates $(-3, -1)$ and $(9, -6)$? They can be found from the coordinates of the endpoints, as shown below. The x-value of the midpoint is half-way between -3 and 9, the x-values of the endpoints.

$$\frac{-3 + 9}{2} = \frac{6}{2} = 3$$

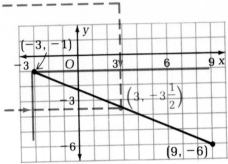

The y-value of the midpoint is half-way between -1 and -6, the y-values of the endpoints.

$$\frac{-1 + (-6)}{2} = \frac{-7}{2} = -3\frac{1}{2}$$

The coordinates of the midpoint of the segment are $(3, -3\frac{1}{2})$. In general, the coordinates of the midpoint of any segment can be found using the following formula.

Midpoint Formula

The midpoint of the segment joining two points with coordinates (x_1, y_1) and (x_2, y_2) has the coordinates

$$\left(\frac{x_1 + x_2}{2}, \frac{y_1 + y_2}{2} \right)$$

EXAMPLE 4

Find the coordinates of the midpoint of the segment connecting $A(-5, 1)$ and $B(3, -7)$.

x-value: $\dfrac{-5 + 3}{2} = \dfrac{-2}{2} = -1$ The x-value of the midpoint is the average of the x-values of A and B.

y-value: $\dfrac{1 + (-7)}{2} = \dfrac{-6}{2} = -3$ The y-value of the midpoint is the average of the y-values of A and B.

The midpoint of segment AB is located at $(-1, -3)$.

CHAPTER 9

CLASS EXERCISES

Find the distance between the two points.

1. (2, 3) and (2, 11)
2. (5, −1) and (5, 6)
3. (−4, 1) and (−10, 1)
4. (7, −2) and (−9, −2)
5. (1, 3) and (−3, 0)
6. (−3, −3) and (3, 5)

Find the coordinates of the midpoint of the segment connecting the two points.

7. (6, 2) and (−4, 2)
8. (−5, −3) and (3, 2)
9. (2, −1) and (6, 5)
10. (0, −4) and (6, 0)
11. (2, 2) and (6, 10)
12. (1.5, −1) and (−3.5, 1)

EXERCISES

A

Find the distance between the two points.

1. (2, 5) and (−2, 5)
2. (3, 7) and (7, 7)
3. (1, 4) and (1, 10)
4. (0, 0) and (0, −17)
5. (−11, −3) and (1, −3)
6. (−2, −1) and (−2, 2)
7. (−2, −1) and (1, −5)
8. (8, 0) and (−1, −12)
9. (8, −9) and (−7, −1)
10. (3, 4) and (5, 7)
11. (−1, 2) and (4, −4)
12. (0, 0) and $\left(\frac{1}{2}, \frac{1}{4}\right)$

Find the distance between the point (−7, 24) and

13. the x-axis.
14. the y-axis.
15. the origin.
16. the point (7, 24).
17. the point (−7, −24).
18. the point (7, −24).

Find the coordinates of the midpoint of the segment connecting the two points.

19. (6, 5) and (14, 5)
20. (−2, 3) and (−2, −3)
21. (−1, −4) and (−6, −4)
22. (8, −2) and (3, −6)
23. (1, 10) and (−1, −10)
24. (5, 6) and (−6, 5)
25. (−4, 7) and (−7, −8)
26. (4, 4) and (−2, −2)

Segment AB has endpoints A(−1, 5) and B(9, −9) and midpoint C.

27. Find the coordinates of point C.
28. Find the length of segment AC.
29. Find the distance from the origin to point C.

B Segment **PQ** has midpoint **M**. Find the coordinates of point **M** for each location of **P** and **Q**.

30. $P(2, -4)$ and $Q(-3, -5)$

31. $P\left(1\frac{1}{2}, 1\right)$ and $Q\left(-\frac{1}{2}, \frac{1}{2}\right)$

32. $P(4\sqrt{2}, -2\sqrt{2})$ and $Q(\sqrt{2}, 2\sqrt{2})$

33. $P(c, d)$ and $Q(2c, 3d)$

Find the coordinates of point **Q** for each location of **P** and **M**.

34. $P(3, 1)$ and $M(1, 0)$

35. $P(-2, 5)$ and $M(1, -1)$

36. $P\left(\frac{1}{2}, 2\right)$ and $M\left(-1, -1\frac{1}{2}\right)$

37. $P(0, 1.3)$ and $M(2.8, -1.2)$

Find the coordinates of point **P** for each location of **M** and **Q**.

38. $M(0, a)$ and $Q(0, 2a)$

39. $M(b, b)$ and $Q(0, b)$

40. $M(c, 2c)$ and $Q(2c, c)$

41. $M(d, e)$ and $Q(f, g)$

Point **C** is the midpoint of the segment connecting **A**$(2, -3)$ and **B**$(-6, 9)$. Find the coordinates of the midpoint of

42. segment AC.

43. segment CB.

The midpoint of a segment is **R**$(6, -5)$. Find the coordinates of the endpoints of the segment if

44. it is parallel to the x-axis and 12 units long.

45. it is parallel to the y-axis and 7 units long.

C Point **C**$(-1, -2)$ is the midpoint of segment **AB**, and point **D**$(2, 3)$ is the midpoint of segment **AC**.

46. Find the length of segment AB.

47. Find the coordinates of points A and B.

Points that lie on the same line are said to be **collinear**. Use the distance formula to determine if the three points are **collinear** or **not collinear**.

48. $A(-7, 8)$, $B(1, 2)$, $C(5, -1)$

49. $D(0, -2)$, $E(-6, -5)$, $F(8, 4)$

If the sum of the squares of the measures of the two shorter sides of a triangle equals the square of the measure of the longest side, then the triangle is a right triangle. Use the distance formula to determine if the three points form a right triangle.

50. $G(-2, -3)$, $H(3, -3)$, $I(-2, 10)$

51. $J(20, -10)$, $K(20, -3)$, $L(-4, -10)$

52. Find the perimeter of triangle ABC with vertices at $A(-1, -6)$, $B(-7, 2)$ and $C(2, -2)$.

53. Square $PQRS$ has vertices at $P(1, 2)$ and $Q(-7, -4)$. Find the length of a diagonal of the square.

54. P, Q, and R are the midpoints of the sides of triangle ABC. Show that the perimeter of triangle PQR is one-half the perimeter of triangle ABC.

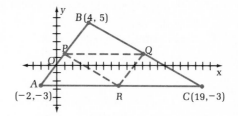

*55. Let point P have the coordinates (x_1, y_1) and point Q have the coordinates (x_2, y_2). Use the distance formula to verify that $PM = MQ$, where the coordinates of point M are

$$\left(\frac{x_1 + x_2}{2}, \frac{y_1 + y_2}{2}\right)$$

EXTRA TOPIC

Analytic Geometry

René Descartes (1596–1650) was a famous French mathematician and philosopher. The familiar rectangular coordinate plane is often called the *Cartesian plane* in his honor. When he developed this coordinate system, he combined two branches of mathematics, algebra and geometry, into one new subject, analytic geometry.

Using the distance and midpoint formulas, some interesting theorems can be proved using analytic geometry. Try to prove those given below.

1. The two diagonals of a rectangle have the same length.

2. The two diagonals of a rectangle intersect at their midpoints.

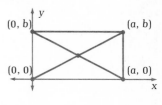

3. The midpoint of the hypotenuse of a right triangle is the same distance from each of its three vertices.

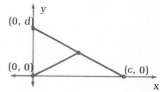

9-2 Circles

To find the center and radius of a circle from its equation.
To graph a circle, given its equation.
To write the equation of a circle in *h, k* form.

When you draw a circle with a compass, all points
are the same distance from the center.

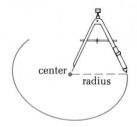

> A **circle** is the set of all points in a plane at a
> fixed distance from a point called the **center.**
> The fixed distance is called the **radius.**

The distance formula can be used to find the equation of a circle.

EXAMPLE 1   Find the equation of a circle with center
at the origin and radius 5.

A point $P(x, y)$ is on the circle with center $(0, 0)$ if and only if its distance from
the center is 5.

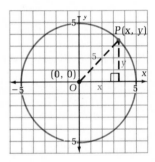

$$d = \sqrt{(x - 0)^2 + (y - 0)^2} = 5 \qquad \text{Use the distance formula.}$$
$$\sqrt{x^2 + y^2} = 5 \qquad \text{Simplify.}$$
$$x^2 + y^2 = 25 \qquad \text{Square each side.}$$

The equation of the circle is $x^2 + y^2 = 25$.

This table gives the coordinates of selected points on the circle, each
5 units from the center.

x	−5	−4	−3	0	3	4	5
y	0	±3	±4	±5	±4	±3	0

**The equation of a circle with center at the origin (0, 0) and
radius *r* is**

$$x^2 + y^2 = r^2$$

EXAMPLE 2   Find the center and radius of the circle with the equation
$x^2 + y^2 = \frac{1}{4}$.

The center is (0, 0) and the radius is $\sqrt{\frac{1}{4}} = \frac{1}{2}$.   Take the positive root.

EXAMPLE 3   Find the equation of a circle with center
(3, 2) and radius 4.

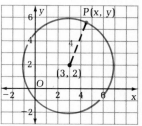

The distance from the center (3, 2) to any
point on the circle is 4. Substitute in the
distance formula to find the equation.

$\sqrt{(x_1 - x_2)^2 + (y_1 - y_2)^2} = d$ Use the distance formula.

$\sqrt{(x - 3)^2 + (y - 2)^2} = 4$ Substitute.

$(x - 3)^2 + (y - 2)^2 = 16$ Square each side to obtain the equation of the circle.

The equation of a circle with center at (h, k) and radius r is

$$(x - h)^2 + (y - k)^2 = r^2$$

A circle with the equation $(x - h)^2 + (y - k)^2 = r^2$ is congruent to
a circle with the equation $x^2 + y^2 = r^2$, if r has the same value in each
equation. The circle with center (h, k) can be obtained by translating
every point on $x^2 + y^2 = r^2$ a distance of h units horizontally and k
units vertically.

EXAMPLE 4   Find the center and radius of the circle with the equation
$(x - 3)^2 + (y + 2)^2 = 25$.

$(x - 3)^2 + [y - (-2)]^2 = 5^2$ Compare to $(x - h)^2 + (y - k)^2 = r^2$.

The center is (3, −2) and the radius is 5.

EXAMPLE 5   Find the equation of a circle with center (−2, 7) and *diameter* d = 12.

Let h = −2, k = 7, and r = $\frac{1}{2}$d = 6, and substitute in
$(x - h)^2 + (y - k)^2 = r^2$.

$[x - (-2)]^2 + (y - 7)^2 = 6^2$

$(x + 2)^2 + (y - 7)^2 = 36$

The equation is $(x + 2)^2 + (y - 7)^2 = 36$.

Sometimes the equation of a circle is not given in h, k form. In order to graph the circle, write the h, k form by completing the square in x, in y, or in both x and y.

EXAMPLE 6   Graph the circle with the equation $x^2 + y^2 + 4x - 10y - 52 = 0$.

Complete the square in x and y to get the equation in h, k form.

$$x^2 + y^2 + 4x - 10y - 52 = 0$$
$$(x^2 + 4x + 4) + (y^2 - 10y + 25) = 52 + (4 + 25)$$
$$(x + 2)^2 + (y - 5)^2 = 81$$

Find the coordinates of the center and find the radius from the equation.

Center: $(-2, 5) \longleftarrow (h, k)$

Radius: $9 \longleftarrow r = \sqrt{81}$

Then draw the graph.

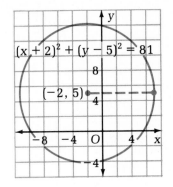

CLASS EXERCISES

Give the center and radius of each circle from its equation.

1. $x^2 + y^2 = 100$

2. $x^2 + y^2 = 0.25$

3. $x^2 + y^2 = \dfrac{4}{25}$

4. $x^2 + y^2 = 2\dfrac{3}{4}$

5. $(x - 2)^2 + (y - 8)^2 = 64$

6. $(x + 1)^2 + (y + 3)^2 = 0.01$

*Give the equation of the circle with the given center and radius **r**.*

7. $(0, 0), r = 4$

8. $(0, 0), r = 11$

9. $(0, -3), r = 6$

10. $(5, 0), r = 1$

11. $(-5, -6), r = 20$

12. $(2, -2), r = 1\dfrac{1}{2}$

EXERCISES

A   *Find the center and radius of each circle from its equation.*

1. $x^2 + y^2 = 49$

2. $x^2 + y^2 = 1$

3. $x^2 + y^2 = 0.09$

4. $x^2 + y^2 = 5$

5. $(x - 2)^2 + y^2 = 4$

6. $x^2 + (y + 1)^2 = 144$

7. $(x + 3)^2 + (y - 3)^2 = \dfrac{9}{49}$

8. $(x - 5)^2 + \left(y - \dfrac{1}{2}\right)^2 = 225$

Find the equation of the circle with the given center and radius or diameter.

9. $(0, 0)$, $r = 3$

10. $(0, 0)$, $r = 0.6$

11. $(-1, 2)$, $r = 6$

12. $(4, 0)$, $d = 8$

13. $(-3, -7)$, $r = \sqrt{3}$

14. $(2, -8)$, $d = 5$

B

Give the center and radius of the circle. Then graph the circle.

15. $x^2 + y^2 - 2y = 0$

16. $x^2 + 6x + y^2 = 0$

17. $x^2 + 4x + y^2 + 4y = 8$

18. $x^2 + y^2 + 10y = 144$

19. $x^2 - 8x + y^2 - 20y = -35$

20. $x^2 + y^2 + 16x + 2y + 1 = 0$

Explain why the equation does not have a circle as its graph.

21. $(x - 3)^2 + (y + 1)^2 = 0$

22. $(x + 2)^2 + (y - 5)^2 = -12$

23. $x^2 + 2x + y^2 + 1 = 0$

24. $x^2 + y^2 - 6y + 15 = 0$

Find the radius using the distance formula, and then find the equation of the circle

25. with center at $(5, -12)$ and passing through the origin.

26. with center at $(-6, 5)$ and passing through $(-2, 8)$.

27. Find the equations of two circles that have centers on the x-axis and radii 5, and that pass through the origin.

28. Find the equations of four circles with radii 12, each tangent to both the x- and y-axes.

C

29. Find the equation of a circle inscribed in square $ABCD$ with vertices $A(2, 2)$, $B(6, 2)$, $C(6, -2)$, and $D(2, -2)$.

30. Find the equation of a circle concentric to $(x - 2)^2 + (y - 1)^2 = 4$, but with a radius of twice the length.

31. Find the equations of four circles tangent to both of the lines $x = 3$ and $y = 4$, with radii 5.

32. Write the equation of the line tangent to the circle $x^2 + y^2 = 25$ at the point $(3, 4)$.
Hint: The slope of the tangent is the negative reciprocal of the slope of the radius to the point of tangency.

9-3 Parabolas

To find the vertex, axis of symmetry, focus, and directrix of a parabola
   from its equation.
To sketch a parabola, given its equation.
To write the equation of a parabola in h, k form.

_____

What is the set of all points the same distance from both the point
$F(0, 1)$ and line l, with the equation $y = -1$? We can examine several
such points to find out.

The distance between $P_1(-4, 4)$ and $F(0, 1)$ is 5.

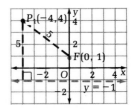

$$\sqrt{(-4 - 0)^2 + (4 - 1)^2} = \sqrt{(-4)^2 + 3^2}$$
$$= \sqrt{25}$$
$$= 5$$

The distance between $P_1(-4, 4)$ and $y = -1$
is also 5.

$$|4 - (-1)| = |5| = 5$$

Thus point P_1 is 5 units from point F and also 5 units from line l.
   We say point P_1 is *equidistant* from point F and line l. The following
list includes some other points equidistant from both point F and line l.

$P_1(-4, 4)$	5 units
$P_2(-2, 1)$	2 units
$P_3(0, 0)$	1 unit
$P_4(2, 1)$	2 units
$P_5(4, 4)$	5 units

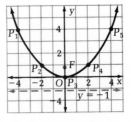

It appears that the set of all points equidistant from F and l is a parabola. The points do, in fact, satisfy the definition of a parabola.

> A **parabola** is the set of all points in a plane that are equi-
> distant from a fixed point, called the **focus,** and a fixed line,
> called the **directrix.**

EXAMPLE 1   Find the equation of the parabola whose points are equidistant from the focus $F(0, 1)$ and the directrix $y = -1$.

Let $P(x, y)$ be any point on the parabola. The distance between P and F is

$$d_1 = \sqrt{(x - 0)^2 + (y - 1)^2} = \sqrt{x^2 + (y - 1)^2}$$

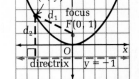

The distance between P and line l is

$$d_2 = |y - (-1)| = |y + 1|$$

Since point P is equidistant from point F and line l, set d_1 equal to d_2.

$$\sqrt{x^2 + (y - 1)^2} = |y + 1|$$
$$x^2 + (y - 1)^2 = |y + 1|^2 \qquad \text{Square each side.}$$
$$x^2 + y^2 - 2y + 1 = y^2 + 2y + 1 \qquad \text{Expand.}$$
$$x^2 = 4y$$
$$y = \frac{1}{4}x^2 \qquad \text{The equation, in the form } y = ax^2$$

The *vertex* of the parabola shown above is at the origin. It lies on the axis of symmetry, $x = 0$, midway between the focus $F(0, 1)$ and the directrix $y = -1$. The distance from the vertex to the focus and to the directrix is 1, which can be expressed in terms of the coefficient of the x^2 term as $1 = \dfrac{1}{4\left(\dfrac{1}{4}\right)} = \dfrac{1}{4a}$.

In general, $y = ax^2$ is the equation of a parabola that has its vertex at the origin. The distance from the vertex to the focus and to the directrix is $\left|\dfrac{1}{4a}\right|$. The parabola opens upward when $a > 0$ and downward when $a < 0$.

EXAMPLE 2   Graph the parabola $y = -2x^2$. Find the focus and the directrix.

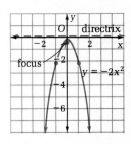

x	-2	-1	0	1	2
y	-8	-2	0	-2	-8

The equation is in the form $y = ax^2$, with $a = -2$.

Focus: $\left(0, -\dfrac{1}{8}\right) \longleftarrow \left(0, \dfrac{1}{4a}\right)$

Directrix: $y = \dfrac{1}{8} \longleftarrow y = -\dfrac{1}{4a}$

The coordinates of the vertex and focus can be found directly from the equation of a parabola when given in h, k form. The equations of the axis of symmetry and the directrix can also be found from this equation.

> **Parabola with Equation in the Standard Form $y = a(x - h)^2 + k$**
>
> Vertex: (h, k) Axis of symmetry: $x = h$
>
> Focus: $\left(h, k + \dfrac{1}{4a}\right)$ Directrix: $y = k - \dfrac{1}{4a}$
>
> The parabola opens upward if $a > 0$, and downward if $a < 0$.

EXAMPLE 3

The equation of a parabola is $y = -x^2 - 4x - 1$. Find the vertex, axis of symmetry, focus, and directrix. State whether the parabola opens upward or downward.

First write the equation in h, k form by completing the square.

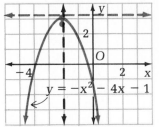

$$y = -x^2 - 4x - 1$$
$$= -(x^2 + 4x) - 1$$
$$= -(x^2 + 4x + \mathbf{4}) - 1 + \mathbf{4}$$
$$= -(x + 2)^2 + 3$$

Compare the resulting equation to $y = a(x - h)^2 + k$, where $h = -2$, $k = 3$, and $a = -1$.

Coordinates of vertex: $(-2, 3) \longleftarrow (h, k)$

Equation of axis of symmetry: $x = -2 \longleftarrow x = h$

Coordinates of focus: $\left(-2, 2\dfrac{3}{4}\right) \longleftarrow \left(h, k + \dfrac{1}{4a}\right)$

Equation of directrix: $y = 3\dfrac{1}{4} \longleftarrow y = k - \dfrac{1}{4a}$

The parabola opens downward. $\longleftarrow a < 0$

A parabola may have a horizontal, rather than vertical, axis. If the vertex is at (h, k) and the axis of symmetry is $y = k$, the parabola has the standard form $x = a(y - k)^2 + h$. It opens to the right if $a > 0$ and to the left if $a < 0$.

EXAMPLE 4

Sketch the parabola with the equation $x = 2(y - 1)^2$.

Make a brief table of values.

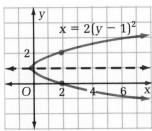

y	-1	0	1	2	3
x	8	2	0	2	8

The vertex is $(0, 1)$. $\longleftarrow (h, k)$
The axis of symmetry is $y = 1$. $\longleftarrow y = k$
The parabola opens to the right. $\longleftarrow a > 0$

Plot the points and sketch the curve.

CLASS EXERCISES

*Give the vertex and axis of symmetry of the parabola from its equation. State whether the parabola opens **upward, downward, left,** or **right.***

1. $y = 3x^2$

2. $y = -x^2$

3. $y = (x - 1)^2$

4. $y = (x + 5)^2 + 4$

5. $y = x^2 - 3$

6. $y = -(x - 1)^2$

7. $x = y^2$

8. $x = -\dfrac{1}{2}y^2$

9. $x = (y - 5)^2 + 2$

EXERCISES

A

*Find the vertex and axis of symmetry of the parabola from its equation. State whether the parabola opens **upward** or **downward.***

1. $y = 5x^2$

2. $y = -2x^2$

3. $y = (x + 2)^2$

4. $y = x^2 + 2$

5. $y = (x - 1)^2 + 3$

6. $y = (x + 3)^2 - 4$

7. $y = -(x + 1)^2 - 1$

8. $y = 2(x - 3)^2 + 4$

9. $y = -2(x + 3)^2 - 3$

Find the focus and directrix of the parabola.

10. $y = 4x^2$

11. $y = \dfrac{1}{4}x^2$

12. $y = \dfrac{1}{8}x^2$

13. $y = -12x^2$

14. $y = \dfrac{3}{4}x^2$

15. $y = \dfrac{1}{2}x^2$

16. $y = x^2 - 2$

17. $y = -(x + 1)^2$

18. $y = (x - 2)^2 + 6$

Complete the table of values for the given parabola. Then sketch the parabola.

19. $y = (x - 2)^2$

x	−1	0	1	2	3	4	5
y							

20. $y = -2x^2 + 1$

x	−3	−2	−1	0	1	2	3
y							

21. $y = (x - 1)^2 - 2$

x	−2	−1	0	1	2	3	4
y							

Sketch the parabola with the given equation.

22. $y = -3x^2$

23. $y = x^2 + 1$

24. $y = (x + 3)^2$

25. $y = 2x^2 + 1$

26. $y = -(x - 2)^2 - 1$

27. $y = (x + 4)^2 + 2$

B A parabola consists of all points that are equidistant from $(0, 6)$ and $y = 2$.

28. Find the focus of the parabola.   **29.** Find the directrix.

30. Find the vertex.   **31.** Find the axis of symmetry.

32. Find an equation of the parabola.   **33.** Sketch the parabola.

Find an equation for the set of all points equidistant from

34. the point F $(0, 2)$ and the line $y = -2$.

35. the point F $\left(0, -\frac{1}{3}\right)$ and the line $y = \frac{1}{3}$.

36. the point F $(2, 3)$ and the line $y = 1$.

Find the coordinates of the vertex and focus and the equations of the axis of symmetry and the directrix. Then sketch each parabola.

37. $y = x^2 + 6x + 9$ **38.** $y = x^2 - 2x + 1$ **39.** $y = -x^2 - 8x$

40. $y = x^2 + 4x + 5$ **41.** $y = x^2 + x$ **42.** $y = 6 + 2x + x^2$

43. $y = -2 + 3x - x^2$ **44.** $y = 2x^2 - 12x$ **45.** $y = -x^2 - x + 3$

Sketch each parabola.

46. $x = 4y^2 + 1$ **47.** $x = (y - 3)^2$ **48.** $x = y^2 - 4y + 1$

C **49.** Graph a parabola with the point $(0, 8)$ as focus and the x-axis as directrix.

50. Find the equation of a parabola with vertex $(0, 1)$ and focus $(0, -1)$.

51. Find the equation of a parabola with vertex $(0, -4)$ and focus $(0, -2)$.

Show by completing the square that the parabola $y = ax^2 + bx + c$

52. has $y = -\frac{b}{2a}$ as its axis of symmetry.

53. has $\left(-\frac{b}{2a}, \frac{4ac - b^2}{4a}\right)$ as its vertex.

The **latus rectum** of a parabola is a segment through the focus, parallel to the directrix. Its endpoints are on the parabola. Find the length of the latus rectum of each parabola.

*54. $y = 4x^2$ ***55.** $y = x^2 + 2x + 1$

*56. The focus of a parabola is at F $\left(0, \frac{1}{4a}\right)$ and the directrix is $y = -\frac{1}{4a}$. Show that the equation of the parabola is $y = ax^2$.

9-4 Ellipses

OBJECTIVES

To sketch an ellipse centered at the origin.
To find the foci, vertices, and axes of such an ellipse.
To write the equation of an ellipse.

Tie a piece of string into a loop and put the loop around two thumbtacks. Then pull the string taut with a pencil and move the pencil around, drawing the curve shown here.

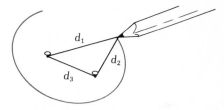

In the figure above, the distance d_3 between the two thumbtack points is fixed. But so is the entire length of the loop of string, $d_1 + d_2 + d_3$. It follows that while the lengths d_1 and d_2 change, their sum is constant. The curve that is traced is called an *ellipse*.

> An **ellipse** is the set of all points in a plane such that the sum of the distances from each point to two fixed points, called the **foci,** is constant.

EXAMPLE 1

Point $P(x, y)$ moves such that the sum of its distances from the two fixed points $F_1 (-3, 0)$ and $F_2 (3, 0)$ is always 10. Find the equation of the resulting ellipse.

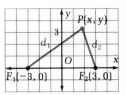

Use the distance formula to find d_1 and d_2.

$$d_1 = \sqrt{(x + 3)^2 + (y - 0)^2} \qquad d_2 = \sqrt{(x - 3)^2 + (y - 0)^2}$$

Then $d_1 + d_2 = 10$

$$d_1 = 10 - d_2$$

$$\sqrt{(x + 3)^2 + y^2} = 10 - \sqrt{(x - 3)^2 + y^2}$$

$(x + 3)^2 + y^2 = 100 - 20\sqrt{(x - 3)^2 + y^2} + (x - 3)^2 + y^2$ Square each side.

$3x - 25 = -5\sqrt{(x - 3)^2 + y^2}$ Simplify.

$9x^2 - 150x + 625 = 25[(x - 3)^2 + y^2]$ Square each side again.

$16x^2 + 25y^2 = 400$ Simplify.

$$\frac{x^2}{25} + \frac{y^2}{16} = 1$$ Divide each side by 400.

The equation of the ellipse is $\frac{x^2}{25} + \frac{y^2}{16} = 1$.

EXAMPLE 2   Sketch the ellipse $\frac{x^2}{25} + \frac{y^2}{16} = 1$.

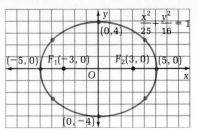

Let $y = 0$. The x-intercepts are at (5, 0) and (−5, 0).

Let $x = 0$. The y-intercepts are at (0, 4) and (0, −4).

These and other coordinate values are shown in this table.

x	−5	−4	0	4	5
y	0	$\pm\frac{12}{5}$	±4	$\pm\frac{12}{5}$	0

Plot these points and connect them with a smooth curve.

The longer axis of an ellipse is the **major axis.** The shorter axis is the **minor axis.** The two axes intersect at their common midpoint, the **center** of the ellipse. In the ellipse $\frac{x^2}{25} + \frac{y^2}{16} = 1$, the length of the major axis is 10 and the length of the minor axis is 8. The center is at (0, 0).

The *standard form* of an ellipse with center at the origin is

$$\frac{x^2}{a^2} + \frac{y^2}{b^2} = 1$$

The x-intercepts are at $(a, 0)$ and $(−a, 0)$, and the y-intercepts are at $(0, b)$ and $(0, −b)$. The foci lie equidistant from the center of the ellipse on the major axis. If the major axis is horizontal, then $a > b$. If the major axis is vertical, then $a < b$. The segment from the origin to the intercept on the major axis is called the **semi-major axis.** For an ellipse with horizontal major axis, a is the length of the semi-major axis, and b is the length of the **semi-minor axis.** All ellipses are symmetric about both their major and minor axes.

Suppose $\frac{x^2}{a^2} + \frac{y^2}{b^2} = 1$ is the equation of an ellipse. If the major axis is horizontal, the points at $(c, 0)$ and $(−c, 0)$ are the foci, and it can be shown that $c^2 = a^2 − b^2$.

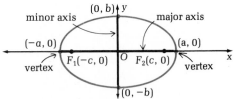

If the major axis is vertical, the points at $(0, c)$ and $(0, −c)$ are the foci, and $c^2 = b^2 − a^2$.

The points of intersection of an ellipse with its major axis are the **vertices** of the ellipse.

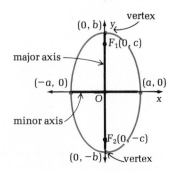

EXAMPLE 3

Sketch the ellipse with the equation $25x^2 + 9y^2 = 225$. Locate and label the foci.

Write the equation in standard form.

$25x^2 + 9y^2 = 225$

$\dfrac{x^2}{9} + \dfrac{y^2}{25} = 1$ Divide each side by 225.

$\dfrac{x^2}{3^2} + \dfrac{y^2}{5^2} = 1$ $a = 3$, $b = 5$

The ellipse with this equation is centered at the origin.

The x-intercepts are at $(3, 0)$ and $(-3, 0)$, and the y-intercepts are at $(0, 5)$ and $(0, -5)$. The major axis is vertical, since $a < b$. Therefore, use $c^2 = b^2 - a^2$ to find c.

$c^2 = b^2 - a^2$

$c^2 = 5^2 - 3^2$

$c^2 = 16$

$c = 4$

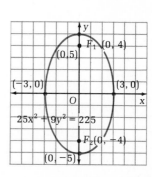

The foci are at $(0, 4)$ and $(0, -4)$. Plot the x- and y-intercepts and sketch the ellipse.

CLASS EXERCISES

Find the length of the

1. semi-major axis.   **2.** semi-minor axis.

Find the coordinates of the

3. center.   **4.** foci.

5. Give the equation of the ellipse in standard form.

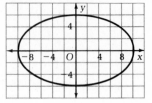

An ellipse has the equation $\dfrac{x^2}{225} + \dfrac{y^2}{625} = 1$. *Find the length of*

6. the major axis.   **7.** the minor axis.   **8.** the segment connecting the foci.

EXERCISES

A

Find the coordinates of the

1. y-intercepts.   **2.** x-intercepts.

Find the length of the

3. semi-major axis.   **4.** semi-minor axis.

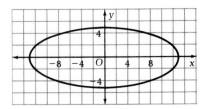

Find the coordinates of the

5. center.   **6.** foci.

7. Write the equation of the ellipse in standard form.

Sketch the ellipses with the given equations. Locate and label the foci.

8. $\dfrac{x^2}{16} + \dfrac{y^2}{25} = 1$ **9.** $\dfrac{x^2}{25} + \dfrac{y^2}{9} = 1$ **10.** $\dfrac{x^2}{100} + \dfrac{y^2}{64} = 1$

11. $\dfrac{x^2}{169} + \dfrac{y^2}{144} = 1$ **12.** $\dfrac{x^2}{4} + \dfrac{y^2}{16} = 1$ **13.** $\dfrac{x^2}{81} + \dfrac{y^2}{36} = 1$

14. $4x^2 + 49y^2 = 196$ **15.** $25x^2 + 9y^2 = 225$ **16.** $x^2 + 4y^2 = 4$

B

Write an equation for each ellipse.

17. Foci on the x-axis, semi-major axis 6, semi-minor axis 2, center at (0, 0)

18. Foci on the y-axis, major axis 10, minor axis 8, center at (0, 0)

19. x-intercepts at (4, 0) and (−4, 0), y-intercepts at (0, 2) and (0, −2)

20. x-intercepts at (2, 0) and (−2, 0), y-intercepts at (0, 6) and (0, −6)

21. Foci at $(0, 3)$ and $(0, -3)$, x-intercepts at $(4, 0)$ and $(-4, 0)$

    Hint: From the given information, $a = 4$ and $c = 3$. Since the major axis is vertical, substitute in $c^2 = b^2 - a^2$ and solve for b.

22. Foci at $(6, 0)$ and $(-6, 0)$, x-intercepts at $(10, 0)$ and $(-10, 0)$

23. Foci at $(5, 0)$ and $(-5, 0)$, x-intercepts at $(6, 0)$ and $(-6, 0)$

24. Foci at $(0, 8)$ and $(0, -8)$, semi-major axis 10

25. Foci at $(2, 0)$ and $(-2, 0)$, minor axis 4

26. Write the equations of two ellipses with centers at the origin and semi-major and semi-minor axes of 12 and 3, respectively.

27. Write the equations of two ellipses, each with intercepts at $(0, 7)$ and $(0, -7)$ and each with their foci 10 units apart.

C

Find an equation for the set of points such that the sum of the distances from each point to

28. $(4, 0)$ and $(-4, 0)$ is 10.

29. $(0, 4)$ and $(0, -4)$ is 10.

Find an equation for the ellipse with foci at $(7, 0)$ and $(-7, 0)$ that contains

30. the point $(0, 2)$.

31. the point $(-10, 0)$

The ellipse $\dfrac{x^2}{a^2} + \dfrac{y^2}{b^2} = 1$ contains the points $P(a, 0)$ and $Q(0, b)$.

*32. If $a > b$, the foci are on the x-axis at $F_1(-c, 0)$ and $F_2(c, 0)$. Show that $c^2 = a^2 - b^2$.

    Hint: Find $PF_1 + PF_2$ and $QF_1 + QF_2$ and set them equal to each other.

*33. If $a < b$, the foci are on the y-axis at $F_1(0, c)$ and $F_2(0, -c)$. Show that $c^2 = b^2 - a^2$.

Not every ellipse has its center at the origin. The equation $\dfrac{(x - h)^2}{a^2} + \dfrac{(y - k)^2}{b^2} = 1$ describes an ellipse with center at (h, k). Graph the ellipse for each equation.

34. $\dfrac{x^2}{25} + \dfrac{(y + 2)^2}{16} = 1$

x	−5	−4	−3	0	3	4	5
y							

35. $\dfrac{(x - 2)^2}{25} + \dfrac{(y + 1)^2}{16} = 1$

x	−3	−2	−1	2	5	6	7
y							

*36. $4x^2 + 8x + y^2 - 8y + 4 = 0$

    Hint: Write the equation in h, k form.

CHALLENGE

Astronomy

Long before the beginning of recorded history, people studied the heavens, watching the motion of the planets and stars. Indeed, astronomy is one of the oldest of all sciences. Students who plan careers in astronomy or related fields should study as much mathematics as possible in high school. Mathematics is needed to describe the motion of the planets and stars and to theorize on the design of the universe itself.

The German mathematician Johannes Kepler (1571–1630) used mathematics when he discovered these two famous laws of planetary motion.

Each planet moves in an ellipse, with the sun at one of its foci.

The segment between each planet and the sun sweeps out equal areas in equal intervals of time.

Both the area of an ellipse and its circumference can be expressed in terms of its semi-major and semi-minor axes.

Area of ellipse: $A = \pi ab$ Circumference of ellipse: $C = 2\pi\sqrt{\dfrac{a^2 + b^2}{2}}$

1. The circle may be considered a special case of an ellipse in which $a = b$. Show that the formulas for the area and circumference of an ellipse are transformed into the familiar formulas for the area and circumference of a circle when you let $a = b$.

2. Find the area and circumference of the ellipse $\dfrac{x^2}{25} + \dfrac{y^2}{16} = 1$. Leave your answers in terms of π.

3. Assume that the earth is nearest the sun at 90 million miles and farthest from the sun at 96 million miles. Use a calculator to find the length of the semi-major and semi-minor axes of its elliptical orbit. Calculate the length of the semi-minor axis to the nearest ten thousand miles. Then compute the area enclosed by the orbit. Compare your answer to the area found, assuming a circular orbit with a radius of 93 million miles.

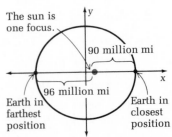

The sun is one focus.

90 million mi

96 million mi

Earth in farthest position

Earth in closest position

9-5 Hyperbolas

OBJECTIVES

To find the foci, vertices, and asymptotes, given the equation of a hyperbola centered at the origin.

To sketch a hyperbola, given its equation.

To write the equation of a hyperbola.

A **hyperbola** is the set of all points in a plane such that the difference of the distances from each point to two fixed points, called the **foci,** is constant.

EXAMPLE 1

Point P (x, y) moves such that the difference of its distances from F_1 $(-5, 0)$ and F_2 $(5, 0)$ is always 8. Find the equation of the resulting hyperbola.

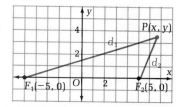

Use the distance formula to find d_1 and d_2.

$$d_1 = \sqrt{(x + 5)^2 + (y - 0)^2} \qquad d_2 = \sqrt{(x - 5)^2 + (y - 0)^2}$$

Set the difference of these distances from the foci equal to 8. Then simplify the resulting equation. We show here the case where $d_1 > d_2$. The same final equation is obtained if $d_2 > d_1$.

$$d_1 - d_2 = 8$$

$$d_1 = 8 + d_2$$

$$\sqrt{(x + 5)^2 + y^2} = 8 + \sqrt{(x - 5)^2 + y^2}$$

$$(x + 5)^2 + y^2 = 64 + 16\sqrt{(x - 5)^2 + y^2} + (x - 5)^2 + y^2 \quad \text{Square each side.}$$

$$5x - 16 = 4\sqrt{(x - 5)^2 + y^2} \quad \text{Simplify.}$$

$$25x^2 - 160x + 256 = 16[(x - 5)^2 + y^2] \quad \text{Square each side again.}$$

$$9x^2 - 16y^2 = 144 \qquad \text{Simplify.}$$

$$\frac{x^2}{16} - \frac{y^2}{9} = 1 \qquad \text{Divide each side by 144.}$$

A hyperbola has two branches that curve around the foci and extend outward in opposite directions. The branches approach, but never meet, two intersecting lines called **asymptotes.** The asymptotes are very helpful in sketching hyperbolas.

CONIC SECTIONS

337

EXAMPLE 2   Sketch the hyperbola $\frac{x^2}{16} - \frac{y^2}{9} = 1$.

Step 1   *Find the intercepts.* Let $y = 0$ and solve for x. The x-intercepts are at $(4, 0)$ and $(-4, 0)$, which are called the **vertices** of the hyperbola. There are no y-intercepts.

Step 2   *Locate the asymptotes* by drawing the rectangle shown.

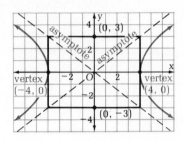

$$\frac{x^2}{16} - \frac{y^2}{9} = 1$$

The square roots of 16 and 9 are ± 4 and ± 3. These values are used to locate the midpoints of the sides of the rectangle.

Extend the diagonals of the rectangle to form the asymptotes. Their equations are $y = \frac{3}{4}x$ and $y = -\frac{3}{4}x$.

Step 3   *Draw the two branches of the hyperbola* through the vertices so that they approach the asymptotes. For more accuracy, use the equation to locate additional points on the hyperbola. Values are given here to the nearest hundredth.

x	−6	−5	−4	4	5	6
y	±3.35	±2.25	0	0	±2.25	±3.35

There are no points on the curve for x-values between −4 and 4.

Note that the two branches of the hyperbola open to the left and right and are symmetric about the y-axis.

There are also hyperbolas centered at the origin with branches that open vertically. The features of both types are given in this table.

Hyperbolas with Equations in Standard Form

$$\frac{x^2}{a^2} - \frac{y^2}{b^2} = 1 \qquad\qquad \frac{y^2}{a^2} - \frac{x^2}{b^2} = 1$$

Center:	**(0, 0)**	**(0, 0)**
Vertices:	$(a, 0)$ and $(-a, 0)$	$(0, a)$ and $(0, -a)$
Foci:	$(c, 0)$ and $(-c, 0)$	$(0, c)$ and $(0, -c)$
	$c^2 = a^2 + b^2$	$c^2 = a^2 + b^2$
Asymptotes:	$y = \pm\dfrac{b}{a}x$	$y = \pm\dfrac{a}{b}x$

Opens right and left with vertices and foci on the x-axis.   **Opens up and down with vertices and foci on the y-axis.**

EXAMPLE 3   Sketch the hyperbola $9y^2 - 16x^2 = 576$. Locate and label the foci and give the equations of the asymptotes.

Write the equation in standard form.

$$9y^2 - 16x^2 = 576$$

$$\frac{y^2}{64} - \frac{x^2}{36} = 1 \qquad \text{Divide each side by 576.}$$

$$\frac{y^2}{8^2} - \frac{x^2}{6^2} = 1 \qquad a = 8, \ b = 6$$

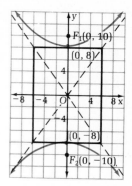

Then find the value of c.

$$c^2 = a^2 + b^2$$

$$c^2 = 64 + 36$$

$$c^2 = 100$$

$$c = 10$$

The vertices are on the y-axis at $(0, 8)$ and $(0, -8)$. The foci are on the y-axis at $(0, 10)$ and $(0, -10)$. Draw the rectangle and extend its diagonals to locate the asymptotes. Their equations are $y = \pm\frac{4}{3}x$. Then sketch the curve. Note that the two branches open up and down and are symmetric about the x-axis.

Thus far we have considered hyperbolas that open vertically or horizontally. There are other hyperbolas of special importance. These are **rectangular hyperbolas** that have the x- and y-axes as asymptotes. Their equations are of the form $xy = c$. More advanced methods can be used to show that graphs of such equations satisfy the definition of a hyperbola.

EXAMPLE 4   Graph the rectangular hyperbola $xy = 1$.

Make a table of values and plot the points. Then draw the two branches of the hyperbola through the points, asymptotic to the axes.

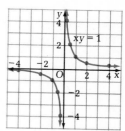

x	-4	-2	-1	$-\frac{1}{2}$	$-\frac{1}{4}$	$\frac{1}{4}$	$\frac{1}{2}$	1	2	4
y	$-\frac{1}{4}$	$-\frac{1}{2}$	-1	-2	-4	4	2	1	$\frac{1}{2}$	$\frac{1}{4}$

In the last example, notice the inverse relationship between x and y in the first quadrant. As x gets very large, y approaches 0. As x approaches 0, y gets very large.

CLASS EXERCISES

A hyperbola has the equation $\frac{y^2}{16} - \frac{x^2}{4} = 1$.

1. Find the coordinates of the vertices.   **2.** Find the coordinates of the foci.

3. Find the equations of the asymptotes.   **4.** Sketch the hyperbola.

EXERCISES

A   State whether the vertices of the hyperbola are on the **x**-axis or on the **y**-axis. Then find the coordinates of the vertices.

1. $\dfrac{x^2}{36} - \dfrac{y^2}{9} = 1$

2. $\dfrac{y^2}{36} - \dfrac{x^2}{9} = 1$

3. $\dfrac{x^2}{9} - \dfrac{y^2}{36} = 1$

4. $\dfrac{y^2}{9} - \dfrac{x^2}{36} = 1$

5. $x^2 - 9y^2 = 36$

6. $y^2 - 9x^2 = 36$

Find the coordinates of the foci of the hyperbola.

7. $\dfrac{x^2}{9} - \dfrac{y^2}{16} = 1$

8. $\dfrac{y^2}{9} - \dfrac{x^2}{16} = 1$

9. $\dfrac{x^2}{16} - \dfrac{y^2}{9} = 1$

Find the equations of the asymptotes.

10. $\dfrac{x^2}{25} - \dfrac{y^2}{4} = 1$

11. $\dfrac{y^2}{25} - \dfrac{x^2}{4} = 1$

12. $\dfrac{x^2}{36} - \dfrac{y^2}{81} = 1$

Locate the vertices and foci. Then draw the asymptotes and sketch the hyperbola.

13. $\dfrac{x^2}{9} - \dfrac{y^2}{16} = 1$

14. $\dfrac{x^2}{64} - \dfrac{y^2}{225} = 1$

15. $\dfrac{y^2}{144} - \dfrac{x^2}{25} = 1$

16. $\dfrac{y^2}{36} - \dfrac{x^2}{64} = 1$

17. $\dfrac{y^2}{9} - \dfrac{x^2}{4} = 1$

18. $x^2 - y^2 = 1$

B   Find an equation of the hyperbola that has its center at the origin and satisfies the given conditions.

19. Vertex (6, 0), focus (10, 0)

20. Vertex (−5, 0), focus (−13, 0)

21. Vertex (0, 3), focus (0, 4)

22. Vertex (−1, 0), focus (−2, 0)

23. The difference of the distances from each point on the hyperbola to (5, 0) and to (−5, 0) is always 6.

24. The difference of the distances from each point on the hyperbola to (0, 8) and to (0, −8) is always 8.

Sketch the hyperbola. Locate and label the foci in Exercises 25–28.

25. $9y^2 - 4x^2 = 16$

26. $x^2 - 4y^2 = 4$

27. $16y^2 - 9x^2 = 25$

28. $x^2 - y^2 = 100$ **29.** $xy = 2$ **30.** $xy = -5$

C *Find the equations of the two asymptotes of the hyperbola.*

31. $x^2 - y^2 = 49$ **32.** $x^2 - 4y^2 = 25$ **33.** $2y^2 - 3x^2 = 6$

Find the equations of two hyperbolas with

34. asymptotes $y = \pm x$ and a distance of 2 units between vertices.

35. asymptotes $y = \pm\frac{3}{4}x$ and a distance of 10 units between foci.

36. asymptotes $y = \pm\frac{5}{12}x$ and foci each 39 units from the center.

37. Find the equation of a hyperbola, with center at (0, 0) and one vertex at (2, 0), that passes through the point (4, 3).

The equation $\frac{x^2}{a^2} - \frac{y^2}{b^2} = 1$ describes a hyperbola with center at the origin and vertices on the **x**-axis. The equation $\frac{(x - h)^2}{a^2} - \frac{(y - k)^2}{b^2} = 1$ describes a hyperbola with center at (**h, k**) and vertices on a line parallel to the **x**-axis. For each hyperbola, find its center and vertices.

38. $\dfrac{(x - 2)^2}{9} - \dfrac{(y + 3)^2}{16} = 1$ **39.** $\dfrac{(x + 6)^2}{144} - \dfrac{(y - 5)^2}{25} = 1$

*Find the equation of each hyperbola with vertices on a line parallel to the **x**-axis. Then graph the hyperbola.*

40. Center (3, 4), $a = 2$, $b = 4$ **41.** Center $(-2, 1)$, $a = 3$, $b = 1$

CHECKPOINT

Find the distance between the two points. Then find the coordinates of the midpoint of the segment joining the points.

1. (5, 4) and (1, 7)   **2.** $(-4, 6)$ and $(-6, 8)$ **3.** $(-2, -7)$ and $(-3, -9)$

Find the center and radius of each circle from its equation. Graph the circle.

4. $x^2 + y^2 = 81$ **5.** $(x + 1)^2 + (y - 1)^2 = 49$

For each parabola, find the coordinates of the vertex and the focus and the equations of the axis of symmetry and the directrix. Then graph the parabola.

6. $y = 2x^2$ **7.** $y = -(x + 2)^2 + 3$ **8.** $y = x^2 - 4x + 1$

9. Graph the ellipse with the equation $x^2 + \dfrac{y^2}{16} = 1$.

10. Graph the hyperbola with the equation $4x^2 - 9y^2 = 36$.

9-6 Classifying Conic Sections

OBJECTIVE

To classify an equation in the form $Ax^2 + Bxy + Cy^2 + Dx + Ey + F = 0$ as that of a circle, ellipse, parabola, or hyperbola.

A circle, ellipse, parabola, and hyperbola can be formed by cutting a hollow double cone as shown below. The curves were explored this way by the ancient Greeks and, to this day, are called the **conic sections.**

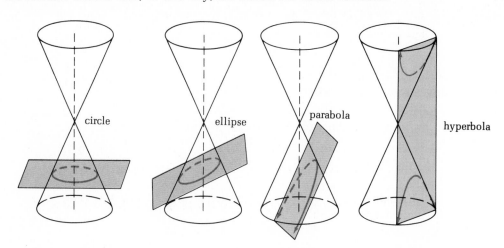

circle   ellipse   parabola   hyperbola

It was not until the invention of coordinate geometry in the seventeenth century that the algebra and geometry of the conic sections were brought together. Every conic section can be expressed by the general second degree equation

$$Ax^2 + Bxy + Cy^2 + Dx + Ey + F = 0$$

where A, B, and C are not all 0. To classify an equation given in this form, rewrite the equation in one of the standard forms you have just learned. It is often necessary to complete the square in order to do this.

EXAMPLE 1   Classify $y = x^2 - 4x + 1$ as the equation of a circle, ellipse, parabola, or hyperbola by writing it in standard form.

$y = x^2 - 4x + 1$
$y = (x^2 - 4x + \mathbf{4}) + 1 - \mathbf{4}$ Complete the square in x.
$y = (x - 2)^2 - 3$

This is the standard form of the equation of a parabola, $y = a(x - h)^2 + k$, where $a = 1$, $h = 2$, and $k = -3$. The vertex of the parabola is at $(2, -3)$.

EXAMPLE 2   Classify the conic with the equation $x^2 + y^2 - 6y - 40 = 0$.

$$x^2 + y^2 - 6y - 40 = 0$$
$$x^2 + (y^2 - 6y + 9) - 40 - 9 = 0 \qquad \text{Complete the square in } y.$$
$$x^2 + (y - 3)^2 = 49$$

This is the standard form of the equation of a circle, $(x - h)^2 + (y - k)^2 = r^2$, where $h = 0$, $k = 3$, and $r = 7$. The center of the circle is at $(0, 3)$.

This table summarizes the standard forms of the equations of conic sections centered at $(0, 0)$ or at some other point (h, k).

Conic	Location	Equation	
Circle	Center at $(0, 0)$	$x^2 + y^2 = r^2$	
	Center at (h, k)	$(x - h)^2 + (y - k)^2 = r^2$	
Ellipse	Center at $(0, 0)$	$\dfrac{x^2}{a^2} + \dfrac{y^2}{b^2} = 1$	
	Center at (h, k)	$\dfrac{(x - h)^2}{a^2} + \dfrac{(y - k)^2}{b^2} = 1$	
Parabola	Vertex at $(0, 0)$	$y = ax^2$	$x = ay^2$
	Vertex at (h, k)	$y = a(x - h)^2 + k$	$x = a(y - k)^2 + h$
Hyperbola	Center at $(0, 0)$	$\dfrac{x^2}{a^2} - \dfrac{y^2}{b^2} = 1$	$\dfrac{y^2}{a^2} - \dfrac{x^2}{b^2} = 1$
	Center at (h, k)	$\dfrac{(x - h)^2}{a^2} - \dfrac{(y - k)^2}{b^2} = 1$	$\dfrac{(y - k)^2}{a^2} - \dfrac{(x - h)^2}{b^2} = 1$

EXAMPLE 3   Classify and graph the conic with the equation $x^2 - 4y^2 - 6x = 7$.

$$x^2 - 4y^2 - 6x = 7$$
$$(x^2 - 6x + 9) - 4y^2 = 7 + 9 \qquad \text{Complete the square in } x.$$
$$\frac{(x - 3)^2}{16} - \frac{4y^2}{16} = 1 \qquad \text{Divide each side by 16.}$$
$$\frac{(x - 3)^2}{4^2} - \frac{y^2}{2^2} = 1$$

The conic is a hyperbola with center at $(3, 0)$ and vertices at $(-1, 0)$ and $(7, 0)$.

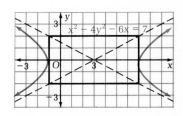

CLASS EXERCISES

*Classify the equation as that of a **circle**, **ellipse**, **parabola**, or **hyperbola**.*

1. $y^2 + x^2 = 1$

2. $y = \dfrac{3}{x}$

3. $y = 2(x - 1)^2 + 3$

4. $\dfrac{x^2}{9} - \dfrac{y^2}{25} = 1$

5. $\dfrac{(x - 4)^2}{4} + y^2 = 1$

6. $(x + 2)^2 + (y - 1)^2 = 16$

7. $3x^2 + 3y^2 = 12$

8. $x + 2y^2 = 3$

9. $x^2 + 2x + y^2 - 6y = 15$

EXERCISES

A

*Classify the equation as that of a **circle**, **ellipse**, **parabola**, or **hyperbola**.*

1. $(x - 2)^2 + (y + 5)^2 = 9$

2. $y = 2(x + 4)^2$

3. $y - 2 = 3(x - 1)^2$

4. $x = \dfrac{2}{3y}$

5. $\dfrac{(x - 3)^2}{25} - \dfrac{(y + 2)^2}{16} = 1$

6. $\dfrac{(x - 1)^2}{64} + \dfrac{(y - 2)^2}{49} = 1$

7. $(x - 1)^2 + (y + 4)^2 = 16$

8. $9x^2 + 4y^2 = 36$

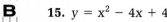

Classify and graph the conic with the given equation.

9. $(x + 2)^2 + y^2 = 4$

10. $y + 2 = (x + 4)^2$

11. $\dfrac{(x + 2)^2}{9} + \dfrac{y^2}{4} = 1$

12. $\dfrac{(x + 1)^2}{4} - \dfrac{y^2}{9} = 1$

13. $\dfrac{(x - 1)^2}{4} + \dfrac{(y + 2)^2}{16} = 1$

14. $\dfrac{(x - 3)^2}{16} - \dfrac{(y - 1)^2}{25} = 1$

B

15. $y = x^2 - 4x + 4$

16. $x^2 + y^2 + 2y + 1 = 9$

17. $x^2 - y^2 + 4y - 8 = 0$

18. $x = y^2 - 6y + 4$

19. $x^2 - 4x + 4y^2 - 16y + 4 = 0$

20. $y^2 - 8y + x^2 + 2x = 8$

21. $x^2 - 12x - y + 30 = 0$

22. $-25x^2 + 4y^2 - 50x - 16y - 109 = 0$

C

Consider the equation $Ax^2 + By^2 = 1$. Give the conditions, if they exist, on the coefficients A and B such that the resulting conic section is

23. a circle.　　24. an ellipse.　　25. a hyperbola.　　26. a parabola.

Assume that the equation $Ax^2 + By^2 + Cx + Dy + E = 0$ is the equation of a conic section. Identify the conic under each of the following conditions.

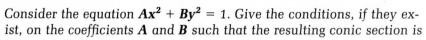

27. $A = B, A \neq 0, B \neq 0$

28. $B = 0, A \neq 0$

29. $A > 0, B < 0$

30. $A < 0, B > 0$

31. $A > 0, B > 0, A \neq B$

32. $A < 0, A = B$

How good are you at visualizing figures? In particular, can you visualize the intersections of planes and three-dimensional figures? This skill can be very useful in solving problems.

You have just learned that every time a plane cuts a cone, the intersection is a conic section. An ellipse is shown in this figure. Cutting the cone at a different angle can form a circle, a parabola, or one branch of a hyperbola.

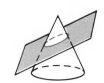

Any way you cut a sphere with a plane, the intersection is a circle. If the plane just touches the sphere at a single point, the intersection can be thought of as a circle with radius 0.

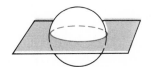

Cutting a cube with a plane is another matter entirely. In the figure shown, the intersection is a triangle. The plane cuts three edges at the points shown, forming the vertices of the triangle. The plane also cuts three faces of the cube, forming the sides of the triangle.

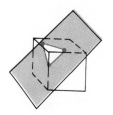

Imagine a plane cutting the cube through the three points shown. Visualize which edges and faces are cut. Then copy the figure, draw the intersection, and name the shape of that intersection. Each marked point is the midpoint of an edge.

1. **2.** **3.** **4.**

The figure at the right is a regular tetrahedron. It has four faces, all congruent triangles. Show how it can be cut by a plane to form

5. a triangle.   **6.** a square.

Sketch a pyramid with a square base and four congruent equilateral triangles as sides. Show how it can be cut by a plane to form

7. a triangle.   **8.** a square.   **9.** a trapezoid.   **10.** a pentagon.

9-7 Linear-Quadratic Systems

OBJECTIVES

To find the points of intersection of the graphs of a linear and a quadratic equation.

To solve linear-quadratic systems by substitution.

Each figure below shows the intersection of the graphs of a linear and a quadratic equation. The solution to each system can be read from its graph.

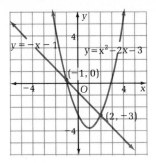

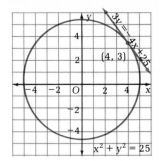

It appears that $(-1, 0)$ and $(2, -3)$ are points of intersection of the graphs of $y = -x - 1$ and $y = x^2 - 2x - 3$. Substitute these values in the equations to show that they are solutions to the system.

It appears that $(4, 3)$ is the only point of intersection of the graphs of $3y = -4x + 25$ and $x^2 + y^2 = 25$. Substitute in the equations to show that this ordered pair is a solution to the system.

Any linear-quadratic system has two, one, or no real solutions. It is usually not efficient to try to solve such systems by graphing. Algebraic methods based on substitution give exact solutions.

EXAMPLE 1

Solve the system: $\begin{aligned} x - 2y &= -4 \\ x^2 + 4y^2 &= 16 \end{aligned}$

$x - 2y = -4$

$\qquad x = 2y - 4$ Solve the linear equation for x in terms of y.

$x^2 + 4y^2 = 16$

$(2y - 4)^2 + 4y^2 = 16$ Substitute for x in the quadratic equation.

$4y^2 - 16y + 16 + 4y^2 = 16$

$y^2 - 2y = 0$

$y(y - 2) = 0$

$y = 0 \qquad \text{or} \qquad y = 2$ Solve for y.

$x = 2(0) - 4 = -4 \qquad x = 2(2) - 4 = 0$ Substitute in the linear equation and solve for x.

Check the ordered pairs $(-4, 0)$ and $(0, 2)$ in both equations.

$$x - 2y = -4 \qquad\qquad x^2 + 4y^2 = 16$$
$$-4 - 2(0) = -4 - 0 = -4 \; ✔ \qquad (-4)^2 + 4(0)^2 = 16 + 0 = 16 \; ✔$$
$$0 - 2(2) = 0 - 4 = -4 \; ✔ \qquad (0)^2 + 4(2)^2 = 0 + 4(4) = 16 \; ✔$$

The solutions are $(-4, 0)$ and $(0, 2)$, the coordinates of the two points of intersection of the line and the ellipse in the given system.

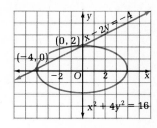

EXAMPLE 2

Solve the system: $\begin{array}{l} 3y^2 - 4x^2 = 8 \\ 2x + 3y = 4 \end{array}$

$2x + 3y = 4$

$\qquad x = -\dfrac{3}{2}y + 2$ \qquad\qquad Solve the linear equation for x.

$\qquad\qquad 3y^2 - 4x^2 = 8$

$\qquad 3y^2 - 4\left(-\dfrac{3}{2}y + 2\right)^2 = 8$ \qquad Substitute for x in the quadratic equation.

$3y^2 - 4\left(\dfrac{9}{4}y^2 - 6y + 4\right) = 8$

$\qquad\qquad -6y^2 + 24y - 24 = 0$

$\qquad\qquad\qquad y^2 - 4y + 4 = 0$

$\qquad\qquad\qquad\quad (y - 2)^2 = 0$

$\qquad\qquad\qquad\qquad\quad y = 2$ \qquad Solve for y.

$x = -\dfrac{3}{2}(2) + 2 = -1$ \qquad\qquad Substitute in the linear equation
\qquad\qquad\qquad\qquad\qquad\qquad\qquad and solve for x.

Check the ordered pair $(-1, 2)$ in both equations. The solution is $(-1, 2)$, the single point of intersection of the line and the hyperbola.

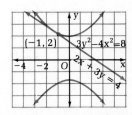

In Example 2, we could have solved the linear equation for y in terms of x and then substituted for y in the quadratic equation. However, the resulting equation is somewhat more difficult to solve than the one used above. When solving a system of equations, it is often worthwhile to do some preliminary investigation to find the method that will prove to be easiest.

In Example 2 the solution was a pair of real numbers, called a *real solution*. When a system has no real solutions, the graphs of the equations do not intersect.

EXAMPLE 3 Find the points of intersection, if any, of the line $x + y = 3$ and the ellipse $4x^2 + y^2 = 1$.

$x + y = 3$

$\qquad y = 3 - x$ Solve the linear equation for y.

$\qquad 4x^2 + y^2 = 1$

$4x^2 + (3 - x)^2 = 1$ Substitute in the quadratic equation.

$\quad 5x^2 - 6x + 8 = 0$ Simplify.

$$x = \frac{-(-6) \pm \sqrt{(-6)^2 - 4(5)(8)}}{2(5)}$$ Use the quadratic formula to solve for x.

$$x = \frac{6 \pm \sqrt{-124}}{10} = \frac{3 \pm i\sqrt{31}}{5}$$

The x-values are imaginary numbers, and the y-values must also be imaginary. Since the solutions are not real numbers, the line and the ellipse do not intersect.

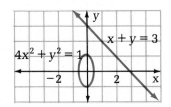

CLASS EXERCISES

Find the points of intersection of the circle $x^2 + y^2 = 100$ and the given line.

1. $y = 10$

2. $x = -10$

3. $y = -6$

4. $y = -\dfrac{4}{3}x$

5. $y = -x + 14$

6. $y = x + 10$

Solve each system by substitution.

7. $y = 2$
$\quad y = x^2 - 4x + 5$

8. $25x^2 + 16y^2 = 400$
$\quad 5x - 4y = 20$

9. $x^2 - 5y^2 = 11$
$\quad x - 4y = 0$

EXERCISES

 A

Graph the conic. Then find its points of intersection, if any, with the given line.

Parabola $y = x^2 - 3$

1. $x = 1$

2. $y = -2$

3. $x - y = -3$

4. $y = -5$

5. $2x + y = 0$

6. $3x - y = 3$

Circle $x^2 + y^2 = 25$

7. $y = -5$ **8.** $x = 0$ **9.** $y = 4$

10. $3y = 4x$ **11.** $x + y = 1$ **12.** $x - 2y = -5$

Ellipse $4x^2 + y^2 = 4$

13. $y = 4$ **14.** $y = 2x - 2$ **15.** $x = -1$

Hyperbola $y^2 - x^2 = 16$

16. $y = x$ **17.** $y = \dfrac{5}{3}x$ **18.** $3x + 5y = 16$

B   Solve each system.

19. $x^2 + y^2 = 169$
$x + y = -17$

20. $y = x^2$
$y = -x + 2$

21. $xy = 1$
$x = y$

22. $y = x^2 - 2x + 1$
$2x - y = 3$

23. $x^2 - y^2 = 16$
$5x + 3y = -16$

24. $x^2 + 4y^2 = 4$
$2y = x + 2$

25. $xy = -1$
$y - 2x = 3$

26. $x^2 - y^2 = 3$
$y - 3x = -5$

27. $y = (x - 3)^2 + 1$
$y + 2x = 6$

28. $x^2 + y^2 = 16$
$x = -2$

29. $4x^2 + 3y^2 = 11$
$y = 1$

30. $x^2 - 4y^2 = 5$
$x + y = 2$

Solve and graph each system.

31. $y = 2x^2 + 3$
$y = x + 4$

32. $x^2 + 9y^2 = 9$
$2y - 2 = x$

33. $y - x = 1$
$x^2 + y^2 = 9$

C   **34.** For what values of k will the line $x = k$ and the hyperbola $25x^2 - 4y^2 = 100$ have two points in common?

35. For what values of r will the circle $x^2 + y^2 = r^2$ and the line $x = -4$ have two points in common?

36. For what values of k will the parabola $y = x^2 - k$ and the line $y = 5$ have no points in common?

37. For what values of b will the line $y = -x + b$ and the hyperbola $xy = 1$ have exactly one point in common?

38. For what values of m will the line $y = mx$ and the hyperbola $y^2 - x^2 = 9$ have no points in common?

39. For what values of m will the line $y = mx + 2$ and the circle $x^2 + y^2 = 25$ have exactly one point in common?

*40. Show that if l is the length of a rectangle with area A and perimeter P, then $l = \dfrac{P + \sqrt{P^2 - 16A}}{4}$.

9-8 Quadratic Systems

OBJECTIVES

To find the points of intersection of the graphs of two quadratic equations.
To solve quadratic systems by substitution or addition.
To graph a system of quadratic inequalities.

A system of two quadratic equations in two variables may have up to four real solutions, as illustrated in the diagrams below.

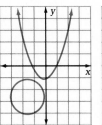 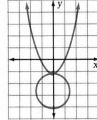 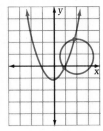 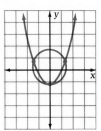 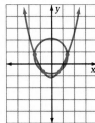

No points of intersection	One point of intersection	Two points of intersection	Three points of intersection	Four points of intersection
No real solutions	One real solution	Two real solutions	Three real solutions	Four real solutions

The substitution method can be used to solve systems of quadratic equations.

EXAMPLE 1   Find the real solutions of the system: $\begin{array}{l} y^2 - x^2 = 3 \\ xy = 2 \end{array}$

Use the substitution method.

$xy = 2$

$y = \dfrac{2}{x}$ Solve $xy = 2$ for y in terms of x.

$y^2 - x^2 = 3$

$\left(\dfrac{2}{x}\right)^2 - x^2 = 3$ Substitute in the other equation.

$\dfrac{4}{x^2} - x^2 = 3$

$4 - x^4 = 3x^2$ Multiply each side by x^2.

$x^4 + 3x^2 - 4 = 0$

$(x^2 + 4)(x^2 - 1) = 0$ Factor.

$x^2 + 4 = 0$ or $x^2 - 1 = 0$

No real solutions $x = 1$ or $x = -1$ Solve for x.

If $x = 1$, then $1(y) = 2$, or $y = 2$.
If $x = -1$, then $-1(y) = 2$, or $y = -2$.

Solve for y by substituting in $xy = 2$.

Check the ordered pairs $(1, 2)$ and $(-1, -2)$ in both equations to show that they are solutions to the system. The two hyperbolas intersect in two points, as shown on the graph.

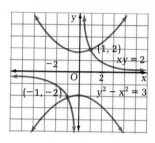

It is sometimes convenient to use the addition method to solve a quadratic system.

EXAMPLE 2

Find the real solutions of the system: $\begin{aligned} x^2 + 2y^2 &= 11 \\ 2x^2 - y^2 &= 2 \end{aligned}$

Use the addition method.

$$\begin{array}{l} x^2 + 2y^2 = 11 \\ \underline{4x^2 - 2y^2 = 4} \\ 5x^2 + 0 = 15 \end{array}$$

Multiply each side of the second equation by 2.
Align like terms and add.

$$x^2 = 3$$
$$x = \pm\sqrt{3}$$

Solve for x.

$$\begin{array}{ll} (\sqrt{3})^2 + 2y^2 = 11 & (-\sqrt{3})^2 + 2y^2 = 11 \\ 3 + 2y^2 = 11 & 3 + 2y^2 = 11 \\ y^2 = 4 & y^2 = 4 \\ y = \pm 2 & y = \pm 2 \end{array}$$

Substitute in one of the original equations and solve for y. Here we use $x^2 + 2y^2 = 11$.

Check in the original equations to show that $(\sqrt{3}, 2)$, $(\sqrt{3}, -2)$, $(-\sqrt{3}, 2)$, and $(-\sqrt{3}, -2)$ are solutions to the system. The hyperbola and ellipse intersect in four points, as shown in the graph.

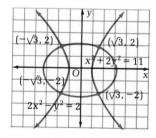

The system above could also have been solved by using the substitution method. Show this by solving the first equation for x^2 in terms of y^2 and substituting in the second equation, or by solving the second equation for y^2 and substituting in the first equation.

To graph a system of inequalities, graph the corresponding equations on the same coordinate plane. Use test points to determine the region that satisfies both inequalities.

EXAMPLE 3 Graph the system: $x^2 + y^2 < 25$
$$y \le \tfrac{4}{9}x^2$$

The circle with the equation $x^2 + y^2 = 25$ has its center at $(0, 0)$ and a radius of 5. Graph the circle using a dashed curve. The points *inside* the circle satisfy the first inequality.

The parabola $y = \tfrac{4}{9}x^2$ has its vertex at $(0, 0)$ and opens upward. Graph the parabola using a solid curve. The points *on and below* the parabola satisfy the second inequality.

The solution to the system consists of all points that satisfy both inequalities.

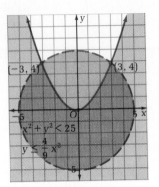

CLASS EXERCISES

Find the points of intersection, if any, of the circle $x^2 + y^2 = 4$ and

1. the hyperbola $x^2 - y^2 = 4$.

2. the ellipse $x^2 + 4y^2 = 16$.

3. the parabola $y = x^2 + 2$.

4. the circle $x^2 + y^2 = 36$.

5. the line $y = x$.

6. the ellipse $4x^2 + 9y^2 = 36$.

Find the real solutions of the system.

7. $x^2 - y^2 = 8$
$xy = 3$

8. $x^2 + y^2 = 13$
$x^2 - y^2 = 5$

9. $x^2 - 2y^2 = 4$
$2x^2 + y^2 = 8$

EXERCISES

A *Find the real solutions of the system.*

1. $y = x^2$
$y = (x + 2)^2$

2. $x^2 + y^2 = 25$
$x^2 + 2y^2 = 34$

3. $x^2 + y^2 = 34$
$x^2 - y^2 = 16$

4. $4x^2 + y^2 = 45$
$4x^2 - y^2 = 27$

5. $2y = x^2 - 8$
$x^2 + 4y^2 = 10$

6. $x^2 + y^2 = 17$
$2y = x^2 - 9$

7. $x^2 + y^2 = 29$
$xy = 10$

8. $x^2 - y^2 = 27$
$xy = 18$

9. $y = -x^2$
$x^2 + y^2 = 20$

10. $x^2 + y^2 = 25$
$25x^2 + 16y^2 = 400$

11. $xy = 12$
$x^2 + y^2 = 25$

12. $y = 2x^2$
$y^2 - x^2 = 3$

Graph the system.

13. $y \geq \dfrac{1}{2}x^2$
  $y \geq x$

14. $x^2 + y^2 < 9$
  $y > x - 1$

15. $xy \leq 4$
  $x^2 + y^2 \leq 16$

B *Find the real solutions, if any, of the system.*

16. $x^2 + y^2 = 25$
  $y = x^2 - 5$

17. $9x^2 + 16y^2 = 144$
  $4y^2 - 64x^2 = 256$

18. $xy = 6$
  $2x^2 - 1 = y^2$

19. $xy = 4$
  $9x^2 + 32 = y^2$

20. $x^2 - 3y^2 = -15$
  $2x^2 + y^2 = 26$

21. $5x^2 - y^2 = 15$
  $x^2 + 3y^2 = 19$

Graph the system.

22. $x > y$
  $x^2 + y^2 < 9$

23. $y \leq 2$
  $y \geq x^2$

24. $x^2 + y^2 \geq 16$
  $25x^2 + 4y^2 \leq 100$

25. $x^2 - y^2 > 1$
  $x^2 + y^2 \leq 4$

26. $xy < 4$
  $xy > -4$

27. $y > x^2 - 4x + 5$
  $x^2 + y^2 < 9$

C

28. Find the points common to the two parabolas $y = x^2 + 1$ and $x = (y - 1)^2$.

29. Find the equations of two circles, each with radius 2, that intersect at (0, 0) and (2, 2). The center of one circle is on the x-axis, and the center of the other is on the y-axis.

30. The hyperbola $xy = -9$ is tangent to a circle at $(-3, 3)$ and $(3, -3)$. The circle is centered at the origin. Find the equation of the circle.

31. The ellipse $4x^2 + 9y^2 = 1$ is tangent to two circles with centers at the origin. Find their equations.

CHECKPOINT

1. Find the length and the coordinates of the midpoint of $\overline{AB}$, with endpoints $A(-3, -7)$ and $B(5, 12)$.

2. Write an equation for the circle with center at $(-2, 8)$ and passing through the point $(-6, 5)$.

3. Write an equation for the parabola with vertex $(-4, 5)$ and focus $(-4, 6)$.

*Classify the equation as that of a **circle, ellipse, parabola,** or **hyperbola.***

4. $y = \dfrac{1}{20}(x - 2)^2 + 3$

5. $\dfrac{(y + 2)^2}{16} - \dfrac{(x - 1)^2}{9} = 1$

6. $16(x - 1)^2 + 25(y - 4)^2 = 400$

7. $x^2 + y^2 + 6x - 6y - 7 = 0$

9-9   Problem Solving: Using Systems Involving Quadratic Equations

OBJECTIVE ────────────────────────────────

To solve problems by writing and solving systems involving quadratic equations.

────────────────────────────────

Certain types of problems can be solved using systems involving quadratic equations. Study the following examples.

EXAMPLE 1   The sum of the squares of two positive numbers is 832, while the difference of their squares is 320. Find the numbers.

Strategy: Use two equations in two variables, one equation for the sum and the other for the difference.

Use variables to represent the numbers.

Let x be the larger number and y the smaller number.

Write a system of two equations.

The sum of the squares of the numbers is 832. $\qquad x^2 + y^2 = 832$

The difference of their squares is 320. $\qquad x^2 - y^2 = 320$

Find the solution.

$$
\begin{array}{ll}
x^2 + y^2 = \ \ 832 & \\
\underline{x^2 - y^2 = \ \ 320} & \\
2x^2 \qquad\ \ = 1152 & \text{Add to eliminate the } y\text{-terms.} \\
\qquad x^2 = 576, \text{ so } x = \pm24 & \text{Solve for } x. \\
\qquad\quad 576 + y^2 = 832 & \text{Substitute and solve for } y. \\
\qquad\qquad\quad y^2 = 256, \text{ so } y = \pm16 &
\end{array}
$$

Number pairs that satisfy the equations are 24 and 16, 24 and −16, −24 and 16, and −24 and −16. However, only the first pair satisfies the conditions of the problem.

Answer the question.

The numbers are 24 and 16.

EXAMPLE 2   A pool is twice as long as it is wide. It took 1224 square feet of material to cover a 6-foot wide deck around the pool. How wide is the pool?

y + 12

y

x

x + 12

Use variables.

Let x be the length and y the width of the pool, in feet.

CHAPTER 9

The area of the pool, in square feet, is xy.

The total area of the pool and deck, in square feet, is $(x + 12)(y + 12)$.

Write a system of equations.

The length of the pool is twice its width.

$x = 2y$

The total area, less the area of the pool, is the area of the deck.

$(x + 12)(y + 12) - xy = 1224$

Find the solution.

$(x + 12)(y + 12) - xy = 1224$

$xy + 12x + 12y + 144 - xy = 1224$ Simplify the second equation.

$12x + 12y = 1080$

$12(2y) + 12y = 1080$ Substitute $2y$ for x,
and solve for y.

$y = 30$

Check to see that the solution 30 satisfies the conditions of the original problem.

Answer the question.   The pool is 30 feet wide.

EXAMPLE 3

It takes 230 feet of fencing to enclose a rectangular garden with an area of 3000 square feet. Find the dimensions of the garden.

Let x be the length and y be the width, in feet.

Area of the garden: $xy = 3000$

Perimeter of the garden: $2x + 2y = 230$

$2x + 2y = 230$ Simplify the second equation and solve
for y.

$x + y = 115$

$y = 115 - x$

$xy = 3000$

$x(115 - x) = 3000$ Substitute $115 - x$ for y in the first
equation and solve for x.

$x^2 - 115x + 3000 = 0$

$(x - 75)(x - 40) = 0$

$x = 75$ or $x = 40$

$75y = 3000$ $40y = 3000$ Substitute for x in $xy = 3000$
and solve for y.

$y = 40$ $y = 75$

Check with the conditions in the problem to verify that the garden is 75 by 40 feet.

CLASS EXERCISES

Solve each problem.

1. The sum of two positive numbers is 22, and the sum of their squares is 250. Find the numbers.

2. The product of two numbers is 16, and the sum of their reciprocals is $\frac{1}{2}$. Find the numbers.

EXERCISES

A *Solve each problem.*

1. The sum of the squares of two positive numbers is 610. The difference of their squares is 272. Find the numbers.

2. The sum of the squares of two positive numbers is 117. The square of one number equals 4 times the other number. Find the numbers.

3. The sum of two positive numbers is 25 and the sum of their squares is 397. Find the numbers.

4. A rectangle has an area of 6 square centimeters and a perimeter of 10 centimeters. Find its dimensions.

5. A rectangle has a perimeter of 80 inches and an area of 375 square inches. Find its dimensions.

B 6. Find two numbers with a sum of 9, if the sum of their reciprocals is $\frac{1}{2}$.

7. Find two numbers with a sum of 10, if the difference between their reciprocals is $\frac{1}{12}$. Two answers are possible.

8. The sum of the reciprocals of two positive numbers is 7 times one-third of the reciprocal of the greater number. The product of the two numbers is 48. Find the numbers.

9. It requires 200 feet of fencing to enclose a rectangular plot with an area of 2475 square feet. Find the dimensions of the plot.

10. Find the dimensions of a rectangle with a perimeter of 34 meters and diagonals each 13 meters in length.

11. The area of one circle is 4 times greater than the area of a second circle. If the difference between the lengths of their radii is 6 inches, find the length of each radius.

12. The sum of the areas of two circles is 25π square inches and the difference of the areas is 7π square inches. Find the length of each radius.

13. If a 6-foot deck is constructed around a rectangular pool, the area enclosed by the entire structure will be increased by 768 square feet. If the width of the pool itself is $\frac{5}{8}$ of the length, how wide is the pool?

C 14. Two-inch squares are cut from the corners of a rectangular sheet of metal with an area of 92 square inches. The metal is then folded into an open box with a volume of 60 cubic inches. Find the dimensions of the original sheet of metal.

Parabolic Reflectors

Communications engineers design equipment to transmit and receive signals. Microwave transmission between communications satellites and earth stations is accomplished by using parabolic reflectors as antennas. Faint signals from space are reflected off the parabolic surface and concentrated at the *focal point*, where a receiver is located.

Example   A three-dimensional parabolic reflector is formed by rotating a parabola about its axis of symmetry. Suppose $y = \frac{1}{12}x^2$ is the equation describing the parabola used. How far from the surface of the reflector should the receiver be placed?

The receiver must be located at the focal point. For the parabola $y = ax^2$, the focus is at $\left(0, \frac{1}{4a}\right)$. Since $a = \frac{1}{12}$ for this parabola, its focus is at $(0, 3)$. Hence, the receiver must be located 3 units from the surface.

The parabolic reflector in a microwave antenna is often called a "dish." Suppose a dish antenna has a surface generated by the parabola $y = \frac{1}{8}x^2$ and has an outside diameter of 6 feet.

1. Graph the shape of the reflector, using the two-dimensional equation $y = \frac{1}{8}x^2$ over the interval $-3 \leq x \leq 3$. Locate and label the focus.

2. How far from the vertex of the dish would the receiver be located?

3. What would be the circumference of the parabolic dish? Use 3.14 for π.

4. How deep would the dish antenna be?

CHAPTER 9 REVIEW

VOCABULARY

distance formula (p. 317)
midpoint (p. 318)
circle (p. 322)
center of a circle (p. 322)
radius (p. 322)
diameter (p. 323)
equidistant (p. 326)
parabola (p. 326)
focus of a parabola (p. 326)
directrix (p. 326)
vertex of a parabola (p. 327)
axis of symmetry (p. 327)
ellipse (p. 331)
foci of an ellipse (p. 331)
major axis (p. 332)

minor axis (p. 332)
center of an ellipse (p. 332)
semi-major axis (p. 332)
semi-minor axis (p. 332)
hyperbola (p. 337)
foci of a hyperbola (p. 337)
asymptotes (p. 337)
vertices of a hyperbola (p. 338)
center of a hyperbola (p. 338)
rectangular hyperbola (p. 339)
conic sections (p. 342)
coordinate geometry (p. 342)
linear-quadratic system (p. 346)
quadratic system (p. 350)

SUMMARY

In this chapter the circle, parabola, ellipse, and hyperbola are defined, illustrated, and analyzed. Fundamental to this study is the distance formula, which is derived in the first lesson. This work provides an insight into analytic geometry by bringing together geometric and algebraic ideas. This is an association that will continue throughout much of the advanced mathematics awaiting you. Each conic section has a unique shape and a unique type of equation, and both the graph and the equation should be recognized readily. Linear-quadratic and quadratic systems are also introduced, along with methods of finding their solutions. In the final lesson, problems are solved by solving such systems.

REVIEW EXERCISES

9-1   *Find the distance between the two points. Then find the coordinates of the midpoint of the segment joining the points.*

1. $(-5, 7)$ and $(1, -1)$

2. $(-7, -4)$ and $(-2, 8)$

3. $(3, -8)$ and $(9, -12)$

4. $(0, 0)$ and $(3, 4)$

Find the distance between the point $(5, 4)$ and

5. the origin.

6. the x-axis.

7. the y-axis.

Segment AB has midpoint M. Given the coordinates of M and A, find the coordinates of point B.

8. $M(-5, 7)$; $A(6, 1)$

9. $M(-7, -4)$; $A(-2, 8)$

10. $M(3, -8)$; $A(9, 12)$

11. The midpoint of a segment is $P(-2, 6)$. The segment is perpendicular to the y-axis, and it is 16 units in length. Find the coordinates of its endpoints.

9-2 *Find the center and radius of each circle from its equation.*

12. $x^2 + y^2 = 144$

13. $(x - 1)^2 + y^2 = 7$

14. $(x + 1)^2 + (y + 1)^2 = \dfrac{49}{16}$

15. $x^2 - 4x + y^2 + 4y + 7 = 0$

Write the equation of the circle with the given center and radius or diameter.

16. $(0, 0)$, $r = 2$

17. $(-7, -6)$, $r = \sqrt{2}$

18. $\left(\dfrac{5}{8}, -\dfrac{3}{16}\right)$, $d = \dfrac{3}{2}$

19. Write the equation of the circle with center $(-2, 8)$ and passing through $(4, 0)$.

20. Write the equation of a circle concentric to $(x - 3)^2 + (y + 2)^2 = 15$, with a radius equal to that of the circle $(x + 7)^2 + (y + 9)^2 = 25$.

9-3 *State the direction in which each parabola opens. Then give the coordinates of its vertex and focus and the equations of its axis of symmetry and directrix.*

21. $y = x^2$

22. $x = 3y^2$

23. $y = -(x - 3)^2$

24. $y = -(x + 1)^2 - 1$

25. $y = x^2 - 4x + 1$

26. $y = -x^2 - x + 3$

27. A parabola consists of the set of points in a plane that are equidistant from $(3, -4)$ and the line $y = 4$. Find the coordinates of its vertex and the equation of its line of symmetry.

9-4 *For each ellipse, give the coordinates of the center and the foci and the lengths of the semi-major and semi-minor axes.*

28. $\dfrac{x^2}{25} + \dfrac{y^2}{16} = 1$

29. $\dfrac{x^2}{36} + \dfrac{y^2}{100} = 1$

30. $9x^2 + y^2 = 9$

31. Find an equation for the set of points such that the sum of the distances from each point to $(2, 0)$ and $(-2, 0)$ is 6.

9-5 *For each hyperbola, give the coordinates of the center, vertices, and foci, and the equations of the asymptotes.*

32. $\dfrac{x^2}{16} - \dfrac{y^2}{9} = 1$

33. $16x^2 - 9y^2 = 144$

34. $y^2 - 25x^2 = 25$

35. The difference of the distances from each point on a hyperbola to the points $(4, 0)$ and $(-4, 0)$ is always 6. Find an equation of the hyperbola.

9-6 *Classify the conic with the given equation. Then sketch its graph.*

36. $x^2 + y^2 - 6x + 8y = 0$

37. $3x^2 - 12x + y^2 + 2y + 4 = 0$

38. $y^2 - 4y + 2x - 8 = 0$

39. $y^2 - 6y - 4x^2 - 16x - 23 = 0$

9-7   *Solve each system.*

40. $x^2 + y^2 = 9$ **41.** $y = x^2 - 1$ **42.** $x - 3y = 0$
     $x = -3$ $y = 0$ $x^2 - y^2 = 2$

43. For what values of k will the graphs of $x = k$ and $x^2 + 4y^2 = 36$ intersect in exactly two points?

9-8   *Find the real solutions, if any, for each system.*

44. $x^2 + y^2 = 6$ **45.** $4x^2 - y^2 = 4$ **46.** $x^2 + y^2 = 9$
     $y = x^2$ $x^2 + y = 4$ $16x^2 + 25y^2 = 400$

9-9   *Solve each problem.*

47. Find two numbers with a sum of 16, if the sum of their reciprocals is $\frac{1}{3}$.

48. A rectangular garden is enclosed by 19.4 meters of picket fencing. If the area of the garden is 18.0 square meters, what are its dimensions?

49. The area of one circle is 16π square inches greater than the area of a second circle. The radius of the larger circle is 2 inches longer than that of the smaller one. Find the length of each radius.

CHAPTER 9 TEST

1. Find the distance between points $X(3, 7)$ and $Y(-6, -2)$. Then find the coordinates of the midpoint of segment XY.

2. Write the equation of the circle with center $(-5, 7)$ and radius $2\sqrt{3}$.

3. For the parabola $y = \frac{1}{4}(x - 1)^2 - 2$, find the coordinates of the vertex and the focus and the equations of the axis of symmetry and the directrix. Then sketch the parabola.

4. For the ellipse $\frac{x^2}{36} + y^2 = 1$, find the coordinates of the foci and the lengths of the semi-major and semi-minor axes. Then sketch the ellipse.

5. For the hyperbola $\frac{x^2}{4} - \frac{y^2}{25} = 1$, find the coordinates of the vertices and foci and the equations of the asymptotes. Then sketch the hyperbola.

*Classify the equation as that of a **circle, ellipse, parabola,** or **hyperbola.***

6. $x^2 - 4x + 2y = 0$ **7.** $25x^2 + 4y^2 - 50x = 75$

Find the real solutions for each system.

8. $4x^2 + 9y^2 = 10$ **9.** $x^2 + y^2 = 16$
     $y = 2x$ $x^2 = 2y + 1$

10. A positive number is 4 less than another number. The difference between the squares of the two numbers is 72. Find the two numbers.

Distance Between Points

The program below uses the *square root function,* SQR(N), to evaluate the distance formula, $d = \sqrt{(x_1 - x_2)^2 + (y_1 - y_2)^2}$.

Most computers permit a variable to be named by a letter followed by a single digit. Therefore we can express x_1 as $X1$.

When entering or copying a program, be careful to distinguish between the letter I and the digit 1, and between the letter O and the digit 0. Many computers use a slashed zero, $\emptyset$.

Since some computers are not exact when raising a number to a power or when taking a root, line 210 rounds the distance to the nearest hundredth.

The Program	What It Does

```
100 REM DISTANCE FORMULA
110 PRINT "ENTER COORDINATES OF POINT A"
120 INPUT X1, Y1
130 PRINT "ENTER COORDINATES OF POINT B"
140 INPUT X2, Y2
200 LET D = SQR((X1 - X2) ↑ 2 + (Y1 - Y2) ↑ 2)
210 LET D = INT(D * 100 + .5)/100
220 PRINT "DISTANCE FROM A TO B IS "; D
300 PRINT
310 PRINT "ANOTHER? (1 = YES, 0 = NO)"
320 INPUT Z
330 IF Z = 1 THEN 110
900 END
```

What It Does

Waits for (x, y), separated by a comma.
Waits for coordinates of B.

Note the symbol ((.
Rounds the result.

Leaves a blank line.
If a message is displayed on two lines, insert blank spaces to avoid breaking words.

What does the program display as the distance between the following?

1. $A(9, 6)$, $B(32, 6)$ **2.** $A(6, 2)$, $B(-1, 0)$ **3.** $A(645, 120)$, $B(200, 560)$

4. $A(-5, -13)$, $B(13, -5)$ **5.** $A(6.75, -3.5)$, $B(-8.2, 12)$ **6.** $A(4, -8)$, $B(5, -7)$

7. If m is an odd positive integer, m, $\dfrac{m^2 - 1}{2}$, and $\dfrac{m^2 + 1}{2}$ form a Pythagorean triple. That is, $m^2 + \left(\dfrac{m^2 - 1}{2}\right)^2 = \left(\dfrac{m^2 + 1^2}{2}\right)^2$. Write a program to display the Pythagorean triple for each of the first ten values of m.

8. If M is the midpoint of a line segment joining points $A(x_1, y_1)$ and $B(x_2, y_2)$, the coordinates of M are $\left(\dfrac{x_1 + x_2}{2}, \dfrac{y_1 + y_2}{2}\right)$. Write a program to compute and display the coordinates of M when the coordinates of A and B are entered.

For more information about BASIC, see the Computer Handbook at the back of the book.

CHAPTER 10

Logarithms can be used to calculate compound interest. When many such calculations are required, a computer does the job quickly and accurately.

EXPONENTIAL AND LOGARITHMIC FUNCTIONS

Prerequisite Skills Review

Write the letter for the correct answer.

1. 100,000,000,000 is equal to __?__.

   a. 10^{10} **b.** 10^{11} **c.** 10^{12} **d.** 10^{13}

2. 10^{-5} is equal to __?__.

   a. 0.0001   **b.** 0.00001   **c.** 0.00005   **d.** 0.000001

3. $36^{-\frac{1}{2}} = $ __?__

   a. 6   **b.** $-\frac{1}{6}$ **c.** $\frac{1}{6}$ **d.** none of these

4. $64^{\frac{2}{3}} = $ __?__

   a. $42\frac{2}{3}$ **b.** 512   **c.** 16   **d.** none of these

5. $\left(\dfrac{9}{16}\right)^{-\frac{3}{2}} = $ __?__

   a. $\dfrac{27}{64}$ **b.** $\sqrt[3]{\dfrac{256}{81}}$ **c.** $\dfrac{64}{27}$ **d.** $\dfrac{4}{3}$

6. $(n^3 \cdot n^3)^2 = $ __?__

   a. n^{12} **b.** n^8 **c.** n^{18} **d.** n^{11}

7. $0.9031 - 1 = $ __?__

   a. -0.9031 **b.** $8.0969 - 10$ **c.** $9.0969 - 10$ **d.** $9.9031 - 10$

8. $-1.3979 = $ __?__

   a. $0.3979 - 1$ **b.** $8.6021 - 10$ **c.** $0.6021 - 10$ **d.** $0.3979 - 2$

9. $2.3802 - 2(-0.3010 + 0.7782) = $ __?__

   a. 1.4258   **b.** 0.2218   **c.** 4.5386   **d.** none of these

10. $0.7782 - 3(0.3010 - 2.3802) = $ __?__

   a. 7.0158   **b.** -5.5494 **c.** -2.5050 **d.** none of these

10-1 Scientific Notation

To write numbers in scientific notation.
To write numbers given in scientific notation as whole numbers or
  decimals.
To identify significant digits.

In 1980, the world's population reached about 4.5 billion. While an
exact count was not possible, this represents a reasonable estimate. The
number can be expressed in many ways, including *scientific notation*.

scientific notation

4.5 billion = 4,500,000,000 = 4.5 × 1,000,000,000 = **4.5 × 10^9** ⟵

> **A positive number *N* is written in *scientific notation* as**
>
> $$N = a \times 10^n$$
>
> **where $1 \leq a < 10$ and *n* is an integer.**

EXAMPLE 1   According to the census, the 1980 population of the United States was
226,504,825. Round this number to the nearest million and then write
the rounded number in scientific notation.

226,504,825, to the nearest million, is 227,000,000.

227,000,000 = 2.27 × 10^8

Scientific notation is usually used with approximate numbers. All
significant digits are included in the first factor, *a*. A **significant digit** is
any nonzero digit or any zero that is not used simply to locate the decimal point.

0.0034 has two significant digits.	0.00**34**
0.0304 has three significant digits.	0.0**304**
3.004 has four significant digits.	**3.004**
3.40 has three significant digits.	**3.40**
34,000 has two significant digits.	**34**,000

In numbers such as 34,000, it is possible that one or more of the final
zeros is significant. However, in whole numbers of this kind it is assumed
that the final zero or zeros are not significant, unless otherwise indicated.

EXAMPLE 2   Give the number of significant digits in each approximate number. Then write the number in scientific notation.

    a. The speed of light: **186,000 miles per second**

    There are three significant digits.

    $186,000 = 1.86 \times 10^5$ Move the decimal point 5 places to the *left*.

    b. The radius of a hydrogen atom: **0.00000000053 cm**

    There are two significant digits.

    $0.00000000053 = 5.3 \times 10^{-10}$ Move the decimal point 10 places to the *right*.

EXAMPLE 3   Write each number as a decimal or as a whole number.

    a. 1.62×10^2

    $1.62 \times 10^2 = 162$ Move the decimal point 2 places to the *right*.

    b. 8×10^{-4}

    $8 \times 10^{-4} = 0.0008$ Move the decimal point 4 places to the *left*.

    Scientific notation is useful for making rough estimates of products and quotients.

EXAMPLE 4   Estimate the time it takes electricity to travel the length of a 63-meter wire at a rate of 24,000,000,000 centimeters per second.

    Round each number to one significant digit and express the rounded numbers in scientific notation.

    63 m = 6300 cm ≈ 6000 cm $6000 = 6 \times 10^3$

    24,000,000,000 cm ≈ 20,000,000,000 cm $20,000,000,000 = 2 \times 10^{10}$

    Then $\dfrac{6 \times 10^3}{2 \times 10^{10}} = 3 \times 10^{-7}$.

    It will take approximately $3 \times 10^{-7} = 0.0000003$ second, or three ten-millionths of a second.

CLASS EXERCISES

Give the number of significant digits in each approximate number.

    1. 5,600,000   **2.** 50,600   **3.** 5006   **4.** 5.60   **5.** 0.056

Name each approximate number using scientific notation.

    6. 125,000   **7.** 0.00037   **8.** 5,000,000   **9.** 8.09   **10.** 0.805

EXERCISES

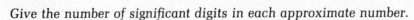

A   *Give the number of significant digits in each approximate number.*

1. 6700   **2.** 6007   **3.** 6070   **4.** 67.00   **5.** 0.067

6. 40,000,000   **7.** 25.04   **8.** 0.0006   **9.** 60,072   **10.** 16.90

Write each approximate number using scientific notation.

11. 14,000   **12.** 4020   **13.** 0.111   **14.** 0.000089   **15.** 5.11

16. 0.135   **17.** 333   **18.** 23,006   **19.** 500,000   **20.** 0.0002

21. 500.1   **22.** 7,000,000   **23.** 0.000002   **24.** 0.0503   **25.** 0.240

Write each number as a decimal or as a whole number.

26. 2.73×10^3 **27.** 8.76×10^9 **28.** 1.01×10^{-1} **29.** 6.6×10^{-7}

30. 5×10^0 **31.** 6.67×10^5 **32.** 4.20×10^{-2} **33.** 4.4×10^{-4}

34. 6.08×10^1 **35.** 7.0×10^{-4} **36.** 8×10^{-10} **37.** 2.6×10^8

B   *Round each number to two significant digits. Then write the rounded number in scientific notation.*

38. 86.17   **39.** 0.0844   **40.** 32,100   **41.** 5666   **42.** 4001

43. 0.353   **44.** 0.00119   **45.** 38.26   **46.** 4.5710   **47.** 0.000294

48. 0.0000555   **49.** 70.735   **50.** 698,400   **51.** 0.1109   **52.** 0.000195

Estimate each product or quotient using scientific notation. First round each number to one significant digit.

53. 306.7×0.00089 **54.** $4785 \times 63,476$ **55.** 0.00000238×593

56. $48.33 \times 51,025$ **57.** 0.0062×0.00099 **58.** $0.0000278 \times 31,459$

59. $\dfrac{0.000425}{188}$ **60.** $\dfrac{0.00875}{0.00000032}$ **61.** $\dfrac{79}{0.00000022}$

C   **62.** The mass of a hydrogen atom, in grams, is 1.663×10^{-30}. Express this number as a decimal.

63. Approximately how long will it take for light from the star Sirius to reach Earth, which is 3.3×10^{13} kilometers away, if light travels 300,000,000 meters per second?

64. 3×10^{18} electrons per second flow past a given point in the filament of a 60-watt light bulb. How many electrons flow past that point in 3 hours?

Using Diagrams for Rate Problems

In order to solve a rate problem, it is often helpful to draw a diagram. For example, suppose two trains are passing each other on adjacent tracks. One train is 250 feet long and is going 40 miles per hour. The other train is 366 feet long and its rate is 30 miles per hour. How long does it take from the time they meet until they pass each other?

The trains meet.   **The trains pass.**

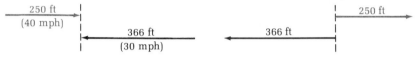

From the diagrams, you can see that the trains travel in opposite directions a total of 616 feet from the time they meet until they pass. Also, they are separating at a rate of $40 + 30 = 70$ miles per hour. Use the formula $d = rt$, and solve for t.

$$t = \frac{d}{r} = \frac{616 \text{ ft}}{70 \text{ mph}} = \frac{616 \text{ ft}}{\frac{308}{3} \text{ ft per sec}} = 6 \text{ sec} \qquad 70 \text{ mph} = 70 \cdot \frac{5280}{3600} \text{ ft per sec} = \frac{308}{3} \text{ ft per sec}$$

It will take 6 seconds for the trains to pass each other.

Solve each problem. Draw diagrams!

1. A 2300-foot freight train moves at a rate of 40 miles per hour. A 1000-foot passenger train going 50 miles per hour passes the freight train going in the opposite direction. How long does it take from the time they meet until they pass each other?

Beth drives a certain distance at a constant rate of 40 miles per hour. Carmen starts at the same time and travels the same route.

2. Assume that Carmen drives at a rate of 36 miles per hour for the first half of the distance. How fast must she drive during the second half in order to arrive when Beth does?

3. Suppose Carmen's rate for the first half is 20 miles per hour. How fast must she drive during the second half in order to arrive when Beth does?

*4. Two boats start at the same time from opposite sides of a river. They travel back and forth without stopping, each at a constant rate. The first time that they pass each other they are 700 feet from one shore. After they each make one turn, they pass each other again 400 feet from the other shore. How wide is the river?

10-2 Real-Number Exponents

OBJECTIVES _____

To simplify expressions involving irrational exponents.
To solve exponential equations by inspection or by using the fact that
if $a^x = a^y$, then $x = y$.

_____

Any integer can be used as an exponent. In particular, recall these properties.

$$b^{-n} = \frac{1}{b^n} \text{ and } b^0 = 1 \text{ for } b \neq 0$$

This table shows decimal values of some integral powers of 2.

$2^{-3} = \frac{1}{8} = 0.125$	$2^0 = 1 = 1.000$
$2^{-2} = \frac{1}{4} = 0.250$	$2^1 = 2 = 2.000$
	$2^2 = 4 = 4.000$
$2^{-1} = \frac{1}{2} = 0.500$	$2^3 = 8 = 8.000$

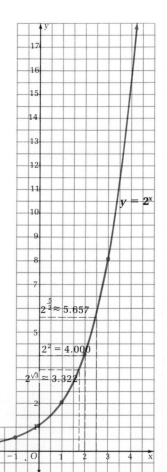

Other rational numbers can also be used as exponents. Recall the following property.

$$b^{\frac{m}{n}} = \sqrt[n]{b^m}$$

Each expression in the following table has a unique decimal value determined by the exponent on the base 2. These values can be approximated using the exponent key on a scientific calculator.

$2^{-\frac{5}{2}} = \sqrt{\frac{1}{32}} \approx 0.177$	$2^{\frac{1}{2}} = \sqrt{2} \approx 1.414$
$2^{-\frac{3}{2}} = \sqrt{\frac{1}{8}} \approx 0.354$	$2^{\frac{3}{2}} = \sqrt{8} \approx 2.828$
$2^{-\frac{1}{2}} = \sqrt{\frac{1}{2}} \approx 0.707$	$2^{\frac{5}{2}} = \sqrt{32} \approx 5.657$

Decimals can be used to evaluate expressions with irrational exponents. The table at the right shows how decimal approximations for the irrational number $\sqrt{3}$ can be used to approximate the value of $2^{\sqrt{3}}$. A scientific calculator was used to obtain the values shown.

$$2^{1.7} \approx 3.24900958$$
$$2^{1.732} \approx 3.32188010$$
$$2^{1.73205} \approx 3.32199523$$
$$2^{1.7320508} \approx 3.32199707$$
$$2^{\sqrt{3}} \approx 3.32199709$$

This illustrates the fact that any real number may be used as an exponent. The graph of $y = 2^x$ shows that for every real number x, 2^x is a positive real number.

The properties of exponents apply for all real-number exponents, rational and irrational.

EXAMPLE 1   Simplify, using the properties of exponents.

a. $5^{\sqrt{2}} \cdot 5^{2\sqrt{2}}$

The bases are the same, so add the exponents using the property $b^m b^n = b^{m+n}$.
$$5^{\sqrt{2}} \cdot 5^{2\sqrt{2}} = 5^{\sqrt{2}+2\sqrt{2}}$$
$$= 5^{3\sqrt{2}}, \text{ or } 125^{\sqrt{2}}$$

b. $(4^{\sqrt{2}})^{\sqrt{2}}$

Multiply the exponents, using the property $(b^m)^n = b^{mn}$.
$$(4^{\sqrt{2}})^{\sqrt{2}} = 4^{\sqrt{2} \cdot \sqrt{2}}$$
$$= 4^2$$
$$= 16$$

c. $2^{\sqrt{3}} \cdot 3^{\sqrt{3}}$

The exponents are the same, so multiply the bases using the property $a^m b^m = (ab)^m$.
$$2^{\sqrt{3}} \cdot 3^{\sqrt{3}} = (2 \cdot 3)^{\sqrt{3}}$$
$$= 6^{\sqrt{3}}$$

When an equation contains a variable in an exponent, it is called an **exponential equation.** Some exponential equations can be solved by inspection, using your knowledge of powers and roots.

EXAMPLE 2   Solve for x.

a. $2^x = 8$ 8 is the cube of 2, so $x = 3$.

b. $16^x = 4$ 4 is the square root of 16, so $x = \frac{1}{2}$.

Many equations containing exponents can be solved using the following properties.

> If each side of an equation is an exponential expression with the same base, then the exponents are equal.
>
> If $a^m = a^n$, where $a > 0$ and $a \neq 1$, then $m = n$.
>
> If each side of an equation is raised to the same power, then the resulting expressions are equal.
>
> If $a = b$, then $a^n = b^n$ for all n.

EXAMPLE 3   Solve.

a. $4^{\sqrt{x}} = 2^6$

$\quad\quad 4^{\sqrt{x}} = 4^3$ Express each side using the same base. $2^6 = (2^2)^3 = 4^3$

$\quad\quad \sqrt{x} = 3$ Set the exponents equal.

$\quad\quad\quad x = 9$ Square each side.   If $a = b$, then $a^n = b^n$.

Check $4^{\sqrt{9}} = 4^3 = 64 = 2^6$ The solution is 9.

b. $3^{2y+1} = \sqrt{3}$

$\quad\quad 3^{2y+1} = 3^{\frac{1}{2}}$

$\quad\quad 2y + 1 = \dfrac{1}{2}$ Set the exponents equal.

$\quad\quad\quad\quad y = -\dfrac{1}{4}$ Check to show that the solution is $-\dfrac{1}{4}$.

c. $x^{\frac{2}{3}} = 9$

$\quad\quad \left(x^{\frac{2}{3}}\right)^{\frac{3}{2}} = 9^{\frac{3}{2}}$ Raise each side to the $\frac{3}{2}$ power.

$\quad\quad\quad\quad x = (\sqrt{9})^3$

$\quad\quad\quad\quad x = 27$ Check to show that the solution is 27.

CLASS EXERCISES

Simplify, using the properties of exponents.

1. $7^{\sqrt{3}} \cdot 7^{\sqrt{3}}$ **2.** $(5^{\sqrt{2}})^{\sqrt{3}}$ **3.** $3^{\sqrt{2}} \cdot 5^{\sqrt{2}}$ **4.** $4^{\sqrt{5}} \cdot 2^{\sqrt{5}}$

Solve and check.

5. $5^{2x} = 25$ **6.** $4^x = \dfrac{1}{2}$ **7.** $2^{4x} = 32$ **8.** $3^{2x+3} = 81$

9. $2^{3x+2} = 4^{2x}$ **10.** $10^{4x} = 100^3$ **11.** $5^{-x} = \dfrac{1}{125}$ **12.** $x^{\frac{3}{4}} = 27$

EXERCISES

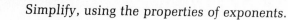

A *Simplify, using the properties of exponents.*

1. $2^{\sqrt{3}} \cdot 6^{\sqrt{3}}$

2. $4^{\sqrt{5}} \cdot 7^{\sqrt{5}}$

3. $5^{\sqrt{2}} \cdot 5^{\sqrt{2}}$

4. $3^{\sqrt{5}} \cdot 3^{2\sqrt{5}}$

5. $2^{\sqrt{3}} \cdot 2^{\sqrt{3}}$

6. $8^{-\sqrt{3}} \cdot 8^{\sqrt{3}}$

7. $(2^{\sqrt{3}})^{\sqrt{3}}$

8. $(5^{\sqrt{2}} \cdot 5^{\sqrt{2}})^{\sqrt{2}}$

9. $(3^{\sqrt{2}} \cdot 2^{\sqrt{2}})^{2\sqrt{2}}$

10. $3^{-\sqrt{2}} \cdot 3^{\sqrt{8}}$

11. $(6^{-\sqrt{3}})^{-\sqrt{6}}$

12. $(2^{\sqrt{2}} \cdot 5^{\sqrt{2}})^{\sqrt{5}}$

Solve and check.

13. $3^{2x} = 9$

14. $5^{x+1} = 125$

15. $2^{6x} = 64$

16. $4^{x-1} = 64$

17. $4^{x} = 32$

18. $9^{x} = 27$

19. $32^{x} = 16$

20. $27^{2x} = 9$

21. $x^{\frac{1}{2}} = 4$

22. $x^{\frac{1}{3}} = 8$

23. $x^{\frac{2}{3}} = 16$

24. $x^{\frac{3}{4}} = 8$

B *Simplify, using the properties of exponents.*

25. $(12^{\sqrt[3]{5}})^{\sqrt[3]{2}}$

26. $(6^{\sqrt{2}} \cdot 5^{\sqrt{3}})^0$

27. $4^{\sqrt[3]{2}} \cdot 4^{\sqrt[3]{16}}$

28. $2^{\sqrt{3}} \cdot 2^{3\sqrt{3}}$

29. $x^{-\sqrt{2}} x^{\sqrt{3}}$

30. $(x^{\sqrt{5}} x^{\sqrt{3}})^{\sqrt{2}}$

31. $(3^{\sqrt{2}} a^2)^{\sqrt{2}}$

32. $(a^{\sqrt{2}} b^0)^{-\sqrt{2}}$

33. $(b^{\sqrt{2}})^{\sqrt{8}}$

34. $(2m^{\sqrt{2}}) m^{\sqrt{2}}$

35. $2m^{\sqrt{2}} \cdot 2m^2$

36. $(3m^{2\sqrt{3}})^{\sqrt{3}}$

37. $a^{\sqrt{2}} a^{\sqrt{2}} a^{\sqrt{2}}$

38. $a^{\sqrt{3}} a^{2\sqrt{3}} a^{3\sqrt{3}}$

39. $[(a^{\sqrt{3}})^{\sqrt{2}}]^{\sqrt{6}}$

40. $(a^{\sqrt{2}} b)^{\sqrt{2}} c$

41. $(a^{\sqrt{2}} + b^{\sqrt{2}})^2$

42. $(c^{\sqrt{3}} - c^{\sqrt{2}})^2$

43. $(b^{\sqrt{3}} - c^{\sqrt{3}})^2$

44. $a^3 b^{\sqrt{3}} (ab)^{\sqrt{3}}$

Solve and check.

45. $4^{3+x} = 8^x$

46. $8^{2x} = 2^{2x-4}$

47. $2^{4x} = 32^{x-1}$

48. $4^{2x+1} = 16$

49. $9^2 = 3^{x+4}$

50. $27^{2x} = 3^{x-5}$

51. $16^{\frac{1}{2}x} = 32^{\frac{1}{4}x+1}$

52. $49^{3x} = 7^{2x-1}$

53. $25^{3x} = 5^{2x+2}$

54. $(6^{\sqrt{x}})^{\sqrt{x}} = \sqrt{6}$

55. $9^{-x} = 3^{-4}$

56. $16^{2x+1} = 2^{5-x}$

57. $\left(\frac{1}{2}\right)^x = \left(\frac{1}{8}\right)^{x+2}$

58. $2^{\sqrt{x}} = 4^{\sqrt{x}-1}$

59. $\left(\frac{1}{8}\right)^x = \left(\frac{1}{4}\right)^{x+3}$

60. $\left(\frac{1}{9}\right)^{\sqrt{x}} = \left(\frac{1}{3}\right)^{\sqrt{x}+1}$

61. $(2x)^{\frac{1}{2}} = 1$

62. $\left(\frac{x}{3}\right)^{\frac{2}{3}} = 9$

63. $(4x)^{\frac{3}{2}} = 64$

64. $\left(\frac{9}{16}x\right)^{\frac{5}{2}} = 32$

C *Find the value of each expression, rounded to the nearest hundredth. Use $\sqrt{2} = 1.414$ and $2^{\sqrt{2}} = 2.665$.*

65. $2^{\frac{1}{2}}$

66. $2^{\frac{3}{2}}$

67. $2^{-\frac{1}{2}}$

68. $2^{2\sqrt{2}}$

69. $2^{\sqrt{2}+1}$

70. $2^{\frac{1}{2}-\sqrt{2}}$

*Solve each exponential equation for all values of **x**.*

71. $2^{x^2} = 16$

72. $9^{2x} = 3^{x^2}$

73. $4^{x^2} = 2^x$

74. $3^{x^2+2x} = 27$

75. $6^{\sqrt{x}} = 36^{\sqrt{2}}$

76. $2^{\sqrt{x}} = 8^x$

77. $2^x 3^x = 36^{\sqrt{x}}$

78. $3^{\sqrt[4]{x}} = 9^{\sqrt{x}}$

10-3 Exponential Functions

To graph exponential functions.
To evaluate functions of the form $f(x) = ka^x$ for given values of x.

For every positive real number a and every real number x, there is a corresponding unique real number a^x. The exponential equation $y = a^x$, with $a > 0$ and $a \neq 1$, determines the **exponential function** $f(x) = a^x$.

To graph an exponential function, make a table of ordered pairs $(x, f(x))$. Then plot the corresponding points and connect them with a smooth curve.

EXAMPLE 1 Graph each exponential function.

a. $f(x) = 4^x$

x	−2	−1	0	1	2
$f(x)$	$\dfrac{1}{16}$	$\dfrac{1}{4}$	1	4	16

b. $g(x) = 2^x$

x	−2	−1	0	1	2
$g(x)$	$\dfrac{1}{4}$	$\dfrac{1}{2}$	1	2	4

c. $h(x) = (\sqrt{2})^x$

x	−2	−1	0	1	2
$h(x)$	0.5	0.7	1	1.4	2

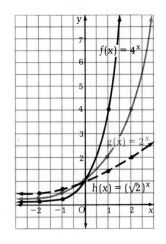

Each of the above functions has the set of real numbers for its domain. Each has the set of positive real numbers for its range. Its graph lies entirely above the x-axis. Furthermore, each graph passes through the point (0, 1). The curves represent *increasing functions*, since the value of each function increases as x increases.

EXAMPLE 2 If $g(x) = 2^x$, find $g(-20)$, $g(0)$, $g(20)$, and $g(21)$.

$$g(-20) = 2^{-20} = \frac{1}{2^{20}} \approx 0.000001$$

$$g(0) = 2^0 = 1$$

$$g(20) = 2^{20} = 1{,}048{,}576$$

$$g(21) = 2^{21} = 2 \cdot 2^{20} = 2{,}097{,}152$$

As x increases, $g(x) = 2^x$ increases without bound. For each unit increase in x, the value of 2^x doubles, as illustrated by the fact that $g(21) = 2g(20)$. Exponential functions are not always increasing functions, however.

When $a > 1$, $f(x) = a^x$ is an increasing function.

When $0 < a < 1$, $f(x) = a^x$ is a *decreasing function*.

EXAMPLE 3

Graph $f(x) = \left(\frac{1}{2}\right)^x$ and evaluate the function for x equal to 20 and 21.

x	-2	-1	0	1	2
$f(x)$	4	2	1	$\frac{1}{2}$	$\frac{1}{4}$

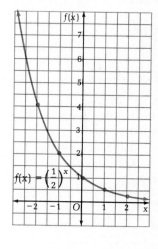

Here, as x increases, $f(x)$ decreases toward 0. For each unit increase in x, the value of $\left(\frac{1}{2}\right)^x$ is halved.

$$f(20) = \left(\frac{1}{2}\right)^{20} \approx 0.000001$$

$$f(21) = \frac{1}{2}f(20) \approx \frac{1}{2}(0.000001)$$

$$f(21) \approx 0.0000005$$

EXAMPLE 4

Graph $h(x) = -\left(\frac{1}{2}\right)^x$. Give the domain and range and tell whether it is an increasing or a decreasing function.

x	-2	-1	0	1	2
$h(x)$	-4	-2	-1	$-\frac{1}{2}$	$-\frac{1}{4}$

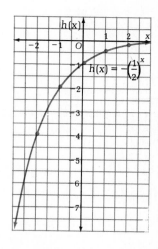

The domain of $h(x) = -\left(\frac{1}{2}\right)^x$ is the set of real numbers, and the range is the set of negative real numbers. It is an increasing function.

If you multiply a^x $(a > 0)$ by a nonzero constant k, each ordinate value $y = a^x$ is multiplied by k. If $k = -1$, the curve is reflected about the x-axis. Every function of the form $f(x) = ka^x$, with x a real number, is an exponential function if $k \neq 0$, $a > 0$, and $a \neq 1$.

CLASS EXERCISES

Use the graphs from Examples 1, 3, and 4 in this section.

1. Compare the graphs of $f(x) = \left(\frac{1}{2}\right)^x$ and $h(x) = -\left(\frac{1}{2}\right)^x$.
   Are they symmetric to each other about the x-axis?
   Do they have any points in common?

2. Compare the graphs of $g(x) = 2^x$ and $f(x) = \left(\frac{1}{2}\right)^x$.
   Are they symmetric to each other about the y-axis?
   Do they have any points in common?

3. Compare the graphs of $g(x) = 2^x$ and $h(x) = -\left(\frac{1}{2}\right)^x$.
   Are they symmetric to each other about either axis?
   Do they have any points in common?

Consider the exponential function $f(x) = 3^x$.

4. Is $f(x)$ positive for all real values of x?

5. Is x positive for all real values of $f(x)$?

6. Is $f(x)$ an *increasing* function or is it a *decreasing* function?

EXERCISES

1. If $f(x) = 3^x$, find $f(3)$, $f(-1)$, $f(-2)$, and $f(6)$.

2. If $g(x) = 25^x$, find $g(0)$, $g(-1)$, $g\left(\frac{1}{2}\right)$, and $g\left(-\frac{1}{2}\right)$.

3. If $h(x) = 10^x$, find $h(2)$, $h(6)$, $h(-1)$, and $h(-3)$.

*Graph each exponential function. Give the domain and range and tell whether it is an **increasing** or a **decreasing** function.*

4. $f(x) = 3^x$ 5. $f(x) = -(3)^x$ 6. $f(x) = \left(\frac{1}{3}\right)^x$ 7. $f(x) = -\left(\frac{1}{3}\right)^x$.

Let $y = 4(2)^x$.

8. Find y if $x = 3$.   9. Find y if $x = -2$.   10. Find x if $y = 64$.

Let $y = -3\left(\frac{1}{4}\right)^x$.

11. Find y if $x = \frac{1}{2}$.   12. Find x if $y = -3$.   13. Find x if $y = -24$.

Graph each exponential function. Give the domain and range.

14. $f(x) = 3(2^x)$ 15. $f(x) = -2\left(\frac{1}{2}\right)^x$ 16. $f(x) = \frac{1}{2}\left(1\frac{1}{2}\right)^x$ 17. $f(x) = \frac{1}{2}(3)^{-x}$

CHAPTER 10

Let $y = \frac{1}{10}(4)^x$.

18. For what values of x will y be positive?

19. For what values of y will x be positive?

20. Is y an *increasing* function or a *decreasing* function?

21. At what point, if any, will the graph cross the x-axis? the y-axis?

Let $f(x) = 3(5)^x$. If $f(10) = 29{,}296{,}875$, find the value of

22. $f(11)$.   **23.** $f(9)$.   **24.** $f(8)$.   **25.** $f(7)$.

C

Let $f(x) = ka^x$, where x, k, and a are real numbers and $a > 0$. For what values of k and a will $f(x)$ be

26. positive?   **27.** negative?   **28.** increasing?   **29.** decreasing?

Give the equation of the curve symmetric to $y = 4^x$ with respect to

30. the x-axis.   **31.** the y-axis.

Find the points of intersection, if any, of the graphs of the two given exponential functions.

32. $y = 10^x$ and $y = \left(\dfrac{1}{10}\right)^x$

33. $y = -\left(\dfrac{1}{5}\right)^x$ and $y = \left(\dfrac{1}{5}\right)^x$

34. $y = 8^x$ and $y = 8^{-x}$

35. $y = 12^x$ and $y = -\left(\dfrac{1}{12}\right)^x$

36. $y = 2^x$ and $y = \left(\dfrac{1}{2}\right)^{x+2}$

37. $y = 9^{3-x}$ and $y = \left(\dfrac{1}{3}\right)^{x-4}$

CHECKPOINT

1. The radius of a hydrogen atom is about 5.3×10^{-8} millimeters. Write this number as a decimal.

2. Every second, about 1.4×10^{10} drops of water flow over Niagara Falls. Each drop contains about 1.7×10^{21} molecules. Estimate the number of molecules of water that pass over the falls in one minute.

Simplify.

3. $3^{\sqrt{6}} \cdot 3^{\sqrt{6}}$ **4.** $2^{\sqrt{8}} \cdot 2^{\sqrt{2}}$ **5.** $6^{\sqrt{2}} \cdot 5^{\sqrt{2}}$ **6.** $\left(7^{\sqrt{3}}\right)^{\sqrt{3}}$

Solve and check.

7. $3^x = 27$ **8.** $3^{x^2} = 81$ **9.** $6^{-\sqrt{x}} = \dfrac{1}{1296}$ **10.** $7^{3x+1} = 49^{2x-2}$

Inverse Functions and Relations

Consider these points on the line $y = 2x + 2$.

x	−3	−2	−1	0	1
y	−4	−2	0	2	4

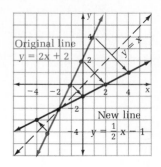

Original line
$y = 2x + 2$

New line
$y = \frac{1}{2}x - 1$

If the x- and y-values are interchanged, a new set of number pairs is formed.

x	−4	−2	0	2	4
y	−3	−2	−1	0	1

Each original point has been reflected about the line $y = x$ to a new point on a new line. The *line of symmetry*, $y = x$, is perpendicular to and bisects the segments connecting each pair of corresponding points.

To find the slope-intercept form of the equation of the new line from the old one, interchange the variables x and y, and solve for y.

$$y = 2x + 2 \;\rightarrow\; x = 2y + 2 \;\rightarrow\; 2y = x - 2 \;\rightarrow\; y = \frac{1}{2}x - 1$$

original equation   Interchange variables.   Solve for y.   new equation

Both equations define functions of x.

$$f(x) = 2x + 2 \qquad g(x) = \frac{1}{2}x - 1$$

The two functions $f(x)$ and $g(x)$ are called **inverse functions.** Each does the inverse mapping of the other. For every point (a, b), if $f(x)$ maps a into b, then $g(x)$ maps b into a.

$f(x)$ maps 1 uniquely into 4. $f(1) = 2(1) + 2 = 2 + 2 = 4$

The point $(1, 4)$ lies on the graph of $y = 2x + 2$.

$g(x)$ maps the 4 uniquely back into 1. $g(4) = \frac{1}{2}(4) - 1 = 2 - 1 = 1$

The point $(4, 1)$ lies on the graph of $y = \frac{1}{2}x - 1$.

Taking the cube root of a number is the inverse of cubing a number. For example, 2 cubed is 8, and the cube root of 8 is 2. The equations $y = x^3$ and $y = \sqrt[3]{x}$ define inverse functions. The graphs are symmetric about the line $y = x$.

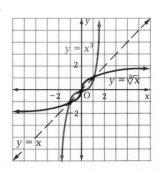

$y = x^3$

$y = \sqrt[3]{x}$

$y = x$

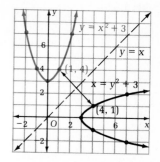

Not every function has an inverse that is also a function. The inverse of the function $y = x^2 + 3$ is the relation $x = y^2 + 3$. The two parabolas are symmetric about the line $y = x$.

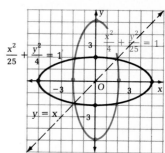

The equations of these two ellipses are $\frac{x^2}{4} + \frac{y^2}{25} = 1$ and $\frac{x^2}{25} + \frac{y^2}{4} = 1$. Neither equation defines a function. However, the relations are inverses, and the graphs are symmetric with respect to the line $y = x$. For every point (a, b) on one, there corresponds a point (b, a) on the other. $\frac{x^2}{4} + \frac{y^2}{25} = 1$ and $\frac{x^2}{25} + \frac{y^2}{4} = 1$ are called **inverse relations.**

EXERCISES

1. Find $g(x)$, the inverse function for $y = f(x) = 3x - 2$. Show that $f(x)$ maps 4 into 10 and that $g(x)$ maps the 10 back into 4.

2. Find $g(x)$, the inverse function for $y = f(x) = -\frac{1}{2}x + 4$. Show that $f(x)$ maps 12 into -2 and that $g(x)$ maps the -2 back into 12.

3. Graph $y = |x|$ and its inverse. Are $y = |x|$ and its inverse both functions?

4. Graph $y = 2x^2 - 1$ and its inverse. Do both equations represent functions?

5. Graph $xy = 12$ and its inverse. Do both equations represent functions?

6. Graph $y = \frac{1}{x}$ and its inverse. Do both equations represent functions?

7. What is the inverse relation for the circle $x^2 + y^2 = 4$?

8. Are the hyperbolas $\frac{x^2}{9} - \frac{y^2}{16} = 1$ and $\frac{x^2}{16} - \frac{y^2}{9} = 1$ symmetric about the line $y = x$? Find the equation of the relation that is the inverse of $\frac{x^2}{9} - \frac{y^2}{16} = 1$.

9. Graph the inverse of the exponential function $y = 2^x$.

10-4 Logarithmic Functions

To express a logarithm in exponential form, and the reverse.
To evaluate logarithms to various bases.
To graph logarithmic functions.

The exponential function $y = 2^x$ gives powers of 2 for specific real values of the exponent x. The inverse of this exponential function is $x = 2^y$. Note that y is the exponent needed on the base 2 to produce the number x. This exponent y is called the **logarithm**, or **log**, of x to the base 2. The resulting *logarithmic equation* is

$$y = \log_2 x \qquad \text{Read: } \textbf{\textit{y}} \text{ \textit{equals the logarithm of} } \textbf{\textit{x}} \text{ \textit{to the base 2,}}$$
$$\text{or } \textbf{\textit{y}} \text{ \textit{equals log} } \textbf{\textit{x}}, \text{ \textit{base 2}}.$$

The two tables below show that the exponential and logarithmic forms of the equation express the same relationship between x and y.

Exponential Equation	
y	$2^y = x$
0	$2^0 = 1$
1	$2^1 = 2$
2	$2^2 = 4$
3	$2^3 = 8$

Logarithmic Equation	
x	$\log_2 x = y$
1	$\log_2 1 = 0$
2	$\log_2 2 = 1$
4	$\log_2 4 = 2$
8	$\log_2 8 = 3$

EXAMPLE 1

Express in logarithmic form.

a. $2^4 = 16$ $\qquad \log_2 16 = 4$ $\qquad$ *log 16, base 2, equals 4*

b. $2^5 = 32$ $\qquad \log_2 32 = 5$ $\qquad$ *log 32, base 2, equals 5*

c. $2^6 = 64$ $\qquad \log_2 64 = 6$ $\qquad$ *log 64, base 2, equals 6*

EXAMPLE 2

Express in exponential form.

a. $\log_2 1024 = 10$ $\qquad 2^{10} = 1024$

b. $\log_2 1,048,576 = 20$ $\qquad 2^{20} = 1,048,576$

c. $\log_2 0.03125 = -5$ $\qquad 2^{-5} = 0.03125$

Since a logarithm is an exponent, it can be any real number. Here is a table of logarithms to the base 2 of some numbers from 2.0 to 2.5.

x	$\log_2 x$
2.0	1.0000
2.1	1.0704
2.2	1.1375
2.3	1.2016
2.4	1.2630
2.5	1.3219

$$\log_2 2.3 = 1.2016$$
$$2^{1.2016} = 2.3$$

Entries in the table have been rounded to four decimal places, so $\log_2 2.3$ is approximately equal to 1.2016. However, we use the symbol = for convenience.

EXAMPLE 3   Solve.

a. $\log_2 x = 1.1375$

Find 1.1375 in the right column of the table.
Find the corresponding value of x, 2.2.

$$\log_2 x = 1.1375$$
$$x = 2.2$$

b. $2^y = 2.5$

The exponential equation $2^y = 2.5$ is equivalent to the logarithmic equation $y = \log_2 2.5$.

Find 2.5 in the left column of the table.

Find the corresponding value of $\log_2 x$, 1.3219.

$$y = \log_2 2.5 = 1.3219$$

The graph in the next example shows that $y = \log_2 x$ is a function. It is called a **logarithmic function,** and it assigns a unique real number y to every positive value of x.

EXAMPLE 4   Graph $y = \log_2 x$.

Since $y = \log_2 x$ is equivalent to $x = 2^y$, a table may be constructed.

y	-2	-1	0	1	2
x	$\frac{1}{4}$	$\frac{1}{2}$	1	2	4

Note that $y = \log_2 x$ is the inverse of the exponential function $y = 2^x$. Hence, the two graphs are symmetric about the line $y = x$. See the Extra Topic on pages 376–377.

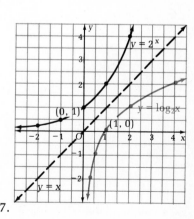

The graph of such a logarithmic function lies entirely to the right of the y-axis. The curve for $y = \log_2 x$ contains the point $(1, 0)$. It drops downward, asymptotic to the y-axis, as x approaches 0 from the right. It rises at a decreasing rate as x becomes large without bound. Do you see that $y = \log_2 x$ is an *increasing function*? Explain why $y = \log_{\frac{1}{2}} x$ is a *decreasing function*.

All logarithmic functions of the form $y = \log_b x$ have these two important properties.

- The domain of the function is $x > 0$.

    You can find the logarithm of any positive real number.

- The range of the function is the set of all real numbers.

    The logarithms of all numbers greater than 1 are positive.
    The logarithm of 1, to any base, is 0.
    The logarithms of all numbers between 0 and 1 are negative.

The base b of a logarithm can be any positive real number except 1. Remember, you can evaluate $\log_b x$ by finding the exponent y such that b^y is equal to x.

$$\overbrace{y = \log_b x \qquad\qquad b^y = x}^{\text{logarithm = exponent}}$$
$$\underbrace{\qquad\qquad\qquad\qquad}_{\text{base}}$$

EXAMPLE 5   Evaluate.

a. $\log_{16} 4$ $16^{\frac{1}{2}} = \sqrt{16} = 4$, so $\log_{16} 4 = \dfrac{1}{2}$.

b. $\log_8 4$ $8^{\frac{2}{3}} = (\sqrt[3]{8})^2 = 4$, so $\log_8 4 = \dfrac{2}{3}$.

c. $\log_{\frac{1}{2}} 4$ $\left(\dfrac{1}{2}\right)^{-2} = 2^2 = 4$, so $\log_{\frac{1}{2}} 4 = -2$.

d. $\log_{10} 1000$ $10^3 = 1000$, so $\log_{10} 1000 = 3$.

If you cannot find the value of a logarithm by inspection, solve the equivalent exponential equation for y. For Example 5b we have

$$\log_8 4 = y \text{ means } 8^y = 4$$
$$(2^3)^y = 2^2 \qquad \text{Use the same base, 2.}$$
$$2^{3y} = 2^2$$
$$3y = 2 \qquad \text{Set the exponents equal.}$$
$$y = \frac{2}{3}$$

Therefore, $\log_8 4 = \frac{2}{3}$.

CLASS EXERCISES

Express in logarithmic form.

1. $10^4 = 10,000$

2. $10^5 = 100,000$

3. $10^8 = 100,000,000$

4. $10^{-2} = 0.01$

5. $10^{-4} = 0.0001$

6. $10^{-7} = 0.0000001$

Express in exponential form.

7. $2 = \log_{10}100$

8. $6 = \log_{10}1,000,000$

9. $-5 = \log_{10}0.00001$

Find the logarithm of

10. one billion, to the base 10.

11. one thousandth, to the base 1000.

Solve for the indicated variable.

12. $\log_{10}1 = y$

13. $\log_{10}x = -1$

14. $\log_b 10 = -1$

EXERCISES

A

Express in logarithmic form.

1. $3^2 = 9$

2. $3^0 = 1$

3. $3^{-2} = \dfrac{1}{9}$

4. $5^3 = 125$

5. $5^{-1} = \dfrac{1}{5}$

6. $5^{-3} = 0.008$

7. $9^{-1} = \dfrac{1}{9}$

8. $9^{\frac{1}{2}} = 3$

9. $9^{-\frac{1}{2}} = \dfrac{1}{3}$

10. $20^4 = 160,000$

11. $20^{-1} = 0.05$

12. $20^{-2} = 0.0025$

Express in exponential form.

13. $\log_4 64 = 3$

14. $\log_4 2 = \dfrac{1}{2}$

15. $\log_4\left(\dfrac{1}{2}\right) = -\dfrac{1}{2}$

16. $\log_{10}100 = 2$

17. $\log_6 36 = 2$

18. $\log_{\frac{1}{2}}\left(\dfrac{1}{4}\right) = 2$

19. $\log_2 16 = 4$

20. $\log_{\frac{1}{2}}16 = -4$

21. $\log_8 16 = \dfrac{4}{3}$

22. $\log_{0.1}1 = 0$

23. $\log_{0.1}10 = -1$

24. $\log_{0.1}0.01 = 2$

Evaluate.

25. $\log_3 81$

26. $\log_8 64$

27. $\log_5 125$

28. $\log_{10}0.1$

29. $\log_9 3$

30. $\log_{49}7$

31. $\log_{\frac{1}{2}}\left(\dfrac{1}{2}\right)$

32. $\log_{\frac{1}{3}}9$

33. $\log_{\frac{1}{4}}64$

34. $\log_4 8$

35. $\log_{100}10,000$

36. $\log_{16}8$

Copy and complete each table. Then graph the function.

37. $\log_3 x = y$, or $x = 3^y$

y	−2	−1	0	1	2
x					

38. $\log_4 x = y$, or $x = 4^y$

y	−2	−1	0	1	2
x					

B *Express in exponential form.*

39. $\log_a 3 = 2$ **40.** $\log_2 x = 5$ **41.** $\log_4 9 = c$ **42.** $\log_a x = 4$

Evaluate.

43. $\log_2 0.25$ **44.** $\log_5 0.04$ **45.** $\log_{\frac{1}{2}} 0.125$ **46.** $\log_4 (4^3)$

47. $\log_2 (2^{-5})$ **48.** $\log_3 (9^2)$ **49.** $\log_{\frac{1}{4}}\left(\dfrac{1}{8}\right)$ **50.** $\log_{\frac{1}{4}} 8$

Use the table to solve each equation.

51. $\log_2 1.2 = y$

52. $\log_2 0.4 = y$

53. $2^y = 0.8$

54. $2^y = 1.6$

x	$\log_2 x$
0.4	−1.322
0.8	−0.322
1.2	0.263
1.6	0.678
2.0	1.000

55. Use the values in the table to graph $y = \log_2 x$ for $0 < x \leq 2$.

C *Graph each logarithmic function. Give the domain and range and tell whether it is an **increasing** or a **decreasing** function.*

56. $y = \log_{\frac{1}{2}} x$ **57.** $y = -\log_2 x$ **58.** $y = -\log_{\frac{1}{2}} x$

59. Compare the graphs from Exercises 56–58 with the graph of $y = \log_2 x$. Which graph is the same as the graph of $y = \log_2 x$? About which axis are the other two graphs symmetrical to the graph of $y = \log_2 x$?

Solve.

60. $\log_b 16 = 4$ **61.** $\log_{100} x = -\dfrac{1}{2}$ **62.** $\log_9 27 = y$ **63.** $\log_4 x = \dfrac{5}{2}$

64. $\log_{\frac{3}{4}}\left(\dfrac{\sqrt{3}}{2}\right) = y$ **65.** $\log_b 4 = \dfrac{1}{4}$ **66.** $\log_{a+1} 32 = 5$ **67.** $\log_4 (b - 3) = -\dfrac{3}{2}$

Find the domain of each logarithmic function.

68. $\log_2 (x - 1)$ **69.** $\log_2 (x + 3)$ **70.** $\log_2 (2x - 1)$

10-5 Properties of Logarithms

OBJECTIVES

To find the logarithm of a product, quotient, or power.
To find the logarithm of a number, using a table.
To find a number, given its logarithm.

Since logarithms are exponents, they have certain useful properties that can be derived from the properties of exponents. The first of these properties states that the logarithm of a product is equal to the *sum* of the logarithms of the factors.

Logarithm of a Product

If M, N, and b are positive real numbers, $b \neq 1$, then

$$\log_b(MN) = \log_b M + \log_b N$$

To show that the above property is true, let $r = \log_b M$ and $s = \log_b N$.

$b^r = M$ and $b^s = N$	Write the exponential forms.
$MN = b^r \cdot b^s$	Multiply equals by equals.
$MN = b^{r+s}$	Add exponents.
$\log_b(MN) = r + s$	Change to logarithmic form.
$\log_b(MN) = \log_b M + \log_b N$	Substitute for r and s.

EXAMPLE 1   Find the logarithm of the product.

a. 16 × 64, to the base 4

$$\log_4(16 \times 64) = \log_4 16 + \log_4 64$$
$$= 2 + 3 \qquad \log_4 16 = 2 \text{ and } \log_4 64 = 3$$
$$= 5$$

b. $256 \times \dfrac{1}{8}$, to the base 2

$$\log_2\left(256 \times \frac{1}{8}\right) = \log_2 256 + \log_2\left(\frac{1}{8}\right)$$
$$= 8 + (-3) \qquad \log_2 256 = 8 \text{ and } \log_2\left(\frac{1}{8}\right) = -3$$
$$= 5$$

It can also be shown that the logarithm of a quotient is equal to the logarithm of the dividend *minus* the logarithm of the divisor.

Logarithm of a Quotient

If *M*, *N*, and *b* are positive real numbers, *b* ≠ 1, then

$$\log_b(M \div N) = \log_b M - \log_b N$$

EXAMPLE 2   Find the logarithm of the quotient.

a. 256 ÷ 32, to the base 2

$$\log_2(256 \div 32) = \log_2 256 - \log_2 32$$
$$= 8 - 5$$
$$= 3$$

b. $\frac{1}{125} \div \frac{1}{25}$, to the base 5

$$\log_5\left(\frac{1}{125} \div \frac{1}{25}\right) = \log_5\left(\frac{1}{125}\right) - \log_5\left(\frac{1}{25}\right)$$
$$= -3 - (-2)$$
$$= -1$$

Recall that any positive number is associated with a unique logarithm for each positive base except 1. The two tables that follow can be used to find the logarithms of the integers from 1 through 10 to the base 2 and to the base 10. They can also be used to find the integer when its logarithm is given.

Logarithms to Base 2

x	$\log_2 x$
1	0.0000
2	1.0000
3	1.5850
4	2.0000
5	2.3219
6	2.5850
7	2.8074
8	3.0000
9	3.1699
10	3.3219

← The logarithm of 3, to the base 2, is 1.5850.

$$\log_2 3 = 1.5850$$

The integer with the logarithm 0.9031, to the base 10, is 8. →

$$\log_{10} 8 = 0.9031$$

Logarithms to Base 10

x	$\log_{10} x$
1	0.0000
2	0.3010
3	0.4771
4	0.6021
5	0.6990
6	0.7782
7	0.8451
8	0.9031
9	0.9542
10	1.0000

The next two examples illustrate how the use of the tables can be extended by applying the properties of logarithms.

EXAMPLE 3   Find the logarithm of 30 to the base 10.

The logarithm of 30 is not in the table, but it can be found using the logarithm of 3.

$$\log_{10} 30 = \log_{10}(3 \times 10) \qquad \text{Write 30 as } 3 \times 10.$$
$$= \log_{10} 3 + \log_{10} 10 \qquad \text{Add the logarithms.}$$
$$= 0.4771 + 1.0000$$
$$= 1.4771$$

What is the logarithm of 300, to the base 10?

EXAMPLE 4   Find the logarithm of 0.5 to the base 2.

Method 1 $\log_2 0.5 = \log_2\left(\dfrac{1}{2}\right) = -1 \qquad \text{Recall that } 2^{-1} = \frac{1}{2}.$

Method 2 $\log_2 0.5 = \log_2(5 \div 10)$
$$= \log_2 5 - \log_2 10 \qquad \text{Subtract the logarithms.}$$
$$= 2.3219 - 3.3219$$
$$= -1.0000$$

What is the logarithm of 0.5, to the base 10?

A third important property of logarithms states that the logarithm of the kth power of a number is equal to k times the logarithm of that number.

Logarithm of a Power

If N and b are positive numbers, $b \neq 1$, and k is any real number, then

$$\log_b N^k = k \log_b N$$

EXAMPLE 5   Find the logarithm of 2^{20} to the base 10.

$$\log_{10}(2^{20}) = 20 \log_{10} 2 \qquad \text{Logarithm of a power}$$
$$= 20(0.3010) \qquad \text{Use the table of logarithms base 10.}$$
$$= 6.0200$$

The value of $2^{20} = 10^{6.0200}$ is slightly more than 10^6, or one million.

EXPONENTIAL AND LOGARITHMIC FUNCTIONS

EXAMPLE 6   Find $\log_2 \sqrt{15}$.

$$\log_2 \sqrt{15} = \log_2 (15^{\frac{1}{2}})$$

$$= \frac{1}{2} \log_2 15 \qquad\qquad \text{Logarithm of a power property}$$

$$= \frac{1}{2} \log_2 (3 \times 5) \qquad \begin{array}{l}\text{Log}_2\ 15 \text{ is not in the table, so} \\ \text{write 15 as } 3 \times 5.\end{array}$$

$$= \frac{1}{2}(\log_2 3 + \log_2 5) \qquad \text{Logarithm of a product property}$$

$$= \frac{1}{2}(1.5850 + 2.3219) \qquad \text{Use the table of logarithms base 2.}$$

$$= \frac{1}{2}(3.9069)$$

$$= 1.9535$$

The value of $\sqrt{15} = 2^{1.9535}$ is slightly less than 2^2, or 4.

CLASS EXERCISES

Find the logarithm of the product, quotient, or power, to the base 3 by using the appropriate rule for logarithms.

1. 9×3 **2.** 27×81 **3.** $729 \times \dfrac{1}{9}$ **4.** $\dfrac{1}{3} \times \dfrac{1}{27}$

5. $81 \div 27$ **6.** $243 \div \dfrac{1}{9}$ **7.** $\dfrac{27}{729}$ **8.** $\dfrac{243}{27}$

9. 9^2 **10.** 27^5 **11.** $\left(\dfrac{1}{81}\right)^2$ **12.** 243^{10}

EXERCISES

A   *Find the logarithm of the product, quotient, or power, to the base 2.*

1. 4×16 **2.** 32×128 **3.** $64 \times \dfrac{1}{4}$ **4.** $\dfrac{1}{8} \times 128$

5. $256 \div 16$ **6.** $4 \div 64$ **7.** $128 \div \dfrac{1}{8}$ **8.** $\dfrac{512}{16}$

9. 4^3 **10.** 16^5 **11.** 64^2 **12.** 256^4

Find the logarithm, given $\log_5 3 = 0.6826$.

13. $\log_5 15$ **Hint:** $15 = 3 \times 5$ **14.** $\log_5 0.6$ **Hint:** $0.6 = 3 \div 5$

15. $\log_5 243$ **Hint:** $243 = 3^5$ **16.** $\log_5 9$

17. $\log_5 \sqrt{3}$ **18.** $\log_5 225$

B

Given $\log_3 10 = 2.0959$, find the logarithm to the base 3 of each number.

19. 9   **20.** 90   **21.** 900   **22.** 9000

23. 27   **24.** 2.7   **25.** 0.27   **26.** 0.027

Given $\log_{10} 4 = 0.6021$ and $\log_{10} 5 = 0.6990$, find the logarithm to the base 10 of each number.

27. 4×10 **28.** 50   **29.** 400   **30.** $5 \div 10$

31. 0.04   **32.** 0.005   **33.** 4^3 **34.** 125

35. 256   **36.** 20^3 **37.** $\dfrac{1}{4}$ **38.** $\dfrac{1}{20}$

39. 64   **40.** $\dfrac{4}{5}$ **41.** $\sqrt{40}$ **42.** $\sqrt[3]{50}$

Find the number that has the given logarithm to the base 10.

43. $0.6990 + 1.0000$ **44.** 2.6021   **45.** 4.6990

46. $0.6021 - 1.0000$ **47.** -0.3010 **48.** -1.3979

Use the logarithm table to the base 2 on page 384. Explain why each statement is true, using the three properties of logarithms.

49. The logarithm of 8 is 3 times the logarithm of 2.

50. The logarithm of 6 is 1 more than the logarithm of 3.

51. The logarithm of 5 is 1 less than the logarithm of 10.

C

Solve. Use the logarithm tables on page 384.

52. $\log_{10} 3 = x$ **53.** $\log_{10} 60 = x$ **54.** $\log_{10} 900 = x$

55. $\log_{10} x = 0.8451$ **56.** $\log_{10} x = 1.9542$ **57.** $\log_{10} x = 5.3010$

58. $\log_{10} \sqrt{3} = x$ **59.** $\log_{10} x = -0.7782$ **60.** $\log_{10} \left(\dfrac{1}{80}\right) = x$

61. $\log_2 (5^4) = x$ **62.** $\log_2 \left(\dfrac{1}{72}\right) = x$ **63.** $\log_2 (12^2) = x$

64. $\log_2 \sqrt{6} = x$ **65.** $\log_2 \sqrt{35} = x$ **66.** $\log_2 \sqrt[3]{20} = x$

67. On the same coordinate plane, graph the two logarithmic functions $y = \log_2 x$ and $y = \log_{10} x$, between $x = 1$ and $x = 10$. Use the tables of values on page 384, rounded to tenths.

*68. Use exponents to show that the quotient property on page 384 is true.

Hint: $\dfrac{b^r}{b^s} = b^{r-s}$

*69. Use exponents to show that the power property on page 385 is true.

Hint: $(b^r)^s = b^{rs}$

10-6 Common Logarithms

To find the common logarithm of a number.
To find the antilogarithm, given the common logarithm.

Base 10 logarithms, or **common logarithms,** can be used in computation. If no base is shown, it is understood that the common logarithm is intended. That is,

$$\log x \text{ means } \log_{10} x.$$

The common logarithms of numbers from 1.00 through 9.99 can be obtained directly from the table on pages 670–671. The table can also be used to find the common logarithms of many other positive numbers. A portion of the table is reproduced here.

Common Logarithms

n	0	1	2	3	4	5	6	7	8	9
46	6628	6637	6646	6656	6665	6675	6684	6693	6702	6712
47	6721	6730	6739	6749	6758	6767	6776	**6785**	6794	6803
48	6812	6821	6830	6839	6848	6857	6866	6875	6884	6893

To find the common logarithm of 4.77, locate the row with the first two digits 47. Then read across to column 7 to find the logarithm, correct to four decimal places. Note that the decimal points are not shown in the table.

$$\log 4.77 = 0.6785$$

To find the logarithm of a number between 0 and 1 or greater than 10, the number is first written in scientific notation.

EXAMPLE 1

Find the common logarithm of 468.

Begin by writing 468 in scientific notation: $468 = 4.68 \times 10^2$. The table shows that log 4.68 is equal to 0.6702.

$$\begin{aligned} \log 468 &= \log (4.68 \times 10^2) \\ &= \log 4.68 + \log 10^2 \\ &= 0.6702 + 2 \qquad \log 10^2 = 2 \\ &= 2.6702 \end{aligned}$$

The decimal portion of a logarithm, read from the table, is called the **mantissa.** The integral part of the logarithm, *not* found in the table, is called the **characteristic.** In the preceding example the mantissa is 0.6702 and the characteristic is 2. Note that the characteristic is the exponent of 10 when the original number is written in scientific notation.

CHAPTER 10

The logarithm of a number between 0 and 1 is negative. However, in order to use the table of common logarithms, we show such a logarithm with a positive mantissa and a negative characteristic.

EXAMPLE 2 Find the common logarithm of 0.481.

$$\log 0.481 = \log (4.81 \times 10^{-1})$$
$$= \log 4.81 + \log 10^{-1}$$
$$= 0.6821 + (-1) \qquad \text{From the table, } \log 4.81 = 0.6821.$$
$$= 0.6821 - 1$$

Actually, a negative logarithm may be written in various ways for convenience in computation. To illustrate, any of the expressions below may be used to show the logarithm of 0.481.

$$\log 0.481 = -0.3179 \qquad \text{Not in mantissa/characteristic form}$$
$$= \quad 0.6821 - 1 \qquad \text{Mantissa: } 0.6821 \quad \text{Characteristic: } 0 - 1 = -1$$
$$= \quad 3.6821 - 4 \qquad \text{Mantissa: } 0.6821 \quad \text{Characteristic: } 3 - 4 = -1$$
$$= \quad 9.6821 - 10 \qquad \text{Mantissa: } 0.6821 \quad \text{Characteristic: } 9 - 10 = -1$$

We have illustrated the use of a table to find the common logarithm of a given number N. The inverse procedure is to find the original number N when its logarithm is given. The original number is called the **antilogarithm,** or **antilog,** of the given logarithm.

If $\log N = x$, then antilog $x = N$.

EXAMPLE 3 Find each antilogarithm. Use the table on pages 670–671.

a. antilog 0.9455

The characteristic is 0, so the number is between 1 and 10, and it can be found directly from the table. Find 9455 in the body of the table. Read across to the left to find the first two digits, 88, of the antilogarithm. The third digit, 2, is read from the top of the column containing 9455.

antilog $0.9455 = 8.82$

b. antilog 4.9455

The antilogarithm is the product of the antilogs of the mantissa, 0.9455, and the characteristic, 4.

antilog $4.9455 = (\text{antilog } 0.9455)(\text{antilog } 4)$
$$= 8.82 \times 10^4 = 88{,}200$$

c. antilog (8.9455 − 10)

The characteristic is $8 - 10$, or -2.

antilog $(8.9455 - 10) = (\text{antilog } 0.9455)(\text{antilog } -2)$
$$= 8.82 \times 10^{-2} = 0.0882$$

CLASS EXERCISES

Give the characteristic of the common logarithm of each number. Then find each mantissa, using the table on pages 670–671.

1. 3.86 2. 93.6 3. 574 4. 6.66 5. 17.2

6. 1730 7. 900 8. 0.271 9. 0.0152 10. 0.0077

EXERCISES

A Give the characteristic and the mantissa of the common logarithm of each number.

1. 255 2. 4020 3. 19,900 4. 1.66

5. 4.5 6. 0.521 7. 30.3 8. 25

9. 0.013 10. 0.005 11. 3,650,000 12. 160,000,000

13. 0.000124 14. 0.9 15. 88.8 16. 0.0000007

Find the common logarithm of each number.

17. 2.43 18. 24.3 19. 243 20. 2430

21. 7.07 22. 0.707 23. 0.0707 24. 0.00707

25. 8 26. 8000 27. 0.0008 28. 0.00008

29. 72,000 30. 0.0072 31. 0.72 32. 7,200,000

Find the antilogarithm of each common logarithm.

33. 0.6474 34. 1.6474 35. 2.6474 36. 5.6474

37. 0.3054 38. 0.3054 − 1 39. 0.3054 − 2 40. 0.3054 − 4

41. 0.9542 42. 1.9542 43. 6.9542 44. 0.9542 − 3

Evaluate.

45. log 6.73 46. log 44.9 47. log 968 48. log 50,000

49. log 0.44 50. log 0.038 51. log 0.00292 52. log 0.000875

53. log 6850 54. log 0.0003 55. log 320,000 56. log 0.000029

B 57. antilog 0.5378 58. antilog 2.3464 59. antilog 1.5250

60. antilog 3.8241 61. antilog (9.7505 − 10) 62. antilog (3.1038 − 4)

63. antilog 4.4609 64. antilog (0.9074 − 4) 65. antilog (5.3711 − 10)

66. antilog 5.8451 67. antilog 3.0000 68. antilog (9.3010 − 10)

Find the common logarithms of the first five

69. perfect squares. Start with 1.

70. powers of 0.3. Start with $(0.3)^1$.

C

*71. Prove the formula for changing bases: $\log_a N = \dfrac{\log_b N}{\log_b a}$.
Hint: Let $\log_a N = r$, $\log_b N = s$, and $\log_b a = t$.

*72. Find $\log_8 1024$, given that $\log_2 1024 = 10$. Use the formula in Exercise 71.

*73. Find $\log_{10} 400$ and $\log_{10} 5$ in the table of common logarithms. Then find $\log_5 400$.

USING THE CALCULATOR

The Number *e*

In advanced mathematics *logarithms* are often found to a special base, *e*. Here are two ways in which the value of *e* can be found.

I $\quad e = 1 + \dfrac{1}{1} + \dfrac{1}{2 \cdot 1} + \dfrac{1}{3 \cdot 2 \cdot 1} + \dfrac{1}{4 \cdot 3 \cdot 2 \cdot 1} + \cdots$

II $\quad e = $ the limit of $\left(1 + \dfrac{1}{n}\right)^n$,
as *n* increases without bound

1. Evaluate the first eight terms in the series shown in **I**. Find the sum to four decimal places, as an estimate of *e*.

2. Use a table of common logarithms to evaluate $\left(1 + \dfrac{1}{n}\right)^n$ for $n = 100$, to one decimal place.

Hint: $\log \left(1 + \dfrac{1}{100}\right)^{100} = \log (1.01)^{100} = 100 \log 1.01$.

Use a calculator with an exponent key to evaluate $\left(1 + \dfrac{1}{n}\right)^n$

3. for *n* equal to one thousand.

4. for *n* equal to one million.

The number *e* is an irrational number. The calculator display below gives its value correct to 10 digits.

$$e \approx 2.718281828$$

10-7 Computing with Logarithms

OBJECTIVES _____

To find products, quotients, powers, and roots using common logarithms.
To solve problems using logarithms.

_____

When computing with logarithms, familiar procedures are changed dramatically. Since logs are exponents, multiplication is done by *adding* logarithms, and division is done by *subtracting* logarithms.

Multiplication: log(*a* · *b*) = log *a* + log *b*

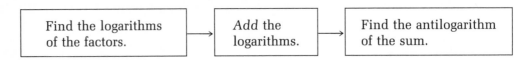

Division: log(*a* ÷ *b*) = log *a* − log *b*

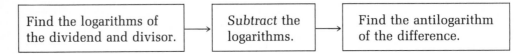

The two procedures are combined here in a single example.

EXAMPLE 1 Evaluate $N = \frac{(28.9)(66,800)}{0.00135}$ using common logarithms.

Step 1 Find the logarithms of the given numbers.

$\log 28.9 \quad = \log(2.89 \times 10^1) \quad = 1.4609$

$\log 66,800 = \log(6.68 \times 10^4) \quad = 4.8248$

$\log 0.00135 = \log(1.35 \times 10^{-3}) = 0.1303 - 3$

Step 2 Add and subtract the logarithms, as required.

$\log N = \log(28.9 \times 66,800) - \log 0.00135$

$= \log 28.9 + \log 66,800 - \log 0.00135$

$= 1.4609 + 4.8248 - (0.1303 - 3)$

$= 9.1554$

Step 3 Find the antilogarithm of the result.

$$N = \text{antilog } 9.1554 = 1.43 \times 10^9$$

Use the nearest mantissa in the table, 0.1553.

$$= 1{,}430{,}000{,}000$$

The result is very close to 1,430,014,815, the answer obtained by performing the multiplication and division and rounding to the nearest whole number.

While logarithms can be used to simplify multiplication and division, they are especially helpful when finding powers and roots.

Powers and Roots: $\log a^b = b \log a$

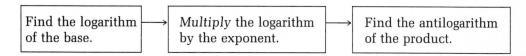

Find the logarithm of the base. → *Multiply* the logarithm by the exponent. → Find the antilogarithm of the product.

EXAMPLE 2   Evaluate $N = (0.8)^7$ using common logarithms.

Step 1 Find the logarithm of the base.

$$\log 0.8 = \log(8 \times 10^{-1}) = 0.9031 - 1$$

Step 2 Multiply the logarithm by the exponent.

$$\log N = 7 \log 0.8 = 7(0.9031 - 1)$$
$$= 6.3217 - 7, \text{ or } 0.3217 - 1$$

Step 3 Find the antilogarithm of the product.

$$N = \text{antilog}(0.3217 - 1)$$
$$= 2.10 \times 10^{-1}$$

Use the nearest mantissa in the table, 0.3222.

$$= 0.210$$

The result is close to the exact value of $(0.8)^7$, which is 0.2097152.

EXAMPLE 3   Evaluate $N = 3.46(12)^{-5}$ using common logarithms.

$$\log 3.46 = 0.5391$$
$$\log 12^{-5} = -5(\log 12) = -5(1.0792) = -5.3960$$

$$\log N = \log 3.46 + \log 12^{-5}$$
$$= 0.5391 + (-5.3960)$$
$$= -4.8569$$

$$N = \text{antilog}(-4.8569)$$
$$= \text{antilog}(0.1431 - 5)$$
$$= 1.39 \times 10^{-5}$$
$$= 0.0000139$$

$-4.8569 = 5 + (-4.8569) - 5$
$= 0.1431 - 5$

Practice in computing with logarithms helps increase understanding of the properties of logarithmic functions. The expressions in the examples can, of course, be evaluated quickly on a scientific calculator. The next example compares the results obtained using a table of common logs and using one type of scientific calculator.

EXAMPLE 4 Find the fourth root of 0.2.

a. Use common logarithms.

Let $N = \sqrt[4]{0.2} = (0.2)^{\frac{1}{4}}$.

Then $\log N = \dfrac{1}{4}(\log 0.2)$

$\qquad = \dfrac{1}{4}(0.3010 - 1)$

$\qquad = \dfrac{1}{4}(3.3010 - 4)$ $0.3010 - 1$ is written as $3.3010 - 4$ so that multiplication by $\frac{1}{4}$ will give an integer for the characteristic.

$\qquad = 0.8253 - 1$

$N = \text{antilog}(0.8253 - 1) = 0.669$

b. Use a scientific calculator.

Can you explain why these keys are used, and in the sequence shown?

CLASS EXERCISES

Evaluate to three significant digits, using common logarithms.

1. 1580×67 2. 44.9×0.0338 3. 0.404×0.000987

4. $450 \div 89.1$ 5. $3000 \div 0.0401$ 6. $0.00111 \div 63{,}300$

7. $(0.00475)^3$ 8. $\sqrt{668}$ 9. $\sqrt[5]{239{,}000}$

EXERCISES

A   *Evaluate to three significant digits, using common logarithms.*

1. 632×94 2. 55.5×0.125 3. 0.00334×0.0808

4. $235{,}000 \times 162$ 5. 46.5×12.9 6. 0.0149×0.000783

7. $48{,}000 \times 7.21$ 8. $6 \times 120 \times 3650$ 9. $0.011 \times 0.0547 \times 98$

10. $\dfrac{6240}{977}$ **11.** $\dfrac{47.3}{0.258}$ **12.** $\dfrac{0.137}{0.00464}$

13. $\dfrac{720}{23.6}$ **14.** $\dfrac{5850}{0.821}$ **15.** $\dfrac{0.0121}{77,500}$

16. $4.65 \div 4.56$ **17.** $8 \div 0.067$ **18.** $29.6 \times 4.33 \div 0.351$

19. $\dfrac{(66)(5450)}{273}$ **20.** $\dfrac{(256)(328)}{475}$ **21.** $\dfrac{(27.5)(36.8)}{108}$

22. 24^3 **23.** $(4.8)^4$ **24.** $(78.6)^4$

25. $\sqrt{117}$ **26.** $\sqrt[3]{671,000}$ **27.** $\sqrt{0.0397}$

B

28. $\dfrac{4.89}{(11.2)(363)}$ **29.** $\dfrac{(57.5)(48.2)}{(0.12)(59.7)(806)}$ **30.** $\dfrac{(0.14)(0.027)}{(0.38)(1.25)}$

31. $(0.5)^5$ **32.** $(11.3)^{-4}$ **33.** $52(3.5)^6$

34. $12(4.6)^3$ **35.** $1.8(2.4)^{-3}$ **36.** $73(4.5)(3.25)^{-2}$

37. $\dfrac{6(4.5)^3}{(2.8)(167)}$ **38.** $\dfrac{(3270)(2650)}{11^4}$ **39.** $\dfrac{0.8(19)^4}{35.8}$

40. $\sqrt[3]{0.529}$ **41.** $\sqrt[5]{0.0411}$ **42.** $\sqrt[4]{0.89}$

43. $35\sqrt{325}$ **44.** $2.4\sqrt{3.86}$ **45.** $624\sqrt[3]{12}$

Evaluate to three significant digits, using common logarithms.
Let $a = 257$, $b = 1120$, and $c = 0.0354$.

46. a^2b **47.** ab^3 **48.** $(ac)^2$ **49.** abc^2

50. $\dfrac{a}{b^2c}$ **51.** $\dfrac{a^2c^4}{b^3}$ **52.** $\sqrt{abc}$ **53.** $\sqrt[3]{a^2c}$

54. $\sqrt[4]{b\sqrt{c^2}}$ **55.** $\sqrt{b\sqrt{a}}$ **56.** $\sqrt[3]{b^2\sqrt{c}}$ **57.** $\sqrt[5]{a\sqrt{bc^2}}$

Evaluate to three significant digits, using common logarithms.

C

58. $\dfrac{52\sqrt[3]{0.49}}{(0.015)^4}$ **59.** $\sqrt{\dfrac{\sqrt[3]{0.8}}{225,000}}$ **60.** $\sqrt[3]{(4.8)^2\sqrt{927}}$

Use your knowledge of logarithms.

61. Evaluate $1750(1 + i)^n$, for $i = 0.09$ and $n = 15$.

62. Evaluate $\dfrac{1}{\sqrt{2\pi}}e^{-0.32}$, using $\pi = 3.14$ and $e = 2.72$.

63. Determine the number of digits in the standard numeral for 5^{20}.

64. Find the smallest positive integer n that will make 7^n a 20-digit numeral.

Use your knowledge of logarithms.

65. Find the square root of $\frac{1}{2}$.

66. Find the cube root of $\frac{3}{4}$.

67. Find the fourth root of $\frac{1}{3}$.

68. Find the sixth root of $\frac{2}{3}$.

69. Find the fifth root of the fourth power of 5.25, to the nearest hundredth.

70. Find the fifth power of the fourth root of 5.25, to the nearest hundredth.

One formula for compound interest is $A = P\left(1 + \frac{r}{n}\right)^{nt}$. P is the principal invested, r is the annual interest rate, expressed as a decimal, and n is the number of times the interest is compounded yearly. A is the total amount at the end of t years. Use this formula and logarithms in Exercises 71–73.

71. A deposit of $2500 earns 12%, compounded monthly. Approximately how much money will be in the account at the end of 7 years?

72. A $6000 bond pays 8% interest, compounded quarterly. Find the approximate value of the bond in 15 years.

73. An investment of $22,500 earns 10%, compounded every six months. How much *interest* will the investment earn in 5 years?

74. Use logarithms and the formula $A = \frac{1}{4}a^2\sqrt{3}$ to find the area of an equilateral triangle in which a, the length of each side, is 2.35 centimeters.

75. Use logarithms and the formula $V = \frac{1}{3}b^3\sqrt{2}$ to find the volume of a regular octahedron in which b, the length of each edge, is 12.8 centimeters.

76. Use logarithms and the formula $V = 2\pi^2 R r^2$ to find the volume of a donut-shaped figure called a *torus*, if $R = 126$ centimeters and $r = 98.5$ centimeters. Use 3.14 as an approximation for π.

*77. If $\log (p^2) = 4 - \log q$, find p in terms of q.

CHECKPOINT

Solve and check.

1. $\left(\frac{1}{3}\right)^x = \left(\frac{1}{27}\right)^{x-1}$

2. $2^{x^2-5x} = 64$

3. $5^x 4^x = 20^{\sqrt{x}}$

Express in logarithmic form.

4. $36^{\frac{1}{2}} = 6$

5. $10^{-1} = \frac{1}{10}$

6. $5^3 = 125$

7. Copy and complete the table. Then graph the function $\log_2 x = y$, or $x = 2^y$.

y	-2	-1	0	1	2
$x = 2^y$					

Solve and check.

8. $\log_b 36 = 2$

9. $\log_{144} a = -\frac{1}{2}$

10. $\log_3 81 = n$

Linear Interpolation

Values from the table of common logarithms can be used to graph the logarithmic function $y = \log x$. The function
is always increasing.

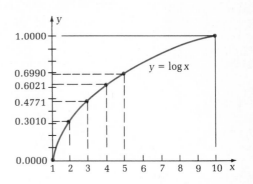

Over the interval $2.00 \le x \le 2.04$,
the graph barely curves at all.

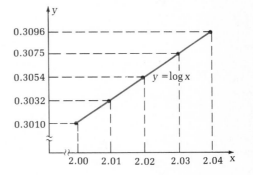

Over the interval $2.00 \le x \le 2.01$,
the graph is very nearly a straight line
connecting the points $(2.00, 0.3010)$
and $(2.01, 0.3032)$.

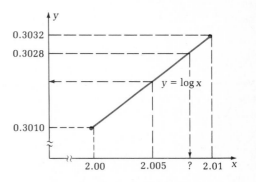

Over small intervals in x, a procedure known as **linear interpolation** can
be used to estimate the value of log x. The method is based on the fact that
the corresponding sides of similar triangles are proportional.

Example 1 illustrates the use of such a proportion in linear interpolation.
It is assumed that $y = \log x$ is a straight line over a small interval, and that
the differences between numbers in that interval are proportional to the differences between their logarithms.

EXPONENTIAL AND LOGARITHMIC FUNCTIONS

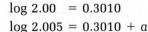

Example 1 Estimate the value of log 2.005, using linear interpolation.

Log 2.005 is more than log 2.00, which is known.

log 2.00 = 0.3010

log 2.005 = 0.3010 + a

Draw the similar triangles, as shown. Write a proportion and solve for a to four decimal places.

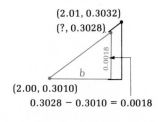

$$\frac{a}{0.005} = \frac{0.0022}{0.01}$$

$$a = \frac{(0.005)(0.0022)}{0.01} = 0.0011$$

Then log 2.005 = 0.3010 + a = 0.3010 + 0.0011 = 0.3021.
A scientific calculator gives a more precise estimate, 0.3021144.

Example 2 Estimate the value of antilog 0.3028, using linear interpolation.

Antilog 0.3028 is more than antilog 0.3010, which is 2.00.

antilog 0.3028 = 2.00 + b

Draw the similar triangles, write a proportion, and solve for b to three decimal places.

(2.01, 0.3032)
(?, 0.3028)
(2.00, 0.3010)
0.3028 − 0.3010 = 0.0018

$$\frac{b}{0.0018} = \frac{0.01}{0.0022}$$

$$b = \frac{(0.0018)(0.01)}{0.0022} = 0.008$$

Then antilog 0.3028 = 2.00 + b = 2.00 + 0.008 = 2.008. The value found on a scientific calculator is 2.0081678.

EXERCISES

Use the table on pages 670–671 and linear interpolation to estimate each value. Check using a scientific calculator, if one is available.

1. log 2.004

2. log 5.618

3. log 38.05

4. log 0.1242

5. log 0.01633

6. antilog 0.3006

7. antilog 0.7784

8. antilog 2.4414

9. antilog (0.2314 − 1)

10-8 Exponential and Logarithmic Equations

OBJECTIVES

To solve exponential and logarithmic equations.
To solve problems involving such equations.

In an *exponential equation*, the variable appears in an exponent. In this chapter you have solved some simple exponential equations by inspection, using your knowlege of powers and roots. A more general method for solving such equations is to take the logarithm of the expression on each side of the equation. If the result is a linear or quadratic equation, it can readily be solved for the variable.

EXAMPLE 1   Solve $10^{x+3} = 100$.

$$10^{x+3} = 100$$
$$\log 10^{x+3} = \log 100 \qquad \text{Take the logarithm of each side.}$$
$$(x + 3) \log 10 = \log 100$$
$$(x + 3)(1) = 2$$
$$x = -1$$

Check $10^{-1+3} = 10^2 = 100$ ✔

The solution is -1.

In a **logarithmic equation,** the variable often appears in the logarithm. To solve such an equation, take the antilogarithm of the expression on each side.

EXAMPLE 2   Solve $\frac{1}{3} \log x = -2$.

$$\frac{1}{3} \log x = -2$$
$$\log x = -6$$
$$\text{antilog } (\log x) = \text{antilog } (-6) \qquad \text{Take the antilog of each side.}$$
$$x = 10^{-6}$$
$$x = 0.000001$$

Check $\frac{1}{3} \log 0.000001 = \frac{1}{3}(-6) = -2$ ✔

The solution is 0.000001.

EXAMPLE 3   Solve $\log x + \log(x + 15) = 2$.

$$\log x + \log(x + 15) = 2$$
$$\log[x(x + 15)] = 2 \qquad \text{Why?}$$
$$x(x + 15) = 10^2 \qquad \text{Take the antilog of each side.}$$
$$x(x + 15) = 100$$
$$x^2 + 15x - 100 = 0 \qquad \text{Solve the resulting quadratic equation.}$$
$$(x + 20)(x - 5) = 0$$
$$x = -20 \quad or \quad x = 5$$

Test each root as a possible solution to the original equation.

$x = -20$ is *not* a solution, since $\log x$ is not defined for a negative x.

For $x = 5$: $\log 5 + \log 20 = \log 5(20) = \log 100 = 2$ ✔

The solution is 5.

Exponential equations can be used in many banking applications. One use is with the *compound interest formula.*

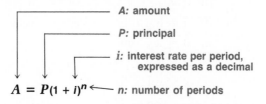

A: amount
P: principal
i: interest rate per period, expressed as a decimal
$$A = P(1 + i)^n \longleftarrow \text{n: number of periods}$$

EXAMPLE 4   At 1% monthly, how long will it take for an amount of money to double, assuming interest is compounded monthly?

Strategy: Substitute in the compound interest formula and solve for n.

$i = 1\% = 0.01$ If you let $P = 1$, then $A = 2$.

Solve for n: $A = P(1 + i)^n$
$$2 = 1(1 + 0.01)^n$$
$$2 = (1.01)^n$$
$$\log 2 = \log(1.01)^n$$
$$\log 2 = n \log 1.01$$
$$0.3010 = n(0.0043) \qquad \text{Use the table of common logarithms.}$$
$$n = 70$$

The money will double in 70 months, or 5 years 10 months.

Exponential equations are useful in solving growth and decay problems. For example, the growth of bacteria is exponential under certain conditions, as time increases.

EXAMPLE 5   An exponential equation relates the number N of bacteria in a culture to the elapsed time t, in hours. If there are 300 bacteria initially, then the equation for the number at time t is $N = 300 \cdot 2^{5t}$. For example, after $t = 2$ hours, there are $N = 300 \cdot 2^{10}$, or 307,200 bacteria. Find how long it will take, under these conditions, for the bacteria count to grow to one million.

Solve the exponential equation $1{,}000{,}000 = 300 \cdot 2^{5t}$ for t.

$$1{,}000{,}000 = 300 \cdot 2^{5t}$$
$$\log 1{,}000{,}000 = \log 300 + 5t(\log 2)$$
$$6 = 2.4771 + 5t(0.3010)$$
$$5t(0.3010) = 6 - 2.4771$$
$$1.505t = 3.5229$$
$$t = 2.34 \qquad \text{To the nearest hundredth}$$

The time needed is 2.34 hours, or approximately 2 hours 20 minutes.

CLASS EXERCISES

Solve, using common logarithms.

1. $10^x = 10{,}000$

2. $10^{x+5} = 1000$

3. $100^{x-1} = 10$

4. $\log x = 3$

5. $\frac{1}{4} \log x = -1$

6. $\log x + \log(x - 9) = 1$

EXERCISES

A *Solve, using common logarithms.*

1. $10^x = 1000$

2. $10^{x+4} = 1000$

3. $10^{x(x-2)} = 1000$

4. $10^x = 0.01$

5. $10^{x-3} = 0.01$

6. $10^{x^2} = 10{,}000$

7. $\frac{1}{2} \log x = 1$

8. $\frac{1}{3} \log x = -2$

9. $\log(x + 1) = 1$

10. $\log(x - 5) = -2$

11. $\frac{1}{2} \log(x + 2) = -1$

12. $\log[x(x + 21)] = 2$

13. $\log x + \log 5 = 3$

14. $\log x + \log 5 = 1$

15. $\log 5 - \log x = 1$

16. $10^x = 12$

17. $10^x = 1.2$

18. $10^x = 0.12$

19. $\log x = 2.525$

20. $2 \log x = 1.6$

21. $\log(x + 1) = 0.941$

22. $\log x = 0.9355$

23. $2 \log x = 2.4244$

24. $\log(x - 2) = 1.179$

25. $3^{x^2} = 3^{3x-2}$ **26.** $2^x = 4^5$ **27.** $10^x = 10^{5x}$

28. $2 \log(x - 2) = 2$ **29.** $3 \log(x - 4) = 0$ **30.** $\log x + \log(x + 3) = 1$

Solve. Give each answer to three significant digits.

31. $3^x = 4$ **32.** $3^x = 65$ **33.** $3^x = 2$

34. $10^x = 5^{x+1}$ **35.** $4^{x+1} = 3^x$ **36.** $2^{x+1} = 5^{2x}$

37. $2^x = 7^{x-1}$ **38.** $2^x(3^{x-1}) = 10$ **39.** $\log x - \log(x + 1) = -1$

Use the equation $A = P(1 + i)^n$ in Exercises 40–44.

40. Find A, if $P = \$1000$, $i = 3\%$, and $n = 5$.

41. Find P, if $A = \$5000$, $i = 2\%$, and $n = 20$.

42. Find n to the nearest whole number, if $A = \$2000$, $P = \$500$, $i = 1\%$.

43. Find i to the nearest percent, if $A = \$3000$, $P = \$2030$, and $n = 10$.

44. In a certain account, the interest is compounded monthly. If the amount in the account doubles in 70 months, what is the interest rate per month? How long would it take for the original amount to be tripled?

The number of bacteria in a certain culture can be found using the equation $N = k \cdot 2^{3t}$. N is the number of bacteria present after t hours and k is the initial number of bacteria.

45. If $k = 100$ and $t = 2$, find N to three significant digits.

46. If $N = 500$ and $t = 3$, find k to three significant digits.

47. If $k = 200$ and $N = 10{,}000$, find t to three significant digits.

A mechanical engineer is designing a large spherical tank. He knows the volume of a sphere can be found using the formula $V = \frac{4}{3}\pi r^3$. Use logarithms and use 3.14 as an approximation of π to find the following to three significant digits.

48. The volume of the tank, if the radius is 3.75 meters

49. The radius needed to give a volume of 2500 cubic meters

The period of a simple pendulum with a small amplitude can be found using the equation $t = 2\pi\sqrt{\frac{l}{980}}$, where t is the period in seconds and l is the length of the pendulum in centimeters. Use logarithms and use 3.14 as an approximation of π to find the following to three significant digits.

50. The period, if the length is 50 centimeters

51. The length, if the period is 0.8 second

Depreciation

The *total depreciation* of an object is the difference between its original value and the estimated salvage or scrap value after it is no longer useful. One method of computing the rate of depreciation is the *constant-percentage* method. The value of an object at the end of a given year is computed at a fixed percentage of its value at the beginning of that year. The following formula can be used to find the rate of depreciation, D, expressed as a decimal. V is the scrap value, and F is the initial, or first, cost, both in dollars. n is the useful life of the object in years.

$$D = 1 - \sqrt[n]{\frac{V}{F}}$$

Example A piece of construction equipment costs $60,000. It has a useful life of 4 years and a scrap value of $4000. Find the rate of depreciation and the value at the end of the first year.

$$D = 1 - \sqrt[4]{\frac{4000}{60,000}}$$

$$1 - D = \sqrt[4]{\frac{4000}{60,000}}$$

$$\log(1 - D) = \frac{1}{4}(\log 4000 - \log 60,000)$$

$$\log(1 - D) = \frac{1}{4}(3.6021 - 4.7782)$$

$$\log(1 - D) = -0.2940$$

$$\log(1 - D) = 9.7060 - 10$$

$$1 - D = 0.508$$

$$D = 0.492 \quad \text{The depreciation rate is 49.2\%.}$$

Since the equipment depreciates 49.2% the first year, its value at the end of that year is $100\% - 49.2\% = 50.8\%$ of $60,000.

$0.508 \times 60,000 = 30,480$ After one year, the value is $30,480.

A machine costs $128,000. Its useful life is 3 years; its scrap value is $600.

1. Find the rate of depreciation. Use logarithms.

2. Find the value of the machine after 1 year.

3. Find its value at the end of 2 years.

4. Use the rate of depreciation to verify that its scrap value after 3 years is about $600.

CHAPTER 10 REVIEW

VOCABULARY

scientific notation (p. 364)
significant digits (p. 364)
exponential equation (p. 369)
exponential function (p. 372)
increasing function (p. 372)
decreasing function (p. 373)
inverse function (p. 376)

logarithm, log (p. 378)
logarithmic function (p. 379)
common logarithm (p. 388)
mantissa (p. 388)
characteristic (p. 388)
antilogarithm, antilog (p. 389)
logarithmic equation (p. 399)

SUMMARY

Initially, this chapter deals with scientific notation and the extension of the exponential concept to include all real numbers. This makes it possible to introduce exponential functions, which are then used to develop logarithmic functions. Since logarithms are exponents, the properties of exponents are used to show how computation is done with logarithms. These ideas are incorporated in the development of methods of solving exponential and logarithmic equations and problems that deal with exponential growth.

REVIEW EXERCISES

10-1 Give the number of significant digits in each approximate number.

1. 3800   **2.** 3080   **3.** 3008   **4.** 0.038

Write each approximate number in scientific notation.

5. 23,000   **6.** 0.305   **7.** 8,000,000   **8.** 0.000072

Write each number as a decimal or as a whole number.

9. 4.6×10^5 **10.** 1.03×10^{-6} **11.** 5×10^{-7} **12.** 9.9×10^6

10-2 Simplify using the properties of exponents.

13. $5^{\sqrt{3}} \cdot 3^{\sqrt{3}}$ **14.** $(6^{\sqrt{3}} \cdot 2^{\sqrt{2}})^0$ **15.** $7^{\sqrt{2}} \cdot 7^{-\sqrt{2}}$ **16.** $4^{\sqrt{2}} \cdot 4^{2\sqrt{2}}$

17. $(4^{\sqrt{5}})^{\sqrt{5}}$ **18.** $(3^{\sqrt{2}} \cdot 2^{\sqrt{2}})^{\sqrt{2}}$ **19.** $a^{\sqrt{3}} \cdot a^{\sqrt{3}}$ **20.** $(a^{\sqrt{3}}b)^{\sqrt{3}}$

Solve and check.

21. $2^{3x} = 64$ **22.** $4^{x-1} = 256$ **23.** $27^x = 9$ **24.** $8^x = 16$

25. $16^x = 8$ **26.** $2^{x+4} = 8^x$ **27.** $3^{3x-1} = 243$ **28.** $16^{2x-1} = 8^{x+2}$

10-3 Find each of the following if $f(x) = 2(4)^x$.

29. $f(2)$ **30.** $f(-3)$ **31.** $f(5)$ **32.** $f\left(\dfrac{3}{2}\right)$

Let $y = 5(2)^x$.

33. Find y if $x = -3$.   **34.** Find x if $y = 10\sqrt{2}$.

Graph each exponential function. Give the domain and range.

35. $f(x) = 4^x$ **36.** $f(x) = 5\left(\dfrac{1}{2}\right)^x$

10-4   Express in logarithmic form.

37. $3^4 = 81$ **38.** $4^{-3} = \dfrac{1}{64}$ **39.** $5^4 = 625$ **40.** $8^{\frac{2}{3}} = 4$

Express in exponential form.

41. $\log_8 2 = \dfrac{1}{3}$ **42.** $\log_{32} 16 = \dfrac{4}{5}$ **43.** $\log_{10} 0.1 = -1$ **44.** $\log_{10} 1000 = 3$

Evaluate.

45. $\log_3 27$ **46.** $\log_5\left(\dfrac{1}{5}\right)$ **47.** $\log_{\frac{1}{4}} 64$ **48.** $\log_{32} 8$

49. Graph $y = \log_5 x$ **50.** Graph $y = \log_{\frac{1}{3}} x$

10-5   Given that $\log_2 5 = 2.3219$, find each logarithm.

51. $\log_2 10$ **52.** $\log_2 25$ **53.** $\log_2 100$ **54.** $\log_2 500$

Given that $\log_{10} 7 = 0.8451$, find the logarithm to the base 10 of each number.

55. 49   **56.** 4.9   **57.** 0.49   **58.** 0.049

10-6   Find the common logarithm of each number. Use the tables on pages 670–671.

59. 3.14   **60.** 0.812   **61.** 21,600   **62.** 0.0012

Use the table to find the antilogarithm of each number.

63. 0.8727   **64.** $7.9619 - 10$ **65.** 3.7067   **66.** -1.0969

10-7   Evaluate to three significant digits, using common logarithms.

67. 2.45×71.3 **68.** $(2.08)^3$ **69.** $\dfrac{6.38(2.17)}{72.4(0.513)}$ **70.** $\sqrt[5]{909}$

Let $a = 436$ and $b = 0.0216$. Evaluate to three significant digits.

71. $a^2 b$ **72.** $\dfrac{a}{b^2}$ **73.** $\sqrt{ab}$ **74.** $\sqrt[4]{a^2 b^3}$

10-8   Solve, using common logarithms.

75. $10^x = 100,000$ **76.** $10^{x(x-1)} = 100$ **77.** $\dfrac{1}{2} \log x = -1$

Solve. Give answers to three significant digits.

78. $3^x = 5$ **79.** $4^x = 5$ **80.** $2^{x+1} = 3^x$

1. Write 0.000305 in scientific notation.

2. Write 5.9×10^7 as a whole number.

Simplify, using the properties of exponents.

3. $8^{\sqrt{2}} \cdot 4^{\sqrt{2}}$

4. $(5 \cdot 2^{\sqrt{5}})^{\sqrt{5}}$

5. Solve and check: $2^{6x-1} = 2^{4x}$

6. If $f(x) = -2(9)^x$, find $f\left(\dfrac{1}{2}\right)$.

7. The graph shown at the right is that of which of the following functions?

   a. $y = 2^x$ **b.** $y = -(2)^x$

   c. $y = \log_{\frac{1}{2}} x$ **d.** $y = \log_2 x$

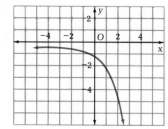

8. Express $5^3 = 125$ in logarithmic form.

9. Express $\log_{81} 3 = \frac{1}{4}$ in exponential form.

Evaluate.   *Given $\log_2 9 = 3.1699$, find each logarithm.*

10. $\log_4 64$ 11. $\log_{\frac{1}{3}} 27$ 12. $\log_2 81$ 13. $\log_2 36$

Given that $\log 0.0125 = 8.0969 - 10$, find

14. $\log 1.25$.   15. $\log 125$.   16. antilog 5.0969.

Choose the letter for the correct answer in Exercises 17 and 18. Assume that s and t represent positive real numbers.

17. $\log (st^2) =$

   a. $2(\log s + \log t)$ **b.** $(\log s)(2 \log t)$

   c. $\log s + 2 \log t$ **d.** $(\log s)(\log t^2)$

18. $\log \left(\dfrac{\sqrt[3]{s}}{t}\right) =$

   a. $3 \log s - \log t$ **b.** $\dfrac{\frac{1}{3} \log s}{\log t}$

   c. $\frac{1}{3}(\log s - \log t)$ **d.** $\frac{1}{3} \log s - \log t$

Solve.

19. $10^{2x+1} = 0.1$

20. $\log x + \log 2 = 1$

Doubling Your Money

Have you ever wondered how long it will take for the money you have saved to double? The compound interest formula is $A = P\left(1 + \frac{R}{N}\right)^{NT}$, with R the annual rate of interest compounded N times per year, and T the number of years. Since we want the principal to double, we substitute $P = 1$ and $A = 2$, giving $2 = \left(1 + \frac{R}{N}\right)^{NT}$. Using logarithms, write $\log 2 = \log\left(1 + \frac{R}{N}\right)^{NT}$. Solving for T gives $T = \dfrac{\log 2}{N \log\left(1 + \frac{R}{N}\right)}$.

The program below displays in decimal form the number of years it takes for an investment to double.

On most computers, the function LOG(X) computes the natural logarithm of X, which is based on the number e. Since the formula we are using is independent of the type of logarithms involved, there is no need for any conversion.

The Program	What It Does
`100 REM DOUBLE INVESTMENT`	
`110 PRINT "ANNUAL RATE AS DECIMAL";`	If a message or prompt is too long for your screen display, rewrite it on two lines.
`120 INPUT R`	
`130 PRINT "INTEREST PERIODS PER YEAR";`	
`140 INPUT N`	
`200 LET T = LOG(2)/(N*LOG(1+R/N))`	Computes T; note double)).
`210 PRINT "AT "; R*100; " PERCENT "`	Converts R to a percent.
`220 PRINT "YOUR MONEY WILL DOUBLE IN"`	On some computers the display may require some modification.
`230 PRINT T; " YEARS."`	
`900 END`	

Computers can also display the antilog when the natural logarithm is entered. The inverse function of LOG(X) is EXP(X). Some computers have functions for both the natural logarithm and the common logarithm of a number.

When interest is compounded monthly ($N = 12$), what is the time needed to double an investment at each of these rates?
1. 6% **2.** 9% **3.** 12% **4.** 8.25% **5.** 16% **6.** 9.45%

7. To obtain the common logarithm of X, use LOG(X)/LOG(10). What does the computer display as the common logarithm of 1492?

8. To obtain the antilog of a common logarithm, use EXP(X*LOG(10)). What does the computer display as the antilog of the common logarithm 3.17376882?

9. Write a program that asks for the common logarithm of a number and displays its antilog.

For more information about BASIC, see the Computer Handbook at the back of the book.

PART I

Write the letter for the correct answer.

1. $|2(-1)^3 - 3(-1)^2|$ is equal to __?__.

   a. -5 **b.** -1 **c.** 0 **d.** 1 **e.** 5

2. The slope of a line perpendicular to $3x + 2y = 6$ is __?__.

   a. $-\dfrac{3}{2}$ **b.** $-\dfrac{2}{3}$ **c.** $\dfrac{2}{3}$ **d.** $\dfrac{3}{2}$ **e.** 3

3. The lines $2x + 5y = 8$ and $y = -3x - 1$ intersect at the point __?__.

   a. $(-6, 4)$ **b.** $(2, -1)$ **c.** $(4, 0)$ **d.** $(-1, 2)$ **e.** $(1, -2)$

4. Solve: $\dfrac{5x - 4}{x - 1} - x = \dfrac{x}{x - 1}$

   a. -1 **b.** 4 **c.** -1 and 4

   d. 1 and 4 **e.** 1 and -4

5. Simplify: $-2\sqrt[3]{40} + 5\sqrt[3]{625} - 3\sqrt[3]{5}$

   a. $18\sqrt[3]{5}$ **b.** $\sqrt[3]{5}$ **c.** $75 - 7\sqrt[3]{5}$ **d.** 0 **e.** $20\sqrt[3]{5}$

6. $8^{-\frac{2}{3}} \div 4^{-\frac{3}{2}} = $ __?__.

   a. -2 **b.** 2 **c.** $-\dfrac{1}{2}$ **d.** 1 **e.** $\dfrac{1}{2}$

7. The minimum value of $y = 3x^2 - 6x + 7$ is __?__.

   a. -4 **b.** 4 **c.** 1 **d.** 3 **e.** -1

8. A rational root of $6x^3 + 7x^2 - x - 2 = 0$ is __?__.

   a. $-\dfrac{2}{3}$ **b.** 6 **c.** $\dfrac{1}{7}$ **d.** -3 **e.** $-\dfrac{1}{4}$

9. The distance between the points $(6, -1)$ and $(-4, 5)$ is __?__.

   a. 4 **b.** 8 **c.** $2\sqrt{34}$ **d.** $2\sqrt{5}$ **e.** $2\sqrt{29}$

10. The radius of the circle $x^2 - 4x + y^2 + 6y - 3 = 0$ is __?__.

    a. 4 **b.** $\sqrt{13}$ **c.** $2\sqrt{2}$ **d.** 16 **e.** $\sqrt{3}$

11. The ellipse $\dfrac{x^2}{9} + \dfrac{y^2}{16} = 1$ has x-intercepts __?__.

    a. ± 3 **b.** ± 4 **c.** ± 9 **d.** ± 16 **e.** ± 8

12. If $9^{3+x} = 27^x$, then $x = $ __?__.

    a. -3 **b.** 0 **c.** $2\dfrac{1}{2}$ **d.** 3 **e.** 6

13. If $\log x + \log 5 = 2$, then $x = $ __?__.

    a. 10 **b.** 20 **c.** 100 **d.** 200 **e.** 1000

PART II

Solve and graph on a number line.

14. $6x - 9 > 15$ or $8 - 4x > 20$

15. $|3(x - 2)| \geq 9$

16. If $f(x) = x^2 - 4$, find $f(-3)$.

17. If $g(x) = x - 4(x - 3)$, find $g(5)$.

18. Solve the system: $\begin{aligned}9x &= 45 - 4y \\ 8x - 12y &= 5\end{aligned}$

19. Graph the system: $\begin{aligned}y &\geq 2 - x \\ -2 &\leq x \leq 1\end{aligned}$

20. Factor completely: $6x^3y - 24x^2y^2 - 16xy^2 + 4x^2y$

Simplify.

21. $\dfrac{x + 3}{x^2 - 6x + 9} \div \dfrac{3x + 9}{x^2 - 3x}$

22. $\dfrac{2x^2 - x - 3}{3x^2 + x - 2} \cdot \dfrac{3x^2 + 10x - 8}{2x^2 + 5x - 12}$

23. $\sqrt[3]{54} - \sqrt[3]{16}$

24. $\dfrac{\sqrt{2} + \sqrt{3}}{\sqrt{2} - \sqrt{3}}$

25. $\dfrac{3 - \sqrt{x + y}}{3 + \sqrt{x + y}}$

Solve.

26. $\sqrt{x - 5} - \sqrt{x} = -2$

27. $(x + 1)^2 = 8$

28. $x^2 + 4x = -1$

29. Write a quadratic equation with the roots 2 and $-\frac{1}{2}$.

30. Write the equation $y = -2x^2 + 4x - 3$ in h, k form. Find the coordinates of the vertex of the parabola and the equation of its axis of symmetry.

31. Find the minimum or maximum value of the function $f(x) = \frac{1}{2}x^2 - 4x + 5$.

32. Find the rational roots of the equation $x^3 - 4x^2 - 25x + 28 = 0$.

Simplify.

33. $\dfrac{3}{4}\sqrt{-\dfrac{32}{81}}$

34. $3\sqrt{-12} + 2\sqrt{-48}$

35. $\dfrac{\sqrt{3} - i\sqrt{2}}{\sqrt{2} - i}$

36. Find the radius and the coordinates of the center of the circle $x^2 - 20x + y^2 = 8y - 35$. Then graph the circle.

37. Find the x- and y-intercepts and the foci of the ellipse $16x^2 + 25y^2 = 400$. Then sketch the ellipse.

38. Solve: $27^{2x} = 3^{2x-4}$

39. If $f(x) = 3^x$, find $f(-2)$.

40. Express the equation $7^2 = 49$ in logarithmic form.

41. Express the equation $\log_9 4 = c$ in exponential form.

42. If $\log 2 = a$ and $\log 3 = b$, express $\log 18$ in terms of a and b.

43. Given that $\log 5.74 = 0.7589$, find $\log 574{,}000$.

CHAPTER 11

The increase in elevation between the ski lift supports can be found if the horizontal distance and the angle of elevation between them are known.

TRIGONOMETRIC RATIOS

Prerequisite Skills Review

Write the letter for the correct answer. Use this figure for Exercises 1–3.

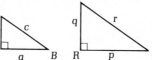

1. If $r = 26$ and $x = 24$, then $y =$? .

a. $2\sqrt{313}$ **b.** $5\sqrt{2}$ **c.** 10   **d.** none of these

2. If $r = 25$ and $y = 7$, then $\dfrac{x}{r} =$? .

a. $\dfrac{24}{25}$ **b.** $\dfrac{7}{25}$ **c.** $\dfrac{3\sqrt{2}}{25}$ **d.** none of these

3. If $r = 17$ and $x = 15$, then the reciprocal of $\dfrac{y}{x}$ equals ? .

a. $\dfrac{8}{15}$ **b.** $\dfrac{15}{17}$ **c.** $\dfrac{17}{8}$ **d.** none of these

4. If triangle ABC is similar to triangle PQR, then ? .

a. $\dfrac{a}{c} = \dfrac{q}{r}$ **b.** $\dfrac{a}{b} = \dfrac{q}{p}$

c. $\dfrac{b}{c} = \dfrac{q}{r}$ **d.** $\dfrac{c}{a} = \dfrac{p}{r}$

5. $\dfrac{2}{\sqrt{3}} =$?

a. $2\sqrt{3}$ **b.** $\dfrac{\sqrt{3}}{3}$ **c.** $\dfrac{2\sqrt{2}}{3}$ **d.** $\dfrac{2\sqrt{3}}{3}$

6. In triangle KLM, angle K measures $44°$ and angle L measures $18°$. The measure of angle M is ? .

a. $28°$ **b.** $62°$ **c.** $118°$ **d.** $128°$

7. If $\dfrac{p}{q} = \dfrac{s}{t}$, then $q =$? .

a. pts **b.** $\dfrac{pt}{s}$ **c.** $\dfrac{ps}{t}$ **d.** $\dfrac{s}{pt}$

8. Given that $\sqrt{2} \approx 1.414$ and $\sqrt{3} \approx 1.732$, find $\dfrac{100\sqrt{3}}{\sqrt{2}}$ to the nearest tenth.

a. 12.2 **b.** 122.5 **c.** 1224.9 **d.** none of these

11-1 Angles of Rotation

OBJECTIVE _____

To sketch an angle of given measure in standard position.

_____

The part of a line consisting of a point and all of the points on one side of it is called a **ray.** Ray AB ($\overrightarrow{AB}$) is named by its initial point A, followed by any other point B on the ray.

An **angle** is formed by rotating a ray in a plane about its initial point. The angle at the right is called angle CAB ($\angle CAB$), angle BAC ($\angle BAC$), or angle A ($\angle A$). The **sides** of the angle are rays AB and AC, and the **vertex** of the angle is point A.

When an angle is in **standard position** on the coordinate plane,

- its vertex is at the origin,

- its **initial side** lies on the positive portion of the horizontal axis, and

- its **terminal side** is located by either a counterclockwise or a clockwise rotation about the origin.

The measure of an angle is determined by the direction and the amount of rotation of the terminal side about the vertex. A common unit of angle measurement is the **degree** (°), and the measure of one complete rotation is 360°. Each degree can be subdivided into 60 equal parts called **minutes** ('). That is, one degree equals 60 minutes. The Greek letter θ (_theta_) is often used to denote the measure of an angle in standard position.

Counterclockwise rotations produce angles with positive measures, while clockwise rotations produce angles with negative measures. A **quadrantal angle** is an angle in standard position, with its terminal side on one of the coordinate axes. Quadrantal angles may have positive, negative, or zero measures.

Some Quadrantal Angles

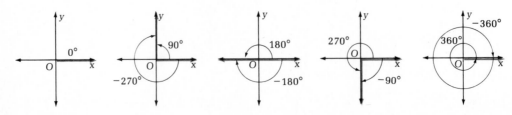

Angles in standard position having the same terminal side are called **coterminal angles.** For example, you can see from the diagrams at the bottom of page 412 that angles with measures of 90° and −270° are coterminal. Are angles of 0° and 360° also coterminal?

EXAMPLE 1   Sketch the angle of measure θ in standard position.

a. $\theta = 50°$

Since 50° is between 0° and 90°, the terminal side is in the first quadrant.

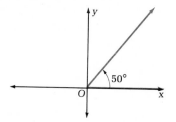

b. $\theta = 200°$

Since 200° is between 180° and 270°, the terminal side is in the third quadrant.

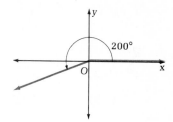

c. $\theta = -40°$

Since −40° is between 0° and −90°, the terminal side is in the fourth quadrant.

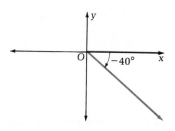

d. $\theta = -195°$

Since −195° is between −180° and −270°, the terminal side is in the second quadrant.

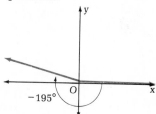

To sketch an angle that measures more than 360°, subtract a multiple of 360° to obtain an angle measure between 0° and 360°.

EXAMPLE 2   Sketch a 480° angle in standard position.

$480° - 360° = 120°$

Sketch a 120° angle, which is coterminal with a 480° angle.

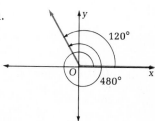

To sketch an angle that measures less than −360°, add a multiple of
360° to obtain an angle measure between −360° and 0°.

EXAMPLE 3   Sketch a −735° angle in standard position.

$$-735° + 2(360°) = -735° + 720°$$
$$= -15°$$

Sketch a −15° angle, which is coterminal
with a −735° angle.

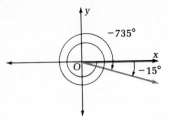

CLASS EXERCISES

For an angle in standard position with the given measure, name the
quadrant that contains the terminal side.

1. 45°   **2.** 135°   **3.** 225°   **4.** 315°   **5.** −45°

6. −135°   **7.** −225°   **8.** −315°   **9.** 28°   **10.** 128°

11. 228°   **12.** 328°   **13.** −84°   **14.** −184°   **15.** −284°

Find the measure of the smallest positive angle that is coterminal with
the angle of given measure.

16. 400°   **17.** 450°   **18.** 900°   **19.** 370°   **20.** 740°

EXERCISES

A   Sketch, in standard position, the angle with the given measure.

1. 15°   **2.** 130°   **3.** 190°   **4.** 315°   **5.** 60°

6. −45°   **7.** −90°   **8.** −300°   **9.** −210°   **10.** −115°

11. −360°   **12.** 180°   **13.** 350°   **14.** −70°   **15.** 260°

Find the measure of the smallest positive angle that is coterminal with
the angle of given measure.

16. 460°   **17.** 540°   **18.** 730°   **19.** 950°   **20.** 700°

B   Sketch the angle with measure θ in standard position.

21. $\theta = 550°$ **22.** $\theta = 765°$ **23.** $\theta = 1020°$ **24.** $\theta = 1170°$

25. $\theta = -390°$ **26.** $\theta = -765°$ **27.** $\theta = -1200°$ **28.** $\theta = -1440°$

29. Start with 0° and list the measures of the next eight quadrantal
angles, obtained by rotating in a clockwise direction.

30. Start with 0° and list the measures of the next eight quadrantal
angles, obtained by rotating in a counterclockwise direction.

Sketch, in standard position, the angle with the given counterclockwise rotation of its terminal side. Find the measure of the angle.

31. $\frac{1}{4}$ of a complete rotation

32. $\frac{5}{6}$ of a complete rotation

33. $3\frac{1}{2}$ complete rotations

34. $1\frac{2}{3}$ complete rotations

C Draw the ray that is the graph of the equation for the given values of **x**. Then give the measure of the smallest positive angle, in standard position, that has that ray as its terminal side.

35. $y = x; x \geq 0$

36. $y = x; x \leq 0$

37. $y = 0; x \leq 0$

38. $x = 0; y \geq 0$

39. $y = -x; x \geq 0$

40. $y = 0; x \geq 0$

CHALLENGE

Angle Constructions

Draw a coordinate system on graph paper. Use a compass to draw a circle with center at the origin and radius 5 units. Then use a straightedge and a compass to construct the following angles.

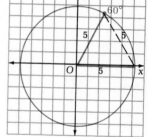

1. Construct angles with measures of 30°, 45°, and 60°, in standard position. Draw dots at the points of intersection of the terminal sides of the angles and the circle. Label the points with appropriate degree measures.

   Hint: Recall that an equilateral triangle has 60° angles. Obtain the 45° and 30° angles by bisecting the 90° and 60° angles, respectively.

2. Use similar procedures to construct and label angles with measures of 120°, 135°, and 150°. Also label the points corresponding to the measures of the quadrantal angles from 0° to 360°.

3. Use the straightedge to extend the terminal sides of the angles constructed in Exercises 1 and 2, so that these lines intersect the lower half of the circle. Label the points of intersection with the appropriate measures: 210°, 225°, 240°, 300°, 315°, and 330°.

4. For each angle constructed in standard position, find the coordinates (x, y) of the point of intersection of the terminal side with the circle.

   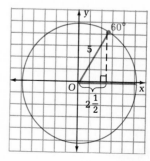

   Hint: Use the Pythagorean theorem. Also, recall that in a 30°-60°-90° triangle, the leg opposite the 30° angle is $\frac{1}{2}$ the length of the hypotenuse. In a 45°-45°-90° triangle, the legs are of equal length. Leave irrational coordinates in radical form.

11-2 Reference Angles and Reference Triangles

OBJECTIVES _____

To find the measure of the reference angle for a nonquadrantal angle in
  standard position.
To draw a reference triangle for a given angle in standard position.
To find the missing value, x, y, or r, for a reference triangle, given the
  other two values.

_____

An angle in standard position with its terminal side within one of the
four quadrants has a *reference angle*. The **reference angle** is the smallest positive angle between the terminal side of the given angle and the
x-axis.

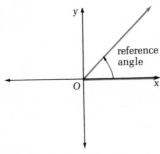

The terminal side of the given
angle is in the first quadrant.

The terminal side of the given
angle is in the second quadrant.

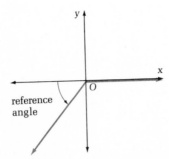

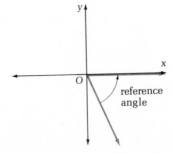

The terminal side of the given
angle is in the third quadrant.

The terminal side of the given
angle is in the fourth quadrant.

The reference angle is always a positive acute angle. That is, its measure is between 0° and 90°. The measure of a reference angle will be
denoted by the Greek letter ϕ (*phi*).

EXAMPLE 1

Sketch the angle with measure θ in standard position. Then find the measure ϕ of its reference angle.

a. $\theta = 43°$

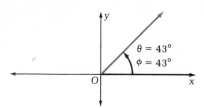

b. $\theta = 127°$

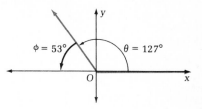

c. $\theta = -560°$

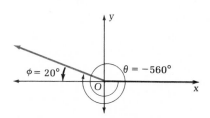

d. $\theta = -70°$

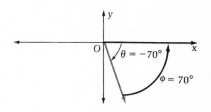

Draw a perpendicular to the x-axis from any point P on the terminal side of a nonquadrantal angle in standard position. The resulting right triangle is called a **reference triangle.** Quadrantal angles do not have reference triangles.

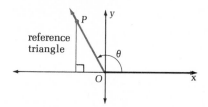

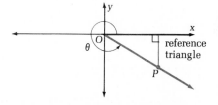

The length of the hypotenuse r of a reference triangle is a positive number. The signs of x and y depend on the quadrant of the reference triangle.

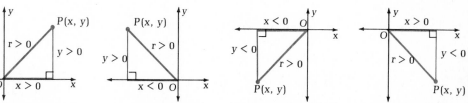

First Quadrant	**Second Quadrant**	**Third Quadrant**	**Fourth Quadrant**
x and y are both positive.	x is negative and y is positive.	x and y are both negative.	x is positive and y is negative.

If two of the three values, x, y, and r, are known, the Pythagorean theorem can be used to find the third value.

EXAMPLE 2 Find the missing value, x, y, or r, for each reference triangle.

a.

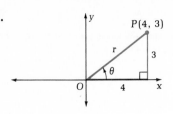

$$r^2 = x^2 + y^2$$
$$r^2 = 4^2 + 3^2$$
$$r^2 = 25$$
$$r = \sqrt{25}$$ Take the positive
$$r = 5$$ square root,
since $r > 0$.

b.

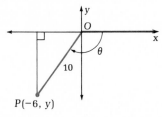

$$x^2 + y^2 = r^2$$
$$(-6)^2 + y^2 = 10^2$$
$$36 + y^2 = 100$$
$$y^2 = 64$$
$$y = -\sqrt{64}$$ Take the negative
$$y = -8$$ root, since $y < 0$.

c.

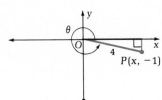

$$x^2 + y^2 = r^2$$
$$x^2 + (-1)^2 = 4^2$$
$$x^2 + 1 = 16$$
$$x^2 = 15$$
$$x = \sqrt{15}$$ Take the positive
root, since $x > 0$.

CLASS EXERCISES

Find the measure of the reference angle for each angle of measure θ, in standard position.

1. $\theta = 32°$ **2.** $\theta = 95°$ **3.** $\theta = 300°$ **4.** $\theta = 400°$ **5.** $\theta = 560°$

6. $\theta = -75°$ **7.** $\theta = -175°$ **8.** $\theta = -200°$ **9.** $\theta = -410°$ **10.** $\theta = -655°$

*Find the missing value, **x**, **y**, or **r**, for each reference triangle.*

11.

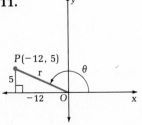

12.

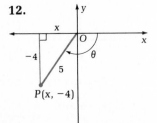

13.

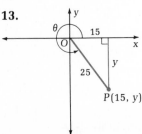

EXERCISES

A

Sketch the angle with measure θ in standard position. Then find the measure ϕ of its reference angle.

1. $\theta = 120°$ **2.** $\theta = 240°$ **3.** $\theta = 72°$ **4.** $\theta = -72°$ **5.** $\theta = -120°$

6. $\theta = 45°$ **7.** $\theta = 315°$ **8.** $\theta = 225°$ **9.** $\theta = -60°$ **10.** $\theta = -150°$

11. $\theta = -240°$ **12.** $\theta = 135°$ **13.** $\theta = -330°$ **14.** $\theta = 385°$ **15.** $\theta = 565°$

16. $\theta = 490°$ **17.** $\theta = 600°$ **18.** $\theta = -380°$ **19.** $\theta = -400°$ **20.** $\theta = -460°$

Find the missing value, x, y, or r, for each reference triangle.

21.
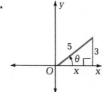

22.
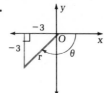

23.
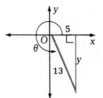

B

The given point $P(x, y)$ is on the terminal side of an angle in standard position. Draw the reference triangle with P as a vertex, and find the length of the hypotenuse r.

24. $P(-3, -4)$ **25.** $P(5, -12)$ **26.** $P(-8, 6)$ **27.** $P(20, 15)$

28. $P(-8, -15)$ **29.** $P(12, -16)$ **30.** $P(10, -24)$ **31.** $P(-30, -16)$

Find the value of a in the given reference triangle.

32.
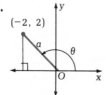

33.
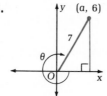

34.
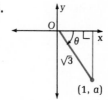

C

Find the measure of the reference angle. Then use properties of isosceles right triangles to find x and y.

35.
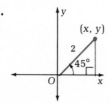

36.
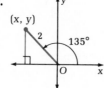

37.
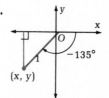

TRIGONOMETRIC RATIOS

419

11-3 Trigonometric Ratios

To find the six trigonometric ratios of θ, the measure of a nonquadrantal angle in standard position.

Let θ be the measure of a nonquadrantal angle in standard position. Let r be the distance from the origin to some other point $P(x, y)$ on the terminal side of the angle. The values x, y, and r are used to define three trigonometric ratios: the **sine (sin)**, the **cosine (cos)**, and the **tangent (tan)** of θ.

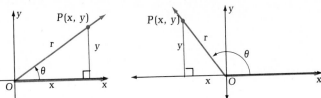

$$\sin \theta = \frac{y}{r} = \frac{\text{y-coordinate of P}}{\text{distance from (0, 0) to P}} \qquad \text{Sin } \theta \text{ is read } sine \text{ of } \theta.$$

$$\cos \theta = \frac{x}{r} = \frac{\text{x-coordinate of P}}{\text{distance from (0, 0) to P}} \qquad \text{Cos } \theta \text{ is read } cosine \text{ of } \theta.$$

$$\tan \theta = \frac{y}{x} = \frac{\text{y-coordinate of P}}{\text{x-coordinate of P}} \qquad \text{Tan } \theta \text{ is read } tangent \text{ of } \theta.$$

Observe that neither x nor y can be 0, since the angle is not quadrantal. Consequently, the defined ratios are not 0.

The reciprocals of the sine, cosine, and tangent ratios are called the **cosecant (csc)**, the **secant (sec)**, and the **cotangent (cot)**, respectively. For values of θ as described above, these ratios are defined as follows.

$$\csc \theta = \frac{1}{\sin \theta} = \frac{r}{y} \qquad \text{Csc } \theta \text{ is read } cosecant \text{ of } \theta.$$

$$\sec \theta = \frac{1}{\cos \theta} = \frac{r}{x} \qquad \text{Sec } \theta \text{ is read } secant \text{ of } \theta.$$

$$\cot \theta = \frac{1}{\tan \theta} = \frac{x}{y} \qquad \text{Cot } \theta \text{ is read } cotangent \text{ of } \theta.$$

EXAMPLE 1

Find the six trigonometric ratios for θ.

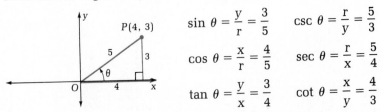

$$\sin \theta = \frac{y}{r} = \frac{3}{5} \qquad \csc \theta = \frac{r}{y} = \frac{5}{3}$$

$$\cos \theta = \frac{x}{r} = \frac{4}{5} \qquad \sec \theta = \frac{r}{x} = \frac{5}{4}$$

$$\tan \theta = \frac{y}{x} = \frac{3}{4} \qquad \cot \theta = \frac{x}{y} = \frac{4}{3}$$

EXAMPLE 2   Find the sine, cosine, and tangent of θ. Then use reciprocals to find the remaining three trigonometric ratios.

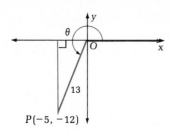

$$\sin \theta = \frac{y}{r} = \frac{-12}{13} = -\frac{12}{13} \qquad \csc \theta = \frac{1}{\sin \theta} = -\frac{13}{12}$$

$$\cos \theta = \frac{x}{r} = \frac{-5}{13} = -\frac{5}{13} \qquad \sec \theta = \frac{1}{\cos \theta} = -\frac{13}{5}$$

$$\tan \theta = \frac{y}{x} = \frac{-12}{-5} = \frac{12}{5} \qquad \cot \theta = \frac{1}{\tan \theta} = \frac{5}{12}$$

Any point P, other than $(0, 0)$, on the terminal ray of an angle in standard position will give the same trigonometric ratios. To illustrate, we take points $P_1(x_1, y_1)$ and $P_2(x_2, y_2)$ on the terminal side. Observe that the right triangles OQ_1P_1 and OQ_2P_2 are *similar*, so the lengths of the corresponding sides are proportional. Thus,

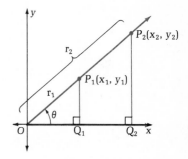

$$\sin \theta = \frac{y_1}{r_1} = \frac{y_2}{r_2} \qquad \cos \theta = \frac{x_1}{r_1} = \frac{x_2}{r_2} \qquad \tan \theta = \frac{y_1}{x_1} = \frac{y_2}{x_2}$$

The size of the reference triangle does not affect the values of the trigonometric ratios for a given value of θ. Each value of θ has just one set of trigonometric ratios.

Sometimes only two of the three values, x, y, and r, are known. In such cases the Pythagorean theorem can be used to find the third value. Then the six trigonometric ratios can be written.

EXAMPLE 3   Find the missing value r. Then write the six trigonometric ratios for θ.

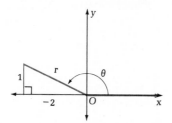

First, solve for r.

$$r^2 = x^2 + y^2$$
$$r^2 = (-2)^2 + 1^2$$
$$r^2 = 5$$
$$r = \sqrt{5} \qquad \text{Take the positive root, since } r > 0.$$

Then find the ratios.

$$\sin \theta = \frac{1}{\sqrt{5}} = \frac{\sqrt{5}}{5} \qquad \cos \theta = \frac{-2}{\sqrt{5}} = -\frac{2\sqrt{5}}{5} \qquad \tan \theta = \frac{1}{-2} = -\frac{1}{2}$$

$$\csc \theta = \frac{\sqrt{5}}{1} = \sqrt{5} \qquad \sec \theta = \frac{\sqrt{5}}{-2} = -\frac{\sqrt{5}}{2} \qquad \cot \theta = \frac{-2}{1} = -2$$

The next example shows how the sine and cosine ratios can be used to find the remaining trigonometric ratios.

EXAMPLE 4   If $\sin \theta = -\frac{1}{2}$ and $\cos \theta = -\frac{\sqrt{3}}{2}$, find the other four trigonometric ratios for θ.

First find values for x, y, and r.

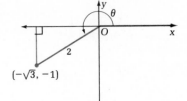

$$\sin \theta = -\frac{1}{2} = \frac{-1}{2} = \frac{y}{r}$$

$$\cos \theta = -\frac{\sqrt{3}}{2} = \frac{-\sqrt{3}}{2} = \frac{x}{r}$$

$(-\sqrt{3}, -1)$

Thus, $x = -\sqrt{3}$, $y = -1$, $r = 2$.
A reference triangle for θ
is shown at the right.

Write the remaining ratios.

$$\tan \theta = \frac{-1}{-\sqrt{3}} = \frac{1}{\sqrt{3}} = \frac{\sqrt{3}}{3} \qquad \cot \theta = \frac{-\sqrt{3}}{-1} = \sqrt{3}$$

$$\sec \theta = \frac{2}{-\sqrt{3}} = -\frac{2\sqrt{3}}{3} \qquad \csc \theta = \frac{2}{-1} = -2$$

CLASS EXERCISES

Find the six trigonometric ratios for θ.

1.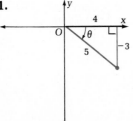

2.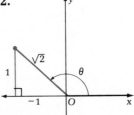

3,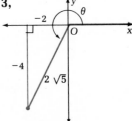

Find the missing value, **x**, **y**, or **r**. Then write the six trigonometric ratios for θ.

4.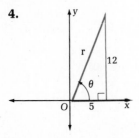

5.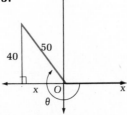

6.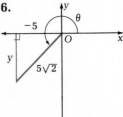

EXERCISES

Find the six trigonometric ratios for θ.

1.
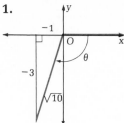

2.
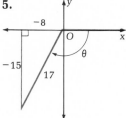

3.
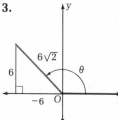

4.
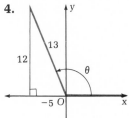

5.
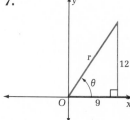

6.
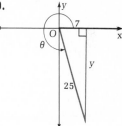

Find the missing value, **x**, **y**, or **r**. Then write the six trigonometric ratios for θ.

7.
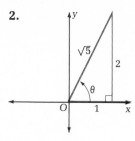

8.
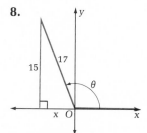

9.
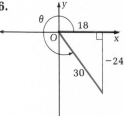

10.
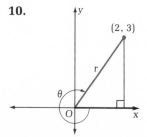

11.
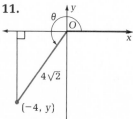

12.
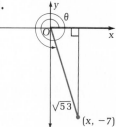

Find the missing value, **x**, **y**, or **r**. Then write the six trigonometric ratios for θ.

13.

(−16, 24)

14.

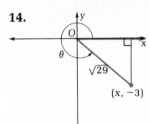

15.

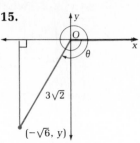

The point **P(x, y)** is on the terminal side of an angle of measure θ, in standard position. Find the six trigonometric ratios for θ.

16. $P(3, 4)$ **17.** $P(-5, 12)$ **18.** $P(-16, -12)$ **19.** $P(9, -12)$

20. $P(-4, 5)$ **21.** $P(1, 2)$ **22.** $P(-5, -6)$ **23.** $P(\sqrt{2}, \sqrt{6})$

Two trigonometric ratios are given for a specific value of θ. Find the other four trigonometric ratios for that value of θ.

24. $\sin \theta = -\dfrac{3}{5}$, $\cos \theta = -\dfrac{4}{5}$ **25.** $\tan \theta = \dfrac{2}{3}$, $\sec \theta = \dfrac{\sqrt{13}}{3}$

26. $\csc \theta = \dfrac{17}{15}$, $\sec \theta = \dfrac{17}{8}$ **27.** $\tan \theta = 3$, $\csc \theta = -\dfrac{\sqrt{10}}{3}$

C   **28.** $\cot \theta = \dfrac{\sqrt{3}}{3}$, $\cos \theta = \dfrac{1}{2}$ **29.** $\sin \theta = \dfrac{1}{3}$, $\cot \theta = -2\sqrt{2}$

One trigonometric ratio is given for a specific value of θ, with the reference triangle in the given quadrant. Find the other five trigonometric ratios for that value of θ.

30. $\sin \theta = \dfrac{3}{5}$; quadrant I   **31.** $\cot \theta = -\dfrac{5}{12}$; quadrant II

32. $\tan \theta = 2$; quadrant III   **33.** $\csc \theta = -2$; quadrant IV

Use the definitions $\sin \theta = \dfrac{y}{r}$ and $\cos \theta = \dfrac{x}{r}$ to show that

34. $\dfrac{\sin \theta}{\cos \theta} = \tan \theta.$ **35.** $\dfrac{\cos \theta}{\sin \theta} = \cot \theta.$

36. In the reference triangle for an angle of measure θ, x = 3 and y = 4. Show that $(\sin \theta)^2 + (\cos \theta)^2 = 1$.

37. Prove the statement in Exercise 36 for any nonquadrantal angle of measure θ. That is, write sin θ and cos θ in terms of x, y, and r, and show that $(\sin \theta)^2 + (\cos \theta)^2 = 1$.

11-4 Special Reference Triangles

To find the trigonometric ratios of θ, where the reference angle for θ is 45°, 30°, or 60°.

In the preceding lesson, we used reference triangles to find the trigonometric ratios for θ, the measure of an angle in standard position. The actual value of θ was not known. Now we will consider the ratios for some specific values of θ. In particular, the trigonometric ratios of 45°, 30°, and 60° can be found using basic geometric concepts.

The figure at the right shows a 45° angle in standard position. The reference triangle is an *isosceles right triangle*. That is, the legs are the same length and the acute angles have the same measure, 45°. The size of the reference triangle does not affect the trigonometric ratios. Therefore, for convenience, we let x and y each equal 1, and solve for r.

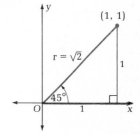

$$r^2 = 1^2 + 1^2 = 2$$
$$r = \sqrt{2}$$

The trigonometric ratios for 45° are found using these values for x, y, and r.

$$\sin 45° = \frac{1}{\sqrt{2}} = \frac{\sqrt{2}}{2} \qquad \cos 45° = \frac{1}{\sqrt{2}} = \frac{\sqrt{2}}{2} \qquad \tan 45° = \frac{1}{1} = 1$$

$$\csc 45° = \frac{\sqrt{2}}{1} = \sqrt{2} \qquad \sec 45° = \frac{\sqrt{2}}{1} = \sqrt{2} \qquad \cot 45° = \frac{1}{1} = 1$$

EXAMPLE 1

Sketch a 135° angle and its reference triangle. Then find the six trigonometric ratios of 135°.

The reference angle measures 45°.

$$180° - 135° = 45°$$

The reference triangle is in the second quadrant, so let x = −1 and y = 1, and solve for r.

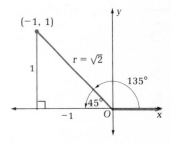

$$r^2 = (-1)^2 + 1^2 = 2$$
$$r = \sqrt{2}$$

The trigonometric ratios are found from the reference triangle.

$$\sin 135° = \frac{1}{\sqrt{2}} = \frac{\sqrt{2}}{2} \qquad \cos 135° = \frac{-1}{\sqrt{2}} = -\frac{\sqrt{2}}{2} \qquad \tan 135° = \frac{1}{-1} = -1$$

$$\csc 135° = \frac{\sqrt{2}}{1} = \sqrt{2} \qquad \sec 135° = \frac{\sqrt{2}}{-1} = -\sqrt{2} \qquad \cot 135° = \frac{-1}{1} = -1$$

Another useful reference triangle has acute angles of 30°
and 60°. For convenience, let the side opposite the 30° angle
be 1 unit in length. Extend the base and form an *equilateral
triangle,* which has sides of equal length and angles of
equal measure. The hypotenuse of the original triangle measures 2 units, and the measure h of the third side is $\sqrt{3}$.

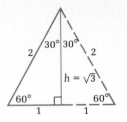

$$h^2 = 2^2 - 1^2 = 3$$
$$h = \sqrt{3}$$

The measures of the sides are shown again below, on the reference
triangles for angles of 30° and 60°, in standard position. From these we
obtain the trigonometric ratios for 30° and 60°, which are given in the
table below the reference triangles.

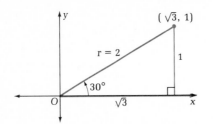

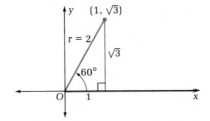

θ	$\sin\theta$	$\cos\theta$	$\tan\theta$	$\cot\theta$	$\sec\theta$	$\csc\theta$
30°	$\dfrac{1}{2}$	$\dfrac{\sqrt{3}}{2}$	$\dfrac{\sqrt{3}}{3}$	$\sqrt{3}$	$\dfrac{2\sqrt{3}}{3}$	2
45°	$\dfrac{\sqrt{2}}{2}$	$\dfrac{\sqrt{2}}{2}$	1	1	$\sqrt{2}$	$\sqrt{2}$
60°	$\dfrac{\sqrt{3}}{2}$	$\dfrac{1}{2}$	$\sqrt{3}$	$\dfrac{\sqrt{3}}{3}$	2	$\dfrac{2\sqrt{3}}{3}$

Since these ratios for 30°, 45°, and 60° will be used frequently in your
study of trigonometry, you should become familiar with them.

EXAMPLE 2   Sketch a −30° angle and its reference
triangle. Then find the six trigonometric
ratios of −30°.

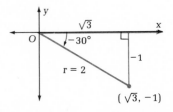

The 30° reference angle is in the fourth
quadrant, so use a reference triangle in
which $x = \sqrt{3}$, $y = -1$, and $r = 2$.

$$\sin(-30°) = \frac{-1}{2} = -\frac{1}{2} \qquad \cos(-30°) = \frac{\sqrt{3}}{2} \qquad \tan(-30°) = \frac{-1}{\sqrt{3}} = -\frac{\sqrt{3}}{3}$$

$$\csc(-30°) = \frac{2}{-1} = -2 \qquad \sec(-30°) = \frac{2}{\sqrt{3}} = \frac{2\sqrt{3}}{3} \qquad \cot(-30°) = \frac{\sqrt{3}}{-1} = -\sqrt{3}$$

EXAMPLE 3

Sketch a 600° angle and its reference triangle. Then find cos 600°.

Since 600° − 360° = 240°, it follows that a 600° angle is coterminal with a 240° angle. Thus, the reference angle measures 60°.

Let x = −1 and r = 2.

Then $\cos 600° = \dfrac{x}{r} = \dfrac{-1}{2} = -\dfrac{1}{2}$

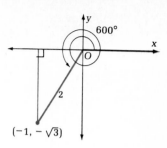

$(-1, -\sqrt{3})$

CLASS EXERCISES

Sketch an angle with the given measure θ, and its reference triangle. Then find the six trigonometric ratios for θ.

1. θ = 60°   **2.** θ = −225°   **3.** θ = 330°   **4.** θ = −315°

Sketch an angle with the given measure, and its reference triangle. Then find the required ratio.

5. sin 120°   **6.** tan 210°   **7.** cos (−135°)   **8.** sec (−330°)

EXERCISES

A

Sketch an angle with the given measure θ, and its reference triangle. Then find the six trigonometric ratios for θ.

1. θ = −45°   **2.** θ = 150°   **3.** θ = −120°   **4.** θ = 315°

Sketch an angle with the given measure, and its reference triangle. Then find the required ratio.

5. cos 120°   **6.** tan 225°   **7.** sec 240°   **8.** csc 300°

9. sin (−60°)   **10.** csc (−135°)   **11.** cot (−240°)   **12.** sin (−300°)

13. cos (−330°)   **14.** tan (−210°)   **15.** sec 210°   **16.** sin 240°

17. cot (−150°)   **18.** csc 225°   **19.** sin (−210°)   **20.** cos 300°

B

21. tan 405°   **22.** cot 480°   **23.** sec (−420°)   **24.** csc (−390°)

25. tan 495°   **26.** cos 510°   **27.** cot (−765°)   **28.** sec (−840°)

29. tan (−405°)   **30.** sin 420°   **31.** cos 390°   **32.** sec (−495°)

33. cot (−510°)   **34.** csc 585°   **35.** sin (−480°)   **36.** tan 765°

37. cos 870°   **38.** sec (−600°)   **39.** csc 660°   **40.** cot (−585°)

41. sec (−570°)   **42.** csc 570°   **43.** tan (−660°)   **44.** cot (−675°)

45. sin (−855°)   **46.** cos 930°   **47.** tan 840°   **48.** sec (−870°)

TRIGONOMETRIC RATIOS

427

Find the missing values, **x**, **y**, or **r**, for the given reference triangle.
Make use of an appropriate similar triangle to find the six trigonometric
ratios of θ.

Sample

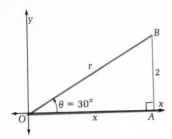

Triangle OAB is similar to triangle PQR.

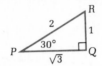

Since the length of $\overline{AB}$ is twice that of
$\overline{QR}$, each side of triangle OAB is twice
the length of the corresponding side of
triangle PQR.

$$OA = x = 2\sqrt{3} \qquad OB = r = 4$$

Then, using triangle OAB,

$$\sin 30° = \frac{2}{4} = \frac{1}{2} \qquad \cos 30° = \frac{2\sqrt{3}}{4} = \frac{\sqrt{3}}{2} \qquad \tan 30° = \frac{2}{2\sqrt{3}} = \frac{\sqrt{3}}{3}$$

$$\csc 30° = \frac{4}{2} = 2 \qquad \sec 30° = \frac{4}{2\sqrt{3}} = \frac{2\sqrt{3}}{3} \qquad \cot 30° = \frac{2\sqrt{3}}{2} = \sqrt{3}$$

49.

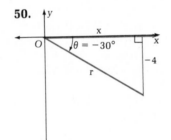

50.

51.

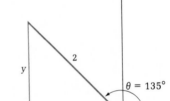

C Find the six trigonometric ratios of θ_1 and θ_2.

52.

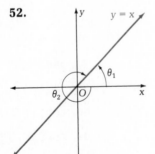

53.

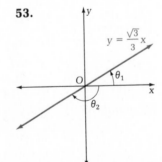

54.

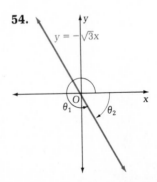

11-5 The Unit Circle

OBJECTIVE _____

To find the trigonometric ratios of angles, including quadrantal angles, using the unit circle.

_____

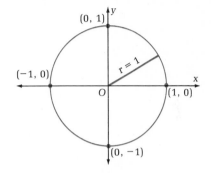

A circle with center at the origin and radius 1 unit is called the **unit circle.**

The points on the unit circle can be used to find the trigonometric ratios of *any* angle. Let $P(x, y)$ be a point on the unit circle and on the terminal side of angle θ, in standard position. Note that we said "the terminal side of angle θ," rather than "the terminal side of the angle of measure θ." From now on we will, at times, use the briefer phrase for the sake of simplicity. Thus, θ will sometimes stand for the name of the angle and sometimes for its measure. The context should make it clear how θ is being used.

Since $\sin \theta = \frac{y}{1}$ and $\cos \theta = \frac{x}{1}$, we have these useful definitions for the coordinates of a point $P(x, y)$ on the unit circle.

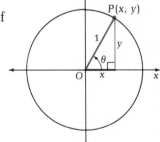

$\sin \theta = y$ The second coordinate is the sine of θ.

$\cos \theta = x$ The first coordinate is the cosine of θ.

The remaining ratios are found using the appropriate definitions.

$$\tan \theta = \frac{y}{x} \qquad\qquad \cot \theta = \frac{x}{y} = \frac{1}{\tan \theta}$$

$$\csc \theta = \frac{1}{y} = \frac{1}{\sin \theta} \qquad \sec \theta = \frac{1}{x} = \frac{1}{\cos \theta}$$

EXAMPLE 1   Find the coordinates of $P(x, y)$ on the unit circle. Then find the six trigonometric ratios of 120°.

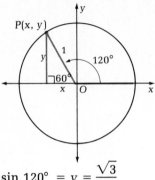

The reference angle measures 60°, and $r = 1$. Recall that the side opposite the 30° angle in this reference triangle is one-half the length of the hypotenuse. Thus,

$$x = -\frac{1}{2}$$

$$y = \sqrt{1^2 - \left(-\frac{1}{2}\right)^2} = \sqrt{\frac{3}{4}} = \frac{\sqrt{3}}{2}$$

$$\sin 120° = y = \frac{\sqrt{3}}{2} \qquad\qquad \csc 120° = \frac{1}{\sin 120°} = \frac{2}{\sqrt{3}} = \frac{2\sqrt{3}}{3}$$

$$\cos 120° = x = -\frac{1}{2} \qquad\qquad \sec 120° = \frac{1}{\cos 120°} = -2$$

$$\tan 120° = \frac{y}{x} = \frac{\frac{\sqrt{3}}{2}}{-\frac{1}{2}} = -\sqrt{3} \qquad \cot 120° = \frac{1}{\tan 120°} = -\frac{1}{\sqrt{3}} = -\frac{\sqrt{3}}{3}$$

Recall that quadrantal angles have no reference triangles. However, the trigonometric ratios of such angles can be found using the unit circle and the definitions $\sin \theta = y$ and $\cos \theta = x$.

EXAMPLE 2   Find the trigonometric ratios of 180°.

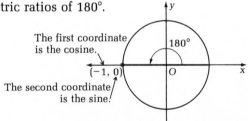

The first coordinate is the cosine.

$(-1, 0)$

The second coordinate is the sine.

$$\sin 180° = y = 0 \qquad\qquad \csc 180° = \frac{1}{\sin 180°} \qquad \text{Csc 180° is undefined, since division by 0 is not possible.}$$

$$\cos 180° = x = -1 \qquad\qquad \sec 180° = \frac{1}{\cos 180°} = \frac{1}{-1} = -1$$

$$\tan 180° = \frac{y}{x} = \frac{0}{-1} = 0 \qquad \cot 180° = \frac{1}{\tan 180°} \qquad \text{Cot 180° is also undefined.}$$

The table on the next page summarizes the trigonometric ratios for all quadrantal angles.

Trigonometric Ratios of Quadrantal Angles

Terminal Side of θ	$\sin \theta$	$\cos \theta$	$\tan \theta$	$\cot \theta$	$\sec \theta$	$\csc \theta$
Positive x-axis	0	1	0	undefined	1	undefined
Positive y-axis	1	0	undefined	0	undefined	1
Negative x-axis	0	−1	0	undefined	−1	undefined
Negative y-axis	−1	0	undefined	0	undefined	−1

It is not necessary to memorize this table. Just decide which one of the four points, (1, 0), (0, 1), (−1, 0), or (0, −1), is on the terminal side of the angle. The first coordinate is the cosine and the second is the sine. The remaining ratios, if they exist, are found by using the appropriate definitions.

CLASS EXERCISES

Find the coordinates of $P(x, y)$ on the unit circle. Then find the six trigonometric ratios of the given angle.

1.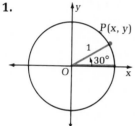

2.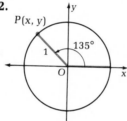

3.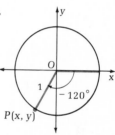

Find the trigonometric ratios for the quadrantal angle with the given measure.

4. 0° **5.** 90° **6.** 270° **7.** −180°

EXERCISES

Find the given trigonometric ratio, if it exists. If not, write **undefined.**

1. sin 360° **2.** cos (−270°) **3.** tan (−90°) **4.** csc (−90°)

$\overline{AC}$ and $\overline{BD}$ are diameters of a unit circle. Find the coordinates of points **A, B, C,** and **D.** Then write the six trigonometric ratios of an angle with the given measure.

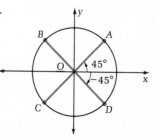

5. 45° **6.** 135° **7.** 225° **8.** 315°

9. For each angle in Exercises 5–8, find the measure of the angle between 0° and −360° that has the same trigonometric ratios.

$\overline{PR}$ and $\overline{QS}$ are diameters of a unit circle. Find the coordinates of points **P, Q, R,** and **S.** Then write the six trigonometric ratios of an angle with the given measure.

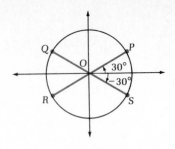

10. 30°

11. 150°

12. 210°

13. 330°

14. For each angle in Exercises 10–13 find the measure of the angle between 0° and −360° that has the same trigonometric ratios.

B

15. Follow the directions for Exercises 10–14, using the four points on the unit circle related to 60° reference angles.

Use the definitions of sin θ and cos θ on the unit circle to explain why

16. −1 ≤ sin θ ≤ 1, for all θ.

17. −1 ≤ cos θ ≤ 1, for all θ.

Find the given trigonometric ratio, if it exists. If not, write **undefined.**

18. sin (−90°)

19. cos 360°

20. tan (−270°)

21. cot (−360°)

22. sec 450°

23. csc 630°

24. sin 540°

25. cos (−450°)

26. tan 270°

27. cot 450°

28. sec (−270°)

29. sin (−630°)

30. sec 360°

31. cot (−540°)

32. sec 720°

33. cos (−900°)

C

34. Write the equation of the unit circle in terms of x and y, where (x, y) is any point on the circle.

35. Let θ be the measure of any angle in standard position. Let P (x, y) be the point of intersection of the terminal side of the angle with the unit circle. Use the result from Exercise 34 to write the equation of the unit circle in terms of sin θ and cos θ.

CHECKPOINT

Sketch the angle with measure θ in standard position and write the measure φ of its reference angle. Then write the six trigonometric ratios for θ.

1. 120°

2. 315°

3. −225°

4. −510°

Find the indicated ratio or state that it is **undefined.**

5. tan 180°

6. sin (−240°)

7. sec 330°

8. sec (−270°)

9. cot 360°

10. csc 150°

11. cos (−540°)

12. tan (−90°)

11-6 Trigonometric Tables

OBJECTIVES

To find the trigonometric ratios of a positive acute angle, using a table.
To find the measure of a positive acute angle, given one of its trigonometric ratios.

Other than the quadrantal angles, the only angles whose trigonometric ratios we have found are those with reference angles of 30°, 45°, and 60°. More advanced methods were used to construct the table on pages 672–676. This table gives the values in decimal form for angles from 0° through 90°, in intervals of 10 minutes. A part of the table is shown below.

θ Degrees	θ Radians	Sin θ	Cos θ	Tan θ	Cot θ	Sec θ	Csc θ		
28° 00′	.4887	.4695	.8829	.5317	1.881	1.133	2.130	1.0821	62° 00′
10′	.4916	.4720	.8816	.5354	1.868	1.134	2.118	1.0792	50′
20′	.4945	.4746	.8802	.5392	1.855	1.136	2.107	1.0763	40′
30′	.4974	.4772	.8788	.5430	1.842	1.138	2.096	1.0734	30′
40′	.5003	.4797	.8774	.5467	1.829	1.140	2.085	1.0705	20′
50′	.5032	.4823	.8760	.5505	1.816	1.142	2.074	1.0676	10′
29° 00′	.5061	.4848	.8746	.5543	1.804	1.143	2.063	1.0647	61° 00′
10′	.5091	.4874	.8732	.5581	1.792	1.145	2.052	1.0617	50′
20′	.5120	.4899	.8718	.5619	1.780	1.147	2.041	1.0588	40′
30′	.5149	.4924	.8704	.5658	1.767	1.149	2.031	1.0559	30′
40′	.5178	.4950	.8689	.5696	1.756	1.151	2.020	1.0530	20′
50′	.5207	.4975	.8675	.5735	1.744	1.153	2.010	1.0501	10′
30° 00′	.5236	.5000	.8660	.5774	1.732	1.155	2.000	1.0472	60° 00′
		Cos θ	Sin θ	Cot θ	Tan θ	Csc θ	Sec θ	θ Radians	θ Degrees

EXAMPLE 1   Find tan 28°40′.

Locate the row for 28°40′ at the *left*. Then locate the column headed *Tan θ*. This row and column intersect at the entry .5467. Thus, tan 28°40′ = 0.5467.

Note that most of the decimal entries in the table are approximations of exact ratios. Here is a comparison.

$$\cos 30° = \frac{\sqrt{3}}{2} = 0.866025$$

Exact value, found by using the reference triangle for a 30° angle

Decimal for $\frac{\sqrt{3}}{2}$, correct to six decimal places

$$\cos 30° = 0.8660 \longleftarrow$$

Approximate value from table, correct to four decimal places

We use the equal sign for convenience, even though 0.8660 is not the exact value of cos 30°.

In a right triangle, the trigonometric ratios of an acute angle can be found using the sides of the triangle. This is possible because in standard position the acute angle has a first-quadrant reference triangle that is similar to the given triangle.

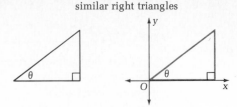

similar right triangles

Now consider both acute angles in a right triangle. Observe that they are **complementary.** That is, the sum of their measures is 90°. The trigonometric ratios of complementary angles are related in a special way.

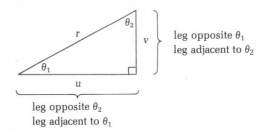

leg opposite θ_1
leg adjacent to θ_2

leg opposite θ_2
leg adjacent to θ_1

$$\sin \theta_1 = \frac{\text{leg opposite } \theta_1}{\text{hypotenuse}} = \frac{v}{r} = \frac{\text{leg adjacent to } \theta_2}{\text{hypotenuse}} = \cos \theta_2$$

The other relationships listed below can be checked in the same way.

$$\sin \theta_1 = \cos \theta_2 \qquad \cos \theta_1 = \sin \theta_2 \qquad \tan \theta_1 = \cot \theta_2$$
$$\csc \theta_1 = \sec \theta_2 \qquad \sec \theta_1 = \csc \theta_2 \qquad \cot \theta_1 = \tan \theta_2$$

Because of these relationships, pairs of complementary angles are listed at the left and right of each row of the trigonometric table. The column headings across the top are for the angles from 0° to 45°, which are shown on the left. The headings across the bottom are for the complementary angles at the right. For example, here is a part of the table showing the complementary angles measuring 28°40′ and 61°20′. The sine of one is equal to the cosine of the other, and so forth.

θ Degrees	θ Radians	Sin θ	Cos θ	Tan θ	Cot θ	Sec θ	Csc θ		
28°40′	.5003	.4797	.8774	.5467	1.829	1.140	2.085	1.0705	61°20′
		Cos θ	Sin θ	Cot θ	Tan θ	Csc θ	Sec θ		
								θ Radians	θ Degrees

——— complementary angles ———

EXAMPLE 2   Find cos 74°10′.

Use the table on page 673. Locate the row for 74°10′ at the *right*. Then locate the column labeled *Cos* θ at the bottom. This row and column intersect at the entry .2728. Thus, cos 74°10′ = 0.2728.

When a trigonometric ratio is given, the table can be used to find the approximate measure of the reference angle that has that ratio.

EXAMPLE 3   Find the measure of the positive acute angle θ, if sin θ = 0.8897.

Use the table on page 675. The entry .8897 is in the column labeled *Sin θ* at the bottom. This entry corresponds to the angle measure at the *right* in that row. Therefore, θ = 62°50'.

If a ratio is not an exact table entry, use the closest entry.

EXAMPLE 4   If θ is a positive acute angle, and cot θ = 1.321, find θ, to the nearest 10 minutes.

The closest entry for the cotangent is 1.319. Therefore, we use θ = 37°10'.

CLASS EXERCISES

Use the table on pages 672–676.

Find the six trigonometric ratios of each angle.

1. 15°   **2.** 39°   **3.** 64°   **4.** 85°

Find each ratio.

5. cos 18°10'   **6.** tan 42°30'   **7.** csc 89°40'   **8.** cot 71°50'

Find the positive acute angle θ, to the nearest 10 minutes.

9. sin θ = 0.2756   **10.** tan θ = 1.402   **11.** sec θ = 1.382

EXERCISES

Use the table on pages 672–676 for Exercises 1–49.

 Find the six trigonometric ratios of each angle, if they are defined.

1. 23°30'   **2.** 38°20'   **3.** 45°   **4.** 64°10'

5. 81°40'   **6.** 3°50'   **7.** 0°   **8.** 90°

 Find each ratio.

9. sin 89°   **10.** sin 89°30'   **11.** cos 1°   **12.** cos 0°30'

13. sin 27°10'   **14.** cos 61°20'   **15.** tan 40°30'   **16.** cot 15°40'

17. sec 75°50'   **18.** csc 46°20'   **19.** cos 6°50'   **20.** cot 84°30'

21. csc 30°30'   **22.** sin 3°   **23.** sec 20°40'   **24.** cot 59°10'

25. tan 11°   **26.** csc 80°10'   **27.** sin 19°50'   **28.** sec 45°10'

Find the positive acute angle θ, to the nearest 10 minutes.

29. $\cos \theta = 0.9781$ **30.** $\sin \theta = 0.9781$ **31.** $\tan \theta = 0.4877$

32. $\cot \theta = 0.4877$ **33.** $\csc \theta = 1.346$ **34.** $\sec \theta = 1.346$

35. $\sin \theta = 0.9730$ **36.** $\cos \theta = 0.9038$ **37.** $\tan \theta = 0.8050$

38. $\cot \theta = 0.9545$ **39.** $\sec \theta = 1.068$ **40.** $\csc \theta = 85.95$

B   **41.** $\cot \theta = 1.361$ **42.** $\sin \theta = 0.8674$ **43.** $\sec \theta = 1.730$

44. $\cos \theta = 0.1841$ **45.** $\csc \theta = 3.134$ **46.** $\cos \theta = 0.4420$

47. $\tan \theta = 6.710$ **48.** $\sin \theta = 0.7000$ **49.** $\sec \theta = 4.190$

Complete each equation by writing the appropriate trigonometric ratio for the complementary angle.

   Sample $\sec 36°20' = \csc 53°40'$

50. $\sin 23° = $ ___?___   **51.** $\tan 52°30' = $ ___?___

52. $\sec 86°20' = $ ___?___   **53.** $\cos 5°10' = $ ___?___

54. $\cot 63°30' = $ ___?___   **55.** $\csc 41°40' = $ ___?___

USING THE CALCULATOR

Decimal Degrees

An angle measure given in degrees and minutes can be written in *decimal degrees* by expressing the number of minutes as a decimal part of a degree. If your calculator does not have the capacity to make such conversions directly, you can proceed as in the following illustration.

$$32°24' = 32° + \left(\frac{24}{60}\right)^{\circ} \qquad \text{Divide 24 by 60, since } 1' = \left(\frac{1}{60}\right)^{\circ}.$$
$$= 32° + 0.4° = 32.4°$$

Similarly, an angle measure given in decimal degrees can be written in degrees and minutes.

$$86.85° = 86° + (60 \times 0.85)' \qquad \text{Multiply 0.85 by 60, since } 1° = 60'.$$
$$= 86° + 51', \text{ or } 86°51'$$

1. Use a calculator to find θ in decimal degrees and to find $\sin \theta$, each to four decimal places. (If your calculator does not give trigonometric ratios, estimate $\sin \theta$ using the table on pages 672–676.)
   a. $\theta = 4°15'$ **b.** $\theta = 28°23'$ **c.** $\theta = 57°36'$ **d.** $\theta = 86°52'$

2. Express each measure in degrees and minutes, to the nearest minute.
   a. $16.72°$ **b.** $35.14°$ **c.** $43.6°$ **d.** $61.43°$

11-7 Solving Right Triangles

OBJECTIVES _____

To find missing side or angle measures in right triangles, using
   trigonometric ratios.
To solve problems, using right triangles.

The trigonometric ratios can be used to find the measures of sides and
angles in right triangles.

EXAMPLE 1   Solve for a, without using a table.

Since the measure of the angle opposite
a is given and the length of the hypotenuse is also known, we use the sine
ratio.

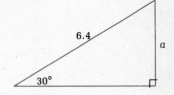

$$\sin 30° = \frac{a}{6.4}$$
$$a = 6.4(\sin 30°)$$
$$a = 6.4\left(\frac{1}{2}\right) \qquad \sin 30° = \frac{1}{2}$$
$$a = 3.2$$

In the last example we used the known value of the sine of 30°. In the
next example, the trigonometric table is needed to find the required ratio.

EXAMPLE 2   Solve for b, to the nearest tenth.

Since the length of the side opposite the
41°50′ angle is given, either the tangent
or cotangent ratio can be used. It is easier to use the cotangent, since multiplication is involved, rather than division. Both methods are shown below.

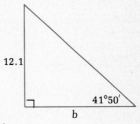

$$\cot 41°50' = \frac{b}{12.1} \qquad\qquad \tan 41°50' = \frac{12.1}{b}$$

$$b = 12.1(\cot 41°50') \qquad\qquad b = \frac{12.1}{\tan 41°50'}$$

$$b = 12.1(1.117) \qquad\qquad b = \frac{12.1}{0.8952}$$

$$b = 13.5 \qquad\qquad\qquad b = 13.5$$

The measures of the angles of triangle ABC may be denoted by the Greek letters α (*alpha*), β (*beta*), and γ (*gamma*).

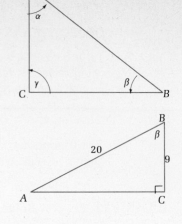

EXAMPLE 3 Solve for β.

Since the lengths of the hypotenuse and the leg adjacent to angle B are known, we can find the cosine of β.

$$\cos \beta = \frac{9}{20} = 0.45$$

The closest table entry for the cosine is .4488, which corresponds to $63°20'$. Thus, $\beta = 63°20'$.

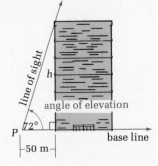

EXAMPLE 4 A point P is 50 meters from the base of a building. The angle of elevation to the top of the building is $72°$. Find the height h of the building, to the nearest meter.

Note that the **angle of elevation** is the angle between the *base line* and the *line of sight*.

Strategy: Write and solve an equation, using the tangent ratio.

$$\tan 72° = \frac{h}{50}$$
$$h = 50(\tan 72°)$$
$$h = 50(3.078)$$
$$h = 153.9$$

The building is approximately 154 meters tall.

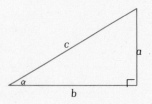

CLASS EXERCISES

In the triangle at the right, $\sin \alpha = \frac{a}{c}$. *Thus we can express* a *in terms of* $\sin \alpha$: $a = c \sin \alpha$.

1. Write a similar expression for a in terms of $\tan \alpha$.

2. Write an expression for b in terms of $\cos \alpha$.

3. Write an expression for c in terms of $\sec \alpha$.

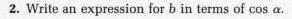

In the triangle at the right, $\cos \beta = \frac{a}{c}$. *Thus we can express* a *in terms of* $\cos \beta$: $a = c \cos \beta$.

4. Write a similar expression for a in terms of $\cot \beta$.

5. Write an expression for b in terms of $\sin \beta$.

6. Write an expression for c in terms of $\sec \beta$.

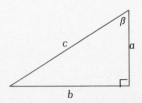

EXERCISES

A

*Solve for **a**, **b**, **c**, or θ, without using a table. Leave irrational answers in radical form.*

1.
6
30°
b

2.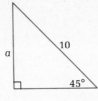
a
10
45°

3.
8
60°
b

4.
c
10
45°

5.
15
θ
7.5

6.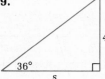
5
θ
5√3

7.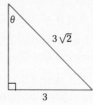
θ
3√2
3

8.
6
θ
3√3

*Solve for **s**, to the nearest whole number of units, or θ, to the nearest 10 minutes. Use the trigonometric table on pages 672–676.*

9.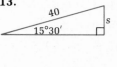
4
36°
s

10.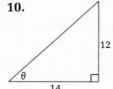
12
θ
14

11.
15
68°
s

12.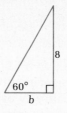
100   90
θ

13.
40
15°30′
s

14.
42°
30
s

15.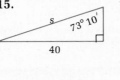
s
73° 10′
40

16.
θ
19
9

B

Solve for the indicated measure in right triangle ABC. Compute lengths to the nearest whole number and angle measures to the nearest 10 minutes.

17. Find b if $\alpha = 40°$ and $a = 10$.

18. Find c, if $\alpha = 40°$ and $a = 10$.

19. Find b, if $\beta = 46°30'$ and $a = 24$.

20. Find c, if $\beta = 46°30'$ and $a = 24$.

21. Find β, if $a = 2$ and $b = 3$.

22. Find α, if $a = 80$ and $b = 95$.

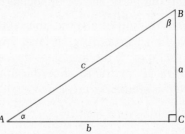

B
β
c
a
A α
b
C

TRIGONOMETRIC RATIOS

439

Solve each problem. Round lengths to the nearest unit.

23. A building casts a shadow 60 meters long when the angle of elevation of the top of the building from the tip of the shadow is 62°10′. How high is the building?

24. The distance from the base of a tree to a point P on the ground is 72 feet. The angle of elevation of the top of the tree from P is 55°. How tall is the tree?

25. An airplane is flying at an altitude of 3000 feet. When the plane is directly over a point G on the ground, the **angle of depression** of an airport is 70°40′. What is the distance from G to the airport?

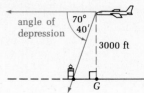

26. In Exercise 25, find the distance between the airplane and the airport along the line of sight between them.

27. Assume that a kite string anchored to the ground forms a straight line. If the string makes an angle of 67°20′ with the ground, and 625 feet of string are out, how high above the ground is the kite?

28. The top of a 25-foot ladder leaning against a house is 23 feet above the ground. Find the measure of the angle that the ladder makes with the ground. Give your answer to the nearest degree.

29. An airplane takes off at a point on a runway that is 525 feet away from a point under some high-tension wires that are 144 feet high. The angle made with the runway at takeoff is kept constant until the wires are cleared. What is that angle, to the nearest 10 minutes, if the wires are cleared by 50 feet?

30. An observer in a lighthouse standing along the shoreline measures the **angle of depression** of a ship at sea to be 8°20′. If the observer is 350 feet above sea level, how far is the ship from the shoreline?

31. The base of an isosceles triangle measures 64 inches, and the vertex angle measures 27°. Find the lengths of the two congruent sides. **Hint:** Consider the altitude from the vertex.

32. A circle inscribed in a regular octagon has a radius of 7.5 centimeters. Find the perimeter of the octagon, to the nearest tenth of a centimeter.

33. From the top of a skyscraper 1000 feet above the street, you can see two houses standing on level ground due north of the skyscraper. If the angles of depression of the houses are 18°20′ and 9°10′, how far apart are the houses?

Interpolation

When you wish to find a trigonometric ratio of an angle measure not given in a multiple of 10 minutes, it is not necessary to round to the nearest 10 minutes. Greater accuracy can be obtained by using *linear interpolation*, a method based on proportional parts. For example, to find sin 16°27′, first observe that this value is between sin 16°20′ and sin 16°30′.

Use a display to show the differences between the angle measures and the difference between the tabular values of their sines.

$$10'\left\{7'\left\{\begin{matrix}\sin 16°20' = 0.2812\\ \sin 16°27' = \ ?\\ \sin 16°30' = 0.2840\end{matrix}\right\}0.0028\right.$$

Note that the difference between 20′ and 27′ is $\frac{7}{10}$ of the difference between 20′ and 30′. Then assume that the difference between sin 16°20′ and sin 16°27′ is $\frac{7}{10}$ of 0.0028. The sine *increases* as the angle measure increases over this interval. Therefore, sin 16°27′ is found by *adding* $\frac{7}{10}$ of 0.0028 to sin 16°20′.

$$\sin 16°27' = 0.2812 + \frac{7}{10}(0.0028)$$

$$= 0.2812 + 0.0020 \qquad \text{Round to four decimal places.}$$

$$= 0.2832$$

When using this method to find other trigonometric ratios, always note whether the values increase or decrease over the interval. For instance, the cosine *decreases* as the angle increases between 0° and 90°. Therefore, to find cos 16°27′, $\frac{7}{10}$ of the positive difference between cos 16°20′ and cos 16°30′ would be *subtracted* from cos 16°20′. Try it!

A similar procedure is used to find the angle measure when a given ratio is not in the table.

For example, to find θ when cos θ = 0.4576 and 0° < θ < 90°, first note that the cosine value is between 0.4566 and 0.4592.

$$10'\left\{\begin{matrix}\cos 62°40' = 0.4592\\ \cos \theta \quad = 0.4576\\ \cos 62°50' = 0.4566\end{matrix}\right\}0.0016\right\}0.0026$$

$$\theta = 62°40' + \frac{8}{13}(10') \qquad \frac{0.0016}{0.0026} = \frac{8}{13} \text{ Assume that the difference between } \theta \text{ and } 62°40' \text{ is } \frac{8}{13} \text{ of } 10'.$$

$$= 62°40' + 6' \qquad \text{Round to the nearest minute.}$$

$$= 62°46'$$

Use linear interpolation to find each ratio.

1. sin 48°43′   **2.** cos 17°38′   **3.** tan 30°5′   **4.** cot 78°54′

Use linear interpolation to find θ, where 0° < θ < 90°.

5. sin θ = 0.2510   **6.** sec θ = 1.393   **7.** csc θ = 2.094

11-8 Using Reference Angles

OBJECTIVES

To find the trigonometric ratios of any angle, using a table.
To find the measure of an angle, given a trigonometric ratio.

The table of trigonometric ratios can be used to find the ratios for angles other than those between 0° and 90°. This can be done using reference angles. To illustrate, for an angle θ with terminal side in the third quadrant and reference angle ϕ,

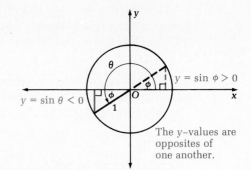

The y-values are opposites of one another.

$$\sin \theta = -\sin \phi$$

That is, $\sin \theta$ is the opposite of $\sin \phi$, which can be found in the table. Similarly, $\cos \theta = -\cos \phi$ and $\tan \theta = \tan \phi$.

In general, to find the trigonometric ratios of an angle of measure θ, in standard position:

- Find ϕ, the measure of the reference angle.
- Find the ratio for ϕ in the table on pages 672–676.
- Determine the quadrant in which the terminal side of θ is located.

This gives the signs of the ratios, as summarized in the following chart.

	Terminal side in quadrant I	Terminal side in quadrant II	Terminal side in quadrant III	Terminal side in quadrant IV
sine and cosecant	positive	positive	negative	negative
cosine and secant	positive	negative	negative	positive
tangent and cotangent	positive	negative	positive	negative

EXAMPLE 1   Find the sine, cosine, and tangent ratios of 162°10′.

First, find the measure of the reference angle.

$\phi = 180° - 162°10′$

$\phi = 179°60′ - 162°10′$ Write 180° as 179°60′ in order to be able to subtract.

$\phi = 17°50′$

Then find the ratios for ϕ in the table.

sin 17°50′ = 0.3062   cos 17°50′ = 0.9520   tan 17°50′ = 0.3217

Since the terminal side of an angle measuring 162°10′ is in the second quadrant, the sine is positive and the cosine and tangent are negative.

sin 162°10′ = sin 17°50′ = 0.3062

cos 162°10′ = −cos 17°50′ = −0.9520

tan 162°10′ = −tan 17°50′ = −0.3217

EXAMPLE 2   Find tan 260°.

The terminal side of a 260° angle is in quadrant III, and $\phi = 80°$.

tan 260° = tan 80° = 5.671

EXAMPLE 3   Find sin (−43°30′).

An angle of −43°30′ has its terminal side in quadrant IV, and $\phi = 43°30′$.

sin (−43°30′) = −sin 43°30′ = −0.6884

The measure of an angle can also be determined, if enough information is given.

EXAMPLE 4   Find θ, if cos $\theta = -0.9703$ and 90° < θ < 180°.

First locate 0.9703 in the Cos column of the table to find ϕ.

0.9703 = cos 14°, so $\phi = 14°$

Since 90° < θ < 180°, the terminal side of θ is in the second quadrant. Therefore, subtract the value of ϕ from 180°.

$\theta = 180° - 14° = 166°$

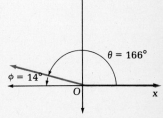

CLASS EXERCISES

Find each difference.

1. $180° - 97°20'$ **2.** $360° - 325°30'$ **3.** $180° - 142°50'$

Find the measure of the reference angle for θ, and find the quadrant containing the terminal side of θ.

4. $\theta = 89°$ **5.** $\theta = 193°$ **6.** $\theta = -300°$ **7.** $\theta = -243°$

8. $\theta = 251°30'$ **9.** $\theta = -333°50'$ **10.** $\theta = 311°10'$ **11.** $\theta = -185°40'$

EXERCISES

A   *Copy and complete the table.*

	θ	Quadrant of Terminal Side of θ	Measure of Reference Angle ϕ	$\sin \theta$	$\cos \theta$	$\tan \theta$	$\cot \theta$	$\sec \theta$	$\csc \theta$
1.	25°								
2.	155°								
3.	205°								
4.	335°								
5.	78°20′								
6.	281°40′								
7.	−101°40′								
8.	−258°20′								

Find the sine, cosine, and tangent ratios for θ.

9. $\theta = 110°$ **10.** $\theta = 190°$ **11.** $\theta = 333°20'$ **12.** $\theta = 135°50'$

13. $\theta = -161°$ **14.** $\theta = -203°$ **15.** $\theta = -342°50'$ **16.** $\theta = -5°30'$

Find the given ratio.

17. $\sin 100°$ **18.** $\cos 182°$ **19.** $\tan 198°$ **20.** $\cot 294°$

21. $\sec(-54°)$ **22.** $\csc(-112°)$ **23.** $\cos(-200°)$ **24.** $\tan(-353°)$

25. $\sin 79°10'$ **26.** $\sec 131°50'$ **27.** $\csc 300°20'$ **28.** $\cot(-19°40')$

29. $\cos 384°30'$ **30.** $\tan 472°$ **31.** $\sin(-272°10')$ **32.** $\csc(-563°)$

33. $\sec 360°10'$ **34.** $\cot 600°$ **35.** $\cos(-700°)$ **36.** $\csc(-360°30')$

Find θ to the nearest 10 minutes.

37. $\sin \theta = 0.2079, \ 0° < \theta < 90°$

38. $\sin \theta = 0.2079, \ 90° < \theta < 180°$

39. $\cos \theta = 0.6756, \ 0° < \theta < 90°$

40. $\cos \theta = 0.6756, \ 270° < \theta < 360°$

41. $\tan \theta = 0.5735, \ 0° < \theta < 90°$

42. $\tan \theta = 0.5735, \ 180° < \theta < 270°$

43. $\cot \theta = 0.9543, \ 0° < \theta < 90°$

44. $\sec \theta = 1.803, \ 270° < \theta < 360°$

45. $\csc \theta = 1.313, \ 90° < \theta < 180°$

46. $\sec \theta = 18.13, \ 360° < \theta < 450°$

47. $\cos \theta = -0.5250, \ 90° < \theta < 180°$

48. $\tan \theta = -0.3040, \ 90° < \theta < 180°$

49. $\sec \theta = -2.597, \ 90° < \theta < 180°$

50. $\cot \theta = -4.121, \ 90° < \theta < 180°$

B Find all possible values of θ between $0°$ and $180°$.

51. $\sin \theta = 0.9283$

52. $\cos \theta = 0.6670$

53. $\tan \theta = 1.422$

54. $\cos \theta = -0.9481$

55. $\cot \theta = -0.1792$

56. $\sin \theta = 0.1082$

57. $\cot \theta = 24.54$

58. $\csc \theta = 1.116$

59. $\sec \theta = -1.192$

Find all possible values of θ between $0°$ and $360°$.

60. $\sin \theta = -0.2000$

61. $\tan \theta = 20.00$

62. $\cos \theta = 0.2000$

63. $\cot \theta = -20.00$

64. $\sec \theta = -2.000$

65. $\csc \theta = -2.000$

CHECKPOINT

Find the missing values, **x**, **y**, or **r**, for the given reference triangle. Then find the six trigonometric ratios for θ.

1.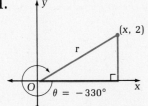

2.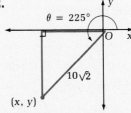

3.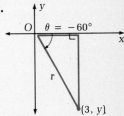

4. A statue casts a 6-meter shadow when the angle of elevation from the tip of the shadow to the sun is 71°20′. How tall is the statue, to the nearest meter?

5. A pilot, flying at an altitude of 1 mile, is directly over a point that is 5 miles from the airport. What is the angle of depression from the plane to the airport, to the nearest 10 minutes?

11-9　The Law of Cosines

OBJECTIVES _____

To find the measure of a side or an angle of a triangle, using the law of
　cosines.
To solve problems, using the law of cosines.

You have learned how to solve for unknown measures of sides and
angles in right triangles. Now we will develop a formula that makes it
possible to do the same for triangles that do not contain right angles.
　Consider triangle ABC with sides measuring a, b,
and c units. The altitude from B to side AC is of
length h, and the two parts of side AC are of lengths
x and $b - x$. Solve for h^2, using right triangle ABD.

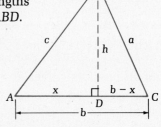

$$x^2 + h^2 = c^2 \qquad \text{Pythagorean theorem}$$
$$h^2 = c^2 - x^2$$

Also solve for h^2 using right triangle CBD.

$$(b - x)^2 + h^2 = a^2$$
$$h^2 = a^2 - (b - x)^2$$

Then set the two expressions for h^2 equal to each other.

$$a^2 - (b - x)^2 = c^2 - x^2$$
$$a^2 - b^2 + 2bx - x^2 = c^2 - x^2$$
$$a^2 = b^2 + c^2 - 2bx \qquad \text{Cos } A = \tfrac{x}{c}, \text{ so } x = c \text{ cos } A.$$
$$a^2 = b^2 + c^2 - 2bc \text{ cos } A \qquad \text{Note that the letter } A \text{ for the vertex is}$$

also used to designate the measure
of the angle.

　Similar formulas can be derived for b^2 and c^2. Collectively, these results are called the **law of cosines.**

Law of Cosines
For any triangle ABC, $a^2 = b^2 + c^2 - 2bc$ cos A
$$b^2 = a^2 + c^2 - 2ac \text{ cos } B$$
$$c^2 = a^2 + b^2 - 2ab \text{ cos } C$$

Translating the law of cosines into words may help you to memorize it:

　*The square of a side of a triangle equals the sum of the squares of
　the other two sides, minus twice their product times the cosine of
　their included angle.*

The law of cosines is used to solve for the length of a side of a triangle when the measures of the other two sides and the included angle are known.

EXAMPLE 1 Find a to the nearest whole number.

$$a^2 = b^2 + c^2 - 2bc \cos A$$
$$a^2 = 10^2 + 4^2 - 2(10)(4) \cos 60°$$
$$a^2 = 100 + 16 - 2(10)(4)\left(\frac{1}{2}\right)$$
$$a^2 = 76 \qquad \text{Take the positive square root}$$
$$a = 8.718 \qquad \text{Use the table on page 668.}$$

To the nearest whole number, $a = 9$.

The law of cosines is also used to solve for angle measures when the lengths of the three sides of the triangle are known.

EXAMPLE 2 Find the measure of angle A.

$$a^2 = b^2 + c^2 - 2bc \cos A$$
$$2bc \cos A = b^2 + c^2 - a^2 \qquad \text{Solve for cos A.}$$
$$\cos A = \frac{b^2 + c^2 - a^2}{2bc}$$
$$\cos A = \frac{12^2 + 22^2 - 14^2}{2(12)(22)} = 0.8182$$

The closest entry in the table is .8175, so we use $\angle A = 35°10'$.

The law of cosines is particularly helpful in some problems that require you to find distances that cannot be measured directly.

EXAMPLE 3 Points A and B are on the shoreline of a pond. A surveyor is at point C, which is 54 meters from A and 70 meters from B. If $\gamma = 108°$, what is the distance between A and B, to the nearest meter?

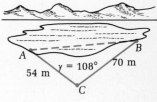

Strategy: Use the law of cosines.

$$AB^2 = BC^2 + AC^2 - 2(BC)(AC) \cos \gamma \qquad c^2 = a^2 + b^2 - 2ab \cos C$$
$$AB^2 = 70^2 + 54^2 - 2(70)(54) \cos 108°$$
$$AB^2 = 4900 + 2916 - 7560(-0.3090) \qquad \cos 108° = -\cos 72°$$
$$AB^2 = 10152.04$$
$$AB = \sqrt{10152.04}$$

$\sqrt{10{,}152}$ is not in the table on page 668. Use a calculator, or estimate as follows:

$100^2 = 10{,}000$, so $\sqrt{10{,}000} = 100$. $101^2 = 10{,}201$, so $\sqrt{10{,}201} = 101$.

The distance between points A and B is about 101 meters.

Note that if an angle of a triangle measures 90°, the law of cosines gives us a familiar result, the Pythagorean theorem. Suppose the measure of angle C is 90°. Then,

$$c^2 = a^2 + b^2 - 2ab \cos C$$
$$c^2 = a^2 + b^2 - 2ab(0) \qquad \cos 90° = 0$$
$$c^2 = a^2 + b^2$$

CLASS EXERCISES

State the law of cosines by completing each equation.

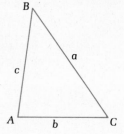

1. $a^2 = \underline{\ ?\ }$ **2.** $b^2 = \underline{\ ?\ }$ **3.** $c^2 = \underline{\ ?\ }$

*Use the law of cosines to express each ratio in terms of **a**, **b**, and **c**.*

4. $\cos A = \underline{\ ?\ }$ **5.** $\cos B = \underline{\ ?\ }$ **6.** $\cos C = \underline{\ ?\ }$

EXERCISES

A   Find **a**, **b**, or **c** to the nearest whole number, or α, β, or γ to the nearest degree.

1. $a = \underline{\ ?\ }$

2. $c = \underline{\ ?\ }$

3. $b = \underline{\ ?\ }$

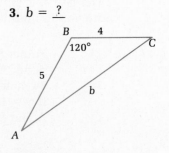

4. $\gamma = \underline{\ ?\ }$

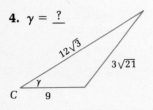

5. $\beta = \underline{\ ?\ }$

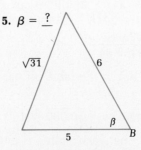

6. $\alpha = \underline{\ ?\ }$

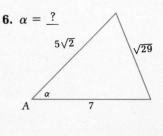

B

7. In triangle ABC, find b to the nearest tenth and α to the nearest degree.

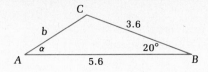

8. In triangle PQR, find p to the nearest tenth and $\angle R$ to the nearest degree.

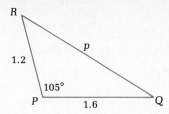

*In triangle **ABC**, find each angle measure to the nearest 10 minutes.*

9. Find γ, if $a = 8$, $b = 6$, and $c = 10$.

10. Find γ, if $a = b = 50$ and $c = 30$.

11. Find α, β, and γ, if $a = b = c = 12$.

12. Find α, if $b = 4$, $c = 5$, and $a = 6$.

13. Find β in Exercise 12.

14. Find γ in Exercise 12. Use the fact that the sum of the angle measures of a triangle is 180°.

*Use the law of cosines and the given side and angle measures to find the measures of the three remaining angles, or the two remaining angles and one side of triangle **ABC**. Give lengths to the nearest tenth and angle measures to the nearest degree.*

15. $\alpha = 60°$, $b = 3.0$, $c = 8.0$

16. $\beta = 30°$, $a = 5.0$, $c = 4.0$

17. $\gamma = 45°$, $a = 1.0$, $b = 3.0$

18. $\gamma = 120°$, $a = 6.0$, $b = 3.2$

19. $a = 7.0$, $b = 9.0$, $c = 10.0$

20. $\alpha = 64°$, $b = 4.0$, $c = 3.5$

21. $\beta = 28°$, $a = 2.4$, $c = 4.0$

22. $a = 8.0$, $b = 10.8$, $c = 15.0$

23. $a = 9.6$, $b = 8.0$, $c = 5.8$

24. $a = 6.0$, $b = 10.2$, $c = 14.5$

Solve each problem. Round lengths to the nearest unit and angle measures to the nearest degree.

25. A railroad tunnel passes through a mountain, as shown at the right. Find the length AB of the tunnel.

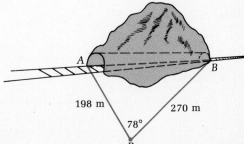

26. Points A and B lie on opposite sides of a field. A surveyor stands at a point P, such that $\overline{PA}$ measures 100 meters and $\overline{PB}$ 135 meters. The surveyor uses a transit and finds that angle APB measures $128°20'$. Find the distance between A and B.

C

27. Two adjacent sides of a parallelogram, with lengths 15 and 25 inches, form a $58°$ angle. Find the length of the longer diagonal.

28. Circles A, B, and C are tangent to each other, and the sides of triangle ABC pass through the points of tangency. Circles A and B have 4-unit radii, and circle C has a radius of 2 units. Find the measures of the angles of triangle ABC.

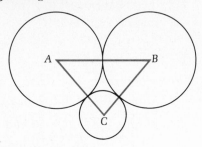

29. Two cars start at the intersection of two straight highways at 12:00 noon. One travels at an average rate of 44 miles per hour, and the other at 52 miles per hour. If the angle between their paths measures $38°$, how far apart are the cars at 12:45 P.M.?

30. A baseball diamond is in the shape of a square with 90 feet between consecutive bases. The center fielder is standing in line with home plate and second base, at a distance of 150 feet from second base. How far is the center fielder from third base?

31. For triangle ABC, show that

$$c = a \cos B + b \cos A$$

Hint: First draw the altitude from vertex C and find expressions for $\cos A$ and $\cos B$.

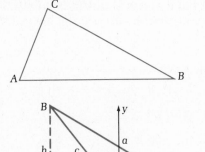

32. The law of cosines holds for any triangle. However, in the derivation of the law on page 446, all three angles of triangle ABC are acute. Refer to obtuse triangle ABC at the right, and prove that

$$a^2 = b^2 + c^2 - 2bc \cos A$$

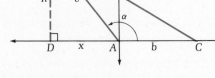

Use the *law of cosines to derive the following formulas for any triangle ABC.*

*33. $2(ab \cos C + ac \cos B + bc \cos A) = a^2 + b^2 + c^2$

*34. $\dfrac{\cos A}{a} + \dfrac{\cos B}{b} + \dfrac{\cos C}{c} = \dfrac{a^2 + b^2 + c^2}{2abc}$

Quick Geometric Checks

When solving for the measures of sides or angles of a triangle, certain types of errors can be discovered without doing involved computations. A quick glance will tell you that your "solution" must be wrong, since it contradicts a basic geometric rule. Here are some of the familiar rules that can be used.

  a. The sum of the angle measures of a triangle is 180°.

  b. The sum of the measures of two sides of a triangle is greater than the measure of the third side.

  c. Two sides of a triangle are of equal measure if and only if the angles opposite them are of equal measure.

  d. One side of a triangle is longer than a second side if and only if the angle opposite the first side is greater than the angle opposite the second side.

  e. The hypotenuse of a right triangle is longer than either leg.

  f. The longest side of an obtuse triangle is opposite the obtuse angle.

Suppose, for example, that you solve for p in triangle PQR, obtaining the answer $p = 4$. A glance at the diagram should tell you that this answer gives a situation in which rule **b** is contradicted. If p equals 4, then $p + r = 4 + 3 = 7$, and 7 is *not* greater than 8, the measure of the third side of the triangle.

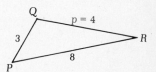

Now you try it! The measure shown in red on each figure is incorrect. Write the letter of the rule that is contradicted.

1.

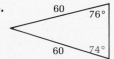

2.

3.

4.

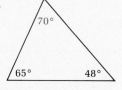

5.

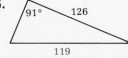

6.

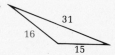

11-10   The Law of Sines: Two Angles and a Side

To solve a triangle, when the measures of two angles and a side are known.

To solve problems, using the law of sines.

In this triangle, the measures of two angles and a side are given. To find the length of another side we cannot use the law of cosines, which requires known measures of two sides of the triangle. However, another law can be derived that enables us to find b or c.

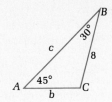

The triangle at the right has sides measuring a, b, and c units, and altitude h. Thus,

$$\sin A = \frac{h}{c} \text{ and } \sin C = \frac{h}{a}$$

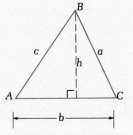

We solve each equation for h and then set the two expressions for h equal to each other.

$$h = c \sin A \qquad h = a \sin C$$

Then, $c \sin A = a \sin C$

$$\frac{\sin A}{a} = \frac{\sin C}{c}$$

If the altitude is drawn from A, the result is similar.

$$\frac{\sin B}{b} = \frac{\sin C}{c}$$

Taken together, these results are called the **law of sines.**

Law of Sines

For any triangle ABC,

$$\frac{\sin A}{a} = \frac{\sin B}{b} = \frac{\sin C}{c}$$

In the first example, the law of sines is used to solve for b in the triangle shown at the top of this page.

EXAMPLE 1

Find the exact value of b in radical form. Then find b to the nearest whole number.

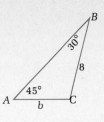

Use the law of sines. Since the measures of angle A and the side opposite that angle are given, use $\frac{\sin A}{a} = \frac{\sin B}{b}$ and solve for b.

$b \sin A = a \sin B$

$b = \dfrac{a \sin B}{\sin A}$ Divide each side by $\sin A$.

$b = \dfrac{8 \sin 30°}{\sin 45°}$ Substitute 8 for a, 30° for B, 45° for A.

$b = \dfrac{8\left(\dfrac{1}{2}\right)}{\dfrac{\sqrt{2}}{2}}$

$b = 4\sqrt{2}$ Exact value of b

$b = 6$ Value of b, to the nearest whole number

To *solve a triangle* means to find all of the unknown measures of its angles and sides.

EXAMPLE 2

Solve triangle ABC, where $\angle A = 43°$, $\angle C = 115°$, and $AC = 5$.

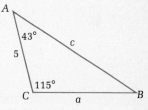

Sketch and label the triangle. Then find the measure of the third angle, B. Since the sum of the measures of the angles of a triangle is 180°,

$\angle B = 180° - (43° + 115°) = 22°$

Now, since the measures of angle B and the side opposite angle B are known, we can use the law of sines to find a and c. First, we solve $\frac{\sin B}{b} = \frac{\sin C}{c}$ for c, and substitute the known values.

$c = \dfrac{b \sin C}{\sin B} = \dfrac{5 \sin 115°}{\sin 22°} = \dfrac{5 \sin 65°}{\sin 22°} = \dfrac{5(0.9063)}{0.3746} = 12$ To the nearest whole number

Now solve $\frac{\sin B}{b} = \frac{\sin A}{a}$ for a, and substitute the known values.

$a = \dfrac{b \sin A}{\sin B} = \dfrac{5 \sin 43°}{\sin 22°} = \dfrac{5(0.6820)}{0.3746} = 9$ To the nearest whole number

In Example 2, the law of cosines could have been used to solve for a, since the measures of angle A and the two sides adjacent to that angle are already known. The law of sines was used because it usually involves fewer calculations than the law of cosines.

EXAMPLE 3

The angle of elevation to the top of a mountain from point A on the ground is $22°$. The angle of elevation from point B to the top is $58°$. The distance from A to B is 1000 feet, and points A, B, and D are on the same line. How high is the mountain?

Strategy: Use the law of sines to find a. Then use $\sin 58°$ to find h.

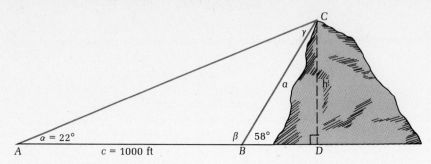

For triangle ABC: $\alpha = 22°$

$$\beta = 180° - 58° = 122°$$

$$\gamma = 180° - (22° + 122°) = 36°$$

Use the law of sines to solve for a.

$$\frac{\sin 22°}{a} = \frac{\sin 36°}{1000}$$

$$a = \frac{1000 \sin 22°}{\sin 36°} = \frac{1000(0.3746)}{0.5878} = 637 \qquad \text{To the nearest whole number}$$

Then use right triangle BCD to solve for h.

$$\sin 58° = \frac{h}{a}$$

$$h = a \sin 58° = 637(0.8480) = 540 \qquad \text{To the nearest whole number}$$

The height of the mountain is approximately 540 feet.

CLASS EXERCISES

Use $\frac{\sin A}{a} = \frac{\sin B}{b}$ to express each of the following in terms of the other three quantities.

1. a **2.** b **3.** $\sin A$ **4.** $\sin B$

Find the indicated measure without using a table or a calculator. Leave irrational answers in radical form.

5. If $a = \dfrac{10 \sin 45°}{\sin 30°}$, find a.

6. If $\sin A = \dfrac{14\sqrt{2} \sin 30°}{14}$, find $\angle A$.

7. If $\sin C = \dfrac{14\sqrt{3} \sin 90°}{28}$, find $\angle C$.

8. If $b = \dfrac{6 \sin 60°}{\sin 30°}$, find b.

EXERCISES

A Find the exact measure of the indicated side. If the answer is irrational, give it to the nearest whole number also.

1. $a =$ ___?___

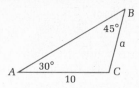

2. $c =$ ___?___

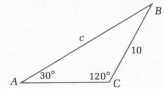

3. $b =$ ___?___

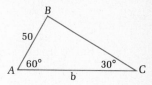

4. $\angle B = 75°$, $\angle C = 45°$, $a = 14$; $c =$ ___?___

5. $\angle A = 60°$, $\angle B = 45°$, $a = 9$; $b =$ ___?___

6. $\angle A = 120°$, $\angle C = 45°$, $c = 8\sqrt{3}$; $a =$ ___?___

7. $\angle A = 15°$, $\angle B = 30°$, $b = 10\sqrt{2}$; $c =$ ___?___

8. Let $\angle A = 30°$, $\angle C = 40°$, and $a = 10$. First solve for c, using the law of sines. Then solve for b, using the law of sines. Solve for b again, using the law of cosines. Give answers to the nearest whole number.

9. Let $\angle A = 70°$, $\angle B = 30°$, and $b = 15$. First solve for c using the law of sines. Then solve for a using the law of sines. Solve for a again, using the law of cosines. Give answers to the nearest whole number.

10. Find the distance across the pond, between points A and B, to the nearest meter.

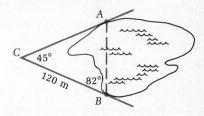

B Solve triangle **ABC**. Give lengths to the nearest whole number and angle measures to the nearest 10 minutes.

11. $\alpha = 37°20'$, $\beta = 71°30'$, $a = 40$ **12.** $\alpha = 68°10'$, $\gamma = 76°50'$, $c = 65$

13. $\beta = 55°40'$, $\gamma = 80°30'$, $c = 2500$ **14.** $\alpha = 32°50'$, $\beta = 126°10'$, $a = 180$

15. $\beta = 110°40'$, $\gamma = 29°30'$, $a = 22$ **16.** $\alpha = 155°$, $\beta = 15°50'$, $c = 20$

Solve. Round answers to the nearest unit except where otherwise specified.

17. One angle of a rhombus measures 34°, and the length of the longer diagonal of the rhombus is 50 centimeters. Find the length of a side of the rhombus.
Hint: All sides of a rhombus are of equal length, and the sum of the measures of any pair of consecutive angles is 180°.

18. Two guy wires that support a telephone pole stretch from the top of the pole to points on the ground on opposite sides of the pole. The wires form angles of 62°10′ and 68°50′ with the ground, and the distance between the points on the ground is 46 feet. Find the lengths of the guy wires.

C

19. Use the law of sines to find the length of segment CD in the triangle shown below.

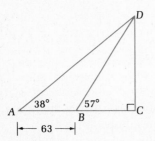

20. In the figure below, the plane containing triangle ACD is perpendicular to the plane containing triangle ABC. Find the length of segment CD.

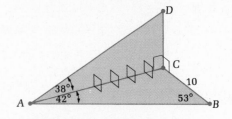

21. Two points, A and B, on the edge of a straight beach are 1000 meters apart. A ship at point S is simultaneously observed from both points, such that ∠ABS = 63°20′ and ∠BAS = 81°40′. Find the distance from the ship to the beach, to the nearest 10 meters.

22. Points P and Q are observation points in the same building, with P 150 feet directly above Q. The angles of depression from these points to a point G at ground level are 23°20′ and 14°10′. Find the distance from G to the building and the height of P above the ground.

23. Find the measures of segments AB and AD.

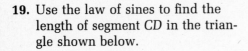

*24. Points A and B lie along a straight shoreline and 500 meters apart. Two ships are anchored at points P and Q. Find the distance between the ships, to the nearest 10 meters, if the angles measured at A and B are as indicated on the diagram.

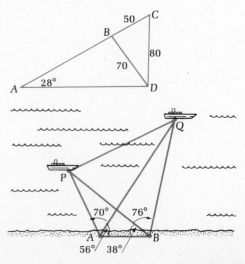

11-11 The Law of Sines: Two Sides and an Angle

OBJECTIVES _____

To determine the number of triangles possible when the measures of two
  sides and the angle opposite one of them are known.
To solve triangles when the measures of such parts are known.

When the measures of two sides and an angle opposite one of them are
given, you may be able to draw one triangle, two different triangles, or
no triangle. To illustrate, angle A and sides with measures a and c are
given in the figures below.

I Suppose $\angle A$ is an acute angle.

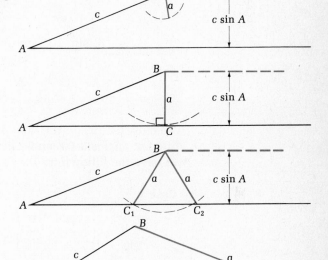

If $a < c \sin A$, there is
no triangle.

If $a = c \sin A$, there is
one triangle.

If $a > c \sin A$ and $a < c$,
there are *two* possible
triangles.

If $a \geq c$, there is *one*
triangle.

II Suppose $\angle A$ is a right angle or an obtuse angle.

If $a \leq c$, there is
no triangle.

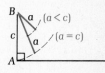

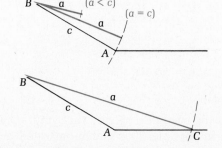

If $a > c$, there is
one triangle.

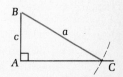

EXAMPLE 1

Solve triangle ABC, where $a = 10$, $c = 13$, and $\angle A = 25°$. Give lengths to the nearest tenth and angle measures to the nearest 10 minutes.

$\angle A$ is acute.

$a > c \sin A$ $13 \sin 25° = 5.4938$, and $10 > 5.4938$.

$a < c$ $10 < 13$

Thus, there are two possible solutions. Sketch the two triangles.

Case 1   **Case 2**

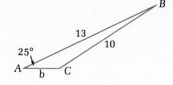

Find $\angle C$, using $\dfrac{\sin A}{a} = \dfrac{\sin C}{c}$.

$$\sin C = \frac{c \sin A}{a} = \frac{13 \sin 25°}{10} = 0.5494$$

The closest entry in the table is .5495. Since there are two different angles between 0° and 180° with this sine ratio, we have the following:

Case 1

$\angle C = 33°20'$

$\angle B = 180° - (25° + 33°20')$
$\angle B = 121°40'$

$\dfrac{\sin A}{a} = \dfrac{\sin B}{b}$

$b = \dfrac{a \sin B}{\sin A}$

$b = \dfrac{10 \sin 121°40'}{\sin 25°}$

$b = \dfrac{10(0.8511)}{0.4226}$

$b = 20.1$

Case 2

$\angle C = 180° - 33°20' = 146°40'$

$\angle B = 180° - (25° + 146°40')$
$\angle B = 8°20'$

$\dfrac{\sin A}{a} = \dfrac{\sin B}{b}$

$b = \dfrac{a \sin B}{\sin A}$

$b = \dfrac{10 \sin 8°20'}{\sin 25°}$

$b = \dfrac{10(0.1449)}{0.4226}$

$b = 3.4$

When solving triangles, be sure that your answers do not include values that are impossible. This is demonstrated in the next example.

EXAMPLE 2   Solve triangle ABC, if $a = 10$, $c = 21$, and $\angle A = 30°$.

$\angle A$ is acute.

$a < c \sin A$ $21 \sin 30° = 21\left(\dfrac{1}{2}\right) = 10.5$,

and $10 < 10.5$.

Therefore, there is no triangle.

If you did not realize, from the given data, that no triangle was possible in Example 2, you would have discovered this fact when you tried to solve for $\angle C$ using the law of sines.

$\dfrac{\sin C}{c} = \dfrac{\sin A}{a}$, so $\sin C = \dfrac{21\left(\frac{1}{2}\right)}{10} = 1.05$ No angle has a sine ratio greater than 1, so there is no solution.

CLASS EXERCISES

Determine the number of triangles possible, without attempting to solve the triangle(s).

1. $\angle A = 65°$, $a = 11$, $c = 8$

2. $\angle A = 30°$, $a = 5$, $c = 10$

3. $\angle A = 150°$, $a = 20$, $c = 14$

4. $\angle A = 140°$, $a = 6$, $c = 9$

5. $\angle A = 53°$, $a = 17$, $c = 17$

6. $\angle A = 45°$, $a = 12$, $c = 10\sqrt{2}$

7. $\angle A = 90°$, $a = 12$, $c = 8$

8. $\angle A = 90°$, $a = 6$, $c = 8$

9. $\angle A = 100°$, $a = 6$, $c = 6$

10. $\angle A = 60°$, $a = 10$, $c = 8\sqrt{3}$

EXERCISES

A   *Determine the number of triangles possible, without attempting to solve the triangle(s).*

1. $\angle A = 32°10'$, $a = 5$, $c = 10$

2. $\angle A = 74°30'$, $a = 19.5$, $c = 20$

3. $\angle A = 162°20'$, $a = 27.1$, $c = 30.4$

4. $\angle A = 135°$, $a = 34$, $c = 34\sqrt{2}$

5. $\angle A = 170°50'$, $a = 0.7$, $c = 0.5$

6. $\angle A = 10°40'$, $a = 1.7$, $c = 1.7$

Find the indicated angle measures, to the nearest 10 minutes.

7.

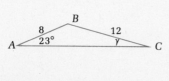

8.

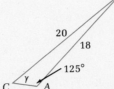

9.

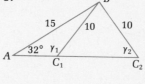

B

Solve the triangle or triangles with the given measures, if a triangle is possible. Give lengths to the nearest whole number and angle measures to the nearest 10 minutes.

10. $\alpha = 40°$, $a = 18$, $c = 10$ **11.** $\alpha = 130°$, $a = 15$, $c = 5$

12. $\alpha = 53°$, $a = 20$, $c = 22$ **13.** $\alpha = 36°$, $b = 12$, $a = 12$

14. $\alpha = 48°$, $c = 30$, $a = 10$ **15.** $\alpha = 110°30'$, $a = 5$, $c = 3$

16. $\beta = 153°10'$, $b = 100$, $c = 80$ **17.** $\gamma = 16°40'$, $c = 44$, $b = 28$

Solve the triangle or triangles with the given measures. Give lengths to the nearest tenth and angle measures to the nearest 10 minutes.

18. $\alpha = 160°30'$, $a = 29$, $c = 19$ **19.** $\alpha = 10°50'$, $a = 48$, $c = 64$

Solve each problem. Round lengths to the nearest unit and angle measures to the nearest degree.

20. A 40-foot conveyor belt moves packages from ground level at a point Q to a platform at point P. The belt is inclined at an angle of 44° with the ground. A 28-foot ladder reaches from a point R on the ground *behind* the platform to P. Find the angle the ladder makes with the ground.

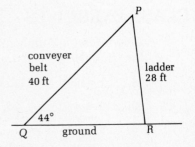

C

21. A diagonal of a parallelogram is 30 centimeters long and forms an angle of 53° with one of the sides of the parallelogram. The other side of the parallelogram is 42 centimeters long. Find the length of the other diagonal.

*22. In the figure at the right, $\overline{HT}$ represents a 50-foot tower standing on top of a hill. S is the tip of the 39-foot shadow made by the tower. Point A is at the base of the hill. The measures of angles HST and HAT are shown. Find the height of the hill, BH.

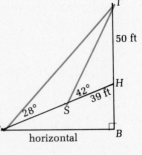

*23. Find the length of diagonal AC in quadrilateral ABCD, if diagonal BD is 120 units long.

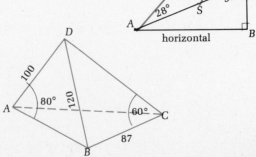

Navigation

In some navigation problems the direction or *bearing* from a point P to a point Q is important. The bearing can be defined as the measure of the acute angle formed by the north-south line through P and the line PQ.

In the figure at the right, the bearing from P to Q is N 35° E (*north 35° east*). The letter N or S is written first, then the angle measure, and then the letter E or W.

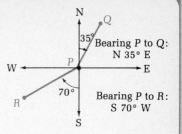

Bearing P to Q:
N 35° E

Bearing P to R:
S 70° W

Example   A cruise ship sailed 50 nautical miles with a bearing N 60° W. It changed course and sailed 75 nautical miles with a bearing N 20° E.

a. How far was the ship from its starting point?

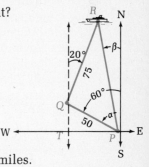

The dashed line is parallel to line NP. Thus angles QPN and PQT are congruent, and $\angle PQT = 60°$. Then

$$\angle PQR = 180° - (20° + 60°) = 100°$$

Use the law of cosines to find PR.

$$(PR)^2 = 50^2 + 75^2 - 2(50)(75)\cos 100°$$
$$(PR)^2 \approx 9427, \text{ so } PR \approx 97.$$

The distance is approximately 97 nautical miles.

b. What was the bearing from the starting point to the final point?

Use the law of sines to find α.

$$\frac{75}{\sin \alpha} = \frac{97}{\sin 100°}, \text{ or } \sin \alpha = \frac{75 \sin 100°}{97}. \text{ Thus, } \alpha \approx 50°.$$

Then find β. $\beta \approx 60° - 50°$, or 10°.

The bearing of R from P is approximately N 10° W.

1. Ship A leaves a dock at 12 noon and sails with a bearing N 40° W at a speed of 25 knots (25 nautical miles per hour). Ship B leaves the same dock at 1 P.M. and sails at 20 knots with a bearing N 60° E. Find the distance between the ships at 2:30 P.M., to the nearest nautical mile. Find the bearing from B to A to the nearest degree. Find the bearing from A to B.

*2. A ship at point P is to sail to point Q, 40 nautical miles north and 200 nautical miles east of P. The ship cannot take a direct course to Q, so it first sails S 70° E to point R, 100 nautical miles from P. Find the distance from R to Q to the nearest nautical mile. Find the bearing from R to Q to the nearest degree.

VOCABULARY

ray (p. 412)
angle (p. 412)
sides of an angle (p. 412)
vertex of an angle (p. 412)
standard position (p. 412)
initial side (p. 412)
terminal side (p. 412)
degree (p. 412)
minute (p. 412)
positive angle (p. 412)
negative angle (p. 412)
quadrantal angle (p. 412)
coterminal angles (p. 413)
reference angle (p. 416)
reference triangle (p. 417)
Pythagorean theorem (p. 418)
trigonometric ratios (p. 420)

sine, sin (p. 420)
cosine, cos (p. 420)
tangent, tan (p. 420)
cosecant, csc (p. 420)
secant, sec (p. 420)
cotangent, cot (p. 420)
similar triangles (p. 421)
isosceles right triangle (p. 425)
equilateral triangle (p. 426)
unit circle (p. 429)
complementary angles (p. 434)
angle of elevation (p. 438)
angle of depression (p. 440)
law of cosines (p. 446)
law of sines (p. 452)
solving a triangle (p. 453)

SUMMARY

Our study of trigonometry begins with angles in standard position. Degree measure is used and, for the most part, the measures of angles are given to the nearest 10 minutes. The trigonometric ratios for nonquadrantal angles are defined using reference triangles. The ratios for quadrantal angles are introduced by using the unit circle to extend the definitions of the ratios.

Trigonometric tables are used initially for finding the ratios for acute angles. Then the tables are applied to angles of any size by making use of reference angles. The applications in this chapter involve solving for the unknown measures of angles and sides of triangles. The law of sines and the law of cosines are used in applications involving triangles that do not have right angles.

REVIEW EXERCISES

11-1   *Find the measure of the smallest positive angle that is coterminal with the angle of given measure.*

   1. $450°$ **2.** $560°$ **3.** $640°$ **4.** $700°$ **5.** $850°$

11-2   *The given point $P(x, y)$ is on the terminal side of an angle in standard position. Draw the reference triangle with P as a vertex, and find the length of the hypotenuse r.*

   6. $P(-6, -8)$ **7.** $P(1, -3)$ **8.** $P(-15, 8)$ **9.** $P(4, 3)$

1-3   The point $P(x, y)$ is on the terminal side of an angle of measure θ, in standard position. Find the six trigonometric ratios for θ.

10. $P(8, 8)$ **11.** $P(-1, 6)$ **12.** $P(3, -5)$ **13.** $P(-4, -6)$

11-4   Sketch an angle with the given measure, and its reference triangle. Then find the required ratio.

14. csc 240°   **15.** tan $(-240°)$ **16.** cos $(-45°)$ **17.** sec 300°

11-5   Find the coordinates of the point on the terminal side of θ and on the unit circle. Then write all of the defined trigonometric ratios for θ.

18. $\theta = 30°$ **19.** $\theta = 135°$ **20.** $\theta = -120°$ **21.** $\theta = 90°$ **22.** $\theta = -540°$

11-6   Find each ratio. Use the table on pages 672–676.

23. sin 1°   **24.** tan 49°30′   **25.** cos 89°   **26.** sec 4°10′

Find the positive acute angle θ, to the nearest 10 minutes.

27. cos $\theta = 0.9730$ **28.** csc $\theta = 1.106$ **29.** cot $\theta = 0.8053$

11-7   **30.** The hypotenuse of a right triangle measures 80 feet. If one leg measures 40 feet, find the measure of the angle adjacent to that leg.

31. A forest ranger in a lookout tower sees a fire through a telescope that is 30 meters above the ground. If the angle of depression to the fire is 3°, how far is the fire from the tower?

11-8   **32.** Find cos 100°.   **33.** Find cot 198°20′.   **34.** Find tan $(-294°50′)$.

35. Find θ to the nearest 10 minutes, if sin $\theta = 0.6756$ and $0° \leq 0 \leq 90°$.

11-9   **36.** In triangle ABC, $b = 4$, $c = 6$, and $\angle A = 40°$. Find a to the nearest tenth and find $\angle B$ and $\angle C$ to the nearest degree.

37. A parallelogram has sides 5 inches and 8 inches long, and the longest diagonal is 10 inches long. Find the measures of the angles of the parallelogram, to the nearest 10 minutes.

11-10   Solve triangle **ABC**. Give lengths to the nearest whole number.

38. $\alpha = 40°$, $\beta = 110°$, $a = 13$ **39.** $\gamma = 120°$, $\beta = 30°$, $c = 24$

11-11   Solve the triangle or triangles with the given measures, if a triangle is possible. Give lengths to the nearest whole number and angle measures to the nearest 10 minutes.

40. $\alpha = 42°$, $a = 20$, $c = 25$ **41.** $\alpha = 144°$, $a = 14$, $b = 14$

1. Sketch a $-300°$ angle in standard position.

2. Sketch a $495°$ angle in standard position.

The point $P(x, y)$ *is on the terminal side of an angle of measure* θ *in standard position. Draw the reference triangle with* P *as a vertex. Then find the six trigonometric ratios for* θ.

3. $P(-5, -12)$ 4. $P(15, 20)$ 5. $P(-5, 7)$

Sketch an angle with the given measure, and its reference triangle. Then find the required ratio.

6. $\sec(-135°)$ 7. $\cot 660°$

Find the given trigonometric ratio, if it exists. If not, write **undefined.**

8. $\cos(-540°)$ 9. $\csc 720°$

Use the brief trigonometric table at the right, where applicable, for Exercises 10–20.

Find each ratio.

10. $\tan 25°10'$ 11. $\cos 54°$

12. $\cos 144°$ 13. $\sin 514°30'$

Angle	Sin	Cos	Tan
25°00′	.4226	.9063	.4663
25°10′	.4253	.9051	.4699
25°20′	.4279	.9038	.4734
25°30′	.4305	.9026	.4770
36°00′	.5878	.8090	.7265
36°10′	.5901	.8073	.7310
36°20′	.5925	.8056	.7355
36°30′	.5948	.8039	.7400

Solve for **s,** *to the nearest whole number of units, or for* θ, *to the nearest 10 minutes.*

14.

15.

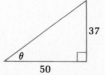

16. In triangle ABC, $a = 2$, $b = 4$, and $c = 2\sqrt{3}$. Find the measure of $\angle C$.

17. In triangle ABC, $\angle A = 25°$, $\angle B = 30°$, and $b = 5$. Find a, to the nearest whole number.

18. A tree stands 10 meters from a house and 10 meters from a barn. If the house and barn are 19 meters apart, find the angle between the lines to the house and to the barn from the tree, to the nearest 10 minutes.

19. The measure of each leg of an isosceles triangle is $10\sqrt{3}$, and each base angle measures $30°$. How long is the base of the triangle?

20. How many triangles ABC are possible if $\alpha = 30°$, $a = 4$, and $c = 10$?

Orbital Speed

For a satellite to remain in orbit, it must be traveling at a minimum velocity that varies according to its height above the earth. This velocity can be approximated by using the formula $V = \sqrt{\dfrac{1.24 \times 10^{12}}{3960 + M}}$, where M is its height above the earth in miles.

Because of its size, the numerator of the above fraction is expressed in *scientific notation*. In BASIC exponential notation, 1.24×10^{12} is written as 1.24E+12. When a number is extremely large or extremely small, a computer automatically displays it in exponential notation. For example, 0.00025 may be shown as 2.5E–04.

The Program   **What It Does**

```
100 REM SATELLITE IN ORBIT
110 PRINT "INPUT HEIGHT IN MILES"
120 INPUT M
130 IF M < 0 THEN 110

140 LET V = SQR(1.24E+12/(3960 + M))
150 PRINT "MINIMUM VELOCITY IS"
160 PRINT V; " MILES PER HOUR."
900 END
```

Asks for a new entry if the input is negative.

Computes minimum velocity.

You may wish to insert additional statements so the program runs again automatically.

Without line 130 to reject a negative entry, the computer may accept it and display an invalid result.

Write each of the following in scientific notation.
1. 3.7E+06   **2.** 8.8E+12   **3.** 4.25E-06   **4.** 4.09E-08

Write each of the following in BASIC exponential notation.
5. 8×10^6 **6.** 4.9×10^8 **7.** 2.5×10^{-5} **8.** 0.0000075

What does the program SATELLITE IN ORBIT display for these entries?
9. 140 miles   **10.** 220 miles   **11.** 100 miles   **12.** 300 miles

13. 1000 miles   **14.** 500 miles   **15.** 2000 miles   **16.** 5000 miles

17. A steel bar's increase in length due to expansion is the product of 1.1×10^{-5} (its coefficient of expansion), the original length, and the number of degrees Celsius the temperature has increased. Write a program to display the increase in length when the appropriate data are entered.

18. The increase in volume of a quantity of petroleum is the product of the original volume, the number of degrees Celsius increase in temperature, and 8.99×10^{-4}. Write a program to display the increase in volume for the data input.

For more information about BASIC, see the Computer Handbook at the back of the book.

This tower is located on the Canadian side of Niagara Falls. If the angle of elevation from a point of known distance from a tower is twice that from another point, then a double-angle identity can be used to find the height of the tower.

TRIGONOMETRIC EQUATIONS AND IDENTITIES

Prerequisite Skills Review

Write the letter for the correct answer.

1. For which value of θ is $\tan \theta$ undefined?

    a. $225°$ **b.** $450°$ **c.** $180°$ **d.** $-360°$

2. For which value of θ is $\dfrac{\sin \theta}{1 + \cos \theta}$ undefined?

    a. $0°$ **b.** $90°$ **c.** $180°$ **d.** $270°$

3. $\dfrac{\dfrac{1}{\sin \theta}}{\dfrac{\cos \theta}{\sin \theta}} = \underline{\ ?\ }$

    a. $\dfrac{1}{\cos \theta}$ **b.** $\dfrac{\cos \theta}{\sin^2 \theta}$ **c.** $\cos \theta$ **d.** none of these

4. If $\cos \theta = -\dfrac{\sqrt{3}}{2}$ and $0° \le \theta < 360°$, then the possible values of θ are $\underline{\ ?\ }$.

    a. $210°$ and $330°$ **b.** $120°$ and $240°$ **c.** $150°$ and $210°$ **d.** $240°$ and $300°$

5. $\dfrac{\sqrt{3}}{2}\left(\dfrac{\sqrt{2}}{2}\right) - \dfrac{1}{2}\left(\dfrac{\sqrt{2}}{2}\right) = \underline{\ ?\ }$

    a. $\dfrac{1}{2}(\sqrt{6} - \sqrt{2})$ **b.** $\dfrac{\sqrt{3} - 1}{2}$ **c.** $\dfrac{1}{4}(6 - \sqrt{2})$ **d.** $\dfrac{1}{4}(\sqrt{6} - \sqrt{2})$

6. $\dfrac{1 + \dfrac{\sqrt{3}}{3}}{1 - \dfrac{\sqrt{3}}{3}} = \underline{\ ?\ }$

    a. 1 **b.** 2 **c.** $2 + 6\sqrt{3}$ **d.** none of these

7. $\dfrac{2\left(\dfrac{4}{3}\right)}{1 - \left(\dfrac{4}{3}\right)^2} = \underline{\ ?\ }$

    a. -8 **b.** $-\dfrac{24}{7}$ **c.** $-\dfrac{8}{13}$ **d.** $-\dfrac{24}{15}$

8. $\sqrt{\dfrac{1 + \dfrac{\sqrt{3}}{2}}{2}} = \underline{\ ?\ }$

    a. $\dfrac{1}{2}\sqrt{2 + \sqrt{3}}$ **b.** $\dfrac{1}{2}\sqrt{1 + \sqrt{3}}$ **c.** $\dfrac{1}{4}\sqrt{2 + \sqrt{3}}$ **d.** none of these

12-1 Basic Trigonometric Identities

OBJECTIVES _____

To develop the basic trigonometric identities.
To show when a given trigonometric equation is not an identity.
To write trigonometric expressions using only sine and cosine ratios.

Recall that the unit circle can be used to find the trigonometric ratios for any angle of measure θ. In particular,

$$\sin \theta = y \qquad \cos \theta = x$$

If the angle is not coterminal with an angle of 90° or 270°, then $\cos \theta \neq 0$ and we can write the following identity.

$$\tan \theta = \frac{\sin \theta}{\cos \theta} \qquad \tan \theta = \frac{y}{x}$$

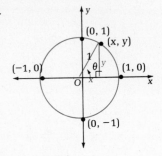

A **trigonometric identity** is an equation that is true for all values of the variable for which both sides of the equation are defined.

EXAMPLE 1 Write an identity expressing $\cot \theta$ in terms of $\sin \theta$ and $\cos \theta$. State any restrictions on θ.

$$\cot \theta = \frac{\cos \theta}{\sin \theta} \qquad \cot \theta = \frac{x}{y}$$

$\frac{\cos \theta}{\sin \theta}$ is not defined for $\sin \theta = 0$. Therefore, the identity does not hold for any angle coterminal with an angle of 0° or 180°.

The equation $\sin \theta = \cos \theta$ is true for $\theta = 45°$, but the equation is *not* an identity. To show that such a trigonometric equation is not an identity, you must find at least one value of θ for which each side of the equation is defined, but the equation is false. This is shown in the next example.

EXAMPLE 2 Show that $\sin \theta = \cos \theta$ is *not* an identity.

Many values can be chosen. Try $\theta = 30°$.
Both $\sin 30°$ and $\cos 30°$ are defined. $\sin 30° = \frac{1}{2}$ $\cos 30° = \frac{\sqrt{3}}{2}$
Since $\sin 30° \neq \cos 30°$, the equation $\sin \theta = \cos \theta$ is not an identity.

If θ is not coterminal with an angle of 0° or 180°, then $\sin \theta \neq 0$ and $\csc \theta = \frac{1}{\sin \theta}$ is an identity. The identity can be written in several alternate equivalent forms, all of which have the same restrictions on θ.

$$\csc \theta = \frac{1}{\sin \theta} \qquad \sin \theta = \frac{1}{\csc \theta} \qquad \sin \theta \csc \theta = 1$$

Similarly, if θ is not coterminal with an angle of 90° or 270°, then $\cos \theta \neq 0$ and $\sec \theta = \dfrac{1}{\cos \theta}$ is an identity. If the angle is not quadrantal, then $\cot \theta = \dfrac{1}{\tan \theta}$ is an identity. Here are alternate equivalent forms.

$$\sec \theta = \frac{1}{\cos \theta} \qquad \cos \theta = \frac{1}{\sec \theta} \qquad \cos \theta \sec \theta = 1$$

$$\cot \theta = \frac{1}{\tan \theta} \qquad \tan \theta = \frac{1}{\cot \theta} \qquad \tan \theta \cot \theta = 1$$

The terminal side of any angle in standard position intersects the unit circle at some point (x, y). Then, by the Pythagorean theorem,

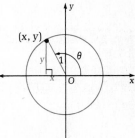

$$y^2 + x^2 = 1$$

Substituting $\sin \theta$ for y and $\cos \theta$ for x, we obtain

$\sin^2 \theta + \cos^2 \theta = 1$ It is customary to write $\sin^2 \theta$ for $(\sin \theta)^2$ and $\cos^2 \theta$ for $(\cos \theta)^2$.

The above identity, known as the **Pythagorean identity,** is valid for all values of θ. When each side of $\sin^2 \theta + \cos^2 \theta = 1$ is divided by $\cos^2 \theta$, another identity is obtained.

$$\frac{\sin^2 \theta}{\cos^2 \theta} + \frac{\cos^2 \theta}{\cos^2 \theta} = \frac{1}{\cos^2 \theta} \qquad \cos \theta \neq 0$$

$$\left(\frac{\sin \theta}{\cos \theta} \right)^2 + 1 = \left(\frac{1}{\cos \theta} \right)^2$$

$$\tan^2 \theta + 1 = \sec^2 \theta$$

Similarly, dividing each side of $\sin^2 \theta + \cos^2 \theta = 1$ by $\sin^2 \theta$ produces

$$1 + \cot^2 \theta = \csc^2 \theta \qquad \sin \theta \neq 0$$

The following table summarizes the basic trigonometric identities.

Basic Trigonometric Identities

$$\tan \theta = \frac{\sin \theta}{\cos \theta} \quad (\cos \theta \neq 0) \qquad \sin^2 \theta + \cos^2 \theta = 1$$

$$\cot \theta = \frac{\cos \theta}{\sin \theta} \quad (\sin \theta \neq 0) \qquad \tan^2 \theta + 1 = \sec^2 \theta \quad (\cos \theta \neq 0)$$

$$\csc \theta = \frac{1}{\sin \theta} \quad (\sin \theta \neq 0) \qquad 1 + \cot^2 \theta = \csc^2 \theta \quad (\sin \theta \neq 0)$$

$$\sec \theta = \frac{1}{\cos \theta} \quad (\cos \theta \neq 0)$$

$$\cot \theta = \frac{1}{\tan \theta} \quad (\sin \theta \neq 0, \cos \theta \neq 0)$$

EXAMPLE 3   Express $\dfrac{\cot\theta}{1+\csc\theta}$ using only $\sin\theta$ and $\cos\theta$. Simplify the expression.

$$\frac{\cot\theta}{1+\csc\theta} = \frac{\dfrac{\cos\theta}{\sin\theta}}{1+\dfrac{1}{\sin\theta}} \qquad \text{Use basic identities.} \quad \cot\theta = \frac{\cos\theta}{\sin\theta} \quad \csc\theta = \frac{1}{\sin\theta}$$

$$= \frac{\dfrac{\cos\theta}{\sin\theta}}{1+\dfrac{1}{\sin\theta}}\cdot\frac{\sin\theta}{\sin\theta} \qquad \text{Simplify.} \quad \frac{\sin\theta}{\sin\theta}=1$$

$$= \frac{\cos\theta}{\sin\theta+1}$$

EXAMPLE 4   Express $(\tan^2\alpha)(\csc^2\alpha)$ using only $\sin\alpha$.

$$(\tan^2\alpha)(\csc^2\alpha) = \left(\frac{\sin\alpha}{\cos\alpha}\right)^2\left(\frac{1}{\sin\alpha}\right)^2$$

$$= \frac{\sin^2\alpha}{\cos^2\alpha}\cdot\frac{1}{\sin^2\alpha}$$

$$= \frac{1}{\cos^2\alpha}$$

$$= \frac{1}{1-\sin^2\alpha} \qquad \cos^2\alpha = 1-\sin^2\alpha$$

CLASS EXERCISES

Complete each equation, using a basic identity.

1. $\dfrac{1}{\cos\theta} = \underline{\ ?\ }$ **2.** $\sin\theta\csc\theta = \underline{\ ?\ }$ **3.** $1-\sin^2\theta = \underline{\ ?\ }$

Name all values of θ, if any, for which the given ratio is undefined.
Assume that $0° \le \theta < 360°$.

4. $\sin\theta$ **5.** $\cos\theta$ **6.** $\tan\theta$ **7.** $\cot\theta$ **8.** $\sec\theta$ **9.** $\csc\theta$

EXERCISES

A   *Complete each equation, using a basic identity.*

1. $\sin^2\theta - 1 = \underline{\ ?\ }$ **2.** $\tan\theta\cot\theta = \underline{\ ?\ }$ **3.** $\sec^2\theta - \tan^2\theta = \underline{\ ?\ }$

4. $-\dfrac{1}{\sin\theta} = \underline{\ ?\ }$ **5.** $\dfrac{\cos\theta}{\cot\theta} = \underline{\ ?\ }$ **6.** $\dfrac{\tan\theta}{\sin\theta} = \underline{\ ?\ }$

Assume that $0° \le \theta < 360°$. Find all values of θ, if any, for which the expression is undefined.

7. $\dfrac{1}{\sin\theta}$ **8.** $\dfrac{1}{\sec\theta}$ **9.** $\tan\theta\cot\theta$ **10.** $\sin\theta\cos\theta$

Write each expression, using only sine and/or cosine ratios.
Simplify wherever possible.

11. $\tan \theta \csc^2 \theta$

12. $\dfrac{\cot \theta}{\tan \theta}$

13. $\dfrac{1 + \sec \alpha}{\tan \alpha}$

14. $\dfrac{\tan^2 \beta}{1 + \tan^2 \beta}$

15. $\dfrac{\sin x - \cos x}{\csc x - \sec x}$

16. $\dfrac{\csc \beta}{\tan \beta + \cot \beta}$

Show that the given equation is **not** an identity. Use $\theta = 30°$.

17. $\tan \theta = \cot \theta$

18. $\tan^2 \theta - 1 = \sec^2 \theta$

B

Use this list for Exercises 19 and 20. **0°, 45°, 60°, 90°**

19. Which listed values of θ can be used to show that $\sin \theta + \csc \theta = 1$ is not an identity?

20. Which listed values of θ can be used to show that $1 - \sin \theta \tan \theta = \cos \theta$ is not an identity?

Find the value of each expression without using tables or a calculator.

21. $\sin^2 63° + \cos^2 63°$

22. $\tan(-19°)\cot(-19°)$

23. $\tan^2 126° - \sec^2 126°$

24. Express $\sin^2 \theta - \cos^2 \theta$ in terms of $\sin \theta$ only.

25. Express $\cot^2 \theta \sec^2 \theta$ in terms of $\cos \theta$ only.

26. Express $\dfrac{\cos x}{\sec x - \tan x}$ in terms of $\sin x$ only.

27. Express $\dfrac{\cot x - \sin x}{\sin x}$ in terms of $\cos x$ only.

28. Express $(\tan A + \csc A)(\tan A)$ in terms of $\cos A$ only.

Show that the first expression is equivalent to the second expression.

29. $(\sin \theta)(\sec \theta)(\cot \theta)$; 1

30. $\dfrac{\cos \alpha}{\sec \alpha} + \dfrac{\sin \alpha}{\csc \alpha}$; 1

C

31. $\csc \beta - \cos \beta \cot \beta$; $\sin \beta$

32. $\dfrac{\sin^2 x - \cot x \tan x}{\cot x \sin x}$; $-\cos x$

33. $(1 + \tan^2 \theta)(1 - \sin^2 \theta)$; 1

34. $\dfrac{2 + \tan^2 \theta}{\sec^2 \theta} - 1$; $\cos^2 \theta$

Express each trigonometric ratio in terms of $\sin \theta$.

Sample Express $\cos \theta$ in terms of $\sin \theta$.

$$\sin^2 \theta + \cos^2 \theta = 1$$
$$\cos^2 \theta = 1 - \sin^2 \theta$$
$$\cos \theta = \pm\sqrt{1 - \sin^2 \theta}$$

35. $\csc \theta$

36. $\tan \theta$

37. $\sec \theta$

38. $\cot \theta$

12-2 Proving Identities

To prove that certain trigonometric equations are identities.

As seen in the preceding section, a given expression such as $\dfrac{\cot \theta}{1 + \csc \theta}$ can be written in an equivalent form involving only the sine and cosine ratios.

$$\frac{\cot \theta}{1 + \csc \theta} = \frac{\dfrac{\cos \theta}{\sin \theta}}{1 + \dfrac{1}{\sin \theta}}$$

$$= \frac{\cos \theta}{\sin \theta + 1}$$

Therefore $\dfrac{\cot \theta}{1 + \csc \theta} = \dfrac{\cos \theta}{\sin \theta + 1}$ is an identity.

A similar procedure can be used to prove that a given equation is an identity.

Proving Identities—Method I

Start with one side of the given equation. Change it into the form of the other side, using known identities.

EXAMPLE 1   Prove that $\dfrac{\cos^2 \theta}{1 - \sin \theta} = 1 + \sin \theta$ is an identity.
State any restrictions on θ.

To avoid a zero denominator, $\sin \theta$ cannot be equal to 1. Therefore, the angle cannot be coterminal with a 90° angle.

$$\frac{\cos^2 \theta}{1 - \sin \theta} = \frac{1 - \sin^2 \theta}{1 - \sin \theta}$$ Start with the side that has the more involved expression. Substitute $1 - \sin^2 \theta$ for $\cos^2 \theta$.

$$= \frac{(1 - \sin \theta)(1 + \sin \theta)}{1 - \sin \theta}$$ Factor the numerator.

$$= 1 + \sin \theta$$ Simplify.

The proof is complete, since $1 + \sin \theta$ is exactly the same as the right side of the given equation.

For the sake of convenience, an identity is often given without specifying the restrictions on the variable. However, it is always understood that the identity is valid only for the values of the variable for which the expressions on both sides of the equation are meaningful.

EXAMPLE 2   Prove that $\cot \alpha = \dfrac{1 + \cot^2 \alpha}{\cot \alpha \sec^2 \alpha}$ is an identity.

$$\frac{1 + \cot^2 \alpha}{\cot \alpha \sec^2 \alpha} = \frac{\csc^2 \alpha}{\cot \alpha \sec^2 \alpha} \qquad$$

Begin with the right side of the given equation. Substitute $\csc^2 \alpha$ for $1 + \cot^2 \alpha$.

$$= \frac{\dfrac{1}{\sin^2 \alpha}}{\dfrac{\cos \alpha}{\sin \alpha} \cdot \dfrac{1}{\cos^2 \alpha}} \qquad$$

It is often helpful to write each expression in terms of the sine and cosine.

$$= \frac{\dfrac{1}{\sin^2 \alpha}}{\dfrac{1}{\sin \alpha \cos \alpha}}$$

$$= \frac{1}{\sin^2 \alpha} \cdot \frac{\sin \alpha \cos \alpha}{1}$$

$$= \frac{\cos \alpha}{\sin \alpha}$$

$$= \cot \alpha \qquad \text{The proof is complete.}$$

A second method of proving identities is sometimes useful.

Proving Identities—Method II

Work with each side of the given equation. Change both sides to the same form, using known identities.

EXAMPLE 3   Prove that $(\sec \theta - \tan \theta)^2 = \dfrac{\csc \theta - 1}{\csc \theta + 1}$ is an identity.

Use a vertical line of separation when working with both sides of the equation.

$(\sec \theta - \tan \theta)^2$	$\dfrac{\csc \theta - 1}{\csc \theta + 1}$
$\left(\dfrac{1}{\cos \theta} - \dfrac{\sin \theta}{\cos \theta}\right)^2$	$\dfrac{\dfrac{1}{\sin \theta} - 1}{\dfrac{1}{\sin \theta} + 1}$
$\left(\dfrac{1 - \sin \theta}{\cos \theta}\right)^2$	$\dfrac{\left(\dfrac{1}{\sin \theta} - 1\right)}{\left(\dfrac{1}{\sin \theta} + 1\right)} \cdot \dfrac{\sin \theta}{\sin \theta}$
$\dfrac{(1 - \sin \theta)^2}{\cos^2 \theta}$	
$\dfrac{(1 - \sin \theta)^2}{1 - \sin^2 \theta}$	$\dfrac{1 - \sin \theta}{1 + \sin \theta}$
$\dfrac{(1 - \sin \theta)^2}{(1 + \sin \theta)(1 - \sin \theta)}$	
$\dfrac{1 - \sin \theta}{1 + \sin \theta}$	$\dfrac{1 - \sin \theta}{1 + \sin \theta}$

Write each expression in terms of $\sin \theta$ and $\cos \theta$.

The proof is complete, since the same expression is obtained on each side.

CLASS EXERCISES

Prove in two ways that each equation is an identity. Use Method I, then Method II.

1. $\cos \theta \csc \theta = \cot \theta$

2. $\dfrac{\sec \theta}{\sin \theta} = \dfrac{\csc \theta}{\cos \theta}$

3. $\dfrac{1}{\csc^2 \theta} = 1 - \dfrac{1}{\sec^2 \theta}$

EXERCISES

A *Prove that each equation is an identity, using Method I.*

1. $\sin^2 \theta - \cos^2 \theta = 1 - 2\cos^2 \theta$

2. $\cos \theta = \dfrac{\sin \theta}{\tan \theta}$

3. $(\tan \alpha + 1)^2 = \sec^2 \alpha + 2\tan \alpha$

4. $(1 + \sin \beta)(1 - \sin \beta) = \dfrac{1}{1 + \tan^2 \beta}$

5. $\csc \theta = \dfrac{\tan^2 \theta + 1}{\sec \theta \tan \theta}$

6. $(\sec^2 \gamma - 1)\cos^2 \gamma = 1 - \cos^2 \gamma$

7. $\dfrac{\csc^2 \theta}{\csc^2 \theta - 1} = \sec^2 \theta$

8. $\sec^2 \theta - 4\tan^2 \theta = 4 - 3\sec^2 \theta$

9. $2\cos^2 \beta - 1 = 1 - 2\sin^2 \beta$

10. $\cot^2 \theta - \cos^2 \theta = \cos^2 \theta \cot^2 \theta$

11. $\dfrac{\cos \alpha + \cot \alpha}{1 + \csc \alpha} = \cos \alpha$

12. $\cot \gamma + \tan \gamma = \dfrac{\csc \gamma}{\cos \gamma}$

13. $\dfrac{1 + \tan^2 \theta}{1 + \cot^2 \theta} = \tan^2 \theta$

14. $\dfrac{1 + \csc \beta}{\sec \beta} = \cos \beta + \cot \beta$

B *Prove that each equation is an identity, using either Method I or Method II. For Exercises 15–18, state the restrictions, if any, on the variable.*

15. $\dfrac{\sin \theta \sec \theta}{\tan \theta + \cot \theta} = \dfrac{1}{\csc^2 \theta}$

16. $\sin^4 \theta - \cos^4 \theta = \sin^2 \theta - \cos^2 \theta$

17. $\dfrac{\cot x + 1}{\cot x - 1} = \dfrac{1 + \tan x}{1 - \tan x}$

18. $\dfrac{1 - \sin x}{1 + \sin x} = (\sec x - \tan x)^2$

19. $\dfrac{\tan^2 y}{\sec y - 1} = \sec y + 1$

20. $\sec^2 y + \csc^2 y = \sec^2 y \csc^2 y$

21. $\dfrac{1 - \sin A}{\cos A} + \dfrac{\cos A}{1 - \sin A} = 2\sec A$

22. $\dfrac{\csc B}{\sec B - \cos B} = \cot B \csc^2 B$

C **23.** $\dfrac{\cos \theta}{1 - \sin \theta} = \dfrac{1 + \sin \theta}{\cos \theta}$ **Hint:** Multiply the left side by $\dfrac{1 + \sin \theta}{1 + \sin \theta}$.

24. $\dfrac{1}{\sec x - \tan x} = \sec x + \tan x$

25. $\left(\dfrac{1 + \cot x}{\sec x + \csc x}\right)^2 = \sin^2 x \cot^2 x$

*26. $\dfrac{\sin x}{\sec x + 2\cos x} = \dfrac{\cot x}{1 + 3\cot^2 x}$

*27. $\dfrac{\cos^3 x}{\cot x - \cos x} = \dfrac{1 + \sin x}{\csc x}$

12-3 Solving Trigonometric Equations

OBJECTIVE

To solve trigonometric equations for θ, where $0° \leq \theta < 360°$.

For what values of θ is the equation $2 \sin \theta = 1$ true? To find out, begin by solving the equation for $\sin \theta$.

$$2 \sin \theta = 1, \text{ so } \sin \theta = \frac{1}{2}$$

Since $\sin \theta = \frac{1}{2}$, the reference angle for θ must be 30°. Furthermore, since the sine is positive in the first and second quadrants, two solutions are $\theta = 30°$ and $\theta = 150°$. Many more solutions can be obtained by adding or subtracting multiples of 360°. For example, 390° and $-210°$ are solutions, since $30° + 360° = 390°$ and $150° - 360° = -210°$. To avoid the necessity of describing all possible solutions to such trigonometric equations, we will restrict θ to values such that $0° \leq \theta < 360°$, unless otherwise specified.

EXAMPLE 1   Solve $4 \cos^2 \theta + 2 = 3$.

$$4 \cos^2 \theta + 2 = 3$$
$$4 \cos^2 \theta = 1$$
$$\cos^2 \theta = \frac{1}{4}$$
$$\cos \theta = \pm \sqrt{\frac{1}{4}} = \pm \frac{1}{2} \qquad \text{The reference angle is } 60°.$$

$$\cos \theta = \frac{1}{2} \quad \text{or} \quad \cos \theta = -\frac{1}{2}$$
$$\theta = 60°, 300° \qquad \theta = 120°, 240°$$

$\quad$ Cos $\theta > 0$ in quadrants I and IV. $\qquad$ Cos $\theta < 0$ in quadrants II and III.

Check by substituting each value of θ in the given equation.

For $\theta = 60°$: $4 \cos^2 60° + 2 = 4\left(\frac{1}{2}\right)^2 + 2 = 1 + 2 = 3$ ✔

For $\theta = 120°$: $4 \cos^2 120° + 2 = 4\left(-\frac{1}{2}\right)^2 + 2 = 1 + 2 = 3$ ✔

For $\theta = 240°$: $4 \cos^2 240° + 2 = 4\left(-\frac{1}{2}\right)^2 + 2 = 1 + 2 = 3$ ✔

For $\theta = 300°$: $4 \cos^2 300° + 2 = 4\left(\frac{1}{2}\right)^2 + 2 = 1 + 2 = 3$ ✔

The solutions are 60°, 120°, 240°, and 300°.

TRIGONOMETRIC EQUATIONS AND IDENTITIES

The next example shows how factoring can be used in solving a trigonometric equation.

EXAMPLE 2   Solve $\sin^2 \theta = \sin \theta$.

$$\sin^2 \theta = \sin \theta$$
$$\sin^2 \theta - \sin \theta = 0$$
$$\sin \theta \, (\sin \theta - 1) = 0$$

$\sin \theta = 0$ or $\sin \theta - 1 = 0$ If $rs = 0$, then $r = 0$ or $s = 0$.
$\theta = 0°, 180°$ $\sin \theta = 1$
                                $\theta = 90°$

Check to show that the solutions are 0°, 90°, and 180°.

In the preceding example it would have been incorrect to divide each side of $\sin^2 \theta = \sin \theta$ by $\sin \theta$, since the solutions for which $\sin \theta = 0$ would have been lost. In situations where it is clear that no solutions will be lost, it is permissible to divide by a trigonometric ratio.

EXAMPLE 3   Solve $\sin \theta = \cos \theta$.

$$\sin \theta = \cos \theta$$

$$\frac{\sin \theta}{\cos \theta} = \frac{\cos \theta}{\cos \theta}$$ Divide each side by $\cos \theta$. No solutions are lost, since $\cos \theta = 0$ for $\theta = 90°$ or $\theta = 270°$, and $\sin \theta \neq \cos \theta$ for these values.

$$\tan \theta = 1$$
$$\theta = 45°, 225°$$

Check to show that the solutions are 45° and 225°.

Sometimes it is helpful to rewrite an equation so that it contains just one trigonometric ratio.

EXAMPLE 4   Solve $\cos^2 \theta + \frac{1}{2} \sin \theta - \frac{1}{2} = 0$.

$$\cos^2 \theta + \frac{1}{2} \sin \theta - \frac{1}{2} = 0$$

$$1 - \sin^2 \theta + \frac{1}{2} \sin \theta - \frac{1}{2} = 0 \qquad \cos^2 \theta = 1 - \sin^2 \theta$$

$$2 - 2 \sin^2 \theta + \sin \theta - 1 = 0 \qquad \text{Multiply each side by 2.}$$

$$2 \sin^2 \theta - \sin \theta - 1 = 0 \qquad \text{Simplify.}$$

$$(2 \sin \theta + 1)(\sin \theta - 1) = 0 \qquad \text{Factor.}$$

$2 \sin \theta + 1 = 0$ or $\sin \theta - 1 = 0$

$$\sin \theta = -\frac{1}{2} \qquad\qquad \sin \theta = 1$$

$$\theta = 210°, 330° \qquad\qquad \theta = 90°$$

Check to show that the solutions are 90°, 210°, and 330°.

CLASS EXERCISES

If $0° \leq \theta < 360°$, give the possible values of θ under the given conditions.

1. The reference angle for θ is 30°.

2. The reference angle for θ is 45°, and $\sin \theta > 0$.

3. The reference angle for θ is 60°, and $\cos \theta < 0$.

4. The reference angle for θ is 30°, and $\tan \theta < 0$.

Solve for θ, where $0° \leq \theta < 360°$.

5. $\sin \theta = \dfrac{1}{2}$ **6.** $\tan \theta = -1$ **7.** $\cos \theta = -\dfrac{\sqrt{2}}{2}$

8. $\sec \theta = 2$ **9.** $\csc \theta = \dfrac{2\sqrt{3}}{3}$ **10.** $\cot \theta = 0$

EXERCISES

A   Solve for θ, where $0° \leq \theta < 360°$, and check.

1. $\sin \theta = 0$ **2.** $\sec \theta = -1$ **3.** $\cot \theta = -\dfrac{\sqrt{3}}{3}$

4. $2 \cos \theta = 1$ **5.** $\sqrt{3} \sec \theta = 2$ **6.** $2 \cot \theta = -2$

7. $\sqrt{2} \sin \theta - 1 = 0$ **8.** $2 \csc \theta + 4 = 0$ **9.** $2 \cos \theta - \sqrt{3} = 0$

10. $\sin \theta + 1 = 0$ **11.** $\sin \theta + 1 = 2$ **12.** $\sec \theta - 1 = 0$

13. $\cos^2 \theta = 1$ **14.** $3 \tan^2 \theta = 1$ **15.** $4 \sin^2 \theta - 3 = 0$

16. $\sin \theta \cos \theta = 0$ **17.** $(\sin \theta - 1) \cos \theta = 0$ **18.** $\tan^2 \theta - \tan \theta = 0$

19. $(\cot \theta - 1)^2 = 0$ **20.** $\sin \theta = -\cos \theta$ **21.** $\sin \theta - \dfrac{1}{2} \csc \theta = 0$

B   **22.** $(2 \sin \theta + 1)(\cos \theta - 1) = 0$ **23.** $(\cot^2 \theta - 1)\cos \theta = 0$

24. $\sin^2 \theta (4 \sin^2 \theta - 3) = 0$ **25.** $\sin \theta \cos \theta - \sin \theta = 0$

26. $\sqrt{3} \sin \theta \tan \theta - \sin \theta = 0$ **27.** $2 \cos^2 \theta \tan \theta = \tan \theta$

Solve for x, where $0° \leq x < 360°$, and check.

28. $\tan x = 3 \cot x$ **29.** $\tan x - \sqrt{2} \sin x = 0$

30. $\tan^2 x - 2 \tan x + 1 = 0$ **31.** $\cos^2 x + \cos x - 2 = 0$

32. $2 \sin^2 x - 3 \sin x = -1$ **33.** $\sec^2 x = 3 \sec x - 2$

34. $\cos^2 x - \sin^2 x = 1$ **35.** $3 \sin^2 x = \cos^2 x$

36. $\tan^2 x + \sec^2 x = 1$ **37.** $2 \cos^2 x - 1 = \cos x$

38. $2 \cos^2 x - \sin x - 1 = 0$ **39.** $\sec x = \csc x$

TRIGONOMETRIC EQUATIONS AND IDENTITIES

Solve for **x** to the nearest 10 minutes, where $0° \leq x < 180°$. Use the table on pages 672–676.

40. $5 \sin x = 2$

41. $\frac{1}{2} \tan x - 1 = 0$

42. $12 \sin^2 x + 5 \sin x - 3 = 0$

43. $4 \sin x \cos x = \cos x$

44. $\sec^2 x - 4 \sec x + 1 = 0$ **Hint:** Use the quadratic formula.

C   Solve for **all values of x,** and check. Use the table, when necessary.

Sample $\tan x - 1 = 0$

$\tan x = 1$ The solution consists of all values of x such that $x = 45° + n(180°)$, where n is any integer.

45. $\dfrac{\sin^2 x}{1 + \cos x} = 1$

46. $\sin x + \cos x = 1$
Hint: Square each side.

47. $\sin x - 1 = \sqrt{2} \cos x$
Hint: Square each side.

48. $\sin x \cos x - \cos x + \sin x - 1 = 0$
Hint: Factor by grouping.

49. Solve the system $\begin{array}{l} r \sin \theta = 1 \\ r \cos \theta = \sqrt{3} \end{array}$ for r and θ, where $r > 0$ and $0° \leq \theta < 360°$.

Hint: Square each side of each equation, and add.

*50. Solve the equation $\sin^2 x - \cos^2 x + \sin x + \cos x = 0$ for x, where $0° \leq x < 360°$.
Hint: Start by factoring $\sin^2 x - \cos^2 x$ as the difference of two squares.

CHECKPOINT

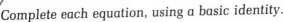

Complete each equation, using a basic identity.

1. $\sec x \sin x = \underline{\ ?\ }$

2. $\csc^2 x - \cot^2 x = \underline{\ ?\ }$

3. $\cos^2 x - 1 = \underline{\ ?\ }$

Write each expression by using only sine and/or cosine ratios. Simplify wherever possible.

4. $\dfrac{\csc x}{\sec x}$

5. $\dfrac{1 + \csc x}{\cot x}$

6. $\dfrac{\sec x}{\sec x + \csc x}$

Prove that each equation is an identity.

7. $\dfrac{\sin \theta - \tan \theta}{\tan \theta} = \cos \theta - 1$

8. $\dfrac{\sin^2 x}{1 - \cos x} - 1 = \cos x$

Solve for **x**, where $0° \leq x < 360°$, and check.

9. $\cot x = 3 \tan x$

10. $2 \sin^2 x - \cos x - 1 = 0$

Transforming Equations into Familiar Forms

If a trigonometric equation appears to be complicated, it might be easier to solve it by first transforming it into a more familiar form. This can usually be done by making appropriate substitutions. Two equations are solved below using this technique. Assume $0° \leq x < 360°$.

Example 1

$$\frac{1}{\cos^2 x} - \frac{3}{\cos x} = -2$$

$$\left(\frac{1}{\cos x}\right)^2 - 3\left(\frac{1}{\cos x}\right) + 2 = 0$$

$$u^2 - 3u + 2 = 0$$ Let $u = \frac{1}{\cos x}$ and substitute
to obtain a quadratic
equation in u.

$$(u - 2)(u - 1) = 0$$

$$u = 2 \quad \text{or} \quad u = 1$$

$$\frac{1}{\cos x} = 2 \quad \text{or} \quad \frac{1}{\cos x} = 1 \quad \text{Substitute } \frac{1}{\cos x} \text{ for } u.$$

$$\cos x = \frac{1}{2} \quad \text{or} \quad \cos x = 1$$

Solutions $0°, 60°, 300°$

Example 2 $\sin x + \sqrt{1 - \sin^2 x} = 1$

$$u + \sqrt{1 - u^2} = 1 \qquad \text{Let } u = \sin x.$$

$$\sqrt{1 - u^2} = 1 - u$$

$$1 - u^2 = 1 - 2u + u^2 \qquad \text{Square each side.}$$

$$2u^2 - 2u = 0$$

$$2u(u - 1) = 0$$

$$u = 0 \quad \text{or} \quad u = 1$$

$$\sin x = 0 \quad \text{or} \quad \sin x = 1$$

Solutions $0°, 90°, 180°$

Use the substitution technique to solve each equation for $0° \leq x < 360°$.

1. $2\cos^2 x + 3\cos x = -1$

2. $\tan^2 x + 1 = 2\tan x$

3. $\dfrac{3}{\sin x} = \dfrac{2}{\sin^2 x} - 2$

4. $\sin x - 1 = \sqrt{3 - 3\sin^2 x}$

5. $\sqrt{1 - \cos^2 x} - \cos x - 1 = 0$

6. $\csc^4 x - \csc^3 x - \csc^2 x + \csc x = 0$

7. $4\sin^4 x - 4\sin^2 x + 1 = 0$
   Hint: Let $u = \sin^2 x$.

8. $2\sin x \tan^2 x + \tan^2 x - 6\sin x = 3$
   Hint: Let $u = \sin x$ and $v = \tan x$.

12-4 The Sine of a Sum

OBJECTIVES _____

To find the area of a triangle, using the measures of two sides and the sine of the included angle.

To evaluate trigonometric expressions, using the formula for the sine of the sum of two angle measures.

Consider triangle PQR, with the altitude drawn from Q. The area of the triangle can be expressed in terms of the lengths of sides PQ and PR and the sine of the *included angle* P. We start with the familiar formula for the area of a triangle.

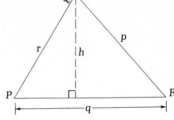

$$\text{area } \triangle PQR = \frac{1}{2}(\text{base})(\text{altitude})$$

$$= \frac{1}{2}qh$$

$$= \frac{1}{2}qr \sin P \qquad \text{Sin } P = \frac{h}{r}, \text{ so } h = r \sin P.$$

Similar formulas can be derived using the sines of the other two angles.

$$\text{area } \triangle PQR = \frac{1}{2}pq \sin R \qquad \text{area } \triangle PQR = \frac{1}{2}pr \sin Q$$

In general, we have the following rule for finding the area of any triangle.

Formula for the Area of a Triangle

The area of a triangle is one-half the product of the lengths of two sides and the sine of the included angle.

EXAMPLE 1 Find the area of triangle STV.

$$\text{area } \triangle STV = \frac{1}{2}tv \sin S$$

$$= \frac{1}{2}(8)(25)(\sin 30°)$$

$$= \frac{1}{2}(8)(25)\left(\frac{1}{2}\right)$$

$$= 50$$

The area is 50 square units.

The ideas just developed can be used to derive a formula for the sine of the sum of two angle measures. Think of the area of triangle ABC as the sum of the areas of triangles ABD and CBD.

$$\text{area } \triangle ABC = \text{area } \triangle ABD + \text{area } \triangle CBD$$

$$\frac{1}{2}ac \sin \theta = \frac{1}{2}hc \sin \alpha + \frac{1}{2}ha \sin \beta$$

$$ac \sin \theta = hc \sin \alpha + ha \sin \beta$$

$$ac \sin(\alpha + \beta) = hc \sin \alpha + ha \sin \beta \qquad \theta = \alpha + \beta$$

$$\sin(\alpha + \beta) = \frac{hc \sin \alpha}{ac} + \frac{ha \sin \beta}{ac}$$

$$\sin(\alpha + \beta) = \frac{h}{a} \sin \alpha + \frac{h}{c} \sin \beta$$

$$\sin(\alpha + \beta) = \cos \beta \sin \alpha + \cos \alpha \sin \beta \qquad \frac{h}{a} = \cos \beta;\ \frac{h}{c} = \cos \alpha$$

or $\textbf{sin}(\boldsymbol{\alpha} + \boldsymbol{\beta}) = \textbf{sin } \boldsymbol{\alpha} \textbf{ cos } \boldsymbol{\beta} + \textbf{cos } \boldsymbol{\alpha} \textbf{ sin } \boldsymbol{\beta}$

The formula just derived for the sum of the measures of two acute angles turns out to be valid for angles of any size.

EXAMPLE 2   Use the formula for $\sin(\alpha + \beta)$ to find $\sin 105°$.

Use two angle measures with known ratios. Let $\alpha = 60°$ and $\beta = 45°$, since $105° = 60° + 45°$. Substitute in the formula.

$$\sin 105° = \sin(60° + 45°) = \sin 60° \cos 45° + \cos 60° \sin 45°$$

$$= \frac{\sqrt{3}}{2}\left(\frac{\sqrt{2}}{2}\right) + \frac{1}{2}\left(\frac{\sqrt{2}}{2}\right) = \tfrac{1}{4}(\sqrt{6} + \sqrt{2})$$

EXAMPLE 3   Show that $\sin(90° + \theta) = \cos \theta$ is an identity.

$$\sin(90° + \theta) = \sin 90° \cos \theta + \cos 90° \sin \theta = 1(\cos \theta) + 0(\sin \theta) = \cos \theta$$

CLASS EXERCISES

Find the area of each triangle to the nearest whole number of square units.

1.

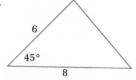

2.

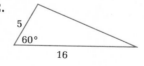

3.

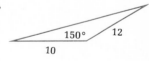

Verify each result, using the formula for $\sin(\alpha + \beta)$.

4. $\sin 120° = \dfrac{\sqrt{3}}{2}$; $\alpha = 30°$, $\beta = 90°$ **5.** $\sin 120° = \dfrac{\sqrt{3}}{2}$; $\alpha = 60°$, $\beta = 60°$

EXERCISES

A

Find the area of each triangle to the nearest whole number of square units.

1.

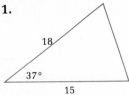

18

37°

15

2.

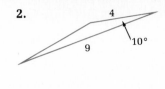

4

9

10°

3.

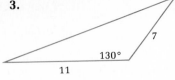

7

130°

11

Complete each equation to get a specific case of the formula
$\sin \alpha \cos \beta + \cos \alpha \sin \beta = \sin(\alpha + \beta)$.

4. $\sin 10° \cos 25° + \cos 10° \sin 25° = \sin$ ___?___

5. $\sin 23° \cos(-7°) + \cos 23° \sin(-7°) = \sin$ ___?___

6. $\sin 51° \cos \theta + \cos 51° \sin \theta = \sin$ ___?___

7. $\sin x \cos x + \cos x \sin x = \sin$ ___?___

8. $\sin\left(\dfrac{x + y}{2}\right)\cos\left(\dfrac{x - y}{2}\right) + \cos\left(\dfrac{x + y}{2}\right)\sin\left(\dfrac{x - y}{2}\right) = \sin$ ___?___

Verify each result, using the formula for $\sin(\alpha + \beta)$ and the given values
for α and β.

9. $\sin 135° = \dfrac{\sqrt{2}}{2}$; $\alpha = 45°$, $\beta = 90°$

10. $\sin 135° = \dfrac{\sqrt{2}}{2}$; $\alpha = 180°$, $\beta = -45°$

11. $\sin 150° = \dfrac{1}{2}$; $\alpha = 60°$, $\beta = 90°$

12. $\sin 225° = -\dfrac{\sqrt{2}}{2}$; $\alpha = 270°$, $\beta = -45°$

13. $\sin(-225°) = \dfrac{\sqrt{2}}{2}$; $\alpha = -270°$, $\beta = 45°$

14. $\sin(-60°) = -\dfrac{\sqrt{3}}{2}$; $\alpha = 30°$, $\beta = -90°$

Find each ratio, using the formula for $\sin(\alpha + \beta)$ and the given values
of α and β. Leave the answers in radical form.

15. $\sin 75°$; $\alpha = 30°$, $\beta = 45°$

16. $\sin 165°$; $\alpha = 120°$, $\beta = 45°$

B

Find the area of each triangle to the nearest whole number of square units.

17.

18   18

15°

18.

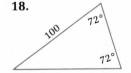

100

72°

72°

19.

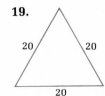

20   20

20

Find each ratio, using the formula for $\sin(\alpha + \beta)$. Choose values for α and β so that you will not need a table or a calculator. Leave the answers in radical form.

20. $\sin(-165°)$ **21.** $\sin 345°$ **22.** $\sin 195°$

23. $\sin(-75°)$ **24.** $\sin 15°$ **25.** $\sin(-15°)$

Use the table on pages 672–676 to find $\sin \alpha$, $\sin \beta$, $\cos \alpha$, $\cos \beta$, and $\sin(\alpha + \beta)$. Then verify that $\sin(\alpha + \beta) = \sin \alpha \cos \beta + \cos \alpha \sin \beta$, by using substitution.

26. $\alpha = 10°,\ \beta = 40°$ **27.** $\alpha = 25°,\ \beta = 53°$

28. $\alpha = 23°40',\ \beta = 35°30'$ **29.** $\alpha = 62°10',\ \beta = 74°50'$

Prove that each equation is an identity.

30. $\sin(x + 30°) = \frac{1}{2}(\sqrt{3} \sin x + \cos x)$ **31.** $\sin(45° + x) = \frac{\sqrt{2}}{2}(\cos x + \sin x)$

32. $\sin(x + 60°) = \frac{1}{2}(\sin x + \sqrt{3} \cos x)$ **33.** $\sin(x + 360°) = \sin x$

34. $\sin 2x = 2 \sin x \cos x$

C

35. Show that the area of triangle ABC equals $\frac{1}{2} bc \sin \alpha$, where α is the measure of obtuse angle CAB. **Hint:** $\sin \alpha = \sin(180° - \alpha)$

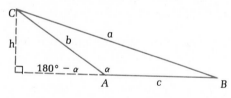

Find the area of each triangle to the nearest whole number of square units.

36.

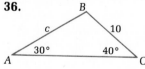

37.

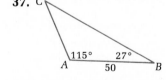

38.

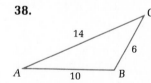

***39.** When the measures of two angles and the *included side* of a triangle ABC are given, the area of the triangle equals $\frac{c^2 \sin A \sin B}{2 \sin C}$, where c is the given side. Derive this result.

***40.** Prove that the following equation is an identity.

$$\frac{\sin(x + h) - \sin x}{h} = \left(\frac{\sin h}{h}\right) \cos x + \left(\frac{\cos h - 1}{h}\right) \sin x \quad (h \neq 0)$$

CHALLENGE

Heron's Formula

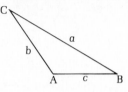

The area K of a triangle can be found by using Heron's formula, which depends only on the lengths of the sides. The formula is expressed in terms of the semiperimeter s, where $s = \frac{1}{2}(a + b + c)$.

$$K = \sqrt{s(s - a)(s - b)(s - c)} \qquad \text{Heron's formula}$$

To derive this formula, begin with $K = \frac{1}{2}bc \sin A$, multiply each side by 2, and square each side.

$$4K^2 = b^2c^2 \sin^2 A = b^2c^2(1 - \cos^2 A) = b^2c^2(1 + \cos A)(1 - \cos A)$$

From the Law of Cosines, substitute $\dfrac{b^2 + c^2 - a^2}{2bc}$ for $\cos A$. Then

$$4K^2 = b^2c^2\left(1 + \frac{b^2 + c^2 - a^2}{2bc}\right)\left(1 - \frac{b^2 + c^2 - a^2}{2bc}\right)$$

$$4K^2 = b^2c^2\left(\frac{2bc + b^2 + c^2 - a^2}{2bc}\right)\left(\frac{2bc - b^2 - c^2 + a^2}{2bc}\right)$$

$$16K^2 = [(b^2 + 2bc + c^2) - a^2][a^2 - (b^2 - 2bc + c^2)]$$

$$16K^2 = [(b + c)^2 - a^2][a^2 - (b - c)^2]$$

$$16K^2 = (b + c + a)(b + c - a)(a - b + c)(a + b - c)$$

$$16K^2 = 2s(2s - 2a)(2s - 2b)(2s - 2c) \quad 2s = a + b + c, \text{ so } \begin{cases} 2s - 2a = b + c - a \\ 2s - 2b = a - b + c \\ 2s - 2c = a + b - c \end{cases}$$

$$16K^2 = 16s(s - a)(s - b)(s - c)$$

$$K = \sqrt{s(s - a)(s - b)(s - c)}$$

To illustrate the use of the formula, note that for a triangle with sides measuring 3, 4, and 5 units, $s = \frac{1}{2}(3 + 4 + 5) = 6$. Then

$$K = \sqrt{6(6 - 3)(6 - 4)(6 - 5)} = 6 \quad \text{The area is 6 square units.}$$

Since a 3-4-5 triangle is a right triangle, you can verify this result by using the area formula $K = \frac{1}{2}(\text{base})(\text{altitude})$.

Use Heron's formula to find the areas of the triangles with sides of given lengths. Use a calculator, if possible. Round each answer to the same number of significant digits as in the given data.

1. 14, 21, 12   **2.** 114, 200, 241   **3.** 8.4, 3.7, 6.5

4. Explain why s is greater than each of the measures a, b, and c.

5. Show that the radius of the inscribed circle is given by

$$r = \sqrt{\frac{(s - a)(s - b)(s - c)}{s}}$$

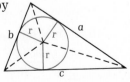

6. Find the radii of the inscribed circles for the triangles in Exercises 1 and 2.

12.5 Sum and Difference Formulas

OBJECTIVES

To evaluate expressions by using the formulas for the trigonometric ratios of sums and differences of angle measures.
To prove identities involving such formulas.

Reference triangles in the unit circle show that sin $(-\theta)$ and sin θ are opposites.

$$\sin (-\theta) = -\sin \theta$$

They also show that cos $(-\theta)$ and cos θ are equal.

$$\cos (-\theta) = \cos \theta$$

Sin $(-\theta) = -\sin \theta$ and cos $(-\theta) = \cos \theta$ are identities for all values of θ.

The two identities given above are used to derive the formula for the sine of the difference of two angle measures.

$$\sin (\alpha - \beta) = \sin [\alpha + (-\beta)]$$
$$= \sin \alpha \cos (-\beta) + \cos \alpha \sin (-\beta)$$
$$= \sin \alpha \cos \beta + \cos \alpha (-\sin \beta) \qquad \cos (-\beta) = \cos \beta$$
$$\mathbf{\sin (\alpha - \beta) = \sin \alpha \cos \beta - \cos \alpha \sin \beta} \qquad \sin (-\beta) = -\sin \beta$$

EXAMPLE 1

Use the formula for sin $(\alpha - \beta)$ to find sin 15°.

Use two angle measures with known ratios. Let $\alpha = 45°$ and $\beta = 30°$, since $15° = 45° - 30°$. Substitute in the formula.

$$\sin 15° = \sin (45° - 30°)$$
$$= \sin 45° \cos 30° - \cos 45° \sin 30°$$
$$= \frac{\sqrt{2}}{2}\left(\frac{\sqrt{3}}{2}\right) - \frac{\sqrt{2}}{2}\left(\frac{1}{2}\right)$$
$$= \frac{1}{4}(\sqrt{6} - \sqrt{2})$$

EXAMPLE 2

Prove that the equation sin $(90° - \theta) = \cos \theta$ is an identity.

$$\sin (90° - \theta) = \sin 90° \cos \theta - \cos 90° \sin \theta$$
$$= 1(\cos \theta) - 0(\sin \theta)$$
$$= \cos \theta$$

TRIGONOMETRIC EQUATIONS AND IDENTITIES

EXAMPLE 3   Prove that the equation $\sin \gamma = \cos (90° - \gamma)$ is an identity.

$$\sin (90° - \theta) = \cos \theta \qquad \text{Start with the identity in Example 2.}$$
$$\sin[90° - (90° - \gamma)] = \cos(90° - \gamma) \qquad \text{Substitute } 90° - \gamma \text{ for } \theta.$$
$$\sin \gamma = \cos(90° - \gamma)$$

The identities in Examples 2 and 3 were introduced in Chapter 11. That is, the sine of an angle equals the cosine of its complement, and the cosine equals the sine of its complement. Here is a list of the identities that apply to complementary angles.

$$\sin(90° - \theta) = \cos \theta \qquad \tan(90° - \theta) = \cot \theta \qquad \sec(90° - \theta) = \csc \theta$$
$$\cos(90° - \theta) = \sin \theta \qquad \cot(90° - \theta) = \tan \theta \qquad \csc(90° - \theta) = \sec \theta$$

The formula for $\cos (\alpha + \beta)$ can be derived as follows.

$$\cos \theta = \sin(90° - \theta) \qquad \text{Start with the identity in Example 2.}$$
$$\cos(\alpha + \beta) = \sin[90° - (\alpha + \beta)] \qquad \text{Substitute } \alpha + \beta \text{ for } \theta.$$
$$= \sin[(90° - \alpha) - \beta]$$
$$= \sin(90° - \alpha) \cos \beta - \cos(90° - \alpha) \sin \beta$$
$$\mathbf{\cos(\alpha + \beta) = \cos \alpha \cos \beta - \sin \alpha \sin \beta} \qquad \text{Substitute, using the identities in Examples 2 and 3.}$$

EXAMPLE 4   Use the formula for $\cos(\alpha + \beta)$ to derive a formula for $\cos(\alpha - \beta)$.

$$\cos(\alpha - \beta) = \cos[\alpha + (-\beta)]$$
$$= \cos \alpha \cos (-\beta) - \sin \alpha \sin (-\beta)$$
$$= \cos \alpha \cos \beta - \sin \alpha (-\sin \beta) \qquad \cos (-\beta) = \cos \beta$$
$$\cos(\alpha - \beta) = \cos \alpha \cos \beta + \sin \alpha \sin \beta \qquad \sin (-\beta) = -\sin \beta$$

EXAMPLE 5   Angle α terminates in quadrant III, and angle β terminates in quadrant II. Find $\cos(\alpha - \beta)$, if $\cos \alpha = -\frac{5}{13}$ and $\cos \beta = -\frac{3}{5}$.

First find the missing y-values for the reference triangles.

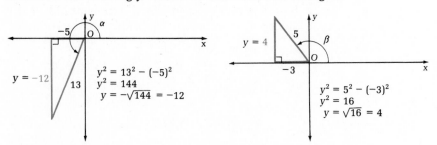

$$y^2 = 13^2 - (-5)^2 \qquad\qquad y^2 = 5^2 - (-3)^2$$
$$y^2 = 144 \qquad\qquad\qquad\quad y^2 = 16$$
$$y = -\sqrt{144} = -12 \qquad\qquad y = \sqrt{16} = 4$$

$\text{Sin } \alpha = -\frac{12}{13}$, and $\sin \beta = \frac{4}{5}$. Substitute these values in the formula
$\cos(\alpha - \beta) = \cos \alpha \cos \beta + \sin \alpha \sin \beta$.

$$\cos(\alpha - \beta) = -\frac{5}{13}\left(-\frac{3}{5}\right) + \left(-\frac{12}{13}\right)\left(\frac{4}{5}\right) = \frac{15}{65} - \frac{48}{65} = -\frac{33}{65}$$

The formula for $\tan(\alpha + \beta)$ is derived using the basic identity $\tan \theta = \frac{\sin \theta}{\cos \theta}$.

$$\tan(\alpha + \beta) = \frac{\sin(\alpha + \beta)}{\cos(\alpha + \beta)}$$

$$= \frac{\sin \alpha \cos \beta + \cos \alpha \sin \beta}{\cos \alpha \cos \beta - \sin \alpha \sin \beta}$$

$$= \frac{\dfrac{\sin \alpha \cos \beta}{\cos \alpha \cos \beta} + \dfrac{\cos \alpha \sin \beta}{\cos \alpha \cos \beta}}{\dfrac{\cos \alpha \cos \beta}{\cos \alpha \cos \beta} - \dfrac{\sin \alpha \sin \beta}{\cos \alpha \cos \beta}}$$

$$= \frac{\dfrac{\sin \alpha}{\cos \alpha} + \dfrac{\sin \beta}{\cos \beta}}{1 - \dfrac{\sin \alpha}{\cos \alpha}\left(\dfrac{\sin \beta}{\cos \beta}\right)}$$

$$\tan(\alpha + \beta) = \frac{\tan \alpha + \tan \beta}{1 - \tan \alpha \tan \beta}$$

If $-\beta$ is used in place of β in the formula above, a similar formula is derived for $\tan(\alpha - \beta)$. It is included in the following table, which summarizes the **sum and difference formulas.**

Sum and Difference Formulas

$$\sin(\alpha + \beta) = \sin \alpha \cos \beta + \cos \alpha \sin \beta$$

$$\sin(\alpha - \beta) = \sin \alpha \cos \beta - \cos \alpha \sin \beta$$

$$\cos(\alpha + \beta) = \cos \alpha \cos \beta - \sin \alpha \sin \beta$$

$$\cos(\alpha - \beta) = \cos \alpha \cos \beta + \sin \alpha \sin \beta$$

$$\tan(\alpha + \beta) = \frac{\tan \alpha + \tan \beta}{1 - \tan \alpha \tan \beta}$$

$$\tan(\alpha - \beta) = \frac{\tan \alpha - \tan \beta}{1 + \tan \alpha \tan \beta}$$

CLASS EXERCISES

Express each angle as the sum of two of these special angle measures.

30°   45°   60°   120°   135°   150°   210°

1. 75°   **2.** 165°   **3.** 195°   **4.** 285°

Express each angle as the difference of two of the special angle measures.

5. 15°   **6.** 75°   **7.** 105°   **8.** 165°

Find each ratio, using the given formula. Choose values for α and β in such a way that you will not need to use a table or a calculator. Leave answers in radical form.

9. Find $\sin 75°$, using $\sin(\alpha - \beta)$.   **10.** Find $\cos 75°$, using $\cos(\alpha + \beta)$.

TRIGONOMETRIC EQUATIONS AND IDENTITIES

EXERCISES

A

Find each ratio using the given formula. Choose values for α and β so that you will not need to use a table or a calculator. Leave answers in radical form.

1. Find $\sin 75°$ using $\sin(\alpha + \beta)$.

2. Find $\cos 75°$ using $\cos(\alpha - \beta)$.

3. Find $\tan 75°$ using $\tan(\alpha + \beta)$.

4. Find $\tan 75°$ using $\tan(\alpha - \beta)$.

5. Find $\sin 105°$ using $\sin(\alpha - \beta)$.

6. Find $\tan 165°$ using $\tan(\alpha - \beta)$.

7. Find $\cos 195°$ using $\cos(\alpha + \beta)$.

8. Find $\cos 285°$ using $\cos(\alpha + \beta)$.

B

Follow these instructions for Exercises 9–12.
   a. Use a sum or difference formula to find the exact ratio, in radical form.
   b. Use a calculator or a table of square roots to estimate the result in **a** to three decimal places.
   c. Use a calculator or a table of trigonometric ratios to find the ratio, and compare it to the result in **b**.

9. $\tan 15°$ **10.** $\cos 105°$ **11.** $\sin 225°$ **12.** $\tan 300°$

Suppose $\sin \alpha = \frac{3}{5}$, with $0° < \alpha < 90°$, and $\sin \beta = \frac{12}{13}$, with $90° < \beta < 180°$. Find

13. $\sin(\alpha + \beta)$.   **14.** $\cos(\alpha + \beta)$.   **15.** $\tan(\alpha - \beta)$.

Suppose $\cos \alpha = \frac{7}{25}$, with $0° < \alpha < 90°$, and $\tan \beta = -\frac{8}{15}$, with $90° < \beta < 180°$. Find

16. $\sin(\alpha + \beta)$.   **17.** $\sin(\alpha - \beta)$.   **18.** $\cos(\alpha - \beta)$.

Suppose $\cos \alpha = -\frac{4}{5}$, with $90° < \alpha < 180°$, and $\tan \beta = -\frac{9}{40}$, with $270° < \beta < 360°$. Find

19. $\tan(\alpha + \beta)$.   **20.** $\tan(\alpha - \beta)$.   **21.** $\cos(\alpha + \beta)$.

22. Find $\tan(\alpha - \beta)$, given that $\sin \alpha = \frac{5}{13}$ and $\tan \beta = \frac{12}{5}$, with the terminal sides of both angles in the first quadrant.

23. Given that $\sin 35° = 0.5736$, $\tan 35° = 0.7002$, and $\sec 35° = 1.2208$, find $\cos 55°$, $\cot 55°$, and $\csc 55°$. Use identities that apply to complementary angles.

24. Given that $\cos 72° = 0.3090$, $\cot 72° = 0.3249$, and $\csc 72° = 1.0515$, find $\tan 18°$, $\sin 18°$, and $\sec 18°$.

Prove that each equation is an identity.

25. $\cos(\theta + 90°) = -\sin \theta$

26. $\sin(180° - \theta) = \sin \theta$

27. $\tan(\theta - 135°) = \dfrac{\tan \theta + 1}{1 - \tan \theta}$

28. $\sec(\theta - 90°) = \csc \theta$

29. The equations $\sin(-\theta) = -\sin \theta$ and $\cos(-\theta) = \cos \theta$ are sometimes called **negative angle identities.** Prove that the equation $\tan(-\theta) = -\tan \theta$ is a negative angle identity.

C   ***30. a.** Find $\tan \beta$, using the measures of the sides of right triangle AEC.

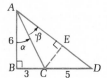

   b. Find $\tan \beta$, using the formula for $\tan(\alpha + \beta)$. Do not use the measures of the sides of triangle AEC.

31. Derive $\cot(\alpha + \beta) = \dfrac{\cot \alpha \cot \beta - 1}{\cot \alpha + \cot \beta}$, using $\cot(\alpha + \beta) = \dfrac{1}{\tan(\alpha + \beta)}$.

CHALLENGE

More About Proofs

In the proof of the formula for $\sin(\alpha + \beta)$ on page 481, we assumed that α and β were positive and less than $90°$. However, all of the sum and difference formulas are valid for more general values of α and β. The first four exercises below outline a derivation of the formula for $\cos(\alpha - \beta)$, in which the terminal sides of the two angles are in the second quadrant. The argument could be adapted for any measures α and β.

In the unit circle diagram at the left below, α and β are the measures of two angles in standard position with terminal sides in the second quadrant, and $\alpha > \beta$. Angle $B'OA'$ is drawn congruent to angle BOA in the diagram at the right.

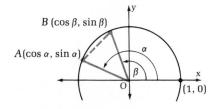
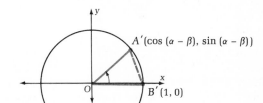

1. Explain why the coordinates of point A' are $(\cos(\alpha - \beta), \sin(\alpha - \beta))$.

2. Use the distance formula to show that
$AB = \sqrt{2 - 2(\cos \alpha \cos \beta + \sin \alpha \sin \beta)}$.

3. Show that $A'B' = \sqrt{2 - 2 \cos(\alpha - \beta)}$.

4. Triangles $OB'A'$ and OBA are congruent, so $A'B' = AB$. Show that $\cos(\alpha - \beta) = \cos \alpha \cos \beta + \sin \alpha \sin \beta$.

5. Use the formula for $\cos(\alpha - \beta)$ and the identities $\sin \theta = \cos(90° - \theta)$ and $\cos \theta = \sin(90° - \theta)$ to derive the formula for $\sin(\alpha + \beta)$.
Hint: Start with $\sin(\alpha + \beta) = \cos[90° - (\alpha + \beta)] = \cos[(90° - \alpha) - \beta]$.

12-6 Double-Angle Formulas

OBJECTIVES

To evaluate trigonometric expressions by using the double-angle formulas.
To prove identities and solve equations using such formulas.

The formula for $\sin(\alpha + \beta)$ can be used to derive a formula for $\sin 2\theta$, as shown below. The result is known as a **double-angle formula.**

$$\begin{aligned}
\sin(\alpha + \beta) &= \sin \alpha \cos \beta + \cos \alpha \sin \beta \\
\sin(\theta + \theta) &= \sin \theta \cos \theta + \cos \theta \sin \theta \qquad \text{Let } \alpha = \beta = \theta. \\
\sin 2\theta &= \sin \theta \cos \theta + \sin \theta \cos \theta \\
\sin 2\theta &= 2 \sin \theta \cos \theta
\end{aligned}$$

Substituting θ for α and for β in formulas for $\cos(\alpha + \beta)$ and $\tan(\alpha + \beta)$ produces double-angle formulas for the cosine and the tangent.

$$\begin{aligned}
\cos(\alpha + \beta) &= \cos \alpha \cos \beta - \sin \alpha \sin \beta & \tan(\alpha + \beta) &= \frac{\tan \alpha + \tan \beta}{1 - \tan \alpha \tan \beta} \\
\cos(\theta + \theta) &= \cos \theta \cos \theta - \sin \theta \sin \theta & \tan(\theta + \theta) &= \frac{\tan \theta + \tan \theta}{1 - \tan \theta \tan \theta} \\
\cos 2\theta &= \cos^2 \theta - \sin^2 \theta & \tan 2\theta &= \frac{2 \tan \theta}{1 - \tan^2 \theta}
\end{aligned}$$

EXAMPLE 1 Use the Pythagorean identity, $\sin^2 \theta + \cos^2 \theta = 1$, to derive two alternate forms of the formula for $\cos 2\theta$.

$$\begin{aligned}
\cos 2\theta &= \cos^2 \theta - \sin^2 \theta & \cos 2\theta &= \cos^2 \theta - \sin^2 \theta \\
&= \cos^2 \theta - (1 - \cos^2 \theta) & &= (1 - \sin^2 \theta) - \sin^2 \theta \\
\cos 2\theta &= 2 \cos^2 \theta - 1 & \cos 2\theta &= 1 - 2 \sin^2 \theta
\end{aligned}$$

The double-angle formulas are summarized below.

Double-Angle Formulas

$$\begin{aligned}
\sin 2\theta &= 2 \sin \theta \cos \theta & \cos 2\theta &= \cos^2 \theta - \sin^2 \theta \\
\tan 2\theta &= \frac{2 \tan \theta}{1 - \tan^2 \theta} & &= 2 \cos^2 \theta - 1 \\
& & &= 1 - 2 \sin^2 \theta
\end{aligned}$$

EXAMPLE 2 Verify that $\cos 2\theta = \cos^2 \theta - \sin^2 \theta$ for $\theta = 30°$.

$$
\begin{array}{c|c}
\cos 2(30°) & \cos^2 30° - \sin^2 30° \\[4pt]
\cos 60° & \left(\dfrac{\sqrt{3}}{2}\right)^2 - \left(\dfrac{1}{2}\right)^2 \\[10pt]
\dfrac{1}{2} & \dfrac{1}{2}
\end{array}
$$

EXAMPLE 3 A positive acute angle has measure θ, and $\cos \theta = \frac{4}{5}$. Find $\sin 2\theta$, $\cos 2\theta$, and $\tan 2\theta$.

Draw the reference triangle and show that

$$\sin \theta = \frac{3}{5} \qquad \tan \theta = \frac{3}{4}$$

$$\sin 2\theta = 2 \sin \theta \cos \theta = 2\left(\frac{3}{5}\right)\left(\frac{4}{5}\right) = \frac{24}{25}$$

$$\cos 2\theta = \cos^2 \theta - \sin^2 \theta = \left(\frac{4}{5}\right)^2 - \left(\frac{3}{5}\right)^2 = \frac{7}{25}$$

$$\tan 2\theta = \frac{2 \tan \theta}{1 - \tan^2 \theta} = \frac{2\left(\frac{3}{4}\right)}{1 - \left(\frac{3}{4}\right)^2} = \frac{\frac{3}{2}}{1 - \frac{9}{16}} = \frac{24}{7}$$

Note that an alternate method for finding $\tan 2\theta$ is to evaluate $\frac{\sin 2\theta}{\cos 2\theta}$.

EXAMPLE 4 Prove that $\sin 2\theta \tan \theta = 2 \sin^2 \theta$ is an identity.

$$
\begin{aligned}
\sin 2\theta \tan \theta &= (2 \sin \theta \cos \theta)\tan \theta \\
&= (2 \sin \theta \cos \theta)\frac{\sin \theta}{\cos \theta} \\
&= 2 \sin \theta \sin \theta \\
&= 2 \sin^2 \theta
\end{aligned}
$$

CLASS EXERCISES

Complete each equation to get a specific case of a double-angle formula.

1. $2 \sin 30° \cos 30° = \underline{\ ?\ }$

2. $\sin 45° \cos 45° = \underline{\ ?\ }$

3. $\cos^2 10° - \sin^2 10° = \underline{\ ?\ }$

4. $1 - 2 \sin^2 10° = \underline{\ ?\ }$

5. $2 \cos^2 10° - 1 = \underline{\ ?\ }$

6. $\dfrac{1}{2} - \sin^2 17° = \underline{\ ?\ }$

7. $\dfrac{2 \tan 5°}{1 - \tan^2 5°} = \underline{\ ?\ }$

8. $\dfrac{4 \tan 26°}{1 - \tan^2 26°} = \underline{\ ?\ }$

9. $2 \sin 2\theta \cos 2\theta = \underline{\ ?\ }$

10. $2 \cos^2 4x - 1 = \underline{\ ?\ }$

EXERCISES

A

1. Verify that $\sin 2\theta = 2 \sin \theta \cos \theta$ for $\theta = 90°$.

2. Verify that $\tan 2\theta = \dfrac{2 \tan \theta}{1 - \tan^2 \theta}$ for $\theta = 60°$.

3. Verify all three forms of the formula for $\cos 2\theta$ for $\theta = 45°$.

Evaluate using double-angle formulas. Do not use trigonometric tables or calculators. Leave irrational answers in radical form.

4. $2 \sin 15° \cos 15°$

5. $\cos^2 75° - \sin^2 75°$

6. $2 \cos^2 15° - 1$

7. $1 - 2 \sin^2(22°30')$

8. $\sin(-15°) \cos(-15°)$

9. $2 \cos^2(22°30') - 2 \sin^2(22°30')$

B

10. $\dfrac{\tan 75°}{1 - \tan^2 75°}$

11. $\dfrac{4 \tan^2 165°}{(1 - \tan^2 165°)^2}$

Find the sine, cosine, and tangent of 2θ for θ terminating in the given quadrant.

12. Quadrant I; $\cos \theta = \dfrac{3}{5}$

13. Quadrant II; $\tan \theta = -\dfrac{12}{5}$

14. Quadrant III; $\sin \theta = -\dfrac{7}{25}$

15. Quadrant IV; $\sin \theta = -\dfrac{40}{41}$

Prove that each equation is an identity.

16. $\csc 2\theta = \dfrac{1}{2} \csc \theta \sec \theta$

17. $\sec 2\theta = \dfrac{\sec^2 \theta}{2 - \sec^2 \theta}$

18. $\cot 2\theta = \dfrac{\cot^2 \theta - 1}{2 \cot \theta}$

19. $\sin 2\theta = \dfrac{2 \cot \theta}{\csc^2 \theta}$

20. $\sin 2\theta = \dfrac{2 \tan \theta}{1 + \tan^2 \theta}$

21. $\cos 2\theta = \cos^4 \theta - \sin^4 \theta$

22. $(\sin x + \cos x)^2 = 1 + \sin 2x$

23. $2 \sin x \csc 2x = \sec x$

24. $\sec^2 x \cos 2x = \sec^2 x - 2 \tan^2 x$

25. $\dfrac{1 + \cos 2x}{1 - \cos 2x} = \cot^2 x$

C

26. $\dfrac{1 + \tan x}{1 - \tan x} = \dfrac{1 + \sin 2x}{\cos 2x}$

27. $\sin 3\theta = 3 \sin \theta - 4 \sin^3 \theta$
    Hint: $3\theta = 2\theta + \theta$

28. The angle of elevation of a tower is twice as great from a point 245 feet from the base of the tower as from a point 1120 feet from the base. Find the height of the tower.

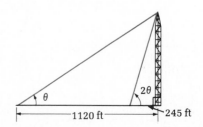

29. In the figure at the right, $BC = 15$, $CD = 25$, and the measures of angles BAC and CAD are equal. Solve for d.

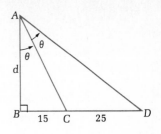

Solve for x, where $0° \le x < 360°$, and check.

Sample $2 \sin x \cos x - 1 = 0$
$$2 \sin x \cos x = 1$$
$$\sin 2x = 1 \qquad 2 \sin x \cos x = \sin 2x$$

Since $0° \le x < 360°$, values for $2x$ satisfy $0° \le 2x < 720°$. Then $\sin 2x = 1$ implies $2x = 90°$ or $2x = 450°$, and the solutions are $x = 45°$ and $x = 225°$. Check by substituting these values in the original equation.

30. $\sin 2x - \cos x = 0$

31. $\cos 2x + \sin x - 1 = 0$

32. $\sin^2 2x = \sin 2x$

33. $\tan x - 2 \tan 2x = 0$

34. $2 \cos^2 x + \sqrt{3} \sin 2x = 0$

35. $\tan 2x \sin x - \cos x = 0$

36. $\tan x + \cot x - 2 = 2 \sec x \csc x$

*37. $\dfrac{\sin^3 x - \cos^3 x}{\sin x - \cos x} = -\sin x \cos x$

CHECKPOINT

Prove that each equation is an identity.

1. $\dfrac{1 - \cos x}{\sin x} + \dfrac{\sin x}{1 - \cos x} = \dfrac{2}{\sin x}$

2. $\dfrac{\cos 2x - 1}{\cos 2x + 1} = -\tan^2 x$

Solve for x, where $0° \le x < 360°$, and check.

3. $(\tan^2 x - 1) \sin x = 0$

4. $2 \sin^2 x \cot x = \cot x$

5. Two sides of a triangle measure 9 and 12, and the angle included by these sides measures 30°. Find the area of the triangle.

Find each ratio by using the given formula. Choose values for x and y in such a way that you will not need a table or a calculator. Leave answers in radical form.

6. Find $\sin 105°$, using $\sin(x + y)$.

7. Find $\sin 225°$, using $\sin(x - y)$.

8. Find $\cos 105°$, using $\cos(x - y)$.

9. Find $\tan 315°$, using $\tan(x - y)$.

10. Evaluate $2 \sin 75° \cos 75°$ by using a double-angle formula. Do not use a table or a calculator.

TRIGONOMETRIC EQUATIONS AND IDENTITIES

12-7 Half-Angle Formulas

OBJECTIVES

To evaluate trigonometric expressions by using the half-angle formulas.
To prove identities and solve equations by using such formulas.

A formula that allows us to evaluate $\sin \frac{\theta}{2}$ in terms of $\cos \theta$ is derived using a double-angle formula for the cosine.

$$1 - 2 \sin^2 \alpha = \cos 2\alpha$$

$$\sin^2 \alpha = \frac{1 - \cos 2\alpha}{2}$$

$$\sin \alpha = \pm \sqrt{\frac{1 - \cos 2\alpha}{2}}$$

$$\sin \frac{\theta}{2} = \pm \sqrt{\frac{1 - \cos \theta}{2}} \qquad \text{Let } \theta = 2\alpha \text{ and substitute } \tfrac{\theta}{2} \text{ for } \alpha.$$

The formula just derived is called a **half-angle formula.** Another form of the double-angle formula for the cosine, $2 \cos^2 \alpha - 1 = \cos 2\alpha$, is used to derive the half-angle formula for the cosine.

$$2 \cos^2 \alpha - 1 = \cos 2\alpha$$

$$\cos^2 \alpha = \frac{1 + \cos 2\alpha}{2}$$

$$\cos \alpha = \pm \sqrt{\frac{1 + \cos 2\alpha}{2}}$$

$$\cos \frac{\theta}{2} = \pm \sqrt{\frac{1 + \cos \theta}{2}} \qquad \text{Substitute } \tfrac{\theta}{2} \text{ for } \alpha.$$

We divide the expressions for $\sin \frac{\theta}{2}$ and $\cos \frac{\theta}{2}$ to get a formula for $\tan \frac{\theta}{2}$.

$$\tan \frac{\theta}{2} = \frac{\sin \frac{\theta}{2}}{\cos \frac{\theta}{2}} = \frac{\pm \sqrt{\dfrac{1 - \cos \theta}{2}}}{\pm \sqrt{\dfrac{1 + \cos \theta}{2}}}$$

$$\tan \frac{\theta}{2} = \pm \sqrt{\frac{1 - \cos \theta}{1 + \cos \theta}}$$

The half-angle formulas are summarized below.

Half-Angle Formulas

$$\sin \frac{\theta}{2} = \pm \sqrt{\frac{1 - \cos \theta}{2}} \qquad \cos \frac{\theta}{2} = \pm \sqrt{\frac{1 + \cos \theta}{2}} \qquad \tan \frac{\theta}{2} = \pm \sqrt{\frac{1 - \cos \theta}{1 + \cos \theta}}$$

When using the half-angle formulas, the quadrant or portion of an axis where $\frac{\theta}{2}$ terminates determines the sign of the trigonometric ratio.

EXAMPLE 1   Use a half-angle formula to evaluate $\sin 22.5°$.

Let $\theta = 45°$, so that $\frac{\theta}{2} = 22.5°$.

$$\sin \frac{45°}{2} = \sqrt{\frac{1 - \cos 45°}{2}} \qquad \text{A 22.5° angle terminates in the first quadrant, so the sine is positive.}$$

$$\sin 22.5° = \sqrt{\frac{1 - \frac{\sqrt{2}}{2}}{2}} = \sqrt{\frac{2 - \sqrt{2}}{4}} = \frac{\sqrt{2 - \sqrt{2}}}{2}$$

EXAMPLE 2   If $270° < \theta < 360°$ and $\tan \theta = -\frac{15}{8}$, find $\tan \frac{\theta}{2}$.

Draw the reference triangle and find $\cos \theta$.

$$\cos \theta = \frac{8}{17}$$

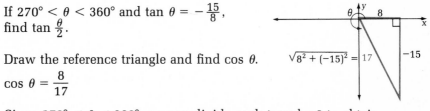

$$\sqrt{8^2 + (-15)^2} = 17$$

Since $270° < \theta < 360°$, we can divide each term by 2 to obtain $135° < \frac{\theta}{2} < 180°$. Therefore, $\frac{\theta}{2}$ is in the second quadrant, and its tangent is negative.

$$\tan \frac{\theta}{2} = -\sqrt{\frac{1 - \cos \theta}{1 + \cos \theta}} = -\sqrt{\frac{1 - \frac{8}{17}}{1 + \frac{8}{17}}} = -\sqrt{\frac{17 - 8}{17 + 8}} = -\sqrt{\frac{9}{25}} = -\frac{3}{5}$$

CLASS EXERCISES

Find the quadrant containing the terminal side of the angle of measure $\frac{\theta}{2}$, if θ satisfies the given conditions.

1. $0° < \theta < 90°$ **2.** $90° < \theta < 180°$ **3.** $270° < \theta < 360°$

4. $-90° < \theta < 0°$ **5.** $-360° < \theta < -270°$ **6.** $540° < \theta < 630°$

Complete each equation to get a specific case of a half-angle formula.

7. $\sqrt{\dfrac{1 - \cos 20°}{2}} = \dfrac{?}{}$ **8.** $\sqrt{\dfrac{1 - \cos 210°}{2}} = \dfrac{?}{}$

9. $-\sqrt{\dfrac{1 + \cos 210°}{2}} = \dfrac{?}{}$ **10.** $\sqrt{\dfrac{1 + \cos 610°}{2}} = \dfrac{?}{}$

11. $-\sqrt{\dfrac{1 - \cos (-60°)}{2}} = \dfrac{?}{}$ **12.** $\sqrt{\dfrac{1 - \cos 380°}{1 + \cos 380°}} = \dfrac{?}{}$

EXERCISES

A

1. Using $\cos 90° = 0$ and the half-angle formulas, find $\sin 45°$, $\cos 45°$, and $\tan 45°$. Leave irrational answers in radical form.

2. Using $\cos 120° = -\frac{1}{2}$ and the half-angle formulas, find $\sin 60°$, $\cos 60°$, and $\tan 60°$. Leave irrational answers in radical form.

Evaluate using half-angle formulas. Do not use trigonometric tables or a calculator. Leave irrational answers in radical form.

3. $\sin 15°$

4. $\tan 22.5°$

5. $\sin 105°$

6. $\tan (-75°)$

7. $\sin (-67.5°)$

8. $\cos 165°$

B

Use half-angle formulas to find $\sin \frac{\theta}{2}$, $\cos \frac{\theta}{2}$, and $\tan \frac{\theta}{2}$, where θ satisfies the given conditions. Leave irrational answers in radical form.

9. $0° < \theta < 90°$; $\tan \theta = \frac{3}{4}$

10. $180° < \theta < 270°$; $\tan \theta = \frac{8}{15}$

11. $270° < \theta < 360°$; $\sin \theta = -\frac{24}{25}$

12. $180° < \theta < 270°$; $\cot \theta = 2\sqrt{2}$

Prove that each equation is an identity.

13. $\sec^2 \frac{\theta}{2} = \frac{2}{1 + \cos \theta}$

14. $\tan^2 \frac{\theta}{2} = \frac{\sec \theta - 1}{\sec \theta + 1}$

15. $\dfrac{\cos^2 \frac{x}{2} - \sin^2 \frac{x}{2}}{\cos^2 \frac{x}{2} + \sin^2 \frac{x}{2}} = \cos x$

16. $\left(\sin \frac{x}{2} + \cos \frac{x}{2} \right)^2 = 1 + \sin x$

C

17. Verify that the equation $\tan \alpha = \dfrac{\sin 2\alpha}{1 + \cos 2\alpha}$ is an identity.

18. Let $\theta = 2\alpha$ in the identity in Exercise 17, and prove that $\tan \frac{\theta}{2} = \dfrac{\sin \theta}{1 + \cos \theta}$ is an identity.

19. Explain how the identity in Exercise 18 is demonstrated in the unit circle diagram at the right.

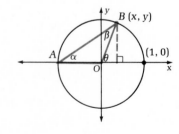

20. Use the identity in Exercise 18 to prove that $\tan \frac{\theta}{2} = \dfrac{1 - \cos \theta}{\sin \theta}$ is an identity.

Solve for x, where $0° \leq x < 360°$, and check.

21. $2 \cos \frac{x}{2} - 1 = 0$

22. $\sqrt{2} \sin \frac{x}{2} = 1$

23. $3 \tan^2 \frac{x}{2} = 1$

*24. $\cos^2 \frac{x}{2} = 1 - \frac{1}{2} \cos x$

*25. $\cos 2x + 4 \sin^2 \frac{x}{2} = 1$

Vectors

A directed line segment, or arrow, is called a **vector**.
Vectors are used to represent quantities that have
magnitude *and* direction. The length of the vector
represents magnitude; the arrowhead shows direction.

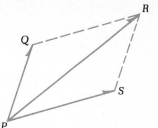

Vectors $\overrightarrow{PQ}$, $\overrightarrow{PR}$, and $\overrightarrow{PS}$ have the initial point P. $\overrightarrow{PR}$ is
the diagonal of the parallelogram formed by $\overrightarrow{PQ}$
and $\overrightarrow{PS}$. $\overrightarrow{PR}$ is called the sum, or **resultant**, of $\overrightarrow{PQ}$ and $\overrightarrow{PS}$.

Example   What is the minimum force needed to keep a 200-pound block from
sliding down a ramp that makes an angle of 35° with the ground?
Assume there is no friction.

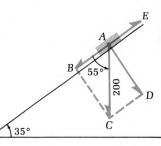

Let $\overrightarrow{AC}$ be the force vector due to
gravity. The magnitude of this
vector, $|\overrightarrow{AC}|$, is 200. Resolve $\overrightarrow{AC}$
into two vectors, $\overrightarrow{AB}$ and $\overrightarrow{AD}$, such
that $\overrightarrow{AB}$ is parallel to the ramp and
$\overrightarrow{AD}$ is perpendicular to the ramp.
$|\overrightarrow{AD}|$, the force on the ramp, is
counteracted by the ramp itself.

$\overrightarrow{AB}$ is the force vector tending to move the block down the ramp.
A force vector $\overrightarrow{AE}$ in the opposite direction from $\overrightarrow{AB}$, such that
$|\overrightarrow{AE}| = |\overrightarrow{AB}|$, will hold the block. Since $\angle BAC = 90° - 35° = 55°$,

$$|\overrightarrow{AE}| = |\overrightarrow{AB}| = 200 \cos 55° = 114.72$$

Thus, a force of 115 pounds, to the nearest pound, will hold the
block stationary. Note that a force of over 200 pounds is needed to
lift the block vertically, while about 115 pounds will *slide* it up the
ramp. The ramp provides an advantage of $200 - 115 = 85$ pounds.

*Find the minimum force required to hold a 200-pound block stationary
on a ramp with the given angle. Give each answer to the nearest pound.*

1. 25°   **2.** 45°   **3.** 50°

4. What happens as the ramp angle gets closer to 90°?

5. If the minimum force is to be 35 pounds, to the nearest pound,
what should be the ramp angle, to the nearest degree?

6. A 50-pound force acts on an object in a horizontal direction. A
25-pound force acts simultaneously on the object at an angle of 60°
to the horizontal. Find the magnitude and direction of the resultant.
Hint: Use the laws of cosines and sines.

CHAPTER 12
REVIEW

VOCABULARY

trigonometric equation (p. 468)

trigonometric identity (p. 468)

Pythagorean identity (p. 469)

sum and difference formulas (p. 484)

double-angle formula (p. 490)

half-angle formula (p. 494)

SUMMARY

Trigonometric equations that are identities are presented in the first two sections of this chapter. Such equations are shown to be identities by using either of two methods of proof. In the third section, trigonometric equations that are not identities are solved, where the solutions are restricted to the interval $0° \leq x < 360°$. The remainder of the chapter focuses on some important trigonometric formulas. In particular, the results derived are the sum and difference formulas, the double-angle formulas, and the half-angle formulas. These formulas are fundamental to the study of trigonometry and its applications.

REVIEW EXERCISES

12-1   *Complete each equation by using a basic identity. State the restrictions on x, if any, in each case.*

1. $\dfrac{1}{\sin x} = \underline{\ ?\ }$

2. $\cos x \sec x = \underline{\ ?\ }$

3. $2(1 - \cos^2 x) = \underline{\ ?\ }$

Write each expression by using only sine and/or cosine ratios. Simplify wherever possible.

4. $\dfrac{\sin x}{\csc x - \cot x}$

5. $\dfrac{\tan x - \cos x}{\cos x}$

6. $(\cot x + \sec x)(\cot x)$

Show that the first expression is equivalent to the second expression.

7. $(1 + \cot^2 x)(1 - \cos^2 x); \ 1$

8. $\dfrac{2 + \cot^2 x}{\csc^2 x} - 1; \ \sin^2 x$

12-2   *Prove that each equation is an identity.*

9. $(1 + \cos x)(1 - \cos x) = \dfrac{1}{1 + \cot^2 x}$

10. $(\csc^2 x - 1)\sin^2 x = 1 - \sin^2 x$

11. $\csc^2 x - 4 \cot^2 x = 4 - 3 \csc^2 x$

12. $\dfrac{\cos x - 1}{\sin x - \tan x} = \dfrac{1}{\tan x}$

12-3   *Solve for x, where $0° \leq x < 360°$, and check.*

13. $2 \sec x + 4 = 0$

14. $2 \sin x - \sqrt{3} = 0$

15. $\cot x - \sqrt{2} \cos x = 0$

16. $\sin^2 x + \sin x = 2$

17. $2 \tan^2 x = 2 - \sec^2 x$

18. $2 \cos^2 x \tan x = \sin x$

12-4 *Find the area of each triangle to the nearest whole number of square units.*

19.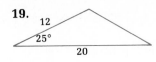

20.

21.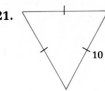

22. Use the formula for sin $(\alpha + \beta)$ to evaluate sin 165°. Leave the answer in radical form. Do not use a table or a calculator.

12-5 *Find each ratio by using a suitable sum or difference formula. Choose values for α and β in such a way that you will not need a table or calculator. Leave answers in radical form, where appropriate.*

23. tan 75°

24. sin 135°

25. cos 150°

26. tan 315°

27. sin 210°

28. cos 300°

Prove that each equation is an identity.

29. $\cos (\theta + 180°) = -\cos \theta$

30. $\sin (\theta - 90°) = -\cos \theta$

12-6 *Find the sine, cosine, and tangent of 2θ for θ terminating in the given quadrant.*

31. Quadrant I; $\sin \theta = \dfrac{3}{5}$

32. Quadrant II; $\cot \theta = -\dfrac{12}{5}$

33. Quadrant III; $\cos \theta = -\dfrac{7}{25}$

34. Quadrant IV; $\cos \theta = \dfrac{40}{41}$

Prove that each equation is an identity.

35. $\dfrac{\csc 2x}{\sec x} = \dfrac{1}{2} \csc x$

36. $\sin 2x = \dfrac{2 \cos^2 x}{\cot x}$

37. $\dfrac{1 + \sin 2x}{1 - \sin 2x} = \dfrac{(\sin x + \cos x)^2}{(\sin x - \cos x)^2}$

38. $\cos 3x = \cos^3 x - 3 \sin^2 x \cos x$

Solve for x, where $0° \le x < 360°$

39. $\cos 2x - \sin x = 0$

40. $2 \sin^2 x + 3 \cos 2x = 0$

12-7 Use half-angle formulas to find $\sin \frac{x}{2}$, $\cos \frac{x}{2}$, and $\tan \frac{x}{2}$, where **x** satisfies the given conditions. Leave answers in radical form.

41. $0° < x < 90°$; $\tan x = \dfrac{4}{3}$

42. $180° < x < 270°$; $\cot x = \dfrac{15}{8}$

43. $90° < x < 180°$; $\cos x = -\dfrac{24}{25}$

44. $270° < x < 360°$; $\sin x = -\dfrac{12}{13}$

45. Solve $2 \cos^2 \dfrac{x}{2} - 1 = 0$ for $0° < x < 360°$

CHAPTER 12
TEST

Write each expression by using only sine and/or cosine ratios. Simplify wherever possible.

1. $\dfrac{\cot^2 \theta}{\csc^2 \theta}$

2. $\sec \theta - \dfrac{\tan^2 \theta}{\sec \theta}$

Prove that each equation is an identity.

3. $\dfrac{1 - \tan^2 x}{1 - \cot^2 x} = 1 - \sec^2 x$

4. $\tan^2 \theta - \sin^2 \theta = \dfrac{\sin^2 \theta}{\cot^2 \theta}$

Solve for **x**, where $0° \le x < 360°$.

5. $\sin x \cos x = \cos x$

6. $\cot^2 x + \csc x - 1 = 0$

7. Find the area of the triangle, to the nearest whole number of square units.

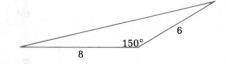

8. Prove that $\tan (\theta + 180°) = \tan \theta$ is an identity.

Use the given formula to find the required ratio. Choose values for the angle measures in such a way that you will not need a table or a calculator. Leave answers in radical form, where appropriate.

9. Find $\sin 105°$ by using the formula for $\sin (\alpha + \beta)$.

10. Find $\sin 75°$ by using the formula for $\sin (\alpha - \beta)$.

11. Find $\tan 195°$ by using the formula for $\tan (\alpha - \beta)$.

12. Find $\cos 22°30'$ by using the formula for $\cos \dfrac{\theta}{2}$.

13. Find $\tan 105°$ by using the formula for $\tan \dfrac{\theta}{2}$.

14. Find $\sin 2x$, where $\tan x = \dfrac{12}{5}$, and $180° < x < 270°$.

15. Find $\tan 2x$, where $\csc x = 3$, and $0° < x < 90°$.

The Richter Scale

The strength of an earthquake is measured as a value on a scale developed by Charles Richter, an American seismologist. The scale is related to powers of ten and to common logarithms. Since 10^3 is ten times as great as 10^2, a quake with a rating of 3 on the Richter scale is ten times as strong as a quake with a rating of 2.

The program below compares the strength of two earthquakes when their ratings on the Richter scale are entered. By using the absolute-value function in line 130, we obtain the positive difference between the two values, regardless of the order in which they are entered.

The Program

```
100 REM RICHTER SCALE COMPARISON
110 PRINT "INPUT TWO RATINGS"
120 INPUT A, B
130 LET D = ABS(A - B)
140 LET X = 10↑D
150 LET X = INT(X*10 + .5)/10
160 PRINT "ONE QUAKE WAS ";X
170 PRINT " TIMES AS STRONG. "
200 PRINT "ANOTHER? (1 = YES, 0 = NO)"
210 INPUT Z
220 IF Z = 1 THEN 110
900 END
```

What It Does

Line 130: Computes positive difference.

Line 150: Rounds to the nearest tenth.

```
RUN
INPUT TWO RATINGS
? 3.6, 5.4
ONE QUAKE WAS 63.1
TIMES AS STRONG.
ANOTHER? (1 = YES, 0 = NO)
```

Sample run for earthquakes with readings of 3.6 and 5.4 on the Richter scale

What does the program display for each pair of Richter scale values?

1. 2.3, 4.3   **2.** 3.1, 6.1   **3.** 2.8, 4.5   **4.** 3.9, 7.4

5. 3.4, 6.1   **6.** 5.8, 8.5   **7.** 7.6, 4.9   **8.** 8.7, 2.7

9. The intensity of a sound is measured on the *decibel scale,* which is logarithmic. A sound 20 decibels higher than another sound is 100 times as intense ($\frac{20}{10} = 2$, and $10^2 = 100$.) A sound 35 decibels higher than another is $10^{3.5}$ times as intense ($\frac{35}{10} = 3.5$). Write a program that compares the intensity of two sounds when their decibel ratings are entered.

For more information about BASIC, see the Computer Handbook at the back of the book.

CHAPTER 13

A computer display can be used to compare the periods and amplitudes of the graphs of the equations $y = \sin x$, $y = 2 \sin x$, and $y = \sin 2x$.

CIRCULAR FUNCTIONS

Prerequisite Skills Review

Write the letter for the correct answer.

1. $\dfrac{5\pi}{4} \cdot \dfrac{180}{\pi} = \underline{\ ?\ }$

   a. $\dfrac{225}{\pi}$
   b. 225π
   c. 225
   d. none of these

2. To the nearest 10 minutes, 68.3° is equal to $\underline{\ ?\ }$.
   a. 68°10′
   b. 68°20′
   c. 68°30′
   d. none of these

3. To the nearest tenth of a degree, 56°50′ is equal to $\underline{\ ?\ }$.
   a. 56.8°
   b. 56.9°
   c. 56.5°
   d. none of these

4. The solid curve can be obtained by
   a. translating the dashed curve $2a$ units up.
   b. reflecting the dashed curve through the x-axis.
   c. reflecting the dashed curve through the y-axis.
   d. rotating the dashed curve 180° about its highest point.

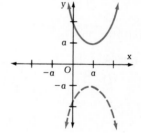

5. If $\theta = 120°$, then $2 \cos \dfrac{\theta}{2} = \underline{\ ?\ }$.

   a. 1
   b. $2\sqrt{3}$
   c. -1
   d. none of these

6. If $-\dfrac{\pi}{2} \le x \le \dfrac{\pi}{2}$, then $\underline{\ ?\ }$.

   a. $-2\pi \le 2x \le 2\pi$
   b. $-\pi \le 2x \le \pi$
   c. $-\dfrac{\pi}{4} \le 2x \le \dfrac{\pi}{4}$
   d. none of these

7. If $0 \le \dfrac{x}{2} \le \pi$, then $\underline{\ ?\ }$.

   a. $0 \le 2x \le 4\pi$
   b. $4 \le 2x \le 4\pi$
   c. $0 \le 2x \le 2\pi$
   d. none of these

8. If a second-quadrant angle has a sine of $\dfrac{8}{17}$, then its tangent is $\underline{\ ?\ }$.

   a. $-\dfrac{15}{17}$
   b. $\dfrac{8}{15}$
   c. $-\dfrac{15}{8}$
   d. $-\dfrac{8}{15}$

13-1 Radian Measure

To express degree measure in radians, and the reverse.
To find the trigonometric ratios of angle measures given in radians.

Length can be measured in many different units, such as inches, feet, centimeters, or meters. The size of an angle can also be expressed in more than one way. You are already familiar with degrees and minutes. The *radian* is another common unit of angle measure. It is particularly useful in scientific work.

A **central angle** of a circle is an angle whose vertex is the center of the circle. One **radian** is the measure of a central angle that intercepts an arc of length equal to the radius of the circle. Angle *AOB* is a central angle of circle *O*. Since the length of arc *AB* is equal to r, the measure of the radius, angle *AOB* measures one radian.

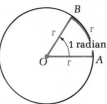

The circumference of a circle with radius r is $2\pi r$. Since the circumference is 2π times the length of a radius, there are 2π radians in one revolution.

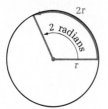 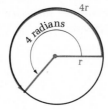 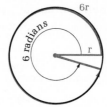 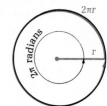

Since there are 360° in one complete revolution, $360° = 2\pi$ radians, or

$$180° = \pi \text{ radians}$$

Divide each side by 180 to get

$$1° = \frac{\pi}{180} \text{ radians} \approx 0.0175 \text{ radians}$$

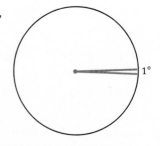

Changing Degrees to Radians

To change degree measure to radian measure, multiply the number of degrees by $\frac{\pi}{180}$.

EXAMPLE 1   Express each special angle measure in radians, using π.

a. $30° = \left(30 \cdot \dfrac{\pi}{180} \right)$ radians

$= \dfrac{\pi}{6}$ radians

b. $45° = \left(45 \cdot \dfrac{\pi}{180} \right)$ radians

$= \dfrac{\pi}{4}$ radians

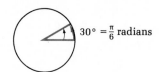

c. $60° = \left(60 \cdot \dfrac{\pi}{180} \right)$ radians

$= \dfrac{\pi}{3}$ radians

d. $90° = \left(90 \cdot \dfrac{\pi}{180} \right)$ radians

$= \dfrac{\pi}{2}$ radians

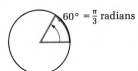

Sometimes it is convenient to use a decimal approximation rather than the exact radian measure expressed in terms of π. The table on pages 672–676 can be used to find radian measures accurate to four decimal places for degree measures from 0° to 90°. Such values can also be found by using an appropriate approximation for π.

EXAMPLE 2   Express 110° in radians, giving a decimal approximation correct to two decimal places.

Use 3.14 as an approximation for π.

$110° = \left(110 \cdot \dfrac{\pi}{180} \right)$ radians $\approx \dfrac{11(3.14)}{18}$ radians ≈ 1.92 radians

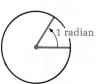

Dividing each side of the equation, π **radians = 180°**, by π produces

1 radian $= \left(\dfrac{180}{\pi} \right)° \approx 57°20'$ To the nearest 10 minutes

---

Changing Radians to Degrees

To change radian measure to degree measure, multiply the number of radians by $\dfrac{180}{\pi}$.

CIRCULAR FUNCTIONS

EXAMPLE 3   Express each angle measure in degrees.

$\textbf{a.}\ \dfrac{2\pi}{3}$ **radians** $= \left(\dfrac{2\pi}{3} \cdot \dfrac{180}{\pi}\right)^{\!\circ} = 120°$

$\textbf{b.}\ -\dfrac{7\pi}{4}$ **radians** $= \left(-\dfrac{7\pi}{4} \cdot \dfrac{180}{\pi}\right)^{\!\circ} = -315°$

Radian measure is often written without using the word *radian*. An angle measure of 2 radians may be given simply as 2, whereas a measure of 2 degrees is written with the degree symbol, 2°. Similarly, sin 2 means *the sine of an angle measuring 2 radians.*

EXAMPLE 4   Find $\sin \frac{4\pi}{3}$, $\cos \frac{4\pi}{3}$, and $\tan \frac{4\pi}{3}$.

Express $\frac{4\pi}{3}$ radians in degrees.

$$\frac{4\pi}{3} \text{ radians} = \left(\frac{4\pi}{3} \cdot \frac{180}{\pi}\right)^{\!\circ} = 240°$$

Since the reference angle is 60°, it is not necessary to use a table to find the required ratios.

$$\sin \frac{4\pi}{3} = \sin 240° \qquad \cos \frac{4\pi}{3} = \cos 240° \qquad \tan \frac{4\pi}{3} = \tan 240°$$
$$= -\frac{\sqrt{3}}{2} \qquad\qquad\qquad = -\frac{1}{2} \qquad\qquad\qquad = \sqrt{3}$$

EXAMPLE 5   Find sin 2, cos 2, and tan 2, using the table on pages 672–676.

First express 2 radians in degrees and minutes, to the nearest 10 minutes. Use 3.14 as an approximation for π.

$$2 \text{ radians} = \left(2 \cdot \frac{180}{\pi}\right)^{\!\circ} = \left(\frac{360}{\pi}\right)^{\!\circ} \approx 114.6° \approx 114°40' \qquad \begin{array}{l} 1° = 60', \text{ and} \\ 0.6 \cdot 60' \approx 40'. \end{array}$$

Then find the required ratios in the table.

$\sin 2 \approx \sin 114°40' = \sin 65°20' = 0.9088$
$\cos 2 \approx \cos 114°40' = -\cos 65°20' = -0.4173$
$\tan 2 \approx \tan 114°40' = -\tan 65°20' = -2.177$

CLASS EXERCISES

Express in radians, using π.

1. 15°   **2.** 165°   **3.** $-30°$ **4.** $-180°$ **5.** 330°   **6.** 450°

Express each radian measure in degrees.

7. $\dfrac{3\pi}{4}$ **8.** $\dfrac{3\pi}{2}$ **9.** $-\dfrac{2\pi}{9}$ **10.** $\dfrac{\pi}{18}$ **11.** $\dfrac{4\pi}{3}$ **12.** $\dfrac{5\pi}{12}$

EXERCISES

A   *Express in radians, using π.*

1. 120°   **2.** 180°   **3.** 225°   **4.** −90°   **5.** −240°   **6.** −330°

Express each radian measure in degrees.

7. $\dfrac{\pi}{2}$ **8.** $\dfrac{\pi}{9}$ **9.** $\dfrac{\pi}{15}$ **10.** $-\dfrac{3\pi}{2}$ **11.** $-\dfrac{5\pi}{4}$ **12.** $\dfrac{7\pi}{18}$

13. Complete by writing the equivalent radian measures.

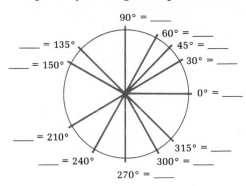

Find each trigonometric ratio, if it exists, without using a table or a calculator.

14. $\sin\dfrac{\pi}{6}$ **15.** $\cos\dfrac{\pi}{4}$ **16.** $\tan\dfrac{\pi}{2}$ **17.** $\cot\dfrac{2\pi}{3}$ **18.** $\sec(-\pi)$

19. $\csc\left(-\dfrac{\pi}{2}\right)$ **20.** $\cos\dfrac{5\pi}{6}$ **21.** $\tan\left(-\dfrac{3\pi}{4}\right)$ **22.** $\sin 2\pi$ **23.** $\cot(-5\pi)$

Express each radian measure in degrees. Then find the trigonometric ratio, using the table on pages 672–676.

24. $\sec\dfrac{\pi}{12}$ **25.** $\cot\dfrac{\pi}{15}$ **26.** $\sin\dfrac{5\pi}{36}$ **27.** $\cos\left(-\dfrac{\pi}{18}\right)$ **28.** $\cos\dfrac{5\pi}{9}$

B   *Express each angle measure in radians, giving a decimal approximation correct to two decimal places. Use 3.14 as an approximation for π.*

29. 125°   **30.** 200°   **31.** 94°   **32.** 285°   **33.** 450°

Express each angle measure in radians, giving a decimal approximation correct to four decimal places. Use the table on pages 674–678.

34. 25°   **35.** 68°   **36.** 33°30′   **37.** 52°30′   **38.** 73°50′

Express each radian measure in degrees and minutes. Use the table.

39. 0.3694   **40.** 0.8290   **41.** 1.0007   **42.** 0.0640   **43.** 0.9977

Express each radian measure in degrees and minutes, to the nearest 10 minutes. Use 3.14 for π. Then find the trigonometric ratio, using the table.

44. $\sin 3$ **45.** $\cos 2.5$ **46.** $\tan 4$ **47.** $\sec 5$ **48.** $\cot 3.5$

Evaluate.

49. $\dfrac{\sin \dfrac{\pi}{4} - \cos \dfrac{\pi}{2}}{\tan \dfrac{\pi}{6}}$

50. $\dfrac{\tan \dfrac{3\pi}{4} + \cot \left(-\dfrac{3\pi}{4}\right)}{\left(\sin \dfrac{2\pi}{3}\right)\left(\cos \dfrac{5\pi}{6}\right)}$

Solve for **x** in radians, where **$0 \le x < 2\pi$.**

51. $(\cos x)(\sin x + 1) = 0$ **52.** $2 \sin \dfrac{x}{2} = 1$ **53.** $\cos x - \sqrt{3} \sin x = 0$

54. $2 \cos^2 x - 1 = \cos x$ **55.** $\sin x - \sin 2x = 0$ **56.** $4 \sin x \cos x - \sqrt{2} = 0$

Evaluate without using a table.

57. $\dfrac{\sin^2 \dfrac{2\pi}{7} + \cos^2 \dfrac{2\pi}{7}}{2 \sin \dfrac{\pi}{12} \cos \dfrac{\pi}{12}}$

58. $1 - 2 \sin^2 \dfrac{\pi}{8}$

59. $\tan \dfrac{\pi}{8}$

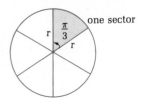

USING THE CALCULATOR

The Area of a Circular Sector

The circular region with radius r has been divided into six congruent *circular sectors*. Since the area of the circle is πr^2, each of these sectors has area $\frac{1}{6}(\pi r^2) = \frac{1}{2}(\frac{\pi}{3} r^2)$, where $\frac{\pi}{3}$ is the measure of the central angle of the sector. In general, $\frac{1}{2}\theta r^2$ is the area of a circular sector with radius r and central angle θ, expressed in radians.

Use a calculator.

1. A circle has a radius of 21.38 centimeters. Find the area of each sector with the given central angle. Use $\pi = 3.14$, and round each answer to two decimal places. Note that degrees must be changed to radians in **c** and **d**.

   a. $\theta = \dfrac{\pi}{6}$ **b.** $\theta = \dfrac{35\pi}{36}$ **c.** $\theta = 135°$ **d.** $\theta = 40°$

2. A circular sector has a radius of 8.5 centimeters and an area of 48.41 square centimeters. Find its central angle in radians, rounded to two decimal places.

*3. Find the area of the shaded region, which is generated by revolving a 12-foot rope in both directions around the right triangle. Leave the answer in terms of π.

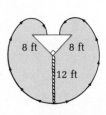

13-2 The Sine and Cosine Functions

To graph functions with equations of the form $y = c + a \sin x$ and
$y = c + a \cos x$.
To determine the periods and amplitudes of such functions.

In the unit circle, a central angle of 1 radian intercepts an arc of length 1. Similarly, a central angle of
2 radians intercepts an arc of length 2, and so forth.
This is stated below in general terms.

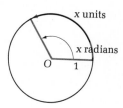

> The radian measure of a central angle in
> the unit circle is the same as the arc length.

Real numbers are used to indicate direction and distance.
On line AB, the numbers -2 and 2 indicate that point A is 2 units to the left
of the origin and point B is 2 units to
the right.

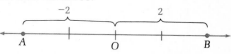

On unit circle O, the same numbers are used to
show that points C and D are each 2 units from the
point $(1, 0)$ along arcs of the circle. For C, this distance is measured in the positive direction, counterclockwise. For D, it is measured in the negative direction, clockwise. Note that it makes sense to think of a
ratio such as **sin 2** not only as the sine of 2 radians,
but also as the sine of the real number 2.

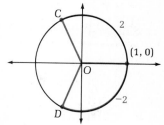

Recall that $(\cos \theta, \sin \theta)$ are the coordinates of the point where the
unit circle intersects the terminal side of an angle of θ degrees. Similarly, you can think of $(\cos x, \sin x)$ as the coordinates of the point on
the unit circle where the arc of x radians terminates.

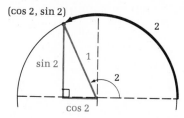

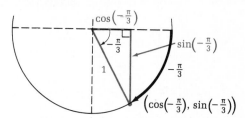

Since $y = \sin x$ and $y = \cos x$ are uniquely defined for all real numbers
x, we say that these equations define **trigonometric**, or **circular**, **functions**
with domain all real numbers.

From the unit circle diagrams, it is clear that for all real x

$$-1 \le \sin x \le 1 \qquad -1 \le \cos x \le 1$$

That is, the range of each function consists of all real numbers from -1 through 1.

To graph the functions defined by $y = \sin x$ and $y = \cos x$, first construct a table of selected values from $x = 0$ to $x = 2\pi$ and connect the resulting points with a smooth curve.

x	$y = \sin x$	$y = \cos x$
0	0	1
$\dfrac{\pi}{6}$	$\dfrac{1}{2} = 0.5$	$\dfrac{\sqrt{3}}{2} \approx 0.9$
$\dfrac{\pi}{3}$	$\dfrac{\sqrt{3}}{2} \approx 0.9$	$\dfrac{1}{2} = 0.5$
$\dfrac{\pi}{2}$	1	0
$\dfrac{2\pi}{3}$	$\dfrac{\sqrt{3}}{2} \approx 0.9$	$-\dfrac{1}{2} = -0.5$
$\dfrac{5\pi}{6}$	$\dfrac{1}{2} = 0.5$	$-\dfrac{\sqrt{3}}{2} \approx -0.9$
π	0	-1
$\dfrac{7\pi}{6}$	$-\dfrac{1}{2} = -0.5$	$-\dfrac{\sqrt{3}}{2} \approx -0.9$
$\dfrac{4\pi}{3}$	$-\dfrac{\sqrt{3}}{2} \approx -0.9$	$-\dfrac{1}{2} = -0.5$
$\dfrac{3\pi}{2}$	-1	0
$\dfrac{5\pi}{3}$	$-\dfrac{\sqrt{3}}{2} \approx -0.9$	$\dfrac{1}{2} = 0.5$
$\dfrac{11\pi}{6}$	$-\dfrac{1}{2} = -0.5$	$\dfrac{\sqrt{3}}{2} \approx 0.9$
2π	0	1

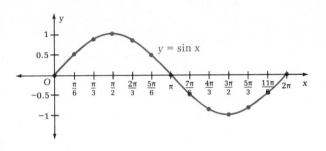

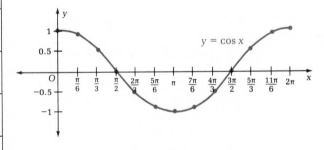

EXAMPLE 1   Determine the intervals from $x = 0$ to $x = 2\pi$ for which $\sin x$ increases and those for which it decreases.

Sin x increases from $x = 0$ to $x = \frac{\pi}{2}$ The curve for $y = \sin x$ rises
and from $x = \frac{3\pi}{2}$ to $x = 2\pi$.   over these intervals.

Sin x decreases from $x = \frac{\pi}{2}$ to $x = \frac{3\pi}{2}$.   The curve falls over this interval.

It is unnecessary to make a table of values for x less than 0 or greater than 2π, since the values of sin x and cos x repeat. This is illustrated below, using the unit circle.

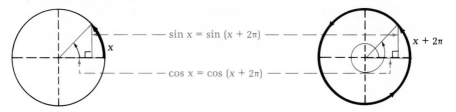

Note that the following identities hold for any real number x:

$$\sin(x + 2\pi) = \sin x \qquad \cos(x + 2\pi) = \cos x$$

Since the values of sin x and cos x repeat, the curves just shown for $y = \sin x$ and $y = \cos x$ repeat endlessly to the right and left of the y-axis. The sine and cosine functions are said to be **periodic,** with *period* 2π. The graph over one period is called a **cycle.**

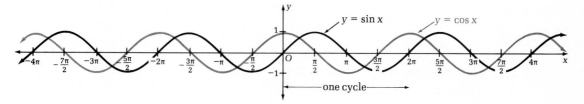

The sine and cosine curves have the same shape and are described as **sine waves.** Note that the cosine curve can be obtained by shifting the sine curve $\frac{\pi}{2}$ units to the left. Similarly, the sine curve can be obtained by shifting the cosine curve $\frac{\pi}{2}$ units to the right.

One-half of the vertical distance from the lowest to the highest point on each curve is called the **amplitude** of the function.

The Amplitude of a Periodic Function

If a periodic function has a maximum value M and a minimum value m, the amplitude of the function is

$$\frac{M - m}{2}$$

For both $y = \sin x$ and $y = \cos x$, $M = 1$ and $m = -1$. Thus the amplitude of each function is 1.

$$\frac{M - m}{2} = \frac{1 - (-1)}{2} = 1$$

CIRCULAR FUNCTIONS

511

EXAMPLE 2

Graph $y = 2 \sin x$ and $y = \frac{1}{2} \sin x$ for $0 \le x \le 2\pi$. Find the period and amplitude of each function.

First graph $y = \sin x$. Choose several points on the curve and multiply each ordinate by 2 to find the corresponding points on the graph of $y = 2 \sin x$. Similarly, multiply each ordinate by $\frac{1}{2}$ to find the corresponding points on the graph of $y = \frac{1}{2} \sin x$.

The period of each function is 2π.
The amplitude of $y = 2 \sin x$ is
$$\frac{2 - (-2)}{2} = 2$$
The amplitude of $y = \frac{1}{2} \sin x$ is
$$\frac{\frac{1}{2} - \left(-\frac{1}{2}\right)}{2} = \frac{1}{2}$$

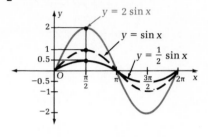

EXAMPLE 3

Graph $y = -\cos x$ and $y = -2 \cos x$ for $-2\pi \le x \le 2\pi$. Find the period and amplitude of each function.

First graph $y = \cos x$. The ordinate of each point on the graph of $y = -\cos x$ is the opposite of the ordinate of the corresponding point on the graph of $y = \cos x$. That is, the dashed curve is reflected through the x-axis to obtain the graph of $y = -\cos x$. To obtain points on the graph of $y = -2 \cos x$, the ordinates of points on the graph of $y = -\cos x$ are multiplied by 2.

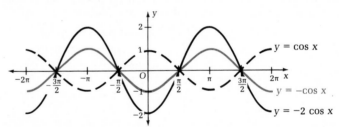

The period of each function is 2π. The amplitude of $y = -\cos x$ is 1. The amplitude of $y = -2 \cos x$ is 2.

Notice that each function described so far has the same period. In general, any function of the form $y = c + a \sin x$ or $y = c + a \cos x$ has a period of 2π.

EXAMPLE 4

Graph $y = 2 + \sin x$ for $0 \le x \le 2\pi$. Find the period and amplitude.

First graph $y = \sin x$. To obtain the graph of $y = 2 + \sin x$, the curve for $y = \sin x$ is translated 2 units upward.

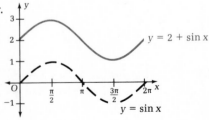

The period is 2π. The amplitude is 1.

512

CLASS EXERCISES

Find the period and amplitude of each function.

1. $y = -\sin x$ **2.** $y = \frac{3}{2} \sin x$ **3.** $y = -\frac{1}{2} \cos x$

4. Use the graph of $y = \cos x$ to determine the intervals from $x = 0$ to $x = 2\pi$ for which the cosine increases and those for which it decreases.

*Find the values of **x** from 0 to 2π where*

5. $\sin x > 0$.   **6.** $\sin x < 0$.   **7.** $\cos x > 0$.   **8.** $\cos x < 0$.

EXERCISES

A

Find the period and amplitude of each function.

1. $y = 3 \sin x$ **2.** $y = -\frac{1}{3} \sin x$ **3.** $y = 4 \cos x$

4. $y = -\frac{3}{4} \cos x$ **5.** $y = 1 + \sin x$ **6.** $y = 5 + \cos x$

*Find the values of **x** from 0 to 2π where*

7. $\sin x > 0$ and $\cos x > 0$.   **8.** $\sin x > 0$ and $\cos x < 0$.

9. $\sin x < 0$ and $\cos x > 0$.   **10.** $\sin x < 0$ and $\cos x < 0$.

11. Complete the table. Use a calculator or trigonometric tables, where necessary, and round ratios to the nearest tenth.

x	0	$\frac{\pi}{8}$	$\frac{\pi}{4}$	$\frac{3\pi}{8}$	$\frac{\pi}{2}$	$\frac{5\pi}{8}$	$\frac{3\pi}{4}$	$\frac{7\pi}{8}$	π
sin x									
cos x									

12. Use the table above to graph $y = \sin x$ for $0 \le x \le \pi$.

13. Use the table to graph $y = \cos x$ for $0 \le x \le \pi$.

14. Graph $y = \sin x$ for $-2\pi \le x \le 0$.

15. Use the graph from Exercise 14 to determine the intervals from $x = -2\pi$ to $x = 0$ for which $\sin x$ increases and those for which it decreases.

B

Graph each pair of functions on the same coordinate axes for $0 \le x \le 2\pi$. Find the amplitude of each function.

16. $y = \sin x,\ y = 3 \sin x$ **17.** $y = \cos x,\ y = 2 \cos x$

18. $y = \sin x,\ y = -\sin x$ **19.** $y = \cos x,\ y = \frac{1}{3} \cos x$

20. $y = -\sin x,\ y = -2 \sin x$

21. $y = \cos x,\ y = 1 + \cos x$

22. $y = \sin x,\ y = -1 + \sin x$

23. $y = \cos x,\ y = -3 + \cos x$

24. Prove that $\sin(x + 2\pi) = \sin x$ and $\cos(x + 2\pi) = \cos x$, using the formulas for $\sin(\alpha + \beta)$ and $\cos(\alpha + \beta)$.

Graph each function for $-2\pi \leq x \leq 2\pi$.

25. $y = 3 \cos x$

26. $y = -3 \sin x$

27. $y = -\dfrac{1}{2} \cos x$

C | *Graph each function for* $0 \leq x \leq 2\pi$.

28. $y = 1 - \sin x$

29. $y = -1 - \sin x$

30. $y = 2 - \cos x$

31. $y = 2 - 2 \cos x$

32. $y = \sin(-x)$

33. $y = \cos(-x)$

34. Graph $y = \sin x$ for $\dfrac{\pi}{2} \leq x \leq \dfrac{5\pi}{2}$.

35. Graph $y = \sin\left(x + \dfrac{\pi}{2}\right)$ by translating the curve in Exercise 34 to the left $\dfrac{\pi}{2}$ units.

36. Use the formula for $\sin(\alpha + \beta)$ to show that $\sin\left(x + \dfrac{\pi}{2}\right) = \cos x$.

37. Graph $y = \cos x$ for $-\dfrac{\pi}{2} \leq x \leq \dfrac{3\pi}{2}$.

38. Graph $y = \cos\left(x - \dfrac{\pi}{2}\right)$ by translating the curve in Exercise 37 to the right $\dfrac{\pi}{2}$ units.

39. Use the formula for $\cos(\alpha - \beta)$ to show that $\cos\left(x - \dfrac{\pi}{2}\right) = \sin x$.

40. Graph $y = \sin x$ and $y = \cos x$ for $0 \leq x \leq 2\pi$ on the same axes. Then find the x-values for which the two curves intersect by solving $\sin x = \cos x$.

41. Complete the following table of values, using decimals to the nearest tenth.

x	0	$\dfrac{\pi}{4}$	$\dfrac{\pi}{2}$	$\dfrac{3\pi}{4}$	π	$\dfrac{5\pi}{4}$	$\dfrac{3\pi}{2}$	$\dfrac{7\pi}{4}$	2π
sin x	0								
cos x	1								
sin x + cos x	$0 + 1 = 1$								

a. Use the table of values to graph $y = \sin x$ and $y = \cos x$ on the same axes, using dashed curves.

b. Use the table to graph $y = \sin x + \cos x$ on the same axes used in **a**. Use a solid curve.

c. Find the amplitude of the function $y = \sin x + \cos x$.

13-3 Graphing $y = a \sin bx$ and $y = a \cos bx$

OBJECTIVES

To graph functions with equations of the form $y = a \sin bx$ and $y = a \cos bx$.
To determine the periods and amplitudes of such functions.

Compare the graphs of $y = \sin x$ and $y = \sin 2x$, shown below.

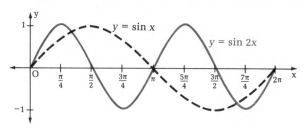

The graphs of the two functions behave in much the same way. However, the period of $y = \sin x$ is 2π, while $y = \sin 2x$ has a shorter period, π.

The period of $y = \sin 2x$ could have been determined without graphing. Since one cycle of $y = \sin x$ is completed as x varies from 0 to 2π, it follows that one cycle of $y = \sin 2x$ is completed as 2x varies from 0 to 2π, or as x varies from 0 to π.

EXAMPLE 1

Find the period p and the amplitude of $y = 2 \cos \frac{x}{2}$. Sketch the curve from $x = -p$ to $x = p$.

Since $0 \le \frac{x}{2} \le 2\pi$, is equivalent to $0 \le x \le 4\pi$, p is equal to 4π. The maximum value of $2 \cos \frac{x}{2}$ is 2, and the minimum value is -2, so the amplitude is 2.

Make a table of values, plot the points, and sketch the curve from $x = 0$ to $x = 4\pi$. Copy the graph for $x = -4\pi$ to $x = 0$.

x	0	π	2π	3π	4π
$\dfrac{x}{2}$	0	$\dfrac{\pi}{2}$	π	$\dfrac{3\pi}{2}$	2π
$\cos \dfrac{x}{2}$	1	0	-1	0	1
$2 \cos \dfrac{x}{2}$	2	0	-2	0	2

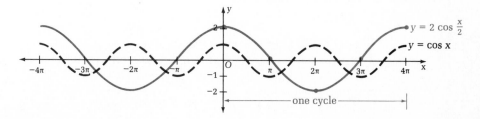

Compare the graph of $y = 2 \cos \frac{x}{2}$ to that of $y = \cos x$, shown as a dashed curve in Example 1. The amplitude and period of $y = 2 \cos \frac{x}{2}$ are twice the amplitude and period of $y = \cos x$. The relationships between the graphs of $y = \sin x$ and $y = \sin 2x$, and between the graphs of $y = \cos x$ and $y = 2 \cos \frac{x}{2}$, suggest the following steps for sketching sine and cosine functions.

To sketch one cycle of $y = a \sin bx$ and of $y = a \cos bx$, where $b > 0$:

- First find the period p. Divide the interval from 0 to p into four equal parts.

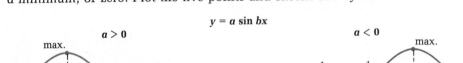

- For each of the five x-values, the corresponding y-value will be *a maximum, a minimum*, or *zero*. Plot the five points and sketch one cycle.

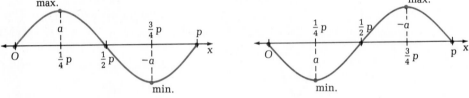

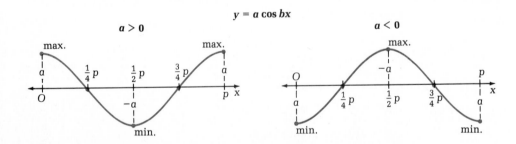

The next example shows how one cycle is used to obtain a more extensive graph.

EXAMPLE 2   Sketch $y = \sin 4x$ for $0 \le x \le 2\pi$. Find the number of cycles from $x = 0$ to $x = 2\pi$.

The period p of $y = \sin 4x$ is $\frac{\pi}{2}$, since $0 \le 4x \le 2\pi$ is equivalent to $0 \le x \le \frac{\pi}{2}$. Show the following points on the horizontal axis:

$$0 \qquad \frac{1}{4}p = \frac{1}{4}\left(\frac{\pi}{2}\right) = \frac{\pi}{8} \qquad \frac{1}{2}p = \frac{1}{2}\left(\frac{\pi}{2}\right) = \frac{\pi}{4} \qquad \frac{3}{4}p = \frac{3}{4}\left(\frac{\pi}{2}\right) = \frac{3\pi}{8} \qquad p = \frac{\pi}{2}$$

Since the maximum value of sin 4x is 1 and the minimum value is −1, the amplitude is 1. Plot the points for each of the five x-values and sketch one cycle.

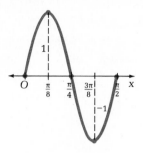

There are four cycles from x = 0 to x = 2π. Complete the graph by sketching the cycle three more times. Show the y-axis.

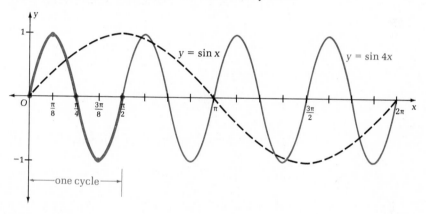

—one cycle—

CLASS EXERCISES

Complete the table. Give the required **x**-values for **0 ≤ x ≤ p**.

	period p	No. of Cycles, or Part of a Cycle, for 0 ≤ x ≤ 2π	amplitude	y is max. for x =	y is min. for x =	y = 0 for x =
1. $y = \cos 2x$						
2. $y = \sin \dfrac{x}{2}$						
3. $y = -\sin 3x$						
4. $y = 3 \sin 6x$						
5. $y = \dfrac{1}{3} \cos \dfrac{x}{4}$						

EXERCISES

A Complete the table. Give the required *x*-values for $0 \le x \le p$.

	period p	No. of Cycles, or Part of a Cycle, for $0 \le x \le 2\pi$	amplitude	y is max. for $x =$	y is min. for $x =$	$y = 0$ for $x =$
1. $y = \sin 4x$						
2. $y = -\cos 2x$						
3. $y = \cos \dfrac{x}{3}$						
4. $y = 2 \sin 5x$						
5. $y = 4 \cos \dfrac{x}{2}$						

Sketch one cycle for each function.

6. $y = \cos 2x$ **7.** $y = -\cos 2x$ **8.** $y = \sin 8x$ **9.** $y = -\sin 8x$

B **10.** $y = 2 \cos 4x$ **11.** $y = -3 \sin 3x$ **12.** $y = \sin \dfrac{x}{2}$ **13.** $y = -\cos \dfrac{x}{2}$

14. $y = 2 \cos 5x$ **15.** $y = 2 \sin 5x$ **16.** $y = \sin \dfrac{3x}{2}$ **17.** $y = \dfrac{3}{2} \cos \dfrac{3x}{2}$

Find positive numbers *a* and *b* so that $y = a \sin bx$ has

18. amplitude 1 and period $\frac{\pi}{2}$.   **19.** amplitude 2 and period 4π.

Find positive numbers *a* and *b* so that $y = a \cos bx$ has

20. amplitude 4 and period $\frac{\pi}{3}$.   **21.** amplitude $\frac{1}{3}$ and period 6π.

Sketch the graph from $x = -p$ to $x = p$, where *p* is the period of the function.

22. $y = 2 + 2 \sin 2x$ **23.** $y = -1 + \cos \dfrac{x}{2}$

C **24.** Show that the amplitude of $y = a \sin bx$ or $y = a \cos bx$ equals $|a|$.

25. Show that for $b > 0$, the period of $y = a \sin bx$ or $y = a \cos bx$ is $\dfrac{2\pi}{b}$.

26. Write the equation of a sine function with period $\frac{\pi}{2}$, maximum value 4, and minimum value -2.

27. Write the equation of a cosine function with period 5π, maximum value $\frac{7}{2}$, and minimum value $\frac{1}{2}$.

13-4 The Tangent and Cotangent Functions

OBJECTIVES

To graph functions with equations of the form $y = a \tan bx$ and
$y = a \cot bx$.
To determine the periods of such functions.

Since $\tan x = \frac{\sin x}{\cos x}$, the tangent is undefined whenever $\cos x$ is equal
to 0. In particular, $\tan x$ is undefined for x equal to $\pm\frac{\pi}{2}$ or any odd multiples of these values. $\text{Tan}(x + \pi) = \tan x$ is an identity, so the period
of the function $y = \tan x$ is π. There is one full cycle of the graph between $x = -\frac{\pi}{2}$ and $x = \frac{\pi}{2}$. A table of values can be used to obtain the
coordinates of points on this cycle, which repeats endlessly.

x	$y = \tan x$
$-\dfrac{\pi}{2}$	undefined
$-\dfrac{\pi}{3}$	$-\sqrt{3} \approx -1.7$
$-\dfrac{\pi}{4}$	-1
$-\dfrac{\pi}{6}$	$-\dfrac{\sqrt{3}}{3} \approx -0.6$
0	0
$\dfrac{\pi}{6}$	$\dfrac{\sqrt{3}}{3} \approx 0.6$
$\dfrac{\pi}{4}$	1
$\dfrac{\pi}{3}$	$\sqrt{3} \approx 1.7$
$\dfrac{\pi}{2}$	undefined

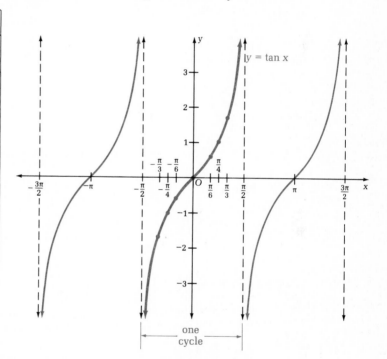

The vertical lines at x-values for which $\tan x$ is undefined are
asymptotes. That is, the curve approaches these lines more and more
closely. Each cycle of the curve gets arbitrarily high or low as it approaches the asymptotes, so the tangent function has no maximum or
minimum values and therefore no amplitude.

To sketch a function of the form $y = a \tan bx$, $b > 0$, first find the
period p. Divide the interval from $-\frac{p}{2}$ to $\frac{p}{2}$ into four equal parts and
draw the vertical asymptotes through $(\pm\frac{p}{2}, 0)$ to "enclose" one cycle.
Also, use the points $(\pm\frac{p}{4}, \pm a)$ and $(0, 0)$.

EXAMPLE 1   Graph one cycle of $y = \tan 2x$.

$0 \le 2x \le \pi$ is equivalent to $0 \le x \le \frac{\pi}{2}$, so the period p is $\frac{\pi}{2}$. The asymptotes are $x = \pm\frac{p}{2}$, or $x = \pm\frac{\pi}{4}$. Make a brief table of values, including $\left(\pm\frac{p}{4}, \pm a\right)$ and $(0, 0)$.

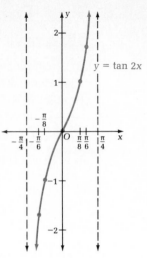

$y = \tan 2x$

x	$2x$	$\tan 2x$
0	0	0
$\pm\dfrac{\pi}{8}$	$\pm\dfrac{\pi}{4}$	± 1
$\pm\dfrac{\pi}{6}$	$\pm\dfrac{\pi}{3}$	$\pm\sqrt{3} \approx \pm 1.7$

$\cot(x + \pi) = \cot x$ is an identity, so the period of the cotangent function $y = \cot x$ is also π. The asymptotes for the graph of the cotangent function are $x = 0$, $x = \pm\pi$, $x = \pm 2\pi$, and so forth, since $\cot x$ is undefined for these values. A table of values can be used to obtain one cycle between $x = 0$ and $x = \pi$. The cycle repeats to the left and right.

x	$y = \cot x$
0	undefined
$\dfrac{\pi}{6}$	$\sqrt{3} \approx 1.7$
$\dfrac{\pi}{4}$	1
$\dfrac{\pi}{3}$	$\dfrac{\sqrt{3}}{3} \approx 0.6$
$\dfrac{\pi}{2}$	0
$\dfrac{2\pi}{3}$	$-\dfrac{\sqrt{3}}{3} \approx -0.6$
$\dfrac{3\pi}{4}$	-1
$\dfrac{5\pi}{6}$	$-\sqrt{3} \approx -1.7$
π	undefined

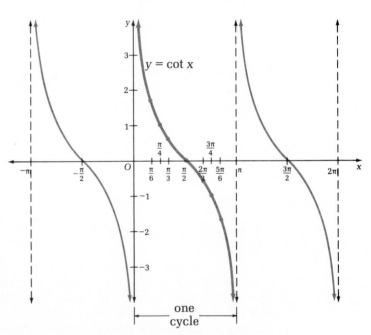

$y = \cot x$

Notice that the cotangent function, like that of the tangent, has no maximum or minimum values. Therefore it has no amplitude.

To sketch a function of the form $y = a \cot bx$, we can use a method similar to that used for graphing $y = a \tan bx$. In the next example, however, we vary the procedure by first graphing $y = \cot bx$ and then multiplying the ordinates by a to obtain the graph of $y = a \cot bx$.

EXAMPLE 2   Find the period p of the function $y = \frac{1}{2} \cot \frac{x}{2}$ and sketch its graph between $x = -p$ and $x = p$.

Since $0 < \frac{x}{2} < \pi$ and $0 < x < 2\pi$ are equivalent, the period is 2π. Draw the asymptote through $(2\pi, 0)$ and lightly sketch one cycle of $y = \cot \frac{x}{2}$. Each ordinate is multiplied by $\frac{1}{2}$ to get one cycle of $y = \frac{1}{2} \cot \frac{x}{2}$. Repeat the cycle to the left of the y-axis.

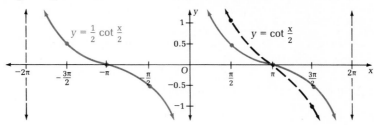

CLASS EXERCISES

Give the values of **x** from -2π to 2π for which the given function is undefined. Then give the values of **x** for which the value of the function is 0.

1. $y = \tan x$ **2.** $y = \tan \frac{x}{2}$ **3.** $y = \cot x$ **4.** $y = \cot 2x$

Find the period **p** of each function and the equations of the asymptotes from $x = -p$ to $x = p$. Then sketch each graph between $x = -p$ and $x = p$.

5. $y = \tan \frac{x}{2}$ **6.** $y = \cot 2x$

EXERCISES

A   Find the period for each function. Then sketch one cycle.

1. $y = \tan 3x$ **2.** $y = \tan \frac{x}{3}$ **3.** $y = \cot 4x$ **4.** $y = \cot \frac{x}{4}$

Find the period **p** for each function. Then sketch the graph between $x = -p$ and $x = p$.

5. $y = \tan 2x$ **6.** $y = \tan \frac{x}{4}$ **7.** $y = \cot 3x$ **8.** $y = \cot \frac{x}{2}$

Find the values of **x** from $-\pi$ to π where

9. $\tan x > 0$.   **10.** $\tan x < 0$.   **11.** $\cot x > 0$.   **12.** $\cot x < 0$.

B   **13.** Determine the intervals from $x = -\pi$ to $x = \pi$ for which tan x increases.

14. Determine the intervals between $x = -\pi$ and $x = \pi$ for which cot x decreases.

Find the period **p** for each function. Then sketch the graph of each function between **x = −2π** and **x = 2π**.

15. y = −tan x   **16.** y = 2 cot x   **17.** y = −2 cot 2x   **18.** $y = \frac{1}{2} \tan \frac{x}{2}$

19. Find the period of y = tan πx and sketch the graph over the interval $-\frac{1}{2} < x < \frac{1}{2}$.

20. Find the period of y = −cot 2πx and sketch the graph over the interval $0 < x < \frac{1}{2}$.

21. Prove that tan(x + π) = tan x and cot(x + π) = cot x, using the formula for tan(α + β).

C   **22.** Sketch the graph of $y = \tan \frac{3x}{2}$ from x = 0 to x = 2π.

23. Sketch the graph of $y = \cot \frac{2x}{3}$ between x = 0 and x = 3π.

Sketch one cycle of each function by making an appropriate horizontal and/or vertical translation of **y = tan x** or **y = cot x**.

24. $y = \tan\left(x - \frac{\pi}{4}\right)$ **25.** $y = \cot\left(x + \frac{\pi}{4}\right)$ **26.** y = tan x + 2

27. y = cot x − 1   **28.** $y = \tan\left(x + \frac{\pi}{2}\right) + 1$ **29.** $y = \cot\left(x - \frac{\pi}{2}\right) - 2$

CHALLENGE

Circular Functions on the Unit Circle

Circle 0 is a unit circle. $\overline{CD}$ and $\overline{EF}$ are tangent to the circle at C and E, respectively. $\overline{OB}$, a side of acute angle COB, is extended to intersect these tangents at D and at F. $\overline{OE}$ is perpendicular to $\overline{EF}$ and to $\overline{OA}$. $\overline{OC}$ is perpendicular to $\overline{AB}$ and to $\overline{CD}$.

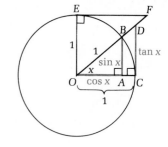

Recall that for acute angle COB, with measure x, sin x and cos x are the lengths of the perpendicular sides of triangle OAB. Also, since triangles OAB and OCD are similar, tan x is the length of $\overline{CD}$.

$$\tan x = \frac{\sin x}{\cos x} = \frac{AB}{OA} = \frac{CD}{OC} = \frac{CD}{1} = CD$$

Name the segment with length equal to the given ratio.

1. sec x   **2.** cot x   **3.** csc x

4. Tan 0 is equal to 0, and cot 0 is undefined. Explain this in geometric terms, using the unit circle. **Hint:** In this case, A, B, C, and D all name the same point.

13-5 The Secant and Cosecant Functions

The secant is the reciprocal of the cosine. The period of both functions,
$y = \cos x$ and $y = \sec x$, is 2π.
   To graph one cycle of $y = \sec x$, first
graph $y = \cos x$ from $x = -\frac{\pi}{2}$ to $x = \frac{3\pi}{2}$.
Then take reciprocals of the y-values.
Notice that the curve has a *positive
branch* and a *negative branch*. The
asymptotes for $y = \sec x$ occur at
the values of x for which $\cos x$ is
equal to 0.

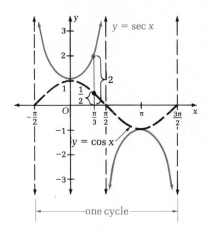

EXAMPLE 1   Find the period of $y = \sec 2x$. Then sketch the function from $x = -\pi$
to $x = \pi$.

Since $0 \le 2x \le 2\pi$ is equivalent to $0 \le x \le \pi$, the period of the function $y = \sec 2x$ is π. Sketch $y = \cos 2x$. Then draw the asymptotes
through the points on the x-axis for which $\cos 2x = 0$. Sketch the
given secant function by taking reciprocals of y-values for $y = \cos 2x$.

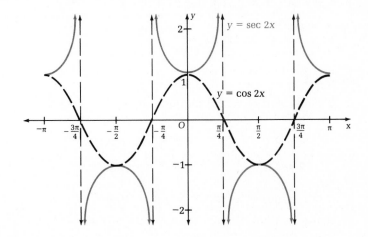

The graph of $y = \csc x$ is similar to that of $y = \sec x$.

EXAMPLE 2   Find the period of $y = \csc x$. Then sketch the function between $x = -2\pi$ and $x = 2\pi$.

The cosecant is the reciprocal of the sine, so the period of $y = \csc x$ is 2π, the same period as that of $y = \sin x$. First, graph $y = \sin x$. Draw the asymptotes through the points on the x-axis for which $\sin x = 0$. Then take reciprocals of $\sin x$ to sketch the curve of $y = \csc x$.

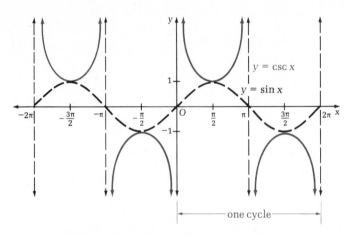

Notice that the secant and cosecant functions, like those of the tangent and cotangent, have no maximum or minimum values. Therefore, neither the secant nor the cosecant function has an amplitude.

CLASS EXERCISES

Find the period of each function and the equations of the asymptotes from $x = 0$ to $x = p$. Then sketch the graph from $x = 0$ to $x = p$.

1. $y = \sec 4x$ **2.** $y = \csc \dfrac{x}{2}$ **3.** $y = -\csc x$

EXERCISES

A   *Find the period of each function and sketch the graph from $x = 0$ to $x = p$.*

1. $y = \sec \dfrac{x}{2}$ **2.** $y = \csc 2x$ **3.** $y = -\sec x$

4. $y = 2 \sec x$ **5.** $y = \dfrac{1}{2} \csc x$ **6.** $y = -2 \csc x$

Find the values of x from $-\dfrac{\pi}{2}$ to $\dfrac{3\pi}{2}$ where

7. $\sec x \geq 1$.   **8.** $\sec x \leq -1$.

*Find the values of **x** from 0 to 2π where*

9. csc x ≥ 1.

10. csc x ≤ −1.

B

11. Determine the intervals from $x = -\frac{\pi}{2}$ to $x = \frac{3\pi}{2}$ for which sec x increases and those for which it decreases.

12. Determine the intervals from $x = 0$ to $x = 2\pi$ for which csc x increases and those for which it decreases.

*Find the period **p** and sketch the graph between **x** = −**p** and **x** = **p**.*

13. $y = 2 \sec 2x$ **14.** $y = 3 \sec \frac{x}{3}$ **15.** $y = -\csc 3x$ **16.** $y = 2 \csc \frac{x}{3}$

C

17. $y = \sec \frac{2}{3}x$ **18.** $y = \csc \frac{3}{2}x$ **19.** $y = \sec \pi x$ **20.** $y = \csc 2\pi x$

*If **p** is the period of the function **y** = **sec bx**, then $x = \frac{1}{4}p$ and $x = \frac{3}{4}p$ are the equations of the asymptotes over the interval **0 ≤ x ≤ p**. Also, **y** is either 1 or −1 when **x** = **0**, **x** = $\frac{1}{2}$**p**, and **x** = **p**. Use this information to sketch the graph of each function from **x** = **0** to **x** = **p**, without using a cosine curve.*

21. $y = \sec 4x$

22. $y = \sec \frac{x}{4}$

*Let **p** be the period of the function **y** = **csc bx**.*

23. Express the equations of the asymptotes in terms of p, over the interval 0 ≤ x ≤ p.

24. Use p to express the x-values for which $y = 1$ or $y = -1$, over the interval 0 ≤ x ≤ p.

25. Sketch the graph of $y = \csc 4x$, without using a sine curve.

*Use horizontal and vertical translations of **y** = **sec x** or **y** = **csc x** to obtain one complete cycle of each function.*

26. $y = \sec\left(x - \frac{\pi}{2}\right) + 1$

27. $y = \csc\left(x + \frac{\pi}{2}\right) - 1$

CHECKPOINT

1. Express 165° in radians.

2. Express −80° in radians.

3. Express $\frac{9\pi}{4}$ radians in degrees. Then find $\sin \frac{9\pi}{4}$.

*Find the period **p** and sketch the graph from **x** = **0** to **x** = **p**.*

4. $y = -\sin 2x$ **5.** $y = 3 \cos 3x$ **6.** $y = -\cot x$

7. $y = 2 \tan 2x$ **8.** $y = 2 \csc 2x$ **9.** $y = \sec \frac{3}{2}x$

13-6 The Inverse Sine Function

OBJECTIVES

To graph functions with equations of the form $y = a$ Arcsin bx.
To evaluate expressions involving Arcsin x for given values of x.

When the variables in the equation $y = \sin x$ are interchanged, the resulting sine wave is vertical.

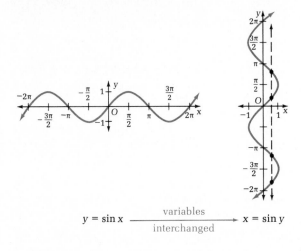

y is not a function of
x, since there is
more than one y-
value for the same x.

$$y = \sin x \xrightarrow[\text{interchanged}]{\text{variables}} x = \sin y$$

If the domain of $y = \sin x$ is restricted to $-\frac{\pi}{2} \le x \le \frac{\pi}{2}$, the relation
produced by interchanging the variables is a function. This new func-
tion is called the **inverse sine function.** The equation $x = \sin y$ tells us
that y is the measure of the angle whose sine is x or

$y = $ Arcsin x The arc length on the unit circle is equal to
the measure of the central angle in radians.
Arcsin x is an abbreviation for *the arc whose
sine is x,* or *the angle whose sine is x.*

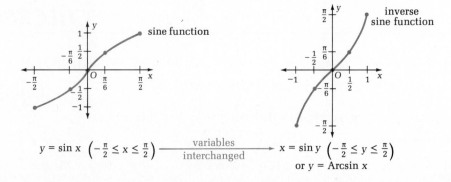

$$y = \sin x \left(-\frac{\pi}{2} \le x \le \frac{\pi}{2}\right) \xrightarrow[\text{interchanged}]{\text{variables}} x = \sin y \left(-\frac{\pi}{2} \le y \le \frac{\pi}{2}\right)$$
$$\text{or } y = \text{Arcsin } x$$

> **The Inverse Sine Function**
>
> $$y = \text{Arcsin } x \qquad \text{(means } x = \sin y\text{)}$$
>
> **Domain: $-1 \le x \le 1$ \qquad Range: $-\dfrac{\pi}{2} \le y \le \dfrac{\pi}{2}$**

The graph of $y = \text{Arcsin } x$ shows the following properties of the function.

If $-1 < x < 0$, then $-\dfrac{\pi}{2} < y < 0$. \qquad The reference angle of measure y is in quadrant IV.

If $0 < x < 1$, then $0 < y < \dfrac{\pi}{2}$. \qquad The reference angle of measure y is in quadrant I.

This information is helpful when we evaluate Arcsin x for specific values of x. Note that when Arcsin x is evaluated for a given x, the angle measure is given in radians unless otherwise specified.

EXAMPLE 1 Evaluate $\text{Arcsin}\left(-\dfrac{\sqrt{2}}{2}\right)$.

$\text{Arcsin}\left(-\dfrac{\sqrt{2}}{2}\right)$ means *the angle whose sine is* $-\dfrac{\sqrt{2}}{2}$. Since $-1 < -\dfrac{\sqrt{2}}{2} < 0$, the angle is in quadrant IV.

$\text{Arcsin}\left(-\dfrac{\sqrt{2}}{2}\right) = -\dfrac{\pi}{4}$

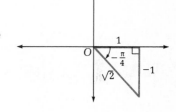

In the next example, it is not necessary to find the angle measure in order to evaluate the given expression.

EXAMPLE 2 Evaluate $\cos\left(\text{Arcsin }\dfrac{5}{13}\right)$.

Begin by letting $\theta = \text{Arcsin }\dfrac{5}{13}$. Since $0 < \dfrac{5}{13} < 1$, the angle is in quadrant I. Construct a reference triangle in the first quadrant, and use the Pythagorean theorem to find the third side, t.

$t = \sqrt{13^2 - 5^2} = \sqrt{169 - 25} = 12$

Then

$\cos\left(\text{Arcsin }\dfrac{5}{13}\right) = \cos \theta = \dfrac{12}{13}$

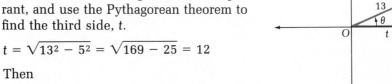

When graphing an inverse sine function, keep in mind the domain and range of $y = \text{Arcsin } x$. Also note that $y = \text{Arcsin } x$ is *not* a periodic function.

EXAMPLE 3   Find the domain and range of $y = 3 \text{ Arcsin } \frac{x}{2}$. Then graph the function.

Domain: $-2 \leq x \leq 2$ $-1 \leq \frac{x}{2} \leq 1$ and $-2 \leq x \leq 2$ are equivalent.

Range: $-\dfrac{3\pi}{2} \leq y \leq \dfrac{3\pi}{2}$ $-\frac{\pi}{2} \leq \text{Arcsin } \frac{x}{2} \leq \frac{\pi}{2}$ and
$-\frac{3\pi}{2} \leq 3 \text{ Arcsin } \frac{x}{2} \leq \frac{3\pi}{2}$ are equivalent.

Make a table of values for $-2 \leq x \leq 2$, and graph the function.

x	0	± 1	± 2
$\dfrac{x}{2}$	0	$\pm\dfrac{1}{2}$	± 1
$\text{Arcsin } \dfrac{x}{2}$	0	$\pm\dfrac{\pi}{6}$	$\pm\dfrac{\pi}{2}$
$3 \text{ Arcsin } \dfrac{x}{2}$	0	$\pm\dfrac{\pi}{2}$	$\pm\dfrac{3\pi}{2}$

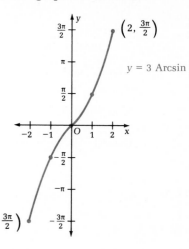

$\left(2, \frac{3\pi}{2}\right)$

$y = 3 \text{ Arcsin } \frac{x}{2}$

$\left(-2, -\frac{3\pi}{2}\right)$

CLASS EXERCISES

Evaluate, without using a table or a calculator.

1. $\text{Arcsin } (-1)$ **2.** $\text{Arcsin } \dfrac{\sqrt{2}}{2}$ **3.** $\text{Arcsin } 0$

4. $\text{Arcsin } \left(-\dfrac{1}{2}\right)$ **5.** $\text{Arcsin } \dfrac{\sqrt{3}}{2}$ **6.** $\text{Arcsin } 1$

Find the domain and the range of the function defined by each equation.

7. $y = \text{Arcsin } 2x$ **8.** $y = 2 \text{ Arcsin } x$ **9.** $y = \dfrac{1}{2} \text{ Arcsin } \dfrac{x}{2}$

EXERCISES

A   *Evaluate, without using a table or a calculator.*

1. $\text{Arcsin } \dfrac{1}{2}$ **2.** $\text{Arcsin } \left(-\dfrac{\sqrt{3}}{2}\right)$ **3.** $-\text{Arcsin } \dfrac{\sqrt{3}}{2}$

4. $-6 \text{ Arcsin } \dfrac{\sqrt{2}}{2}$ **5.** $2 \text{ Arcsin } (-1)$ **6.** $-4 \text{ Arcsin } \left(-\dfrac{1}{2}\right)$

Find the domain and the range of the function defined by each equation.

7. $y = 3 \text{ Arcsin } x$ **8.** $y = -3 \text{ Arcsin } x$ **9.** $y = \text{Arcsin } 3x$

10. $y = -\text{Arcsin } 3x$ **11.** $y = \frac{1}{2} \text{ Arcsin } 3x$ **12.** $y = \frac{3}{2} \text{ Arcsin } \frac{x}{3}$

Sketch the graph of each function. Show the coordinates of the endpoints of the curve.

13. $y = 2 \text{ Arcsin } x$ **14.** $y = -\text{Arcsin } x$ **15.** $y = \text{Arcsin } 2x$

B

16. $y = \text{Arcsin } 4x$ **17.** $y = \frac{1}{2} \text{ Arcsin } \frac{x}{2}$ **18.** $y = 4 \text{ Arcsin } \frac{x}{3}$

*Use the table on pages 672–676 to evaluate each expression in terms of radians **and** in terms of degrees.*

19. $\text{Arcsin } 0.3090$ **20.** $\text{Arcsin } 0.6225$ **21.** $\text{Arcsin}(-0.1536)$

Evaluate.

22. $\tan(\text{Arcsin } 0)$ **23.** $\tan\left(\text{Arcsin } \frac{\sqrt{2}}{2}\right)$ **24.** $\cos\left(\text{Arcsin } \frac{1}{2}\right)$

25. $\cos\left(\text{Arcsin}\left(-\frac{\sqrt{3}}{2}\right)\right)$ **26.** $\sin\left(\text{Arcsin } \frac{1}{2}\right)$ **27.** $\text{Arcsin}\left(\sin \frac{\pi}{4}\right)$

28. $\text{Arcsin}\left(\cos \frac{\pi}{3}\right)$ **29.** $\text{Arcsin}\left(\tan \frac{\pi}{4}\right)$ **30.** $\cos\left(\text{Arcsin } \frac{3}{5}\right)$

31. $\tan\left(\text{Arcsin } \frac{12}{13}\right)$ **32.** $\tan\left(\text{Arcsin } \frac{5}{13}\right)$ **33.** $\cos\left(\text{Arcsin } \frac{8}{17}\right)$

C

34. $\sin\left(\text{Arcsin } \frac{\sqrt{2}}{2} + \text{Arcsin } 1\right)$ **35.** $\tan\left(2 \text{ Arcsin } \frac{\sqrt{3}}{2}\right)$

Prove that each equation is an identity for $-1 \leq x \leq 1$.

Sample $\sin(\text{Arcsin } x) = x$

Let $\text{Arcsin } x = y$

Then $\sin(\text{Arcsin } x) = \sin y$
$\sin(\text{Arcsin } x) = x$ Since $\text{Arcsin } x = y$, then by definition,
$\sin y = x$.

36. $\cos(\text{Arcsin } x) = \sqrt{1 - x^2}$
Hint: Use the Pythagorean identity. Also, use the identity given above in the *sample*.

37. $\sin(2 \text{ Arcsin } x) = 2x\sqrt{1 - x^2}$
Hint: Use the double-angle formula for the sine. Also, use the identities in the *sample* and in Exercise 36.

*38. Sketch the graph of $y = \text{Arcsin}(-x)$. Then prove that the equation $\text{Arcsin}(-x) = -\text{Arcsin } x$ is an identity for $-1 \leq x \leq 1$.

13-7 The Inverse Cosine and Inverse Tangent Functions

The same procedure used to obtain the inverse sine function can be used to find the **inverse cosine** and **inverse tangent functions.** To graph the inverse cosine, we begin by restricting the domain of $y = \cos x$ to $0 \leq x \leq \pi$. Then we interchange the variables to obtain $x = \cos y$, or $y =$ **Arccos** x. **Arccos x** means *the arc whose cosine is x or the angle whose cosine is x.*

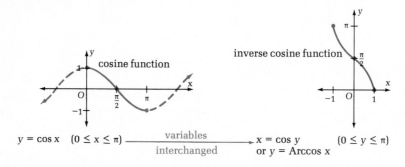

$y = \cos x \quad (0 \leq x \leq \pi)$ ——— variables interchanged ——→ $x = \cos y$ or $y =$ Arccos x $\quad (0 \leq y \leq \pi)$

The Inverse Cosine Function

$$y = \text{Arccos } x \qquad \text{(means } x = \cos y\text{)}$$

Domain: $-1 \leq x \leq 1$ Range: $0 \leq y \leq \pi$

The graph of $y =$ Arccos x shows the following properties of the function, which are useful when Arccos x is evaluated for specific values of x.

If $-1 < x < 0$, then $\dfrac{\pi}{2} < y < \pi$. The reference angle of measure y is in quadrant II.

If $0 < x < 1$, then $0 < y < \dfrac{\pi}{2}$. The reference angle of measure y is in quadrant I.

EXAMPLE 1 Evaluate Arccos $\frac{1}{2}$.

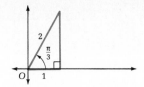

Arccos $\frac{1}{2}$ means *the angle whose cosine is* $\frac{1}{2}$. Since $0 < \frac{1}{2} < 1$, the angle is in quadrant I, and Arccos $\frac{1}{2} = \frac{\pi}{3}$.

To graph the inverse tangent function, we begin by restricting the domain to $-\frac{\pi}{2} < x < \frac{\pi}{2}$. Then we interchange the variables in $y = \tan x$ to obtain $x = \tan y$, or $y = $ Arctan x, where **Arctan x** means *the arc or angle whose tangent is* **x**.

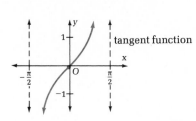

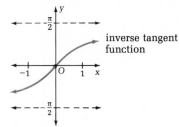

$$y = \tan x \ \left(-\frac{\pi}{2} < x < \frac{\pi}{2}\right) \xrightarrow[\text{interchanged}]{\text{variables}} x = \tan y \atop \text{or } y = \text{Arctan } x \ \left(-\frac{\pi}{2} < y < \frac{\pi}{2}\right)$$

Inverse Tangent Function

$$y = \textbf{Arctan } x \qquad \textbf{(means x = tan y)}$$

Domain: all real numbers   **Range:** $-\dfrac{\pi}{2} < y < \dfrac{\pi}{2}$

Note the following properties of the function $y = $ Arctan x.

If $x < 0$, then $-\dfrac{\pi}{2} < y < 0$.   The reference angle of measure y is in quadrant IV.

If $x > 0$, then $0 < y < \dfrac{\pi}{2}$.   The reference angle of measure y is in quadrant I.

EXAMPLE 2 Evaluate each expression.

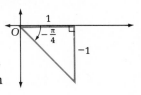

a. Arctan (−1)

Arctan (−1) means *the angle whose tangent is* −1. Since −1 < 0, the angle is in quadrant IV, and Arctan (−1) = $-\frac{\pi}{4}$.

b. $\sin\left(\text{Arctan } \dfrac{\sqrt{3}}{3} + \text{Arccos } \dfrac{\sqrt{2}}{2}\right) = \sin\left(\dfrac{\pi}{6} + \dfrac{\pi}{4}\right) = \sin\dfrac{\pi}{6}\cos\dfrac{\pi}{4} + \cos\dfrac{\pi}{6}\sin\dfrac{\pi}{4}$

$$= \dfrac{1}{2}\left(\dfrac{\sqrt{2}}{2}\right) + \dfrac{\sqrt{3}}{2}\left(\dfrac{\sqrt{2}}{2}\right) = \dfrac{1}{4}(\sqrt{2} + \sqrt{6})$$

EXAMPLE 3 Find the domain and range of $y = \frac{1}{2}$ Arctan $2x$. Then graph the function.

Domain: all real numbers

x is a real number if and only if
$2x$ is a real number.

Range: $-\frac{\pi}{4} < y < \frac{\pi}{4}$

$-\frac{\pi}{2} < $ Arctan $2x < \frac{\pi}{2}$ and
$-\frac{\pi}{4} < \frac{1}{2}$ Arctan $2x < \frac{\pi}{4}$ are equivalent.

Make a table of values and graph the function.

x	0	$\pm\frac{1}{2}$	$\pm\frac{\sqrt{3}}{2}$
$2x$	0	± 1	$\pm\sqrt{3}$
Arctan $2x$	0	$\pm\frac{\pi}{4}$	$\pm\frac{\pi}{3}$
$\frac{1}{2}$ Arctan $2x$	0	$\pm\frac{\pi}{8}$	$\pm\frac{\pi}{6}$

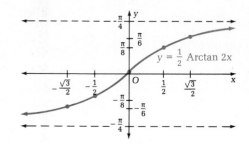

CLASS EXERCISES

Evaluate, without using a table or a calculator.

1. Arccos 0

2. Arccos $\frac{\sqrt{3}}{2}$

3. Arccos (-1)

4. Arctan 0

5. Arctan $(-\sqrt{3})$

6. Arctan 1

Find the domain and the range of the function defined by each equation.

7. $y = $ Arccos $4x$

8. $y = $ Arccos $\frac{x}{4}$

9. $y = $ Arctan $2x$

10. $y = 3$ Arccos x

11. $y = 2$ Arctan x

12. $y = \frac{1}{2}$ Arctan $3x$

EXERCISES

 A *Evaluate, without using a table or a calculator.*

1. Arccos 1

2. Arccos$\left(-\frac{\sqrt{3}}{2}\right)$

3. 2 Arccos$\left(-\frac{1}{2}\right)$

4. $\frac{1}{3}$ Arccos$\left(-\frac{\sqrt{2}}{2}\right)$

5. $\frac{1}{2}$ Arctan $\sqrt{3}$

6. 4 Arctan$\left(-\frac{\sqrt{3}}{3}\right)$

Find the domain and the range of the function defined by each equation.

7. $y = 2$ Arccos x

8. $y = 3$ Arctan x

9. $y = $ Arccos $2x$

10. $y = $ Arctan $3x$

11. $y = \frac{1}{2}$ Arccos $\frac{x}{2}$

12. $y = -$Arctan x

Sketch the graph of each function.

13. $y = 2 \text{ Arccos } x$ **14.** $y = 3 \text{ Arctan } x$ **15.** $y = \text{Arccos } 2x$

B   **16.** $y = \text{Arctan } \dfrac{x}{3}$ **17.** $y = \dfrac{1}{2} \text{ Arctan } \dfrac{x}{2}$ **18.** $y = -\text{Arccos } 4x$

*Use the table on pages 672–676 to evaluate each expression in terms of radians **and** in terms of degrees.*

19. $\text{Arccos } 0.4488$ **20.** $\text{Arccos}(-0.7771)$ **21.** $\text{Arctan } 0.2462$

Evaluate.

22. $\sin\left(\text{Arccos } \dfrac{\sqrt{3}}{2}\right)$ **23.** $\cos(\text{Arctan}(-1))$ **24.** $\tan\left(\text{Arctan } \dfrac{\sqrt{3}}{3}\right)$

25. $\cos\left(\text{Arccos } \dfrac{\sqrt{2}}{2}\right)$ **26.** $\sec\left(\text{Arccos}\left(-\dfrac{1}{2}\right)\right)$ **27.** $\cot(\text{Arctan } \sqrt{3})$

28. $\csc\left(\text{Arccos } \dfrac{3}{5}\right)$ **29.** $\sin\left(\text{Arctan}\left(-\dfrac{12}{5}\right)\right)$ **30.** $\cot\left(\text{Arccos } \dfrac{15}{17}\right)$

Use an appropriate sum, difference, or double-angle formula to evaluate each expression.

31. $\cos\left(\text{Arccos } \dfrac{1}{2} + \text{Arctan}(-1)\right)$ **32.** $\tan(\text{Arctan } 5 - \text{Arctan } 3)$

33. $\sin\left(\text{Arctan } \dfrac{5}{12} - \text{Arccos } \dfrac{3}{5}\right)$ **34.** $\tan\left(\text{Arccos } \dfrac{15}{17} + \text{Arctan } \dfrac{24}{7}\right)$

35. $\sin\left(2 \text{ Arctan } \dfrac{8}{15}\right)$ **36.** $\tan\left(2 \text{ Arccos } \dfrac{4}{5}\right)$

C   *Show that each equation is an identity.*

37. $\tan(\text{Arccos } x) = \dfrac{\sqrt{1 - x^2}}{x}$, for $0 < |x| \le 1$

***38.** $\sin(2 \text{ Arctan } x) = \dfrac{2x}{x^2 + 1}$, for all real x

CHECKPOINT

1. Solve $\sin x - \sqrt{3} \cos x = 0$ for x in radians, where $0 \le x \le 2\pi$.

2. Evaluate: $\cos\left(\text{Arcsin } \dfrac{\sqrt{3}}{2}\right)$ **3.** Evaluate: $\sin(\text{Arctan } (-1))$

4. Graph the function $y = -1 + \cos x$ for $0 \le x \le 2\pi$.

5. Graph: $y = -\text{Arcsin } 2x$ **6.** Graph: $y = \dfrac{1}{2} \text{ Arctan } \dfrac{x}{3}$

13-8 Complex Numbers in Trigonometric Form

To graph complex numbers in the complex plane.
To express a complex number x + yi in trigonometric form, and the
reverse.

A complex number written in the form x + yi is in *rectangular form.*
Such a number can be associated with a unique ordered pair of real
numbers (x, y). Consequently, it is possible to match complex numbers
with points in a rectangular system called a **complex plane.**

In the complex plane, the horizontal axis is called
the **real axis.** The points on this axis represent the real
numbers x. The vertical axis is called the **imaginary
axis.** The points on this axis represent the pure imaginary numbers yi. To locate the point for z = x + yi,
move x units from the origin horizontally, then y units
vertically. Draw an arrow from the origin to the point.

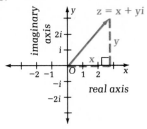

EXAMPLE 1   Graph the following complex numbers in the
same complex plane.

   a. **2 + 3i**   b. **−3 + 2i**

   c. **−1 − 4i**   d. **4 − 3i**

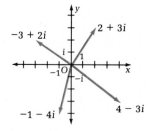

A complex number z = x + yi can also be located in the complex
plane if we know its distance from the origin and the angle it forms
with the positive real axis.

The distance from z to the origin is denoted by the
letter r and is found using the Pythagorean theorem.
r is also called the **modulus** of z or the *absolute
value of z.*

$$r = |z| = |x + yi| = \sqrt{x^2 + y^2}$$

From the reference triangle, we have

$$x = r \cos \theta \qquad y = r \sin \theta$$

Substituting the above values for x and y in the equation z = x + yi
produces the **trigonometric form** of z.

$$z = x + yi = r \cos \theta + (r \sin \theta)i$$
$$z = r(\cos \theta + i \sin \theta) \qquad \text{Trigonometric form}$$

The angle θ is called an **argument** of the complex number. The sine and cosine are periodic functions, so a given complex number z can be written in more than one way. For example, if $z = r\left(\cos \frac{\pi}{4} + i \sin \frac{\pi}{4}\right)$, we could write

$$z = r\left[\cos\left(\frac{\pi}{4} + 2\pi\right) + i \sin\left(\frac{\pi}{4} + 2\pi\right)\right]$$

However, in this text we will make the restriction that $0 \le \theta < 2\pi$, or $0° \le \theta < 360°$, in which case θ is called the **principal argument.**

EXAMPLE 2   Write the complex number $1 + i$ in trigonometric form, expressing θ in radians.

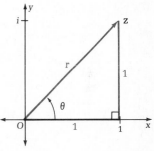

First draw the reference triangle and find the values of r and θ.

$r = \sqrt{1^2 + 1^2} = \sqrt{2}$

$\theta = \frac{\pi}{4}$

Then write the number in the form $r(\cos \theta + i \sin \theta)$.

$1 + i = \sqrt{2}\left(\cos \frac{\pi}{4} + i \sin \frac{\pi}{4}\right)$

EXAMPLE 3   Write the complex number $-1 - i\sqrt{3}$ in trigonometric form, expressing θ in degrees.

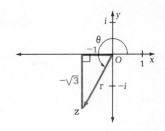

$r = \sqrt{(-1)^2 + (-\sqrt{3})^2} = \sqrt{1 + 3} = 2$

$\theta = 240°$

Then

$-1 - i\sqrt{3} = 2(\cos 240° + i \sin 240°)$

EXAMPLE 4   Write each complex number in rectangular form.

a. $\cos \frac{\pi}{2} + i \sin \frac{\pi}{2} = 0 + i(1) = i$

b. $\sqrt{2}\left(\cos \frac{7\pi}{4} + i \sin \frac{7\pi}{4}\right) = \sqrt{2}\left(\frac{\sqrt{2}}{2} - \frac{\sqrt{2}}{2}i\right) = 1 - i$

c. $5(\cos 50° + i \sin 50°) = 5(0.6428 + 0.7660i)$ Use the table on
$= 3.2140 + 3.8300i$ pages 672–676.

CLASS EXERCISES

Graph each complex number in the same complex plane.

1. $2 + 2i$ **2.** $-2 + 2i$ **3.** $3i$

4. $1 - i\sqrt{3}$ **5.** -3 **6.** $-\sqrt{2} - i\sqrt{2}$

Write each complex number in trigonometric form, expressing θ in radians.

7. $2 + 2i$　　　　　　　　**8.** $-2 + 2i$　　　　　　　　**9.** $3i$

Write each complex number in trigonometric form, expressing θ in degrees.

10. $1 - i\sqrt{3}$　　　　　　**11.** -3　　　　　　　　**12.** $-\sqrt{2} - i\sqrt{2}$

Write each complex number in rectangular form.

13. $2\left(\cos\dfrac{\pi}{3} + i\sin\dfrac{\pi}{3}\right)$　　　　　　　**14.** $10(\cos 180° + i\sin 180°)$

EXERCISES

A　Graph each set of complex numbers in the same complex plane.

1. $3 - 4i, \ -3 + 4i, \ -3 - 4i, \ 3 + 4i$

2. $-5 + 3i, \ -5 - 5i, \ \dfrac{3}{2} - \dfrac{3}{2}i, \ 2\sqrt{2} + 2i\sqrt{2}, \ 5i$

Write each complex number in trigonometric form, expressing θ in radians.

3. $-1 + i\sqrt{3}$　　**4.** $\sqrt{2} + i\sqrt{2}$　　**5.** $-1 - i$　　**6.** $5 + 5i$

7. $\sqrt{3} - i$　　　　**8.** $-1 + i$　　　　**9.** $\sqrt{3} + i$　　**10.** $1 + i\sqrt{3}$

Write each complex number in trigonometric form, expressing θ in degrees.

11. $-\sqrt{2} + i\sqrt{2}$　　**12.** $1 - i$　　　　**13.** $\sqrt{3} - i$　　**14.** $1 + i\sqrt{3}$

Write each complex number in rectangular form.

15. $\cos\dfrac{\pi}{4} + i\sin\dfrac{\pi}{4}$

16. $2\left(\cos\dfrac{3\pi}{4} + i\sin\dfrac{3\pi}{4}\right)$

17. $3\left(\cos\dfrac{\pi}{6} + i\sin\dfrac{\pi}{6}\right)$

18. $6\left(\cos\dfrac{11\pi}{6} + i\sin\dfrac{11\pi}{6}\right)$

19. $7(\cos 150° + i\sin 150°)$

20. $\dfrac{1}{2}(\cos 180° + i\sin 180°)$

21. $2(\cos 90° + i\sin 90°)$

22. $4(\cos 0° + i\sin 0°)$

B　Write each complex number in rectangular form. Use a table or a calculator.

23. $\cos 63° + i\sin 63°$

24. $2(\cos 141° + i\sin 141°)$

25. $3(\cos 235° + i\sin 235°)$

26. $4(\cos 287° + i\sin 287°)$

Write each complex number in trigonometric form, expressing θ in radians. Do not use a table or a calculator.

27. $\dfrac{\sqrt{3}}{2} + \dfrac{1}{2}i$　　**28.** $\dfrac{1}{2} - \dfrac{\sqrt{3}}{2}i$　　**29.** $\dfrac{\sqrt{2}}{3} + \dfrac{\sqrt{2}}{3}i$　　**30.** $-\dfrac{\sqrt{2}}{2} - \dfrac{\sqrt{2}}{2}i$

31. $2\sqrt{3} + 2i$　　**32.** $2 + 2i\sqrt{3}$　　**33.** $7i$　　　　　**34.** -12

Write each complex number in trigonometric form, expressing θ in degree measure to the nearest 10 minutes. Use a table or a calculator.

35. $4 + 3i$ **36.** $24 - 7i$ **37.** $-12 + 5i$ **38.** $-12 - 9i$

C

Let $w = 2 + 2i\sqrt{3}$ and $z = -1 - i\sqrt{3}$.

39. Evaluate $w \cdot z$, using the given rectangular forms.

40. Evaluate $w \cdot z$, using trigonometric forms. Verify that the result is the same as that obtained in Exercise 39.

41. Evaluate $\frac{w}{z}$, using the given rectangular forms.

42. Evaluate $\frac{w}{z}$, using trigonometric forms. Verify that the result is the same as that obtained in Exercise 41.

The *product formula* derived below simplifies the work involved in the multiplication of complex numbers in trigonometric form.

If $u = r(\cos \alpha + i \sin \alpha)$ and $v = s(\cos \beta + i \sin \beta)$, then

$uv = [r(\cos \alpha + i \sin \alpha)][s(\cos \beta + i \sin \beta)]$

$uv = rs[(\cos \alpha \cos \beta - \sin \alpha \sin \beta) + i(\sin \alpha \cos \beta + \cos \alpha \sin \beta)]$

$\boldsymbol{uv = rs[\cos(\alpha + \beta) + i \sin(\alpha + \beta)}$ product formula for complex numbers in trigonometric form

Note that the modulus of the product is the product of the moduli, and the argument of the product is the sum of the arguments. It is customary to convert to the principal argument when expressing the product.

Sample   Find uv, if $u = 2(\cos 150° + i \sin 150°)$ and $v = 3(\cos 240° + i \sin 240°)$. Then graph u, v, and uv.

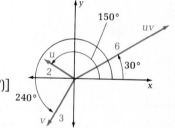

     product of the moduli   sum of the arguments

$uv = (2 \cdot 3)[\cos(150° + 240°) + i \sin(150° + 240°)]$

$uv = 6(\cos 390° + i \sin 390°)$

$uv = 6(\cos 30° + i \sin 30°)$ principal argument

43. For $u = 2 + 2i\sqrt{3}$ and $v = -1 - i\sqrt{3}$, evaluate uv using the rectangular forms and also using trigonometric forms. Verify that the two answers are equivalent. Then graph the trigonometric forms of u, v, and uv.

DeMoivre's Theorem states that if $u = r(\cos \theta + i \sin \theta)$ and n is a positive integer, then $u^n = r^n(\cos n\theta + i \sin n\theta)$.

*44. Use the product formula above to verify DeMoivre's Theorem for $n = 2$ and for $n = 3$. That is, show that $[r(\cos \theta + i \sin \theta)]^2 = r^2(\cos 2\theta + i \sin 2\theta)$ and $[r(\cos \theta + i \sin \theta)]^3 = r^3(\cos 3\theta + i \sin 3\theta)$.

*45. Write $u = 1 - i\sqrt{3}$ in trigonometric form. Then use DeMoivre's Theorem to find u^2, u^3, and u^8, and convert the answers to rectangular form.

STRATEGIES for PROBLEM SOLVING

Changing the Coordinate System

It is difficult to graph the equation $x^2 + y^2 = \sqrt{x^2 + y^2} + x$ using a rectangular coordinate system. However, if the equation is converted into *polar form*, it is easier to graph.

A point (x, y) with trigonometric form $r(\cos \theta + i \sin \theta)$ has *polar coordinates* (r, θ). A point with polar coordinates is graphed in a *polar system*, as shown at the right. For example, the point $P(2, 45°)$ is located by rotating a ray on the *polar axis* through $45°$. The point is 2 units from the *pole* on this ray. The point $Q(-2, 45°)$ is 2 units from the pole on the opposite ray.

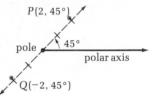

Note that there are many different polar coordinates for a point. To illustrate, the coordinates $(2, 405°)$ and $(-2, -135°)$ also name point P.

When rectangular and polar systems are superimposed, the relationship between the two types of coordinates can be observed.

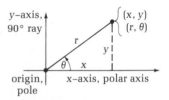

$$x = r \cos \theta$$
$$y = r \sin \theta$$
$$x^2 + y^2 = r^2$$

The equation $x^2 + y^2 = \sqrt{x^2 + y^2} + x$ can now be written in polar form.

$$x^2 + y^2 = \sqrt{x^2 + y^2} + x \longrightarrow r^2 = r + r \cos \theta \longrightarrow \mathbf{r = 1 + \cos \theta}$$

To graph the equation $r = 1 + \cos \theta$, make a table of values, plot the points in a polar system, and connect the points with a smooth curve.

θ	0°	45°	60°	90°	120°	180°
r	2.0	1.7	1.5	1.0	0.5	0.0

θ	180°	240°	270°	300°	315°	360°
r	0.0	0.5	1.0	1.5	1.7	2.0

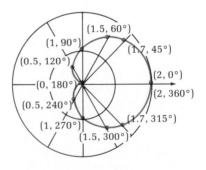

This curve is called a **cardioid.**

1. Plot the points $(3, 60°)$, $(-3, 60°)$, $(3, -60°)$, $(-3, -60°)$, $(3, 120°)$, and $(-3, 300°)$ in the same polar coordinate system.

2. Graph the equation $r = 4 \sin \theta$.

3. Graph the equation $r = 1 - \cos \theta$.

4. Write $x^2 + y^2 = 2x$ in polar form. Then graph the equation.

Linear and Angular Speeds

The circumference of a circle of radius r is $2\pi r$. A semicircle has length πr, and a quarter-circle has length $\frac{\pi}{2}r$. In general, in a circle of radius r, an arc intercepted by a central angle of θ radians has length $s = r\theta$, where θ is in radians and r and s are expressed in the same units.

The *linear speed* v of a point A on a circle is defined as

$$v = \frac{\text{linear distance}}{\text{time}} = \frac{s}{t}$$

The *angular speed* ω (the Greek letter *omega*) of the radial line OA is defined as the amount of angular rotation per unit of time.

$$\omega = \frac{\text{angular distance}}{\text{time}} = \frac{\theta}{t}$$

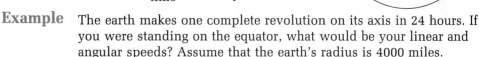

Example   The earth makes one complete revolution on its axis in 24 hours. If you were standing on the equator, what would be your linear and angular speeds? Assume that the earth's radius is 4000 miles.

$$v = \frac{s}{t} = \frac{r\theta}{t} = \frac{4000 \cdot 2 \cdot \pi}{24} \approx \frac{4000 \cdot 2 \cdot 3.14}{24} \approx 1047$$

The linear speed is 1047 miles per hour, to the nearest mile per hour.

$$\omega = \frac{\theta}{t} = \frac{2\pi}{24} = \frac{\pi}{12}$$

The angular speed is $\frac{\pi}{12}$ radians per hour.

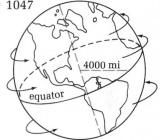

1. What are the angular speeds, in radians per minute, of the minute and hour hands of a clock? Express the answers in terms of π.

2. A satellite has a circular orbit 500 miles above the earth. One revolution around the earth takes 2 hours 30 minutes. What is the satellite's linear speed in miles per hour? (Use 4000 miles as the radius of the earth.)

3. The angular speed of a spoke of a wheel is 82 radians per minute. If the radius of the wheel is 20 inches, what is the linear speed of a point on the rim?

4. Karen rode her bicycle 7065 feet in 5 minutes. Find her linear speed in feet per minute. Also, find the angular speed of a spoke in one of the wheels, which has a 27-inch diameter. Express the answer in radians per minute.

CHAPTER 13 REVIEW

VOCABULARY

central angle (p. 504)
radian (p. 504)
trigonometric function (p. 509)
circular function (p. 509)
periodic function (p. 511)
period (p. 511)
cycle (p. 511)
sine wave (p. 511)
amplitude (p. 511)
asymptote (p. 519)
positive branch (p. 523)
negative branch (p. 523)
inverse sine function (p. 526)

Arcsin (p. 526)
inverse cosine function (p. 530)
Arccos (p. 530)
inverse tangent function (p. 531)
Arctan (p. 531)
rectangular form (p. 534)
complex plane (p. 534)
real axis (p. 534)
imaginary axis (p. 534)
modulus (p. 534)
trigonometric form (p. 534)
argument (p. 535)
principal argument (p. 535)

SUMMARY

This is the last of three chapters on trigonometry. The first section introduces radian measure, which is then used throughout the remainder of the chapter. The six trigonometric ratios are used to develop the six circular, or trigonometric, functions. Considerable emphasis is given to the study of their graphs, using the periodicity of the functions. The amplitudes and asymptotes are used as aids in sketching the graphs, where applicable.

After the circular functions have been studied, the inverse functions and their graphs are developed for the sine, cosine, and tangent. The chapter concludes with a section dealing with the use of the sine and cosine to obtain the trigonometric form of a complex number.

REVIEW EXERCISES

13-1   *Express in radians, using π.*

1. $210°$ **2.** $270°$ **3.** $-315°$ **4.** $0°$ **5.** $-150°$

Express each radian measure in degrees.

6. $\dfrac{\pi}{4}$ **7.** $\dfrac{\pi}{12}$ **8.** $-\dfrac{7\pi}{15}$ **9.** $-\dfrac{5\pi}{6}$ **10.** $\dfrac{3\pi}{5}$

Solve for x in radians, where $0 \leq x < 2\pi$.

11. $\cos x - \cos 2x = 0$ **12.** $2 \sin^2 x = \sqrt{2} \sin x$

13-2 Find the period and amplitude of each function.

13. $y = -3 \sin x$ 　　　　**14.** $y = \dfrac{1}{3} \cos x$ 　　　　**15.** $y = 5 - \cos x$

Graph each function for $0 \le x \le 2\pi$.

16. $y = \sin(-x)$ 　　　　**17.** $y = 2 - \dfrac{1}{2} \cos x$ 　　　　**18.** $y = 1 + \cos(-x)$

13-3 **19.** Find positive numbers a and b so that $y = a \sin bx$ has amplitude $\dfrac{1}{2}$ and period 2π.

20. Find positive numbers a and b so that $y = a \cos bx$ has amplitude 4 and period 4π.

Graph each function for $0 \le x \le 2\pi$.

21. $y = 5 \cos 2x$ 　　　　**22.** $y = 2 \sin \dfrac{x}{2}$ 　　　　**23.** $y = -\dfrac{3}{2} \sin \dfrac{2x}{3}$

13-4 Find the period p for each function. Then sketch the graph between $x = -p$ and $x = p$.

24. $y = -\cot x$ 　　　　**25.** $y = -2 \tan 2x$ 　　　　**26.** $y = \dfrac{1}{2} \cot \dfrac{x}{4}$

13-5 **27.** $y = \dfrac{1}{2} \sec \dfrac{x}{2}$ 　　　　**28.** $y = 3 \csc 2x$ 　　　　**29.** $y = 4 \sec 3x$

13-6 Evaluate, without using a table or a calculator.

30. Arcsin 1 　　　　**31.** $-\text{Arcsin } \dfrac{\sqrt{2}}{2}$ 　　　　**32.** 4 Arcsin (-1)

Sketch the graph of each function. Show the coordinates of the endpoints of the curve.

33. $y = -2 \text{ Arcsin } x$ 　　　　**34.** $y = \text{Arcsin } \dfrac{x}{2}$ 　　　　**35.** $y = 3 \text{ Arcsin } 2x$

Evaluate.

36. $\cos\left(\text{Arcsin } \dfrac{\sqrt{3}}{2}\right)$ 　　　　**37.** $\tan\left(\text{Arcsin } -\dfrac{\sqrt{2}}{2}\right)$ 　　　　**38.** $\cot\left(\text{Arcsin } \dfrac{1}{2}\right)$

13-7 Evaluate without using a table or a calculator.

39. Arccos (-1) 　　　　**40.** $\text{Arctan } \dfrac{\sqrt{3}}{3}$ 　　　　**41.** $-2 \text{ Arccos } \dfrac{1}{2}$

Sketch the graph of each function.

42. $y = \text{Arctan } 2x$ 　　　　**43.** $y = 2 \text{ Arccos } 3x$ 　　　　**44.** $y = -\text{Arctan } \dfrac{x}{3}$

Evaluate.

45. $\sec\left(\text{Arccos } \dfrac{3}{5}\right)$ **46.** $\cos\left[\text{Arctan }\left(-\dfrac{12}{5}\right)\right]$ **47.** $\tan\left(\text{Arccos } \dfrac{15}{17}\right)$

Write each complex number in trigonometric form, expressing θ in radians.

48. $1 - i\sqrt{3}$ **49.** $-\sqrt{2} - i\sqrt{2}$ **50.** $1 + i$ **51.** $-\sqrt{3} + i$

Write each complex number in rectangular form.

52. $\cos\dfrac{\pi}{3} + i\sin\dfrac{\pi}{3}$ **53.** $2\left(\cos\dfrac{\pi}{4} + i\sin\dfrac{\pi}{4}\right)$

54. $\dfrac{1}{2}(\cos 150° + i\sin 150°)$ **55.** $3[\cos(-90°) + i\sin(-90°)]$

Write each complex number in rectangular form. Use a table or a calculator.

56. $\cos 50° + i\sin 50°$ **57.** $5(\cos 95° + i\sin 95°)$

58. $\dfrac{1}{2}(\cos 260° + i\sin 260°)$ **59.** $10(\cos 325° + i\sin 325°)$

CHAPTER 13 TEST

1. Express each angle measure in radians, using π.
   a. 300°   **b.** −45°

2. Express each radian measure in degrees.
   a. $\dfrac{15\pi}{18}$ **b.** $\dfrac{13\pi}{15}$

3. Find the period and amplitude of the function $y = -3\cos x$. Then graph the function for $0 \le x \le 2\pi$.

4. Find positive numbers a and b so that $y = a\sin bx$ has amplitude 3 and period $\dfrac{\pi}{2}$.

*Find the period **p** for each function. Then sketch the graph between* $x = -p$ *and* $x = p$.

5. $y = -\tan\dfrac{x}{2}$ **6.** $y = 2\sec 3x$

Evaluate.

7. $\csc\left(\text{Arcsin } \dfrac{3}{5}\right)$ **8.** $\cos(\text{Arctan } \sqrt{3})$

9. Write the complex number $\sqrt{3} + i\sqrt{3}$ in trigonometric form.

10. Write the complex number $\cos\dfrac{2\pi}{3} + i\sin\dfrac{2\pi}{3}$ in rectangular form.

Trigonometric Functions

When many similar trigonometric problems must be solved, a computer can be helpful because BASIC contains programs to compute the sine, cosine, and tangent. The keywords for these functions are SIN(X), COS(X), and TAN(X). The value of X, however, must be expressed in radians on most computers.

To change a given number of degrees to radians, multiply by π and divide by 180. The program below uses 3.14 for π. If your computer has a key for π, you may use it in line 200.

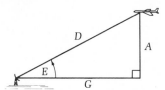

$$\sin E = \frac{A}{D}$$

$$D \sin E = A$$

At an airport, radar determines the distance D to an aircraft, and its angle of elevation E. A computer uses these values in the program below to determine the plane's altitude A to the nearest 10 units.

The Program	What It Does

```
100 REM ALTITUDE OF PLANE
110 PRINT "ENTER DISTANCE";
120 INPUT D
130 PRINT "ENTER ANGLE OF ELEVATION";
140 INPUT E
200 LET R = E * 3.14/180          Computes the number of radians.
210 LET A = D * SIN(R)            Computes the altitude.
220 LET A = INT(A/10 + .5) * 10   Rounds to nearest ten units.
230 PRINT "ALTITUDE IS "; A
900 END
```

What does this program display for each of these entries?

1. 6500 ft at 23° **2.** 5200 yd at 18° **3.** 55,100 ft at 27°
4. 8750 yd at 8.4° **5.** 7200 m at 31° **6.** 1075 m at 5.9°

7. What is the output for an entry of 3.6 miles at 24.7°? Modify line 220 so it rounds to the nearest tenth. What does the revised program display for this entry?

8. Modify the program ALTITUDE OF PLANE so that it also displays the ground distance G of the plane from the radar.

9. Write a program that displays the following, or its equivalent, for the angle entered:

```
ANGLE      SIN       COS        TAN
  41      .6561     .7547      .8693
```

For more information about BASIC, see the Computer Handbook at the back of the book.

PART I

Write the letter for the correct answer.

1. If $|x - 1| = 3$, then $x = $ _?_ .

   a. 4   **b.** -2 **c.** 2 or -2 **d.** 2 or 4   **e.** 4 or -2

2. Simplify: $(x^{-1} + y^{-1})^{-1}$

   a. $x + y$ **b.** $-x - y$ **c.** $\dfrac{1}{x} + \dfrac{1}{y}$ **d.** $\dfrac{xy}{x + y}$ **e.** $\dfrac{x - y}{x + y}$

3. The vertex of the parabola $y = \frac{3}{2}x^2 - 4$ has the coordinates _?_ .

   a. $(3, 2)$ **b.** $(0, -4)$ **c.** $(3, -4)$ **d.** $(0, 4)$ **e.** $(-4, 0)$

4. A rational root of $4x^4 + 8x^3 + 3x^2 + 10x + 5 = 0$ is _?_ .

   a. $-\dfrac{1}{2}$ **b.** 5   **c.** -2 **d.** -4 **e.** $\dfrac{1}{8}$

5. The center of the circle $x^2 - 4x + y^2 - 10y = 7$ has the coordinates _?_ .

   a. $(2, -5)$ **b.** $(-4, 5)$ **c.** $(-2, -5)$ **d.** $(2, 5)$ **e.** $(4, 10)$

6. If $8^{x^2} = 2^x$, then $x = $ _?_ .

   a. 0   **b.** 0 or $\dfrac{1}{9}$ **c.** 0 or $\dfrac{1}{3}$ **d.** $\dfrac{1}{3}$ or $-\dfrac{1}{3}$ **e.** $-\dfrac{1}{3}$

7. If $\log_2 x = 3$, then $x = $ _?_ .

   a. $\sqrt[3]{2}$ **b.** $\sqrt{3}$ **c.** 9   **d.** 8   **e.** $\dfrac{3}{2}$

8. If $\sin \theta = \dfrac{-3\sqrt{10}}{10}$ and $\cot \theta = \frac{1}{3}$, then $\sec \theta = $ _?_ .

   a. $-\sqrt{10}$ **b.** $-\dfrac{\sqrt{10}}{10}$ **c.** 3   **d.** $\dfrac{-3\sqrt{10}}{10}$ **e.** $-\dfrac{3}{10}$

9. The angle of depression from the top of a flagpole to a point 8 meters from its base is $60°$. The height of the flagpole is _?_ .

   a. $\dfrac{8\sqrt{3}}{3}$ m   **b.** 16 m   **c.** $\dfrac{16\sqrt{3}}{3}$ m   **d.** 4 m   **e.** $8\sqrt{3}$ m

10. If $\dfrac{\cos^2 \theta}{1 + \sin \theta} = 1$, where $0 \le \theta < 360°$, then $\theta = $ _?_ .

   a. $90°$ or $270°$ **b.** $0°$ or $90°$ **c.** $180°$ or $270°$ **d.** $270°$ or $0°$ **e.** $0°$ or $180°$

11. If $\sin x = \frac{4}{5}$ and $\cos x = -\frac{3}{5}$, then $\tan 2x = $ _?_ .

   a. $-\dfrac{24}{25}$ **b.** $-\dfrac{4}{3}$ **c.** $\dfrac{24}{7}$ **d.** $-\dfrac{3}{4}$ **e.** $-\dfrac{6}{7}$

12. The expression $\cot (\text{Arccos } 0) + \tan (\text{Arcsin } \frac{\sqrt{2}}{2})$ is equal to _?_ .

   a. 0   **b.** 1   **c.** -1 **d.** 2   **e.** -2

PART II

Write an equation for the line that has the given slope **m** and contains the given point.

13. $m = -2;\ (6, 6)$ **14.** $m = \frac{1}{4};\ (7, -4)$ **15.** $m = -\frac{3}{4};\ (0, 8)$

Solve each system.

16. $5x - 3y = 4$
    $6x + y = 14$

17. $\frac{3}{4}x - \frac{1}{2}y = 5$
    $\frac{1}{3}x + \frac{5}{6}y = -2$

18. $2x + y - 2z = -3$
    $x + 3y + z = 0$
    $4x - 2y - 3z = 0$

Factor completely.

19. $121 - 49x^2$ **20.** $16x^2 + 24x + 9$ **21.** $10xy - 20y^2 - 2x + 4y$

Solve.

22. $6x^2 - 7x + 2 = 0$ **23.** $x^2 + 2x = 2$ **24.** $6x^2 + x - 5 = 0$

Simplify.

25. $(3 - 2i)(4 + 5i)$ **26.** $i^{15} + i^{33}$ **27.** $\dfrac{1 - i}{1 - 2i}$

Classify each equation as that of a *circle*, *ellipse*, *parabola*, or *hyperbola*.

28. $4x^2 - 32x + y^2 + 2y + 49 = 0$ **29.** $x^2 - 10x + y^2 + 2y - 30 = 0$

Solve.

30. $\log_x 216 = 3$ **31.** $\log_6 x = -2$ **32.** $\log_2\left(\dfrac{1}{32}\right) = x$

The given point is on the terminal side of an angle θ in standard position. Find the six trigonometric functions of the angle.

33. $(-4, -3)$ **34.** $(-12, 5)$ **35.** $(6, -8)$

Solve for **x**, where $0° \leq x < 360°$.

36. $\sin x + \csc x = 2$ **37.** $\cot x = 2 \cos x$ **38.** $2\cos^2 x - 1 = \cos x$

Give the period, if any, of each function. Sketch the graph.

39. $y = -\sin \frac{1}{2}x$ **40.** $y = \tan \frac{1}{4}x$ **41.** $y = 3\,\text{Arccos}\,x$

Evaluate.

42. $\sin\left[\text{Arcsin}\,\frac{1}{2} + \text{Arccos}\,(-1)\right]$ **43.** $\cos\left(2\,\text{Arctan}\,\dfrac{\sqrt{3}}{3}\right)$

CHAPTER 14

Sequences and series are of interest to demographers, who study statistics relating to the characteristics and the distribution of populations.

SEQUENCES AND SERIES

Prerequisite Skills Review

Write the letter for the correct answer.

1. If $a = -4$, $n = 25$, and $d = -\dfrac{1}{2}$, then $a + (n - 1)d = \underline{\ ?\ }$.

   a. -16 b. 48 c. 8 d. -8

2. Solve the system: $\begin{array}{l} -1 = a + d \\ 11 = a + 5d \end{array}$

   a. $a = -3$, $d = 2$ b. $a = 1$, $d = 2$

   c. $a = -4$, $d = 3$ d. none of these

3. If $a = 3$, $n = 4$, and $r = -2$, then $ar^{n-1} = \underline{\ ?\ }$.

   a. -18 b. -216 c. 24 d. none of these

4. If $a = 1$, $n = 5$, and $r = \dfrac{1}{2}$, then $\dfrac{a(1 - r^n)}{1 - r} = \underline{\ ?\ }$.

   a. $\dfrac{31}{16}$ b. $\dfrac{1}{16}$ c. $\dfrac{15}{8}$ d. none of these

5. Which of the following is not equal to $\dfrac{2}{3}$?

   a. $0.\overline{6}$ b. $0.666\ldots$

   c. 0.67 d. $0.6 + 0.06 + 0.006 + \cdots$

6. $(x - 2)^0 + (x - 2)^1 + (x - 2)^2 = \underline{\ ?\ }$

   a. $x^2 - 2x$ b. $x^2 - 3x + 3$ c. $x^2 - x + 3$ d. $x^2 - 3x + 2$

7. $(x + 1)^3 = \underline{\ ?\ }$

   a. $x^3 + 3x^2 + 3x + 1$ b. $x^3 + 1$

   c. $x^3 + 2x^2 + 2x + 1$ d. $x^3 + 3x^2 + 4x + 2$

8. $\dfrac{9 \cdot 8 \cdot 7 \cdot 6 \cdot 5 \cdot 4}{1 \cdot 2 \cdot 3 \cdot 4 \cdot 5 \cdot 6} = \underline{\ ?\ }$

   a. 126 b. 84 c. 504 d. 28

9. $\dfrac{7 \cdot 6 \cdot 5 \cdot 4 \cdot 3 \cdot 2 \cdot 1}{(4 \cdot 3 \cdot 2 \cdot 1)(3 \cdot 2 \cdot 1)} = \underline{\ ?\ }$

   a. 210 b. 70 c. 42 d. 35

14-1 Sequences

OBJECTIVES

To write the first few terms of a sequence, given the mathematical rule.
To write a rule for a sequence, given the first few terms.

This set of numbers follows a pattern. Try to guess the next number.

$$2, 4, 8, 16, \ldots$$

A good choice for the next number would be 32. This would be a description of the pattern that is followed:

Start with 2. Each number thereafter
is twice the preceding number.

A set of ordered numbers is called a **sequence.** Each number is called a **term** of the sequence. To find a mathematical rule that describes the pattern in the sequence above, list each term with its position in the sequence. This diagram shows how each term is paired with a counting number.

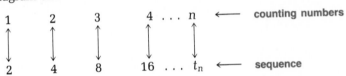

The rule tells how each counting number n is related to the nth term t_n in the sequence. For the example above, one rule that may be given is $t_n = 2^n$. To find the next three terms in the sequence, replace n with 5, 6, and 7.

$$t_5 = 2^5 = 32 \qquad \text{The fifth term is 32.}$$
$$t_6 = 2^6 = 64 \qquad \text{The sixth term is 64.}$$
$$t_7 = 2^7 = 128 \qquad \text{The seventh term is 128.}$$

To go from one term to the next in this sequence, multiply by 2. Thus, another way to write the mathematical rule is $t_{n+1} = 2t_n$, where $t_1 = 2$.

EXAMPLE 1 Find the first four terms in the sequence with the rule $t_n = 3n^2$.

$$t_1 = 3(1)^2 = 3$$
$$t_2 = 3(2)^2 = 12$$
$$t_3 = 3(3)^2 = 27$$
$$t_4 = 3(4)^2 = 48$$

The first four terms are 3, 12, 27, 48.

EXAMPLE 2 A sequence starts with 2. To go from one term to the next, add 3. The rule is $t_{n+1} = t_n + 3$, where $t_1 = 2$. Find the first five terms.

$t_1 = 2$
$t_2 = t_1 + 3 = 2 + 3 = 5$
$t_3 = t_2 + 3 = 5 + 3 = 8$
$t_4 = t_3 + 3 = 8 + 3 = 11$
$t_5 = t_4 + 3 = 11 + 3 = 14$
The first five terms in the sequence are 2, 5, 8, 11, 14.

Any sequence with a last term is called a **finite sequence.** If a sequence goes on without end, it has no last term. A sequence with no last term is called an **infinite sequence.**

EXAMPLE 3 Classify each sequence as finite or infinite. If finite, give the last term and the number of terms in the sequence.

a. 5, 10, 15, 20, 25, 30, 35, 40, 45, 50

The sequence is finite. The last term is 50, and there are 10 terms.

b. 5, 10, 15, 20, 25, . . . , 5000

The sequence is finite, and the last term is 5000. There are 1000 terms in all, but most of them have not been listed.

c. 5, 10, 15, 20, 25, . . .

The sequence is infinite. It continues without end, and there is no last term. Three dots following the last listed term mean that the sequence is infinite.

CLASS EXERCISES

Use the given rule to write the first four terms in the sequence.

1. $t_n = 4n$ **2.** $t_n = n + 11$ **3.** $t_n = 3n - 1$ **4.** $t_n = 2(n + 3)$

5. $t_n = 2^n - 1$ **6.** $t_n = 5(2)^n$ **7.** $t_n = (-2)^n$ **8.** $t_n = n^n$

9. $t_{n+1} = t_n + 6$, where $t_1 = 5$ **10.** $t_{n+1} = 3t_n - 2$, where $t_1 = 2$

*Classify the sequence as **finite** or **infinite.** If finite, give the last term and the number of terms in the sequence.*

11. 6, 10, 14, 18, 22, 26, 30   **12.** 10, 20, 30, 40, . . . , 200

13. 6, 11, 16, 21, . . .   **14.** 2, −4, 6, −8, . . . , −120

EXERCISES

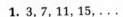

A Describe a pattern in the given sequence. Then write the next three terms.

1. 3, 7, 11, 15, . . .

2. 1, −1, 1, −1, . . .

3. −7, −5, −3, −1, . . .

4. 2, 5, 8, 11, . . .

5. 4, 2, 1, $\frac{1}{2}$, . . .

6. 8, 6, 4, 2, . . .

Classify the sequence as **finite** or **infinite**. If finite, give the last term and the number of terms in the sequence.

7. 1, 3, 5, 7, . . . , 25

8. 2, 8, 14, 20, . . .

9. 7, 27, 47, 67, 87, 107

10. 2, 4, 8, 16, . . . , 1024

Use the given rule to write the first three terms of the sequence.

11. $t_n = 3n$

12. $t_n = \frac{1}{n}$

13. $t_n = n + 7$

14. $t_n = 2n - 1$

15. $t_n = n^2 - 1$

16. $t_n = n(n + 2)$

17. $t_n = 2^n + 1$

18. $t_n = 3^n - 1$

19. $t_n = n(n^2 - 1)$

20. $t_n = (-1)^n$

21. $t_n = (-2)^{-n}$

22. $t_n = n^n + 1$

23. $t_{n+1} = t_n + 4$, where $t_1 = 3$

24. $t_{n+1} = t_n - 2$, where $t_1 = 2$

25. $t_{n+1} = 2t_n + 1$, where $t_1 = 1$

26. $t_{n+1} = (-1)t_n - 1$, where $t_1 = 4$

B Give a rule for the sequence by defining t_n.

27. 1, $\frac{1}{2}$, $\frac{1}{3}$, $\frac{1}{4}$, . . .

28. 1, 4, 9, 16, . . .

29. 3, 4, 5, 6, . . .

30. 2, 4, 6, 8, . . .

31. 3, 9, 27, 81, . . .

32. 1, −2, 3, −4, . . .

Give a rule for the sequence by naming t_1 and defining t_{n+1} in terms of t_n.

33. 1, 3, 5, 7, . . .

34. 20, 15, 10, 5, . . .

35. 1, −3, −7, −11, . . .

36. $\frac{1}{2}$, $1\frac{1}{4}$, 2, $2\frac{3}{4}$, . . .

37. 5, −10, 20, −40, . . .

38. 2, 3, 5, 9, . . .

39. It is important to describe a sequence by its rule, since there can be more than one sequence that begins with the same terms. To illustrate, find the first five terms in the sequence with the rule $t_n = \frac{n^3 - 3n^2 + 8n}{3}$. Compare your results with the first five terms of the sequence with the rule $t_n = 2^n$, which is described on page 548.

C Write the next three terms of each sequence. Describe the pattern you used.

40. 1, 2, 5, 10, 17, . . .

41. 0, 1, 3, 6, 10, . . .

42. −16, 8, −4, 2, −1, . . .

43. 1, $\frac{2}{3}$, $\frac{3}{5}$, $\frac{4}{7}$, $\frac{5}{9}$, . . .

44. $\frac{1}{2}$, $\frac{3}{4}$, $\frac{7}{8}$, $\frac{15}{16}$, $\frac{31}{32}$, . . .

45. $\frac{1}{2}$, $\frac{4}{3}$, $\frac{9}{4}$, $\frac{16}{5}$, $\frac{25}{6}$, . . .

14-2 Arithmetic Sequences

OBJECTIVES _____

To write specified terms of an arithmetic sequence, given the first few
  terms, the first term and the common difference, or two terms and their
  numerical positions in the sequence.
To insert a given number of arithmetic means between two numbers, and
  to find *the* arithmetic mean of the given numbers.

A radio station is sponsoring a contest with a cash
prize. The prize is $10 during the first hour of the
contest and is increased by $5 each hour until it is
won. The amount of the prize for the first 6 hours
is shown in this table.

Hour	1st	2nd	3rd	4th	5th	6th
Amount	10	15	20	25	30	35

The corresponding sequence

$$10, 15, 20, 25, 30, 35$$

is an *arithmetic sequence*. An **arithmetic sequence,** or **arithmetic
progression,** is a sequence in which each term after the first is obtained
by adding a constant d to the preceding term. In the sequence above,
this **common difference** d is 5.

Suppose a is the first term of an arithmetic sequence, and the common difference is d. Then $t_{n+1} = t_n + d$. The sequence may be written

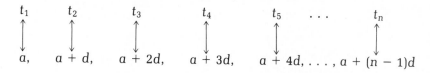

$$t_1 \qquad t_2 \qquad t_3 \qquad t_4 \qquad t_5 \quad \ldots \qquad t_n$$

$$a, \qquad a + d, \qquad a + 2d, \qquad a + 3d, \qquad a + 4d, \ldots, a + (n - 1)d$$

The **nth term in an arithmetic sequence with first term a and common
difference d is given by**

$$t_n = a + (n - 1)d$$

EXAMPLE 1   State whether the sequence is or is not an arithmetic sequence.

a. 3, 9, 15, 21

Find the differences between successive terms.

$t_2 - t_1 = 9 - 3 = 6$
$t_3 - t_2 = 15 - 9 = 6$
$t_4 - t_3 = 21 - 15 = 6$

The differences are equal, so it *is* an arithmetic sequence.

b. 3, 9, 16, 24

Again, find the differences between successive terms.

$t_2 - t_1 = 9 - 3 = 6$
$t_3 - t_2 = 16 - 9 = 7$
$t_4 - t_3 = 24 - 16 = 8$

The differences are not equal, so it *is not* an arithmetic sequence.

EXAMPLE 2   The first term of an arithmetic sequence is 5 and the common difference is 2. List the first seven terms, using the given rule.

5, 7, 9, 11, 13, 15, 17   Add 2 to each term to find the next term.

EXAMPLE 3   A finite arithmetic sequence has 20 terms. The first term is 7 and the common difference is -3. Find the last term.

Substitute in the formula $t_n = a + (n - 1)d$.

$t_{20} = 7 + (20 - 1)(-3)$ $n = 20, a = 7, d = -3$
$\quad\ = 7 + 19(-3)$
$\quad\ = 7 + (-57)$
$\quad\ = -50$

The last, or twentieth, term is -50.

Note that it is possible, but tedious, to check the answer in Example 3 by writing all of the terms of the sequence.

7,   4,   1, -2, -5, -8, -11, -14, -17, -20,

-23, -26, -29, -32, -35, -38, -41, -44, -47, **-50**⟵ twentieth term

EXAMPLE 4   Determine the numerical position of the term 74 in the infinite arithmetic sequence 2, 6, 10, 14, ...

Substitute in the formula $t_n = a + (n - 1)d$ and solve for n.

$74 = 2 + (n - 1)4$ $t_n = 74, a = 2, d = 4$
$72 = (n - 1)4$
$18 = n - 1$
$19 = n$

74 is the 19th term of the sequence.

EXAMPLE 5

The third term of an arithmetic sequence is -7 and the ninth term is 11. Find the seventh term.

Substitute in the formula $t_n = a + (n - 1)d$ to obtain a system of two equations in two variables, a and d.

$$-7 = a + 2d \qquad t_3 = a + (3 - 1)d$$
$$\underline{11 = a + 8d} \qquad t_9 = a + (9 - 1)d$$
$$-18 = -6d \qquad \text{Subtract, and solve for } d.$$
$$3 = d$$

$$-7 = a + 2(3) \qquad \text{Substitute 3 for } d \text{ in one of the above equations,}$$
$$-13 = a \qquad\qquad \text{and solve for } a.$$

Finally, use the formula to find t_7, where $d = 3$ and $a = -13$.

$$t_7 = -13 + (7 - 1)3 = 5 \qquad \text{The seventh term is 5.}$$

The terms between any two nonconsecutive terms of an arithmetic sequence are called **arithmetic means.** If there is a single arithmetic mean between two numbers, it is called **the arithmetic mean,** or the **average** of the numbers.

The arithmetic mean of two numbers p and q is $\dfrac{p + q}{2}$.

EXAMPLE 6

a. **Find *the* arithmetic mean of 16 and 46.**

$$\frac{p + q}{2} = \frac{16 + 46}{2} = \frac{62}{2} = 31 \qquad \text{The arithmetic mean is 31.}$$

b. **Insert four arithmetic means between 16 and 46.**

16, __, __, __, __, 46

Substitute known values in $t_n = a + (n - 1)d$ and solve for d.

$$46 = 16 + (6 - 1)d \qquad t_n = 46, \ a = 16, \ n = 6$$
$$6 = d \qquad\qquad \text{The common difference is 6.}$$

16, $\underline{22}$, $\underline{28}$, $\underline{34}$, $\underline{40}$, 46 \qquad The means are 22, 28, 34, and 40.

CLASS EXERCISES

State whether the sequence is or is not an arithmetic sequence. If it is an arithmetic sequence, identify the first term and the common difference.

1. 2, 4, 6, 8

2. 7, 4, 1, −2

3. 1, 3, 6, 10

4. 4, 4, 4, 4

5. 2, 4, 8, 16

6. −4, −1, 2, 5

*State the first three terms of the arithmetic sequence with the given values of **a** and **d**.*

7. $a = 1, d = 8$

8. $a = 5, d = -3$

9. $a = -1, d = \dfrac{1}{2}$

EXERCISES

A State whether the finite sequence is or is not an arithmetic sequence.

1. 15, 10, 5, 0

2. 5, 11, 17, 23

3. 7, 9, 11, 9

4. −5, −2, 1, 4

5. 2, 3, 5, 8

6. −1, −3, −5, −7

7. $\frac{1}{6}, \frac{1}{3}, \frac{1}{2}, \frac{2}{3}$

8. $1, \frac{1}{2}, \frac{1}{3}, \frac{1}{4}$

9. −2, 4, −6, 8

Write the next three terms of the infinite arithmetic sequence.

10. 7, 5, 3, . . .

11. 5, 2, −1, . . .

12. 8, 7.5, 7, . . .

13. −3, −4$\frac{1}{2}$, −6, . . .

14. −$\sqrt{3}$, 0, $\sqrt{3}$, . . .

15. 6 − i, 6, 6 + i, . . .

Write the first three terms of the arithmetic sequence with the given values.

16. $a = 2, d = 4$

17. $a = -7, d = 3$

18. $a = -9, d = 5$

19. $a = 8, d = -3.5$

20. $a = 4, d = 1 - \sqrt{3}$

21. $a = -i, d = -1.5$

Each finite arithmetic sequence has 15 terms. Find the last term.

22. −10, −7, −4, . . . , __

23. 1, 5, 9, . . . , __

24. −6, −5.5, −5, . . . , __

Find **the** arithmetic mean of the two numbers.

25. 12 and 38

26. 16.7 and 19.3

27. 2 + i and 4 − 3i

B Determine the numerical position of the term 24 in each arithmetic sequence.

28. −1, 4, 9, . . .

29. −9, −6, −3, . . .

30. 80, 76, 72, . . .

31. −25, −18, −11, . . .

32. 4, 5$\frac{1}{3}$, 6$\frac{2}{3}$, . . .

33. 41$\frac{1}{2}$, 39, 36$\frac{1}{2}$, . . .

Find the 31st term of the arithmetic sequence.

34. $-7 + 2\sqrt{2}, -5 + \sqrt{2}, -3, \ldots$

35. 3 + i, 2 − i, 1 − 3i, . . .

36. x + 3y, 3x + 2y, 5x + y, . . .

37. $a - \frac{1}{2}b, \frac{2}{3}a, \frac{1}{3}a + \frac{1}{2}b, \ldots$

Insert the indicated number of arithmetic means between the two numbers.

38. two, between 14 and 23

39. three, between −3 and 18

40. five, between 4 and 29

41. four, between 5 and 27$\frac{1}{2}$

Find the 6th term of the arithmetic sequence containing the given terms.

42. $t_2 = -7, t_8 = 23$

43. $t_5 = 1, t_8 = -26$

44. $t_8 = 19, t_{11} = 33\frac{1}{2}$

C **45.** After the first bank deposit, each successive monthly deposit is increased by the same amount. If the fifth deposit was $41 and the tenth was $76, which deposit was $160?

14-3 Arithmetic Series

OBJECTIVES _____

To find the sum of the first n terms of an arithmetic series.
To write the expanded form of an arithmetic series given in summation
notation, and then find the sum.

_____

A contractor pays a penalty for not completing a project before a given
date. He is billed $400 for the first extra day, and the daily charge is
increased $75 each day thereafter until the project is completed. What
is the total penalty charged if it takes six extra days to finish the
project?

The daily penalty charges form an arithmetic sequence with a first
term of 400 and a common difference of 75.

> daily penalties   400,   475,   550,   625,   700,   775

The total penalty is the sum of the six terms of this sequence.

> total penalty $400 + 475 + 550 + 625 + 700 + 775$

The indicated sum of the terms of an arithmetic sequence is called an
arithmetic series. Add the six terms shown in the series above to find
the total penalty, $3525.

When there is a relatively large number of terms, it is not convenient
to simply add them. The example below shows one way to find the
sum S_n of the first n terms of an arithmetic series.

EXAMPLE 1   Find the sum of the first 100 counting numbers.

First write the series. Then rewrite the series by reversing the order of
the terms. When the equations are added, each term on the right side
of the new equation is 101.

$$S_{100} = 1 + 2 + 3 + \ldots + 98 + 99 + 100 \leftarrow \text{original series}$$
$$\underline{S_{100} = 100 + 99 + 98 + \ldots + 3 + 2 + 1} \leftarrow \text{terms reversed}$$
$$2S_{100} = 101 + 101 + 101 + \ldots + 101 + 101 + 101 \leftarrow \text{sum}$$
$$2S_{100} = 100 \cdot 101 \qquad \text{There are 100 terms. Each term is 101.}$$
$$2S_{100} = 10{,}100$$
$$S_{100} = \frac{10{,}100}{2}$$
$$S_{100} = 5050$$

The sum is 5050.

The same method can be used to find the sum of the first n terms of any arithmetic series. Let the first term be a, the nth term t_n, and the common difference d. Then the sum of the first n terms is given by S_n.

$$S_n = a + (a + d) + (a + 2d) + \ldots + (t_n - 2d) + (t_n - d) + t_n \quad \text{terms}$$
$$S_n = t_n + (t_n - d) + (t_n - 2d) + \ldots + (a + 2d) + (a + d) + a \leftarrow \text{reversed}$$
$$2S_n = (a + t_n) + (a + t_n) + (a + t_n) + \ldots + (a + t_n) + (a + t_n) + (a + t_n)$$
$$2S_n = n(a + t_n) \qquad \text{There are } n \text{ terms. Each term is } a + t_n.$$
$$S_n = \frac{n}{2}(a + t_n) \qquad \text{The sum is equivalent to } n \text{ times the average of the first and last terms.}$$

The sum of the first n terms of an arithmetic series with first term a and nth term t_n is given by

$$S_n = \frac{n}{2}(a + t_n)$$

EXAMPLE 2   Find the sum of the first 15 terms of the arithmetic series in which the first term is -10 and the 15th term is 68.

Substitute in the formula for S_n.

$$S_{15} = \frac{15}{2}(-10 + 68) = \frac{15}{2}(58) = 435 \qquad n = 15, \, a = -10, \, t_n = 68$$

EXAMPLE 3   Find the sum of the arithmetic series $8 + 11 + 14 + 17 + \ldots + 47$.

First find n using the formula for t_n.

$$t_n = a + (n - 1)d$$
$$47 = 8 + (n - 1)3 \qquad a = 8, \, d = 3, \, t_n = 47$$
$$14 = n$$

Then substitute in the formula for S_n.

$$S_{14} = \frac{14}{2}(8 + 47) = 7(55) = 385$$

Another formula for S_n can be derived by substituting $a + (n - 1)d$ for t_n.

$$S_n = \frac{n}{2}(a + t_n)$$

$$S_n = \frac{n}{2}(a + [a + (n - 1)d])$$

$$S_n = \frac{n}{2}[2a + (n - 1)d]$$

EXAMPLE 4   Find the sum of the first 30 odd counting numbers.

$$S_n = \frac{n}{2}[2a + (n - 1)d] = \frac{30}{2}[2(1) + (30 - 1)2] = 900 \qquad n = 30, a = 1, d = 2$$

For the series in Example 4, the general kth term is $2k - 1$, which can be found as follows:

$$t_k = 1 + (k - 1)2 = 2k - 1$$

The series can then be described using the **summation notation** represented by the Greek letter Σ (*sigma*).

Read: the summation from 1 to 30 of $2k - 1$

$$S_{30} = \sum_{k=1}^{30}(2k - 1) = [2(1) - 1] + [2(2) - 1] + \ldots + [2(29) - 1] + [2(30) - 1]$$

$$= 1 + 3 + \ldots + 57 + 59 \qquad \text{Expanded form}$$

$$= 900 \qquad \text{Sum}$$

You can think of Σ as a *command to add*. To write the given series in *expanded form*, you replace k with the integers 1 through 30, in order, and write the indicated sum. To find the *sum*, you add the terms of the indicated sum, or use one of the formulas for the sum.

EXAMPLE 5   Write $\sum_{k=1}^{4}(3k + 1)$ in expanded form. Then find the sum.

$$\sum_{k=1}^{4}(3k + 1) = [3(1) + 1] + [3(2) + 1] + [3(3) + 1] + [3(4) + 1]$$

$$= 4 + 7 + 10 + 13 \qquad \text{Expanded form}$$

$$= 34 \qquad \text{Sum}$$

CLASS EXERCISES

Find the sum for each arithmetic series.

1. $5 + 10 + 15 + 20 + 25 + 30 + 35$ **2.** $\sum_{k=1}^{4} 3k$ **3.** $\sum_{k=1}^{5}(2k + 1)$

Find S_n for each arithmetic series.

4. $a = 4, n = 7, t_n = 40$ **5.** $a = 10, n = 20, d = -2$

EXERCISES

A   *Find the sum for each arithmetic series.*

1. $9 + 21 + 33 + 45 + 57 + 69$ **2.** $5.7 + 7.1 + 8.5 + 9.9 + 11.3$

3. the first 100 terms, where $a = 0$ and $t_{100} = 99$

4. the first 50 terms, where $a = 4$ and $t_{50} = 196$

5. the first 21 terms, where $a = 20$ and $t_{21} = 400$

Find the number of terms in the arithmetic series. Then find S_n.

6. $2 + 4 + 6 + 8 + \ldots + 60$

7. $5 + 11 + 17 + 23 + \ldots + 101$

8. $10 + 20 + 30 + 40 + \ldots + 500$

9. $46 + 43 + 40 + \ldots + 16$

Find t_n and S_n for each arithmetic series.

10. $a = 3, d = 9, n = 20$

11. $a = 8, d = 7, n = 12$

12. $a = -4, d = 10, n = 15$

13. $a = 0, d = 25, n = 60$

Write the arithmetic series in expanded form. Then find the sum.

14. $\sum\limits_{k=1}^{5} 5k$

15. $\sum\limits_{k=1}^{6} (10 - k)$

16. $\sum\limits_{k=1}^{8} (2k - 3)$

17. $\sum\limits_{k=1}^{4} \left(\dfrac{4 - k}{2} \right)$

B

Find the indicated sum for each arithmetic series.

18. the first 40 counting numbers

19. the first 30 positive multiples of 5

20. the first 20 positive multiples of 50

21. the first 150 terms in $1 + 2 + 3 + \ldots$

22. the first 20 terms in $-4 - 9 - \ldots$

23. the first 15 terms in $8 + 1 - \ldots$

24. $\sum\limits_{k=1}^{25} (5k + 6)$ 1775 **25.** $\sum\limits_{k=1}^{11} (11 - 4k)$

26. $\sum\limits_{k=1}^{50} \left(\dfrac{k - 3}{3} \right)$ 375 **27.** $\sum\limits_{k=1}^{35} \left(\dfrac{2k + 1}{2} \right)$

28. A contractor pays a $150 penalty for the first extra day she takes to complete a job. The daily charge is increased $60 each extra day thereafter. What is the total penalty if she takes 5 extra days? if she takes 15 extra days?

29. A bookkeeper earned $12,200 his first year on a job and received a raise of $675 each year thereafter. What did he earn during his 12th year on the job? How much did he earn in all during the 12 years?

C

Find the sum of the first 10 terms of the arithmetic series in which

30. $t_5 = 15$ and $t_{10} = 45.$

31. $t_7 = 7$ and $t_{10} = 13.$

32. $t_6 = -5$ and $t_{12} = 10.$

CHECKPOINT

Use the given rule to write the first three terms in the sequence.

1. $t_n = 5n$

2. $t_n = 1 - n$

3. $t_n = 2n + 1$

4. $t_n = 3^n - 1$

5. Find the 20th term of the arithmetic sequence 3, 8, 13, ...

6. Write $\sum\limits_{k=1}^{10} (3k - 2)$ in expanded form. Then find the sum.

Using Successive Differences

The solutions to many problems can be found through the recognition of number patterns. One useful method involves *successive differences*.

The first five *triangular numbers* are shown here. It appears that each of the second differences is 1. If that is the case, then the first differences always increase by 1. It follows that the next first difference would be 6, and hence the next triangular number would be 21.

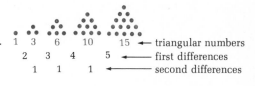

You should readily recognize this sequence of *square numbers*. Look at the successive differences. It appears that each second difference is 2. Then the next first difference would be 11, giving 36 as the next square number.

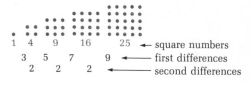

The first two pentagonal numbers are 1 and 5. Successive second differences are always 3.

1. Write the first four first differences.

2. Write the first five pentagonal numbers.

The first two hexagonal numbers are 1 and 6. Successive second differences are always 4.

3. Write the first five first differences.

4. Write the first six hexagonal numbers.

Every triangular, square, pentagonal, and hexagonal number can be expressed as the sum of a finite arithmetic series. Use this idea to write a formula for

5. the nth triangular number.
6. the nth square number.

7. the nth pentagonal number.
8. the nth hexagonal number.

Consider a sequence of octagonal numbers.

9. The second differences are constant. What would you guess is their value?

10. Write the first seven first differences.

11. Write the first eight octagonal numbers.

12. Write a formula for the nth octagonal number.

14-4 Geometric Sequences

OBJECTIVES _____

To write specified terms of a geometric sequence, given the first few
  terms, the first term and the common ratio, or two terms and their
  numerical positions in the sequence.
To insert a given number of geometric means between two numbers, and
  to find *the* geometric mean of the given numbers.

A certain bacteria count starts at 100, and it doubles every hour. The
number of bacteria each hour after that is 2 times the number in the
preceding hour.

Hour	1st	2nd	3rd	4th	5th	6th
Number	100	200	400	800	1600	3200

The corresponding sequence, 100, 200, 400, 800, 1600, 3200, . . . , is
a *geometric sequence*. A **geometric sequence,** or **geometric progression,**
is a sequence in which each term after the first is obtained by multiplying the preceding term by a constant r. In the geometric sequence
above, this **common ratio** r is 2.

Suppose a is the first term of a geometric sequence and the common
ratio of the terms is r. Then the sequence may be written

$$t_1 \quad t_2 \quad t_3 \quad t_4 \quad t_5 \ldots \quad t_n$$

$$a, \quad ar, \quad ar^2, \quad ar^3, \quad ar^4, \ldots, ar^{n-1}$$

> **The nth term in a geometric sequence with first term a and common
> ratio r is given by**
> $$t_n = ar^{n-1}$$

EXAMPLE 1   State whether 5, -10, 20, -40 is or is not a geometric sequence.

Find the ratios of successive terms.

$$\frac{t_2}{t_1} = \frac{-10}{5} = -2 \qquad \frac{t_3}{t_2} = \frac{20}{-10} = -2 \qquad \frac{t_4}{t_3} = \frac{-40}{20} = -2$$

The sequence *is* geometric, with the common ratio $r = -2$.

EXAMPLE 2

The first term of a geometric sequence is 54, and the common ratio is $\frac{2}{3}$. Find the first six terms.

$$t_1 = 54 \qquad\qquad t_2 = \frac{2}{3}(54) = 36 \qquad t_3 = \frac{2}{3}(36) = 24$$

$$t_4 = \frac{2}{3}(24) = 16 \qquad t_5 = \frac{2}{3}(16) = \frac{32}{3} \qquad t_6 = \frac{2}{3}\left(\frac{32}{3}\right) = \frac{64}{9}$$

The first six terms are: 54, 36, 24, 16, $\frac{32}{3}$, $\frac{64}{9}$.

EXAMPLE 3

The first three terms of a geometric sequence are $\frac{1}{27}$, $\frac{2}{9}$, and $\frac{4}{3}$. Find the sixth term.

The common ratio r can be found by dividing any term of the sequence by the preceding term.

$$r = \frac{t_2}{t_1} = \frac{\frac{2}{9}}{\frac{1}{27}} = \frac{2}{9} \cdot \frac{27}{1} = 6 \qquad r = \frac{t_3}{t_2} = \frac{\frac{4}{3}}{\frac{2}{9}} = \frac{4}{3} \cdot \frac{9}{2} = 6$$

The common ratio is $r = 6$. Substitute in the formula $t_n = ar^{n-1}$.

$$t_6 = \left(\frac{1}{27}\right)(6^{6-1}) = \left(\frac{1}{27}\right)(6^5) = 288$$

The sixth term is 288.

The terms between any two nonconsecutive terms of a geometric sequence are called **geometric means.** In Example 3, the four geometric means between $\frac{1}{27}$ and 288 are $\frac{2}{9}$, $\frac{4}{3}$, 8, and 48. You can verify this by showing that each term after the first in the sequence $\frac{1}{27}$, $\frac{2}{9}$, $\frac{4}{3}$, 8, 48, 288 is 6 times the preceding term.

EXAMPLE 4

Find three geometric means between $\frac{1}{8}$ and 32.

$$\frac{1}{8}, \underline{\quad}, \underline{\quad}, \underline{\quad}, 32$$

Substitute known values in $t_n = ar^{n-1}$, and solve for r.

$$32 = \left(\frac{1}{8}\right)(r^{5-1}) \qquad t_5 = 32$$
$$256 = r^4$$
$$\pm 4 = r \qquad \text{There are two solutions.}$$

If $r = 4$, the sequence is $\frac{1}{8}$, $\frac{1}{2}$, 2, 8, 32, and the three geometric means are $\frac{1}{2}$, 2, and 8. If $r = -4$, the sequence is $\frac{1}{8}$, $-\frac{1}{2}$, 2, -8, 32, and the three geometric means are $-\frac{1}{2}$, 2, and -8.

If there is a single geometric mean between two numbers, it is called **the geometric mean**, or the **mean proportional**, of the numbers. The geometric mean between two numbers p and q is either $\sqrt{pq}$ or $-\sqrt{pq}$.

CLASS EXERCISES

*Find the common ratio **r** for each geometric sequence.*

1. 2, 4, 8, 16, . . .   **2.** −3, 6, −12, 24, . . .   **3.** 5, 5, 5, 5, . . .

4. 6000, −1200, 240, −48, . . .   **5.** 0.7, 0.07, 0.007, 0.0007, . . .

What are the next three terms in the geometric sequence?

6. 2, 6, 18, . . .   **7.** $\frac{1}{2}, \frac{1}{6}, \frac{1}{18}, \ldots$ **8.** 24, −12, 6, . . .

EXERCISES

A   *State whether the given sequence is or is not a geometric sequence.*

1. 5, 10, 15, 20   **2.** 9, 9, 9, 9   **3.** 1, 4, 9, 16

4. 16, 24, 36, 54   **5.** $1, \frac{1}{2}, \frac{1}{4}, \frac{1}{8}$ **6.** 10, 20, 30, 40

7. 6, −6, 6, −6   **8.** 14, 7, 14, 7   **9.** 2, 0.2, 0.02, 0.002

*Write the first three terms of the geometric sequence with the given values of **a** and **r**.*

10. $a = 5, r = 2$ **11.** $a = 6, r = -2$ **12.** $a = -4, r = 3$

13. $a = \frac{3}{8}, r = 4$ **14.** $a = 6, r = \frac{2}{3}$ **15.** $a = 8, r = 0.1$

16. $a = 0.1, r = 20$ **17.** $a = \sqrt{3}, r = 2\sqrt{3}$ **18.** $a = i, r = -i$

Write the next three terms in the geometric sequence.

19. 7, 14, 28, . . .   **20.** 64, 32, 16, . . .   **21.** 40, −20, 10, . . .

22. 27, 18, 12, . . .   **23.** $-\frac{1}{6}, -\frac{1}{3}, -\frac{2}{3}, \ldots$ **24.** −8, −0.8, −0.08, . . .

Find the specified term of the geometric sequence.

25. 5th term of 5, 10, 20, . . .   **26.** 10th term of 2, 4, 8, . . .

27. 7th term of −3, 6, −12, . . .   **28.** 8th term of $-\frac{1}{9}, -\frac{1}{3}, -1, \ldots$

29. 9th term of 96, 48, 24, . . .   **30.** 6th term of 108, 18, 3, . . .

31. 7th term of 1, 0.2, 0.04, . . .   **32.** 5th term of 0.96, 0.24, 0.06, . . .

*Find **the positive geometric mean** of*   *Find **the negative geometric mean** of*

33. 16 and 9.   **34.** 8 and $\frac{1}{2}$.   **35.** −3 and −27.   **36.** −0.1 and −40.

B   *Find the missing terms in each geometric sequence.*

37. 2, 6, __, __   **38.** 1, 4, __, __   **39.** __, 15, 5, __

40. __, 18, __, 2   **41.** __, 12, __, 108   **42.** __, 9, −27, __

43. Find two geometric means between $\frac{1}{6}$ and 36.

44. Find four geometric means between -3 and -96.

45. Find three geometric means between 3 and 48. Give two answers.

46. Find three geometric means between $-\frac{1}{2}$ and -648. Give two answers.

47. A bacteria count starts at 500 and doubles every hour. What is the count at the beginning of the 4th hour? the 8th hour?

48. A laboratory technician was hired at an annual salary of $20,000 and was promised a 10% raise for each successive year. What will her salary be for the 3rd year? the 5th year?

C *Find the 5th term of the geometric sequence containing the given terms.*

49. $t_2 = 27,\ t_3 = 81$ **50.** $t_1 = -5,\ t_4 = \dfrac{1}{25}$ **51.** $t_7 = -32,\ t_{10} = 256$

Determine the numerical position of the term 2 in each geometric sequence.

52. $\dfrac{81}{8},\ \dfrac{27}{4},\ \dots$ **53.** $0.016,\ 0.08,\ \dots$ **54.** $32,\ 16\sqrt{2},\ \dots$

USING THE CALCULATOR

The Fibonacci Sequence

The **Fibonacci sequence** is neither an arithmetic nor a geometric sequence. The first two terms are 1 and 1. Each term thereafter is found by adding the two preceding terms. The sequence continues without end.

$$1,\quad 1,\quad 2,\quad 3,\quad 5,\quad 8,\quad 13,\quad 21,\quad 34,\quad \dots$$

Use a calculator to do the calculations required in these exercises.

1. Find the 15th term of the Fibonacci sequence. Find the 25th term.

Another sequence can be formed by taking these ratios of successive terms in the Fibonacci sequence: $\dfrac{1}{1},\ \dfrac{1}{2},\ \dfrac{2}{3},\ \dfrac{3}{5},\ \dfrac{5}{8},\ \dfrac{8}{13},\ \dots$

2. Write decimals for the first 12 such ratios, to six decimal places.

3. Study the results in Exercise 2. Are the terms always decreasing, always increasing, or alternately decreasing and increasing? Discuss the absolute value of the difference between successive terms.

4. It can be shown that as you write more and more terms of the Fibonacci sequence, the ratio of successive terms approaches $\dfrac{2}{1 + \sqrt{5}}$. Evaluate $\dfrac{2}{1 + \sqrt{5}}$ on a calculator. Compare it with the last decimal written for Exercise 2.

14-5 Geometric Series

To find the sum of the first n terms of a geometric series.
To write the expanded form of a geometric series given in summation notation, and then find the sum.

A **geometric series** is the indicated sum of the terms of a geometric sequence. Thus, for every geometric sequence there is a corresponding geometric series.

geometric sequences			corresponding geometric series
	$9, 3, 1, \dfrac{1}{3}$	$9 + 3 + 1 + \dfrac{1}{3}$	
	$1, 2, 4, 8, \ldots$	$1 + 2 + 4 + 8 + \ldots$	

The sum S_n of the first n terms of a geometric series can be found by addition. However, another method is shown in the following example.

EXAMPLE 1

Find the sum of this geometric series:

$$1 + 2 + 4 + 8 + 16 + 32 + 64 + 128 + 256 + 512 + 1024$$

First write the series with sum S_n. Then multiply by the common ratio $r = 2$ to obtain the related series with sum $2S_n$. When the second series is subtracted from the first, all terms become 0 except the first and the last. Solve the resulting equation for S_n.

$$S_n = 1 + 2 + 4 + 8 + 16 + 32 + 64 + 128 + 256 + 512 + 1024$$
$$2S_n = 2 + 4 + 8 + 16 + 32 + 64 + 128 + 256 + 512 + 1024 + 2048$$
$$\overline{S_n - 2S_n = 1 + 0 + 0 + 0 + 0 + 0 + 0 + 0 + 0 + 0 + 0 - 2048}$$
$$(1 - 2)S_n = 1 - 2048$$
$$S_n = \frac{-2047}{-1} = 2047 \qquad \text{The sum is 2047.}$$

The same method can be used to find the sum of any finite geometric series. For a geometric series with first term a and common ratio r, the sum of the first n terms, S_n, is given on the first line below.

$$S_n = a + ar + ar^2 + ar^3 + \ldots + ar^{n-2} + ar^{n-1} \qquad \text{Original series}$$
$$rS_n = ar + ar^2 + ar^3 + \ldots + ar^{n-2} + ar^{n-1} + ar^n \qquad \text{Multiply by } r.$$
$$\overline{S_n - rS_n = a + 0 + 0 + 0 + \ldots + 0 + 0 - ar^n} \qquad \text{Subtract.}$$
$$(1 - r)S_n = a(1 - r^n)$$
$$S_n = \frac{a(1 - r^n)}{1 - r} \qquad (r \neq 1)$$

The sum of the first n terms of a geometric series with first term a and common ratio r is given by

$$S_n = \frac{a(1 - r^n)}{1 - r}$$

EXAMPLE 2

Use the formula to find the sum of this geometric series:

$$24 - 8 + \frac{8}{3} - \frac{8}{9} + \frac{8}{27}$$

There are 5 terms, starting with 24, so $n = 5$ and $a = 24$.
The value of r is found by dividing any term by the preceding term.

$$r = \frac{-8}{24} = -\frac{1}{3}$$

Then $S_5 = \dfrac{24\left[1 - \left(-\dfrac{1}{3}\right)^5\right]}{1 - \left(-\dfrac{1}{3}\right)} = \dfrac{24\left(1 + \dfrac{1}{243}\right)}{\dfrac{4}{3}} = \dfrac{488}{27} = 18\dfrac{2}{27}$

A geometric series may also be expressed using *summation notation*.

EXAMPLE 3

Write each geometric series in expanded form. Then find the sum.

a. $\displaystyle\sum_{k=1}^{4} 5^k = 5^1 + 5^2 + 5^3 + 5^4 = 5 + 25 + 125 + 625 = 780$

b. $\displaystyle\sum_{k=1}^{4} 5^{-k} = 5^{-1} + 5^{-2} + 5^{-3} + 5^{-4} = \frac{1}{5} + \frac{1}{25} + \frac{1}{125} + \frac{1}{625} = \frac{156}{625}$

CLASS EXERCISES

Use the formula to find the sum S_n for each geometric series.

1. $a = 4, r = 3, n = 5$

2. $a = -1, r = -2, n = 8$

3. $a = \dfrac{1}{2}, r = -\dfrac{1}{3}, n = 6$

4. $a = -9, r = -3, n = 4$

5. $25 - 5 + 1 - \dfrac{1}{5} + \dfrac{1}{25}$

6. $\dfrac{1}{100} + \dfrac{1}{10} + 1 + 10 + 100 + 1000$

7. the first 5 terms of $\dfrac{3}{2} + 1 + \dfrac{2}{3} + \ldots$

8. the first 6 terms of $3 + \dfrac{3}{2} + \dfrac{3}{4} + \ldots$

EXERCISES

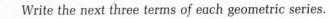

A Write the next three terms of each geometric series.

1. $3 + 6 + 12 + \ldots$ **2.** $2 + 8 + 32 + \ldots$ **3.** $-2 + 4 - 8 + \ldots$

4. $\dfrac{1}{2} + \dfrac{3}{2} + \dfrac{9}{2} + \ldots$ **5.** $-8 + 3 - \dfrac{9}{8} + \ldots$ **6.** $1 + \dfrac{1}{5} + \dfrac{1}{25} + \ldots$

Use the formula to find the sum S_n for each geometric series.

7. $a = 5, r = 2, n = 6$ **8.** $a = 3, r = -2, n = 7$

9. $a = -2, r = 3, n = 5$ **10.** $a = 4, r = \dfrac{1}{4}, n = 4$

11. $a = 1, r = 0.1, n = 5$ **12.** $a = -4, r = -1, n = 9$

13. the first 6 terms of $1 + 3 + \ldots$ **14.** the first 10 terms of $2 - 4 + \ldots$

15. the first 15 terms of $-1 + 1 - \ldots$ **16.** the first 5 terms of $\dfrac{1}{9} + \dfrac{1}{3} + \ldots$

B **17.** $\displaystyle\sum_{k=1}^{5} 2^k$ **18.** $\displaystyle\sum_{k=1}^{6} \left(\dfrac{1}{3}\right)^k$ **19.** $\displaystyle\sum_{k=1}^{4} (-4)^k$ **20.** $\displaystyle\sum_{k=1}^{7} (-1)^{-k}$

21. the first 8 terms of $3 + 0.3 + 0.03 + \ldots$

22. the first 5 terms of $3 - \dfrac{9}{2} + \dfrac{27}{4} - \ldots$

23. the first 9 terms of $12 - 6 + 3 - \ldots$

Write the series in expanded form and find the sum. Indicate whether the series is **arithmetic, geometric,** or **neither.**

24. $\displaystyle\sum_{k=1}^{5} 4^k$ **25.** $\displaystyle\sum_{k=1}^{5} k^4$ **26.** $\displaystyle\sum_{k=1}^{4} 4^{-k}$ **27.** $\displaystyle\sum_{k=1}^{5} 4k$

C Find the sum of each finite geometric series.

28. $2 + 4 + 8 + \ldots + 1024$ **29.** $\dfrac{1}{25} + \dfrac{1}{5} + 1 + \ldots + 625$

30. $0.01 - 0.1 + 1 - \ldots + 1{,}000{,}000$ **31.** $\dfrac{25}{64} + \dfrac{5}{8} + 1 + \ldots + \dfrac{64}{25}$

Write the geometric series using summation notation.

32. $1 + 5 + 25 + 125$ **33.** $1 - 2 + 4 - 8 + 16 - 32$

34. $\dfrac{1}{4} + 1 + 4 + 16 + 64$ **35.** $64 - 16 + 4 - 1 + \dfrac{1}{4}$

*36. A \$1500 investment earns 1% interest per month. The interest is also invested at the same rate. Find the total interest earned over a two-year period.

Mathematical Induction

Some number patterns can become apparent by studying specific cases. For example, consider the pattern at the right, which may be familiar to you.

$$1 = 1^2$$
$$1 + 3 = 2^2$$
$$1 + 3 + 5 = 3^2$$

From these specific cases we can guess that the sum of the first n odd numbers is n^2. The nth odd number can be written as $2n - 1$, so the general form for this pattern would be

$$1 + 3 + 5 + \ldots + 2n - 1 = n^2$$

However, a guess or suspicion based on a finite number of specific cases is not a proof. How, then, can it be proved that the pattern holds for *all* counting numbers n? One way to prove it is to use **mathematical induction.**

Principle of Mathematical Induction

To prove a statement about all counting numbers, both of the following conditions must be established.

I. The statement is true for the number $n = 1$.

II. Whenever the statement is true for the number $n = k$, then it must follow that it is true for the number $n = k + 1$.

This principle is analogous to the process of knocking down a long row of dominoes, all standing so that the distance between any pair is less than the height of a domino.

Comparison with Mathematical Induction   **Condition I Fails**   **Condition II Fails**

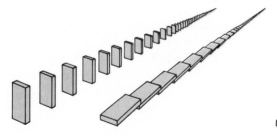

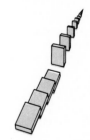

Push the first, and all will eventually fall.

The first cannot knock down the second. The "chain reaction" cannot start.

The "chain reaction" cannot continue because another pair is too far apart.

To illustrate the use of this principle, here is the proof that $1 + 3 + \ldots + 2n - 1 = n^2$ is true for every counting number n.

I. Since $1 = 1^2$, the statement is true for $n = 1$.

II. To prove that the kth case implies the $(k + 1)$st case, assume that the statement is true for $n = k$.

$$1 + 3 + \ldots + (2k - 1) = k^2$$

Add the next odd number, $2k - 1 + 2 = 2k + 1$, to each side.

A $1 + 3 + \ldots + (2k - 1) + (2k + 1) = k^2 + (2k + 1)$

Substitute $k + 1$ for n in the original equation, $1 + 3 + \ldots + 2n - 1 = n^2$, and show that the resulting equation is equivalent to equation **A**.

$$1 + 3 + \ldots + 2(k + 1) - 1 = (k + 1)^2$$
B $1 + 3 + \ldots + 2k + 1 = k^2 + 2k + 1$

Equations **A** and **B** are equivalent. This completes the proof of part II. Since parts I and II have been established, the principle of mathematical induction assures us that $1 + 3 + \ldots + 2n - 1 = n^2$ is true for all counting numbers n.

*Now you try it! Use mathematical induction to prove that each statement is true for all counting numbers **n**.*

1. $1 + 2 + 3 + \ldots + n = \dfrac{n(n + 1)}{2}$

   a. Show that the statement is true for $n = 1$, by substituting 1 for n.

   b. Show that if the statement is true for $n = k$, then it is true for $n = k + 1$. Substitute k for n in the given equation and add $k + 1$ to each side. Show that the result is equivalent to the equation obtained by substituting $k + 1$ for n in the original equation.

2. $1(2) + 2(3) + 3(4) + \ldots + n(n + 1) = \dfrac{n(n + 1)(n + 2)}{3}$

   a. Test the statement for $n = 1$.

   b. Test it for $n = k + 1$, given that it is true for $n = k$. Begin by substituting k for n and adding $(k + 1)(k + 2)$ to each side. Compare the result with that obtained by a direct substitution of $k + 1$ for n.

3. $2 + 4 + 6 + \ldots + 2n = n(n + 1)$ **4.** $5 + 5^2 + 5^3 + \ldots + 5^n = \dfrac{5^{n+1} - 5}{4}$

5. $\dfrac{1}{2} + \dfrac{1}{4} + \dfrac{1}{8} + \ldots + \dfrac{1}{2^n} = 1 - \dfrac{1}{2^n}$ **6.** $1^3 + 2^3 + \ldots + n^3 = \dfrac{n^2(n + 1)^2}{4}$

7. $\dfrac{1}{1(2)} + \dfrac{1}{2(3)} + \dfrac{1}{3(4)} + \ldots + \dfrac{1}{n(n + 1)} = \dfrac{n}{n + 1}$

8. $1^2 + 2^2 + 3^2 + \ldots + n^2 = \dfrac{n(n + 1)(2n + 1)}{6}$

9. $a + ar + ar^2 + \ldots + ar^{n-1} = \dfrac{a(1 - r^n)}{1 - r}, r \neq 0$

14-6 Infinite Geometric Series

OBJECTIVE

To determine whether a given infinite geometric series has a finite sum, and to find that sum if it exists.

Infinite geometric series have terms that go on without end. Can you find the sum of this infinite geometric series, with terms that are powers of 2?

$$2 + 4 + 8 + 16 + 32 + 64 + 128 + \ldots$$

Notice that the sum of the first two terms is 6. The sum of the first three terms is 14, and the sum of the first four terms is 30. These **partial sums** are all finite. However, they become greater and greater, without bound. It would be impossible to find a finite sum for the infinite number of terms of this entire series.

Here is another infinite geometric series.

$$0.3 + 0.03 + 0.003 + 0.0003 + 0.00003 + 0.000003 + \ldots$$

It is clear that this is equivalent to the infinite repeating decimal $0.333333\ldots$, or $0.\overline{3}$, which is equal to $\frac{1}{3}$.

$$0.3 + 0.03 + 0.003 + 0.0003 + 0.00003 + 0.000003 + \ldots = \frac{1}{3}$$

Hence it *is* possible to have an infinite series that has a finite sum.

Consider the partial sum S_n of another infinite geometric series.

$$1 + \frac{1}{2} + \frac{1}{4} + \frac{1}{8} + \ldots$$

nth partial sum, for the first n terms $\qquad S_n = \dfrac{a(1 - r^n)}{1 - r} = \dfrac{1\left[1 - \left(\frac{1}{2}\right)^n\right]}{1 - \frac{1}{2}}$

Any counting number can be used for n. The values of r^{10} and r^{20}, and the 10th and 20th partial sums, are approximated below.

For the 10th partial sum, $n = 10$. $\qquad r^{10} = \left(\dfrac{1}{2}\right)^{10} = \dfrac{1}{1024} \approx 0.001 \qquad S_{10} \approx 1.998$

For the 20th partial sum, $n = 20$. $\qquad r^{20} = \left(\dfrac{1}{2}\right)^{20} = \dfrac{1}{1,048,576} \approx 0.000001 \qquad S_{20} \approx 1.999998$

The value of $r^n = \left(\frac{1}{2}\right)^n$ approaches 0 as n becomes very large. As a result, as n increases without bound, the partial sum S_n approaches 2.

In general, for any infinite geometric series with $|r| < 1$, r^n approaches 0 as n becomes large without bound. Also,

$$S_n = \frac{a(1 - r^n)}{1 - r} \text{ approaches } S = \frac{a}{1 - r}$$

The sum of an infinite geometric series with first term a and common ratio r, where $|r| < 1$, is given by

$$S = \frac{a}{1 - r}$$

EXAMPLE 1

Find the finite sum, if it exists, of the geometric series

$$2 - 1 + \frac{1}{2} - \frac{1}{4} + \frac{1}{8} - \ldots$$

This is an infinite geometric series with $a = 2$ and $r = -\frac{1}{2}$. Since $\left| -\frac{1}{2} \right| < 1$, the sum exists. Use the formula $S = \frac{a}{1 - r}$.

$$S = \frac{2}{1 - \left(-\frac{1}{2} \right)} = \frac{2}{\frac{3}{2}} = \frac{4}{3} = 1\frac{1}{3}$$

The sum is $1\frac{1}{3}$. That is, $2 - 1 + \frac{1}{2} - \frac{1}{4} + \frac{1}{8} - \ldots = 1\frac{1}{3}$.

EXAMPLE 2

Find the finite sum, if it exists, of the geometric series

$$0.9 + 0.009 + 0.00009 + \ldots$$

This is an infinite geometric series with $a = 0.9$ and $r = 0.01$. Since $|0.01| < 1$, the sum exists.

$$S = \frac{0.9}{1 - 0.01} = \frac{0.9}{0.99} = \frac{10}{11}$$

The sum is $\frac{10}{11}$. That is, $0.9 + 0.009 + 0.00009 + \ldots = \frac{10}{11}$.

EXAMPLE 3

Find the finite sum, if it exists, of the geometric series

$$1 + 3 + 9 + \ldots$$

This is an infinite geometric series with $a = 1$ and $r = 3$. Since $|3| > 1$, the series has no finite sum.

CLASS EXERCISES

Determine whether or not each infinite geometric series has a finite sum. Then find that sum, if it exists.

1. $3 + 6 + 12 + \ldots$

2. $9 + 3 + 1 + \ldots$

3. $1 + 0.1 + 0.01 + \ldots$

4. $1 - \frac{1}{6} + \frac{1}{36} - \ldots$

5. $10 + 5 + \frac{5}{2} + \ldots$

6. $2 - 4 + 8 - \ldots$

7. $-\frac{3}{7} - \frac{9}{28} - \frac{27}{112} - \ldots$

8. $8 + 10 + \frac{25}{2} + \ldots$

9. $40 + 0.4 + 0.004 + \ldots$

EXERCISES

A

Determine whether each infinite geometric series has a finite sum. Then find that sum, if it exists.

1. $5 + 10 + 20 + \ldots$
2. $\frac{1}{3} + \frac{1}{6} + \frac{1}{12} + \ldots$
3. $8 - 32 + 128 - \ldots$

4. $6 + 3 + \frac{3}{2} + \ldots$
5. $\frac{1}{4} + \frac{1}{12} + \frac{1}{36} + \ldots$
6. $5 - 15 + 45 - \ldots$

7. $7 - \frac{7}{2} + \frac{7}{4} - \ldots$
8. $-\frac{3}{4} - \frac{1}{4} - \frac{1}{12} - \ldots$
9. $-6 + 18 - 54 + \ldots$

10. $8 + 6 + \frac{9}{2} + \ldots$
11. $9 + 6 + 4 + \ldots$
12. $-\frac{2}{3} + \frac{1}{3} - \frac{1}{6} + \ldots$

Find the sum of the infinite geometric series with given values of **a** and **r**. If the series has no finite sum, state why.

13. $a = 6, r = -\frac{1}{2}$
14. $a = -7, r = -3$
15. $a = -6, r = \frac{1}{3}$

16. $a = -24, r = -\frac{1}{6}$
17. $a = -2, r = -2$
18. $a = -0.3, r = -0.5$

19. $a = -4, r = -\frac{3}{4}$
20. $a = \frac{1}{2}, r = 6$
21. $a = -\frac{2}{3}, r = 9$

B

Find the sum of the infinite geometric series with given values of **a** and **r**. Write each sum as a repeating decimal.

22. $a = 5, r = 0.4$
23. $a = 8, r = 0.1$
24. $a = 0.7, r = 0.1$

25. $a = 0.15, r = 0.01$
26. $a = 0.63, r = 0.01$
27. $a = 0.125, r = 0.001$

28. $a = 0.16, r = 0.01$
29. $a = 0.4, r = 0.1$
30. $a = 0.01, r = 0.01$

31. A force is applied to a particle moving in a straight line in such a fashion that each second it moves one-half the distance it moved the preceding second. If the particle moves 20 centimeters the first second, how far can it move?

32. Each side of an equilateral triangle is 10 centimeters long. The midpoints of the sides are joined to form an inscribed equilateral triangle. Then the midpoints of the sides of that triangle are joined to form another triangle, and the process is continued. Find the sum of the perimeters of the triangles, if the process is continued without end.

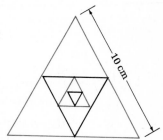

33. Air resistance causes the path of each swing of a pendulum ball to be 0.9 times the length of the preceding swing. If the path of the first swing is 50 centimeters long, find the total distance traveled by the ball before coming to rest.

C

34. A ball returns two-thirds of the distance it falls on each bounce. If the ball is dropped from a height of 6 meters and always bounces in the same place, find the distance through which it travels before coming to rest.

35. A rubber ball dropped 15 meters rebounds on each bounce two-fifths of the height from which it fell. How many meters will it travel, bouncing in place, before coming to rest?

Write each repeating decimal in the form $\frac{p}{q}$, where p and q are integers.
Use the formula for the finite sum of an infinite geometric series.

Sample $0.\overline{24}$ First write the decimal as an infinite geometric series, where $a = 0.24$ and $r = 0.01$.

$$0.\overline{24} = 0.242424\ldots = 0.24 + 0.0024 + 0.000024 + \ldots$$

Then find the sum of the series.

$$S = \frac{0.24}{1 - 0.01} = \frac{0.24}{0.99} = \frac{8}{33} \quad \text{Thus, } 0.\overline{24} = \frac{8}{33}$$

36. $0.\overline{7}$ **37.** $0.\overline{17}$ **38.** $0.\overline{207}$ **39.** $1.\overline{1}$

40. $1.\overline{36}$ **41.** $5.\overline{162}$ **42.** $0.0\overline{5}$ **43.** $0.2\overline{36}$

CHECKPOINT

1. Give a rule for the sequence $1, \frac{1}{4}, \frac{1}{9}, \frac{1}{16}, \ldots$ by defining t_n.

2. Find the number of terms in the arithmetic series $\frac{1}{2} + 1 + 1\frac{1}{2} + \ldots + 100$. Then find the sum of the terms.

3. Find the sixth term of the geometric sequence $0.5, -0.25, 0.125, \ldots$.

4. Find the numerical position of the term $-\frac{5}{243}$ in the geometric sequence $-15, -5, -\frac{5}{3}, \ldots$.

5. Find two arithmetic means between 108 and 256. Then find two geometric means between the same two given numbers.

6. Find the sum of the first 10 terms of the geometric series $192 + 96 + 48 + \ldots$.

7. Write $\sum\limits_{k=1}^{4} (-2)^k$ in expanded form. Then find the sum.

8. Write $\sum\limits_{k=1}^{4} k^{-2}$ in expanded form. Then find the sum.

14-7 Pascal's Triangle and the Binomial Theorem

To write a binomial expansion using patterns observed in Pascal's
  triangle, or using the binomial theorem.
To find specified terms of a binomial expansion.

An important type of series that is neither arithmetic nor geometric is
obtained by the expansion of $(a + b)^n$, where n is a nonnegative integer.

$(a + b)^n$	Expansion
$(a + b)^0 =$	1
$(a + b)^1 =$	$a + b$
$(a + b)^2 =$	$a^2 + 2ab + b^2$
$(a + b)^3 =$	$a^3 + 3a^2b + 3ab^2 + b^3$
$(a + b)^4 =$	$a^4 + 4a^3b + 6a^2b^2 + 4ab^3 + b^4$
$(a + b)^5 =$	$a^5 + 5a^4b + 10a^3b^2 + 10a^2b^3 + 5ab^4 + b^5$
$(a + b)^6 =$	$a^6 + 6a^5b + 15a^4b^2 + 20a^3b^3 + 15a^2b^4 + 6ab^5 + b^6$
$(a + b)^7 =$	$a^7 + 7a^6b + 21a^5b^2 + 35a^4b^3 + 35a^3b^4 + 21a^2b^5 + 7ab^6 + b^7$

There are some interesting patterns to
be observed here. The coefficients of the
terms in the expansion form a pattern
known as **Pascal's triangle.** In this pattern, any number except 1 is the sum of
the two numbers to its right and left in
the row directly above it. The diagram
shows how row 6 is obtained from row 5.
Note that the numbers in each row read
the same from left to right and from
right to left.

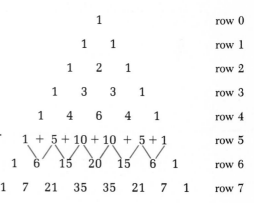

There are n + 1 terms in the expansion of $(a + b)^n$. In each term, the
sum of the exponents of a and b is n. The exponents of a begin with
n and decrease by 1 for each succeeding term. The exponents of b
begin with 0 and increase by 1 for each succeeding term.

$$(a + b)^7 = a^7b^0 + 7a^6b^1 + 21a^5b^2 + 35a^4b^3 + 35a^3b^4 + 21a^2b^5 + 7a^1b^6 + a^0b^7$$

Note that the exponent of b is always one less than the number of the
term. For example, in the third term b has the exponent 2.

To expand expressions of the form $(a + b)^n$ you can use the following rules, which are practical for reasonably small values of n.

1. The first term is a^n.

2. For each succeeding term

   a. the coefficient is the number in the corresponding position in the nth row of Pascal's triangle.

   b. the exponent of a is one less than the exponent of a in the preceding term.

   c. the exponent of b is one greater than the exponent of b in the preceding term.

3. The last term is b^n.

EXAMPLE 1   Expand $(2x - y)^4$ and simplify.

Refer to the form $(a + b)^n$ and let $a = 2x$, $b = -y$, $n = 4$. Use the rules given above.

$$(2x - y)^4 = (2x)^4 + 4(2x)^3(-y) + 6(2x)^2(-y)^2 + 4(2x)(-y)^3 + (-y)^4$$
$$= 16x^4 - 32x^3y + 24x^2y^2 - 8xy^3 + y^4$$

In the example above, note that every other term of the simplified expansion is preceded by a negative sign. This is true in general for the expansion of $(a - b)^n$.

The general expansion of an expression of the form $(a + b)^n$ is called the **binomial theorem.**

Binomial Theorem

If n is any counting number, then

$$(a + b)^n = a^n + \frac{n}{1}a^{n-1}b + \frac{n(n-1)}{1 \cdot 2}a^{n-2}b^2 + \frac{n(n-1)(n-2)}{1 \cdot 2 \cdot 3}a^{n-3}b^3 + \ldots + \frac{n}{1}ab^{n-1} + b^n$$

EXAMPLE 2   Use the binomial theorem to write the first five terms in the expansion of $(x + y)^8$.

$$(x + y)^8 = x^8 + \frac{8}{1}x^7y + \frac{8 \cdot 7}{1 \cdot 2}x^6y^2 + \frac{8 \cdot 7 \cdot 6}{1 \cdot 2 \cdot 3}x^5y^3 + \frac{8 \cdot 7 \cdot 6 \cdot 5}{1 \cdot 2 \cdot 3 \cdot 4}x^4y^4 + \ldots$$

$$= x^8 + 8x^7y + 28x^6y^2 + 56x^5y^3 + 70x^4y^4 + \ldots$$

Products of consecutive counting numbers starting with 1 can be expressed using **factorial notation.**

$$1 \cdot 2 \cdot 3 \cdot 4 \cdot 5 \cdot 6 = 6 \cdot 5 \cdot 4 \cdot 3 \cdot 2 \cdot 1 = 6! \qquad \textit{six factorial}$$

The value of $r!$ is defined as follows, where r is a counting number.

$$r! = r(r - 1)(r - 2)(r - 3) \ldots (4)(3)(2)(1) \qquad \textbf{\textit{r}} \textit{ factorial}$$

Also, by definition, $0!$ is equal to 1.

Factorials can be used to write the coefficients in a binomial expansion. If $(a + b)^n$ is expanded by the rules previously stated, the coefficient of the term containing $a^{n-r}b^r$ is given by

$$\frac{n!}{r! \, (n - r)!}$$

In the expansion of $(a + b)^7$, Pascal's triangle shows that the coefficient of the fourth term is 35. To find this coefficient using factorials, we first find the value of r, the exponent of b. Since the exponent for b is 1 less than the number of the term, we have $r = 4 - 1 = 3$. Then the coefficient of the fourth term is

$$\frac{n!}{r! \, (n - r)!} = \frac{7!}{3! \, (7 - 3)!} = \frac{7!}{3! \, 4!} = \frac{7 \cdot 6 \cdot 5 \cdot \cancel{4} \cdot \cancel{3} \cdot \cancel{2} \cdot \cancel{1}}{(\cancel{3} \cdot \cancel{2} \cdot \cancel{1})(\cancel{4} \cdot \cancel{3} \cdot \cancel{2} \cdot \cancel{1})} = 35$$

EXAMPLE 3   Find and simplify the 9th term of the expansion of $(a + b)^{13}$.

First find r, the exponent for b. $r = 9 - 1 = 8$
                                          └── number of term

Then find $n - r$, the exponent for a. $n - r = 13 - 8 = 5$
The 9th term will contain $a^5 b^8$.

Now, find the coefficient of the 9th term.

$$\frac{n!}{r! \, (n - r)!} = \frac{13!}{8! \, 5!} = \frac{(13 \cdot 12 \cdot 11 \cdot 10 \cdot 9) \cdot 8!}{(8!)(5 \cdot 4 \cdot 3 \cdot 2 \cdot 1)} = 1287$$

The 9th term is $1287 a^5 b^8$.

CLASS EXERCISES

1. State the number of terms in the expansion of $(a + b)^{13}$. Then state the sum of the exponents in each term.

2. Name the first and last terms of the expansion of $(a + b)^{10}$.

3. Name the first and last terms of the expansion of $(a - b)^{10}$.

4. Name the first and last terms of the expansion of $(a - 2)^5$.

5. Name the next-to-last term of the expansion of $(x + y)^9$.

6. Expand $(3 + 2y)^5$, and simplify.

EXERCISES

A   *Simplify.*

1. 7!   **2.** 1!   **3.** 2! 5!   **4.** 3! 3!

5. $\dfrac{6!}{4!\,2!}$ **6.** $\dfrac{8!}{3!\,5!}$ **7.** $\dfrac{12!}{0!\,12!}$ **8.** $\dfrac{15!}{11!\,4!}$

Expand and simplify.

9. $(x + y)^3$ **10.** $(x - 2)^4$ **11.** $(1 - y)^5$ **12.** $(x + 1)^6$

13. $(x + 2)^5$ **14.** $(3 + y)^3$ **15.** $(x - y)^7$ **16.** $(4 - y)^4$

17. $(2a + b)^3$ **18.** $(a - 2b)^4$ **19.** $(2a + 3b)^3$ **20.** $\left(\dfrac{1}{2}a - b\right)^5$

B   *Find and simplify the specified term of each expansion.*

21. the 8th term of $(a + b)^{12}$ **22.** the 6th term of $(a - b)^8$

23. the 5th term of $(x + 2)^{10}$ **24.** the 4th term of $(2x + y)^7$

25. the term containing y^4 in $(x + y)^6$ **26.** the term containing x^3 in $(x - 3)^5$

27. the term containing c^8 in $(c + 1)^{12}$ **28.** the term containing d^4 in $(2 + d)^{10}$

Expand and simplify.

29. $(a + b^2)^3$ **30.** $(a^2 - b)^4$ **31.** $(a + 2b^2)^5$ **32.** $(2a - 3b)^8$

C

33. An expression is of the form $(a + b)^n$, where n is a positive integer. The coefficient of the third term of the expansion of the binomial is 120. Find the value of n.

34. An expression is of the form $(a + 3)^n$, where n is a positive integer. The coefficient of the third term of the *simplified* expansion of the binomial is 189. Find the value of n.

35. Use the binomial expansion to evaluate 2^{10}. **Hint:** $2^{10} = (1 + 1)^{10}$

36. Write the 10th row of Pascal's triangle. Add the terms in the 10th row, and compare the sum to the result in Exercise 35.

37. Evaluate 2^{12}, using the binomial expansion. Compare the result with the sum of the terms in the 12th row of Pascal's triangle.

38. Using the results of Exercises 35–37, write a conjecture about the relationship between Pascal's triangle and the value of 2^n, where n is a counting number.

*39. Show that the following is true:

$$\frac{n!}{(r - 1)!(n - r + 1)!} + \frac{n!}{r!(n - r)!} = \frac{(n + 1)!}{r!(n - r + 1)!}$$

Astronomy

One of the most exciting chapters in the history of science is the discovery that planets behave according to mathematical formulas. Planetary motion is governed by laws that can be expressed by equations. It is important to remember that astronomers discovered these laws only after years of very precise measurements had brought together a vast amount of information.

The table below presents data about the five planets closest to the sun. d is the relative mean distance from the sun, with the earth's distance given as 1.000. T is the time in earth years for a planet's revolution about the sun.

Planet	d	T
Mercury	0.387	0.241
Venus	0.723	0.615
Earth	1.000	1.000
Mars	1.523	1.881
Jupiter	5.203	11.861

Example Compare the cube of each distance, d, in the table above with the square of the corresponding time, T. What do you discover?

Planet	d^3	T^2
Mercury	0.0580	0.0581
Venus	0.378	0.378
Earth	1.000	1.000
Mars	3.533	3.538
Jupiter	140.9	140.7

In each case, the values for d^3 and T^2 are virtually the same. It appears that $d^3 = T^2$.

Estimate each value. Use logarithms.

1. The relative mean distance from the sun to Saturn, given that $T = 29.457$

2. The number of years for one complete revolution of Uranus about the sun, given that $d = 19.190$

3. T for Neptune, given that $d = 30.086$

4. d for Pluto, given that $T = 248.350$

CHAPTER 14 REVIEW

VOCABULARY

sequence (p. 548)
term (p. 548)
finite sequence (p. 549)
infinite sequence (p. 549)
arithmetic sequence (p. 551)
arithmetic progression (p. 551)
common difference (p. 551)
arithmetic mean(s) (p. 553)
average (p. 553)
arithmetic series (p. 555)
summation notation (p. 557)
sigma Σ (p. 557)

expanded form of a series (p. 557)
geometric sequence (p. 560)
geometric progression (p. 560)
common ratio (p. 560)
geometric mean(s) (p. 561)
mean proportional (p. 561)
geometric series (p. 564)
infinite geometric series (p. 569)
partial sum (p. 569)
Pascal's triangle (p. 573)
binomial theorem (p. 574)
factorial notation (p. 575)

SUMMARY

The mathematics explored in this chapter has applications in many fields. These include banking, science, and other areas in which geometric or growth and decay problems are encountered.

After the concept of a sequence is introduced, special kinds of sequences and series are studied. Arithmetic sequences and series are considered first, then geometric sequences and series. Formulas for the general terms of such sequences are established, as are formulas for the sums of the finite series.

Infinite geometric series are considered next, and a formula is given for the sum of an infinite geometric series with a common ratio between -1 and 1. The final lesson introduces Pascal's triangle, which is used to find the coefficients in a binomial expansion. Such expansions are also obtained using the binomial theorem.

REVIEW EXERCISES

14-1   Use the given rule to write the first three terms of the sequence.

1. $t_n = \dfrac{2}{3}n$ **2.** $t_n = \dfrac{1}{2n}$ **3.** $t_n = n - 7$ **4.** $t_n = 3n + 2$

Give a rule for the sequence by defining t_n.

5. 7, 8, 9, 10, . . . **6.** 5, 8, 13, 20, . . . **7.** $6, 5\dfrac{1}{2}, 5\dfrac{1}{3}, 5\dfrac{1}{4}, \ldots$

Give a rule for the sequence by naming t_1 and defining t_{n+1} in terms of t_n.

8. 4, 6, 8, 10, . . . **9.** 23, 18, 13, 8, . . . **10.** $-3, -7, -11, -15, \ldots$

14-2   State whether the finite sequence is or is not an arithmetic sequence.

11. 11, 13, 15, 17 **12.** $-3, -5, -7, -9$ **13.** 2, 20, 200, 2000

Write the first three terms of the arithmetic sequence with the given values.

14. $a = -2, d = -4$ **15.** $a = 7, d = 3$ **16.** $a = -9, d = 5$

17. Find the arithmetic mean of 4.6 and 7.2.

18. Determine the numerical position of the term 19 in the arithmetic sequence $-8, -5, -2, \ldots$.

19. Find the 26th term of the arithmetic sequence $\sqrt{2}, 1 + 2\sqrt{2}, 2 + 3\sqrt{2}, \ldots$.

20. Find three arithmetic means between -16 and 4.

14-3   *Find the number of terms in the arithmetic series. Then find S_n.*

21. $3 + 6 + 9 + \cdots + 90$ **22.** $-1 + 5 + 11 + 17 + \cdots + 95$

23. Find t_n and S_n for the arithmetic series in which $a = -3, d = -9$, and $n = 12$.

24. Write $\sum\limits_{k=1}^{6} \dfrac{6 - k}{3}$ in expanded form. Then find the sum.

14-4   *State whether the given sequence is or is not a geometric sequence.*

25. $1, 2, 3, 5, 8, \ldots$ **26.** $-16, -8, -4, -2, \ldots$

Write the first three terms of the geometric sequence with the given values.

27. $a = 3, r = \dfrac{1}{3}$ **28.** $a = \dfrac{1}{3}, r = 3$ **29.** $a = 3, r = -\dfrac{1}{3}$

30. Find the 7th term of the geometric sequence $0.04, 0.2, 1, \ldots$.

31. Find the positive geometric mean of $\dfrac{3}{5}$ and $\dfrac{5}{3}$.

32. Find three geometric means between -5 and -80. Give two answers.

14-5   *Use the formula to find the sum S_n for each geometric series.*

33. $a = -7, r = 0.1, n = 4$ **34.** $a = 2, r = 2^{-1}, n = 5$

35. the first 4 terms: $\dfrac{1}{64} + \dfrac{1}{16} + \dfrac{1}{4} + \cdots$ **36.** the first 10 terms: $-1 + 3 - 9 + \cdots$

37. $\sum\limits_{k=1}^{4} 5^k$ **38.** $\sum\limits_{k=1}^{4} (-5)^k$ **39.** $\sum\limits_{k=1}^{4} 5^{-k}$

14-6   *Does the infinite geometric series have a finite sum? Find that sum, if it exists.*

40. $7 + 14 + 28 + \cdots$ **41.** $\dfrac{1}{7} + \dfrac{1}{14} + \dfrac{1}{28} + \cdots$ **42.** $3 - 12 + 48 - \cdots$

43. $7 + 3\dfrac{1}{2} + 1\dfrac{3}{4} + \cdots$ **44.** $\dfrac{1}{3} + \dfrac{1}{9} + \dfrac{1}{27} + \cdots$ **45.** $3 + \dfrac{3}{2} + \dfrac{3}{4} + \cdots$

46. Find the sum of an infinite geometric series for which $a = -3$ and $r = \frac{2}{3}$.

47. For an infinite geometric series, $a = 65$ and $r = 0.01$. Write the sum of the series as a repeating decimal.

14-7 **48.** Simplify: $\dfrac{8!0!}{2!4!}$ **49.** Expand and simplify: $(1 - x)^6$

Find and simplify the specified term of each expansion.

50. the 4th term of $(x + 4)^{10}$ **51.** the 9th term of $(2x - y)^9$

52. the term containing x^4 in $(x + 3)^6$ **53.** the term containing x^9 in $(x + 1)^{13}$

CHAPTER 14 TEST

Give a rule for each sequence by defining t_n.

1. $-2, -4, -6, -8, \ldots$ **2.** $5, 25, 125, 625, \ldots$

Consider the arithmetic sequence $10, 8, 6, \ldots$.

3. Find the numerical position of the term -20.

4. Find the 19th term of the sequence.

Consider the arithmetic series $-4 - 1 + 2 + \cdots + 41$.

5. Find the number of terms in the series.   **6.** Find the sum of the series.

Write the 8th term of each geometric sequence.

7. $4, 8, 16, \ldots$ **8.** $0.128, -0.064, 0.032, \ldots$

Consider the geometric series $\frac{1}{4} - \frac{1}{2} + 1 - \cdots - 8$.

9. Find the number of terms in the series.   **10.** Find the sum of the series.

Write in expanded form. Then find the sum.

11. $\displaystyle\sum_{k=1}^{5} (k - 2)$ **12.** $\displaystyle\sum_{k=1}^{7} 2k$ **13.** $\displaystyle\sum_{k=1}^{4} \frac{1}{2^k}$

14. Find two arithmetic means between 20 and 65.

15. Find the positive geometric mean of 1.8 and 5.

16. Find the sum of the infinite geometric series $0.6 + 0.06 + 0.006 + \ldots$.

Expand and simplify.

17. $(x + 1)^5$ **18.** $(1 - y)^5$ **19.** $(2x + y)^4$

20. Find the term containing x^3y^3 in the expansion of $(x + y)^6$.

Simplifying a Radical

You have seen that $\sqrt{-24} = \sqrt{(-1)(4)(6)} = 2i\sqrt{6}$. Simplifying a radical with a computer requires care in programming.

First we test the absolute value of the radicand for possible factors (lines 200, 210, and 240). Each factor that is found is then tested (lines 220 and 230) to see if it is a perfect square. Once the greatest perfect square has been found (it may be a 1), lines 300 through 350 display the result.

Because the computation of square root is not always exact in BASIC, SQR(529) may display 23.0000001. This makes it difficult to recognize that 529 is a perfect square. Therefore we assume that the value computed is slightly inexact, and we allow a very small tolerance, perhaps 0.00001. This is used in line 230 to test whether or not the number F is an integer.

The Program	What It Does
100 REM SIMPLIFY RADICAL	
110 PRINT "ENTER RADICAND";	
120 INPUT R	
130 LET N = ABS(R)	Gives a positive value to factor.
200 FOR D = N TO 1 STEP -1	
210 IF N/D < > INT(N/D) THEN 240	Tests for factors of the radicand.
220 LET F = SQR(D)	Tests whether factors are perfect squares.
230 IF ABS(INT(F) - F) < .00001 THEN 300	
240 NEXT D	
300 PRINT F;	Displays factor removed from radical.
310 IF R > 0 THEN 330	Tests if radicand is positive.
320 PRINT " I ";	Displays I for imaginary.
330 LET C = N/D	Computes factor that will remain under radical sign.
340 IF C = 1 THEN 900	Tests to avoid displaying $\sqrt{1}$.
350 PRINT " SQR("; C; ")"	Displays part of answer still under radical.
900 END	

RUN	This is a sample run for the radicand −24.
ENTER RADICAND ? -24	
2 I SQR(6)	Computer displays $2\,i\sqrt{6}$

What does the program display for each of the following?

1. $\sqrt{867}$ **2.** $\sqrt{6727}$ **3.** $\sqrt{2197}$ **4.** $\sqrt{-9245}$ **5.** $\sqrt{-191}$ **6.** $\sqrt{-16{,}129}$

7. Write a program that tests whether a number entered is a perfect cube. If it is, have the cube root displayed. If not, have it display NOT A PERFECT CUBE. Use X ↑ (1/3) to compute the cube root.

For more information about BASIC, see the Computer Handbook at the back of the book.

In order to obtain useful results from a telephone poll, the people contacted must represent a random sample of the population.

PROBABILITY AND STATISTICS

Prerequisite Skills Review

Write the letter for the correct answer.

1. $\dfrac{6!}{(6-4)!} = \underline{\ ?\ }$

   a. $\dfrac{30}{29}$
   b. 360
   c. 120
   d. 240

2. $\dfrac{9!}{3!\ 3!} = \underline{\ ?\ }$

   a. 1
   b. 40,320
   c. 10,080
   d. none of these

3. $\dfrac{11!}{4!(11-4)!} = \underline{\ ?\ }$

   a. 330
   b. 1980
   c. 2310
   d. none of these

4. $\dfrac{5}{8} \cdot \dfrac{4}{7} \cdot \dfrac{3}{6} = \underline{\ ?\ }$

   a. $\dfrac{5}{56}$
   b. $\dfrac{5}{28}$
   c. $\dfrac{5}{14}$
   d. none of these

5. If $x = 3$, $n = 5$, $p = \dfrac{1}{3}$, and $q = \dfrac{2}{3}$, then $p^x q^{n-x} = \underline{\ ?\ }$.

   a. $\dfrac{4}{9}$
   b. $\dfrac{8}{243}$
   c. $\dfrac{4}{27}$
   d. $\dfrac{4}{243}$

6. $\dfrac{80}{1300}$ is approximately equal to $\underline{\ ?\ }$.

   a. 0.06%
   b. 0.6%
   c. 6%
   d. 60%

7. $\sqrt{\dfrac{(4-7)^2 + (7-2)^2}{2}} = \underline{\ ?\ }$

   a. $2\sqrt{2}$
   b. $\dfrac{1}{2}\sqrt{34}$
   c. $\sqrt{17}$
   d. none of these

8. 47.5% of 800 is $\underline{\ ?\ }$.
   a. 38
   b. 380
   c. 3800
   d. 38,000

15-1 Probability

OBJECTIVES ─────────────────────────────────────

To find the probability of a simple event occurring.
To write a sample space showing all possible outcomes.
To find the probability of mutually exclusive events *A or B* occurring.

The **probability** of an event occurring is the chance that it will occur. It is a prediction based upon available data. Sometimes the probability that an event E will occur, $P(E)$, can be found by counting equally likely outcomes using this formula:

$$P(E) = \frac{\text{number of successful outcomes}}{\text{total number of possible outcomes}} = \frac{s}{n}$$

EXAMPLE 1   Suppose you pick a day at random from this month of June.

JUNE						
S	M	T	W	T	F	S
			1	2	3	4
5	6	7	8	9	10	11
12	13	14	15	16	17	18
19	20	21	22	23	24	25
26	27	28	29	30		

a. What is the probability that it is June ninth?

The chances are 1 in 30.   There is only 1 June ninth.
                                There are 30 days in June.

The probability is $\frac{1}{30}$. $P(\text{ninth}) = \frac{s}{n} = \frac{1}{30}$

b. What is the probability that it is a Wednesday?

The chances are 5 in 30.   There are 5 Wednesdays.
The probability is $\frac{1}{6}$. $P(\text{Wed.}) = \frac{5}{30} = \frac{1}{6}$

c. What is the probability that it falls on a weekend?

The chances are 8 in 30.   There are 8 weekend days.
The probability is $\frac{4}{15}$. $P(\text{weekend}) = \frac{8}{30} = \frac{4}{15}$

In the example just given, the calendar served as a *sample space*. A **sample space** is a list of all equally likely outcomes. That is, each outcome has the same chance of occurring.

EXAMPLE 2   Write a sample space showing the ways three coins can fall when tossed. Then use it to find the probability that all three fall alike.

(HHH)
HHT
HTH
THH
HTT
THT
TTH
(TTT)

Let H represent heads. Let T represent tails.

$$P(\text{all alike}) = \frac{2}{8} = \frac{1}{4}$$

This **tree diagram** is another way of showing the sample space for Example 2.

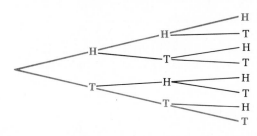 Altogether there are 8 paths. The two successes, *HHH* and *TTT*, are high-lighted.

EXAMPLE 3   Draw a bar graph showing the probability for each possible exact number of heads in the toss of three coins.

$P(0 \text{ heads}) = \dfrac{1}{8}$ *TTT*

$P(1 \text{ head}) = \dfrac{3}{8}$ *HTT, THT, TTH*

$P(2 \text{ heads}) = \dfrac{3}{8}$ *HHT, HTH, THH*

$P(3 \text{ heads}) = \dfrac{1}{8}$ *HHH*

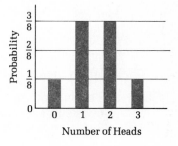

The events 0, 1, 2, and 3 heads are **mutually exclusive.** That is, no two of the events can occur together.

EXAMPLE 4   A number cube labeled 1 through 6 is rolled. Find the probability that the result is

a. 1.

$$P(1) = \frac{1}{6}$$ ① 2 3 4 5 6

b. an even number.

$$P(\text{even}) = \frac{3}{6} = \frac{1}{2}$$ 1 ② 3 ④ 5 ⑥

c. 1 *or* an even number.

$$P(1 \text{ or even}) = \frac{4}{6} = \frac{2}{3}$$ ① ② 3 ④ 5 ⑥

On the roll of a die, the events **1** and **even** are mutually exclusive. They cannot occur together. Hence

$$P(1 \text{ or even}) = P(1) + P(\text{even}) = \frac{1}{6} + \frac{1}{2} = \frac{2}{3}$$

Probability of Mutually Exclusive Events

If events *A* and *B* are mutually exclusive, then

$$P(A \text{ or } B) = P(A) + P(B)$$

Notice that the events **2** and **even** are *not* mutually exclusive. They occur together when a 2 is rolled. We can see from the sample space that $P(2 \text{ or even}) = \frac{3}{6} = \frac{1}{2}$.

1 ② 3 ④ 5 ⑥

If you use the formula, the event **2** will be counted twice, giving an incorrect answer.

Two important properties of probability should be noted.

1. Every event *E* has a probability from 0 through 1.

$$0 \leq P(E) \leq 1$$

When the event is certain to occur, the probability is 1.
When the event is impossible, the probability is 0.

2. The sum of the probabilities of all possible mutually exclusive events in an experiment must be 1. From this we have

$$P(E) + P(\text{not } E) = 1$$

It follows that

$$P(\text{not } E) = 1 - P(E)$$

CLASS EXERCISES

The pointer is spun. Find the probability of each event occurring.

1. B **2.** A vowel

3. A consonant **4.** not B

5. A letter in the word *ACE*

6. A letter in the word *BID*

7. A letter in the word *TRUMP*

8. A letter in the first half of the alphabet

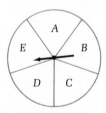

EXERCISES

A die is rolled. Find the probability that the result is

1. 4.

2. not 4.

3. an odd number.

4. a prime number.

5. a perfect square.

6. a factor of 20.

The pointer is spun. Find each probability.

7. $P(A)$

8. $P(B)$

9. $P(not\ A)$

10. $P(A\ or\ B)$

11. $P(D)$

12. $P(A\ or\ B\ or\ C)$

A letter is chosen at random from the alphabet. Find the probability that it is

13. P.

14. P or Q.

15. not W.

16. in the word *EIGHT*.

17. in the word *NINE*.

18. in the word *ELEVEN*.

Four coins are tossed.

19. Write a sample space showing the 16 ways they can fall.

Use the sample space in Exercise 19 to find the probability of each result.

20. All heads

21. All alike

22. Exactly one head

23. At least two heads

24. At most three heads

25. Draw a bar graph showing the probabilities for 0, 1, 2, 3, and 4 heads in the toss of four coins.

A packet of flower seeds has the distribution of colors shown in the circle graph at the right. Find the probability that a randomly chosen flower grown from these seeds is

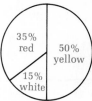

26. yellow.

27. *not* white.

28. neither white nor yellow.

29. A die is rolled three times, and each result is recorded as *even* or *odd*. Write a sample space showing all possible outcomes, using E for even and O for odd.

30. The pointer is spun twice. Write a sample space showing all possible results, using the notation (*first, second*).

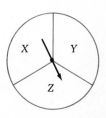

Use the sample space in Exercise 30 to find each probability.

31. $P(X, X)$

32. $P(Y, Z)$

33. P(both the same)

34. P(at least one Z)

A day is chosen at random from the month of January. Find the probability that it is

35. the 17th.　　　　　　**36.** before the 17th.　　　　**37.** after the 17th.

38. a Monday, if the 17th is a Monday.

39. a Friday, if the 17th is a Wednesday.

40. a weekday, if the 17th is a Sunday.

*State whether the two events are **mutually exclusive** or **not mutually exclusive**.*

41. An E; a vowel　　　　　　　**42.** A letter before N; a letter after M

43. A letter in the word *LARGE*; a letter in the word *SMALL*

C *A student is chosen at random from a group. Find the probability of selecting*

44. a boy, if 65% of the group are girls.

45. a girl, if the ratio of girls to boys is 3 to 2.

46. a junior, if there are equal numbers of freshmen, sophomores, juniors, and seniors.

47. a senior, if there are $\frac{1}{4}$ as many seniors as there are all other students.

One of the cards at the right is drawn at random and replaced three successive times.

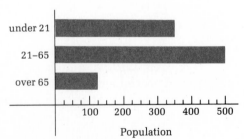

48. Draw a tree diagram showing all possible results.

49. Use the tree diagram to find the probability that exactly one of the three draws is a 2.

The graph at the right shows the distribution of a town's population by age groups. Suppose that a resident is chosen at random. What is the probability that the person is

50. under 21?　　　**51.** 65 or younger?

*52. A hat contains three cards. One card is red on both sides, and one is green on both sides. The third card is red on one side and green on the other side. A card is drawn at random and placed on the table. The side showing is red. What is the probability that the other side of the card is also red? (The answer is *not* $\frac{1}{2}$!)

15-2 Permutations

OBJECTIVES _____

To find the number of ways two events can occur together, using the
multiplication property for counting.
To find the number of permutations of *n* things taken *r* at a time.
To find probabilities using permutations.

_____

How many different sets of three initials are possible?

There are 26 letters in the alphabet. For each of the 26
choices for the first initial, there are 26 choices for the
second and 26 for the third. Any of the 26 letters can be
used in any of the three positions. Multiply to find the
total number of possibilities.

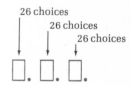

$$26 \times 26 \times 26 = 17{,}576$$

This illustrates the *multiplication property for counting.*

Multiplication Property for Counting

**If a first event can occur in *m* ways and a second event in *n* ways,
then the two events can occur together in *m* × *n* ways.**

The multiplication property can be extended to three or more events.

EXAMPLE 1   In how many ways can the letters in the word *EIGHT* be arranged?

Five choices are possible for the first letter. But then only 4 choices remain for
the second letter, 3 for the third letter,
and so on.

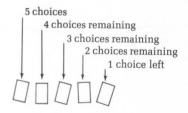

$5 \times 4 \times 3 \times 2 \times 1 = 120$

There are 120 possible arrangements.

Recall that the product of consecutive counting numbers, beginning
with one, can be written using *factorial notation.*

$$n! = n(n - 1)(n - 2)(n - 3) \ldots (3)(2)(1)$$

Thus, in Example 1 we could have written

$$5 \times 4 \times 3 \times 2 \times 1 = 5! = 120$$

EXAMPLE 2

In how many ways can the letters in the word *EIGHT* be arranged, taken 3 at a time?

$5 \times 4 \times 3 = 60$ 5 choices for the first letter, 4 for the second, and 3 for the third

Notice that the answer 60 can be written using factorials.

$$60 = \frac{5 \times 4 \times 3 \times 2 \times 1}{2 \times 1} = \frac{5!}{2!}$$

A **permutation** is an ordering, or arrangement. The number of permutations of n things taken n at a time is $n!$.

$$_nP_n = n!$$

The number of permutations of n things taken r at a time, where $r \leq n$, is $n(n-1)(n-2) \ldots (n-r+1)$. Multiplying by $\frac{(n-r)!}{(n-r)!} = 1$ gives the equivalent expression $\frac{n!}{(n-r)!}$.

Permutation Formula

The number of permutations of n different things taken r at a time is given by

$$_nP_r = \frac{n!}{(n-r)!} \qquad r \leq n$$

EXAMPLE 3

Find the number of permutations of any 4 of the 7 letters in the word *NUMBERS*.

Method I

Use the multiplication property.

$7 \times 6 \times 5 \times 4 = 840$

Method II

Use the formula.

$$_7P_4 = \frac{7!}{(7-4)!} = \frac{7!}{3!} = \frac{7 \cdot 6 \cdot 5 \cdot 4 \cdot \cancel{3 \cdot 2 \cdot 1}}{\cancel{3 \cdot 2 \cdot 1}} = 840$$

There are 840 permutations.

EXAMPLE 4

Five people of different heights stand in a line, side by side. What is the probability that they are arranged by height, increasing from left to right?

Strategy: Find the total number of possibilities, and apply the formula for P(E).

Find the number of permutations. $_5P_5 = 5! = 120$ $n = 120$

Only one has the heights in the correct order. $s = 1$

Hence, the probability of this event is $\frac{1}{120}$. $P(E) = \frac{s}{n} = \frac{1}{120}$

The procedure for counting permutations changes when some elements are alike. The number of permutations of n things, of which n_1 are alike, is

$$\frac{n!}{n_1!}$$

Similarly, the number of permutations of n things, of which n_1 are alike, n_2 are alike, and so forth, is

$$\frac{n!}{n_1! \, n_2! \ldots}$$

EXAMPLE 5   Find the number of permutations of the digits or letters.

a. 8681   There are 4 digits, 2 of which are alike.

$$\frac{4!}{2!} = \frac{4 \cdot 3 \cdot \cancel{2 \cdot 1}}{\cancel{2 \cdot 1}} = 12 \qquad \text{There are 12 permutations.}$$

b. NINETEEN   There are 8 letters, 3 alike and another 3 alike.

$$\frac{8!}{3! \, 3!} = \frac{8 \cdot 7 \cdot \cancel{6} \cdot 5 \cdot 4 \cdot \cancel{3 \cdot 2 \cdot 1}}{(\cancel{3 \cdot 2 \cdot 1})(\cancel{3 \cdot 2 \cdot 1})} = 1120 \qquad \text{There are 1120 permutations.}$$

CLASS EXERCISES

Consider the five digits, 1, 2, 3, 4, and 5.

1. In how many ways can they be arranged in a row?

2. How many such arrangements start with 1?

3. Find the number of permutations of the five digits taken 4 at a time.

4. Find the number of permutations of the five digits taken 2 at a time.

5. What is the probability that a random arrangement of the 5 digits forms an even number?

EXERCISES

The pointer is spun repeatedly. Use the multiplication property for counting to find the number of different results possible

1. in 2 spins.   2. in 5 spins.

*Each question on a true-false test can be answered **T** or **F**. In how many different ways can a set of answers be given*

3. on a 5-question test?   4. on a 10-question test?

In how many ways can the letters in each word be arranged?

5. *BIG*   6. *TINY*   7. *LARGE*   8. *SLIGHT*

Use factorial notation to express the number of arrangements possible using

9. one of each of the 10 digits.　　　　**10.** one of each letter of the alphabet.

Find the number of permutations of

11. 6 different things taken 6 at a time.　　**12.** 7 different things taken 5 at a time.

13. 10 different things taken 3 at a time.

*Two of the 6 letters in the word **JUNIOR** are arranged at random.*

14. Use the formula to find the number of permutations possible.

15. List all the possible permutations.

B

Find the number of permutations of the digits or letters.

16. 6233　　　　**17.** 15255　　　　**18.** 707070　　　　**19.** 269269

20. TALLER　　**21.** TALLEST　　**22.** STEEPER　　**23.** STEEPEST

24. In how many ways can 8 different books be arranged in a row on a shelf?

25. What is the probability that a random arrangement of 8 different books on a shelf has the titles in alphabetical order?

26. A tank car, four different boxcars, and a flatcar are arranged on a straight track. What is the probability that a random arrangement has the tank car first, the flatcar last, and the four boxcars in between?

C

27. The colors yellow, red, blue, green, and orange are to be shown in five vertical stripes on a flag. Find the probability that a random arrangement has the red stripe first and the yellow stripe last.

*A **circular permutation** is an arrangement of objects in a circle. Suppose 3 objects are so arranged. All the possibilities are shown at the right. However, **a**, **b**, and **c** are considered alike, since the relative positions of the objects are the same. Similarly, **d**, **e**, and **f** are alike. Therefore, there are only 2 possible distinct circular permutations of the 3 objects. In general, there are (**n** − 1)! distinct circular permutations of **n** different objects.*

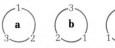

28. In how many different ways can 6 people be seated at a circular table?

29. In how many different ways can 9 players form a circle?

30. In how many different ways can 5 people be seated at a circular table, if two of them must *not* be seated next to each other?

15-3 Combinations

OBJECTIVES

To find the number of combinations of *n* things taken *r* at a time.
To find terms in Pascal's triangle using combinations.
To find probabilities using combinations.

Sometimes selections are made in such a way that the order of selection is not important. Such selections are called **combinations.**

EXAMPLE 1   In how many ways can you pick 3 of the 7 letters in the word *NUMBERS?*

This is a *combination* problem. We are only interested in which letters are picked, not in the way they are arranged.

Method I   Write a sample space and count the combinations.

NUM	NUB	NUE	NUR	NUS	NMB	NME
NMR	NMS	NBE	NBR	NBS	NER	NES
NRS	UMB	UME	UMR	UMS	UBE	UBR
UBS	UER	UES	URS	MBE	MBR	MBS
MER	MES	MRS	BER	BES	BRS	ERS

Method II   Use factorials to find the number of combinations.

In the *permutations* of 7 things taken 3 at a time, each set of 3 things chosen is ordered in 3! different ways. Since combinations do not involve orderings, we divide the number of permutations by 3! to find the number of combinations $_7C_3$.

$$_7C_3 = \frac{_7P_3}{3!} = \frac{7!}{3!(7-3)!} = \frac{7!}{3!\ 4!} = \frac{7 \cdot 6 \cdot 5 \cdot 4 \cdot 3 \cdot 2 \cdot 1}{(3 \cdot 2 \cdot 1)(4 \cdot 3 \cdot 2 \cdot 1)} = 35$$

There are 35 possible combinations.

Example 1 leads to the following formula.

Combination Formula

The number of combinations of *n* different things taken *r* at a time is given by

$$_nC_r = \frac{n!}{r!(n-r)!} \qquad r \leq n$$

EXAMPLE 2

How many diagonals can be drawn in an octagon?

Strategy: Use combinations to find the number of possible segments between any 2 of the 8 vertices, and subtract the number of sides.

Any 2 of the 8 vertices can be connected, but 8 of the segments formed are sides of the octagon, not diagonals. Therefore, find the number of combinations of 8 things taken 2 at a time, and subtract 8.

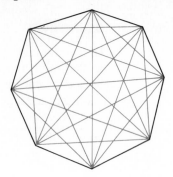

$$_8C_2 - 8 = \frac{8!}{2!\ 6!} - 8 = 28 - 8 = 20$$

Twenty diagonals can be drawn.

The numbers in Pascal's triangle are combinations, as illustrated in Example 3. The nth row of the triangle can be found by computing $_nC_0,\ _nC_1,\ _nC_2,\ \ldots,\ _nC_{n-1},\ _nC_n$.

EXAMPLE 3

Use combinations to write the terms in the 4th row of Pascal's triangle.

$$_4C_0 = \frac{4!}{0!\ 4!} = 1$$

$$_4C_1 = \frac{4!}{1!\ 3!} = 4$$

$$_4C_2 = \frac{4!}{2!\ 2!} = 6$$

$$_4C_3 = \frac{4!}{3!\ 1!} = 4$$

$$_4C_4 = \frac{4!}{4!\ 0!} = 1$$

```
      1   1
    1   2   1
  1   3   3   1
1   4   6   4   1
```

The fourth row of Pascal's triangle is: 1   4   6   4   1

EXAMPLE 4

Eight boys and nine girls are members of a club. Three members are to be chosen at random for a committee. What is the probability that they will all be girls?

Strategy: Use combinations to find s and n, and then use the formula for P(E).

Find the number of combinations of 3 members from among the 17.

$$_{17}C_3 = \frac{17!}{3!\ 14!} = \frac{17 \cdot 16 \cdot 15}{3 \cdot 2 \cdot 1} = 680 \qquad\qquad n = 680$$

Find the number of combinations of 3 girls from among the 9 girls.

$$_9C_3 = \frac{9!}{3!\ 6!} = \frac{9 \cdot 8 \cdot 7}{3 \cdot 2 \cdot 1} = 84 \qquad\qquad s = 84$$

The probability is $\frac{21}{170}$. $\qquad\qquad P(E) = \frac{s}{n} = \frac{84}{680} = \frac{21}{170}$

CLASS EXERCISES

Consider the five digits, 1, 2, 3, 4, and 5. Find the number of combinations of these five digits taken

1. 2 at a time.   **2.** 3 at a time.   **3.** 5 at a time.

4. Two of the digits are chosen at random. What is the probability that both are odd?

5. Three of the digits are chosen at random. What is the probability that each of them is less than 5?

EXERCISES

A

*Three of the 5 letters in the word **STUDY** are chosen at random.*

1. Use the formula to find the number of combinations possible.

2. List all possible combinations.

*Two of the 6 letters in the word **JUNIOR** are chosen at random.*

3. Use the formula to find the number of combinations possible.

4. List all possible combinations.

Find the number of combinations of

5. 5 things taken 4 at a time.   **6.** 7 things taken 3 at a time.

7. 8 things taken 5 at a time.   **8.** 6 things taken 4 at a time.

9. 10 things taken 5 at a time.   **10.** 12 things taken 10 at a time.

Use factorial notation to express the number of combinations possible using the 26 letters of the alphabet

11. 9 at a time.   **12.** 17 at a time.   **13.** 26 at a time.

B

*Assume that **n** is any positive integer. Write **true** or **false** for each statement.*

14. $_nC_n = {_nP_n}$ **15.** $_nC_1 = {_nP_1}$ **16.** $_nC_0 = {_nP_0}$

17. $_nC_{n-1} = {_nP_{n-1}}$ **18.** $_nC_r < {_nP_r}$, if r is an integer, and $1 < r \leq n$

How many diagonals can be drawn in

19. a hexagon?

20. a decagon?

Suppose that 10 points lie in a plane, and no three of the points are collinear.

21. How many distinct segments can be drawn, each connecting two of the points?

22. How many distinct triangles can be drawn, each with three of the given points as vertices?

Use combinations to find the given row or term in Pascal's triangle.

23. The 5th row

24. The 7th row

25. The third term in the 8th row

26. The ninth term in the 10th row

27. In how many ways can three people be selected from a group of 10?

28. Three of the people in a group of 10 are brothers. If three people are chosen at random from the 10, what is the probability that the three brothers are chosen?

29. A box contains a penny, a nickel, a dime, a quarter, a half dollar, and a one-dollar coin. Two coins are chosen at random. Find the probability that the selection contains the quarter.

30. There are 25 students in a class, and 14 of them are girls. If a committee of four is to be chosen at random, find the probability that all members of the committee will be boys.

Assume that cards are dealt from an ordinary deck of 52 that has been well shuffled.

31. How many different four-card hands are possible?

32. What is the probability of being dealt a four-card hand containing all cards with the same value, such as four aces, four jacks, or four 6's?

33. How many different five-card hands are possible?

34. What is the probability of being dealt a five-card hand containing only diamonds?

35. What is the probability of being dealt a five-card hand in which all five cards are of the same suit?

C   *Each of the digits 0 through 9 is written on one of 10 separate cards.*

36. Suppose 3 cards are drawn at random. What is the probability that the sum of the numbers drawn is 12? What is the probability that the product of the three numbers drawn is 48?

37. What is the probability that a random arrangement of all 10 cards forms a numeral greater than 8,500,000,000?

15-4 Independent Events

OBJECTIVES _____

To find the probability of two independent events both occurring.
To find the probability of two dependent events both occurring.

Suppose you were to spin both of these pointers. What is the probability that they both would stop at an *E*?

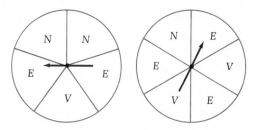

$$P(\text{both } E\text{'s}) = \frac{s}{n} = \frac{2 \times 3}{5 \times 6} \begin{matrix} \longleftarrow \text{Number of ways to spin two } E\text{'s} \\ \longleftarrow \text{Total number of ways to spin two letters} \end{matrix}$$

$$= \frac{1}{5}$$

The probability of spinning two *E*'s is $\frac{1}{5}$.

The separate spins in this illustration are **independent events.** Events are *independent* if the occurrence of one does not affect the others. Another way of calculating the probability that two independent events will both occur is to multiply their respective probabilities.

Probability of Independent Events

If events *A* and *B* are independent, then

$$P(A \text{ and } B) = P(A) \cdot P(B)$$

This rule can be used to find the probability of spinning both *E*'s on the dials shown above. Let *A* be the event ***E on first dial*** and *B* be the event ***E on second dial.*** Then

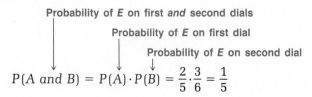

Probability of *E* on first *and* second dials

Probability of *E* on first dial

Probability of *E* on second dial

$$P(A \text{ and } B) = P(A) \cdot P(B) = \frac{2}{5} \cdot \frac{3}{6} = \frac{1}{5}$$

When there are more than two independent events, the probability of all of them occurring is calculated in a similar way.

EXAMPLE 1   A die is rolled three times. Find the probability of rolling three 6's.

Each roll is independent of the others.

Probability of 6 on first roll

Probability of 6 on second roll

Probability of 6 on third roll

$$P(A \text{ and } B \text{ and } C) = P(A) \cdot P(B) \cdot P(C) = \frac{1}{6} \cdot \frac{1}{6} \cdot \frac{1}{6} = \frac{1}{216}$$

The probability of rolling three 6's in three rolls is $\frac{1}{216}$.

Repeated events that occur under identical conditions are independent, as illustrated in Example 2.

EXAMPLE 2   The probability of a particular event occurring is p.

a. Find the probability of the event occurring on each of n successive tries, under identical conditions.

n equal factors

$$\overbrace{p \cdot p \cdot p \cdot \ldots \cdot p}^{} = p^n$$

b. Find the probability that on each of the n tries the event does *not* occur.

n equal factors

$$\overbrace{(1 - p)(1 - p)(1 - p) \ldots (1 - p)}^{} = (1 - p)^n$$

EXAMPLE 3   Three cards are drawn randomly in succession, *with replacement*. That is, each card drawn is replaced before drawing again. Find the probability that all three letters drawn are E's.

SEVENTEEN

Strategy: Use p^3, where p is the probability of success in one trial.

The probability p of drawing an E on a single try is $\frac{4}{9}$.

$$P(\text{three E's}) = p^3 = \frac{4}{9} \cdot \frac{4}{9} \cdot \frac{4}{9}$$

Since each draw is replaced, the events are independent. The probabilities are the same.

$$= \frac{64}{729}$$

The probability of drawing three E's in three tries, with replacement, is $\frac{64}{729}$.

Multiplication is sometimes used to find the probability of the occurrence of two events that are *not* independent.

EXAMPLE 4

Three cards are drawn from the set of cards shown in Example 3, but without replacement. Find the probability that all three letters are E's.

Strategy: Find the different probabilities for the three trials, and multiply.

Without replacement means that once a card has been drawn, it cannot be drawn again. Hence the events are **dependent** upon one another, and the probabilities are not the same.

4 *E*'s in 9 letters

3 *E*'s in remaining 8 letters

2 *E*'s in remaining 7 letters

$$P(\text{three } E\text{'s}) = \frac{4}{9} \cdot \frac{3}{8} \cdot \frac{2}{7} = \frac{1}{21}$$

The probability of drawing three E's in three tries, without replacement, is $\frac{1}{21}$.

CLASS EXERCISES

Find the probability of

1. spinning E on the dial.

2. rolling 5 on the die.

3. spinning E *and* rolling 5.

4. spinning a vowel on the dial.

5. rolling an odd number on the die.

6. spinning a vowel *and* rolling an odd number.

The pointer is spun and the die is rolled. Find each probability.

7. P(a vowel *and* 5)

8. P(A *and* an odd number)

9. P(a vowel *and not* an odd number)

10. P(*not* a vowel *and not* a prime number)

EXERCISES

A card is drawn at random, and the pointer is spun. Find the probability of

1. drawing O *and* spinning N.

2. drawing O *and not* spinning N.

3. no E's. 4. two E's. 5. two O's. 6. two letters alike.

7. two E's or two O's.
Hint: Use P(two E's) + P(two O's).

8. two different letters.
Hint: Use 1 − P(two alike).

B   A die is rolled twice. Find the probability of rolling

9. two 6's.

10. 5 or 6 each time.

11. two 5's or two 6's.

12. 5 on one roll, 6 on the other.
      Hint: Use $P(5, 6) + P(6, 5)$.

The probability of a successful event occurring is **p**. If there are 5 successive trials under identical conditions, find the probability of

13. 5 successes.

14. 5 failures.

15. at least 1 failure.
     Hint: Use $1 - P(5 \text{ successes})$.

16. at least 1 success.

17. at least 1 success and at least 1 failure.

Exercises 18–25 refer to the cards at the right. Cards are drawn at random, in succession.

Two cards are drawn, **with replacement.** Find the probability that

18. both are E's.

19. neither is an E.

Three cards are drawn, **with replacement.** Find the probability that

20. all are I's.

21. all are vowels.

22. none are vowels.

Two cards are drawn, **without replacement.** Find the probability that

23. both are D's.

24. both are N's.

25. exactly one is an N.

C   Cards are dealt from a shuffled deck containing 13 spades, 13 hearts, 13 diamonds, and 13 clubs. Find the probability that

26. the first card dealt is the queen of hearts.

27. the first card dealt is a club.

28. the first card is the queen of hearts *and* the second is the king of hearts.

29. the first three cards are diamonds.

30. the first four cards are aces.

CHECKPOINT

Consider the letters in the word **CUMBERLAND.**

If a letter is chosen at random, find the probability for each result.

1. L   **2.** B or C   **3.** not R   **4.** a vowel   **5.** Z

6. Find the number of permutations of the 10 letters taken 4 at a time.

7. Find the number of combinations of the 10 letters taken 7 at a time.

15-5 The Binomial Distribution

To use a binomial expansion to find the probability of a given number of
  successes in an experiment requiring repeated independent trials.
To use the binomial distribution formula to find probabilities.

_____

Consider an experiment involving three rolls of a die, where a success
is rolling a four.

The probability of a success, a four,
on any single roll is $\frac{1}{6}$.

$$p = \frac{1}{6}$$

The probability of a failure, *not* a
four, on any single roll is $\frac{5}{6}$.

$$q = \frac{5}{6}$$

The sum of probabilities p and q is 1. $p + q = 1$

   Since the repeated rolls are independent of each other, we can multiply to find the probability of a specific sequence of events occurring.

EXAMPLE 1   Find the probability that in three rolls of a die

a. the first two are fours, but the third is *not* a four.

$$P \text{ (fours on first 2 rolls only)} = p \cdot p \cdot q$$

$$= \frac{1}{6} \cdot \frac{1}{6} \cdot \frac{5}{6}$$

$$= \frac{5}{216} \quad \text{The probability is } \frac{5}{216}.$$

b. there are exactly 2 fours.

P (fours on first 2 rolls only)

P (fours on first and third rolls only)

P (fours on last 2 rolls only)

$$P \text{ (2 fours)} = (p \cdot p \cdot q) + (p \cdot q \cdot p) + (q \cdot p \cdot p)$$

$$= \left(\frac{1}{6} \cdot \frac{1}{6} \cdot \frac{5}{6}\right) + \left(\frac{1}{6} \cdot \frac{5}{6} \cdot \frac{1}{6}\right) + \left(\frac{5}{6} \cdot \frac{1}{6} \cdot \frac{1}{6}\right)$$

$$= 3\left(\frac{1}{6}\right)^2\left(\frac{5}{6}\right)$$

$$= \frac{15}{216} \quad \text{The probability is } \frac{15}{216}.$$

The *binomial theorem* can be used to find all such probabilities in an experiment of this type. Here are the terms in the binomial expansion of $(p + q)^3$, and their relationship to the possible results in three rolls of a die.

$$(p + q)^3 = 1p^3q^0 + 3p^2q^1 + 3p^1q^2 + 1p^0q^3$$

$$\left(\frac{1}{6} + \frac{5}{6}\right)^3 = 1\left(\frac{1}{6}\right)^3\left(\frac{5}{6}\right)^0 + 3\left(\frac{1}{6}\right)^2\left(\frac{5}{6}\right)^1 + 3\left(\frac{1}{6}\right)^1\left(\frac{5}{6}\right)^2 + 1\left(\frac{1}{6}\right)^0\left(\frac{5}{6}\right)^3$$

$$= \frac{1}{216} + \frac{15}{216} + \frac{75}{216} + \frac{125}{216}$$

$$P(3) = P(3 \text{ fours}) \qquad = \frac{1}{216}$$

$$P(2) = P(2 \text{ fours}) \qquad = \frac{15}{216}$$

$$P(1) = P(1 \text{ four}) \qquad = \frac{75}{216}$$

$$P(0) = P(0 \text{ fours}) \qquad = \frac{125}{216}$$

$$P(3) + P(2) + P(1) + P(0) = 1 \qquad \text{The sum is 1, since } \left(\frac{1}{6} + \frac{5}{6}\right)^3 = 1^3 = 1.$$

A second illustration of this use of the binomial theorem is given in Example 2. Notice that combinations and factorials are used to express the coefficient of the required term of the binomial expansion.

EXAMPLE 2   A coin is tossed five times. Use the binomial expansion to find the probability of getting exactly 3 heads.

Since there are 5 trials, think of the expansion of $(p + q)^5$. Find the term containing p^3, which gives the probability of exactly 3 successes.

$$P(3 \text{ successes}) = {}_5C_3 p^3 q^2 = \frac{5!}{3! \, 2!} p^3 q^2 = 10p^3q^2$$

The probability p of a head occurring on a single toss is $\frac{1}{2}$. The probability q of a head *not* occurring on a single toss is also $\frac{1}{2}$. Substitute $\frac{1}{2}$ for p and for q.

$$P(3 \text{ heads}) = 10p^3q^2 = 10\left(\frac{1}{2}\right)^3\left(\frac{1}{2}\right)^2 = \frac{5}{16}$$

In probability and statistics, this application of the binomial theorem is called the **binomial distribution.** It can be used in experiments that require
- repeated independent trials, each with only two possible results, success or failure.
- a fixed number of trials and a fixed probability of success per trial.

Binomial Distribution

Let p be the probability of success per trial.
Let q be the probability of failure per trial.
Then the probability of exactly x successes in n repeated independent trials is

$$P(x) = {}_nC_x p^x q^{n-x} \qquad n \geq x$$

EXAMPLE 3

A deck of 52 cards is cut and restacked 6 times. Find the probability of cutting exactly 2 diamonds.

Strategy: Identify the values of n, x, p, q, and use the formula for $P(x)$.

All conditions for the binomial are met.

$n = 6$ There are 6 independent trials, and each has only two possible results, *a diamond* or *not a diamond*.

$x = 2$ Exactly 2 trials are successes.

$p = \dfrac{1}{4}$ $\frac{1}{4}$ of the cards are diamonds.

$q = \dfrac{3}{4}$ $\frac{3}{4}$ of the cards are *not* diamonds.

Use the binomial distribution.

$$P(2 \text{ diamonds}) = {}_6C_2\left(\frac{1}{4}\right)^2\left(\frac{3}{4}\right)^4 = 15 \cdot \frac{1}{16} \cdot \frac{81}{256} = \frac{1215}{4096} \approx 0.297$$

The probability is about 0.30, or 30%.

CLASS EXERCISES

A die is rolled 4 times. Let a success on each roll be a six.

1. What is the probability p of a success per roll?

2. What is the probability q of a failure per roll?

3. What is the number n of repeated trials?

4. Express and expand $(p + q)^n$, using the values from Exercises 1–3.

Find the probability for each number of successes on 4 rolls of the die. Use the binomial distribution from Exercise 4.

5. $P(0 \text{ sixes})$ 6. $P(1 \text{ six})$ 7. $P(2 \text{ sixes})$

8. $P(3 \text{ or more sixes})$ 9. $P(\text{at most 3 sixes})$ 10. $P(\text{less than 3 sixes})$

EXERCISES

A

When the pointer is spun, the probability that it stops at **A** is $\frac{3}{4}$.

Suppose the pointer is spun twice.

1. List all possible results as ordered pairs.

How many of the ordered pairs listed for Exercise 1 have

2. no A's?   **3.** exactly one A?   **4.** two A's?

5. Find the expansion of $(\frac{3}{4} + \frac{1}{4})^2$.

Use the binomial expansion from Exercise 5 to find each probability.

6. P(no A's)   **7.** P(one A)   **8.** P(two A's)

Suppose the pointer is spun three times.

9. Write the appropriate binomial expansion.

Use the binomial expansion from Exercise 9 to find each probability.

10. P(three A's)   **11.** P(one A)   **12.** P(at least one A)

B

Copy and complete. Do not evaluate.

13. $P(6) = {}_9C_\square \left(\frac{2}{3}\right)^\square \left(\frac{1}{3}\right)^\square$ **14.** $P(4) = {}_{10}C_\square \left(\frac{5}{6}\right)^\square (\square)^\square$

Find the binomial probabilities.

15. Find $P(3)$, if $n = 5$ and $p = \frac{1}{5}$.   **16.** Find $P(2)$, if $n = 10$ and $p = \frac{1}{2}$.

A die is repeatedly rolled. Let a three be a success on each roll.

17. Find P(2 threes) in 2 rolls.   **18.** Find P(2 threes) in 3 rolls.

       Hint: $p = \dfrac{1}{6}$, $q = \dfrac{5}{6}$, $n = 2$

19. Find P(2 threes) in 4 rolls.   **20.** Find P(3 threes) in 4 rolls.

C

The probability that a particular student misses the school bus on any given morning is 0.1. Find the probability that in five consecutive school days

21. he misses the bus just once.   **22.** he never misses the bus.

23. he misses the bus more often than he catches it.

24. The probability that a basketball player makes a basket when she takes a shot is 0.6. Find the probability that in 10 consecutive shots she makes exactly 6 baskets. Assume independence. Give the answer to the nearest hundredth.

15-6 Descriptive Statistics

OBJECTIVES

To find the arithmetic mean and the range of a set of numbers.
To find the standard deviation for a set of numbers.

The binomial distribution gives the probabilities expected in certain types of experiments. However, the actual results of an experiment may differ somewhat from the expected values.

The **frequency distribution** on the left below gives the results of an experiment in which four coins were tossed 100 times. The distribution shows the different numbers of heads possible and how many times each such result occurred. The same information is shown in the **histogram** at the right.

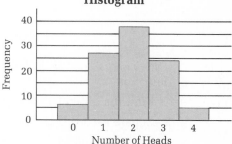

Frequency Distribution			Histogram
Number of Heads	Frequency f		
0	6		
1	27		
2	38		
3	24		
4	5		
	100		

A set of data is often described in terms of a representative value. An *average* is such a measure of central tendency. A common average used in statistics is the *arithmetic mean*. To find the arithmetic mean, find the sum of all the given values. Then divide by the number of values.

EXAMPLE 1 Find the arithmetic mean for the number of heads in the frequency distribution shown above.

$$\text{arithmetic mean} = \frac{6(0) + 27(1) + 38(2) + 24(3) + 5(4)}{100}$$

$$= \frac{195}{100}, \text{ or } 1.95$$

The arithmetic mean for a sample is often represented by $\bar{x}$, read x *bar*. A formula for the arithmetic mean can be written using *summation notation*.

$$\text{arithmetic mean} \longrightarrow \bar{x} = \frac{\sum\limits_{i=1}^{n} x_i}{n}$$

Add all of the values in the sample.

Then divide by the number of values.

The **range** of a set of values is the difference between the highest and lowest values. It is a measure of dispersion, or spread.

EXAMPLE 2   Find the mean and the range of the squares of the first 10 counting numbers.

$$x = 1, 4, 9, 16, 25, 36, 49, 64, 81, 100$$

$$\overline{x} = \frac{\sum_{i=1}^{10} x_i}{10} = \frac{1 + 4 + 9 + 16 + 25 + 36 + 49 + 64 + 81 + 100}{10}$$

$$= 38.5$$

$$\text{range} = 100 - 1 = 99$$

A measure of variation or spread about the mean is the *standard deviation*. The larger the standard deviation, the greater the spread. The **standard deviation** s for the values in a sample is defined by the formula:

$$\text{standard deviation} \longrightarrow s = \sqrt{\frac{\sum_{i=1}^{n} (x_i - \overline{x})^2}{n}}$$

Five steps must be followed in using the formula for the standard deviation.

1. Find the difference between each value in the sample and the mean, $\overline{x}$.
2. Square each difference.
3. Add the squares.
4. Divide this sum by n, the number of values in the sample.
5. Take the positive square root of the result.

EXAMPLE 3   Find the mean and the standard deviation for this set of numbers.

$$9, 6, 5, 12, 13$$

$$\overline{x} = \frac{\sum_{i=1}^{5} x_i}{5} = \frac{9 + 6 + 5 + 12 + 13}{5} = \frac{45}{5} = 9$$

$$s = \sqrt{\frac{\sum_{i=1}^{5} (x_i - \overline{x})^2}{n}} = \sqrt{\frac{(9 - 9)^2 + (6 - 9)^2 + (5 - 9)^2 + (12 - 9)^2 + (13 - 9)^2}{5}}$$

$$= \sqrt{\frac{0 + 9 + 16 + 9 + 16}{5}}$$

$$= \sqrt{10}, \text{ or approximately } 3.16$$

The mean is 9 and the standard deviation is $\sqrt{10}$, or 3.16, to the nearest hundredth.

CLASS EXERCISES

Use the data in the frequency distribution.

1. Find the mean.

2. Find the range.

x	5	6	7	8	9	10
f	1	3	4	8	5	4

Total: 25

Use this set of numbers: 7, 5, 9, 16, 13.

3. Find the mean.

4. Find the standard deviation.

EXERCISES

A

Find the mean and range for each set of numbers.

1. 2, 5, 8, 8, 7

2. 112, 140, 132, 166, 153, 110

3. $1\frac{1}{2}$, 2, $1\frac{1}{2}$, $2\frac{3}{4}$, $1\frac{1}{2}$, $1\frac{1}{4}$, $2\frac{5}{8}$, $1\frac{7}{8}$

4. 3, −2, 1, 0, −2, −3, 2

This frequency distribution gives the ages of 100 students.

Age	14	15	16	17	18
f	1	6	14	62	17

5. Find the mean.

6. Find the range.

7. Find the mean number of children per family, using this survey data.

Number of Children	0	1	2	3	4	5	6
Frequency f	6	18	41	27	15	7	6

B

8. Find the mean of the squares of the first eight odd counting numbers.

9. Find the square of the mean of the first eight odd counting numbers.

10. $\sum_{i=1}^{27} x_i = 7695$ and $n = 27$. Find $\bar{x}$.

11. $\sum_{i=1}^{n} x_i = 992$ and $\bar{x} = 12.4$. Find n.

12. $\sum_{i=1}^{12} (x_i - \bar{x})^2 = 432$; $n = 12$. Find s.

13. $\sum_{i=1}^{n} (x_i - \bar{x})^2 = 968$; $s = 11$. Find n.

Find the mean and the standard deviation.
Express irrational answers as decimals, to the nearest hundredth.

14. 11, 7, 14, 3, 5

15. 6, 1, 4, 10, 6, 9

16. 7, 7, 7, 7, 7

17. 8, 13, 7, 12

18. 42, 34, 40, 26, 28

19. 1, 9, 9, 13, 9, 7

C

Let **y** = 2, 3, 6, 10.

20. Find $\bar{y}$, the mean of the four values of y.

21. Find the mean of the four values of $2y + 3$. Compare to $2\bar{y} + 3$.

Let $y = 2, 3, 6, 10$.

22. Find the mean of the four values of $ay + b$. Is your answer equal to $a\bar{y} + b$?

23. Five coins are tossed 200 times, with the results shown in the frequency distribution below. Draw a histogram for the data. Then compute the mean, to the nearest hundredth.

Number of Heads	Frequency f
0	6
1	34
2	63
3	59
4	30
5	8
	200

24. A coin is tossed repeatedly until a head appears. The results of 20 such experiments are given in the histogram below. Compute the mean and the standard deviation, to the nearest tenth.

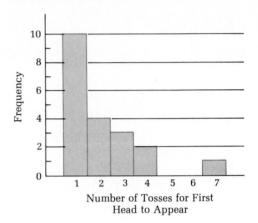

Number of Tosses for First Head to Appear

CHECKPOINT

Consider the letters in the word **TENNESSEE.**

If a letter is chosen at random, find the probability for each result.

1. T   **2.** N   **3.** E   **4.** E or S   **5.** not E or S

6. In how many ways can the letters be arranged?

7. If 2 of the letters are taken at random, what is the probability that both will be consonants?

A die is cast, and a card is drawn from an ordinary deck of 52 cards. What is the probability for each result?

8. 1 and an ace   **9.** 3 and a red card   **10.** 7 and a club

11. An even number and a club   **12.** 6 and the ace of spades

Three cards are drawn, without replacement, from an ordinary deck of cards. What is the probability for each result?

13. All 3 are hearts.   **14.** All 3 are red.   **15.** All 3 are aces.

Using Graphs

Graphs are used to present and describe data. A graphical presentation often makes it easier to see relationships and to make predictions. The graphs below allow us to make quick comparisons and to visualize trends using data dealing with geography and world population.

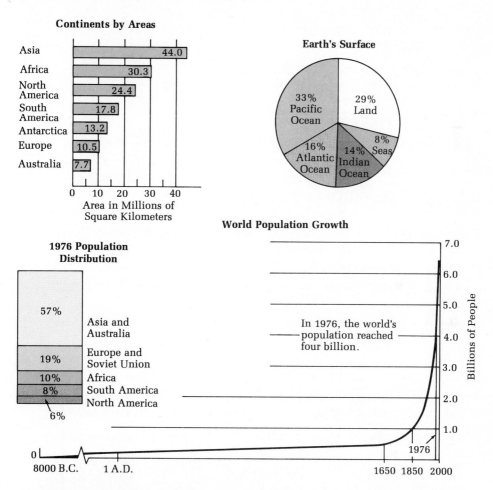

Continents by Areas

Asia	44.0
Africa	30.3
North America	24.4
South America	17.8
Antarctica	13.2
Europe	10.5
Australia	7.7

Area in Millions of Square Kilometers

Earth's Surface

29% Land
33% Pacific Ocean
8% Seas
14% Indian Ocean
16% Atlantic Ocean

1976 Population Distribution

57% Asia and Australia
19% Europe and Soviet Union
10% Africa
8% South America
6% North America

World Population Growth

In 1976, the world's population reached four billion.

Billions of People

8000 B.C.   1 A.D.   1650 1850 2000   1976

Some information can be found directly from the graphs. Other information can be found by solving problems using data given in the graphs.

Use the bar graph.

1. Which continent is largest?

2. What is the total area of Europe and Asia combined?

Use the circle graph.

3. Which is the smallest ocean?

4. What percent of Earth's surface is covered by the Atlantic and Pacific oceans combined?

Use the 100% bar graph.

5. In 1976, what percent of the world's population lived in North and South America?

6. In 1976, what percent of the world's population did *not* live in Europe or the Soviet Union?

Use the population growth curve.

7. Estimate the year in which the world's population reached one-half billion.

8. About how many years did it take the population to double, going from one-half billion to one billion?

Find the percent of the total land area of Earth occupied by each continent. Use information from the bar graph. Give your answer to the nearest tenth of a percent.

9. Asia   **10.** Australia

Find the approximate population of the given continent in 1976. Use the population growth curve and the 100% bar graph.

11. Africa   **12.** North America

Suppose a meteoroid plunges through the atmosphere and crashes into Earth at some random point. What is the probability that it would fall

13. into the Atlantic Ocean?   **14.** into any ocean or sea?

Suppose you spin a globe and stop it at a random point with your finger. Express each probability as a decimal, to the nearest hundredth.

15. The probability that the point is in Africa

16. The probability that the point is in North or South America

15-7 Normal Distribution

OBJECTIVES _____

Given the mean and standard deviation of a normal distribution, to find the
number or percent of scores within a certain range.
To find the probability that a random score lies within a given range of
scores.

The handspans of 100 randomly chosen students were measured to the
nearest 0.5 inch, and the results were shown in a frequency distribution. The same data were used to draw the histogram at the right.

Handspan in Inches	Frequency f
6.5	1
7.0	13
7.5	37
8.0	31
8.5	15
9.0	3
	100

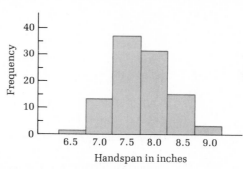

Suppose the handspans of a great many more students of the same
age were measured. The shape of the resulting histogram would not be
exactly the same, but we could expect it to be very similar to the one
above. Furthermore, if the measurements were more precise, say to the
nearest tenth of an inch, more bars would be shown in the graph. The
curve formed by joining the midpoints of the tops of the bars would
appear to be smooth and to approach that of a *normal distribution*.

A **normal distribution** is a distribution
with a bell-shaped curve, symmetric
about the vertical axis. This axis of
symmetry locates the mean of the values
in the distribution. 50% of the values
lie on each side of the mean. The
curve approaches the horizontal axis
on each side of the axis of symmetry.

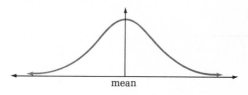

Many measurements, such as weights of apples, daily temperature highs,
and dimensions of some manufactured products, are normally distributed.
The normal curves for such distributions can be used to find probabilities.

- Approximately 68% of the values lie within 1 standard deviation of
  the mean.

- Approximately 95% lie within 2 standard deviations of the mean.

These probabilities are represented as areas under the normal curve.

EXAMPLE 1   A normal distribution has a mean of 30 and a standard deviation of 6.

a. What percent of the values lie between 24 and 36?

24 is 1 standard deviation below the mean. 36 is 1 standard deviation above the mean. Thus, 68% of the values lie between 24 and 36.

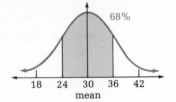

b. What is the probability that a randomly chosen value X lies between 30 and 42?

42 is 2 standard deviations above the mean. 95% of the values lie within 2 standard deviations, half above and half below the mean. Thus, 47.5% lie between 30 and 42.

$P(30 < X < 42) = 0.475$

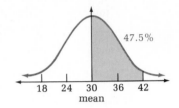

c. Out of 400 values, how many would you expect to be above 42?

50% lie above the mean, but 47.5% lie between 30 and 42. Therefore, 2.5% of the 400, or 10, are above 42.

2.5% of 400 = 0.025 × 400 = 10

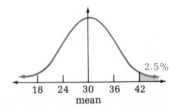

EXAMPLE 2   Assume that heights of people are normally distributed, with a mean of 67 inches and a standard deviation of 2.5 inches. What is the probability that a person is less than 6 feet tall?

Six feet is equivalent to 72 inches, which is 2 standard deviations above the mean. 47.5% of the heights X lie between 67 and 72, and another 50% lie below 67, for a total of 97.5%.

$P(X < 72) = 0.975$

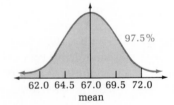

CLASS EXERCISES

Let a set of scores be normally distributed, with mean 200 and standard deviation 40. Find the probability that a randomly chosen score X is

1. between 160 and 240.   2. above 200.   3. between 120 and 240.

4. above 280.   5. below 240.   6. below 160.

7. less than 2 standard deviations from the mean.

8. more than 1 standard deviation from the mean.

EXERCISES

A

A box contains 2000 items with weights that are normally distributed.

1. How many items have weights within 1 standard deviation of the mean?

2. How many have weights more than 1 standard deviation *above* the mean?

The life of a certain automobile battery is normally distributed, with mean 45 months and standard deviation 3 months.

3. What percent of the batteries can be expected to last less than 42 months?

4. What is the probability that a randomly selected battery lasts between 42 and 48 months?

5. Out of 50 batteries, how many will probably last more than 4 years?

B

6. Daily temperature highs in Dallas, Texas, are normally distributed, with an average of 78°F and a standard deviation of 12°F. What percent of the days would you expect a temperature high greater than 90°F?

7. Yearly rainfall in Chicago, Illinois, is normally distributed, with an average of 39 inches and a standard deviation of 9 inches. What is the probability that a random year will have more than 30 inches of rain?

8. Cereal boxes are labeled 12 ounces, but the weights of their contents are normally distributed, with mean 12.3 ounces and standard deviation 0.3 ounces. What percent of the boxes can be expected to contain less than 11.7 ounces of cereal?

9. A drink dispensing machine fills cups with an average of 8 fluid ounces of beverage, with a standard deviation of 0.4 fluid ounces. Out of 50 cupfuls, how many would you expect to be filled within 0.4 fluid ounces of the mean? Assume a normal distribution.

Let a set of scores be normally distributed, with mean 2 and standard deviation 0.6. Find each probability for a randomly selected score **X**.

10. $P(0.8 < X < 3.2)$ **11.** $P(X > 0.8)$ **12.** $P(1.4 < X < 3.2)$

C

More accurate values of the normal distribution probabilities can be obtained from special tables. The tables give probabilities as areas under the normal curve, from the mean to a given number **z** *of standard deviations. Because of symmetry, two* **z** *values with the same absolute value, such as 0.5 and −0.5, cut off the same area from the mean. Use the table at the right to find the following probabilities.*

z	Area
0.5	0.1915
1.0	0.3414
1.5	0.4332
2.0	0.4772
2.5	0.4938
3.0	0.4987

13. $P(-1.0 < z < 1.0)$ **14.** $P(z < 2.5)$ **15.** $P(z > 1.5)$

16. $P(-0.5 < z < 2.5)$ **17.** $P(1.5 < z < 2.0)$ **18.** $P(-3.0 < z < 3.0)$

STRATEGIES for PROBLEM SOLVING

Straight-Line Prediction

Five students studied for a difficult test. Here are the hours studied and the corresponding test scores. What test score would you predict for another student who studies for $6\frac{1}{2}$ hours before taking the same test?

Student	A	B	C	D	E
No. of Hours	1	4	2	6	7
Test Score	12	60	36	66	96

The data points do not all lie on the same line. However, there does appear to be a line that fits the points reasonably well.

Call the equation of the line of "best fit" $y = mx + b$. The *method of least squares* is used to find the equation of this line. This method locates the line so that the sum of the squares of the deviations from the line is minimized.

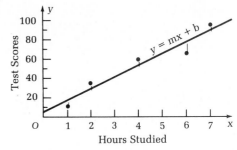

Step 1 Substitute each pair of values x and y in the equation $y = mx + b$. Add the resulting equations.

$$
\begin{array}{rcrcl}
12 &=& m &+& b \\
60 &=& 4m &+& b \\
36 &=& 2m &+& b \\
66 &=& 6m &+& b \\
96 &=& 7m &+& b \\
\hline
270 &=& 20m &+& 5b
\end{array}
$$

Step 2 Multiply through each equation by the coefficient of m. Add the new set of equations.

Multiply by 1.
Multiply by 4.
Multiply by 2.
Multiply by 6.
Multiply by 7.

$$
\begin{array}{rcrcl}
12 &=& m &+& b \\
240 &=& 16m &+& 4b \\
72 &=& 4m &+& 2b \\
396 &=& 36m &+& 6b \\
672 &=& 49m &+& 7b \\
\hline
1392 &=& 106m &+& 20b
\end{array}
$$

Step 3 Find the equation of the line of best fit.
  a. Steps 1 and 2 each produce an equation in m and b. Solve this system of two linear equations for m and b.
  b. Substitute these values for m and b in the equation $y = mx + b$ to get the equation of the line of best fit.

Step 4 Use the line of best fit. Substitute $6\frac{1}{2}$ for x in the equation. Find the resulting y-value, which is the test score estimate for $6\frac{1}{2}$ hours of study, based on straight-line prediction.

Now try it again! Use the method of least squares to fit a line to these values. Then use the equation of the line to predict **y** *for* **x** $= 6.5$.

x	4	6	7	5
y	11	15	16	14

Sampling

Naturalists often need to estimate the population of certain wildlife when they cannot make an actual count. In such cases, they make use of an interesting sampling procedure.

Example A random sample of 100 fish is caught, marked, and returned to a lake. Some time later a second sample of 100 fish is taken from the lake. Of these, only 2 had been marked. Estimate the total number of fish in the lake.

Assume that the marked fish became thoroughly mixed with the others after they were returned to the lake. It can be expected that the ratio of marked fish to the total population is the same as the ratio of marked fish to the number in the second sample.

$$\text{total number marked} \longrightarrow \frac{100}{n} = \frac{2}{100} \longleftarrow \text{number marked in second sample}$$
$$\text{total number in population} \qquad\qquad\qquad\qquad \longleftarrow \text{total number in second sample}$$

$$n = \frac{(100)(100)}{2}$$

$$n = 5000$$

A reasonable estimate of the fish population of the lake is 5000.

A team of naturalists captures and marks 200 deer that inhabit a certain region. The deer are released and allowed to mix with the other deer in that region. Later the team returns and observes that 5 out of the first 40 deer they see are marked.

1. Estimate the deer population of the region.

2. Estimate the population if only 100 deer had been marked initially.

3. Estimate the population if 100 deer had been marked initially and the team spotted only 1 marked deer out of 20 later on.

4. Estimate the deer population if 60 had been marked initially and the team spotted 3 marked deer out of 50 later on.

CHAPTER 15 REVIEW

VOCABULARY

SUMMARY

The chapter begins by introducing the probability of equally likely events. The concepts of permutations and combinations are developed and used to further the study of probability. The probabilities of independent events are computed, which leads into the use of the binomial distribution to find probabilities related to experiments involving repeated independent trials. There is also an introduction to statistics, and the formulas for the arithmetic mean and standard deviation are included. Probability and statistics merge in the final section, where the normal distribution is developed and applied in a variety of practical situations.

REVIEW EXERCISES

15-1   *A pointer is attached to a dial that is divided into 12 equal parts labeled 1 through 12. What is the probability of each event occurring on a single spin?*

1. $P(12)$ **2.** $P(1 \text{ or } 7)$ **3.** $P(\text{not } 3)$ **4.** $P(\text{odd number})$

5. $P(\text{multiple of } 4)$ **6.** $P(\text{factor of } 10)$ **7.** $P(13)$

8. Five coins are tossed. Write a sample space showing the 32 ways they can fall.

9. If 5 coins are tossed, what is the probability of getting exactly 2 heads?

15-2   *Find the number of permutations possible.*

10. 5 different things taken 5 at a time   **11.** 8 different things taken 4 at a time

12. All of the letters in *MISSISSIPPI*   **13.** All of the digits in 55337

15-3   *Find the number of combinations possible.*

14. 5 different things taken 5 at a time   **15.** 8 different things taken 4 at a time

Use combinations to find the given row or term in Pascal's triangle.

16. The 4th row

17. The 4th term in the 7th row

18. Four records in a stack of 10 belong to Karen. If 2 of the 10 records are chosen at random, what is the probability that they will both be Karen's?

15-4 *Assume that 3 of these cards are drawn at random, with replacement. Find each probability.*

19. P(all 9's)   **20.** P(no 5's)   **21.** P(at least one 5)

Assume the 3 cards are drawn without replacement. Find each probability.

22. P(all 9's)   **23.** P(no 5's)   **24.** P(at least one 5)

15-5 *A die is made in the shape of a tetrahedron that has four congruent equilateral triangles as its faces. The faces are labeled **A, B, C,** and **D.** Assume the die is tossed 5 times, and a success is landing with the **A** face down.*

25. What is the probability p of a success per roll?

26. What is the probability q of a failure per roll?

27. What is the number n of repeated trials?

28. Expand $(p + q)^n$, using the values from Exercises 25–27.

Find the probability for each number of successes on 5 rolls of the die. Use the binomial distribution from Exercise 28.

29. P(2 A's)   **30.** P(at most 3 A's)   **31.** P(at least 3 A's)

15-6 *Find the mean, the range, and the standard deviation, to the nearest tenth, for each set of numbers.*

32. 5, 8, 11, 11, 10

33. 109, 137, 129, 163, 150, 107

34. $\sum_{i=1}^{10} x_i = 150$ and $n = 10$. Find $\bar{x}$.

35. $\sum_{i=1}^{n} (x_i - \bar{x})^2 = 1008$ and $s = 12$. Find n.

15-7 *A lumber pile contains 1000 boards with lengths that are normally distributed. The mean length of the boards is 8 feet, with a standard deviation of $\frac{1}{2}$ inch.*

36. What percent of the boards can be expected to be shorter than 97 inches?

37. Find the probability that a randomly selected board is over $96\frac{1}{2}$ inches.

38. If 200 boards are selected randomly, how many can be expected to be longer than 97 inches?

Consider the numeral 658755. If a digit is chosen at random, find the probability for each result.

1. An odd number

2. 7 or 8

3. 5

For the numeral 9876, find the number of permutations of the digits

4. taken 4 at a time.

5. taken 2 at a time.

6. Find the number of possible permutations of the letters in the word *SUCCESS*.

For the word CHAPTER, find the number of combinations of the letters

7. taken 5 at a time.

8. taken 7 at a time.

9. A coin is tossed and a die is rolled. What is the probability of getting a head and an even number?

10. Two of these cards are drawn at random, *with replacement*. What is the probability of drawing two I's?

11. Two of these cards are drawn at random, *without replacement*. What is the probability of drawing two T's?

Three draws, with replacement, are to be made from five cards numbered 1 through 5. A success is drawing an even number.

12. Find p, the probability of a success per draw, and q, the probability of a failure per draw.

13. Expand $(p + q)^n$, using $n = 3$ and the values for p and q from Exercise 12.

14. Find P(exactly 2 even numbers) for the three draws.

Find the given measures for the following set of numbers: 16, 12, 19, 8, 10

15. Mean

16. Range

17. Standard deviation

The diameters of bolts produced by a certain machine are normally distributed.

18. What percent of the diameters will be within 2 standard deviations of the mean?

19. Out of 100 randomly chosen bolts, how many can be expected to have diameters more than 1 standard deviation above the mean?

20. Assume that the mean diameter is 30 millimeters and the standard deviation is 0.5 millimeter. Find the probability that a randomly chosen bolt has a diameter less than 30.5 millimeters.

The Golden Ratio

The ancient Greeks concluded that the rectangles with the most pleasing appearance were those with dimensions that fit the proportion $\dfrac{W}{L} = \dfrac{L}{L + W}$. This proportion became known as the *divine proportion*, while the ratio $\dfrac{L}{L + W}$ came to be known as the *Golden Ratio*.

Golden Rectangles

When $L = 1$, the divine proportion leads to the quadratic equation $W^2 + W = 1$. Solving, we find that W is $\dfrac{\sqrt{5} - 1}{2}$. Using these values for L and W, the Golden Ratio is approximately 0.618.

Many years later, Leonardo of Pisa, known as Fibonacci, wrote about the sequence 1, 1, 2, 3, 5, 8, 13, . . . Each term after the first two is the sum of the two preceding terms. This sequence is related to the Golden Ratio.

This program displays the first twenty terms of the Fibonacci sequence, one pair at a time. After each pair of Fibonacci numbers, the program also displays their ratio and its reciprocal.

The Program	What It Does
| ```
100 REM FIBONACCI
110 LET X = 1
120 LET Y = 1
``` | Sets X and Y equal to the first two terms of the sequence. |
| ```
130 FOR N = 1 TO 10
``` | Allows ten pairs to be displayed. |
| ```
140 PRINT "FIBONACCI NUMBERS:"
150 PRINT X, Y
``` | Displays one pair. |
| ```
160 PRINT "THEIR RATIOS:"
170 PRINT X/Y, Y/X
``` | Displays their ratio and its reciprocal. |
| ```
180 LET X = X + Y
190 LET Y = X + Y
``` | Computes the next two Fibonacci numbers. |
| ```
200 NEXT N
900 END
``` | |

1. What pattern can be seen in the ratios X/Y ?

2. What pattern can be seen in their reciprocals Y/X ?

3. How do the ratios X/Y and Y/X appear to be related?

4. Write a program that displays the first twenty-five triangular numbers: {1, 3, 6, 10, 15, 21, . . .}.
   Hint: The nth triangular number may be obtained by finding the sum of the first n natural numbers.

5. Write a program that starts with $.01 and doubles the amount thirty times.

For more information about BASIC, see the Computer Handbook at the back of the book.

CHAPTER 16

Matrices can be used in solving various problems for large city agencies, such as the Police Department and the Board of Education. Computers store large amounts of data and carry out complex computations by using matrices.

MATRICES, DETERMINANTS, AND LINEAR SYSTEMS

Prerequisite Skills Review

Write the letter for the correct answer.

1. $(3, -4)$ is the solution to which of the following linear systems?

   a. $-2x - 3y = 6$ **b.** $4x - y = 16$ **c.** $3x + y = 5$ **d.** none of these
        $x - y = -1$ $2x - y = 2$ $-x - 3y = 9$

2. $(-1, 2, -3)$ is the solution to which of the following linear systems?

   a. $-x + 2y = 5$ **b.** $x + y = 1$
        $2y - z = 7$ $y + z = -1$
        $3x + 2z = 3$ $x + z = -4$

   c. $x + y + z = -2$ **d.** none of these
        $3x + 2y - z = 4$
        $2x + 3y + z = 7$

3. If $y = -3$ and $3x - 4y = -1$, then $x = \underline{\ ?\ }$.

   a. $\dfrac{11}{3}$ **b.** $\dfrac{13}{3}$ **c.** $-\dfrac{11}{3}$ **d.** $-\dfrac{13}{3}$

4. If $z = 1$, $y - 2z = 2$, and $x - y + z = 3$, then $x = \underline{\ ?\ }$.

   a. 4   **b.** 6   **c.** 8   **d.** 0

5. The multiplicative inverse of 4 is $\underline{\ ?\ }$.

   a. 4^{-1} **b.** 4^0 **c.** $4^{\frac{1}{2}}$ **d.** -4

6. If -4 times -3 is added to -2, the result is $\underline{\ ?\ }$.

   a. -14 **b.** 20   **c.** 10   **d.** none of these

7. If twice $-\dfrac{3}{4}$ is added to $\dfrac{1}{2}$, the result is $\underline{\ ?\ }$.

   a. -2 **b.** -1 **c.** $-\dfrac{1}{4}$ **d.** none of these

8. If $a = 5$, $b = -6$, $c = 7$, and $d = -8$, then $ad - bc = \underline{\ ?\ }$.

   a. -82 **b.** -13 **c.** 26   **d.** none of these

9. If $a = -4$, $b = -1$, $c = -8$, and $d = 5$, then $ad - bc = \underline{\ ?\ }$.

   a. -28 **b.** -12 **c.** 44   **d.** none of these

16-1 Using Matrices to Solve Linear Systems

OBJECTIVE

To solve linear systems by using augmented matrices.

The algebraic methods used in Chapter 3 to solve linear systems can be adapted to solve such systems using *matrices*. A **matrix** is a rectangular array of numbers. For example, the 2×2 (two-by-two) matrix shown below at the right has two rows and two columns. The numbers, or *elements*, in this matrix are the coefficients of the variables in the linear system shown at the left.

$$\begin{aligned} 3x - 5y &= 25 \\ 2x + 4y &= 24 \end{aligned} \qquad \begin{bmatrix} 3 & -5 \\ 2 & 4 \end{bmatrix}$$

By using the constant terms as a third column, we obtain the 2×3 **augmented matrix** of the given system.

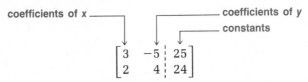

coefficients of x ⎯⎯⎯⎯⎯⎯⎯⎯⎯⎯⎯⎯ coefficients of y ⎯⎯⎯⎯⎯⎯ constants

$$\begin{bmatrix} 3 & -5 & \vdots & 25 \\ 2 & 4 & \vdots & 24 \end{bmatrix}$$

An algebraic solution of the preceding system and the corresponding matrix solution are shown below. In each step, the augmented matrix of the system at the left is shown at the right.

Algebraic Solution	**Augmented Matrix Solution**
Step 1 Write the system.	Write the augmented matrix.
$\begin{aligned} 3x - 5y &= 25 \\ 2x + 4y &= 24 \end{aligned}$	$\begin{bmatrix} 3 & -5 & \vdots & 25 \\ 2 & 4 & \vdots & 24 \end{bmatrix}$
Step 2 Multiply the second equation by $\frac{1}{2}$.	Multiply the second row by $\frac{1}{2}$.
$\begin{aligned} 3x - 5y &= 25 \\ x + 2y &= 12 \end{aligned}$	$\begin{bmatrix} 3 & -5 & \vdots & 25 \\ 1 & 2 & \vdots & 12 \end{bmatrix}$
Step 3 Interchange the first and second equations.	Interchange the first and second rows.
$\begin{aligned} x + 2y &= 12 \\ 3x - 5y &= 25 \end{aligned}$	$\begin{bmatrix} 1 & 2 & \vdots & 12 \\ 3 & -5 & \vdots & 25 \end{bmatrix}$
Step 4 Add -3 times the first equation to the second equation.	Add -3 times the first row to the second row.
$\begin{aligned} x + 2y &= 12 \\ -11y &= -11 \end{aligned}$	$\begin{bmatrix} 1 & 2 & \vdots & 12 \\ 0 & -11 & \vdots & -11 \end{bmatrix}$

Notice the *triangular form* of the coefficients in Step 4. Once such a form is reached, with only zero coefficients outside the triangle, the solution of the system can be completed using *back-substitution*. That is, the value of y is found from the equation for the last row. Then x is found by substituting that y-value back into the equation for the first row.

$$\text{Second equation: } -11y = -11 \rightarrow \quad y = 1$$

$$\text{First equation: } x + 2y = 12 \rightarrow x + 2(1) = 12 \rightarrow x = 10$$

The solution is the ordered pair (10, 1). Check this in the original system.

As demonstrated in the preceding solution, the algebraic operations used to obtain equivalent systems correspond to the following *elementary row operations* for the augmented matrices.

1. Interchange two rows.
2. Multiply a row by a nonzero constant.
3. Add a multiple of one row to another row.

EXAMPLE   Solve the system at the right, using augmented matrices and back-substitution.

$$\begin{aligned} 2x - 7y - z &= 1 \\ x - 3y - 4z &= 8 \\ 6x - 5y + 3z &= 7 \end{aligned}$$

Begin with the augmented matrix. Use elementary row operations until a triangular form for the coefficients is obtained.

$$\begin{bmatrix} 2 & -7 & -1 & \vdots & 1 \\ 1 & -3 & -4 & \vdots & 8 \\ 6 & -5 & 3 & \vdots & 7 \end{bmatrix} \rightarrow \begin{bmatrix} 1 & -3 & -4 & \vdots & 8 \\ 2 & -7 & -1 & \vdots & 1 \\ 6 & -5 & 3 & \vdots & 7 \end{bmatrix}$$

Interchange the first and second rows. It is convenient to have 1 in the upper left corner in order to obtain 0's below.

$$\rightarrow \begin{bmatrix} 1 & -3 & -4 & \vdots & 8 \\ 0 & -1 & 7 & \vdots & -15 \\ 0 & 13 & 27 & \vdots & -41 \end{bmatrix}$$

Add −2 times the first row to the second row. Add −6 times the first row to the third row.

$$\rightarrow \begin{bmatrix} 1 & -3 & -4 & \vdots & 8 \\ 0 & -1 & 7 & \vdots & -15 \\ 0 & 0 & 118 & \vdots & -236 \end{bmatrix}$$

Add 13 times the second row to the third row. This gives the desired triangular form, with zero coefficients outside of the triangle.

Now back-substitute, using the equations corresponding to the three rows in the last augmented matrix.

$$118z = -236 \quad \rightarrow z = -2$$
$$-y + 7z = -15 \quad \rightarrow -y + 7(-2) = -15 \quad \rightarrow y = 1$$
$$x - 3y - 4z = 8 \rightarrow x - 3(1) - 4(-2) = 8 \rightarrow x = 3$$

Check in the original system to show that the solution is (3, 1, −2).

When solving a linear system using matrices, the steps can vary. For instance, the solution in the example above could have started with the addition of $-\frac{1}{2}$ times the first row to the second row.

CLASS EXERCISES

Write the augmented matrix for each system.

1. $x - 3y = -1$
$3x + 2y = 19$

2. $2x + y + 4z = -8$
$-x + 2y - 4z = -2$
$2x - 3y - 2z = -3$

3. $2x - 2y + z = 12$
$x + y = 5$
$x + 3z = 0$

Write the linear system corresponding to each augmented matrix. Then solve the system, using back-substitution.

4. $\begin{bmatrix} 3 & 2 & | & 18 \\ 0 & 13 & | & 39 \end{bmatrix}$

5. $\begin{bmatrix} 1 & -2 & 3 & | & 4 \\ 0 & 1 & -3 & | & -3 \\ 0 & 0 & 2 & | & 4 \end{bmatrix}$

EXERCISES

A

Write the linear system corresponding to each augmented matrix. Then solve the system, using back-substitution.

1. $\begin{bmatrix} 5 & 4 & | & -3 \\ 0 & -8 & | & -4 \end{bmatrix}$

2. $\begin{bmatrix} 1 & -2 & 2 & | & 1 \\ 0 & 5 & 1 & | & 9 \\ 0 & 0 & -4 & | & 4 \end{bmatrix}$

3. $\begin{bmatrix} 1 & 1 & -4 & | & -4 \\ 0 & \frac{1}{2} & 6 & | & 11 \\ 0 & 0 & -\frac{2}{3} & | & -1 \end{bmatrix}$

Solve each system using augmented matrices and back-substitution.

4. $x - 3y = -2$
$-2x + 5y = 2$

5. $-x + 3y = -9$
$4x + 2y = 8$

6. $2x - 3y = 12$
$4x + y = 24$

7. $-9x + 7y = -15$
$3x + 2y = 18$

8. $2x + y = 3$
$3x + 2y = 9$

9. $x - 4y = -10$
$-2x + y = -8$

B

10. $x - 2y + 3z = 4$
$3x - 3y = 3$
$2y - 4z = -2$

11. $x + y = 5$
$x + 3z = 0$
$2x - 2y + z = 12$

12. $2x + 2z = 8$
$4y + z = -3$
$-6x + 2y = 2$

13. $x + 4z = 6$
$2x + 2y - z = -1$
$4x - y = 10$

14. $x - 2y + z = -1$
$2x + y - 3z = 3$
$3x + 2y - 3z = 7$

15. $4x + y + 2z = -8$
$2x + 3y - 2z = 3$
$-4x + 2y - z = -2$

C

16. Solve the system at the right, using augmented matrices and back-substitution.

$w - x - y - z = -4$
$x + z = 1$
$-w + x - y - 2z = -5$
$2w - x + 3z = -1$

17. In an augmented matrix, a row in which each element except the last is 0 corresponds to the false equation $0 = c$, where $c \neq 0$. Such a system has no solution.

Show that the system at the right has no solution.

$x - 2z = 6$
$-2x + 3y + 8z = 2$
$3y + 4z = -4$

16-2 Matrix Algebra

OBJECTIVE —————————————————————

To add, subtract, and multiply matrices, and to find scalar products.

Two matrices can be added provided they have the same number of rows and the same number of columns. The addition is done by adding the elements in corresponding positions in each matrix.

EXAMPLE 1   Find $A + B$, where $A = \begin{bmatrix} 2 & -3 & 1 \\ 0 & 5 & -4 \end{bmatrix}$ and $B = \begin{bmatrix} 4 & 2 & -6 \\ -7 & 1 & 0 \end{bmatrix}$.

$$A + B = \begin{bmatrix} 2 & -3 & 1 \\ 0 & 5 & -4 \end{bmatrix} + \begin{bmatrix} 4 & 2 & -6 \\ -7 & 1 & 0 \end{bmatrix}$$

$$= \begin{bmatrix} 2+4 & -3+2 & 1+(-6) \\ 0+(-7) & 5+1 & -4+0 \end{bmatrix} = \begin{bmatrix} 6 & -1 & -5 \\ -7 & 6 & -4 \end{bmatrix}$$

As illustrated in the last step of the above example, two matrices are equal if and only if they have equal elements in corresponding positions.

It can be shown that for any $m \times n$ matrices A, B, and C, addition is both commutative and associative.

$$A + B = B + A \qquad (A + B) + C = A + (B + C)$$

A matrix in which every element is 0 is called a **zero matrix** and is denoted by O. Since the addition of matrices involves the addition of real numbers, the zero matrix is the additive identity. That is,

$$A + O = O + A = A$$

The **additive inverse** of a matrix A is denoted by $-A$ and is formed by taking the opposite of each element in A. To illustrate:

$$\text{If } A = \begin{bmatrix} 6 & -1 & -2 \\ 0 & 4 & 3 \\ -8 & 7 & 1 \end{bmatrix}, \text{ then } -A = \begin{bmatrix} -6 & 1 & 2 \\ 0 & -4 & -3 \\ 8 & -7 & -1 \end{bmatrix}$$

It is clear that $A + (-A) = -A + A = O$.

Subtraction of two $m \times n$ matrices is defined using the additive inverse.

$$A - B = A + (-B)$$

EXAMPLE 2   Subtract the given matrices, as indicated.

$$\begin{bmatrix} 3 & 0 \\ -1 & 5 \\ -2 & \frac{1}{2} \end{bmatrix} - \begin{bmatrix} 1 & 2 \\ 3 & -3 \\ -2 & -\frac{1}{2} \end{bmatrix} = \begin{bmatrix} 3 & 0 \\ -1 & 5 \\ -2 & \frac{1}{2} \end{bmatrix} + \begin{bmatrix} -1 & -2 \\ -3 & 3 \\ 2 & \frac{1}{2} \end{bmatrix} = \begin{bmatrix} 2 & -2 \\ -4 & 8 \\ 0 & 1 \end{bmatrix}$$

The product of a real number c and a matrix A is denoted cA. The matrix is represented by a capital letter and a real number, or **scalar**, by a lower-case letter. The **scalar product** cA is found by multiplying each element of A by c.

EXAMPLE 3   Find $2D$, where $D = \begin{bmatrix} 6 & -3 \\ -1 & 2 \end{bmatrix}$.

$$2D = 2\begin{bmatrix} 6 & -3 \\ -1 & 2 \end{bmatrix} = \begin{bmatrix} 2(6) & 2(-3) \\ 2(-1) & 2(2) \end{bmatrix} = \begin{bmatrix} 12 & -6 \\ -2 & 4 \end{bmatrix}$$

Scalar multiplication of matrices has the following properties:

$1A = A$ $\qquad\qquad -1A = -A$ $\qquad\qquad$ $0A$ is the zero matrix.

$(cd)A = c(dA)$ $\qquad c(A + B) = cA + cB$ $\qquad (c + d)A = cA + dA$

For two matrices, A and B, the product AB is defined only if the number of columns of A is equal to the number of rows of B. Below is a step-by-step illustration of the computation of the product AB, where

$$A = \begin{bmatrix} 2 & 3 & -4 \\ -1 & 5 & 2 \end{bmatrix} \text{ and } B = \begin{bmatrix} 1 & 6 \\ -2 & 0 \\ 3 & 1 \end{bmatrix}$$

Note how each element in the product is formed. The elements in a row of A are multiplied by the corresponding elements in a column of B, and the results are added.

$$2(1) + 3(-2) + (-4)(3) =$$

$$AB = \begin{bmatrix} 2 & 3 & -4 \\ -1 & 5 & 2 \end{bmatrix}\begin{bmatrix} 1 & 6 \\ -2 & 0 \\ 3 & 1 \end{bmatrix} \qquad \begin{bmatrix} -16 & \end{bmatrix}$$

$$2(6) + 3(0) + (-4)(1) =$$

$$\begin{bmatrix} 2 & 3 & -4 \\ -1 & 5 & 2 \end{bmatrix}\begin{bmatrix} 1 & 6 \\ -2 & 0 \\ 3 & 1 \end{bmatrix} \qquad \begin{bmatrix} -16 & 8 \end{bmatrix}$$

$$\begin{bmatrix} 2 & 3 & -4 \\ -1 & 5 & 2 \end{bmatrix}\begin{bmatrix} 1 & 6 \\ -2 & 0 \\ 3 & 1 \end{bmatrix} \qquad \begin{bmatrix} -16 & 8 \\ -5 & \end{bmatrix}$$

$$-1(1) + 5(-2) + 2(3) =$$

$$AB = \begin{bmatrix} 2 & 3 & -4 \\ -1 & 5 & 2 \end{bmatrix}\begin{bmatrix} 1 & 6 \\ -2 & 0 \\ 3 & 1 \end{bmatrix} = \begin{bmatrix} -16 & 8 \\ -5 & -4 \end{bmatrix}$$

$$-1(6) + 5(0) + 2(1) =$$

Observe that A is a 2×3 matrix, B is a 3×2 matrix, and the product AB is a 2×2 matrix. In general, if A is $m \times p$ and B is $p \times n$, then AB is $m \times n$.

Matrix multiplication is not commutative, as is shown in the next example.

EXAMPLE 4   Find the product BA, using the matrices in the preceding illustration.

$$BA = \begin{bmatrix} 1 & 6 \\ -2 & 0 \\ 3 & 1 \end{bmatrix} \begin{bmatrix} 2 & 3 & -4 \\ -1 & 5 & 2 \end{bmatrix} = \begin{bmatrix} -4 & 33 & 8 \\ -4 & -6 & 8 \\ 5 & 14 & -10 \end{bmatrix} \quad \text{Note that } BA \neq AB.$$

Although matrix multiplication is not commutative, the operation does have the following properties.

$$(AB)C = A(BC) \qquad k(AB) = (kA)B = A(kB)$$
$$A(B + C) = AB + AC \qquad (B + C)A = BA + CA$$

CLASS EXERCISES

Evaluate each expression, if possible, for the given matrices.

$A = \begin{bmatrix} 3 & 6 \\ -2 & 1 \end{bmatrix}$ $B = \begin{bmatrix} -1 & 1 \\ 1 & -1 \end{bmatrix}$ $C = \begin{bmatrix} 5 \\ -2 \end{bmatrix}$

$D = \begin{bmatrix} 2 & 1 & -4 \end{bmatrix}$ $E = \begin{bmatrix} 1 & 0 & -1 \\ 2 & 2 & 1 \\ 0 & -1 & 2 \end{bmatrix}$ $F = \begin{bmatrix} 7 & -5 \\ 0 & 4 \\ -3 & 2 \end{bmatrix}$

1. $A + B$ **2.** $B - A$ **3.** $B + F$ **4.** $3E$ **5.** AB

6. AC **7.** $-4B + A$ **8.** ED **9.** EF **10.** $2C + 0C$

EXERCISES

A   *Evaluate each expression, if possible, for the given matrices.*

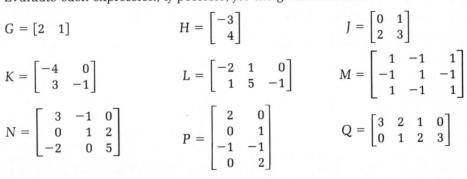

$G = \begin{bmatrix} 2 & 1 \end{bmatrix}$ $H = \begin{bmatrix} -3 \\ 4 \end{bmatrix}$ $J = \begin{bmatrix} 0 & 1 \\ 2 & 3 \end{bmatrix}$

$K = \begin{bmatrix} -4 & 0 \\ 3 & -1 \end{bmatrix}$ $L = \begin{bmatrix} -2 & 1 & 0 \\ 1 & 5 & -1 \end{bmatrix}$ $M = \begin{bmatrix} 1 & -1 & 1 \\ -1 & 1 & -1 \\ 1 & -1 & 1 \end{bmatrix}$

$N = \begin{bmatrix} 3 & -1 & 0 \\ 0 & 1 & 2 \\ -2 & 0 & 5 \end{bmatrix}$ $P = \begin{bmatrix} 2 & 0 \\ 0 & 1 \\ -1 & -1 \\ 0 & 2 \end{bmatrix}$ $Q = \begin{bmatrix} 3 & 2 & 1 & 0 \\ 0 & 1 & 2 & 3 \end{bmatrix}$

1. $G + H$ **2.** $J + K$ **3.** $N - M$ **4.** $K - 4J$ **5.** JK

6. KJ **7.** $2(GH)$ **8.** HG **9.** LM **10.** GJ

11. *KH*   **12.** *LP*   **13.** *PQ*   **14.** *QP*   **15.** (*GK*)*H*

16. *G*(*K* + *J*)   **17.** *0M*   **18.** 3*M* − 2*N*   **19.** (−2*P*)*L*   **20.** *P*(−2*L*)

21. [0 0]*Q*   **22.** $P\begin{bmatrix} 0 \\ 0 \end{bmatrix}$ **23.** *LM* + *LN*   **24.** *L*(*M* + *N*)

25. The matrix *I*, at the left, is called the 3 × 3 **identity matrix**, since *IK* = *KI* = *K* for any 3 × 3 matrix *K*. Verify this result for matrix *K* shown at the right.

$$I = \begin{bmatrix} 1 & 0 & 0 \\ 0 & 1 & 0 \\ 0 & 0 & 1 \end{bmatrix} \qquad K = \begin{bmatrix} a & b & c \\ d & e & f \\ g & h & i \end{bmatrix}$$

26. The zero product rule for real numbers states that if *ab* = 0, then at least one of the two factors *a* and *b* is equal to 0. Verify that this rule does *not* apply to matrix multiplication by finding the product *AB*, where

$$A = \begin{bmatrix} 1 & 2 \\ 3 & 6 \end{bmatrix} \text{ and } B = \begin{bmatrix} -4 & 6 \\ 2 & -3 \end{bmatrix}.$$

*Show that each matrix property is valid for matrices **A**, **B**, and **C**, where*

$$A = \begin{bmatrix} 2 & 1 \\ 0 & -4 \end{bmatrix} \qquad B = \begin{bmatrix} 0 & -1 \\ 3 & 2 \end{bmatrix} \qquad C = \begin{bmatrix} 5 & 2 \\ 1 & -1 \end{bmatrix}$$

27. *A* + *B* = *B* + *A*   **28.** *A*(*B* + *C*) = *AB* + *AC*   **29.** (*B* + *C*)*A* = *BA* + *CA*

30. (*A* + *B*) + *C* = *A* + (*B* + *C*)   **31.** (*AB*)*C* = *A*(*BC*)

*For a positive integer **n**,* $P^n = \overbrace{PP \ldots P}^{n \text{ factors}}$. *Evaluate each expression for matrix P, shown at the right.*

$$P = \begin{bmatrix} 2 & 0 & 0 \\ 0 & 3 & 0 \\ 0 & 0 & 4 \end{bmatrix}$$

32. P^2 **33.** P^3 **34.** P^n

CHECKPOINT

Solve each system by using augmented matrices and back-substitution.

1. x + 2y = 3   **2.** x + y − z = 0   **3.** 5x − 2y + z = 2
   3x − y = −5   2x − y + z = 3   −2x + 5y + 3z = 1
                            3x + 2y − 2z = 1   4x − 3y − 2z = −4

Evaluate each expression, if possible, for the given matrices.

$$R = \begin{bmatrix} -3 & 4 & 1 \end{bmatrix} \qquad S = \begin{bmatrix} 1 & 1 & 3 \\ -3 & -2 & -1 \\ 2 & -1 & 3 \end{bmatrix} \qquad T = \begin{bmatrix} 1 & 0 & 2 \\ -2 & -1 & 1 \\ 0 & -2 & -1 \end{bmatrix}$$

4. *SR*   **5.** 3(*T* + *S*)   **6.** (*RT*)*S*   **7.** *ST* − *TS*

Using Matrices to Organize Data

An appliance manufacturer has two outlet stores in one city. During November, Store I sold 20 dishwashers, 30 refrigerators, and 14 ranges. Store II sold 25 dishwashers, 22 refrigerators, and 11 ranges during the same month. In December, the appliances sold at Store I were 24 dishwashers, 28 refrigerators, and 17 ranges; Store II sold 16 dishwashers, 22 refrigerators, and 20 ranges. These sales figures can be arranged in 2×3 matrix displays.

		Dishwashers	Refrigerators	Ranges	
November sales matrix	$N =$	20	30	14	Store I
		25	22	11	Store II

		Dishwashers	Refrigerators	Ranges	
December sales matrix	$D =$	24	28	17	Store I
		16	22	20	Store II

Matrix displays like these are effective ways of organizing data. Furthermore, matrix algebra can be used to obtain additional information. For example, suppose the manufacturer wants to know the *total* sales of each appliance per store for the two months. Matrix addition gives the required matrix display.

		Dishwashers	Refrigerators	Ranges	
two-month sales matrix	$N + D =$	44	58	31	Store I
		41	44	31	Store II

1. Find $D - N$ for matrices D and N, given above. What is the meaning of a positive element in matrix $D - N$? What is the meaning of a negative element? a zero element?

Two furniture stores held January sales. During the month, Store A sold 37 sofas, 42 tables, 104 chairs, and 29 desks, while Store B sold 31 sofas, 38 tables, 92 chairs, and 33 desks. The following month there were no special sales. In February, Store A sold 22 sofas, 20 tables, 48 chairs, and 13 desks, while Store B sold 25 sofas, 18 tables, 56 chairs, and 8 desks.

2. Write a 2×4 matrix for each month. Show the sales for each item per store.

3. Write a matrix showing the two-month sales totals for each item per store.

4. The total sales made during the three-month period January through March is given by the matrix at the right. Write a matrix showing the number of sales for each item per store in March.

	S	T	C	D	
	73	81	198	49	Store A
	68	72	200	46	Store B

16-3 Solving Systems, Using Inverses

OBJECTIVES

To find the multiplicative inverse of a square matrix.
To solve a linear system, using the inverse of the matrix of coefficients.

A **square matrix** is a matrix with the same number of rows and columns. The *multiplicative identity* for all 2×2 matrices is the square matrix

$$I = \begin{bmatrix} 1 & 0 \\ 0 & 1 \end{bmatrix}$$

since $IR = RI = R$ for any 2×2 matrix R, as shown here.

$$\begin{bmatrix} 1 & 0 \\ 0 & 1 \end{bmatrix} \begin{bmatrix} a & b \\ c & d \end{bmatrix} = \begin{bmatrix} a & b \\ c & d \end{bmatrix} \begin{bmatrix} 1 & 0 \\ 0 & 1 \end{bmatrix} = \begin{bmatrix} a & b \\ c & d \end{bmatrix}$$

The multiplicative identity for all 3×3 matrices is

$$I = \begin{bmatrix} 1 & 0 & 0 \\ 0 & 1 & 0 \\ 0 & 0 & 1 \end{bmatrix}$$

since $IQ = QI = Q$ for any 3×3 matrix Q. Similar observations can be made for square matrices of any size.

Any nonzero number x has a reciprocal, or multiplicative inverse, x^{-1}, so that $xx^{-1} = x^{-1}x = 1$. Certain square matrices also have *multiplicative inverses*. Consider, for example, the following products of the matrices

$$A = \begin{bmatrix} -2 & -4 \\ 4 & 7 \end{bmatrix} \text{ and } B = \begin{bmatrix} \frac{7}{2} & 2 \\ -2 & -1 \end{bmatrix}.$$

$$AB = \begin{bmatrix} -2 & -4 \\ 4 & 7 \end{bmatrix} \begin{bmatrix} \frac{7}{2} & 2 \\ -2 & -1 \end{bmatrix} = \begin{bmatrix} 1 & 0 \\ 0 & 1 \end{bmatrix} = I$$

$$BA = \begin{bmatrix} \frac{7}{2} & 2 \\ -2 & -1 \end{bmatrix} \begin{bmatrix} -2 & -4 \\ 4 & 7 \end{bmatrix} = \begin{bmatrix} 1 & 0 \\ 0 & 1 \end{bmatrix} = I$$

Since $AB = BA = I$, we say that B is the inverse of A and write $B = A^{-1}$ and $AA^{-1} = A^{-1}A = I$. Note that A^{-1} represents the multiplicative inverse of A, not the reciprocal of A. Matrices do not have reciprocals.

Suppose the inverse of A were not known. One way to find A^{-1} is to write a 2×4 matrix containing A and I and to apply elementary row operations until the left half has been transformed into I. When this occurs, the right half will be A^{-1}.

$$A \quad \begin{bmatrix} -2 & -4 & \vdots & 1 & 0 \\ 4 & 7 & \vdots & 0 & 1 \end{bmatrix} \quad I$$

Start with a 2×4 matrix, showing A at the left and I at the right.

$$\begin{bmatrix} -2 & -4 & \vdots & 1 & 0 \\ 0 & -1 & \vdots & 2 & 1 \end{bmatrix}$$

Add 2 times the first row to the second row.

$$\begin{bmatrix} -2 & 0 & \vdots & -7 & -4 \\ 0 & -1 & \vdots & 2 & 1 \end{bmatrix}$$

Add -4 times the second row to the first row.

$$I \quad \begin{bmatrix} 1 & 0 & \vdots & \frac{7}{2} & 2 \\ 0 & 1 & \vdots & -2 & -1 \end{bmatrix} \quad A^{-1}$$

Multiply the first row by $-\frac{1}{2}$ and the second row by -1.

EXAMPLE 1   Find B^{-1} for $B = \begin{bmatrix} 1 & 2 & 4 \\ 0 & -1 & 1 \\ 2 & 3 & 8 \end{bmatrix}$.

$$B \quad \begin{bmatrix} 1 & 2 & 4 & \vdots & 1 & 0 & 0 \\ 0 & -1 & 1 & \vdots & 0 & 1 & 0 \\ 2 & 3 & 8 & \vdots & 0 & 0 & 1 \end{bmatrix} \quad I$$

Start with a 3×6 matrix, showing B at the left and I at the right.

$$\begin{bmatrix} 1 & 2 & 4 & \vdots & 1 & 0 & 0 \\ 0 & -1 & 1 & \vdots & 0 & 1 & 0 \\ 0 & -1 & 0 & \vdots & -2 & 0 & 1 \end{bmatrix}$$

Add -2 times the first row to the third row.

$$\begin{bmatrix} 1 & 2 & 4 & \vdots & 1 & 0 & 0 \\ 0 & -1 & 0 & \vdots & -2 & 0 & 1 \\ 0 & -1 & 1 & \vdots & 0 & 1 & 0 \end{bmatrix}$$

Interchange the second and third rows.

$$\begin{bmatrix} 1 & 0 & 4 & \vdots & -3 & 0 & 2 \\ 0 & -1 & 0 & \vdots & -2 & 0 & 1 \\ 0 & 0 & 1 & \vdots & 2 & 1 & -1 \end{bmatrix}$$

Add 2 times the second row to the first row. Add -1 times the second row to the third row.

$$I \quad \begin{bmatrix} 1 & 0 & 0 & \vdots & -11 & -4 & 6 \\ 0 & 1 & 0 & \vdots & 2 & 0 & -1 \\ 0 & 0 & 1 & \vdots & 2 & 1 & -1 \end{bmatrix} \quad B^{-1}$$

Add -4 times the third row to the first row. Multiply the second row by -1.

Since I is on the left, the inverse of B is on the right.

Thus, $B^{-1} = \begin{bmatrix} -11 & -4 & 6 \\ 2 & 0 & -1 \\ 2 & 1 & -1 \end{bmatrix}$.   Verify that $BB^{-1} = B^{-1}B = I$.

The method just described can also be used to show that a square matrix has no inverse. To illustrate, we will try to find the inverse of $G = \begin{bmatrix} 3 & -1 \\ -6 & 2 \end{bmatrix}$. The first step is to write the appropriate 2×4 matrix. In an effort to transform the left side into I, 2 times the first row is added to the second row.

$$\begin{bmatrix} 3 & -1 & \vdots & 1 & 0 \\ -6 & 2 & \vdots & 0 & 1 \end{bmatrix} \longrightarrow \begin{bmatrix} 3 & -1 & \vdots & 1 & 0 \\ 0 & 0 & \vdots & 2 & 1 \end{bmatrix}$$

The result is a row in which every element of the left part is 0, so it is impossible to transform the left side into I. This means that G has no multiplicative inverse.

The inverse of a matrix can be used to solve a linear system. First note how the linear system on the left can be written as the **matrix equation** on the right.

	matrix of coefficients	matrix of variables	matrix of constants

$$\begin{array}{c} -2x - 4y = 4 \\ 4x + 7y = -3 \end{array} \qquad \begin{bmatrix} -2 & -4 \\ 4 & 7 \end{bmatrix} \quad \begin{bmatrix} x \\ y \end{bmatrix} = \begin{bmatrix} 4 \\ -3 \end{bmatrix}$$

The matrix equation can be abbreviated as $AX = C$. Here A is the matrix of coefficients, X is the matrix of variables, and C is the matrix of constants. Assume that A^{-1} is known. Then

$$AX = C$$
$$A^{-1}(AX) = A^{-1}C$$
$$(A^{-1}A)X = A^{-1}C$$
$$IX = A^{-1}C$$
$$X = A^{-1}C$$

The solution of the given system is presented in the next example.

EXAMPLE 2

Solve the system shown at the right by using the inverse of the matrix of coefficients.

$$\begin{array}{c} -2x - 4y = 4 \\ 4x + 7y = -3 \end{array}$$

$$C = \begin{bmatrix} 4 \\ -3 \end{bmatrix} \qquad A = \begin{bmatrix} -2 & -4 \\ 4 & 7 \end{bmatrix}, \text{ and it has been shown that } A^{-1} = \begin{bmatrix} \frac{7}{2} & 2 \\ -2 & -1 \end{bmatrix}.$$

$$X = A^{-1}C$$

$$\begin{bmatrix} x \\ y \end{bmatrix} = \begin{bmatrix} \frac{7}{2} & 2 \\ -2 & -1 \end{bmatrix} \begin{bmatrix} 4 \\ -3 \end{bmatrix} = \begin{bmatrix} 8 \\ -5 \end{bmatrix}$$

Since the corresponding elements of equal matrices are equal, $x = 8$ and $y = -5$. Check to show that $(8, -5)$ is the solution to the system.

CLASS EXERCISES

Find the multiplicative inverse of each matrix, if it exists.

1. $\begin{bmatrix} 1 & 3 \\ 0 & 1 \end{bmatrix}$ **2.** $\begin{bmatrix} 1 & 2 \\ -1 & -3 \end{bmatrix}$ **3.** $\begin{bmatrix} 2 & -2 \\ 1 & -2 \end{bmatrix}$ **4.** $\begin{bmatrix} 1 & -4 \\ -2 & 8 \end{bmatrix}$

5. Write the system at the right as a matrix equation.

$$3x - 8y = 4$$
$$-x + 5y = 1$$

6. Write the matrix equation $\begin{bmatrix} 5 & -1 \\ -2 & 2 \end{bmatrix} \begin{bmatrix} x \\ y \end{bmatrix} = \begin{bmatrix} 6 \\ 4 \end{bmatrix}$ as a linear system of equations.

7. Solve the matrix equation $\begin{bmatrix} x \\ y \end{bmatrix} = \begin{bmatrix} 1 & -2 \\ 3 & 2 \end{bmatrix} \begin{bmatrix} 7 \\ 4 \end{bmatrix}$ for x and y.

EXERCISES

A

Find the multiplicative inverse of each matrix, if it exists.

1. $\begin{bmatrix} 1 & 6 \\ 0 & 2 \end{bmatrix}$ **2.** $\begin{bmatrix} 1 & 2 \\ -1 & -3 \end{bmatrix}$ **3.** $\begin{bmatrix} 1 & 5 \\ 2 & 8 \end{bmatrix}$ **4.** $\begin{bmatrix} \frac{1}{2} & 4 \\ 1 & 8 \end{bmatrix}$

Solve each linear system using the inverse of the matrix of coefficients. Use your results from Exercises 1–3.

5. $x + 6y = 3$
      $2y = -6$

6. $x + 2y = 7$
      $-x - 3y = 1$

7. $x + 5y = 3$
      $2x + 8y = 2$

B

Find the multiplicative inverse of each matrix, if it exists.

8. $\begin{bmatrix} 0 & 0 & 1 \\ 1 & 0 & 0 \\ 0 & 1 & 0 \end{bmatrix}$ **9.** $\begin{bmatrix} -1 & 1 & 0 \\ 0 & -1 & 1 \\ 0 & 1 & -2 \end{bmatrix}$ **10.** $\begin{bmatrix} 1 & 0 & -2 \\ -2 & 1 & 2 \\ 0 & 5 & -8 \end{bmatrix}$ **11.** $\begin{bmatrix} 1 & -1 & 2 \\ 2 & 1 & 3 \\ 0 & 4 & -1 \end{bmatrix}$

Solve each linear system using the inverse of the matrix of coefficients. Use your results from Exercises 9–11.

12. $-x + y = 4$
      $-y + z = -2$
      $y - 2z = 3$

13. $x - 2z = -6$
      $-2x + y + 2z = 1$
      $5y - 8z = -15$

14. $x - y + 2z = -1$
      $2x + y + 3z = -3$
      $4y - z = 2$

C

15. For $A = \begin{bmatrix} 1 & -2 \\ 0 & 1 \end{bmatrix}$ and $B = \begin{bmatrix} 0 & -2 \\ 1 & 2 \end{bmatrix}$, verify that $(AB)^{-1} = B^{-1}A^{-1}$.

*16. Assume that A and B are $n \times n$ matrices that have inverses. Prove that $(AB)^{-1} = B^{-1}A^{-1}$.

    Hint: $M^{-1} = N$ if and only if $MN = NM = I$.

*17. A matrix can have no more than one multiplicative inverse. Prove this by assuming that matrix A has inverses B and C and showing that $B = C$.

    Hint: Begin with $AB = I$.

*18. Use the inverse of the matrix of coefficients to solve the system given in Exercise 16 on page 624.

MATRICES, DETERMINANTS, AND LINEAR SYSTEMS

16-4 Determinants

OBJECTIVE

To evaluate second- and third-order determinants.

To each square matrix there corresponds a unique number called the determinant of the matrix. For a 2 × 2 matrix A, the **determinant** of A, denoted by **det** A, is defined below.

$$A = \begin{bmatrix} a & b \\ c & d \end{bmatrix} \qquad \det A = \begin{vmatrix} a & b \\ c & d \end{vmatrix} = ad - bc$$

EXAMPLE 1 Evaluate each determinant.

a. $\begin{vmatrix} 3 & 4 \\ 5 & 2 \end{vmatrix} = 3(2) - 5(4) = -14$ **b.** $\begin{vmatrix} 4 & -3 \\ 2 & 5 \end{vmatrix} = 4(5) - 2(-3) = 26$

A 2 × 2 determinant is also called a **second-order determinant.** For a 3 × 3 matrix B, the **third-order determinant** is defined as follows.

$$B = \begin{bmatrix} a_1 & b_1 & c_1 \\ a_2 & b_2 & c_2 \\ a_3 & b_3 & c_3 \end{bmatrix}$$

$$\det B = \begin{vmatrix} a_1 & b_1 & c_1 \\ a_2 & b_2 & c_2 \\ a_3 & b_3 & c_3 \end{vmatrix} = a_1 b_2 c_3 + a_2 b_3 c_1 + a_3 b_1 c_2 - a_1 b_3 c_2 - a_2 b_1 c_3 - a_3 b_2 c_1$$

To avoid having to memorize this definition, the following scheme is used. Begin by copying the first two columns to the right of the determinant, as shown below. Follow the downward arrows to get the three products preceded by plus signs. Follow the upward arrows to get the three products preceded by minus signs.

$$\begin{vmatrix} a_1 & b_1 & c_1 \\ a_2 & b_2 & c_2 \\ a_3 & b_3 & c_3 \end{vmatrix} \begin{matrix} a_1 & b_1 \\ a_2 & b_2 \\ a_3 & b_3 \end{matrix} = a_1 b_2 c_3 + b_1 c_2 a_3 + c_1 a_2 b_3 - a_3 b_2 c_1 - b_3 c_2 a_1 - c_3 a_2 b_1$$

$$+ \quad + \quad +$$

EXAMPLE 2 Evaluate det B.

$$\det B = \begin{vmatrix} 2 & -3 & 1 \\ -1 & 6 & 0 \\ 4 & 5 & 5 \end{vmatrix} = \begin{vmatrix} 2 & -3 & 1 \\ -1 & 6 & 0 \\ 4 & 5 & 5 \end{vmatrix} \begin{matrix} 2 & -3 \\ -1 & 6 \\ 4 & 5 \end{matrix}$$

$$= 60 + 0 + (-5) - 24 - 0 - 15 = 16$$

An alternate way to evaluate a third-order determinant is based on the following algebraic development.

$$\begin{vmatrix} a_1 & b_1 & c_1 \\ a_2 & b_2 & c_2 \\ a_3 & b_3 & c_3 \end{vmatrix} = a_1b_2c_3 + a_2b_3c_1 + a_3b_1c_2 - a_1b_3c_2 - a_2b_1c_3 - a_3b_2c_1$$

$$= (a_1b_2c_3 - a_1b_3c_2) + (a_2b_3c_1 - a_2b_1c_3) + (a_3b_1c_2 - a_3b_2c_1)$$

$$= a_1(b_2c_3 - b_3c_2) - a_2(b_1c_3 - b_3c_1) + a_3(b_1c_2 - b_2c_1)$$

$$= a_1\begin{vmatrix} b_2 & c_2 \\ b_3 & c_3 \end{vmatrix} - a_2\begin{vmatrix} b_1 & c_1 \\ b_3 & c_3 \end{vmatrix} + a_3\begin{vmatrix} b_1 & c_1 \\ b_2 & c_2 \end{vmatrix}$$

This result is called the **expansion of the determinant by minors** along the first column. The first determinant is called the *minor of a_1*, the second determinant is the *minor of a_2*, and the third is the *minor of a_3*. Each minor is easily identified by deleting the row and column for the element preceding that minor in the expansion.

$$\begin{vmatrix} \cancel{a_1} & \cancel{b_1} & \cancel{c_1} \\ \cancel{a_2} & b_2 & c_2 \\ \cancel{a_3} & b_3 & c_3 \end{vmatrix} \qquad \begin{vmatrix} \cancel{a_1} & b_1 & c_1 \\ \cancel{a_2} & \cancel{b_2} & \cancel{c_2} \\ \cancel{a_3} & b_3 & c_3 \end{vmatrix} \qquad \begin{vmatrix} \cancel{a_1} & b_1 & c_1 \\ \cancel{a_2} & b_2 & c_2 \\ \cancel{a_3} & \cancel{b_3} & \cancel{c_3} \end{vmatrix}$$

In the expansion by minors along the first column, notice that the elements a_1, a_2, and a_3 are preceded by the signs $+$, $-$, $+$, respectively. The expansion along any given column or row will have a distinct pattern of signs in these positions. You may find that the diagram at the right helps you to remember these signs.

$$\begin{vmatrix} + & - & + \\ - & + & - \\ + & - & + \end{vmatrix}$$

EXAMPLE 3 Evaluate det A, where $A = \begin{bmatrix} 1 & 2 & 3 \\ -6 & 0 & 1 \\ 2 & -1 & 4 \end{bmatrix}$.

a. Use an expansion by minors along the first column.

$$\begin{vmatrix} 1 & 2 & 3 \\ -6 & 0 & 1 \\ 2 & -1 & 4 \end{vmatrix} = 1\begin{vmatrix} 0 & 1 \\ -1 & 4 \end{vmatrix} - (-6)\begin{vmatrix} 2 & 3 \\ -1 & 4 \end{vmatrix} + 2\begin{vmatrix} 2 & 3 \\ 0 & 1 \end{vmatrix}$$

$$= 1(1) - (-6)(11) + 2(2) = 1 + 66 + 4 = 71$$

b. Use an expansion by minors along the second row.

$$\begin{vmatrix} 1 & 2 & 3 \\ -6 & 0 & 1 \\ 2 & -1 & 4 \end{vmatrix} = -(-6)\begin{vmatrix} 2 & 3 \\ -1 & 4 \end{vmatrix} + 0\begin{vmatrix} 1 & 3 \\ 2 & 4 \end{vmatrix} - 1\begin{vmatrix} 1 & 2 \\ 2 & -1 \end{vmatrix}$$

$$= -(-6)(11) + 0 - 1(-5) = 66 + 5 = 71$$

In Example 3, note that the expansion along the second row is simpler because one element in that row is 0.

CLASS EXERCISES

Evaluate each determinant.

1. $\begin{vmatrix} 4 & -1 \\ 3 & 3 \end{vmatrix}$ **2.** $\begin{vmatrix} -7 & 2 \\ -4 & 1 \end{vmatrix}$ **3.** $\begin{vmatrix} \frac{1}{2} & 9 \\ -2 & 10 \end{vmatrix}$ **4.** $\begin{vmatrix} 2 & 1 \\ -4 & -2 \end{vmatrix}$

Evaluate $\begin{vmatrix} 3 & 1 & 0 \\ -1 & 2 & 4 \\ -2 & 5 & 1 \end{vmatrix}$, *using the given method.*

5. Copy the first two columns to the right of the determinant.

6. Expand along the second column.   **7.** Expand along the first row.

EXERCISES

A

Evaluate each determinant.

1. $\begin{vmatrix} 2 & 3 \\ -2 & 5 \end{vmatrix}$ **2.** $\begin{vmatrix} -6 & 8 \\ 4 & -1 \end{vmatrix}$ **3.** $\begin{vmatrix} 4 & \frac{1}{3} \\ -6 & -1 \end{vmatrix}$ **4.** $\begin{vmatrix} 8 & -16 \\ -5 & 10 \end{vmatrix}$

Evaluate $\begin{vmatrix} 3 & 2 & 1 \\ -2 & -3 & 0 \\ 0 & 4 & -1 \end{vmatrix}$, *using the given method.*

5. Copy the first two columns to the right of the determinant.

6. Expand along the first column.

7. Expand along the third column.

8. Expand along the second row.

9. Expand along the third row.

B

Evaluate.

10. $\begin{vmatrix} 1 & 0 & 0 \\ 0 & 1 & 0 \\ 0 & 0 & 1 \end{vmatrix}$ **11.** $\begin{vmatrix} 0 & 1 & 0 \\ 1 & 0 & 0 \\ 0 & 0 & 1 \end{vmatrix}$ **12.** $\begin{vmatrix} 1 & 2 & -3 \\ 1 & 2 & 4 \\ 1 & 2 & 5 \end{vmatrix}$ **13.** $\begin{vmatrix} 1 & 2 & 3 \\ 2 & 3 & 0 \\ 3 & 0 & 0 \end{vmatrix}$

14. $\begin{vmatrix} 1 & -1 & 0 \\ 0 & 1 & -1 \\ 2 & 0 & 1 \end{vmatrix}$ **15.** $\begin{vmatrix} 2 & 1 & -1 \\ 3 & 0 & -2 \\ 0 & 6 & 4 \end{vmatrix}$ **16.** $\begin{vmatrix} 2 & 4 & 6 \\ -1 & -2 & -3 \\ 8 & 9 & 10 \end{vmatrix}$ **17.** $\begin{vmatrix} 2 & -1 & 3 \\ 3 & -2 & 1 \\ 1 & 2 & 3 \end{vmatrix}$

18. $\begin{vmatrix} 10 & -8 \\ -9 & 5 \end{vmatrix} \div \begin{vmatrix} 10 & 2 \\ -9 & 7 \end{vmatrix}$

19. $\begin{vmatrix} 1 & 0 & 3 \\ 7 & 5 & 5 \\ 2 & 3 & 0 \end{vmatrix} \div \begin{vmatrix} 1 & 3 & 0 \\ -2 & 0 & 3 \\ 0 & 1 & 2 \end{vmatrix}$

20. If $\begin{vmatrix} x & 2 \\ x+3 & -1 \end{vmatrix} = 0$, find x.

21. If $\begin{vmatrix} 1 & y & 2 \\ -2 & 6 & 1 \\ 3 & y-6 & -1 \end{vmatrix} = 0$, find y.

22. Verify that $(\det A)(\det B) = \det (AB)$, using the determinant in Exercise 14 as $\det A$ and the one in Exercise 15 as $\det B$.

Exercises 23–26 illustrate properties of determinants that can be used to simplify the evaluation of determinants.

23. Interchanging any two rows (or columns) changes the sign of the determinant.

Verify this case:
$$\begin{vmatrix} a_1 & b_1 & c_1 \\ a_3 & b_3 & c_3 \\ a_2 & b_2 & c_2 \end{vmatrix} = - \begin{vmatrix} a_1 & b_1 & c_1 \\ a_2 & b_2 & c_2 \\ a_3 & b_3 & c_3 \end{vmatrix}$$

24. If one row (or column) is a multiple of another, the determinant equals 0.

Verify this case:
$$\begin{vmatrix} a_1 & ka_1 & c_1 \\ a_2 & ka_2 & c_2 \\ a_3 & ka_3 & c_3 \end{vmatrix} = 0$$

25. If one row (or column) is multiplied by a number k, the value of the determinant is multiplied by k.

Verify this case:
$$\begin{vmatrix} a_1 & b_1 & kc_1 \\ a_2 & b_2 & kc_2 \\ a_3 & b_3 & kc_3 \end{vmatrix} = k \begin{vmatrix} a_1 & b_1 & c_1 \\ a_2 & b_2 & c_2 \\ a_3 & b_3 & c_3 \end{vmatrix}$$

26. If a multiple of one row (or column) is added to another row (or column), the value of the determinant remains the same.

Verify this case:
$$\begin{vmatrix} a_1 & b_1 & c_1 \\ a_2 & b_2 & c_2 \\ a_3 + ka_1 & b_3 + kb_1 & c_3 + kc_1 \end{vmatrix} = \begin{vmatrix} a_1 & b_1 & c_1 \\ a_2 & b_2 & c_2 \\ a_3 & b_3 & c_3 \end{vmatrix}$$

Explain each step. Refer to the properties in Exercises 23–26.

27.
$$\begin{vmatrix} 2 & 6 & -3 \\ 0 & -4 & 1 \\ -4 & 2 & 2 \end{vmatrix} = - \begin{vmatrix} -4 & 2 & 2 \\ 0 & -4 & 1 \\ 2 & 6 & -3 \end{vmatrix} = -2 \begin{vmatrix} -2 & 1 & 1 \\ 0 & -4 & 1 \\ 2 & 6 & -3 \end{vmatrix} = -2 \begin{vmatrix} -2 & 1 & 1 \\ 0 & -4 & 1 \\ 0 & 7 & -2 \end{vmatrix}$$

28.
$$\begin{vmatrix} 5 & -5 & 10 \\ -3 & 6 & 12 \\ 1 & -1 & 4 \end{vmatrix} = 5 \begin{vmatrix} 1 & -1 & 2 \\ -3 & 6 & 12 \\ 1 & -1 & 4 \end{vmatrix} = 15 \begin{vmatrix} 1 & -1 & 2 \\ -1 & 2 & 4 \\ 1 & -1 & 4 \end{vmatrix} = 15 \begin{vmatrix} 1 & -1 & 2 \\ 0 & 1 & 6 \\ 0 & 0 & 2 \end{vmatrix}$$

*29. Show that $\begin{vmatrix} 1 & 1 & 1 \\ a & b & c \\ a^2 & b^2 & c^2 \end{vmatrix} = (a - b)(a - c)(c - b)$.

*30. Using matrices A and B, shown at the right, prove that $\det (AB) = (\det A)(\det B)$.
$$A = \begin{bmatrix} a & b \\ c & d \end{bmatrix} \qquad B = \begin{bmatrix} e & f \\ g & h \end{bmatrix}$$

*31. Show that the *determinant equation* at the right is an equation of the line through the two distinct points (a_1, b_1) and (a_2, b_2).
$$\begin{vmatrix} 1 & x & y \\ 1 & a_1 & b_1 \\ 1 & a_2 & b_2 \end{vmatrix} = 0$$

16-5 Cramer's Rule

OBJECTIVE _____

To solve linear systems, using second- and third-order determinants.

_____

Second-order determinants can be used to solve linear systems of two equations in two variables. In general, such a system can be written using the subscripts 1 and 2 to identify the coefficients and constants of the first and second equations, respectively. The system is solved for x by eliminating y, as follows.

$$a_1x + b_1y = c_1 \longrightarrow a_1b_2x + b_1b_2y = c_1b_2 \qquad \text{Multiply through by } b_2.$$
$$a_2x + b_2y = c_2 \longrightarrow \underline{a_2b_1x + b_1b_2y = c_2b_1} \qquad \text{Multiply through by } b_1.$$
$$a_1b_2x - a_2b_1x = c_1b_2 - c_2b_1 \qquad \text{Subtract.}$$
$$(a_1b_2 - a_2b_1)x = c_1b_2 - c_2b_1 \qquad \text{Factor the left side.}$$
$$x = \frac{c_1b_2 - c_2b_1}{a_1b_2 - a_2b_1} \qquad \begin{array}{l}\text{Divide, assuming}\\ a_1b_2 - a_2b_1 \neq 0.\end{array}$$

The system can be solved for y in a similar manner, and the numerators and denominators of the expressions for x and y can be written as determinants.

$$x = \frac{c_1b_2 - c_2b_1}{a_1b_2 - a_2b_1} = \frac{\begin{vmatrix} c_1 & b_1 \\ c_2 & b_2 \end{vmatrix}}{\begin{vmatrix} a_1 & b_1 \\ a_2 & b_2 \end{vmatrix}} = \frac{D_x}{D} \qquad y = \frac{a_1c_2 - a_2c_1}{a_1b_2 - a_2b_1} = \frac{\begin{vmatrix} a_1 & c_1 \\ a_2 & c_2 \end{vmatrix}}{\begin{vmatrix} a_1 & b_1 \\ a_2 & b_2 \end{vmatrix}} = \frac{D_y}{D}$$

Observe that the common denominator D is the determinant of the *matrix of coefficients*. The numerator of x, D_x, can be obtained from D by replacing the first column of D by the constants c_1 and c_2. Similarly, the numerator of y, D_y, is obtained by replacing the second column of D by the constants. **Cramer's rule** for solving a system of two linear equations in two variables is stated below, using this new notation.

_____

Cramer's Rule

The solution to a linear system $\begin{array}{l} a_1x + b_1y = c_1 \\ a_2x + b_2y = c_2 \end{array}$ **is**

$$x = \frac{D_x}{D}, \quad y = \frac{D_y}{D} \quad (D \neq 0)$$

_____

EXAMPLE 1 Solve the system $\begin{array}{c} 2x + 5y = -4 \\ 3x - y = 11 \end{array}$ by using Cramer's rule.

$$D = \begin{vmatrix} 2 & 5 \\ 3 & -1 \end{vmatrix} = -17$$

Replace the *first* column in D by the constants in the equations.

$$x = \frac{D_x}{D} = \frac{\begin{vmatrix} -4 & 5 \\ 11 & -1 \end{vmatrix}}{-17} = \frac{-51}{-17} = 3$$

Replace the *second* column in D by the constants in the equations.

$$y = \frac{D_y}{D} = \frac{\begin{vmatrix} 2 & -4 \\ 3 & 11 \end{vmatrix}}{-17} = \frac{34}{-17} = -2$$

Check in the original system to show that the solution is $(3, -2)$.

Cramers's rule can be extended to systems of three linear equations in three variables. The general system is shown on the left below, and the determinant for the matrix of coefficients D is shown on the right.

$$\begin{array}{c} a_1x + b_1y + c_1z = d_1 \\ a_2x + b_2y + c_2z = d_2 \\ a_3x + b_3y + c_3z = d_3 \end{array} \qquad D = \begin{vmatrix} a_1 & b_1 & c_1 \\ a_2 & b_2 & c_2 \\ a_3 & b_3 & c_3 \end{vmatrix}$$

If $D \neq 0$, it can be shown that the solution for the system is given by

$$x = \frac{\begin{vmatrix} d_1 & b_1 & c_1 \\ d_2 & b_2 & c_2 \\ d_3 & b_3 & c_3 \end{vmatrix}}{D} = \frac{D_x}{D} \qquad y = \frac{\begin{vmatrix} a_1 & d_1 & c_1 \\ a_2 & d_2 & c_2 \\ a_3 & d_3 & c_3 \end{vmatrix}}{D} = \frac{D_y}{D} \qquad z = \frac{\begin{vmatrix} a_1 & b_1 & d_1 \\ a_2 & b_2 & d_2 \\ a_3 & b_3 & d_3 \end{vmatrix}}{D} = \frac{D_z}{D}$$

The numerator of x, D_x, can be formed by replacing the first column in D by the column of constants d_1, d_2, and d_3. Similar observations hold for the numerators of y and z.

EXAMPLE 2 Use Cramer's rule to solve the system: $\begin{array}{c} 6x + 2y - 5z = -5 \\ 3x + y - 2z = 0 \\ -3x - 4y + 3z = 11 \end{array}$

$$D = \begin{vmatrix} 6 & 2 & -5 \\ 3 & 1 & -2 \\ -3 & -4 & 3 \end{vmatrix} = 9$$

$$x = \frac{D_x}{D} = \frac{\begin{vmatrix} -5 & 2 & -5 \\ 0 & 1 & -2 \\ 11 & -4 & 3 \end{vmatrix}}{9} = \frac{36}{9} = 4$$

$$y = \frac{D_y}{D} = \frac{\begin{vmatrix} 6 & -5 & -5 \\ 3 & 0 & -2 \\ -3 & 11 & 3 \end{vmatrix}}{9} = \frac{-18}{9} = -2 \qquad z = \frac{D_z}{D} = \frac{\begin{vmatrix} 6 & 2 & -5 \\ 3 & 1 & 0 \\ -3 & -4 & 11 \end{vmatrix}}{9} = \frac{45}{9} = 5$$

Check to show that the solution is $(4, -2, 5)$.

CLASS EXERCISES

Find the following for this system: $\begin{aligned} 4x + 7y &= 10 \\ -2x + 5y &= 12 \end{aligned}$

1. D **2.** D_x **3.** $\dfrac{D_x}{D}$ **4.** D_y **5.** $\dfrac{D_y}{D}$

Find the following for this system: $\begin{aligned} -x + 2y + 4z &= 5 \\ 2x - y - 3z &= 3 \\ 4x - 3y &= -6 \end{aligned}$

6. D **7.** D_x **8.** $\dfrac{D_x}{D}$ **9.** D_z **10.** $\dfrac{D_z}{D}$

EXERCISES

A Use Cramer's rule to solve each system.

1. $\begin{aligned} 2x - 5y &= 18 \\ -x + 3y &= -10 \end{aligned}$

2. $\begin{aligned} -3x + 6y &= -9 \\ 2x - 5y &= 4 \end{aligned}$

3. $\begin{aligned} 4x + 5y &= 1 \\ -6x - 8y &= 1 \end{aligned}$

4. $\begin{aligned} \tfrac{1}{2}x + 7y &= 12 \\ x + 4y &= 4 \end{aligned}$

5. $\begin{aligned} 5x - \tfrac{1}{2}y &= 1 \\ -\tfrac{1}{2}x + \tfrac{1}{4}y &= -\tfrac{3}{2} \end{aligned}$

6. $\begin{aligned} -4x + 2y &= -7 \\ 8x + \tfrac{2}{3}y &= 0 \end{aligned}$

B **7.** $\begin{aligned} x + 2z &= 5 \\ -4x + 6y &= 0 \\ -y + 2z &= 10 \end{aligned}$

8. $\begin{aligned} 4x - 5y &= 6 \\ 3y + 7z &= 1 \\ -6x - 8z &= -2 \end{aligned}$

9. $\begin{aligned} 3x - 2y + z &= 6 \\ -x + 4y &= 5 \\ 3y - 7z &= -1 \end{aligned}$

10. $\begin{aligned} x + 3y + 4z &= 8 \\ -3x - 2y + 3z &= 7 \\ 2x + 4y - z &= -7 \end{aligned}$

11. $\begin{aligned} 6x - 2y - z &= 5 \\ 2x + 4y + 3z &= -2 \\ -x - y &= 1 \end{aligned}$

12. $\begin{aligned} -2x + 2y + 4z &= 6 \\ x - \tfrac{1}{2}y - 3z &= -1 \\ \tfrac{1}{2}x - \tfrac{1}{2}z &= 2 \end{aligned}$

C Solve the system at the right by the indicated method.

$\begin{aligned} -3x + 2y + 5z &= 1 \\ x + 2y &= -6 \\ -x + y + 2z &= 0 \end{aligned}$

13. Augmented matrices

14. The inverse of the matrix of coefficients

15. Cramer's rule

*16. Verify that $x = \dfrac{D_x}{D}$ for the general linear system of three equations in three variables, where D and D_x are defined as on page 639.
Hint: Start by converting the equation on the left below to the one on the right. Use properties of determinants given in Exercises 23–26 on page 637.

$$D = \begin{vmatrix} a_1 & b_1 & c_1 \\ a_2 & b_2 & c_2 \\ a_3 & b_3 & c_3 \end{vmatrix} \qquad xD = \begin{vmatrix} a_1x + b_1y + c_1z & b_1 & c_1 \\ a_2x + b_2y + c_2z & b_2 & c_2 \\ a_3x + b_3y + c_3z & b_3 & c_3 \end{vmatrix}$$

Matrices for Problems in Manufacturing

A manufacturer uses leather (L), fabric (F), and rubber (R) to make three styles of sneakers. The amounts of each material needed to make a pair of each style are given in matrix M, using convenient units.

Number of Units

$$M = \begin{bmatrix} 2 & 3 & 3 \\ 3 & 1 & 2 \\ 4 & 0 & 4 \end{bmatrix} \begin{matrix} \text{Style I} \\ \text{Style II} \\ \text{Style III} \end{matrix}$$

L F R

The manufacturer has a purchase order for 400 pairs of Style I, 300 pairs of Style II, and 200 pairs of Style III. This order can be written as the matrix P.

$$P = [400 \quad 300 \quad 200]$$

I   II   III

The product PM gives the total number of units of each material needed to fill the order. For example, 400(2) + 300(3) + 200(4) = 2500 is the total number of units of leather needed.

$$PM = [400 \quad 300 \quad 200] \begin{bmatrix} 2 & 3 & 3 \\ 3 & 1 & 2 \\ 4 & 0 & 4 \end{bmatrix} = [2500 \quad 1500 \quad 2600]$$

L   F   R

The manufacturer can buy the materials from one of two suppliers. The unit prices of supplier A are $1.00 for leather, $.80 for fabric, and $1.50 for rubber. The corresponding prices of supplier B are $.90, $.60, and $1.70. These prices are shown in cost matrix C.

Supplier

$$C = \begin{bmatrix} 1.00 & 0.90 \\ 0.80 & 0.60 \\ 1.50 & 1.70 \end{bmatrix} \begin{matrix} \text{Leather} \\ \text{Fabric} \\ \text{Rubber} \end{matrix}$$

A   B

The product MC gives the cost of materials needed for a pair of sneakers in each style. That is, the cost of materials from supplier A for a pair of Style I sneakers is $8.90 since 2(1.00) + 3(0.80) + 3(1.50) = 8.90.

$$MC = \begin{bmatrix} 2 & 3 & 3 \\ 3 & 1 & 2 \\ 4 & 0 & 4 \end{bmatrix} \begin{bmatrix} 1.00 & 0.90 \\ 0.80 & 0.60 \\ 1.50 & 1.70 \end{bmatrix} = \begin{bmatrix} 8.90 & 8.70 \\ 6.80 & 6.70 \\ 10.00 & 10.40 \end{bmatrix} \begin{matrix} \text{Style I} \\ \text{Style II} \\ \text{Style III} \end{matrix}$$

A   B

1. Find the 1 × 2 matrix P(MC). This matrix shows the total cost of materials needed to fill the order from supplier A and the total cost to fill it from supplier B. How much money can be saved by using supplier B for the materials for this order?

Another purchase order is received for 100 pairs of Style I, 300 pairs of Style II, and 500 pairs of Style III sneakers.

2. Write a 1 × 3 matrix for this order. Use matrix multiplication to find the total number of units of each material needed to fill the order.

3. Use matrix multiplication to find the total cost of all materials needed to fill the order from supplier A and the total cost to fill it from supplier B. Which supplier can provide these materials at the lower cost? How much is saved by buying from that supplier?

CHAPTER 16
REVIEW

VOCABULARY

matrix, matrices (p. 622)
element (p. 622)
augmented matrix (p. 622)
triangular form (p. 623)
back-substitution (p. 623)
elementary row operations (p. 623)
zero matrix (p. 625)
scalar (p. 626)
scalar product (p. 626)

square matrix (p. 630)
multiplicative identity (p. 630)
multiplicative inverse (p. 630)
matrix equation (p. 632)
determinant (p. 634)
second-order determinant (p. 634)
third-order determinant (p. 634)
expansion by minors (p. 635)
Cramer's rule (p. 638)

SUMMARY

This chapter serves as an introduction to a branch of modern mathematics, *linear algebra*. It begins with a matrix method of solving linear systems by reducing the matrix of coefficients to triangular form. This method, unlike the substitution and addition methods studied earlier, can be readily extended to larger systems. The fundamental operations with matrices are developed, followed by a method of finding the multiplicative inverse of a matrix. This method also shows when a matrix has no inverse. A second procedure for solving linear systems is introduced, making use of the inverse of the matrix of coefficients.

Second- and third-order determinants are defined, and the evaluation of third-order determinants using expansion by minors is developed. The chapter concludes with yet another method of solving linear systems, involving the use of determinants and Cramer's rule.

REVIEW EXERCISES

16-1 Write the linear system corresponding to each augmented matrix. Then solve the system, using back-substitution.

1. $\begin{bmatrix} 3 & 2 & | & -2 \\ 0 & -6 & | & 24 \end{bmatrix}$

2. $\begin{bmatrix} 2 & 1 & -5 & | & 5 \\ 0 & -2 & 5 & | & 4 \\ 0 & 0 & 2 & | & -8 \end{bmatrix}$

3. $\begin{bmatrix} 3 & 2 & 1 & | & 2 \\ 0 & -3 & -3 & | & -6 \\ 0 & 0 & 5 & | & 15 \end{bmatrix}$

Solve each system using augmented matrices and back-substitution.

4. $x - 2y = 3$
   $3x + 5y = -2$

5. $2x + 3y = 23$
   $5x - 4y = 0$

6. $5x + 3y = 1$
   $2x - y = 2$

7. $2x - 3y + 2z = 3$
   $3x + 2y - 3z = 0$
   $-5x + y + 2z = 1$

8. $4x - 3y + 2z = -3$
   $x + 2y + 5z = 0$
   $3x + y + 7z = -1$

9. $x + y + z = 8$
   $3x + 4y - 2z = -1$
   $2x - 3y + 3z = 21$

16-2 *Evaluate each expression, if possible, for the given matrices.*

$$A = \begin{bmatrix} 1 & -2 & 3 \\ -4 & 5 & -6 \\ 7 & -8 & 9 \end{bmatrix} \qquad B = \begin{bmatrix} -4 & 3 \\ 2 & -1 \\ 0 & -1 \end{bmatrix}$$

$$C = \begin{bmatrix} -2 & 2 \\ 3 & -3 \\ -4 & 4 \end{bmatrix} \qquad D = \begin{bmatrix} -1 & 2 & 5 \end{bmatrix}$$

10. $B + C$ **11.** $A(-2C)$ **12.** BC **13.** $(DA)B$ **14.** $-(AB + AC)$

16-3 *Find the multiplicative inverse of each matrix, if it exists.*

15. $\begin{bmatrix} -1 & 3 \\ 2 & -5 \end{bmatrix}$ **16.** $\begin{bmatrix} 3 & -4 \\ 1 & -1 \end{bmatrix}$ **17.** $\begin{bmatrix} -6 & 12 \\ 4 & -8 \end{bmatrix}$

18. $\begin{bmatrix} 1 & 1 & -1 \\ 0 & 2 & 1 \\ 5 & -1 & -2 \end{bmatrix}$ **19.** $\begin{bmatrix} 1 & -1 & 1 \\ 1 & -2 & -2 \\ 2 & -1 & 3 \end{bmatrix}$ **20.** $\begin{bmatrix} 2 & -1 & 1 \\ 1 & 1 & 0 \\ 6 & 0 & -1 \end{bmatrix}$

Solve each system using the multiplicative inverse of the matrix of coefficients. Use your results from Exercises 15–20.

21. $-x + 3y = 5$
$2x - 5y = 3$

22. $3x - 4y = -1$
$x - y = 3$

23. $x + y - z = -4$
$2y + z = 1$
$5x - y - 2z = -5$

24. $x - y + z = 2$
$x - 2y - 2z = -6$
$2x - y + 3z = 8$

25. $2x - y + z = 0$
$x + y = 1$
$6x - z = -1$

16-4 *Evaluate each determinant.*

26. $\begin{vmatrix} 4 & 2 \\ 3 & 1 \end{vmatrix}$ **27.** $\begin{vmatrix} -1 & -7 \\ 3 & -4 \end{vmatrix}$ **28.** $\begin{vmatrix} 8 & 0 \\ -5 & -5 \end{vmatrix}$

29. $\begin{vmatrix} 1 & 3 & 3 \\ 7 & 0 & 1 \\ 2 & 1 & 3 \end{vmatrix}$ **30.** $\begin{vmatrix} 2 & 3 & -1 \\ -1 & 1 & -2 \\ 8 & 3 & 4 \end{vmatrix}$ **31.** $\begin{vmatrix} 5 & 0 & 6 \\ 0 & 1 & 9 \\ -2 & -3 & 0 \end{vmatrix}$

Evaluate.

32. $\begin{vmatrix} 1 & 3 \\ 2 & -6 \end{vmatrix} \div \begin{vmatrix} 0 & 2 \\ 4 & -1 \end{vmatrix}$

33. $\begin{vmatrix} 6 & 0 & -2 \\ 1 & -5 & 8 \\ 4 & -1 & 0 \end{vmatrix} \div \begin{vmatrix} 1 & -3 & -1 \\ 0 & 0 & 2 \\ 1 & -1 & 1 \end{vmatrix}$

34. If $\begin{vmatrix} -1 & x \\ 3 & 2x \end{vmatrix} = 10$, find x.

35. If $\begin{vmatrix} y & 2 & -1 \\ 1 & y & 0 \\ 2 & 8 & 2 \end{vmatrix} = 0$, find y.

16-5   *Use Cramer's rule to solve each system.*

36. $3x - y = 3$
$5x - 2y = 2$

37. $4x + 3y = 7$
$y + x = 2$

38. $x - 8y = -1$
$4x + 10y = 17$

39. $5x + y - z = 15$
$2x - 3y + 2z = 3$
$3x - 2y - 3z = -6$

40. $6x - 5y + 3z = 39$
$-4x + 3y - 2z = -25$
$3x - 4y - 3z = 6$

41. $3x + y + 3z = 1$
$6x - 3y - z = 7$
$-6x + 4y - 5z = -8$

CHAPTER 16 TEST

Solve each system using augmented matrices and back-substitution.

1. $3x - 2y = 0$
$4x + y = -11$

2. $2x + 3y - 2z = 0$
$-4x + 2y + z = -2$
$x - 5y + z = -1$

Evaluate each expression for the given matrices.

$$A = \begin{bmatrix} 3 & -1 & -2 \\ 0 & 4 & 1 \\ 2 & 1 & 3 \end{bmatrix} \quad B = \begin{bmatrix} -2 & 1 & 2 \\ -1 & 2 & -3 \\ 3 & 1 & -1 \end{bmatrix} \quad C = \begin{bmatrix} 1 & -2 & 3 \\ -1 & 3 & -2 \end{bmatrix}$$

3. $2(A - B)$

4. $CA + CB$

Find the multiplicative inverse of each matrix, if it exists.

5. $\begin{bmatrix} 1 & -3 \\ -2 & 6 \end{bmatrix}$

6. $\begin{bmatrix} 1 & -1 & 2 \\ -2 & 1 & -3 \\ -1 & 3 & 1 \end{bmatrix}$

Evaluate each determinant.

7. $\begin{bmatrix} 5 & 8 \\ -1 & -4 \end{bmatrix}$

8. $\begin{bmatrix} 1 & 5 & -1 \\ -1 & 6 & 0 \\ 4 & -3 & 2 \end{bmatrix}$

Use Cramer's rule to solve each system.

9. $3x - 2y = 14$
$7x + 10y = 18$

10. $x - y + 2z = -5$
$-2x + y - 3z = 4$
$-x + 3y + z = 7$

Frequency Distribution

A frequency-distribution table often contains a great many scores. It is impractical to compute the mean by treating each score individually. Programs can be designed to compute the mean by using the number of scores in each category.

This program uses FOR . . . NEXT . . . statements to generate the scores (in this case, the number of books read) and to prompt the user to enter the frequency. The variable C keeps a count of the number of scores entered. For each interval, W is used to compute the weighted sum of that group of scores. For example, 58 responses of 3 books read equals 58×3, or a weighted sum of 174 books read. The variable T contains the total of all the weighted sums computed thus far.

Summer Book Reading Survey

Number of Books Read	Number of Responses
0	10
1	28
2	41
3	58
4	34
5	18
6	9
7	0
8	2

The Program

```
100 REM MEAN FROM TABLE
110 FOR S = 0 TO 8
120 PRINT "HOW MANY SCORES OF "; S
130 INPUT F
140 LET C = C + F
150 LET W = F * S
160 LET T = T + W
170 NEXT S
200 LET M = T/C
210 PRINT "ARITHMETIC MEAN IS "; M
900 END
```

What It Does

Generates scores, 0–8.
Prompts user to enter frequency.

Finds number of scores entered.
Finds weighted sum.
Finds total of weighted sums.

Computes the mean.

1. What is the arithmetic mean of the frequency table above?

What is the arithmetic mean for these frequency tables?

2. Number of Pets	**Number of Families**	**3. Number of TV Sets**	**Number of Homes**
0	126	0	46
1	520	1	294
2	616	2	861
3	413	3	742
4	109	4	212
5	15	5	26
8	1	6	4

For more information about BASIC, see the Computer Handbook at the back of the book.

PART I

Write the letter for the correct answer.

1. Which graph shows the solution to the inequality $|x - 2| \leq 1$?

 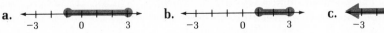

a.

2. If $f(x) = |x + 1|$ and $g(x) = 1 - x^2$, then $f(1) - g(1) = \underline{\ ?\ }$.

    a. -2 **b.** 4   **c.** -4 **d.** 2   **e.** 0

3. What is the remainder when $x^4 + x^2 - 6$ is divided by $x + 2$?

    a. 14   **b.** -26 **c.** 26   **d.** -14 **e.** 0

4. If $\log_x \sqrt{3} = \frac{1}{8}$, then $x = \underline{\ ?\ }$.

    a. 9   **b.** $8\sqrt{3}$ **c.** 27   **d.** 3   **e.** 81

5. If $\sin \theta = -\frac{2}{3}$ and θ is in quadrant III, then $\cos \theta = \underline{\ ?\ }$.

    a. $\dfrac{\sqrt{5}}{3}$ **b.** $-\dfrac{\sqrt{5}}{3}$ **c.** $\dfrac{5}{4}$ **d.** $-\dfrac{5}{9}$ **e.** $-\dfrac{5}{4}$

6. $\dfrac{\tan x + \cot x}{\sec x}$ is equivalent to $\underline{\ ?\ }$.

    a. $\tan x$ **b.** $\cot x$ **c.** $\cos x$ **d.** $\sec x$ **e.** $\csc x$

7. $\text{Arctan}(-1) = \underline{\ ?\ }$.

    a. $-\dfrac{3\pi}{4}$ **b.** $\dfrac{\pi}{4}$ **c.** $-\dfrac{\pi}{4}$ **d.** $\dfrac{3\pi}{4}$ **e.** $\dfrac{5\pi}{4}$

8. Find the finite sum, if there is one, of the infinite geometric series
$3 - 1 + \frac{1}{3} - \frac{1}{9} + \ldots$.

    a. 0   **b.** $\dfrac{9}{2}$ **c.** $\dfrac{9}{4}$ **d.** $\dfrac{4}{9}$ **e.** No finite sum

9. How many combinations are possible, using 10 different letters taken 4 at a time?

    a. 210   **b.** 40   **c.** 1260   **d.** 720   **e.** 5040

10. The multiplicative inverse of $\begin{bmatrix} 1 & 2 \\ -3 & 0 \end{bmatrix}$ is $\underline{\ ?\ }$.

    a. $\begin{bmatrix} -1 & -2 \\ 3 & 0 \end{bmatrix}$ **b.** $\begin{bmatrix} 0 & 0 \\ 0 & 0 \end{bmatrix}$ **c.** $\begin{bmatrix} 1 & 0 \\ 0 & 1 \end{bmatrix}$ **d.** $\begin{bmatrix} 0 & -\frac{1}{3} \\ \frac{1}{2} & \frac{1}{6} \end{bmatrix}$ **e.** $\begin{bmatrix} 1 & \frac{1}{2} \\ -\frac{1}{3} & 0 \end{bmatrix}$

PART II

11. Solve the system: $\begin{aligned}-12x + 3y &= -3\\ y &= 17 - 2x\end{aligned}$ **12.** Graph the system: $\begin{aligned}x &\le y + 2\\ -y + 4 &\le x\end{aligned}$

13. Factor completely: $4xy - 2xy^3 + 4x^2y - 2x^2y^3$

14. Simplify: $3x(x^2 + 2)^{-1} - 3x(x^2 - 2)(x^2 + 2)^{-2}$

15. Solve: $x^2 + 4x = -1$

16. Write the equation $y = 2x^2 - 4x + 3$ in h, k form. Find the coordinates of the vertex of the parabola and the equation of its line of symmetry.

17. Find the minimum or maximum value of the function $f(x) = -\frac{1}{2}x^2 + 4x - 5$.

18. Find the roots of the equation $x^3 + 6x^2 - x - 30 = 0$.

19. Find the radius and the coordinates of the center of the circle $x^2 + 6y + y^2 = 0$. Then sketch the circle.

20. Find the x- and y-intercepts and the foci of the ellipse $4x^2 + 25y^2 = 100$. Then sketch the ellipse.

21. Solve the equation: $\left(\frac{1}{64}\right)^x = \left(\frac{1}{16}\right)^{x+3}$

22. Given that $\log 5.74$ is equal to 0.7589, find $\log 0.0574$.

23. If $\sin \theta = \frac{5}{13}$ and $\cos \theta < 0$, find the other five trigonometric ratios of θ.

24. In triangle ABC, $\beta = 60°$, $b = 2\sqrt{3}$, $c = 4$. Find γ, α, and a.

25. Solve $2\sin^2 \theta + \cos^2 \theta = 1$, where $0° \le \theta < 360°$.

26. Evaluate $\sin\left(\text{Arccsc } \frac{5}{3}\right)$. **27.** Evaluate $\tan\left(\text{Arccos } \frac{1}{2}\right)$.

28. Write $\left(\cos \frac{7\pi}{4} + i \sin \frac{7\pi}{4}\right)$ in rectangular form.

29. For the arithmetic series $10 + 8 + 6 + \dots$, find the sum of the first 21 terms.

30. Find the fifth term of the expansion of $(x - 2)^{10}$.

31. Find the standard deviation for this set of numbers: 20, 16, 23, 12, 14.

32. Evaluate AB, given $A = \begin{bmatrix} 1 & -1 \\ 2 & 0 \\ -3 & 2 \end{bmatrix}$ and $B = \begin{bmatrix} 4 & -2 & 3 \\ 1 & 0 & -1 \end{bmatrix}$.

33. Use Cramer's rule to solve the system: $\begin{aligned}2x - 3y + z &= 0\\ -x + 2y - 3z &= -19\\ 3x - y + 2z &= 11\end{aligned}$

PREREQUISITE SKILLS REVIEW FOLLOW-UP

Chapter One

Rewrite as a decimal.

1. a. $\dfrac{7}{100}$ **b.** $1\dfrac{9}{100}$

   c. $1\dfrac{15}{100}$ **d.** $1\dfrac{7}{10}$

2. a. $\dfrac{28}{25}$ **b.** $\dfrac{7}{5}$

   c. $\dfrac{37}{33}$ **d.** $\dfrac{11}{9}$

3. a. $\dfrac{1}{3}$ **b.** $\dfrac{2}{33}$

   c. $\dfrac{4}{25}$ **d.** $\dfrac{7}{8}$

4. a. $\left(\dfrac{3}{4}\right)^2 = \underline{\ ?\ }$ **b.** $\left(\dfrac{2}{3}\right)^3 = \underline{\ ?\ }$

5. a. $\dfrac{3}{5} + \dfrac{2}{3} = \underline{\ ?\ }$ **b.** $\dfrac{1}{2} + \dfrac{2}{3} = \underline{\ ?\ }$

6. a. $4\dfrac{1}{4} - 2\dfrac{2}{3} = \underline{\ ?\ }$

   b. $6\dfrac{3}{5} - \dfrac{7}{10} = \underline{\ ?\ }$

7. a. $\dfrac{2}{5} \div \dfrac{1}{2} = \underline{\ ?\ }$

   b. $\dfrac{7}{8} \div \dfrac{4}{5} = \underline{\ ?\ }$

8. a. $15.9 - 2.04 = \underline{\ ?\ }$
   b. $19 - 6.8 = \underline{\ ?\ }$

9. a. $0.3 \times 9.6 = \underline{\ ?\ }$
   b. $0.02 \times 36.42 = \underline{\ ?\ }$

10. a. $0.6 \div 0.12 = \underline{\ ?\ }$
    b. $9.9 \div 0.03 = \underline{\ ?\ }$

Chapter Two

1. The coordinate of point A is $\underline{\ ?\ }$.
B is $\underline{\ ?\ }$. C is $\underline{\ ?\ }$.

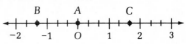

	If	Then
2. a.	$3x + 2y = 7$	$y = \underline{\ ?\ }$
b.	$5x - 3y = 2$	$y = \underline{\ ?\ }$

3. a. $3x + 4y - 13 = 0$
     and $x = 0$ $y = \underline{\ ?\ }$

   b. $2x - 3y + 7 = 0$
     and $x = 0$ $y = \underline{\ ?\ }$

4. a. $y = -\dfrac{1}{3}x - 3$
     and $x = -3$ $y = \underline{\ ?\ }$

   b. $y = -\dfrac{1}{2}x + 2$
     and $x = 4$ $y = \underline{\ ?\ }$

5. a. $y = -2x - 2$
     and $x = -3$ $y = \underline{\ ?\ }$

   b. $y = -4x + 3$
     and $x = 2$ $y = \underline{\ ?\ }$

6. a. $y - 2 = -5(x + 2)$ $y = \underline{\ ?\ }$
   b. $y + 3 = -3(x - 5)$ $y = \underline{\ ?\ }$

7. a. $\dfrac{2 - 6}{-5 - (-6)} = \underline{\ ?\ }$

   b. $\dfrac{3 - 5}{4 - (-2)} = \underline{\ ?\ }$

8. a. If $pq = -1$ and $p = \dfrac{3}{4}$,
     then $q = \underline{\ ?\ }$.

   b. If $rt = -1$ and $t = -\dfrac{2}{5}$,
     then $r = \underline{\ ?\ }$.

Is the point with the given coordinates a solution to the inequality?

9. a. $y < 3x - 4$; $(1, -1)$

  b. $y \le \dfrac{2}{3}x + \dfrac{1}{3}$; $(1, 1)$

  c. $y \ge 4 - x$; $(-2, 2)$

  d. $y > \dfrac{1}{4}x + 3$; $(-1, 2)$

10. a. $y < 3x - 2$; $(0, 0)$

  b. $y > 2x - 5$; $(0, 0)$

  c. $y \le x - 1$; $(0, 0)$

  d. $y \ge x + 9$; $(0, 0)$

Chapter Three

1. Is every solution to the first equation also a solution to the second equation?

  a. $y = 2x + \dfrac{1}{3}$; $6x - 3y = -1$

  b. $y = 2x - \dfrac{1}{4}$; $8x + 4y = 1$

2. The value, in cents, of:

  a. d dimes is _?_.   **b.** n quarters is _?_.

3. Write a mathematical expression for:

  a. one-third of a number n, increased by 7.

  b. three-fourths of a number n, less 5.

4. Solve for x.

  a. $5 - 3x = 2y$ **b.** $7 - 2x = y$

Write the sentence as an equation.

5. a. x is 5 less than y.

  b. y is 7 less than x.

6. a. x is 3 less than 2 times y.

  b. y is 1 less than 4 times x.

7. a. $5x + (-x) =$ _?_

  b. $-2x + (-x) =$ _?_

8. a. $-2x - (-x) =$ _?_

  b. $-8x - (-9x) =$ _?_

Express in terms of x.

9. a. Jeremy is x years old now. Ray's age is 3 times the age that Jeremy was 2 years ago. Ray's age is _?_.

  b. Ann is x years old now. Joe is 4 times the age that Ann will be in 3 years. Joe's age is _?_.

10. a. There are x pounds of an alloy that is 40% tin. The number of pounds of tin is _?_.

  b. There are x ounces of a mixture that is 30% water. The number of ounces of water is _?_.

Chapter Four

1. a. $\left(-\dfrac{2}{3}\right)^4 =$ _?_   **b.** $\left(-\dfrac{2}{5}\right)^3 =$ _?_

2. If $x = -1$ and $y = -4$, then:

  a. $x^3y^2 =$ _?_   **b.** $x^4y^3 =$ _?_

Find the greatest common factor of:

3. a. 24 and 12   **b.** 16 and 20

4. a. 9, 10, and 24   **b.** 25, 28, and 35

5. a. $(8 - 3)$ is the opposite of $(3 -$ _?_ $)$.

  b. $(7 - 2)$ is the opposite of $(-7 +$ _?_ $)$.

Is the number a solution to the equation?

6. a. $3x^2 - 8x - 3 = 0$; -3

  b. $2x^2 - 3x - 5 = 0$; $\dfrac{5}{2}$

7. a. $5x^2 + 14x - 3 = 0$; $-\dfrac{1}{5}$

  b. $4x^2 + 5x + 1 = 0$; $-\dfrac{1}{4}$

8. a. A rectangle is 3 feet long and 10 feet wide. Its area = _?_.

  b. Each side of a square is 5 centimeters long. Its area = _?_.

PREREQUISITE SKILLS FOLLOW-UP

COMPUTER HANDBOOK

TABLES

GLOSSARY

ANSWERS TO CHECKPOINTS

ANSWERS TO SELECTED EXERCISES

INDEX

9. What is the area of a triangle that has the given base b and altitude h?

    a. $b = 5$ in., $h = 10$ in.

    b. $b = 9$ cm, $h = 12$ cm

10. Express in terms of x.

    a. The length, in inches, of a rectangle is 4 inches less than 3 times its width x. The length is ? .

    b. The altitude, in centimeters, of a triangle is 5 centimeters more than twice its base x. The altitude is ? .

Chapter Five

1. Is the fraction defined?

    a. $\dfrac{3}{(-3)^2 + 3}$ **b.** $\dfrac{3}{(-3)^2 - 3}$

    c. $\dfrac{3}{(-3)^2 + 9}$ **d.** $\dfrac{3}{(-3)^2 - 9}$

2. If $b \neq c$, then:

    a. $\dfrac{-a}{c - b} = -\dfrac{a}{?}$ **b.** $\dfrac{-a}{c - b} = \dfrac{a}{?}$

    c. $-\dfrac{a}{c + b} = \dfrac{a}{?}$

3. What is the reciprocal of the given number?

    a. 7   **b.** $-\dfrac{3}{5}$

4. Find the least common multiple of:

    a. 10 and 12   **b.** 15 and 24

5. Find the least common denominator of:

    a. $\dfrac{3}{8}$ and $\dfrac{1}{4}$ **b.** $\dfrac{5}{6}$ and $\dfrac{7}{8}$

6. Multiply each side of the equation by the given number. What equation results?

    a. Multiply by 6.   **b.** Multiply by 10.

    $\dfrac{x}{2} + \dfrac{1}{3} = \dfrac{5}{6}$ $\dfrac{x}{2} - \dfrac{5}{10} = 1$

7. **a.** If $(3x - 1)(x + 2) = 0$, then $x =$? .

    b. If $(x - 3)(2x + 1) = 0$, then $x =$? .

8. Express in terms of x.

    a. The numerator of a fraction is 5 less than 3 times the denominator x. The numerator = ? .

    b. The denominator of a fraction is 2 less than twice the numerator x. The denominator = ? .

9. **a.** If there are 6 red marbles and 7 green marbles, the ratio of the number of red marbles to the total number of marbles is ? .

    b. If 12 out of 30 students in a class wear glasses, then the ratio of the number of students with glasses to the number without glasses is ? .

10. Express in hours and minutes.

    a. 3.2 hr   **b.** $1\dfrac{1}{3}$ hr   **c.** 205 min

Chapter Six

1. **a.** If $x > 0$, then $|x| =$? .

    b. If $x = 0$, then $|x| =$? .

2. Find a perfect square that is also a factor of:

    a. 175   **b.** 405

Find the greatest perfect square that is a factor of:

3. **a.** 72   **b.** 81

4. **a.** 48   **b.** 180

5. Simplify.

    a. $2x - 5(2y - 2)$

    b. $x - 3(4x - 2y)$

6. **a.** $(2a + 3b)(a - 2b) =$?

    b. $(a - 4b)(3a - 5b) =$?

PREREQUISITE SKILLS FOLLOW-UP

COMPUTER HANDBOOK

TABLES

GLOSSARY

ANSWERS TO CHECKPOINTS

ANSWERS TO SELECTED EXERCISES

INDEX

7. Use = or ≠ to make a true sentence.

  a. $x^2 - y^2$ _?_ $(x - y)(x - y)$

  b. $y^2 - 4$ _?_ $(y + 2)(y - 2)$

  c. $16 - a^2$ _?_ $(16 - a)(16 + a)$

  d. $x^2 - t^2$ _?_ $(x + t)(x + t)$

Simplify for $a^2 \neq b^2$.

8. **a.** $\dfrac{a - b}{b - a}$ **b.** $\dfrac{a - b}{a - b}$

  c. $\dfrac{a - b}{-(a - b)}$ **d.** $\dfrac{a + b}{b + a}$

9. **a.** $\dfrac{b^2 - a^2}{a^2 - b^2}$ **b.** $\dfrac{b^2 - a^2}{b^2 - a^2}$

  c. $\dfrac{a^2 - b^2}{(a - b)^2}$ **d.** $\dfrac{(b - a)^2}{(a - b)^2}$

10. Simplify.

  a. $(x^3 \cdot x^5)^2$ **b.** $(y \cdot y^4)^5$

Chapter Seven

Simplify.

1. **a.** $(2\sqrt{3})^2$ **b.** $(4\sqrt{2})^2$

2. **a.** $\sqrt{18}$ **b.** $\sqrt{72}$

3. Factor.

  a. $x^2 - 8x + 16$ **b.** $4x^2 - 4x + 1$

4. Factor only if it is a trinomial square.

  a. $9x^2 - 12x + 4$ **b.** $9x^2 + 12x - 4$

  c. $x^2 - 6x + 9$ **d.** $x^2 - 6x - 9$

Simplify.

5. **a.** $(5 - 3\sqrt{5})^2$ **b.** $(2 - 5\sqrt{3})^2$

6. **a.** $\sqrt{(-9)^2 - 4(2)(-5)}$

  b. $\sqrt{(-6)^2 - 4(4)(-3)}$

Write the two numbers separately and in simplest form.

7. **a.** $\dfrac{-3 \pm \sqrt{25}}{2}$ **b.** $\dfrac{-4 \pm \sqrt{64}}{4}$

8. **a.** $\dfrac{2 \pm \sqrt{108}}{2}$ **b.** $\dfrac{8 \pm \sqrt{192}}{4}$

Is the point with the given coordinates on the graph of the given equation?

9. **a.** $y = (x + 3)^2 + 9$; $(0, 9)$

  b. $y = (x - 1)^2 - 2$; $(0, -1)$

10. **a.** $y = x^2$; $(-2, 4)$

  b. $y = 3(x - 3)^2 + 3$; $(2, 6)$

Chapter Eight

1. **a.** $15x^2 \div 3x = $ _?_

  b. $24x^3 \div 8x^2 = $ _?_

2. **a.** $9x^2 \div x^2 = $ _?_

  b. $9x^3 \div 9x = $ _?_

3. **a.** If $5x^2 - 3x - 8$ is subtracted from $3x^2 - x + 4$, the result is _?_ .

  b. If $3x^2 + 2x - 4$ is subtracted from $4x^2 + x - 4$, the result is _?_ .

Multiply.

4. **a.** $(3x + 2)(4x - 1) - 7$

  b. $(2x - 3)(3x - 5) + 4$

5. **a.** $x(2x + 1)(x - 3) - 8$

  b. $x(3x - 2)(x - 5) + 2$

6. Give the degree of the polynomial.

  a. $3x^5 - 2x^2 + 7$

  b. $x^3 + 2x^2 - 5x + 1$

7. **a.** If $g(x) = 2x^3 - 3x^2 + x - 4$, then $g(-2) = $ _?_ .

  b. If $f(x) = x^4 - 3x^3 + x^2 + x + 1$, then $f(-1) = $ _?_ .

8. **a.** If $g(x) = 9x^3 - 3x^2 + x - 4$, then $g\left(\frac{1}{3}\right) = $ _?_ .

  b. If $h(x) = 4x^3 + 3x^2 - 2x + 2$, then $h\left(-\frac{1}{4}\right) = $ _?_ .

Which of the following name real numbers?

9. **a.** $-\sqrt{1}$ **b.** $\sqrt{-1}$

  c. $\sqrt[3]{-1}$ **d.** $-\sqrt[3]{1}$

10. a. $\sqrt{5^2 - 2(4)(3)}$

    b. $\sqrt{7^2 - 2(4)(6)}$

    c. $\sqrt{12^2 - 4(5)(11)}$

    d. $\sqrt{8^2 - 2(4)(4)}$

Chapter Nine

1. a. $|-7 - (-5)| = \underline{\ ?\ }$

    b. $|13 - (-10)| = \underline{\ ?\ }$

2. Use the given measures of the legs of a right triangle to find the measure of the hypotenuse.

    a. 6, 8   **b.** 7, 8

3. Use the given measures of one leg and the hypotenuse of a right triangle to find the measure of the other leg.

    a. 7, 9   **b.** 3, 6

4. a. If $x^2 - 4x = 2$, then $(x - 2)^2 = \underline{\ ?\ }$.

    b. If $x^2 + 10x = -7$, then $(x + 5)^2 = \underline{\ ?\ }$.

5. Give the equation of the axis of symmetry for the parabola whose equation is:

    a. $y = (x + 1)^2 + 4$

    b. $y = (x - 5)^2 - 3$

6. Give the coordinates of the vertex for the parabola whose equation is:

    a. $y = (x + 2)^2 - 1$

    b. $y = (x + 6)^2 + 5$

7. Give x-intercepts of the graph of:

    a. $x^2 + \dfrac{y^2}{9} = 1$ **b.** $\dfrac{x^2}{4} + \dfrac{y^2}{16} = 1$

8. Does the graph of the equation have x-intercepts, y-intercepts, no intercepts, or both x- and y-intercepts?

    a. $xy = -4$ **b.** $\dfrac{x^2}{2} + \dfrac{y^2}{5} = 1$

    c. $\dfrac{x^2}{4} - y^2 = 1$ **d.** $x^2 + y^2 = 4$

In how many points, at most, can the two figures intersect?

9. a. two lines

    b. a line and a parabola

10. a. a circle and a hyperbola

    b. a line and a hyperbola

Chapter Ten

1. a. $1{,}000{,}000{,}000 = 10^{\underline{\ ?\ }}$

    b. $10{,}000{,}000{,}000 = 10^{\underline{\ ?\ }}$

2. As a decimal: **a.** $10^{-3} = \underline{\ ?\ }$

                   b. $10^{-7} = \underline{\ ?\ }$

3. a. $64^{-\frac{1}{2}} = \underline{\ ?\ }$ **b.** $\dfrac{1}{9^{-\frac{1}{2}}} = \underline{\ ?\ }$

4. a. $27^{\frac{2}{3}} = \underline{\ ?\ }$ **b.** $9^{\frac{3}{2}} = \underline{\ ?\ }$

5. a. $\left(\dfrac{8}{27}\right)^{-\frac{2}{3}} = \underline{\ ?\ }$ **b.** $\left(\dfrac{25}{9}\right)^{-\frac{3}{2}} = \underline{\ ?\ }$

6. Simplify.

    a. $(n^5 \cdot n^5)^2$ **b.** $(n^4 \cdot n^7)^3$

7. a. $0.5079 - 1 = \underline{\ ?\ } - 10$

    b. $0.3032 - 2 = \underline{\ ?\ } - 10$

8. a. $-2.4232 = \underline{\ ?\ }.5768 - 10$

    b. $-1.6345 = 8.3655 - \underline{\ ?\ }$

9. a. $3.9031 - 3(-0.0414 + 0.4183) = \underline{\ ?\ }$

    b. $4.8388 - 2(-1.1523 + 0.7364) = \underline{\ ?\ }$

10. a. $0.8865 - 2(0.4031 - 1.7404) = \underline{\ ?\ }$

    b. $1.9243 - 3(0.0374 - 2.5658) = \underline{\ ?\ }$

Chapter Eleven

Refer to the first diagram on page 411 for Exercises 1–3.

1. a. If $x = 15$ and $r = 25$, then $y = \underline{\ ?\ }$.

    b. If $y = 30$ and $r = 34$, then $x = \underline{\ ?\ }$.

2. a. If $r = 17$ and $y = 15$, then $\dfrac{x}{r} = \underline{\ ?\ }$.

    b. If $r = 24$ and $x = 12$, then $\dfrac{y}{r} = \underline{\ ?\ }$.

3. a. If $r = 26$ and $x = 24$, then the reciprocal of $\frac{y}{x}$ is __?__.

b. If $r = 35$ and $y = 28$, then the reciprocal of $\frac{y}{x}$ is __?__.

4. If $\triangle XYZ$ is similar to $\triangle ABC$, then:

a. $\dfrac{x}{y} = \dfrac{a}{?}$ **b.** $\dfrac{z}{x} = \dfrac{?}{a}$ **c.** $\dfrac{y}{?} = \dfrac{b}{a}$

5. Simplify.

a. $\dfrac{3}{\sqrt{5}}$ **b.** $\dfrac{2}{\sqrt{8}}$

6. The measures of two angles of a triangle are given. Find the measure of the third angle.

a. $51°$, $32°$ **b.** $40°$, $22°$

7. a. If $\dfrac{a}{b} = \dfrac{c}{d}$, then $b =$ __?__.

b. If $\dfrac{f}{g} = \dfrac{t}{r}$, then $r =$ __?__.

8. If $\sqrt{5} \approx 2.236$ and $\sqrt{7} \approx 2.646$, find to the nearest tenth.

a. $\dfrac{100\sqrt{5}}{\sqrt{7}}$ **b.** $\dfrac{1000\sqrt{7}}{\sqrt{5}}$

5. a. $\dfrac{\sqrt{5}}{3}\left(\dfrac{\sqrt{3}}{3}\right) - \dfrac{1}{3}\left(\dfrac{\sqrt{3}}{3}\right) = \dfrac{?}{}(\sqrt{15} - \sqrt{3})$

b. $\dfrac{\sqrt{2}}{4}\left(\dfrac{\sqrt{5}}{2}\right) - \dfrac{1}{2}\left(\dfrac{\sqrt{3}}{4}\right) = \dfrac{1}{8}(\underline{?})$

Write in simplest form. Rationalize the denominator, if necessary.

6. a. $\dfrac{2 + \dfrac{\sqrt{2}}{2}}{2 - \dfrac{\sqrt{2}}{2}}$ **b.** $\dfrac{1 - \dfrac{\sqrt{5}}{3}}{1 + \dfrac{\sqrt{5}}{3}}$

7. a. $\dfrac{2\left(\dfrac{1}{2}\right)}{1 - \left(\dfrac{1}{2}\right)^2}$ **b.** $\dfrac{2\left(\dfrac{5}{3}\right)}{1 - \left(\dfrac{5}{3}\right)^2}$

8. a. $\sqrt{\dfrac{1 + \dfrac{\sqrt{2}}{2}}{2}} = \dfrac{1}{2}\sqrt{?}$

b. $\sqrt{\dfrac{1 + \dfrac{\sqrt{5}}{2}}{2}} = \dfrac{?}{}\sqrt{2 + \sqrt{5}}$

Chapter Twelve

Is the ratio defined at the given value of θ?

1. a. $\tan \theta$; $270°$ **b.** $\tan \theta$; $-180°$

c. $\tan \theta$; $630°$

2. a. $\dfrac{\cos \theta}{1 + \sin \theta}$; $0°$ **b.** $\dfrac{\cos \theta}{1 + \sin \theta}$; $270°$

3. Simplify.

a. $\dfrac{\dfrac{1}{\cos \theta}}{\dfrac{\cos \theta}{\sin \theta}}$ **b.** $\dfrac{\dfrac{\cos \theta}{\sin \theta}}{\cos \theta}$

4. If $0 \le \theta < 360°$, find the possible values of θ if:

a. $\sin \theta = -\dfrac{\sqrt{3}}{2}$ **b.** $\tan \theta = 1$

Chapter Thirteen

1. a. $\dfrac{5\pi}{3} \cdot \dfrac{180}{\pi} = \dfrac{?}{}$ **b.** $\dfrac{3\pi}{2} \cdot \dfrac{180}{\pi} = \dfrac{?}{}$

2. To the nearest 10 minutes:

a. $50.4° = 50°\underline{?}'$ **b.** $72.8° = 72°\underline{?}'$

3. To the nearest tenth of a degree:

a. $32°20' = 32.\underline{?}°$

b. $84°40' = 84.\underline{?}°$

4. On a coordinate plane, show the triangle whose vertices have coordinates $(0, 0)$, $(4, 0)$, and $(4, 3)$. Then show the triangle reflected through the x-axis.

5. a. If $\theta = 120°$, then $2 \sin \dfrac{\theta}{2} =$ __?__.

b. If $\theta = 90°$, then $2 \cos \dfrac{\theta}{2} =$ __?__.

PREREQUISITE SKILLS FOLLOW-UP

COMPUTER HANDBOOK

TABLES

GLOSSARY

ANSWERS TO CHECKPOINTS

ANSWERS TO SELECTED EXERCISES

INDEX

6. a. If $-\pi \le x \le \pi$, then $\underline{}$ $\le \frac{x}{2} \le$ $\underline{}$.

b. If $-\frac{\pi}{4} \le x \le \frac{\pi}{4}$,
then $\underline{}$ $\le 2x \le$ $\underline{}$.

7. a. If $-\pi \le \frac{x}{2} \le \pi$, then $\underline{}$ $\le 2x \le$ $\underline{}$.

b. If $0 \le \frac{x}{2} \le 2\pi$, then $\underline{}$ $\le 2x \le$ $\underline{}$.

8. a. If a third-quadrant angle has a tangent of $\frac{5}{12}$, then its cosine is $\underline{}$.

b. If a fourth-quadrant angle has a cosine of $\frac{3}{5}$, then its sine is $\underline{}$.

8. a. $\dfrac{8 \cdot 7 \cdot 6 \cdot 5 \cdot 4 \cdot 3}{1 \cdot 2 \cdot 3 \cdot 4 \cdot 5 \cdot 6} = \dfrac{?}{}$

b. $\dfrac{11 \cdot 10 \cdot 9 \cdot 8 \cdot 7 \cdot 6 \cdot 5}{1 \cdot 2 \cdot 3 \cdot 4 \cdot 5 \cdot 6 \cdot 7} = \dfrac{?}{}$

9. a. $\dfrac{6 \cdot 5 \cdot 4 \cdot 3 \cdot 2 \cdot 1}{(4 \cdot 3 \cdot 2 \cdot 1)(2 \cdot 1)} = \dfrac{?}{}$

b. $\dfrac{10 \cdot 9 \cdot 8 \cdot 7 \cdot 6 \cdot 5 \cdot 4 \cdot 3 \cdot 2 \cdot 1}{(6 \cdot 5 \cdot 4 \cdot 3 \cdot 2 \cdot 1)(4 \cdot 3 \cdot 2 \cdot 1)} = \dfrac{?}{}$

Chapter Fourteen

1. Find $a + (n - 1)d$ if:

a. $a = -2$, $n = 21$, $d = -\dfrac{1}{4}$

b. $a = 5$, $n = 11$, $d = -\dfrac{1}{2}$

2. Solve the system.

a. $a + d = 1$ **b.** $a + 2d = -4$
   $a + 6d = 11$ $a + 9d = -11$

3. Evaluate ar^{n-1} if:

a. $a = 2$, $n = 5$, $r = -2$

b. $a = 5$, $n = 4$, $r = -3$

4. Evaluate $\dfrac{a(1 - r^n)}{(1 - r)}$ if:

a. $a = 3$, $n = 4$, $r = \dfrac{1}{3}$

b. $a = 2$, $n = 3$, $r = \dfrac{1}{4}$

5. Use $=$ or $\approx$ to make the sentence true.

a. $\dfrac{1}{3}$ $\underline{}$ $0.\overline{3}$

b. $\dfrac{1}{3}$ $\underline{}$ $0.333 \ldots$ **c.** $\dfrac{1}{3}$ $\underline{}$ 0.33

d. $\dfrac{1}{3}$ $\underline{}$ $0.3 + 0.03 + 0.003 + \ldots$

6. a. $(x + 1)^0 + (x + 1)^1 + (x + 1)^2 = \underline{}$

b. $(2x - 1)^0 + (2x - 1)^1$
$+ (2x - 1)^2 = \underline{}$

7. a. $(x - 1)^3 = \underline{}$ **b.** $(x + 2)^3 = \underline{}$

Chapter Fifteen

1. a. $\dfrac{7!}{(7 - 3)!} = \dfrac{?}{}$ **b.** $\dfrac{8!}{(8 - 3)!} = \dfrac{?}{}$

2. a. $\dfrac{10!}{2!5!} = \dfrac{?}{}$ **b.** $\dfrac{6!}{2!2!} = \dfrac{?}{}$

3. a. $\dfrac{12!}{6!(12 - 6)!} = \dfrac{?}{}$

b. $\dfrac{10!}{3!(10 - 3)!} = \dfrac{?}{}$

4. a. $\dfrac{6}{9} \cdot \dfrac{5}{8} \cdot \dfrac{4}{7} = \dfrac{?}{}$ **b.** $\dfrac{10}{12} \cdot \dfrac{9}{11} \cdot \dfrac{8}{10} = \dfrac{?}{}$

5. Evaluate $p^x q^{n-x}$ if:

a. $x = 5$, $n = 8$, $p = \dfrac{1}{2}$, $q = \dfrac{1}{2}$

b. $x = 2$, $n = 4$, $p = \dfrac{1}{4}$, $q = \dfrac{3}{4}$

6. Place the decimal point to show the correct percent.

a. $\dfrac{90}{1400} \approx 0060\%$

b. $\dfrac{5}{800} \approx 0060\%$

7. a. $\sqrt{\dfrac{(3 - 8)^2 + (8 - 1)^2}{2}} = \dfrac{?}{}$

b. $\sqrt{\dfrac{(9 - 3)^2 + (5 - 9)^2}{2}} = \dfrac{?}{}$

8. a. 56.4% of $900 = \underline{}$

b. 82.25% of $600 = \underline{}$

Chapter Sixteen

Is the point whose coordinates are given a solution to the linear system?

1. a. $-2x + y = 8$
   $-x + y = 2$ $(-2, 4)$

   b. $4x - 3y = 17$
   $x + y = -1$ $(2, -3)$

2. a. $-x + 3y = -7$
   $y + z = -3$ $(1, -1, -2)$
   $2x + z = 0$

   b. $x - y = -1$
   $y + z = -1$ $(-3, -2, 1)$
   $x + 2z = -1$

3. a. If $y = -4$ and $4x - 3y = -3$,
   then $x = \underline{\ ?\ }$.

   b. If $x = -2$ and $3x - 2y = 6$, then
   $y = \underline{\ ?\ }$.

4. a. If $z = 2$, $y - 3z = 8$, and
   $x - 2y - z = 4$, then $x = \underline{\ ?\ }$.

   b. If $z = -3$, $x - z = 4$, and
   $x + 2y - 2z = 7$, then $y = \underline{\ ?\ }$.

5. a. $9^{\frac{1}{2}} = \underline{\ ?\ }$ **b.** $9^{-1} = \underline{\ ?\ }$.

   c. $9^0 = \underline{\ ?\ }$

   d. -9 is the $\underline{\ ?\ }$ inverse of 9.

   e. 9^{-1} is the $\underline{\ ?\ }$ inverse of 9.

6. a. If 3 times -6 is added to -4, the
   result is $\underline{\ ?\ }$.

   b. If -2 times -5 is added to 7, the
   result is $\underline{\ ?\ }$.

7. a. If twice $-\frac{5}{8}$ is added to $\frac{1}{4}$, the
   result is $\underline{\ ?\ }$.

   b. If twice $-\frac{7}{16}$ is added to $-\frac{1}{8}$, the
   result is $\underline{\ ?\ }$.

*Evaluate **ad** − **bc** if:*

8. a. $a = -3$, $b = 4$, $c = -5$, $d = 6$

   b. $a = 7$, $b = 2$, $c = -2$, $d = -3$

9. a. $a = -3$, $b = -3$, $c = -4$, $d = 2$

   b. $a = 1$, $b = -5$, $c = -6$, $d = -3$

PREREQUISITE SKILLS FOLLOW-UP

COMPUTER HANDBOOK

TABLES

GLOSSARY

ANSWERS TO CHECKPOINTS

ANSWERS TO SELECTED EXERCISES

INDEX

COMPUTER HANDBOOK

I. Working with BASIC

BASIC is the most popular computer language because it is easy to learn and to use. Computers, however, vary slightly in the BASIC they use. The explanations and programs in this book are designed for use with as many different computers as possible, and can be understood when no computer is available. Because many computers display only capital letters, the programs are written in capitals.

If you enter a program into a computer and find that it does not run properly, first check to see that every line was entered correctly. Even the slightest mistake in entering a program may prevent it from running or may cause an erroneous result. If you still encounter difficulty, consult the section "Some Differences in BASICs" on page 667. Also consult the manual for the computer you are using.

II. Writing a Program

In BASIC, each statement is given a line number. We usually number the statements using multiples of ten. This makes it easy to insert additional statements into the program.

The information immediately following the characters REM does not affect the program itself. This allows you to include comments that make the program easier to read and understand.

Here is a program, written in the language of BASIC, that calculates and displays the sum of two numbers. The PRINT instruction commands the computer to display what follows it on the monitor or TV screen. In order to display words or symbols, we must enclose them in quotation marks, as in line 50. When no quotation marks are used, as in line 60, only the value of S will be displayed on the monitor.

The Program	What It Does
10 REM PROGRAM ONE	Gives the program a title.
20 LET A = 72	Assigns the value 72 to A.
30 LET B = 48	Assigns the value 48 to B.
40 LET S = A + B	Assigns their sum to S.
50 PRINT "THE SUM IS"	Displays a message.
60 PRINT S	Displays the value of S.
70 PRINT	Leaves a blank line.
90 END	Ends the program.

The A, B, and S are called *variables*. In BASIC, a variable is the name of a location in the computer's memory where a number is stored. Line 20 assigns the number 72 to memory location A.

After you have entered the program, you must enter the command RUN. This instructs the computer to run the program, starting with the lowest line number. Here is a sample run of PROGRAM ONE.

```
RUN
THE SUM IS
120
```

If we wish the output to be displayed on one line, as

```
THE SUM IS 120
```

we can combine lines 50 and 60 by using a semicolon.

```
50   PRINT "THE SUM IS "; S
```

EXERCISES   *Insert these lines into PROGRAM ONE.*

```
75   LET D = A - B
80   PRINT "THE DIFFERENCE IS"
85   PRINT D
```

1. For the revised program, what numbers will be displayed?   120 and 24

2. Write a program in BASIC that instructs the computer to display the numbers 541 and 467, their sum, and their difference.

III. Numerical Expressions in BASIC

To perform operations in BASIC, five symbols are used.

+	addition	*	multiplication
-	subtraction	/	division
	↑	raising to a power	

Note: Some computers use the symbol $\wedge$ for raising a number to a power, while others use the symbol ******. Check your user's manual.

Examples

Arithmetic Expression	Equivalent BASIC Expression
$24 + 16$	$24 + 16$
$50 - 39$	$50 - 39$
6×15	$6 * 15$
$72 \div 12$	$72 / 12$
15^2	$15 \uparrow 2$

The order of operations in BASIC is the same as in algebra.

1. Perform the operations within grouping symbols first, starting with the innermost grouping symbol.

2. Raise a number to a power.

3. Multiply and divide in order, from left to right.

4. Add and subtract in order, from left to right.

Since parentheses are the only grouping symbols used in BASIC, we use parentheses within parentheses. Two or more terms in the numerator or denominator of a fraction must be grouped within parentheses.

PREREQUISITE SKILLS FOLLOW-UP

COMPUTER HANDBOOK

TABLES

GLOSSARY

ANSWERS TO CHECKPOINTS

ANSWERS TO SELECTED EXERCISES

INDEX

Examples	Arithmetic Expression	Equivalent BASIC Expression	Value
	$8 \times (20 - 13)$	$8 * (20 - 13)$	56
	$7 + 9 \times 10$	$7 + 9 * 10$	97
	$50 - 3^2$	$50 - 3 \uparrow 2$	41
	$\dfrac{6 + 9}{8 - 3}$	$(6 + 9)/(8 - 3)$	3
	$\dfrac{3 \times (8 + 2)}{5}$	$3 * (8 + 2)/5$	6
	$5 \times [10 - (15 - 8)]$	$5 * (10 - (15 - 8))$	15

EXERCISES   *Write the value of each BASIC expression.*

1. $9 * 13$ **2.** $91/13$ **3.** $2 \uparrow 4$ **4.** $35 - (17 + 4)$
5. $7 * 3 \uparrow 3$ **6.** $75 + 5 * 8$ **7.** $64 - 75/5$ **8.** $72/(7 + 11)$
9. $(17 + 33)/(9 - 4)$ **10.** $(67 - 59) \uparrow 2$ **11.** $64/4 \uparrow 2$ **12.** $9 * (4 + 5)/3$

IV. Algebraic Expressions

A statement in BASIC may look like an algebraic equation, yet have a totally different meaning and use. For example:

```
70   LET X = X + 2
```

In algebra, the equation $x = x + 2$ can never be true. In BASIC, the statement LET X = X + 2 tells the computer to take the value stored in memory location X, increase it by 2, and store the result as the new value for X. On many computers, LET may be omitted.

The left side of a LET statement in BASIC may contain only a variable. The computer evaluates the expression on the right side of the equal sign and assigns that value to the variable on the left side.

The multiplication symbol $*$ must always be used in BASIC.

Examples	Algebraic Expression	Equivalent BASIC Expression
	$5a$	$5 * A$
	$3(r - 4)$	$3 * (R - 4)$
	$6x^2$	$6 * X \uparrow 2$
	$ax^2 + bx - c$	$A * X \uparrow 2 + B * X - C$

EXERCISES   *Tell what output will be displayed.*

1.
```
10   LET K = 42
20   LET K = 5 * K
30   PRINT K
90   END
```

2.
```
10   REM NINE X CUBED
20   LET X = 6
30   LET Y = 9 * X ↑ 3
40   PRINT Y
90   END
```

Write each of the following in BASIC.

3. $19y$ **4.** $6a^3$ **5.** $8d + 24$ **6.** $6(4z - 13)$
7. $-5g^2$ **8.** $r^2 + 5r - 2$ **9.** $8s(7s + 4)$ **10.** $5t + 2t(t + 3)$

Note: Because of the way some computers function, the command PRINT 7 ↑ 2 may result in a display of 49.0000001. To avoid this, most programs in this book use multiplication to raise a number to a power. Thus, 7^2 is programmed as 7 * 7 rather than 7 ↑ 2.

V. Using INPUT Statements

An INPUT statement causes the computer to stop and wait for an entry. On most computers, a question mark is displayed to indicate that the computer is waiting for you to input a value. After an appropriate entry has been made, the computer continues to the next instruction. Here is a program that computes and displays the area of a square after you enter the length of its side.

The Program	What It Does
10 REM AREA OF SQUARE	Tells what the program will compute.
20 PRINT "ENTER LENGTH OF SIDE"	Reminds you what to enter.
30 INPUT S	Waits for you to enter the length.
40 LET A = S * S	Computes $A = s^2$.
50 PRINT "AREA IS "; A	Displays the output.
90 END	Ends the program.

Here is a sample run when the length of a side is 8.

```
RUN
ENTER LENGTH OF SIDE
? 8
AREA IS 64
```
You must enter 8 before the computer will proceed.

Sometimes we wish to enter (input) two or more values. On most computers this can be done with one INPUT statement. The numbers entered must be separated by commas. The following program illustrates a multiple INPUT statement.

The Program	What It Does
10 REM AREA OF RECTANGLE	Tells what the program will compute.
20 PRINT "ENTER LENGTH, WIDTH"	Prompts you to enter the dimensions.
30 INPUT L, W	Waits for you to enter the length and width, separated by a comma.
40 LET A = L * W	Computes $A = lw$.
50 PRINT "AREA IS "; A	
90 END	

Here is a sample run; the length is 9, the width is 6.

```
RUN
ENTER LENGTH, WIDTH
? 9, 6
AREA IS 54
```
You must enter 9, 6 before the computer will proceed.

PREREQUISITE SKILLS FOLLOW-UP

COMPUTER HANDBOOK

TABLES

GLOSSARY

ANSWERS TO CHECKPOINTS

ANSWERS TO SELECTED EXERCISES

INDEX

Here is a program to find the volume of a cylinder.

```
10    REM VOLUME OF CYLINDER
20    PRINT "ENTER RADIUS, HEIGHT"
30    INPUT R, H
40    LET V = 3.14 * R * R * H
50    PRINT "VOLUME IS "; V
90    END
```

1. What does the computer display if you enter the values 4, 5?
2. How would you enter $r = 8$ and $h = 10$? What will be the output?
3. What is the output if you enter 10, 8?
4. Write a program that uses the formula $V = \frac{4}{3} \pi r^3$ to find the volume of a sphere when you enter the radius. (Use 3.14 for π.)

VI. Using GO TO Statements

It is often necessary to have the computer repeat the same set of instructions over and over again. The instruction GO TO (or GOTO on some computers) can be used to direct the computer to do this. The following program directs the computer to display the counting numbers.

The Program	What It Does
`10    REM COUNTING NUMBERS`	
`20    LET N = 1`	Assigns the value 1 to N.
`30    PRINT N`	Displays the number in N.
`40    LET N = N + 1`	Adds 1 to N and assigns the new value to N.
`50    GO TO 30`	Jumps back to line 30 and prints the new value assigned to N.
`90    END`	

When the computer reaches line 50, it jumps back, or "loops," to line 30. The program will display 1, 2, 3, 4, 5, . . . and continue without ever reaching END. The computer is in an "infinite loop."

EXERCISES   *What will the computer display when each of the following programs is entered and run?*

1.
```
10    LET N = 4
20    PRINT N
30    LET N = N + 4
40    GO TO 20
90    END
```

2.
```
10    LET N = 4
20    PRINT N
30    LET N = N + 3
40    GO TO 10
90    END
```

3.
```
10    LET K = 0
20    LET K = K + 12
30    PRINT K
40    GO TO 20
90    END
```

4.
```
10    LET R = 9.5
20    PRINT R
30    LET R = R * R
40    GO TO 10
90    END
```

5. Write a program that displays the positive multiples of 25.
6. Write a program that begins by displaying 400 and counts backwards.

VII. Using FOR. . .NEXT Statements

One way to avoid an infinite loop is to use a FOR. . .NEXT statement. Such a statement tells the computer to repeat a group of instructions a specified number of times. The following program instructs the computer to display the counting numbers from 5 through 8.

The Program	What It Does
10 REM FIVE TO EIGHT	
20 FOR N = 5 TO 8 STEP 1	Assigns the value 5 to N. Increases this value by 1 each time it loops back.
30 PRINT N	Displays the number in N.
40 NEXT N	Jumps back to line 20 to assign next value to N.
50 PRINT	Leaves a blank line.
60 PRINT "FINISHED."	Displays FINISHED to show that the computer has left (exited) the loop.
90 END	

```
RUN
  5
  6
  7
  8

FINISHED.
```

Lines 20 and 40 set up a loop. The computer begins with N = 5. When line 40 is reached, the computer loops back to line 20 and increases the value of N by 1 (STEP 1). Once the last value for N has been reached, line 40 permits the computer to exit, or leave, the loop and continue to lines 50 through 90.

If we omit "STEP 1" in a FOR. . .NEXT statement, the computer will automatically increase the variable by one each step. By placing an appropriate value after "STEP", we can instruct the computer to increase or decrease the value of the variable by any number we choose. These programs illustrate two uses of FOR. . .NEXT. . .STEP.

```
10   REM MULTIPLES OF FIVE
20   FOR F = 5 TO 20 STEP 5
30   PRINT F
40   NEXT F
90   END

RUN
  5
 10
 15
 20
```

```
10   REM BACKWARDS
20   FOR B = 6 TO 3 STEP -1
30   PRINT B
40   NEXT B
90   END

RUN
  6
  5
  4
  3
```

EXERCISES   *What numbers will be output when each program is run?*

```
1. 10   FOR J = 21 TO 30
   20   PRINT J
   30   NEXT J
   90   END
```

```
2. 10   FOR A = 10 TO 15
   20   PRINT A * A
   30   NEXT A
   90   END
```

PREREQUISITE SKILLS FOLLOW-UP

COMPUTER HANDBOOK

TABLES

GLOSSARY

ANSWERS TO CHECKPOINTS

ANSWERS TO SELECTED EXERCISES

INDEX

```
3. 10   FOR M = 0 TO 144 STEP 12        4. 10   FOR T = 1000 TO 0 STEP -100
   20   PRINT M                            20   PRINT T
   30   NEXT M                             30   NEXT T
   90   END                                90   END


5. 10   FOR K = 10 TO -10 STEP -2       6. 10   FOR  X = -15 TO 0 STEP 3
   20   PRINT K                            20   PRINT X, X + 10
   30   NEXT K                             30   NEXT X
   90   END                                90   END
```

Write a program that uses a FOR. . .NEXT statement to display the

7. whole numbers, from 101 to 120.   **8.** multiples of 8, from 0 to 96.

9. integers, from 9 to −9.   **10.** multiples of 10, from 200 to 0.

VIII. Using IF. . .THEN Statements

When a program uses an IF. . .THEN statement, the computer may give
the impression that it is thinking. Actually the computer is only com-
paring two quantities, using one of these symbols:

= is equal to	< > is not equal to
> is greater than	>= is greater than or equal to
< is less than	<= is less than or equal to

To see how an IF. . .THEN statement works, compare these two
programs for counting.

```
10   REM COUNT              10   REM COUNT TO TEN
20   LET K = 1              20   LET K = 1
30   REM LOOP BEGINS        30   REM LOOP BEGINS
40   PRINT K                40   PRINT K
50   LET K = K + 1          50   LET K = K + 1
60   GO TO 40               60   IF K <= 10 THEN 40
90   END                    90   END
```

The first program, COUNT, puts the computer into an infinite loop.
Each time it reaches line 60, the computer loops back to line 40. As a
result, the program never ends.

In the second program, COUNT TO TEN, line 60 tests the value in K.
As long as the value in K is 10 or less, the computer loops back to line
40. But as soon as the value of K is greater than 10, the computer
ignores the THEN command and goes to line 90, ending the program.
Note: The programs in this book use only line numbers after THEN.
Some computers, however, require a GO TO statement. If your computer does not accept line 60 in the above program, make this change:

```
60   IF K <= 10 THEN GO TO 40
```

Study the two programs that follow and note how the location of the
IF. . .THEN statement affects the output.

```
10   REM COUNT BY FIVE          10   REM COUNT BY FIVE
20   LET N = 5                   20   LET N = 5
30   PRINT N                     30   PRINT N
40   IF N = 20 THEN 90           40   LET N = N + 5
50   LET N = N + 5               50   IF N < 20 THEN 30
60   GO TO 30                    90   END
90   END
```

```
RUN        The computer continues        RUN        The computer jumps to
  5        in a loop until N equals         5        line 90 and ends the
 10        20 and 20 has been              10        program without
 15        displayed.                      15        displaying 20.
 20
```

EXERCISES   *What numbers will be displayed when each program is run?*

1.
```
10   REM COUNT BY TEN
20   LET N = 0
30   PRINT N
40   LET N = N + 10
50   IF N < 50 THEN 30
90   END
```

2.
```
10   REM COUNT BY TEN
20   LET N = 0
30   PRINT N
40   IF N > 50 THEN 90
50   LET N = N + 10
60   GO TO 30
90   END
```

3. What will be output when this program is run?
```
10   REM MULTIPLES OF SEVEN
20   LET K = 1
30   PRINT 7 * K
40   LET K = K + 1
50   IF K < 12 THEN 30
90   END
```

*In Exercises 4 and 5, write a program that uses an IF. . .THEN
statement to display*

4. the whole numbers from 31 to 50.

5. the multiples of twelve greater than 12 and less than 200.

6. Write a program that asks for a number to be input and then displays whether it is positive, negative, or zero.

IX. Using READ—DATA Statements

READ—DATA statements are often used to enter data into a computer.
The programs that follow, and the sample run for each, show how
READ—DATA statements can be used. Note that the DATA statement
may appear anywhere in the program before the END statement.

PREREQUISITE SKILLS FOLLOW-UP

COMPUTER HANDBOOK

TABLES

GLOSSARY

ANSWERS TO CHECKPOINTS

ANSWERS TO SELECTED EXERCISES

INDEX

The Program	What It Does
`10   REM AREA OF SQUARE`	
`20   READ S`	The computer reads one value at a time, left to right, from the DATA statement.
`30   DATA 16, 12.5`	Values must be separated by commas.
`40   PRINT "SIDE IS "; S`	Displays current value of S taken from the DATA statement.
`50   LET A = S * S`	Computes $A = s^2$.
`60   PRINT "AREA IS "; A`	Displays current value of A.
`70   PRINT`	Leaves a blank line.
`80   GO TO 20`	Returns for more data.
`90   END`	

`RUN`	
`SIDE IS 16`	Displays output for first
`AREA IS 256`	value in DATA statement.
`SIDE IS 12.5`	Displays output for second
`AREA IS 156.25`	value in DATA statement.
`OUT OF DATA`	Some computers display an error message when out of data.

The Program	What It Does
`100   REM VOLUME OF PRISM`	
`110   READ L, W, H`	Reads three consecutive values from the DATA statement.
`120   PRINT "LENGTH IS "; L`	Displays the values currently
`130   PRINT "WIDTH IS "; W`	in L, W, and H.
`140   PRINT "HEIGHT IS "; H`	
`150   LET V = L * W * H`	Computes $V = lwh$.
`160   PRINT "VOLUME IS "; V`	Displays current value of V.
`170   PRINT`	Leaves a blank line.
`180   GO TO 110`	Returns for more data.
`190   DATA 24, 12, 15`	Gives dimensions of a prism.
`900   END`	

`RUN`	
`LENGTH IS 24`	Displays output for set of three
`WIDTH IS 12`	values in DATA statement.
`HEIGHT IS 15`	
`VOLUME IS 4320`	When a great many values are to be entered, you may use as many DATA statements as necessary.
`OUT OF DATA`	

EXERCISES

1. In the program AREA OF SQUARE, change line 30 to:

   `30 DATA 45, 18, 1.25`

   What areas will be displayed when this revised program is run?

2. In the program VOLUME OF PRISM, change line 190 to:

```
190 DATA 7, 7, 5, 46, 45, 44, 9.5, 6.7, 8.2
```

What volumes will be displayed when this revised program is run?
3. Suppose line 190 becomes: 190 DATA -16, -15, -8, -5, -4, 3
   a. What volume will the computer display?
   b. Can a prism have negative dimensions or negative volume?
   c. Does the output always indicate when the input is invalid?
   d. What does this show about how input and output are related?
4. Write a program, using a READ—DATA statement to find the surface areas of cubes with edges of 8, of 14, and of 6.5. ($S = 6e^2$)

X. Using Exponential Notation

Computers often display numbers in an exponential form that is very similar to scientific notation.

Standard Notation	Scientific Notation	Exponential Notation in BASIC
3,000,000	3×10^6	3E+06
575,000,000,000	5.75×10^{11}	5.75E+11
0.0002	2×10^{-4}	2E−04
0.00425	4.25×10^{-3}	4.25E−03

EXERCISES   *Write each of the following in standard notation.*

1. 4E+07   2. 6.74E+10   3. 5E−08   4. 2.06E−09

Write each of the following in BASIC exponential notation.
5. 600,000   6. 7,800,000   7. 0.00002   8. 0.00000056

XI. Using BASIC Functions

In BASIC, a number of programs, called functions, are stored inside the computer. They can be used by entering the appropriate keyword.

Function	Mathematical Symbol	BASIC Keyword
Absolute Value	$|x|$	ABS(X)
Greatest Integer	$[x]$	INT(X)
Square Root	$\sqrt{x}$	SQR(X)
Sine	$\sin R$	SIN(R)
Cosine	$\cos R$	COS(R)
Tangent	$\tan R$	TAN(R)
Natural Logarithm	$\log N$	LOG(N)
Natural Antilogarithm	antilog N	EXP(N)

ABS(X) causes the computer to obtain the absolute value of X.

LET N = ABS(−19) sets N equal to 19.

Examples

```
PRINT ABS(26)    PRINT ABS(-3)    PRINT ABS(-2.5)
   26               3                2.5
```

PREREQUISITE SKILLS FOLLOW-UP

COMPUTER HANDBOOK

TABLES

GLOSSARY

ANSWERS TO CHECKPOINTS

ANSWERS TO SELECTED EXERCISES

INDEX

INT(X) causes the computer to obtain the greatest integer that is not greater than X. For a decimal numeral, this has the effect of always rounding down to the next lower integer.

LET N = INT(−15.5) sets N equal to −16.

Examples
```
PRINT INT(6)      PRINT INT(2.7)      PRINT INT(-1.8)
 6                 2                   -2
```

SQR(X) causes the computer to obtain the square root of X. If X is negative, the computer displays an error message.

LET N = SQR(49) sets N equal to 7.

Examples
```
PRINT SQR(144)      PRINT SQR(6.25)      PRINT SQR(-16)
 12                  2.5                  ERROR
```

The commands SIN(R), COS(R), and TAN(R) obtain the sine, cosine, and tangent, respectively, of an angle of R radians. To convert the measure of an angle from degrees to radians, multiply by $\pi/180$, or approximately 0.0174532925.

Examples
(Displays
may vary.)
```
PRINT SIN(30 * .0174532925)   PRINT COS(60 * .0174532925)
 .499999999                     .500000001

PRINT TAN(45 * .0174532925)
 .999999998
```

LOG(N) causes the computer to obtain the natural logarithm of N, based upon e. To convert a natural logarithm to a common logarithm, divide by the logarithm of 10.

Examples
```
PRINT LOG(100)/LOG(10)      PRINT LOG(.27)/LOG(10)
 2                           -.568636236
```

EXP(N) causes the computer to obtain the antilogarithm of N, where N is a natural logarithm. To find the antilog of a common logarithm, multiply the common logarithm by the logarithm of 10.

Examples
```
PRINT EXP(2 * LOG(10))      PRINT EXP(.544068044 * LOG(10))
 100                         3.5
```

EXERCISES   *What will the computer display for each entry?*

1. PRINT ABS(-3)   2. PRINT ABS(6.4)   3. PRINT INT(7.5)
4. PRINT INT(-6.2)   5. PRINT SQR(225)   6. PRINT SQR(-4)
7. PRINT LOG(1000)/LOG(10)   8. PRINT LOG(5)/LOG(10)
9. PRINT EXP(3 * LOG(10))   10. PRINT EXP(.397940009 * LOG(10))
11. PRINT SIN(40 * .0174532925)   12. PRINT TAN(23 * .0174532925)

XII. Using Rounding

Because all numbers entered into a computer are converted to base two internally, the results may not always be exact. Some computers are more precise in computation than others. One method of handling this is to round off the results displayed or stored in the computer.

The following can be used to round numbers. The variable N represents the number before rounding. R represents the number after rounding.

To the nearest hundred: R = INT(N/100 + .5) * 100
To the nearest unit: R = INT(N + .5)
To the nearest hundredth: R = INT(N * 100 + .5)/100

EXERCISES   *Write an expression in BASIC to round the number N*

1. to the nearest thousand.   **2.** to the nearest ten-thousandth.

XIII. Some Differences in BASICs

When a program has a statement that does not run on your computer, the following may help you to modify the program.

1. Instead of using ↑ to indicate raising to a power, some computers use ∧ or **.
2. On most computers, if you do not assign a value to a variable (as in LET X = 5), the computer automatically assigns the value zero. On a few computers, however, a program will not run unless you assign a value for each variable used in the program.
3. On most computers the command PRINT 2.6 − 2.5 will result in a display of .1. But on some, the display will be .0999999996. To avoid difficulties caused by inexact answers, you may have to round the results. (See Section XII, Using Rounding)
4. Some computers do not permit multiple INPUT statements. For these computers, write a separate statement for each variable. Instead of 40   INPUT A, B   use   40   INPUT A
                                                45   INPUT B
5. If a computer rejects GO TO, use GOTO.
6. If a computer rejects a statement such as IF A = 8 THEN 60 use IF A = 8 THEN GO TO 60.
7. For a computer without READ-DATA capability, use LET statements or INPUT statements to enter the values.
8. Each computer divides the screen display into "zones." However, the number of zones and their size vary widely. In a PRINT statement, a variable or message following a comma will be printed in the next zone. See your computer manual for further explanation.
9. A semicolon in a PRINT statement that displays a variable has a different effect on different computers. The command PRINT 9; 6 may give any of these displays: 96   9 6   9 6
   See your computer manual for further explanation.
10. Different computers give different "error messages." See your computer manual for an explanation.

As you work with a computer, keep in mind that several different programs can usually be written to solve a problem. The programs in this book were selected because they are easy to understand or because they illustrate certain BASIC commands and programming techniques. Once you learn to program in BASIC, you may be able to write programs that are shorter and more efficient.

PREREQUISITE SKILLS FOLLOW-UP

COMPUTER HANDBOOK

TABLES

GLOSSARY

ANSWERS TO CHECKPOINTS

ANSWERS TO SELECTED EXERCISES

INDEX

TABLE OF SQUARES AND SQUARE ROOTS

n	n^2	$\sqrt{n}$	$\sqrt{10n}$	n	n^2	$\sqrt{n}$	$\sqrt{10n}$
1.0	1.00	1.000	3.162	5.5	30.25	2.345	7.416
1.1	1.21	1.049	3.317	5.6	31.36	2.366	7.483
1.2	1.44	1.095	3.464	5.7	32.49	2.387	7.550
1.3	1.69	1.140	3.606	5.8	33.64	2.408	7.616
1.4	1.96	1.183	3.742	5.9	34.81	2.429	7.681
1.5	2.25	1.225	3.873	6.0	36.00	2.449	7.746
1.6	2.56	1.265	4.000	6.1	37.21	2.470	7.810
1.7	2.89	1.304	4.123	6.2	38.44	2.490	7.874
1.8	3.24	1.342	4.243	6.3	39.69	2.510	7.937
1.9	3.61	1.378	4.359	6.4	40.96	2.530	8.000
2.0	4.00	1.414	4.472	6.5	42.25	2.550	8.062
2.1	4.41	1.449	4.583	6.6	43.56	2.569	8.124
2.2	4.84	1.483	4.690	6.7	44.89	2.588	8.185
2.3	5.29	1.517	4.796	6.8	46.24	2.608	8.246
2.4	5.76	1.549	4.899	6.9	47.61	2.627	8.307
2.5	6.25	1.581	5.000	7.0	49.00	2.646	8.367
2.6	6.76	1.612	5.099	7.1	50.41	2.665	8.426
2.7	7.29	1.643	5.196	7.2	51.84	2.683	8.485
2.8	7.84	1.673	5.292	7.3	53.29	2.702	8.544
2.9	8.41	1.703	5.385	7.4	54.76	2.720	8.602
3.0	9.00	1.732	5.477	7.5	56.25	2.739	8.660
3.1	9.61	1.761	5.568	7.6	57.76	2.757	8.718
3.2	10.24	1.789	5.657	7.7	59.29	2.775	8.775
3.3	10.89	1.817	5.745	7.8	60.84	2.793	8.832
3.4	11.56	1.844	5.831	7.9	62.41	2.811	8.888
3.5	12.25	1.871	5.916	8.0	64.00	2.828	8.944
3.6	12.96	1.897	6.000	8.1	65.61	2.846	9.000
3.7	13.69	1.924	6.083	8.2	67.24	2.864	9.055
3.8	14.44	1.949	6.164	8.3	68.89	2.881	9.110
3.9	15.21	1.975	6.245	8.4	70.56	2.898	9.165
4.0	16.00	2.000	6.325	8.5	72.25	2.915	9.220
4.1	16.81	2.025	6.403	8.6	73.96	2.933	9.274
4.2	17.64	2.049	6.481	8.7	75.69	2.950	9.327
4.3	18.49	2.074	6.557	8.8	77.44	2.966	9.381
4.4	19.36	2.098	6.633	8.9	79.21	2.983	9.434
4.5	20.25	2.121	6.708	9.0	81.00	3.000	9.487
4.6	21.16	2.145	6.782	9.1	82.81	3.017	9.539
4.7	22.09	2.168	6.856	9.2	84.64	3.033	9.592
4.8	23.04	2.191	6.928	9.3	86.49	3.050	9.644
4.9	24.01	2.214	7.000	9.4	88.36	3.066	9.695
5.0	25.00	2.236	7.071	9.5	90.25	3.082	9.747
5.1	26.01	2.258	7.141	9.6	92.16	3.098	9.798
5.2	27.04	2.280	7.211	9.7	94.09	3.114	9.849
5.3	28.09	2.302	7.280	9.8	96.04	3.130	9.899
5.4	29.16	2.324	7.348	9.9	98.01	3.146	9.950
5.5	30.25	2.345	7.416	10	100.00	3.162	10.000

Examples: $\sqrt{5.5} \approx 2.345$ $\sqrt{55} = \sqrt{10(5.5)} \approx 7.416$

TABLE OF CUBES AND CUBE ROOTS

n	n^3	$\sqrt[3]{n}$	$\sqrt[3]{10n}$	$\sqrt[3]{100n}$	n	n^3	$\sqrt[3]{n}$	$\sqrt[3]{10n}$	$\sqrt[3]{100n}$
1.0	1.000	1.000	2.154	4.642	5.5	166.375	1.765	3.803	8.193
1.1	1.331	1.032	2.224	4.791	5.6	175.616	1.776	3.826	8.243
1.2	1.728	1.063	2.289	4.932	5.7	185.193	1.786	3.849	8.291
1.3	2.197	1.091	2.351	5.066	5.8	195.112	1.797	3.871	8.340
1.4	2.744	1.119	2.410	5.192	5.9	205.379	1.807	3.893	8.387
1.5	3.375	1.145	2.466	5.313	6.0	216.000	1.817	3.915	8.434
1.6	4.096	1.170	2.520	5.429	6.1	226.981	1.827	3.936	8.481
1.7	4.913	1.193	2.571	5.540	6.2	238.328	1.837	3.958	8.527
1.8	5.832	1.216	2.621	5.646	6.3	250.047	1.847	3.979	8.573
1.9	6.859	1.239	2.668	5.749	6.4	262.144	1.857	4.000	8.618
2.0	8.000	1.260	2.714	5.848	6.5	274.625	1.866	4.021	8.662
2.1	9.261	1.281	2.759	5.944	6.6	287.496	1.876	4.041	8.707
2.2	10.648	1.301	2.802	6.037	6.7	300.763	1.885	4.062	8.750
2.3	12.167	1.320	2.844	6.127	6.8	314.432	1.895	4.082	8.794
2.4	13.824	1.339	2.884	6.214	6.9	328.509	1.904	4.102	8.837
2.5	15.625	1.357	2.924	6.300	7.0	343.000	1.913	4.121	8.879
2.6	17.576	1.375	2.962	6.383	7.1	357.911	1.922	4.141	8.921
2.7	19.683	1.392	3.000	6.463	7.2	373.248	1.931	4.160	8.963
2.8	21.952	1.409	3.037	6.542	7.3	389.017	1.940	4.179	9.004
2.9	24.389	1.426	3.072	6.619	7.4	405.224	1.949	4.198	9.045
3.0	27.000	1.442	3.107	6.694	7.5	421.875	1.957	4.217	9.086
3.1	29.791	1.458	3.141	6.768	7.6	438.976	1.966	4.236	9.126
3.2	32.768	1.474	3.175	6.840	7.7	456.533	1.975	4.254	9.166
3.3	35.937	1.489	3.208	6.910	7.8	474.552	1.983	4.273	9.205
3.4	39.304	1.504	3.240	6.980	7.9	493.039	1.992	4.291	9.244
3.5	42.875	1.518	3.271	7.047	8.0	512.000	2.000	4.309	9.283
3.6	46.656	1.533	3.302	7.114	8.1	531.441	2.008	4.327	9.322
3.7	50.653	1.547	3.332	7.179	8.2	551.368	2.017	4.344	9.360
3.8	54.872	1.560	3.362	7.243	8.3	571.787	2.025	4.362	9.398
3.9	59.319	1.574	3.391	7.306	8.4	592.704	2.033	4.380	9.435
4.0	64.000	1.587	3.420	7.368	8.5	614.125	2.041	4.397	9.473
4.1	68.921	1.601	3.448	7.429	8.6	636.056	2.049	4.414	9.510
4.2	74.088	1.613	3.476	7.489	8.7	658.503	2.057	4.431	9.546
4.3	79.507	1.626	3.503	7.548	8.8	681.472	2.065	4.448	9.583
4.4	85.184	1.639	3.530	7.606	8.9	704.969	2.072	4.465	9.619
4.5	91.125	1.651	3.557	7.663	9.0	729.000	2.080	4.481	9.655
4.6	97.336	1.663	3.583	7.719	9.1	753.571	2.088	4.498	9.691
4.7	103.823	1.675	3.609	7.775	9.2	778.688	2.095	4.514	9.726
4.8	110.592	1.687	3.634	7.830	9.3	804.357	2.103	4.531	9.761
4.9	117.649	1.698	3.659	7.884	9.4	830.584	2.110	4.547	9.796
5.0	125.000	1.710	3.684	7.937	9.5	857.375	2.118	4.563	9.830
5.1	132.651	1.721	3.708	7.990	9.6	884.736	2.125	4.579	9.865
5.2	140.608	1.732	3.733	8.041	9.7	912.673	2.133	4.595	9.899
5.3	148.877	1.744	3.756	8.093	9.8	941.192	2.140	4.610	9.933
5.4	157.464	1.754	3.780	8.143	9.9	970.299	2.147	4.626	9.967
5.5	166.375	1.765	3.803	8.193	10	1000.000	2.154	4.642	10.000

Examples: $\sqrt[3]{5.5} \approx 1.765$ $\sqrt[3]{55} = \sqrt[3]{10(5.5)} \approx 3.803$ $\sqrt[3]{550} = \sqrt[3]{100(5.5)} \approx 8.193$

PREREQUISITE SKILLS FOLLOW-UP

COMPUTER HANDBOOK

TABLES

GLOSSARY

ANSWERS TO CHECKPOINTS

ANSWERS TO SELECTED EXERCISES

INDEX

TABLE OF COMMON LOGARITHMS

n	0	1	2	3	4	5	6	7	8	9
10	0000	0043	0086	0128	0170	0212	0253	0294	0334	0374
11	0414	0453	0492	0531	0569	0607	0645	0682	0719	0755
12	0792	0828	0864	0899	0934	0969	1004	1038	1072	1106
13	1139	1173	1206	1239	1271	1303	1335	1367	1399	1430
14	1461	1492	1523	1553	1584	1614	1644	1673	1703	1732
15	1761	1790	1818	1847	1875	1903	1931	1959	1987	2014
16	2041	2068	2095	2122	2148	2175	2201	2227	2253	2279
17	2304	2330	2355	2380	2405	2430	2455	2480	2504	2529
18	2553	2577	2601	2625	2648	2672	2695	2718	2742	2765
19	2788	2810	2833	2856	2878	2900	2923	2945	2967	2989
20	3010	3032	3054	3075	3096	3118	3139	3160	3181	3201
21	3222	3243	3263	3284	3304	3324	3345	3365	3385	3404
22	3424	3444	3464	3483	3502	3522	3541	3560	3579	3598
23	3617	3636	3655	3674	3692	3711	3729	3747	3766	3784
24	3802	3820	3838	3856	3874	3892	3909	3927	3945	3962
25	3979	3997	4014	4031	4048	4065	4082	4099	4116	4133
26	4150	4166	4183	4200	4216	4232	4249	4265	4281	4298
27	4314	4330	4346	4362	4378	4393	4409	4425	4440	4456
28	4472	4487	4502	4518	4533	4548	4564	4579	4594	4609
29	4624	4639	4654	4669	4683	4698	4713	4728	4742	4757
30	4771	4786	4800	4814	4829	4843	4857	4871	4886	4900
31	4914	4928	4942	4955	4969	4983	4997	5011	5024	5038
32	5051	5065	5079	5092	5105	5119	5132	5145	5159	5172
33	5185	5198	5211	5224	5237	5250	5263	5276	5289	5302
34	5315	5328	5340	5353	5366	5378	5391	5403	5416	5428
35	5441	5453	5465	5478	5490	5502	5514	5527	5539	5551
36	5563	5575	5587	5599	5611	5623	5635	5647	5658	5670
37	5682	5694	5705	5717	5729	5740	5752	5763	5775	5786
38	5798	5809	5821	5832	5843	5855	5866	5877	5888	5899
39	5911	5922	5933	5944	5955	5966	5977	5988	5999	6010
40	6021	6031	6042	6053	6064	6075	6085	6096	6107	6117
41	6128	6138	6149	6160	6170	6180	6191	6201	6212	6222
42	6232	6243	6253	6263	6274	6284	6294	6304	6314	6325
43	6335	6345	6355	6365	6375	6385	6395	6405	6415	6425
44	6435	6444	6454	6464	6474	6484	6493	6503	6513	6522
45	6532	6542	6551	6561	6571	6580	6590	6599	6609	6618
46	6628	6637	6646	6656	6665	6675	6684	6693	6702	6712
47	6721	6730	6739	6749	6758	6767	6776	6785	6794	6803
48	6812	6821	6830	6839	6848	6857	6866	6875	6884	6893
49	6902	6911	6920	6928	6937	6946	6955	6964	6972	6981
50	6990	6998	7007	7016	7024	7033	7042	7050	7059	7067
51	7076	7084	7093	7101	7110	7118	7126	7135	7143	7152
52	7160	7168	7177	7185	7193	7202	7210	7218	7226	7235
53	7243	7251	7259	7267	7275	7284	7292	7300	7308	7316
54	7324	7332	7340	7348	7356	7364	7372	7380	7388	7396

Examples: log 2.5 = 0.3979   log 25 = 1.3979   log 250 = 2.3979

TABLE OF COMMON LOGARITHMS

n	0	1	2	3	4	5	6	7	8	9
55	7404	7412	7419	7427	7435	7443	7451	7459	7466	7474
56	7482	7490	7497	7505	7513	7520	7528	7536	7543	7551
57	7559	7566	7574	7582	7589	7597	7604	7612	7619	7627
58	7634	7642	7649	7657	7664	7672	7679	7686	7694	7701
59	7709	7716	7723	7731	7738	7745	7752	7760	7767	7774
60	7782	7789	7796	7803	7810	7818	7825	7832	7839	7846
61	7853	7860	7868	7875	7882	7889	7896	7903	7910	7917
62	7924	7931	7938	7945	7952	7959	7966	7973	7980	7987
63	7993	8000	8007	8014	8021	8028	8035	8041	8048	8055
64	8062	8069	8075	8082	8089	8096	8102	8109	8116	8122
65	8129	8136	8142	8149	8156	8162	8169	8176	8182	8189
66	8195	8202	8209	8215	8222	8228	8235	8241	8248	8254
67	8261	8267	8274	8280	8287	8293	8299	8306	8312	8319
68	8325	8331	8338	8344	8351	8357	8363	8370	8376	8382
69	8388	8395	8401	8407	8414	8420	8426	8432	8439	8445
70	8451	8457	8463	8470	8476	8482	8488	8494	8500	8506
71	8513	8519	8525	8531	8537	8543	8549	8555	8561	8567
72	8573	8579	8585	8591	8597	8603	8609	8615	8621	8627
73	8633	8639	8645	8651	8657	8663	8669	8675	8681	8686
74	8692	8698	8704	8710	8716	8722	8727	8733	8739	8745
75	8751	8756	8762	8768	8774	8779	8785	8791	8797	8802
76	8808	8814	8820	8825	8831	8837	8842	8848	8854	8859
77	8865	8871	8876	8882	8887	8893	8899	8904	8910	8915
78	8921	8927	8932	8938	8943	8949	8954	8960	8965	8971
79	8976	8982	8987	8993	8998	9004	9009	9015	9020	9025
80	9031	9036	9042	9047	9053	9058	9063	9069	9074	9079
81	9085	9090	9096	9101	9106	9112	9117	9122	9128	9133
82	9138	9143	9149	9154	9159	9165	9170	9175	9180	9186
83	9191	9196	9201	9206	9212	9217	9222	9227	9232	9238
84	9243	9248	9253	9258	9263	9269	9274	9279	9284	9289
85	9294	9299	9304	9309	9315	9320	9325	9330	9335	9340
86	9345	9350	9355	9360	9365	9370	9375	9380	9385	9390
87	9395	9400	9405	9410	9415	9420	9425	9430	9435	9440
88	9445	9450	9455	9460	9465	9469	9474	9479	9484	9489
89	9494	9499	9504	9509	9513	9518	9523	9528	9533	9538
90	9542	9547	9552	9557	9562	9566	9571	9576	9581	9586
91	9590	9595	9600	9605	9609	9614	9619	9624	9628	9633
92	9638	9643	9647	9652	9657	9661	9666	9671	9675	9680
93	9685	9689	9694	9699	9703	9708	9713	9717	9722	9727
94	9731	9736	9741	9745	9750	9754	9759	9763	9768	9773
95	9777	9782	9786	9791	9795	9800	9805	9809	9814	9818
96	9823	9827	9832	9836	9841	9845	9850	9854	9859	9863
97	9868	9872	9877	9881	9886	9890	9894	9899	9903	9908
98	9912	9917	9921	9926	9930	9934	9939	9943	9948	9952
99	9956	9961	9965	9969	9974	9978	9983	9987	9991	9996

Examples: $\log 6.45 = 0.8096$ $\log 0.645 = 0.8096 - 1 = 9.8096 - 10$
$\log 0.0645 = 0.8096 - 2 = 8.8096 - 10$

PREREQUISITE SKILLS FOLLOW-UP

COMPUTER HANDBOOK

TABLES

GLOSSARY

ANSWERS TO CHECKPOINTS

ANSWERS TO SELECTED EXERCISES

INDEX

TABLE OF TRIGONOMETRIC RATIOS

θ Degrees	θ Radians	Sin θ	Cos θ	Tan θ	Cot θ	Sec θ	Csc θ		
0° 00′	.0000	.0000	1.0000	.0000	-----	1.000	-----	1.5708	90° 00′
10′	.0029	.0029	1.0000	.0029	343.8	1.000	343.8	1.5679	50′
20′	.0058	.0058	1.0000	.0058	171.9	1.000	171.9	1.5650	40′
30′	.0087	.0087	1.0000	.0087	114.6	1.000	114.6	1.5621	30′
40′	.0116	.0116	.9999	.0116	85.94	1.000	85.95	1.5592	20′
50′	.0145	.0145	.9999	.0145	68.75	1.000	68.76	1.5563	10′
1° 00′	.0175	.0175	.9998	.0175	57.29	1.000	57.30	1.5533	89° 00′
10′	.0204	.0204	.9998	.0204	49.10	1.000	49.11	1.5504	50′
20′	.0233	.0233	.9997	.0233	42.96	1.000	42.98	1.5475	40′
30′	.0262	.0262	.9997	.0262	38.19	1.000	38.20	1.5446	30′
40′	.0291	.0291	.9996	.0291	34.37	1.000	34.38	1.5417	20′
50′	.0320	.0320	.9995	.0320	31.24	1.001	31.26	1.5388	10′
2° 00′	.0349	.0349	.9994	.0349	28.64	1.001	28.65	1.5359	88° 00′
10′	.0378	.0378	.9993	.0378	26.43	1.001	26.45	1.5330	50′
20′	.0407	.0407	.9992	.0407	24.54	1.001	24.56	1.5301	40′
30′	.0436	.0436	.9990	.0437	22.90	1.001	22.93	1.5272	30′
40′	.0465	.0465	.9989	.0466	21.47	1.001	21.49	1.5243	20′
50′	.0495	.0494	.9988	.0495	20.21	1.001	20.23	1.5213	10′
3° 00′	.0524	.0523	.9986	.0524	19.08	1.001	19.11	1.5184	87° 00′
10′	.0553	.0552	.9985	.0553	18.07	1.002	18.10	1.5155	50′
20′	.0582	.0581	.9983	.0582	17.17	1.002	17.20	1.5126	40′
30′	.0611	.0610	.9981	.0612	16.35	1.002	16.38	1.5097	30′
40′	.0640	.0640	.9980	.0641	15.60	1.002	15.64	1.5068	20′
50′	.0669	.0669	.9978	.0670	14.92	1.002	14.96	1.5039	10′
4° 00′	.0698	.0698	.9976	.0699	14.30	1.002	14.34	1.5010	86° 00′
10′	.0727	.0727	.9974	.0729	13.73	1.003	13.76	1.4981	50′
20′	.0756	.0756	.9971	.0758	13.20	1.003	13.23	1.4952	40′
30′	.0785	.0785	.9969	.0787	12.71	1.003	12.75	1.4923	30′
40′	.0814	.0814	.9967	.0816	12.25	1.003	12.29	1.4893	20′
50′	.0844	.0843	.9964	.0846	11.83	1.004	11.87	1.4864	10′
5° 00′	.0873	.0872	.9962	.0875	11.43	1.004	11.47	1.4835	85° 00′
10′	.0902	.0901	.9959	.0904	11.06	1.004	11.10	1.4806	50′
20′	.0931	.0929	.9957	.0934	10.71	1.004	10.76	1.4777	40′
30′	.0960	.0958	.9954	.0963	10.39	1.005	10.43	1.4748	30′
40′	.0989	.0987	.9951	.0992	10.08	1.005	10.13	1.4719	20′
50′	.1018	.1016	.9948	.1022	9.788	1.005	9.839	1.4690	10′
6° 00′	.1047	.1045	.9945	.1051	9.514	1.006	9.567	1.4661	84° 00′
10′	.1076	.1074	.9942	.1080	9.255	1.006	9.309	1.4632	50′
20′	.1105	.1103	.9939	.1110	9.010	1.006	9.065	1.4603	40′
30′	.1134	.1132	.9936	.1139	8.777	1.006	8.834	1.4573	30′
40′	.1164	.1161	.9932	.1169	8.556	1.007	8.614	1.4544	20′
50′	.1193	.1190	.9929	.1198	8.345	1.007	8.405	1.4515	10′
7° 00′	.1222	.1219	.9925	.1228	8.144	1.008	8.206	1.4486	83° 00′
10′	.1251	.1248	.9922	.1257	7.953	1.008	8.016	1.4457	50′
20′	.1280	.1276	.9918	.1287	7.770	1.008	7.834	1.4428	40′
30′	.1309	.1305	.9914	.1317	7.596	1.009	7.661	1.4399	30′
40′	.1338	.1334	.9911	.1346	7.429	1.009	7.496	1.4370	20′
50′	.1367	.1363	.9907	.1376	7.269	1.009	7.337	1.4341	10′
8° 00′	.1396	.1392	.9903	.1405	7.115	1.010	7.185	1.4312	82° 00′
10′	.1425	.1421	.9899	.1435	6.968	1.010	7.040	1.4283	50′
20′	.1454	.1449	.9894	.1465	6.827	1.011	6.900	1.4254	40′
30′	.1484	.1478	.9890	.1495	6.691	1.011	6.765	1.4224	30′
40′	.1513	.1507	.9886	.1524	6.561	1.012	6.636	1.4195	20′
50′	.1542	.1536	.9881	.1554	6.435	1.012	6.512	1.4166	10′
9° 00′	.1571	.1564	.9877	.1584	6.314	1.012	6.392	1.4137	81° 00′
		Cos θ	Sin θ	Cot θ	Tan θ	Csc θ	Sec θ	θ Radians	θ Degrees

TABLE OF TRIGONOMETRIC RATIOS

θ Degrees	θ Radians	Sin θ	Cos θ	Tan θ	Cot θ	Sec θ	Csc θ		
9° 00′	.1571	.1564	.9877	.1584	6.314	1.012	6.392	1.4137	81° 00′
10′	.1600	.1593	.9872	.1614	6.197	1.013	6.277	1.4108	50′
20′	.1629	.1622	.9868	.1644	6.084	1.013	6.166	1.4079	40′
30′	.1658	.1650	.9863	.1673	5.976	1.014	6.059	1.4050	30′
40′	.1687	.1679	.9858	.1703	5.871	1.014	5.955	1.4021	20′
50′	.1716	.1708	.9853	.1733	5.769	1.015	5.855	1.3992	10′
10° 00′	.1745	.1736	.9848	.1763	5.671	1.015	5.759	1.3963	80° 00′
10′	.1774	.1765	.9843	.1793	5.576	1.016	5.665	1.3934	50′
20′	.1804	.1794	.9838	.1823	5.485	1.016	5.575	1.3904	40′
30′	.1833	.1822	.9833	.1853	5.396	1.017	5.487	1.3875	30′
40′	.1862	.1851	.9827	.1883	5.309	1.018	5.403	1.3846	20′
50′	.1891	.1880	.9822	.1914	5.226	1.018	5.320	1.3817	10′
11° 00′	.1920	.1908	.9816	.1944	5.145	1.019	5.241	1.3788	79° 00′
10′	.1949	.1937	.9811	.1974	5.066	1.019	5.164	1.3759	50′
20′	.1978	.1965	.9805	.2004	4.989	1.020	5.089	1.3730	40′
30′	.2007	.1994	.9799	.2035	4.915	1.020	5.016	1.3701	30′
40′	.2036	.2022	.9793	.2065	4.843	1.021	4.945	1.3672	20′
50′	.2065	.2051	.9787	.2095	4.773	1.022	4.876	1.3643	10′
12° 00′	.2094	.2079	.9781	.2126	4.705	1.022	4.810	1.3614	78° 00′
10′	.2123	.2108	.9775	.2156	4.638	1.023	4.745	1.3584	50′
20′	.2153	.2136	.9769	.2186	4.574	1.024	4.682	1.3555	40′
30′	.2182	.2164	.9763	.2217	4.511	1.024	4.620	1.3526	30′
40′	.2211	.2193	.9757	.2247	4.449	1.025	4.560	1.3497	20′
50′	.2240	.2221	.9750	.2278	4.390	1.026	4.502	1.3468	10′
13° 00′	.2269	.2250	.9744	.2309	4.331	1.026	4.445	1.3439	77° 00′
10′	.2298	.2278	.9737	.2339	4.275	1.027	4.390	1.3410	50′
20′	.2327	.2306	.9730	.2370	4.219	1.028	4.336	1.3381	40′
30′	.2356	.2334	.9724	.2401	4.165	1.028	4.284	1.3352	30′
40′	.2385	.2363	.9717	.2432	4.113	1.029	4.232	1.3323	20′
50′	.2414	.2391	.9710	.2462	4.061	1.030	4.182	1.3294	10′
14° 00′	.2443	.2419	.9703	.2493	4.011	1.031	4.134	1.3265	76° 00′
10′	.2473	.2447	.9696	.2524	3.962	1.031	4.086	1.3235	50′
20′	.2502	.2476	.9689	.2555	3.914	1.032	4.039	1.3206	40′
30′	.2531	.2504	.9681	.2586	3.867	1.033	3.994	1.3177	30′
40′	.2560	.2532	.9674	.2617	3.821	1.034	3.950	1.3148	20′
50′	.2589	.2560	.9667	.2648	3.776	1.034	3.906	1.3119	10′
15° 00′	.2618	.2588	.9659	.2679	3.732	1.035	3.864	1.3090	75° 00′
10′	.2647	.2616	.9652	.2711	3.689	1.036	3.822	1.3061	50′
20′	.2676	.2644	.9644	.2742	3.647	1.037	3.782	1.3032	40′
30′	.2705	.2672	.9636	.2773	3.606	1.038	3.742	1.3003	30′
40′	.2734	.2700	.9628	.2805	3.566	1.039	3.703	1.2974	20′
50′	.2763	.2728	.9621	.2836	3.526	1.039	3.665	1.2945	10′
16° 00′	.2793	.2756	.9613	.2867	3.487	1.040	3.628	1.2915	74° 00′
10′	.2822	.2784	.9605	.2899	3.450	1.041	3.592	1.2886	50′
20′	.2851	.2812	.9596	.2931	3.412	1.042	3.556	1.2857	40′
30′	.2880	.2840	.9588	.2962	3.376	1.043	3.521	1.2828	30′
40′	.2909	.2868	.9580	.2994	3.340	1.044	3.487	1.2799	20′
50′	.2938	.2896	.9572	.3026	3.305	1.045	3.453	1.2770	10′
17° 00′	.2967	.2924	.9563	.3057	3.271	1.046	3.420	1.2741	73° 00′
10′	.2996	.2952	.9555	.3089	3.237	1.047	3.388	1.2712	50′
20′	.3025	.2979	.9546	.3121	3.204	1.048	3.356	1.2683	40′
30′	.3054	.3007	.9537	.3153	3.172	1.049	3.326	1.2654	30′
40′	.3083	.3035	.9528	.3185	3.140	1.049	3.295	1.2625	20′
50′	.3113	.3062	.9520	.3217	3.108	1.050	3.265	1.2595	10′
18° 00′	.3142	.3090	.9511	.3249	3.078	1.051	3.236	1.2566	72° 00′
		Cos θ	Sin θ	Cot θ	Tan θ	Csc θ	Sec θ	θ Radians	θ Degrees

PREREQUISITE SKILLS FOLLOW-UP

COMPUTER HANDBOOK

TABLES

GLOSSARY

ANSWERS TO CHECKPOINTS

ANSWERS TO SELECTED EXERCISES

INDEX

TABLE OF TRIGONOMETRIC RATIOS

θ Degrees	θ Radians	Sin θ	Cos θ	Tan θ	Cot θ	Sec θ	Csc θ		
18° 00′	.3142	.3090	.9511	.3249	3.078	1.051	3.236	1.2566	72° 00′
10′	.3171	.3118	.9502	.3281	3.047	1.052	3.207	1.2537	50′
20′	.3200	.3145	.9492	.3314	3.018	1.053	3.179	1.2508	40′
30′	.3229	.3173	.9483	.3346	2.989	1.054	3.152	1.2479	30′
40′	.3258	.3201	.9474	.3378	2.960	1.056	3.124	1.2450	20′
50′	.3287	.3228	.9465	.3411	2.932	1.057	3.098	1.2421	10′
19° 00′	.3316	.3256	.9455	.3443	2.904	1.058	3.072	1.2392	71° 00′
10′	.3345	.3283	.9446	.3476	2.877	1.059	3.046	1.2363	50′
20′	.3374	.3311	.9436	.3508	2.850	1.060	3.021	1.2334	40′
30′	.3403	.3338	.9426	.3541	2.824	1.061	2.996	1.2305	30′
40′	.3432	.3365	.9417	.3574	2.798	1.062	2.971	1.2275	20′
50′	.3462	.3393	.9407	.3607	2.773	1.063	2.947	1.2246	10′
20° 00′	.3491	.3420	.9397	.3640	2.747	1.064	2.924	1.2217	70° 00′
10′	.3520	.3448	.9387	.3673	2.723	1.065	2.901	1.2188	50′
20′	.3549	.3475	.9377	.3706	2.699	1.066	2.878	1.2159	40′
30′	.3578	.3502	.9367	.3739	2.675	1.068	2.855	1.2130	30′
40′	.3607	.3529	.9356	.3772	2.651	1.069	2.833	1.2101	20′
50′	.3636	.3557	.9346	.3805	2.628	1.070	2.812	1.2072	10′
21° 00′	.3665	.3584	.9336	.3839	2.605	1.071	2.790	1.2043	69° 00′
10′	.3694	.3611	.9325	.3872	2.583	1.072	2.769	1.2014	50′
20′	.3723	.3638	.9315	.3906	2.560	1.074	2.749	1.1985	40′
30′	.3752	.3665	.9304	.3939	2.539	1.075	2.729	1.1956	30′
40′	.3782	.3692	.9293	.3973	2.517	1.076	2.709	1.1926	20′
50′	.3811	.3719	.9283	.4006	2.496	1.077	2.689	1.1897	10′
22° 00′	.3840	.3746	.9272	.4040	2.475	1.079	2.669	1.1868	68° 00′
10′	.3869	.3773	.9261	.4074	2.455	1.080	2.650	1.1839	50′
20′	.3898	.3800	.9250	.4108	2.434	1.081	2.632	1.1810	40′
30′	.3927	.3827	.9239	.4142	2.414	1.082	3.613	1.1781	30′
40′	.3956	.3854	.9228	.4176	2.394	1.084	2.595	1.1752	20′
50′	.3985	.3881	.9216	.4210	2.375	1.085	2.577	1.1723	10′
23° 00′	.4014	.3907	.9205	.4245	2.356	1.086	2.559	1.1694	67° 00′
10′	.4043	.3934	.9194	.4279	2.337	1.088	2.542	1.1665	50′
20′	.4072	.3961	.9182	.4314	2.318	1.089	2.525	1.1636	40′
30′	.4102	.3987	.9171	.4348	2.300	1.090	2.508	1.1606	30′
40′	.4131	.4014	.9159	.4383	2.282	1.092	2.491	1.1577	20′
50′	.4160	.4041	.9147	.4417	2.264	1.093	2.475	1.1548	10′
24° 00′	.4189	.4067	.9135	.4452	2.246	1.095	2.459	1.1519	66° 00′
10′	.4218	.4094	.9124	.4487	2.229	1.096	2.443	1.1490	50′
20′	.4247	.4120	.9112	.4522	2.211	1.097	2.427	1.1461	40′
30′	.4276	.4147	.9100	.4557	2.194	1.099	2.411	1.1432	30′
40′	.4305	.4173	.9088	.4592	2.177	1.100	2.396	1.1403	20′
50′	.4334	.4200	.9075	.4628	2.161	1.102	2.381	1.1374	10′
25° 00′	.4363	.4226	.9063	.4663	2.145	1.103	2.366	1.1345	65° 00′
10′	.4392	.4253	.9051	.4699	2.128	1.105	2.352	1.1316	50′
20′	.4422	.4279	.9038	.4734	2.112	1.106	2.337	1.1286	40′
30′	.4451	.4305	.9026	.4770	2.097	1.108	2.323	1.1257	30′
40′	.4480	.4331	.9013	.4806	2.081	1.109	2.309	1.1228	20′
50′	.4509	.4358	.9001	.4841	2.066	1.111	2.295	1.1199	10′
26° 00′	.4538	.4384	.8988	.4877	2.050	1.113	2.281	1.1170	64° 00′
10′	.4567	.4410	.8975	.4913	2.035	1.114	2.268	1.1141	50′
20′	.4596	.4436	.8962	.4950	2.020	1.116	2.254	1.1112	40′
30′	.4625	.4462	.8949	.4986	2.006	1.117	2.241	1.1083	30′
40′	.4654	.4488	.8936	.5022	1.991	1.119	2.228	1.1054	20′
50′	.4683	.4514	.8923	.5059	1.977	1.121	2.215	1.1025	10′
27° 00′	.4712	.4540	.8910	.5095	1.963	1.122	2.203	1.0996	63° 00′
		Cos θ	Sin θ	Cot θ	Tan θ	Csc θ	Sec θ	θ Radians	θ Degrees

674   TABLES

TABLE OF TRIGONOMETRIC RATIOS

θ Degrees	θ Radians	Sin θ	Cos θ	Tan θ	Cot θ	Sec θ	Csc θ		
27° 00′	.4712	.4540	.8910	.5095	1.963	1.122	2.203	1.0996	63° 00′
10′	.4741	.4566	.8897	.5132	1.949	1.124	2.190	1.0966	50′
20′	.4771	.4592	.8884	.5169	1.935	1.126	2.178	1.0937	40′
30′	.4800	.4617	.8870	.5206	1.921	1.127	2.166	1.0908	30′
40′	.4829	.4643	.8857	.5243	1.907	1.129	2.154	1.0879	20′
50′	.4858	.4669	.8843	.5280	1.894	1.131	2.142	1.0850	10′
28° 00′	.4887	.4695	.8829	.5317	1.881	1.133	2.130	1.0821	62° 00′
10′	.4916	.4720	.8816	.5354	1.868	1.134	2.118	1.0792	50′
20′	.4945	.4746	.8802	.5392	1.855	1.136	2.107	1.0763	40′
30′	.4974	.4772	.8788	.5430	1.842	1.138	2.096	1.0734	30′
40′	.5003	.4797	.8774	.5467	1.829	1.140	2.085	1.0705	20′
50′	.5032	.4823	.8760	.5505	1.816	1.142	2.074	1.0676	10′
29° 00′	.5061	.4848	.8746	.5543	1.804	1.143	2.063	1.0647	61° 00′
10′	.5091	.4874	.8732	.5581	1.792	1.145	2.052	1.0617	50′
20′	.5120	.4899	.8718	.5619	1.780	1.147	2.041	1.0588	40′
30′	.5149	.4924	.8704	.5658	1.767	1.149	2.031	1.0559	30′
40′	.5178	.4950	.8689	.5696	1.756	1.151	2.020	1.0530	20′
50′	.5207	.4975	.8675	.5735	1.744	1.153	2.010	1.0501	10′
30° 00′	.5236	.5000	.8660	.5774	1.732	1.155	2.000	1.0472	60° 00′
10′	.5265	.5025	.8646	.5812	1.720	1.157	1.990	1.0443	50′
20′	.5294	.5050	.8631	.5851	1.709	1.159	1.980	1.0414	40′
30′	.5323	.5075	.8616	.5890	1.698	1.161	1.970	1.0385	30′
40′	.5352	.5100	.8601	.5930	1.686	1.163	1.961	1.0356	20′
50′	.5381	.5125	.8587	.5969	1.675	1.165	1.951	1.0327	10′
31° 00′	.5411	.5150	.8572	.6009	1.664	1.167	1.942	1.0297	59° 00′
10′	.5440	.5175	.8557	.6048	1.653	1.169	1.932	1.0268	50′
20′	.5469	.5200	.8542	.6088	1.643	1.171	1.923	1.0239	40′
30′	.5498	.5225	.8526	.6128	1.632	1.173	1.914	1.0210	30′
40′	.5527	.5250	.8511	.6168	1.621	1.175	1.905	1.0181	20′
50′	.5556	.5275	.8496	.6208	1.611	1.177	1.896	1.0152	10′
32° 00′	.5585	.5299	.8480	.6249	1.600	1.179	1.887	1.0123	58° 00′
10′	.5614	.5324	.8465	.6289	1.590	1.181	1.878	1.0094	50′
20′	.5643	.5348	.8450	.6330	1.580	1.184	1.870	1.0065	40′
30′	.5672	.5373	.8434	.6371	1.570	1.186	1.861	1.0036	30′
40′	.5701	.5398	.8418	.6412	1.560	1.188	1.853	1.0007	20′
50′	.5730	.5422	.8403	.6453	1.550	1.190	1.844	.9977	10′
33° 00′	.5760	.5446	.8387	.6494	1.540	1.192	1.836	.9948	57° 00′
10′	.5789	.5471	.8371	.6536	1.530	1.195	1.828	.9919	50′
20′	.5818	.5495	.8355	.6577	1.520	1.197	1.820	.9890	40′
30′	.5847	.5519	.8339	.6619	1.511	1.199	1.812	.9861	30′
40′	.5876	.5544	.8323	.6661	1.501	1.202	1.804	.9832	20′
50′	.5905	.5568	.8307	.6703	1.492	1.204	1.796	.9803	10′
34° 00′	.5934	.5592	.8290	.6745	1.483	1.206	1.788	.9774	56° 00′
10′	.5963	.5616	.8274	.6787	1.473	1.209	1.781	.9745	50′
20′	.5992	.5640	.8258	.6830	1.464	1.211	1.773	.9716	40′
30′	.6021	.5664	.8241	.6873	1.455	1.213	1.766	.9687	30′
40′	.6050	.5688	.8225	.6916	1.446	1.216	1.758	.9657	20′
50′	.6080	.5712	.8208	.6959	1.437	1.218	1.751	.9628	10′
35° 00′	.6109	.5736	.8192	.7002	1.428	1.221	1.743	.9599	55° 00′
10′	.6138	.5760	.8175	.7046	1.419	1.223	1.736	.9570	50′
20′	.6167	.5783	.8158	.7089	1.411	1.226	1.729	.9541	40′
30′	.6196	.5807	.8141	.7133	1.402	1.228	1.722	.9512	30′
40′	.6225	.5831	.8124	.7177	1.393	1.231	1.715	.9483	20′
50′	.6254	.5854	.8107	.7221	1.385	1.233	1.708	.9454	10′
36° 00′	.6283	.5878	.8090	.7265	1.376	1.236	1.701	.9425	54° 00′
		Cos θ	Sin θ	Cot θ	Tan θ	Csc θ	Sec θ	θ Radians	θ Degrees

TABLE OF TRIGONOMETRIC RATIOS

θ Degrees	θ Radians	Sin θ	Cos θ	Tan θ	Cot θ	Sec θ	Csc θ		
36° 00′	.6283	.5878	.8090	.7265	1.376	1.236	1.701	.9425	54° 00′
10′	.6312	.5901	.8073	.7310	1.368	1.239	1.695	.9396	50′
20′	.6341	.5925	.8056	.7355	1.360	1.241	1.688	.9367	40′
30′	.6370	.5948	.8039	.7400	1.351	1.244	1.681	.9338	30′
40′	.6400	.5972	.8021	.7445	1.343	1.247	1.675	.9308	20′
50′	.6429	.5995	.8004	.7490	1.335	1.249	1.668	.9279	10′
37° 00′	.6458	.6018	.7986	.7536	1.327	1.252	1.662	.9250	53° 00′
10′	.6487	.6041	.7969	.7581	1.319	1.255	1.655	.9221	50′
20′	.6516	.6065	.7951	.7627	1.311	1.258	1.649	.9192	40′
30′	.6545	.6088	.7934	.7673	1.303	1.260	1.643	.9163	30′
40′	.6574	.6111	.7916	.7720	1.295	1.263	1.636	.9134	20′
50′	.6603	.6134	.7898	.7766	1.288	1.266	1.630	.9105	10′
38° 00′	.6632	.6157	.7880	.7813	1.280	1.269	1.624	.9076	52° 00′
10′	.6661	.6180	.7862	.7860	1.272	1.272	1.618	.9047	50′
20′	.6690	.6202	.7844	.7907	1.265	1.275	1.612	.9018	40′
30′	.6720	.6225	.7826	.7954	1.257	1.278	1.606	.8988	30′
40′	.6749	.6248	.7808	.8002	1.250	1.281	1.601	.8959	20′
50′	.6778	.6271	.7790	.8050	1.242	1.284	1.595	.8930	10′
39° 00′	.6807	.6293	.7771	.8098	1.235	1.287	1.589	.8901	51° 00′
10′	.6836	.6316	.7753	.8146	1.228	1.290	1.583	.8872	50′
20′	.6865	.6338	.7735	.8195	1.220	1.293	1.578	.8843	40′
30′	.6894	.6361	.7716	.8243	1.213	1.296	1.572	.8814	30′
40′	.6923	.6383	.7698	.8292	1.206	1.299	1.567	.8785	20′
50′	.6952	.6406	.7679	.8342	1.199	1.302	1.561	.8756	10′
40° 00′	.6981	.6428	.7660	.8391	1.192	1.305	1.556	.8727	50° 00′
10′	.7010	.6450	.7642	.8441	1.185	1.309	1.550	.8698	50′
20′	.7039	.6472	.7623	.8491	1.178	1.312	1.545	.8668	40′
30′	.7069	.6494	.7604	.8541	1.171	1.315	1.540	.8639	30′
40′	.7098	.6517	.7585	.8591	1.164	1.318	1.535	.8610	20′
50′	.7127	.6539	.7566	.8642	1.157	1.322	1.529	.8581	10′
41° 00′	.7156	.6561	.7547	.8693	1.150	1.325	1.524	.8552	49° 00′
10′	.7185	.6583	.7528	.8744	1.144	1.328	1.519	.8523	50′
20′	.7214	.6604	.7509	.8796	1.137	1.332	1.514	.8494	40′
30′	.7243	.6626	.7490	.8847	1.130	1.335	1.509	.8465	30′
40′	.7272	.6648	.7470	.8899	1.124	1.339	1.504	.8436	20′
50′	.7301	.6670	.7451	.8952	1.117	1.342	1.499	.8407	10′
42° 00′	.7330	.6691	.7431	.9004	1.111	1.346	1.494	.8378	48° 00′
10′	.7359	.6713	.7412	.9057	1.104	1.349	1.490	.8348	50′
20′	.7389	.6734	.7392	.9110	1.098	1.353	1.485	.8319	40′
30′	.7418	.6756	.7373	.9163	1.091	1.356	1.480	.8290	30′
40′	.7447	.6777	.7353	.9217	1.085	1.360	1.476	.8261	20′
50′	.7476	.6799	.7333	.9271	1.079	1.364	1.471	.8232	10′
43° 00′	.7505	.6820	.7314	.9325	1.072	1.367	1.466	.8203	47° 00′
10′	.7534	.6841	.7294	.9380	1.066	1.371	1.462	.8174	50′
20′	.7563	.6862	.7274	.9435	1.060	1.375	1.457	.8145	40′
30′	.7592	.6884	.7254	.9490	1.054	1.379	1.453	.8116	30′
40′	.7621	.6905	.7234	.9545	1.048	1.382	1.448	.8087	20′
50′	.7650	.6926	.7214	.9601	1.042	1.386	1.444	.8058	10′
44° 00′	.7679	.6947	.7193	.9657	1.036	1.390	1.440	.8029	46° 00′
10′	.7709	.6967	.7173	.9713	1.030	1.394	1.435	.7999	50′
20′	.7738	.6988	.7153	.9770	1.024	1.398	1.431	.7970	40′
30′	.7767	.7009	.7133	.9827	1.018	1.402	1.427	.7941	30′
40′	.7796	.7030	.7112	.9884	1.012	1.406	1.423	.7912	20′
50′	.7825	.7050	.7092	.9942	1.006	1.410	1.418	.7883	10′
45° 00′	.7854	.7071	.7071	1.000	1.000	1.414	1.414	.7854	45° 00′
		Cos θ	Sin θ	Cot θ	Tan θ	Csc θ	Sec θ	θ Radians	θ Degrees

GLOSSARY

abscissa (p. 48)   The first number in an ordered pair of numbers (x, y). The abscissa of $(5, -8)$ is 5.

absolute value (pp. 7, 38)   The distance of a real number x from 0 on the number line, denoted by $|x|$. For a real number x, $|x| = x$ if $x \geq 0$, and $|x| = -x$ if $x < 0$.

additive identity (p. 6)   Zero is the additive identity. When 0 is added to a number, the sum is that number: $x + 0 = x$.

additive inverses (p. 6)   Two numbers that are *opposites* of one another; their sum is 0. x and $-x$ are opposites since $x + (-x) = 0$.

algebraic expression (p. 3)   An expression involving variables, such as

$$5x^3 - 3x + 7 \qquad \frac{x}{x^2 + 1} \qquad a(3 - a)$$

amplitude of a periodic function (p. 511)   A periodic function with maximum value M and minimum value m has amplitude $\frac{M - m}{2}$. For functions of the form $y = a \sin b\theta$ and $y = a \cos b\theta$, the amplitude is $|a|$.

angle of depression (p.440)   The angle formed by the horizontal line and the oblique line from the observer's eye to an object below the observer's eye level.

angle of elevation (p. 438)   The angle formed by the horizontal or base line and the oblique line from the observer's eye to an object above the observer's eye level.

antilogarithm (p. 389)   If $\log N = x$, then N is the antilogarithm of x; that is, antilog $x = N$.

argument of a complex number (p. 535)   The angle determined by the real axis and the line from the origin to the point for a complex number in the complex plane. θ is the argument of z in $z = r(\cos \theta + i \sin \theta)$. If $0 \leq \theta < 2\pi$, then θ is the *principal argument*. See also trigonometric form of a complex number.

arithmetic means (p. 553)   The terms between any two nonconsecutive terms of an arithmetic sequence. In case there is only one arithmetic mean between two terms, it is also called the *arithmetic mean*, or the *average* of the two numbers.

arithmetic sequence (p. 551)   A sequence in which each term after the first is obtained by adding a constant called the *common difference*. An arithmetic sequence is also called an *arithmetic progression*.

asymptote (pp. 337, 519)   A line that a curve in a plane approaches more and more closely.

augmented matrix (p. 622)   The matrix associated with a linear system of equations that contains the coefficients and constants of the system.

base (p. 2)   The factor that is repeated in an exponential expression. In $x^3 = x \cdot x \cdot x$, the base is x.

binomial (p. 122)   A polynomial with two terms. $3x^2 - 2$ is a binomial.

binomial distribution (p. 603)   If p is the probability of success per trial and q is the probability of failure per trial, then the probability of exactly x successes in n repeated independent trials is

$$P(x) = {}_nC_x \, p^x q^{n-x} \text{ for } n \geq x$$

PREREQUISITE SKILLS FOLLOW-UP

COMPUTER HANDBOOK

TABLES

GLOSSARY

ANSWERS TO CHECKPOINTS

ANSWERS TO SELECTED EXERCISES

INDEX

binomial theorem (p. 574)   The general expansion of the expression $(a + b)^n$.

central angle (p. 504)   An angle whose vertex is at the center of a circle and whose sides are radii of the circle.

characteristic of a logarithm (p. 388)   The integral part of a common logarithm. The characteristic of $\log_{10}0.0035 = 7.5441 - 10$ is $7 - 10$, or -3.

circle (p.322)   The set of all points in a plane equidistant from a fixed point called the center. The *radius* is the distance from the center to any point on the circle. The general equation of a circle with center at (h, k) and radius r is
$$(x - h)^2 + (y - k)^2 = r^2.$$

circular functions (pp. 509, 520, 524)   Functions defined in terms of the ratios sin x, cos x, tan x, cot x, sec x and csc x—also called trigonometric functions.

coefficient   *See* numerical coefficient.

combination (p. 593)   A set of objects selected without regard to order. A combination of r out of n things may be selected in $_nC_r$ ways:
$$_nC_r = \frac{n!}{r!(n - r)!}, r \le n$$

common logarithm (p. 388)   Logarithm to the base 10.

complex fraction (p. 177)   A fraction in which the numerator or the denominator, or both, contain one or more fractions.

complex number (pp. 296, 534)   A number of the form $a + bi$, where a and b are real numbers, and i is the imaginary unit.

complex plane (pp. 301, 534)   A plane that has a real and an imaginary axis and contains the points corresponding to the complex numbers of the form $a + bi$.

compound inequality (p. 34)   The combination of two inequality statements into a single statement, such as

$x > 2$ and $x < 5$ (which may be written as $2 < x < 5$)

$x < 3$ or $x > 7$

conic sections (p. 342)   The curves formed when a plane cuts a hollow double cone. The general equation of a conic section is
$$Ax^2 + Bxy + Cy^2 + Dx + Ey + F = 0$$
where A, B, and C are not all 0.

conjugates (pp. 221, 297)   The expressions $(\sqrt{a} + \sqrt{b})$ and $(\sqrt{a} - \sqrt{b})$ are conjugate radical expressions. The complex numbers $(a + bi)$ and $(a - bi)$ are conjugates of each other.

consistent system (p. 87)   A system of equations having at least one solution.

constant of proportionality (of variation)   *See* direct variation *and* inverse variation.

constraints (p. 108)   The inequalities of a linear programming problem.

convex region (p. 107)   A region whose boundaries are parts of straight lines such that no extensions of these boundaries intersect the region.

convex

not convex

coordinate plane (p. 48)   Points in a plane located in relation to a pair of perpendicular axes. There is a one-to-one matching of all ordered pairs of real numbers with all of the points in a coordinate plane.

cosecant of θ (pp. 420, 429) $\csc \theta = \dfrac{1}{\sin \theta}$, $\sin \theta \neq 0$

cosine of θ (pp. 420, 429)   For angle θ in standard position, with reference triangle having sides x, y, and r, $\cos \theta = \frac{x}{r}$. When the terminal side of θ intersects the unit circle $x^2 + y^2 = 1$ at the point (x, y), $\cos \theta = x$.

cotangent of θ (pp. 420, 429) $\cot \theta = \dfrac{1}{\tan \theta}$, $\tan \theta \neq 0$, or $\cot \theta = \dfrac{\cos \theta}{\sin \theta}$, $\sin \theta \neq 0$.

coterminal angles (p. 413)   A pair of angles in standard position having the same terminal side, such as 30° and 390°.

counting number (pp. 2, 548)   A member of the set {1, 2, 3, 4, ... }.

Cramer's rule (p. 638)   A method of solving a system of linear equations by using determinants.

cube root (p. 208)   The radical symbol $\sqrt[3]{x}$ indicates the *principal cube root* of x, where $(\sqrt[3]{x})^3 = x$. Every real number has one principal cube root, which has the same sign as the number itself.

degree measure (p. 412)   An angular measure. One degree (1°) is the measure of an angle that is $\frac{1}{360}$ of a complete rotation about a point. A complete rotation is 360°.

degree of a polynomial (p. 122)   The degree of a monomial is the sum of the exponents of its variables. The degree of $7x^3y$ is 4. The degree of any other polynomial is the greatest of the degrees of its terms after it has been simplified. The degree of a constant is 0.

dependent system (p. 87)   A system of equations in which all of the equations have the same graph, such as:

$$y = x$$
$$x - y = 0$$

depressed equation (p. 304)   If $p(x) = 0$ is a polynomial equation and $p(x) = q(x)(x - r) = 0$, then the polynomial equation $q(x) = 0$ is a depressed equation.

determinant (p. 634)   A unique real number assigned to a square matrix A, written as det A, or $|A|$.

direct variation (p. 192)   Two variables, y and x, vary directly if $y = kx$, $k \neq 0$. y is also said to be *directly proportional* to x. k is the *constant of proportionality*.

discriminant (p. 245)   The radicand $b^2 - 4ac$ in the quadratic formula is the discriminant of $ax^2 + bx + c = 0$.

distance formula (p. 317)   For two points (x_1, y_1) and (x_2, y_2), the distance d between them is given by $d = \sqrt{(x_1 - x_2)^2 + (y_1 - y_2)^2}$.

domain of a relation (p. 69)   The set of all first coordinates of the ordered pairs in a relation.

ellipse (p. 331)   The set of all points in a plane such that for each point in the set, the sum of the distances from two fixed points (the *foci*) is constant. The longer and shorter axes of an ellipse are called its *major* and *minor axes*. The standard form for the equation of an ellipse with center at the origin is

$$\frac{x^2}{a^2} + \frac{y^2}{b^2} = 1, \text{ with } a \neq b$$

PREREQUISITE SKILLS FOLLOW-UP

COMPUTER HANDBOOK

TABLES

GLOSSARY

ANSWERS TO CHECKPOINTS

ANSWERS TO SELECTED EXERCISES

INDEX

equivalent expressions (p. 17)   Expressions that have the same value for all possible replacements of the variable(s).

exponent (p. 2)   The number of times the base is used as a factor in an exponential expression. In $x^3 = x \cdot x \cdot x$, the exponent is 3.

exponential function (p. 372)   If $a > 0$ and $a \neq 1$, the equation $y = a^x$ defines an exponential function with base a.

factorial notation (p. 575)   The symbol $n!$ For a positive integer n, $n!$ is the product of the first n consecutive positive integers. 4 factorial is written as $4!$ and $4! = 4 \cdot 3 \cdot 2 \cdot 1$. $0!$ is defined as 1.

fractional equation (p. 181)   An equation containing one or more rational expressions.

frequency distribution (p. 606)   A listing of the number of outcomes of an experiment that shows the frequency with which each outcome occurs.

function (p. 69)   A relation in which each domain value corresponds to exactly one range value.

geometric means (p. 561)   The terms between any two nonconsecutive terms of a geometric sequence. In case there is only one geometric mean between two terms, it is called *the geometric mean*, or the *mean proportional*.

geometric sequence (p. 560)   A sequence in which each term after the first is obtained by multiplying the preceding term by a constant called the *common ratio*. A geometric sequence is also called a *geometric progression*.

greatest common factor of the terms of a polynomial (p. 129)   The product of the GCF of the coefficients and the highest powers of the variables common to all terms. The GCF of $12x^3y^2$ and $18xy^3$ is $6xy^2$.

greatest integer function (p. 75)   The function given by $y = [x]$ in which $[x]$ is the greatest integer not greater than x itself.

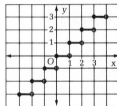

hyperbola (p. 337)   The set of all points in a plane such that for each point in the set, the difference of the distances from two fixed points (the *foci*) is a constant. The standard form for the equation of a hyperbola is one of the following:

$$\frac{x^2}{a^2} - \frac{y^2}{b^2} = 1 \quad \text{or} \quad \frac{y^2}{a^2} - \frac{x^2}{b^2} = 1$$

identity matrix (p. 629)   The square matrix I having 1's on the main diagonal and 0's elsewhere. For a square matrix A, $AI = IA = A$.

imaginary number (p. 292)   A number of the form $a + bi$, where a and b are real numbers. If $a = 0$, then the number is of the form bi and is called a *pure imaginary number*.

imaginary unit (p. 292)   The number $i = \sqrt{-1}$, where $i^2 = -1$.

inconsistent system (p. 88)   A system of equations that has no solution, such as:
$$y = 2x$$
$$y = 2x + 1$$

independent events (p. 597)   Two events are independent if either event can occur without affecting the other.

independent system (p. 87)   A system of equations in which the equations have different graphs.

integer (p. 2)   A member of the set of whole numbers and their opposites; a member of $\{\ldots, -3, -2, -1, 0, 1, 2, 3, \ldots\}$.

intercept form of a linear equation (p. 68)   A linear equation in the form $\frac{x}{p} + \frac{y}{q} = 1$, where p is the x-intercept and q is the y-intercept of the line.

inverse matrices (p. 629)   Square matrices A and B such that $AB = BA = I$ are inverses of each other.

inverse trigonometric functions (pp. 527, 530, 531)   The function given by $y = \text{Arcsin } x$ is the inverse of the sine function and means $x = \sin y$. Its domain is $-1 \le x \le 1$ and its range is $-\frac{\pi}{2} \le y \le \frac{\pi}{2}$. The function given by $y = \text{Arccos } x$ is the inverse of the cosine function and means $x = \cos y$. Its domain is $-1 \le x \le 1$ and its range is $0 \le y \le \pi$. The function given by $y = \text{Arctan } x$ is the inverse of the tangent function and means $x = \tan y$. Its domain is all real numbers and its range is $-\frac{\pi}{2} < y < \frac{\pi}{2}$.

inverse variation (p. 193)   Two variables, y and x, vary inversely if $y = \frac{k}{x}$, $k \ne 0$. y is also said to be *inversely proportional* to x. k is the *constant of proportionality*.

irrational number (p. 2)   A member of the set of those real numbers whose decimal representations are nonterminating and nonrepeating. A real number that is not rational.

law of cosines (p. 446)   For triangle ABC, with sides a, b, and c:
$$a^2 = b^2 + c^2 - 2bc \cos A$$
$$b^2 = a^2 + c^2 - 2ac \cos B$$
$$c^2 = a^2 + b^2 - 2ab \cos C$$

law of sines (p. 452)   For triangle ABC, with sides a, b, and c:
$$\frac{\sin A}{a} = \frac{\sin B}{b} = \frac{\sin C}{c}$$

least common denominator (LCD) (p. 174)   The least common multiple of the denominators of two or more fractions.

least common multiple (LCM) (p. 174)   The LCM of p and q is the polynomial with the least positive coefficient and least degree that is a multiple of p and q.

like terms (p. 16)   Terms that are identical or that differ only in their numerical coefficients, such as $3x^2y$ and $-27x^2y$.

linear equation in two variables (p. 51)   An equation of the form $Ax + By = C$, where A, B, and C are constants such that A and B are not both zero.

linear function (p. 70)   A function that can be described by an equation of the form $y = mx + b$, where m and b are real numbers.

linear programming (p. 107)   A method of finding the maximum or minimum value of an expression $ax + by$ for all (x, y) in a convex region.

PREREQUISITE SKILLS FOLLOW-UP

COMPUTER HANDBOOK

TABLES

GLOSSARY

ANSWERS TO CHECKPOINTS

ANSWERS TO SELECTED EXERCISES

INDEX

logarithm (p. 378)   If $y > 0$, $n > 0$, $n \neq 1$, and $y = n^x$, then $\log_n y = x$. Since $16 = 4^2$, $\log_4 16 = 2$.

logarithmic function (p. 379)   When $b > 0$ and $b \neq 1$, the equation $y = \log_b x$ for $x > 0$ defines a logarithmic function.

mantissa (p. 388)   The decimal part of a common logarithm. The mantissa of $\log_{10} 350 = 2.5441$ is 0.5441.

matrix (p. 622)   A rectangular array of numbers, also called *elements*, enclosed by brackets, such as: $\begin{bmatrix} 3 & -1 \\ 4 & 6 \\ 2 & 0 \end{bmatrix}$

midpoint formula (p. 318)   The midpoint of the segment that joins two points (x_1, y_1) and (x_2, y_2) has coordinates $\left(\dfrac{x_1 + x_2}{2}, \dfrac{y_1 + y_2}{2} \right)$.

modulus (pp. 301, 534)   The distance of a complex number from the origin. The modulus of $3 - 4i$ is 5.

monomial (p. 118)   A constant, a variable, or a product of a constant and one or more variables.

multiplication property of inequality (p. 31)   For real numbers r, s, and t:

$$\text{If } r > s, \text{ then } rt > st \text{ when } t \text{ is positive}$$
$$\text{and } rt < st \text{ when } t \text{ is negative.}$$

multiplicative identity (p. 10)   The multiplicative identity is 1. When 1 is multiplied by a number, the product is that number: $1 \cdot x = x$

multiplicative inverse (p. 11)   The reciprocal of a nonzero number. The multiplicative inverse of r is $\frac{1}{r}$, $r \neq 0$.

mutually exclusive events (p. 585)   Events or outcomes that cannot occur simultaneously.

normal distribution (p. 612)   A distribution with a bell-shaped curve, symmetric about the vertical axis, which locates the mean of the values in the distribution.

numerical coefficient (p. 16)   The numerical factor of a term; also called the *coefficient*. In $-7xy^2$ the numerical coefficient is -7.

opposites (p. 6)   Two numbers that are the same distance from 0 on the number line, but in opposite directions. The sum of opposites is 0.

ordinate (p. 48)   The second number in an ordered pair of numbers (x, y). The ordinate of $(5, -8)$ is -8.

origin (p. 48)   The point labeled O on a number line. The intersection of the x- and y-axes, $(0, 0)$, in a coordinate plane.

parabola (pp. 256, 326)   A set of all points in a plane that are equidistant from a fixed point (the *focus*) and a fixed line (the *directrix*). A parabola is symmetric about a line called the *axis of symmetry*. If this axis is vertical, the parabola opens upward or downward from its *vertex*. If the axis is horizontal, the parabola opens to the left or the right from the vertex. The standard forms of the equations are

$$\text{Vertical axis of symmetry: } y = a(x - h)^2 + k$$
$$\text{Horizontal axis of symmetry: } x = a(y - k)^2 + h$$

Pascal's triangle (p. 573)
A triangular array of numbers whose entries in the nth row are the coefficients of the expansion of $(a + b)^n$.

$$
\begin{array}{ccccccccc}
 & & & & 1 & & & & \text{Row 0} \\
 & & & 1 & & 1 & & & \text{Row 1} \\
 & & 1 & & 2 & & 1 & & \text{Row 2} \\
 & 1 & & 3 & & 3 & & 1 & \text{Row 3} \\
1 & & 4 & & 6 & & 4 & & 1 \quad \text{Row 4} \\
 & & & & \vdots & & & &
\end{array}
$$

periodic function (p. 511)   A function that repeats. The *period* is the change in value of x over one entire nonrepeating section of the curve; the graph over one period is called a *cycle*.

permutation (p. 590)   An ordering, or arrangement, of a number of objects. A set of r out of n things may be arranged in ${}_nP_r$ ways:

$$
{}_nP_r = \frac{n!}{(n - r)!}
$$

point-slope form of a linear equation (p. 65)   The equation of a line in the form $y - y_1 = m(x - x_1)$, where (x_1, y_1) is a point on the line and m is the slope.

polynomial (p. 122)   A monomial or a sum of two or more monomials, such as $4x^3 - 3x^2 - 2x + 5$.

probability (p. 584)   The probability of an event is the ratio of the number of possible successful outcomes for the event to the total number of possible outcomes.

proportion (p. 185)   An equation stating that two ratios are equal.

quadrantal angle (p. 412)   An angle in standard position with its terminal side on one of the coordinate axes.

quadratic equation in one variable (p. 145)   An equation of the form $ax^2 + bx + c = 0$, where a, b, and c are real numbers with $a \neq 0$.

quadratic formula (p. 242)   The solutions of the general quadratic equation $ax^2 + bx + c = 0$ are given by the formula

$$
x = \frac{-b \pm \sqrt{b^2 - 4ac}}{2a}
$$

quadratic function (p. 256)   An equation of the form $y = f(x) = ax^2 + bx + c$, with $a \neq 0$. The graph of a quadratic function is a parabola.

radian (p. 504)   An angular measure. One radian is the measure of a central angle of a circle that intercepts an arc of length equal to the radius of the circle.

radical (p. 208)   An expression such as $\sqrt[n]{x}$, where the *index* n is a positive integer, $n \geq 2$, and x is the *radicand*. In $\sqrt{8}$, the index is 2 and the radicand is 8.

radical equation (p. 227)   An equation with a variable in the radicand.

range of a relation (p. 69)   The set of all second coordinates of the ordered pairs in a relation.

rational expression (p. 166)   A fraction in which both the numerator and the denominator are polynomials.

rational number (p. 2)   A number that can be expressed in the form $\frac{a}{b}$, where a and b are integers, $b \neq 0$.

PREREQUISITE SKILLS FOLLOW-UP

COMPUTER HANDBOOK

TABLES

GLOSSARY

ANSWERS TO CHECKPOINTS

ANSWERS TO SELECTED EXERCISES

INDEX

rationalizing a denominator (p. 220)   To multiply numerator and denominator of a fraction by a common quantity in order to remove the radicals in the denominator of the given fraction, as in

$$\frac{1}{\sqrt{3}} = \frac{1}{\sqrt{3}} \cdot \frac{\sqrt{3}}{\sqrt{3}} = \frac{\sqrt{3}}{3}$$

real number (p. 2)   A member of the set of all rational and all irrational numbers.

reciprocal (p. 11)   The *multiplicative inverse* of a nonzero number. The reciprocal of $r \neq 0$ is $\frac{1}{r}$. The product of a number and its reciprocal is 1.

reference angle (p. 416)   The acute angle between the terminal side of a non-quadrantal angle in standard position and the x-axis.

reference triangle (p. 417)   A right triangle formed by constructing a perpendicular to the x-axis from a point on the terminal side of a nonquadrantal angle.

reflexive property of equality (p. 20)   For any real number a, $a = a$.

relation (p. 69)   A set of ordered pairs.

root of an equation (p. 19)   A replacement for the variable that makes an equation true; also called a *solution* of the equation.

sample space (p. 584)   In probability, the set of all possible outcomes of an experiment.

scalar product (p. 626)   The product of a real number, or *scalar*, and a matrix.

scientific notation (p. 364)   A number expressed in the form $a \times 10^n$, where $1 \leq a < 10$ and n is an integer. In scientific notation, 360,000 is 3.6×10^5 and 0.0023 is 2.3×10^{-3}.

secant of θ (pp. 420, 429) $\sec \theta = \frac{1}{\cos \theta}$, $\cos \theta \neq 0$.

sequence (p. 548)   A set of ordered numbers each of which is called a *term* of the sequence. Sequences may be finite or infinite.

series (pp. 555, 564)   The indicated sum of the terms of a sequence. An *arithmetic series* is the sum of the terms of an arithmetic sequence. A *geometric series* is the sum of the terms of a geometric sequence. Such series may be finite or infinite.

sine of θ (pp. 420, 429)   For angle θ in standard position with reference triangle that has sides x, y, and r, $\sin \theta = \frac{y}{r}$. When the terminal side of θ intersects the unit circle $x^2 + y^2 = 1$ at the point (x, y), $\sin \theta = y$.

slope-intercept form of a linear equation (p. 61)   The equation of a line in the form $y = mx + b$, where m is the slope and b is the y-intercept.

slope of a line (p. 56)   For two distinct points (x_1, y_1) and (x_2, y_2) on a line, the slope is $\frac{y_2 - y_1}{x_2 - x_1}$, provided $x_1 \neq x_2$.

square root (p. 208)   If $x > 0$, x has the two square roots $\pm\sqrt{x}$, where $(\pm\sqrt{x})^2 = x$. The *principal square root* is the positive number, $\sqrt{x}$.

standard deviation (p. 607)   A number that measures the *variation*, or *spread*, of a set of numerical data about the mean.

standard position of an angle (p. 412)   An angle is in standard position when its vertex coincides with the origin of a coordinate system and its initial side is on the positive x-axis.

substitution property of equality (p. 20)   For real numbers a and b, if $a = b$, then a may be replaced by b, or b by a, in any statement.

symmetric property of equality (p. 20)   For real numbers a and b:

$$\text{If } a = b, \text{ then } b = a.$$

synthetic division (p. 278)   A short method of dividing a polynomial in x by $(x - c)$ that uses only the coefficients.

system of equations or inequalities (pp. 86, 105)   Two or more equations or inequalities in the same variables.

tangent of θ (pp. 420, 429) $\tan \theta = \dfrac{\sin \theta}{\cos \theta}$, $\cos \theta \neq 0$.

term (p. 16)   A single number or variable, or a product or quotient of numbers and variables.

transitive property of equality (p. 20)   For real numbers a, b, and c:

$$\text{If } a = b \text{ and } b = c, \text{ then } a = c.$$

trigonometric form of a complex number (p. 535) $z = r(\cos \theta + i \sin \theta)$ is the trigonometric form of a complex number where $r = |z|$ is the *modulus* and θ is the *argument*.

trigonometric function   *See* circular functions.

trigonometric identity (p. 468)   A trigonometric equation that is true for all permissible values of the variable.

trinomial (p. 122)   A polynomial that has three terms, such as $3x^5 + 4x^2 - 3x$.

unit circle (p. 429)   The circle with center at the origin of a coordinate plane and radius $r = 1$; $x^2 + y^2 = 1$ is the equation of the unit circle.

vector (p. 497)   A directed line segment used to represent quantities that have both magnitude and direction.

whole number (p. 2)   A member of the set $\{0, 1, 2, 3, \ldots\}$.

x-intercept (p. 52)   The x-coordinate of the point where a line or curve intersects the x-axis; that is, the x-coordinate when $y = 0$.

y-intercept (p. 52)   The y-coordinate of the point where a line or curve intersects the y-axis; that is, the y-coordinate when $x = 0$.

PREREQUISITE SKILLS FOLLOW-UP

COMPUTER HANDBOOK

TABLES

GLOSSARY

ANSWERS TO CHECKPOINTS

ANSWERS TO SELECTED EXERCISES

INDEX

ANSWERS TO CHECKPOINTS

CHAPTER 1

Page 18. **1.** 60 **2.** 7 **3.** −54 **4.** 32

5. 12 **6.** 0 **7.** 6 **8.** 5 **9.** 5 **10.** $\dfrac{9}{8}$

11. Assoc. prop. of add. **12.** Comm. prop. of mult.

Page 37. **1.** 8 **2.** −5 **3.** 34 **4.** −4
5. $-9x^2 - 3$ **6.** $-6x^2y + 12xyz$
7. $5a + 4ab + 8b$ **8.** $9m + n + mn$
9. $a = 12$ **10.** $c = 5$ **11.** $x = -12$

12. $d = -\dfrac{1}{5}$ **13.** $n + (n - 4) = 24;$

14, 10 **14.** $x > -1$

15. $x < 2$

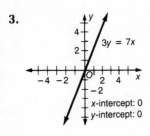

16. $x \geq 2$

CHAPTER 2

Page 60.

1.

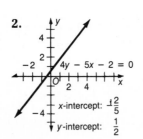

x-intercept: 3
y-intercept: 4
$-4x - 3y + 12 = 0$

2.

$4y - 5x - 2 = 0$
x-intercept: $-\dfrac{2}{5}$
y-intercept: $\dfrac{1}{2}$

3.

$3y = 7x$
x-intercept: 0
y-intercept: 0

4. $-\dfrac{7}{8}$

5.

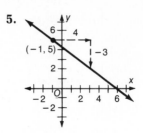

(−1, 5)   −3

Page 74.
1. 1; $y = x - 3$; −3 **2.** 3; $y = 3x$; 0

(6, 3)
(4, 1)
(1, 3)
(−2, −6)

3. −1; $y = -x - 1$; −1

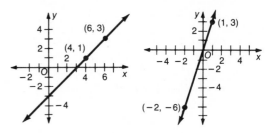

(−2, 1)
(−1, 0)

4. $\dfrac{1}{2}$; $y = \dfrac{1}{2}x - 1$; −1 **5.** 0; $y = -2$; −2

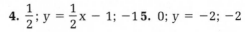

(6, 2)
(−2, −2)
(−5, −2)
(−1, −2)

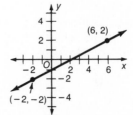

6. $-\dfrac{1}{5}$; $y = -\dfrac{1}{5}x + 3$; 3

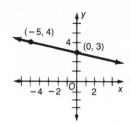

7. $y = \dfrac{1}{2}x - 2$ **8.** $y = -\dfrac{7}{2}x + \dfrac{1}{2}$

9. $y = -2x + 3$ **10.** $y = -3x - \dfrac{1}{3}$

11. Domain: {3}; Range: {1, −1, 2, −2}; Not a function **12.** Domain: {1, −1, 2, −2}; Range: {4}; Function **13.** Domain: {4, 3, 2, 0}; Range: {4, 3, 2, 0}; Function **14.** Domain: {a, c, e}; Range: {b, d, f, z}; Not a function

15. −4 **16.** −1 **17.** −1 **18.** $-\dfrac{13}{4}$

CHAPTER 3

Page 98.

1. (2, 3) **2.** Dependent

3. (2, −2) **4.** (3, −2) **5.** $\left(1, \dfrac{1}{2}\right)$

6. (2, 4) **7.** Sugar, 34¢; Salt, 27¢
Page 106. **1.** (2, −1, 3) **2.** 6, 4, 2
3. 5 touchdowns, 3 points-after-touchdown, 2 field goals
4.

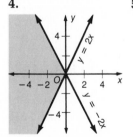

5.

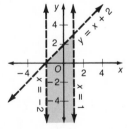

6.

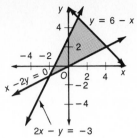

CHAPTER 4

Page 128. **1.** x^4 **2.** x^9 **3.** x^{12}
4. $x^5 y^5$ **5.** $-3x + 5$ **6.** $-9x - 7$
7. $6x - 20$ **8.** $-13x + 9$
9. $7x^3 - 4x^2 + 2x - 44$
10. $10m^2 - 6mn - 9n^2$
11. $10x^2 + 4x + 3$
12. $12x^2 - 48x$ **13.** $-3a^3 + 6a^2$
14. $-21x^3 + 7x^2 + 14x$ **15.** $x^2 - 49$
16. $9x^2 - 4$ **17.** $15x^2 + 4x - 32$
Page 153. **1.** $-7m + 4n$
2. $11x^2 + 26x - 17$ **3.** $7xy(3x - 1)$
4. $(3x - 2)(4y - 3)$ **5.** $(x - 8)(x - 3)$
6. $(2x - 5)(4x + 3)$
7. $(3x - 10y)(9x^2 + 30xy + 100y^2)$
8. $2(3x + 2y)^2$ **9.** 3, −2 **10.** 2, −2
11. 0, 1, −1 **12.** 14 and 16

CHAPTER 5

Page 180. **1.** $\dfrac{4}{9}$ **2.** $\dfrac{x}{4}$ **3.** $\dfrac{1}{3}$ **4.** $\dfrac{x-6}{x-7}$

5. $\dfrac{1}{5}$ **6.** Not defined **7.** Not defined

8. $\dfrac{1}{30}$ **9.** $\dfrac{3}{20}$ **10.** $\dfrac{9}{10}$ **11.** 1 **12.** $-\dfrac{1}{12}$

13. $\dfrac{7b^2}{5a^4}$ **14.** $\dfrac{27by}{4a^2 x^2}$ **15.** $\dfrac{2}{x}$

16. $-\dfrac{2x + 19}{(x + 2)(x - 3)}$ **17.** $\dfrac{3y + 5x}{xy}$

18. $\dfrac{x}{3(x - 1)}$ **19.** $\dfrac{4}{3(x - 1)}$

20. $-\dfrac{10x}{(x + 3)(x - 3)}$ **21.** 144

22. $\dfrac{3x + 2}{x^5}$ **23.** $\dfrac{a + b}{3ab}$ **24.** $\dfrac{4(x - 1)}{3(x - 2)}$

Page 196. **1.** −18 **2.** $\dfrac{3}{2}$ **3.** −10 **4.** $\dfrac{2}{3}$

PREREQUISITE SKILLS FOLLOW-UP

COMPUTER HANDBOOK

TABLES

GLOSSARY

ANSWERS TO CHECKPOINTS

ANSWERS TO SELECTED EXERCISES

INDEX

CHAPTER 6

Page 218. **1.** 7 **2.** Not real **3.** -7
4. $8|x|$ **5.** $-4x$ **6.** 6 **7.** 27 **8.** 3
9. $3\sqrt{11}$ **10.** $9\sqrt{2}$ **11.** 12 **12.** $8\sqrt{2}$
13. $-x\sqrt{7}$ **14.** $2\sqrt[3]{6y}$

Page 226. **1.** $\dfrac{3}{11}$ **2.** $2|x|\sqrt{2}$

3. $\sqrt{5} + \sqrt{3}$ **4.** $\dfrac{7 + 3\sqrt{5}}{2}$
5. $20x + 9\sqrt{xy} - 20y$ **6.** $6x - \sqrt{xy} - y$
7. $-6x - 3y$ **8.** $12x + 8\sqrt{6xy} + 8y$
9. $21^{\frac{1}{2}}$ **10.** $37^{\frac{1}{3}}$ **11.** $5^{\frac{2}{3}}$ **12.** $5^{\frac{2}{3}}$
13. $(8x)^{\frac{1}{3}}$, or $2x^{\frac{1}{3}}$

CHAPTER 7

Page 254. **1.** 3, -5 **2.** $\pm\dfrac{3}{4}$ **3.** $\dfrac{5}{3}$
4. $7 \pm \sqrt{3}$ **5.** One **6.** None **7.** None
8. $x^2 - 14x + 22 = 0$ **9.** $\dfrac{4}{3}$

Page 263. **1.** $\dfrac{7}{5}$, -1 **2.** $\dfrac{-2 \pm 2\sqrt{7}}{3}$
3. $\dfrac{3}{2}$, $-\dfrac{2}{3}$ **4.** $\dfrac{9}{7}$ **5.** $-\dfrac{25}{8}$ **6.** $\pm4\sqrt{3}$
7. 11 and 13 **8.** $a = \dfrac{1}{3}$; $c = -1$
9. $y = -2(x - 1)^2 + 5$; $(1, 5)$; $x = 1$
10. 2, min.

CHAPTER 8

Page 281. **1.** $x + 7 + \dfrac{12}{x - 2}$
2. $3x^2 - x + 3 + \dfrac{12}{2x - 1}$
3. $x - 2 + \dfrac{7}{2x + 1}$ **4.** $x^2 + 3 + \dfrac{3x + 1}{x^2 - 3}$
5. $3x + 4$; 13 **6.** $-5x^2 + 3x + 1$; -9
7. $4x^3 - 4x^2 + 4x - 4$; 8
8. $x^4 + \dfrac{2}{3}x^3 + \dfrac{4}{9}x^2 + \dfrac{8}{27}x + \dfrac{16}{81}$; 0

Page 300. **1.** Yes **2.** No **3.** $\dfrac{1}{3}$,
$\dfrac{2 \pm \sqrt{13}}{3}$ **4.** 5, $\pm2\sqrt{5}$ **5.** $\dfrac{3}{2} - \dfrac{1}{2}i$
6. $-\dfrac{1}{2} + \dfrac{3}{2}i$ **7.** 2 **8.** i

CHAPTER 9

Page 341.

1. 5; $\left(3, 5\dfrac{1}{2}\right)$ **2.** $2\sqrt{2}$; $(-5, 7)$

3. $\sqrt{5}$; $\left(-2\dfrac{1}{2}, -8\right)$ **4.** $(0, 0)$; 9

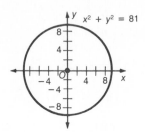
$x^2 + y^2 = 81$

5. $(-1, 1)$; 7

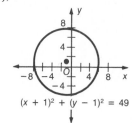
$(x + 1)^2 + (y - 1)^2 = 49$

6. $(0, 0)$; $\left(0, \dfrac{1}{8}\right)$; $x = 0$; $y = -\dfrac{1}{8}$

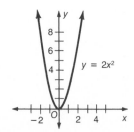
$y = 2x^2$

7. $(-2, 3)$; $\left(-2, 2\dfrac{3}{4}\right)$; $x = -2$; $y = 3\dfrac{1}{4}$

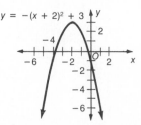
$y = -(x + 2)^2 + 3$

8. $(2, -3)$; $\left(2, -2\frac{3}{4}\right)$; **9.**

$$x = 2; y = -3\frac{1}{4}$$

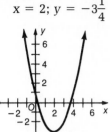

$$y = x^2 - 4x + 1$$

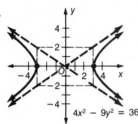

$$x^2 + \frac{y^2}{16} = 1$$

10.

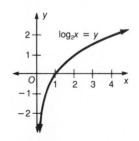

$$4x^2 - 9y^2 = 36$$

Page 353. **1.** $5\sqrt{17}$; $\left(1, 2\frac{1}{2}\right)$

2. $(x + 2)^2 + (y - 8)^2 = 25$

3. $y = \frac{1}{4}(x + 4)^2 + 5$ **4.** Parabola

5. Hyperbola **6.** Ellipse **7.** Circle

CHAPTER 10

Page 375. **1.** 0.000000053
2. 1.428×10^{33} **3.** $9^{\sqrt{6}}$ **4.** $8^{\sqrt{2}}$ **5.** $30^{\sqrt{2}}$
6. 343 **7.** 3 **8.** $2, -2$ **9.** 16 **10.** 5

Page 396. **1.** $\frac{3}{2}$ **2.** $6, -1$ **3.** $0, 1$

4. $\log_{36} 6 = \frac{1}{2}$ **5.** $\log_{10}\left(\frac{1}{10}\right) = -1$

6. $\log_5 125 = 3$ **7.** $\frac{1}{4}; \frac{1}{2}; 1; 2; 4$

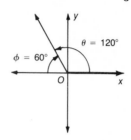

$$\log_2 x = y$$

8. $b = 6$ **9.** $a = \frac{1}{12}$ **10.** $n = 4$

CHAPTER 11
Page 432.
1. $\sin 120° = \frac{\sqrt{3}}{2}$; $\cos 12° = -\frac{1}{2}$;

$\tan 120° = -\sqrt{3}$; $\csc 120° = \frac{2\sqrt{3}}{3}$;

$\sec 120° = -2$; $\cot 120° = -\frac{\sqrt{3}}{3}$

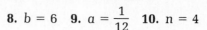

2. $\sin 315° = -\frac{\sqrt{2}}{2}$; $\cos 315° = \frac{\sqrt{2}}{2}$;

$\tan 315° = -1$; $\csc 315° = -\sqrt{2}$;
$\sec 315° = \sqrt{2}$; $\cot 315° = -1$

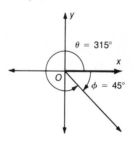

3. $\sin(-225°) = \frac{\sqrt{2}}{2}$; $\cos(-225°) = -\frac{\sqrt{2}}{2}$;

$\tan(-225°) = -1$; $\csc(-225°) = \sqrt{2}$;
$\sec(-225°) = -\sqrt{2}$; $\cot(-225°) = -1$

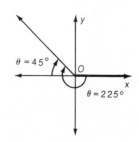

PREREQUISITE SKILLS FOLLOW-UP

COMPUTER HANDBOOK

TABLES

GLOSSARY

ANSWERS TO CHECKPOINTS

ANSWERS TO SELECTED EXERCISES

INDEX

4. $\sin(-510°) = -\frac{1}{2}$; $\cos(-510°) = -\frac{\sqrt{3}}{2}$;

$\tan(-510°) = \frac{\sqrt{3}}{3}$; $\csc(-510°) = -2$;

$\sec(-510°) = -\frac{2\sqrt{3}}{3}$; $\cot(-510°) = \sqrt{3}$

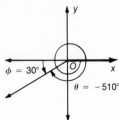

5. 0 **6.** $\frac{\sqrt{3}}{2}$ **7.** $\frac{2\sqrt{3}}{3}$ **8.** Undefined

9. Undefined **10.** 2 **11.** −1

12. Undefined

Page 445. **1.** $x = 2\sqrt{3}$, $r = 4$;

$\sin \theta = \frac{1}{2}$, $\cos \theta = \frac{\sqrt{3}}{2}$, $\tan \theta = \frac{\sqrt{3}}{3}$;

$\csc \theta = 2$, $\sec \theta = \frac{2\sqrt{3}}{3}$, $\cot \theta = \sqrt{3}$

2. $x = -10$, $y = -10$; $\sin \theta = -\frac{\sqrt{2}}{2}$,

$\cos \theta = -\frac{\sqrt{2}}{2}$, $\tan \theta = 1$; $\csc \theta = -\sqrt{2}$,

$\sec \theta = -\sqrt{2}$, $\cot \theta = 1$ **3.** $y = -3\sqrt{3}$,

$r = 6$; $\sin \theta = -\frac{\sqrt{3}}{2}$, $\cos \theta = \frac{1}{2}$,

$\tan \theta = -\sqrt{3}$; $\csc \theta = -\frac{2\sqrt{3}}{2}$, $\cos \theta = 2$,

$\cot \theta = -\frac{\sqrt{3}}{3}$ **4.** 18 m **5.** 11°20′

CHAPTER 12

Page 478. **1.** $\tan x$ **2.** 1 **3.** $-\sin^2 x$

4. $\frac{\cos x}{\sin x}$ **5.** $\frac{\sin x + 1}{\cos x}$ **6.** $\frac{\sin x}{\sin x + \cos x}$

7. $\dfrac{\sin \theta - \tan \theta}{\tan} = \dfrac{\sin \theta - \dfrac{\sin \theta}{\cos \theta}}{\dfrac{\sin}{\cos}}$

$= \dfrac{\sin \theta \cos \theta - \sin \theta}{\sin \theta}$

$= \dfrac{\sin \theta (\cos \theta - 1)}{\sin \theta}$

$= \cos \theta - 1$

8. $\dfrac{\sin^2 x}{1 - \cos x} - 1 = \dfrac{1 - \cos^2 x}{1 - \cos x} - 1$

$= \dfrac{(1 - \cos x)(1 + \cos x)}{1 - \cos x} - 1$

$= 1 + \cos x - 1 = \cos x$

9. 30°, 150°, 210°, 330°

10. 60°, 180°, 300°

Page 493.

1. $\dfrac{1 - \cos x}{\sin x} + \dfrac{\sin x}{1 - \cos x}$

$= \dfrac{1 - \cos x}{\sin x} + \dfrac{\sin}{1 - \cos x}\left(\dfrac{1 + \cos x}{1 + \cos x}\right)$

$= \dfrac{1 - \cos x}{\sin x} + \dfrac{\sin x(1 + \cos x)}{1 - \cos^2 x}$

$= \dfrac{1 - \cos x}{\sin x} + \dfrac{\sin x(1 + \cos x)}{\sin^2 x}$

$= \dfrac{1 - \cos x + 1 + \cos x}{\sin x}$

$= \dfrac{2}{\sin x}$

2. $\dfrac{\cos 2x - 1}{\cos 2x + 1} = \dfrac{(1 - 2 \sin^2 x) - 1}{(2 \cos^2 x - 1) + 1}$

$= \dfrac{-2 \sin^2 x}{2 \cos^2 x}$

$= -\tan^2 x$

3. 0°, 45°, 135°, 180°, 225°, 315°

4. 45°, 90°, 135°, 225°, 270°, 315°

5. 27 sq. units **6.** $\frac{1}{4}(\sqrt{6} + \sqrt{2})$

7. $-\frac{\sqrt{2}}{2}$ **8.** $\frac{1}{4}(\sqrt{2} - \sqrt{6})$ **9.** −1 **10.** $\frac{1}{2}$

CHAPTER 13

Page 525. **1.** $\frac{11\pi}{12}$ **2.** $\frac{4\pi}{9}$ rad. **3.** 405°; $\frac{\sqrt{2}}{2}$

4. $p = \pi$

$y = -\sin 2x$

5. $p = \frac{2\pi}{3}$

$y = 3 \cos 3x$

6. $p = \pi$

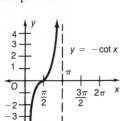

$y = -\cot x$

7. $p = \dfrac{\pi}{2}$

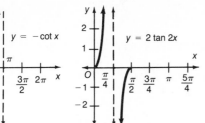

$y = 2 \tan 2x$

8. $p = \pi$

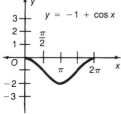

$y = 2 \csc 2x$

9. $p = \dfrac{4\pi}{3}$

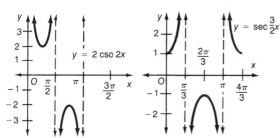

$y = \sec \dfrac{3}{2}x$

Page 533. **1.** $\dfrac{\pi}{3}, \dfrac{4\pi}{3}$ **2.** $\dfrac{1}{2}$ **3.** $-\dfrac{\sqrt{2}}{2}$

4.

$y = -1 + \cos x$

5.

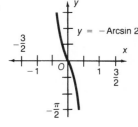

$y = -\text{Arcsin } 2x$

6.

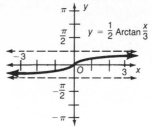

$y = \dfrac{1}{2} \text{Arctan } \dfrac{x}{3}$

CHAPTER 14

Page 558. **1.** 5, 10, 15 **2.** 0, −1, −2
3. 3, 5, 7 **4.** 2, 8, 26 **5.** 98
6. $1 + 4 + 7 + 10 + 13 + 16 + 19 + 22 + 25 + 28 = 145$

Page 572. **1.** $t_n = \dfrac{1}{n^2}$ **2.** 200; 10,050

3. −0.015625 **4.** 7th term **5.** $157\dfrac{1}{3}$,

$206\dfrac{2}{3}$; 144, 192 **6.** $383\dfrac{5}{8}$

7. $-2 + 4 - 8 + 16 = 10$

8. $1 + \dfrac{1}{2^2} + \dfrac{1}{3^2} + \dfrac{1}{4^2} = \dfrac{205}{144}$

CHAPTER 15

Page 600. **1.** $\dfrac{1}{10}$ **2.** $\dfrac{1}{5}$ **3.** $\dfrac{9}{10}$ **4.** $\dfrac{3}{10}$

5. 0 **6.** 5040 **7.** 120

Page 608. **1.** $\dfrac{1}{9}$ **2.** $\dfrac{2}{9}$ **3.** $\dfrac{4}{9}$ **4.** $\dfrac{2}{3}$ **5.** $\dfrac{1}{3}$

6. 3780 **7.** $\dfrac{5}{18}$ **8.** $\dfrac{1}{78}$ **9.** $\dfrac{1}{12}$ **10.** 0

11. $\dfrac{1}{8}$ **12.** $\dfrac{1}{312}$ **13.** $\dfrac{11}{850}$ **14.** $\dfrac{2}{17}$

15. $\dfrac{1}{5525}$ **16.** $\dfrac{1}{32}$ **17.** $\dfrac{1}{2}$ **18.** $\dfrac{5}{16}$

CHAPTER 16

Page 628. **1.** $(-1, 2)$ **2.** $(1, -1, 0)$
3. $(-1, -2, 3)$ **4.** Not possible

5. $\begin{bmatrix} 6 & 3 & 15 \\ -15 & -9 & 0 \\ 6 & -9 & 6 \end{bmatrix}$ **6.** $\begin{bmatrix} 1 & 4 & -36 \end{bmatrix}$

7. $\begin{bmatrix} -6 & -6 & -9 \\ -2 & 5 & -5 \\ 0 & -10 & 1 \end{bmatrix}$

PREREQUISITE SKILLS FOLLOW-UP

COMPUTER HANDBOOK

TABLES

GLOSSARY

ANSWERS TO CHECKPOINTS

ANSWERS TO SELECTED EXERCISES

INDEX

ANSWERS TO SELECTED EXERCISES

CHAPTER 1

Page 1. Prerequisite Skills Review
1. c **2.** a **3.** d **4.** b **5.** d **6.** c **7.** b
8. d **9.** c **10.** a

Page 4. Class Exercises **1.** 2 **3.** 13
5. 2 **7.** 18 **9.** 16 **11.** 21 **13.** 1 **15.** 2

Pages 4–5. Exercises **1.** 2 **3.** $\frac{1}{2}$, 2,

-0.22, $2.\overline{2}$, -2 **5.** True **7.** True **9.** 9
11. 4 **13.** 27 **15.** 92 **17.** 8 **19.** 48
21. 80 **23.** 100 **25.** 5 **27.** 10 **29.** 1

31. 9 **33.** 10 **35.** 25 **37.** 130 **39.** $1\frac{7}{8}$

41. 0 **43.** 1 **45.** $3\frac{1}{4}$ **47.** 28 **49.** 8

51. 18 **53.** 11 **55.** 5 **57.** 13 **59.** 19

61. $4\frac{3}{4}$ **63.** 1 **65.** 7 **67.** $2 \cdot 3 \cdot 4 \cdot 5$

69. $(5 - 2)(3 + 4)$ **71.** $5(2 + 3 - 4)$
73. $3 \cdot 4 \cdot 5 \div 2$ **75.** $4(3 + 5) \div 2$
77. $3(2 + 4) + 5$

Page 8. Class Exercises **1.** -3 **3.** 7

5. -8 **7.** $-\frac{4}{5}$ **9.** $\frac{5}{8}$

Pages 8–9. Exercises **1.** -7 **3.** -14
5. 8 **7.** -24 **9.** -65 **11.** -19
13. -4 **15.** -19 **17.** -4 **19.** -8
21. -22 **23.** -1 **25.** 13 **27.** -12
29. 5 **31.** -15 **33.** -13

35. 0 **37.** $\frac{5}{6}$ **39.** 1 **41.** -2.7

43. -0.3 **45.** 5.7 **47.** $-y$ **49.** 0

51. y **53.** -7.5 **55.** $22\frac{3}{8}$ **57.** 27

59. -1.9 **61.** -2.8 **63.** $-\frac{3}{8}$ **65.** -1

Page 11. Class Exercises **1.** -54
3. -121 **5.** -72 **7.** 0 **9.** -8 **11.** -8
Pages 11–12. Exercises **1.** -56
3. 60 **5.** -5 **7.** 40 **9.** -2 **11.** -14
13. 625 **15.** 216 **17.** 0 **19.** -4

21. $-\frac{4}{5}$ **23.** $1\frac{1}{3}$ **25.** $\frac{1}{15}$ **27.** 2 **29.** 2

31. 1 **33.** -3 **35.** 19 **37.** 0

39. -2.24 **41.** 2.56 **43.** 226 **45.** $-\frac{5}{2}$
47. 144 days **49.** 1 **51.** True
53. True **55.** True

Page 14. Class Exercises **1.** Assoc.
prop. of add. **3.** Inverse prop. of add.
5. Inverse prop. of mult. **7.** Dist. prop.
of mult. over add.

Pages 14–15. Exercises **1.** Equal;
comm. prop. of mult. **3.** Not equal
5. Not equal **7.** Equal; inverse prop. of
add. **9.** Not equal **11.** Equal; dist.
prop. of mult. over add. **13.** Not equal
15. Not equal **17.** $(13 - 4) - 7 = 2$;
$13 - (4 - 7) = 16$; no
19. $(24 \div 4) \div 2 = 3$;
$24 \div (4 \div 2) = 12$; no **21.** 30 **23.** 130
25. 0 **27.** 2 **29.** -4000 **31.** Equal
33. Not equal **35.** Not equal
37. Equal **39.** Not equal

Page 17. Class Exercises **1.** $13x + 19$
3. $8x^2y + 3xy^2$ **5.** $2xy + 3x$
7. $8y - 5y^2$

Page 18. Exercises **1.** 9x, 16y, 8; 8; 9
3. x, $-y$, z; no constant; 1 **5.** $0.1x^2$,
$-1.1x$, $-0.01xy^2$; no constant; -1.1
7. $14x + 3y$ **9.** 0 **11.** $7a + b - 3$
13. $-2s - t$ **15.** $2m^2n^2 - mn^2$
17. $4x - 3y$ **19.** $\pi + 4x$ **21.** $15x^2 + x$
23. $-x^2y + 2xyz$ **25.** -6 **27.** $-11\frac{1}{2}$

29. $-\frac{1}{2}$ **31.** $3\frac{3}{4}$

Page 21. Class Exercises **1.** $x = 8$
3. $x = -12$ **5.** $x = -5$ **7.** $x = 10$
9. $x = 0$ **11.** $x = -4$

Pages 21–22. Exercises **1.** $x = 14$
3. $x = 88$ **5.** $x = -11$ **7.** $y = -6$
9. $y = 9$ **11.** $y = -320$ **13.** $x = 5$
15. $x = 6$ **17.** $x = -22$ **19.** $x = 2.7$
21. $x = 0$ **23.** $x = 0.4$ **25.** Dist. prop.;
add. prop. of equal.; mult. prop. of

equal. **27.** Dist. prop.; add. prop. of equal.; add. prop. of equal.; mult. prop. of equal. **29.** Many **31.** One **33.** None **35.** Symmetric **37.** Reflexive **39.** Transitive **41.** $x = 14$ **43.** $x = 0$ **45.** $x = 3$ **47.** $x = 3$ **49.** $x = 4$

51. $x = -21$ **53.** $x = \dfrac{8}{5}$ **55.** $x = 12$

Page 24. Class Exercises 1. 30

3. $w = \dfrac{P - 2l}{2}$

Pages 24–25. Exercises 1. 15 **3.** 86

5. $w = \dfrac{V}{lh}$ **7.** $b_2 = \dfrac{2A}{h} - b_1$

9. $B = \dfrac{3V}{h}$ **11.** $h = \dfrac{3V}{B}$ **13.** 1132 ft per sec **15.** 2.288 kilowatt-hours

17. 3 hours per day

Page 27. Class Exercises

1. $n + 9 = 20$ **3.** $2n + 2 = 38$

5. $\dfrac{n}{-5} = 12$ **7.** $4n = n + 16$

Page 28. Exercises 1. $n + 4 = 17$; $n = 13$ **3.** $3n = 81$; $n = 27$
5. $2n + 7 = 3$; $n = -2$
7. $16 - n = n + 12$; $n = 2$
9. $-n - 7 = 6n$; $n = -1$
11. $10 + 10x = 200$; $x = 19$
13. $10x + 2x = 360$; $x = 30$
15. $25x + 10(2x + 3) = 1380$; $x = 30$
17. 56 nickels and 62 dimes **19.** 13 and 25 **21.** 280 nickels **23.** 11 years old **25.** 26 years old

Page 32. Class Exercises

1. [number line, open circle at -2, shaded left]

3. [number line, closed circle at -1]

5. [number line, open circles at -4 and -1, shaded between]

7. [number line, open circles at 0 and 4, shaded outside]

9. $x > 1$ **11.** $x < -\dfrac{1}{3}$

Pages 32–33. Exercises

1. $x < -1$ [number line, open circle at -1, shaded left]

3. $x \le 0$ [number line, closed circle at 0, shaded left]

5. $x \le 5$ [number line, closed circle at 5, shaded left]

7. $x < 2$ [number line, open circle at 2, shaded left]

9. $x \le -1$ [number line, closed circle at -1, shaded left]

11. $x > 2\dfrac{1}{2}$ [number line, open circle at $2\tfrac{1}{2}$, shaded right]

13. $x > 1\dfrac{1}{2}$ [number line, open circle at $1\tfrac{1}{2}$, shaded right]

15. $x < 9$ [number line, open circle at 9, shaded left]

17. Add. prop. of ineq.; mult. prop. of ineq. **19.** Dist. prop.; add. prop. of ineq.; mult. prop. of ineq. **21.** $x > 2$
23. $x < -2$ **25.** $x \le 1$ **27.** $x > 2$
29. $x > -26$ **31.** $x < 1$ **33.** $x > 3$
35. 7 quarters **37.** $t < 3380$
39. $232 < t < 2270$ **41.** $r > 0$
43. $r = 0$ **45.** No values of r
47. $r =$ any real number **49.** $r < 0$

Page 36. Class Exercises 1. Is not
3. Is **5.** Is **7.** d **9.** e **11.** a

Pages 36–37. Exercises 1. $x > 0$ and $x < 10$, or $0 < x < 10$ **3.** $x < 2$ and $x < 0$ **5.** $x > -5$ and $x < 2$, or $-5 < x < 2$ **7.** $-1 < x < 4$, or $x > -1$ and $x < 4$

9. 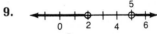 [number line, open circles at 2 and 5, shaded between]

11. [number line, closed circles at -5 and -3, shaded between]

13. [number line, open circle at -5, closed circle at -3, shaded between]

15. $x > -1$ [number line, open circle at -1, shaded right]

17. $x \le -3$ or $x \ge 6$ [number line, closed circle at -3 shaded left, closed circle at 6 shaded right]

19. $-8 < x < -6$ [number line, open circles at -8 and -6, shaded between]

PREREQUISITE SKILLS FOLLOW-UP

COMPUTER HANDBOOK

TABLES

GLOSSARY

ANSWERS TO CHECKPOINTS

ANSWERS TO SELECTED EXERCISES

INDEX

21. $-1 \le x \le 4$

23. $-2 < x \le 2$

25. All real values of x

27. $x \ge 4$ or $x \le -4$

29. $-\dfrac{1}{2} < x < \dfrac{1}{2}$

31. $x \le 1$ or $x \ge 2$ **33.** $x > -3$ and $x \le 5$, or $-3 < x \le 5$ **35.** $x < 0$

37. $x < -8$ or $x > -6$

Page 40. Class Exercises **1.** d **3.** a
5. h **7.** c

Page 40. Exercises **1.** 7 **3.** 35
5. 57 **7.** -51

9. $x = 5$ or $x = -5$

11. $x = -2$ or $x = 4$

13. $-\dfrac{1}{3} \le x \le 1$

15. $-\dfrac{1}{6} < x < 1\dfrac{1}{6}$

17. $x \ge 7\dfrac{1}{2}$ or $x \le -1\dfrac{1}{2}$

19. $x > 1$ or $x < \dfrac{1}{3}$

21. 4 units **23.** x is 10 units from 3.
25. x is less than 10 units from 3.
Pages 43–44. Review Exercises **1.** 19
3. 81 **5.** 8 **7.** 169 **9.** -4 **11.** 4
13. -3.55 **15.** 1.05 **17.** -72 **19.** -27
21. 7 **23.** 4 **25.** Inverse prop. of add.
27. Commut. prop. of add. **29.** $9x - 1$
31. $x^2 - 2x^2y + y^2$ **33.** $x = -24$

35. $y = 120$ **37.** $x = 5$ **39.** $w = \dfrac{P - 2l}{2}$

41. $4n + 6 = -2$; $n = -2$

43. $9(-3 + n) = 63$; $n = 10$

45. $x > 1$

47. $x \le 3$

49. $x < 2$ or $x > 4$

51. 5 **53.** 30 **55.** $x = 4$ or $x = 2$

57. $-4 \le x \le 2$

CHAPTER 2
Page 47. Prerequisite Skills Review
1. c **2.** c **3.** d **4.** b **5.** a **6.** a **7.** c
8. d **9.** b **10.** b
Page 49. Class Exercises **1.** G **3.** C
5. F **7.** A
Pages 49–50. Exercises **1.** $A(6, 0)$, on
x-axis **3.** $C(-7, 2)$, in second quadrant
5. $E(0, 1)$, on y-axis **7.** $G(-8, -1)$, in
third quadrant **9.** $I(-2, 3)$, in second
quadrant **11.** N **13.** R **15.** P **17.** S
19. K
21–32.

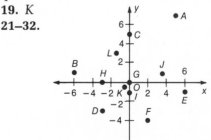

33.

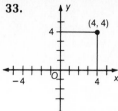

35.

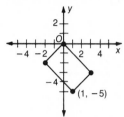

37.

39. First **41.** Second quadrant, plus the nonnegative part of the y-axis and the nonpositive part of the x-axis **43.** First and third **45.** Third **47.** Fourth
49. (5, 2), (5, −2); (−3, 2), (−3, −2); (−1, 0), (3, 0)

Page 53. Class Exercises **1.** −3; −2; −1; 0 **3.** 7; 5; 3; 1 **5.** $y = 5x$
7. $y = -3x$ **9.** $y = x + 3$
11. (−2, −1), (0, 0), (2, 1) **13.** (−2, −5), (0, −3), (2, −1) **15.** (−2, 9), (0, 7), (2, 5)

Pages 53–55. Exercises **1.** 1; −3

3. $-1; \dfrac{1}{4}$ **5.** $\dfrac{1}{2}; -1$ **7.** 8; −6 **9.** −2; −1; 1

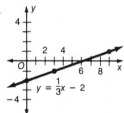

11. 1; 2; 3

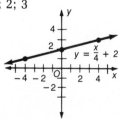

13. −2; 1

15.

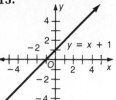

17.

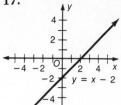

19.

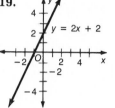

21.

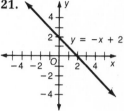

23.

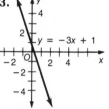

25.

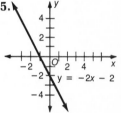

27. 2; −4 **29.** 6; 4 **31.** $5; -\dfrac{5}{3}$ **33.** 0; 0

35. $1; -\dfrac{4}{3}$ **37.** $\dfrac{1}{4}; -\dfrac{1}{3}$

39.

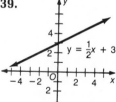

41.

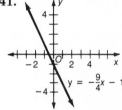

43.

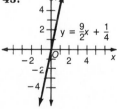

45.

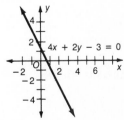

ANSWERS TO SELECTED EXERCISES

PREREQUISITE SKILLS FOLLOW-UP

COMPUTER HANDBOOK

TABLES

GLOSSARY

ANSWERS TO CHECKPOINTS

ANSWERS TO SELECTED EXERCISES

INDEX

47.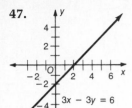

49.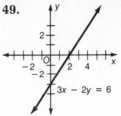

13.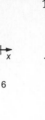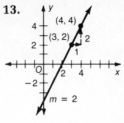

15.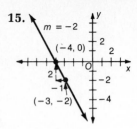

51.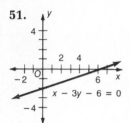

53.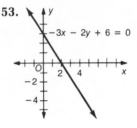

17.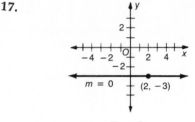

55. The lines appear to be parallel. The coefficient of x is −3.

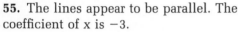
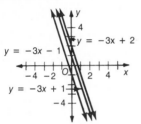

57. $y = -2x + 1$; $y = -\frac{1}{2}x + 1$; As the negative coefficients of x decrease, the graphs become steeper

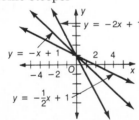

59. $y = -x - 1$ **61.** $y = \frac{1}{3}x$

63. $y = \frac{1}{2}x - 1$

Page 59. Class Exercises   1. 0

3. Not defined   **5.** 1   **7.** $\frac{1}{3}$

Pages 59–60. Exercises   1. $\frac{5}{2}$ **3.** $-\frac{1}{2}$

5. −1   **7.** $\frac{3}{7}$ **9.** 2   **11.** 1

19. Slope of $\overline{AB}$: $\frac{5 - 0}{1 - 0} = 5$

Slope of $\overline{DC}$: $\frac{7 - 2}{4 - 3} = 5$

Slope of $\overline{BC}$: $\frac{7 - 5}{4 - 1} = \frac{2}{3}$

Slope of $\overline{AD}$: $\frac{2 - 0}{3 - 0} = \frac{2}{3}$

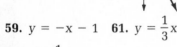

21. Slope of $\overline{IJ}$: $\frac{-5 - (-2)}{1 - 3} = \frac{3}{2}$

Slope of $\overline{LK}$: $\frac{-4 - (-1)}{4 - 6} = \frac{3}{2}$

Slope of $\overline{JK}$: $\frac{-4 - (-5)}{4 - 1} = \frac{1}{3}$

Slope of $\overline{IL}$: $\frac{-1 - (-2)}{6 - 3} = \frac{1}{3}$

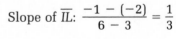
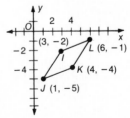

23. Slope of $\overline{DF}$: $\dfrac{0-4}{4-0}=-1$

Slope of $\overline{CE}$: $\dfrac{4-0}{4-0}=1$

$-1(1)=-1$, so $\overline{DF}$ is perpendicular to $\overline{CE}$.

25. Slope of $\overline{NQ}$: $\dfrac{5-7}{9-1}=-\dfrac{1}{4}$

Slope of $\overline{MP}$: $\dfrac{10-2}{6-4}=4$

$-\dfrac{1}{4}(4)=-1$, so $\overline{NQ}$ is perpendicular to $\overline{MP}$.

27. No

29. Slope of $\overline{PQ}$ = Slope of $\overline{RS}=-\dfrac{3}{4}$.

Slope of $\overline{PS}$ = Slope of $\overline{QR}=\dfrac{4}{3}$. Since the slopes of the opposite sides are equal, those sides parallel, and the quadrilateral is a parallelogram. Since $-\dfrac{3}{4}\left(\dfrac{4}{3}\right)=-1$, it is also true that $\overline{PQ}$ is perpendicular to $\overline{QR}$. Thus, angle Q is a right angle. Since a parallelogram with a right angle is a rectangle, $PQRS$ is a rectangle. Finally, the slope of $\overline{PR}$ is $\dfrac{1}{2}$, and the slope of $\overline{QS}$ is $\dfrac{11}{2}$. Since $\dfrac{1}{2}\left(\dfrac{11}{2}\right)\neq-1$, $\overline{PR}$ and $\overline{QS}$ are not perpendicular.

31. $x=-1$ **33.** No. If Q *lies on* $\overleftrightarrow{PR}$, then $\overleftrightarrow{PQ}$ is another name for $\overleftrightarrow{PR}$, and the slopes of $\overleftrightarrow{PQ}$ and $\overleftrightarrow{PR}$ must be the same.

However, the slope of $\overleftrightarrow{PR}$ is 1, while the slope of $\overleftrightarrow{PQ}$ is $\dfrac{3}{2}$. Therefore the three points do not lie on the same line.

35. -3

Page 63. Class Exercises **1.** 1; 0
3. 1; -5 **5.** 3; 1 **7.** 0; 4

Pages 63–64. Exercises **1.** 6; -2
3. -5; 0 **5.** Slope undefined; no y-intercept **7.** -1; 1 **9.** 0; $\dfrac{5}{2}$

11. Slope undefined; no y-intercept
13. $y=x+2$ **15.** $y=-3x-1$

17. $y=\dfrac{1}{2}x+1$ **19.** $\dfrac{3}{2}$; 1 **21.** 3; 3

23. -1; $-\dfrac{1}{2}$ **25.** $y=\dfrac{2}{3}x+1$

27. $y=-\dfrac{3}{2}x-2$

29. $y=-2x+7$ **31.** $y=\dfrac{1}{2}x+3$

33. $y=\dfrac{2}{3}x$ **35.** $y=3x+9$ **37.** Parallel **39.** Neither **41.** Parallel

43. Neither **45.** $\dfrac{3}{2}$ **47.** 0

49. $y=\dfrac{3}{2}x+3$

51. $Ax+By=C$

$$By=-Ax+C$$
$$y=-\dfrac{A}{B}x+\dfrac{C}{B}(B\neq0)$$

The coefficient of x, $-\dfrac{A}{B}$, is the slope.

The constant term, $\dfrac{C}{B}$, is the y-intercept.

53. $n=\dfrac{2}{15}$ **55.** Not possible.

Page 67. Class Exercises **1.** $y=x$

3. $y=3x-5$ **5.** $y=\dfrac{1}{2}x+\dfrac{7}{2}$

7. $y=-\dfrac{3}{2}x$ **9.** $y=\dfrac{1}{4}x-\dfrac{9}{2}$

Pages 67–68. Exercises
1. $y=2x-4$ **3.** $y=x+4$

5. $y=-\dfrac{3}{4}x$ **7.** $y=-1$

PREREQUISITE SKILLS FOLLOW-UP

COMPUTER HANDBOOK

TABLES

GLOSSARY

ANSWERS TO CHECKPOINTS

ANSWERS TO SELECTED EXERCISES

INDEX

9. $y = -5x + 20$ **11.** $y = -x - 7$
13. $y = -x$ **15.** $y = \frac{2}{3}x - \frac{5}{3}$
17. $y = \frac{4}{5}x + \frac{9}{5}$ **19.** $y = x$ **21.** $y = -4$
23. $y = x - 3$ **25.** $x = 5$
27. $y = -2x + 19$ **29.** $x = 1$
31. $y = \frac{1}{2}x + \frac{1}{2}$ **33.** $y = -\frac{7}{5}x + \frac{11}{5}$
35. The slope of the first line is 2, and the slope of the third line is $-\frac{1}{2}$. Since the slopes are negative reciprocals, those two lines are perpendicular and form a right angle.

Page 71. Class Exercises 1. $\{(-3, -2),$ $(-1, 1), (1, -1), (2, 2)\}$; $\{-3, -1, 1, 2\}$; $\{-2, 1, -1, 2\}$; Is a function **3.** $\{(-3, 0),$ $(-2, -1), (-1, 1), (0, 2), (1, -1), (2, 1),$ $(3, 2)\}$; $\{-3, -2, -1, 0, 1, 2, 3\}$; $\{0, -1,$ $1, 2\}$; Is a function **5.** 0 **7.** 15

Pages 72–74. Exercises 1. $\{2, 3, 4, 5\}$; $\{-1, -2, -3, 0\}$; is a function **3.** $\{-2, 0,$ $2, 3\}$; $\{1\}$; is a function **5.** Is a function
7. Is a function **9.** Is not a function
11. 1 **13.** 11 **15.** -1
17. -3 **19.** -1 **21.** 1 **23.** 14
25. -6 **27.** 2 **29.** 12 **31.** $\frac{5}{8}$
33. $\frac{1}{3}$ **35.** $\frac{7}{4}$ **37.** 13 **39.** -10
41. $-\frac{11}{8}$ **43.** There is exactly one y-value for each x-value. Domain: all real numbers. Range: 2 and -2.

45. 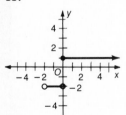 **47.**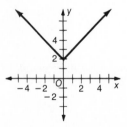

49.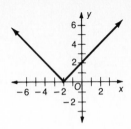

51. Yes **53.** No **55.** No **57. a.** and **c.** describe functions. A real number x has exactly one real cube root and one real fifth root. Part **b.** ($y^4 = x$) does not describe a function since any positive real number x has two real fourth roots.
59. All real numbers except 0 and -1.
61. 7 **63.** $-a^2$ **65.** 82

Page 77. Class Exercises 1. d **3.** c

Page 78. Exercises
1. 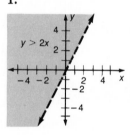 **3.**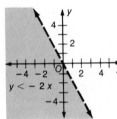

5. 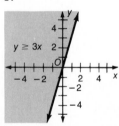 **7.**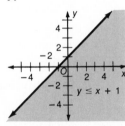

9. 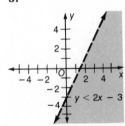 **11.**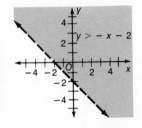

698

13.

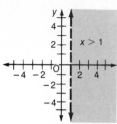

15.

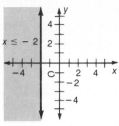

33.

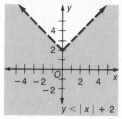

35. $y < 1$ **37.** $y > -x - 1$

39. $y \leq 2x$ **41.** $y < -\dfrac{1}{2}x + 1$

17.

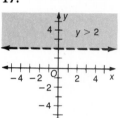

19.

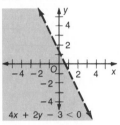

43.

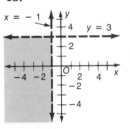

45.

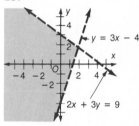

21.

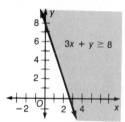

23.

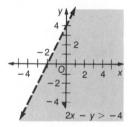

Pages 80–81. Review Exercises

1. $(0, 0)$

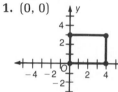

3. $-2; 4; 10$

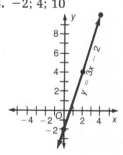

25.

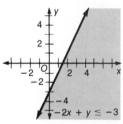

27.

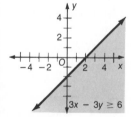

5.

7.

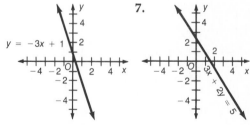

29.

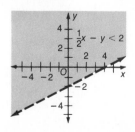

9.

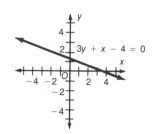

31. No. For every real value of x, there are an unlimited number of real values of y.

ANSWERS TO SELECTED EXERCISES

699

PREREQUISITE SKILLS FOLLOW-UP

COMPUTER HANDBOOK

TABLES

GLOSSARY

ANSWERS TO CHECKPOINTS

ANSWERS TO SELECTED EXERCISES

INDEX

11. 1; 1   **13.** 4; −6   **15.** $\frac{1}{3}$ **17.** D(2, −2)

19. Slope of $\overline{AB}$ = 1; Slope of $\overline{DC}$ = 1; Slope of $\overline{BC}$ = −1; Slope of $\overline{AD}$ = −1

21. Slope of $\overline{AC}$ = 0 (The slope of a horizontal line is 0.)

23.

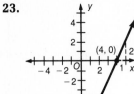

25. $\frac{3}{2}$; −5   **27.** y = 2x + 1

29. $y = \frac{3}{4}x - 3$ **31.** y = −x

33. $y = \frac{1}{3}x - \frac{5}{3}$ **35.** $-\frac{11}{4}$

37.

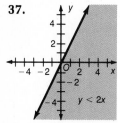

39.

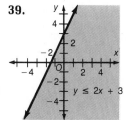

41.

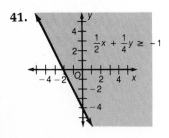

CHAPTER 3

Page 85. Prerequisite Skills Review
1. c   **2.** c   **3.** a   **4.** d   **5.** a   **6.** d   **7.** b
8. d   **9.** c   **10.** d

Page 88. Class Exercises   1. Consistent; (3, −2)   **3.** Consistent; (0, 0)   **5.** Is a solution

Page 89. Exercises   1. (1, 1); consistent   **3.** (0, 2); consistent   **5.** (1, −2); consistent   **7.** No solution; inconsistent   **9.** (2, −1); consistent   **11.** No solution; inconsistent   **13.** (4, 3); consistent   **15.** (−2, −1); consistent   **17.** (−3, 0); consistent   **19. a, c   21.** 4 and 11   **23.** 2 and 3   **25.** 11 holes   **27.** 6 and 10; −6 and −10

Page 92. Class Exercises
1. 3y = x − 1; x   **3.** x − 2y = −3; x   **5.** 6x = 9 − y; y   **7.** (4, 1); (1, 3); (−3, 0)

Page 93.   Exercises   1. (1, 1)
3. (1, −1)   **5.** (−5, 2)   **7.** (12, 4)
9. (8, −3)   **11.** $\left(0, \frac{3}{8}\right)$ **13.** (1, 5)
15. Inconsistent   **17.** (5, −3)
19. 25° and 55°   **21.** 15 lb white onions and 12 lb yellow onions
23. $3000 at 7% and $2500 at 8%
25. 32 field goals

Page 97. Class Exercises   1. Multiply either by −1.   **3.** Multiply second by 3.
5. Multiply first by 8 and second by 3.
7. (1.) Multiply first by −2.   **(2.)** Multiply first by 3 and second by 5.
(3.) Multiply first by 5 and second by 2.   **(4.)** Multiply first by 2.   **(5.)** Multiply first by 2 and second by 5.
(6.) Multiply second by 5.

Pages 97–98. Exercises   1. (1, −3)
3. (12, −5)   **5.** $\left(1, -\frac{3}{4}\right)$ **7.** (2, 2)
9. (2, 3)   **11.** (2, 2)   **13.** (−4, −1)
15. (5, 2)   **17.** $\left(-\frac{1}{3}, 0\right)$ **19.** (20, −10)
21. (6, 8)   **23.** Width is 2 in. and length is 3 in.   **25.** 32 oz of 30% soln and 48 oz of 50% soln   **27.** The plane's rate is 260 m.p.h. and the wind speed is 20 m.p.h.   **29.** 15 grams of silver are added to make 40 grams of alloy.

Page 102. Class Exercises   1. Yes
3. No   **5.** Yes   **7.** 11   **9.** 2   **11.** 0

Pages 102–103. Exercises   1. (1, 2, 3)

3. (2, 3, 3)   **5.** (3, −1, 10)   **7.** $\left(\dfrac{3}{2}, \dfrac{1}{2}, 6\right)$

9. (33, 37, −10)   **11.** (0.5, −0.5, 1)
13. 2 pennies, 3 nickels, and 4 dimes
15. −8, 4, and 12   **17.** 13 cm, 12 cm, and 5 cm   **19.** $3000 at 9%, $1800 at 8%, and $1200 at 7%   **21.** 40 mL of 25% soln, 60 mL of 30% soln, 20 mL of 52% soln   **23.** 746

Page 105. Class Exercises   1. b   **3.** d
5. Yes   **7.** Yes

Pages 105–106. Exercises

1.

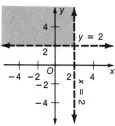

3.

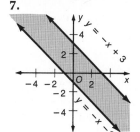

5.

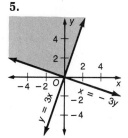

7.

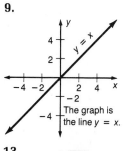

9.

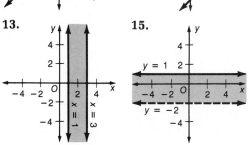

The graph is the line $y = x$.

11.

13.

15.

17.

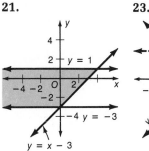

19.

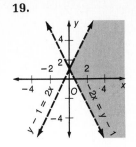

21.

23.

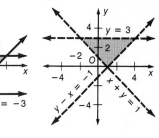

25. $y \geq -x - 1$; $x \leq 2$

27. $y \geq \dfrac{1}{6}x - \dfrac{1}{2}$; $y \leq x + 2$;

$y \leq -\dfrac{2}{3}x + 2$

Page 109. Class Exercises   1. $A(0, 6)$; $B(2, 0)$; $C(6, 0)$; $D(3, 4)$ **3.** 18; 2   **5.** 31; 10   **7.** 46; 12

Pages 109-110. Exercises
1. Max. of p: 8; min. of p: 0
 Max. of q: 8; min. of q: 0
 Max. of r: 24; min. of r: 0
3. Max. of p: 27; min. of p: 5
 Max. of q: 31; min. of q: 10
 Max. of r: 30; min. of r: 5
5. Max. of p: 14; min. of p: 7
 Max. of q: 29; min. of q: 15
 Max. of r: 48; min. of r: 27
7. Max. of p: 12; min. of p: 0
 Max. of q: 74; min. of q: 0
 Max. of r: 60; min. of r: 0
9. 160 standard, 340 special   **11.** 10A, 10B   **13.** 20 acres of Crop I, 40 acres of Crop II

ANSWERS TO SELECTED EXERCISES

PREREQUISITE SKILLS FOLLOW-UP

COMPUTER HANDBOOK

TABLES

GLOSSARY

ANSWERS TO CHECKPOINTS

ANSWERS TO SELECTED EXERCISES

INDEX

Pages 112–114. Review Exercises
1. (2, 1); consistent

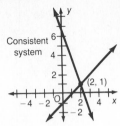

3. (−10, −5); consistent

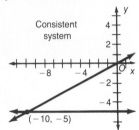

5. (3, −1)   **7.** $\left(\frac{1}{2}, \frac{3}{2}\right)$ **9.** 16   **11.** $\left(\frac{1}{4}, 1\right)$

13. Length: 10 ft; width: 3 ft
15. Current: 4 mph; boat: 15 mph
17. (1, −1, 2)   **19.** 8 pennies, 2 nickels, and 3 dimes
21.   **23.**

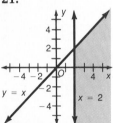   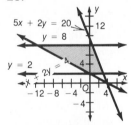

25. 24 standard and 36 deluxe models

CHAPTER 4
Page 117. Prerequisite Skills Review
1. d   **2.** b   **3.** b   **4.** a   **5.** c   **6.** c   **7.** d
8. c   **9.** d   **10.** c
Page 120. Class Exercises   1. 9^8
3. $\left(\frac{2}{3}\right)^{10}$ **5.** $\left(\frac{1}{3}\right)^{18}$ **7.** 15^6 **9.** $(-3)^9$
11. $(xy)^{30}$ **13.** False   **15.** True   **17.** False
19. False   **21.** False   **23.** False   **25.** False
27. True

Page 121. Exercises   1. 7^9 **3.** 2^6
5. 5^{12} **7.** 8^8 **9.** x^{12} **11.** $(ab)^{10}$
13. $\left(\frac{2}{5}\right)^{12}$ **15.** 3^4 **17.** $8x^6$ **19.** $\frac{16}{81}x^4$
21. a^3b^3 **23.** $6x^3y^6$ **25.** $-\frac{1}{6}u^6$
27. $\frac{2}{3}x^5$ **29.** $x^{11}y^{10}$ **31.** $16r^4s^4$
33. 4096   **35.** 1728   **37.** 243   **39.** −1
41. 9   **43.** 216   **45.** 1,000,000
47. 10,000,000,000   **49.** $(xy^2)^{10}$
51. $(x^2y^4)^5$ **53.** $(a^8b^{12}c^4)^2$ **55.** x^{2+n}
57. x^{5n} **59.** x^{n^2}
Page 124. Class Exercises   1. Binomial; 5   **3.** Monomial; 8   **5.** $5x + 5$
7. $-3x - 2$ **9.** $x + 11$
11. $x^2 + 3x - 10$ **13.** $-2xy + 2y^2$
Pages 125–126. Exercises
1. Monomial; 7   **3.** Trinomial; 3   **5.** Binomial; 3   **7.** Monomial; 6   **9.** $8x + 6$
11. $-2x - 4y$ **13.** $11x^2 + 6x - 5$
15. $7x - 2$ **17.** $-5x^3y^2 + 11x^2y - x$
19. $9x + 6y$ **21.** $-9x^2y - 10xy$
23. $8x^2$ **25.** $-27xy + 6x + 5$
27. $8x^2 - 11x - 15$
29. $6x^4 - 2x^3 - 7x^2 - 18$
31. $7x^3 + 9x^2 - 8x - 4$
33. $-2x^5 + 18x^4 + 6x^3 - 60$
35. $-5x^3 + 18x^2 - 10x + 28$
37. $-4x^2 + 3x - 4$ **39.** $6x^2 + 7xy - 2y^2$
39. $6x^2 + 7xy - 2y^2$ **41.** $-8x - 6$
43. $-14x + 8$ **45.** $7x^3 - 3x^2 + x - 42$
47. $8x^2 + 5x + 3$
49. $-x^3 + x^2 - 4x + 2$ **51.** 1
Page 127. Class Exercises
1. $6x^2 - 10x$ **3.** $-5a^3 + 4a^2b$
5. $6x^3y - 21x^2y^2 - 3xy^3$
7. $x^2 + 7x + 10$ **9.** $x^2 + 3x - 10$
11. $4x^2 + 4x + 1$
Pages 127–128. Exercises
1. $5x^2 - 35x$ **3.** $3x^2 - 12x$
5. $x^2y - xy^2$ **7.** $-6x^3 + 6x^2 + 6x$
9. $-21pq^4 + 35q^3$ **11.** $x^2 - 13x + 40$
13. $9x^2 - 1$ **15.** $4x^2 + 27x + 18$
17. $x^2 + 3xy + 2y^2$
19. $6a^2 - 7ab - 3b^2$
21. $9x^2 - 12x + 4$ **23.** $14x^2 - 29x + 2$

25. $x^3 + 13x^2 + 34x - 30$ **27.** $x^3 + 8$
29. $-4x^3 - 13x^2 + 2x + 15$
31. $42x^2 + 19x - 35$ **33.** $x^4 - 1$
35. $p^4 - q^4$ **37.** $8x^3 - 2x$
39. $x^2 - x^2y + 4x - 4xy$
41. $x^3 - 1$ **43.** $6a^3 + a^2b - 4ab^2 + b^3$
45. $15t^3 - 36t^2 - 23t + 14$
47. $3x^5 - 11x^4 + 22x^3 - 14x^2 + 8x - 5$
49. $-4x^4 + 12x^3 + 25x^2 + 10x + 25$
51. $-2x^3 + 7x^2 - 4x + 1$
53. $(x + y + 1)^2 x^2 + 2xy + y^2 + 2x + 2y + 1$
55. $x^6 + 8x^3 + x^2 + x - 2$ **57.** $x^5 - h^5$
59. $-x^3 + x^2y + 2xy^2 - 5xy$

Page 130. Class Exercises **1.** 4 **3.** 6
5. 3 **7.** 14 **9.** 2 **11.** 6 **13.** x^2
15. $4xy$ **17.** 3 **19.** a **21.** 2 **23.** $2rs$

Pages 130–131. Exercises **1.** 6 **3.** 4
5. 2 **7.** 3 **9.** 16 **11.** 14 **13.** y^4
15. $3y$ **17.** 6 **19.** $2a$ **21.** $2(2x - 3)$
23. $5(2 + 3b)$ **25.** $7(x - 6)$
27. $9(x + y)$ **29.** $4x^2(3 - 4x)$
31. $3x(3x + 1)$ **33.** $3b(5a^2 + 4b^2)$
35. $4x(2x + 7)$ **37.** $4x(x - 2)$
39. $a(x + y)$ **41.** $ax(1 - a)$
43. $-7x(4 - 3x^2)$ **45.** $6b^3(b^3 - 2b - 3)$
47. $a(x + y - z)$
49. $2h(32h^2 - 8h + 7)$
51. $3ab(3a^2 + 7ab - 5b^2)$
53. $13x^2(2x^4 - 3x^2 - 4x + 7)$
55. $4x(4x + 1)$ **57.** $2x(3x + 13)$
59. $\frac{1}{2}(x + 4)$ **61.** $\frac{1}{4}x(x - 20)$
63. $\frac{1}{3}y(9x + 2)$ **65.** $\frac{1}{6}(2x - 3)$

Page 133. Class Exercises **1.** $(x + 3)$
3. $(a - b)$ **5.** $(x + 2)$; $(x + 2)$;
$(x + 7)(x + 2)$ **7.** $(x + y)$; $(x + y)$;
$(a + 3)(x + y)$

Pages 133–134. Class Exercises
1. $(x + 2)(y + 5)$ **3.** $(5x + 2)(x + 4)$
5. $(2a + b)(b - 1)$ **7.** $(3v - 8)(u^2 - v)$
9. $(3x + 2)(y + 2)$ **11.** $(a + 5)(b + 3)$
13. $(2v + 5)(6u + 1)$ **15.** $(y + 6)(x - y)$
17. $(x + 9)(5a - 1)$
19. $(4y + 1)(5x - 2y)$
21. $(3 - y^2)(5 + y)$ **23.** $(b + 3)(a^2 - 2)$

25. $(2x^2 - 1)(x + 5)$
27. $(u - v)(u^2 + v^2)$
29. $(r^2 + 5)(s + 2r)$ **31.** $(x - 2)(y + 1)$
33. $(3a - 4)(b + 1)$
35. $(c + d^2)(c^2 - 2d)$
37. $(a + 3)(a + b + c)$
39. $(x^2 + y)(x + y + 3)$
41. $x(y + 1)(x + 1)$
43. $4xy(x + 1)(2 - y^2)$

Page 137. Class Exercises
1. $(x + 4)(x + 3)$ **3.** $(y - 5)(y + 2)$
5. $(n + 2)(n + 5)$ **7.** $(2x + 1)(x + 5)$
9. $(7r + 3)(r + 1)$ **11.** $(3x - 1)(2x + 1)$

Page 138. Class Exercises
1. $(2x + 3)(x + 1)$ **3.** $(y + 8)(y + 1)$
5. $(10b + 1)(b + 1)$ **7.** $(a + 4)(a - 2)$
9. $(b - 10)(b + 2)$ **11.** $(5t - 1)(t - 7)$
13. $(4h - 1)(2h - 7)$
15. $(5x + 6)(x - 1)$
17. $(3y + 2)(5y + 3)$ **19.** $(2x - 3)^2$
21. Not factorable **23.** $(3h + 2)^2$
25. $(2a - 7)(5a + 2)$
27. $(2x - 3)(2x + 5)$
29. $(6z + 1)(3z - 4)$
31. $(2a - 5b)(5a - 3b)$
33. $(6s - t)(s + 4t)$
35. $(2 - y^2)(3 + 4y^2)$
37. $(2a^2 + 5b)(2a^2 - 3b)$
39. $(3y^3 - 4)(y^3 - 2)$
41. $(x^n + 5)(x^n + 3)$
43. $(2x^n + 5)(3x^n + 2)$
45. $(3x^{2n} + 4)(3x^{2n} - 1)$
47. $3(3y - 4)(5y + 2)$ **49.** $xy(x + y)^2$
51. $2(s - 8)(s + 7)$
53. $\frac{1}{5}(x - 10)(x + 5)$
55. $\frac{1}{6}(3x - 2)(2x + 1)$
57. $\frac{1}{4}(2x + 1)(3x - 2)$

Page 140. Class Exercises
1. $(x + 7)(x - 7)$ **3.** $(4s + 9t)(4s - 9t)$
5. $(x + 4)^2$ **7.** $(2c - 1)^2$
9. $(x + 3)(x^2 - 3x + 9)$
11. $(x + 2y)(x^2 - 2xy + 4y^2)$

Page 141. Exercises **1.** $(x + 6)(x - 6)$
3. $(3x + y)(3x - y)$ **5.** $(4c + d)(4c - d)$

PREREQUISITE SKILLS FOLLOW-UP

COMPUTER HANDBOOK

TABLES

GLOSSARY

ANSWERS TO CHECKPOINTS

ANSWERS TO SELECTED EXERCISES

INDEX

7. $(5u + 3v)(5u - 3v)$ 9. $(x - 2)^2$
11. $(x - y)^2$ 13. $(3x - 2)^2$
15. $(a + 2b)^2$ 17. $(x + 1)(x^2 - x + 1)$
19. $(x - 5)(x^2 + 5x + 25)$
21. $(4x - 3)(16x^2 + 12x + 9)$
23. $(6a + 1)(36a^2 - 6a + 1)$
25. $(2x + 7y)(4x^2 - 14xy + 49y^2)$
27. $(9x + 13)(9x - 13)$
29. $(ab - 6)(a^2b^2 + 6ab + 36)$
31. $(8a + 9b)(64a^2 - 72ab + 81b^2)$
33. $(100 + 3cd)(100 - 3cd)$
35. $(17 - 20p)(17 + 20p)$ 37. 396
39. 2496 41. 6375 43. 9999
45. $(y + 0.1)(y - 0.1)$ 47. $(x + 0.5)^2$
49. Area $= a^2 + 2(ab) + b^2 = (a + b)^2$

Page 143. Class Exercises 1. GCF
3. Grouping 5. Trinomial 7. GCF
9. GCF 11. Grouping

Pages 143–144. Exercises
1. $2x(x + 3)(x - 3)$ 3. $3b(a + 4)(a - 4)$
5. $2x(2x - 3)(2x + 1)$ 7. $2h^2(h - 6)^2$
9. $(a^2 + 9)(a + 3)(a - 3)$
11. $b(b^2 + 8)(b^2 - 8)$
13. $3x(x + 6)(x - 1)$
15. $3ab(a + 2b)(a - 2b)$
17. $4x(3 - 2x)^2$
19. $(x + 1)(a + 1)(a - 1)$
21. $(x + y)(x - y)(x^2 + xy + y^2)$
23. $(x + 5)(x - 2)(x^2 + 2x + 4)$
25. $2a(a^2 + 9)(a + 3)(a - 3)$
27. $(2x + 1)^2(2x - 1)^2$ 29. $3x(x^2 + 1)^2$
31. $x(a - 1)(x + y)(x - y)$
33. $(x + 4)(x - 4)(x + 2)(x^2 - 2x + 4)$
35. $10x(x^4 + 10,000)(x^2 + 100)(x + 10)$
$(x - 10)$
37. $(a - 2b)(a^2 + 4b^2)(a + 2b)(a - 2b)$
39. $\frac{1}{16}(4x^2 + 1)(2x + 1)(2x - 1)$
41. $\frac{1}{6}(x - 6)(x - 2)$ 43. $\frac{3}{4}(2x + 1)^2$
45. $\frac{1}{4}(y - 5)(2x - 3)$
47. $\frac{1}{8}(x + 2)(x - 2)^2(x^2 + 2x + 4)$

Page 147. Class Exercises 1. 3, 7
3. 1, -8 5. 0, -1 7. $-2, 4, 6$ 9. 0, 2

Page 147. Exercises 1. 0, 5 3. 0, -4
5. 2, 3 7. $-7, 9$ 9. $-\frac{2}{3}, \frac{3}{2}$ 11. $0, \frac{1}{3}$
13. $0, -\frac{1}{2}$ 15. $-2, 3$ 17. $-5, 2$
19. $1, \frac{2}{3}$ 21. $0, 3, -3$ 23. $\frac{1}{4}, -8$
25. $-\frac{3}{5}, -\frac{1}{5}$ 27. $0, \frac{1}{2}$ 29. 0, 5
31. $-1, 2, -2$ 33. $-2, 1, -1$
35. $1, -1, 2, -2$ 37. $5, -\frac{1}{3}$
39. $3, -3, \frac{1}{2}$ 41. $2, -2$ 43. $\frac{4}{3}, -\frac{5}{4}$
45. $-\frac{2}{3}, 1$ 47. $\frac{3}{4}, -2$ 49. $1, -1, 3$

Page 151. Class Exercises 1. $x^2 + 6x$
3. $x^2 + (x + 1)^2$, or $2x^2 + 2x + 1$
5. $x(x + 5)$, or $x^2 + 5x$

Page 151–152. Exercises 1. 5 and 13
3. 4 and 9 5. 12 7. -12
9. $l = 13$ cm; $w = 5$ cm 11. 15 and 16
13. 11 and 13 15. $l = 16$ m; $w = 9$ m
17. 2 in. 19. 3 in.; 6 in. 21. 3 sec
23. 14 and 47 25. $l = 15$ cm,
$w = 3$ cm, $h = 6$ cm

Page 156. Class Exercises 1. False
3. True 5. True 7. True

Page 156. Exercises
1. $x < -2$ or $x > 0$

3. $2 \leq x \leq 4$

5. $x < -4$ or $x > -3$

7. $-\frac{1}{3} \leq x \leq 2$

9. $x \leq -1$ or $x \geq 1$

11. $x < -2$ or $x > 6$

13. $x \le -8$ or $x \ge -1$

15. $x < -2$ or $x > 2$

17. $-2 < x < 5$

19. $-3 \le x \le 3$

21. $-7 < x < 0$

23. $x < -\dfrac{2}{3}$ or $x > \dfrac{1}{5}$

25. $0 < x < 2$ or $x > 4$

27. $-1 \le x \le 0$ or $x \ge 7$

29. $-3 < x < 0$ or $x > 3$

31. $-3 < x < -1$ or $x > 1$

33. $-3 \le x \le \dfrac{1}{2}$ or $x \ge 3$

35. a. $x^2 - 2x + 4 = (x^2 - 2x + 1) + 3 = (x - 1)^2 + 3$; **b.** $(x - 1)^2 \ge 0$ for all real values of x. Thus, $(x - 1)^2 + 3 \ge 3$ for all real values of x. It follows that $(x - 1)^2 + 3 > 0$, or $x^2 - 2x + 4 > 0$; **c.** $x^3 + 8 = (x + 2)$ $(x^2 - 2x + 4) > 0$. Since the product is

positive and $x^2 - 2x + 4$ is positive, $x + 2$ must also be positive. That is, $x + 2 > 0$, or $x > -2$. The solution to $x^3 + 8 > 0$ is $x > -2$.

Pages 158–160. Review Exercises

1. $9x^6$ **3.** $\dfrac{1}{64}y^6 z^{12}$ **5.** $\dfrac{729}{4096}$ **7.** 36

9. $-4x$ **11.** $8x^2 + 2x - 4$

13. $9x^2 - 13x - 7$

15. $16x^2 - 14x - 15$

17. $12x^4 - 4x^3 + 20x^2$

19. $25x^2 - 20xy + 4y^2$

21. $x^3 + y^3$ **23.** $10x^2 - 9xy + y^2$

25. $2x^2 + 10x + 14$ **27.** 8 **29.** 13

31. $3xy$ **33.** $2(4x - 5)$ **35.** $7(a - b)$

37. $15ab(1 - 3b^2)$

39. $2xy^2(3 - 2xy + 6y^2)$

41. $(x - 1)(y + 3)$ **43.** $(y + 6)(x - 2y)$

45. $(t - w^2)(6t^2 - 1)$ **47.** $(x - 9)(x - 2)$

49. $(x + 3)(x - 1)$ **51.** $(4x - 1)(x - 1)$

53. $(4x + 3)(2x + 1)$

55. $(10w + 9)(w - 2)$ **57.** $(2x + 3)^2$

59. $(2a + 5y)(4a^2 - 10ay + 25y^2)$

61. $(xy - 1)(x^2y^2 + xy + 1)$

63. $(3x - 5y)^2$ **65.** $2(x + y)(x - y)$

67. $(x^2 + 9)(x + 3)(x - 3)$

69. $x(x + 2)(x - 3)$ **71.** $0, -2$

73. $-3, \dfrac{1}{2}$ **75.** 2 **77.** $\dfrac{3}{2}, \dfrac{5}{3}$ **79.** $-\dfrac{3}{2}, 2$

81. $0, \dfrac{1}{4}$ **83.** 9 **85.** 18 cm by 7 cm

87. $0 < x < 4$

89. $-3 \le x \le 3$

91. $-3 < x < 3$

93. $x \le -4$ or $0 \le x \le 4$

95. $x < -2$ or $0 < x < 3$

Pages 162–163. Cumulative Review

1. e **3.** a **5.** b **7.** b **9.** d **11.** a

PREREQUISITE SKILLS FOLLOW-UP

COMPUTER HANDBOOK

TABLES

GLOSSARY

ANSWERS TO CHECKPOINTS

ANSWERS TO SELECTED EXERCISES

INDEX

13. $x = 13$ **15.** $8n - 15 = 22; n = 4\frac{5}{8}$

17. $x < 4$ or $x > 5$

$$\xleftarrow{\hspace{0.3cm}} \overset{-9}{\underset{-8\ -6\ -4\ -2\ \ 0\ \ 2}{\vert\ \vert\ \vert\ \vert\ \vert\ \vert}} \xrightarrow{\hspace{0.3cm}}$$

19. $d = \dfrac{s - a}{n - 1}$

21. -1 **23.** -3 **25.** $\dfrac{2}{3}; -2$ **27.** $(1, 2)$

29. $(2, -1, 6)$ **31.** \$1200 at 8%, \$1400 at 7.5% **33.** $-x^2y^3 - 3y^2$

35. $2(y + 6)(x - 2y)$

CHAPTER 5

Page 165. Prerequisite Skills Review
1. d **2.** b **3.** c **4.** c **5.** c **6.** d **7.** d
8. a **9.** b **10.** a

Page 167. Class Exercises **1.** $\dfrac{3}{5}$

3. $\dfrac{1}{x + 1}$ **5.** $\dfrac{12}{7x}$ **7.** $-\dfrac{4x}{3y^2}$ **9.** $x - 2$ **11.** 1

Page 168. Exercises **1.** $\dfrac{14}{5}$ **3.** $-\dfrac{1}{2}$

5. $\dfrac{1}{3x}$ **7.** $\dfrac{5}{x - 1}$ **9.** xy^3 **11.** $\dfrac{1}{2}$

13. $\dfrac{x - 1}{2}$ **15.** $-\dfrac{1}{2}$ **17.** $\dfrac{4}{5}$ **19.** $\dfrac{8}{7}$

21. -4 **23.** 2 **25.** $\dfrac{36}{7}$ **27.** $-\dfrac{4}{9}$ **29.** $-\dfrac{1}{4}$

31. $\dfrac{1}{12}$ **33.** $-\dfrac{5}{x + 4}$ **35.** $-\dfrac{3y + 2}{3y}$

37. $-\dfrac{x + 4}{4}$ **39.** $\dfrac{1}{x^2 + x + 1}$ **41.** $\dfrac{x - 2}{x + 4}$

43. $\dfrac{p}{p - 3}$ **45.** $\dfrac{(y - 2)^3}{x^{2m} + 1}$

Page 172. Class Exercises **1.** 1 **3.** $\dfrac{9}{16}$

5. $\dfrac{n}{2}$ **7.** $\dfrac{2xy}{x - 3}$

Page 172. Exercises **1.** $\dfrac{3}{10}$ **3.** $\dfrac{1}{2}$

5. $\dfrac{a}{3b^3}$ **7.** $\dfrac{2}{3x^2y}$ **9.** $2xy$ **11.** $\dfrac{5m + n}{5m}$

13. $\dfrac{2x(x + 1)}{x - 1}$ **15.** $\dfrac{3z - 4}{3z^2(z - 2)}$ **17.** $\dfrac{27p^2}{8q^2}$

19. $\dfrac{t(t + 1)}{(t + 5)(t - 5)}$ **21.** $-\dfrac{1}{3(2x + 3)}$

23. $\dfrac{2n(n^2 + 1)}{(n - 1)^2}$ **25.** $\dfrac{2x^2}{x - 1}$ **27.** $\dfrac{acf}{bde}$

29. $\dfrac{adf}{bce}$ **31.** $\dfrac{u^2 + 3u + 9}{u + 3}$

Page 175. Class Exercises **1.** $\dfrac{2}{3}$

3. $\dfrac{11}{6}$, or $1\dfrac{5}{6}$ **5.** $2x$ **7.** $-\dfrac{1}{x + 1}$

9. 1 **11.** $\dfrac{2y^2 + 5}{2y}$

Pages 175–176. Exercises **1.** $\dfrac{2}{3}$ **3.** $\dfrac{7}{8}$

5. $\dfrac{7}{3x}$ **7.** $-\dfrac{2}{x + y}$ **9.** $\dfrac{1}{b}$

11. $\dfrac{5}{r^2}$ **13.** $\dfrac{6 + x}{3}$ **15.** $\dfrac{x^2 + x + 1}{x + 1}$

17. $\dfrac{2r^2 - 9s}{3rs}$ **19.** $\dfrac{17}{5a}$ **21.** $\dfrac{(x + 3)(x - 3)}{3x}$

23. $\dfrac{11}{10x}$ **25.** $\dfrac{6y^2 + 5}{2x^2y^3}$ **27.** $\dfrac{5bc^2 + a}{a^2b^2c^3}$

29. $-\dfrac{x^2 - 2x + 2}{(x^2 + 1)(x + 2)}$

31. $\dfrac{2z^2 + 4z - 15}{(z - 3)(z + 2)}$ **33.** $\dfrac{x^2 - 2x + 3}{x(x - 1)}$

35. $\dfrac{p(22p + 3)}{7p + 1}$ **37.** $\dfrac{ad + bc}{bd}$

39. $\dfrac{h(h + 2)}{(h - 2)^2}$ **41.** $\dfrac{2x}{x + 7}$ **43.** $\dfrac{x}{2x + 1}$

45. $\dfrac{2y}{y + 1}$ **47.** $\dfrac{2x + 1}{x^2(x + 1)}$ **49.** $\dfrac{5}{2}$

51. -2 **53.** $-\dfrac{1}{2}$ **55.** $\dfrac{(a - 3)(a + 1)}{a^3}$

57. $\dfrac{5}{x + 5}$ **59.** $\dfrac{x + 1}{x - 2}$ **61.** $\dfrac{x - 1}{x + 4}$

63. $\dfrac{2a - b}{a - b}$

Page 178. Class Exercises **1.** $\dfrac{1}{2}$

3. $\dfrac{3mn}{n + m}$

Pages 179–180. Exercises **1.** $\dfrac{7}{12}$

3. $-\dfrac{7}{40}$ **5.** $\dfrac{3}{10}$ **7.** -96 **9.** $\dfrac{rt}{s}$

11. $\dfrac{1}{4(x - 1)}$ **13.** $\dfrac{6x(5 + x)}{7x^2 - 45}$ **15.** $-\dfrac{8}{9}$

17. $\dfrac{y^2(2 - x^2y)}{2}$ **19.** $-x$ **21.** 9

23. $y - x$ **25.** 0 **27.** 3 **29.** 1

31. $\dfrac{x}{(x + 4)(x + 5)}$ **33.** $-\dfrac{5}{n^2 - n - 5}$

35. $-\dfrac{2x}{(x-3)(4x+1)}$ **37.** 2

39. $\dfrac{3y+2}{2y+1}$ **41.** 2 **43.** -1

Page 183. Class Exercises 1. 4
3. 12 **5.** $12t$ **7.** $15s$ **9.** $6x(x+2)$
11. $x(x+1)$

Pages 183–184. Exercises 1. 8

3. -7 **5.** -1 **7.** 1 **9.** $3, -\dfrac{1}{3}$ **11.** 8

13. $\dfrac{21}{2}, -3$ **15.** No solution **17.** 6

19. 1 **21.** 5 **23.** $5, -\dfrac{1}{4}$ **25.** $5, \dfrac{10}{7}$

27. 3 and 12 **29.** 36 ft and 8 ft

31. $1, -1$ **33.** $b = \dfrac{11}{7}$

Page 186. Class Exercises 1. 1 **3.** 6

5. $\dfrac{3}{2}$ **7.** 9

Pages 186–187. Exercises 1. 25 **3.** 4

5. 3 **7.** $3, -3$ **9.** $2, 5$ **11.** $\dfrac{12}{13}$ **13.** 2

15. $3, -\dfrac{3}{4}$ **17.** 8 m and 10 m **19.** 23 m

21. 1.5 m **23.** True **25.** True
27. False **29.** $2\sqrt{3}$ **31.** Since each
small triangle is similar to the large triangle, $\dfrac{b}{d} = \dfrac{d}{a+b}$. Thus, d is the mean proportional between b and $a+b$.
Page 190. Class Exercises 1. 50 mph
3. 120 mi

Pages 190–191. Exercises 1. $3\dfrac{1}{4}$ hr

3. 80 items **5.** Tina's rate is 3 mph;
Maria's is 10 mph. **7.** Jim's walking rate
is 6 km/hr; the bus's rate is 60 km/hr.

9. $3\dfrac{1}{2}$ hr **11.** 2 hours and 4 hours

13. 9 hr 36 min
Page 194. Class Exercises 1. $y = 2x$

3. $y = \dfrac{5}{2}x$ **5.** $y = \dfrac{32}{x}$ **7.** $y = \dfrac{10}{x}$

9. $y = 15$

Pages 194–196. Exercises 1. $y = 6x$

3. $y = \dfrac{4}{3}x$ **5.** $y = \dfrac{2}{x}$ **7.** $y = \dfrac{9}{x}$ **9.** 8

11. 14 **13.** 10 **15.** 15 **17.** $\dfrac{2}{3}$ **19.** 14

21. $C = 16\pi$ **23.** 3 lb **25.** 80 lb/sq. in.

27. $\dfrac{3}{2}$ **29.** 3 **31.** 8

33.

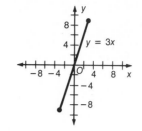

35. $128\,\pi$ cubic units **37.** 9 sec

39. $V = \dfrac{4}{3}\pi r^3$

Page 199. Class Exercises 1. $\dfrac{1}{x^2}$

3. $\dfrac{1}{x^2}$ **5.** 3 **7.** $\dfrac{3b}{a}$

Pages 199–200. Exercises 1. $\dfrac{1}{81}$ **3.** $\dfrac{1}{36}$

5. $\dfrac{1}{x^{12}}$ **7.** $\dfrac{1}{x^4 y^4}$ **9.** y^6 **11.** $\dfrac{1}{ab^2 c^3}$ **13.** x

15. $\dfrac{2x^2}{y^3}$ **17.** $\dfrac{1}{x^6 y^7}$ **19.** $(a+b)^2$

21. $2x - 1$ **23.** $x - 5$ **25.** $\dfrac{2}{(x+3)^2}$

27. $\dfrac{4}{y-1}$ **29.** $\dfrac{h-3}{h+3}$ **31.** $\dfrac{1}{k-8}$

33. $\dfrac{1}{x-3}$ **35.** $\dfrac{7(x+3)^2}{x^3}$ **37.** $\dfrac{1-xy}{x}$

39. 1 **41.** $\dfrac{14x^3}{27}$ **43.** $2(x+3)$ **45.** $-\dfrac{3x}{10y}$

47. $\dfrac{2x}{(x+1)(x-1)}$ **49.** $\dfrac{y^2 - x^2}{xy}$

51. $\dfrac{1}{(x+3)^2}$ **53.** $\dfrac{4x}{(x^2+1)^2}$ **55.** $\dfrac{1-x}{1+x}$

57. $\dfrac{y^2 - x^2}{xy}$ **59.** $\dfrac{y-x}{xy(x+y)}$

Pages 202–204. Review Exercises

1. $\dfrac{3}{5}$ **3.** $\dfrac{1}{x-5}$ **5.** $2x - 3$ **7.** $\dfrac{x-3}{x-2}$

9. -1 **11.** Not defined **13.** $\dfrac{1}{4b}$

PREREQUISITE SKILLS FOLLOW-UP

COMPUTER HANDBOOK

TABLES

GLOSSARY

ANSWERS TO CHECKPOINTS

ANSWERS TO SELECTED EXERCISES

INDEX

15. $\dfrac{2x}{5(4x + 5)}$ **17.** $-\dfrac{5}{x}$ **19.** $\dfrac{3x - y}{x^2y^2}$

21. $\dfrac{x - 1}{x(2x - 3)}$ **23.** $\dfrac{1}{2y + 3x}$ **25.** 3

27. -9 **29.** $-\dfrac{1}{4}$ **31.** 4 ft, 14 ft

33. 6 P.M. **35.** 15 min (hot); $7\dfrac{1}{2}$ min

(cold) **37.** 60 **39.** $S = 4\pi r^2$

41. $\dfrac{3a^7}{2b^6}$ **43.** $\dfrac{2}{x^{10}}$ **45.** $\dfrac{1}{4x}$

CHAPTER 6

Page 207. Prerequisite Skills Review
1. c **2.** d **3.** c **4.** d **5.** a **6.** d **7.** b
8. c **9.** a **10.** c
Page 210. Class Exercises **1.** 8 **3.** Not

real **5.** 10 **7.** $\dfrac{3}{4}$ **9.** $-\dfrac{2}{3}$ **11.** $|n|$

13. n^2 **15.** $-2n$ **17.** 6, -6 **19.** -5
  Pages 210–211. Exercises **1.** 9 **3.** -6

5. -3 **7.** $\dfrac{1}{2}$ **9.** Not real **11.** $|a|$

13. $11|a|$ **15.** $8a$ **17.** -0.5 **19.** -0.1

21. 3, -3 **23.** 5, -5 **25.** $\dfrac{2}{3}, -\dfrac{2}{3}$

27. $\dfrac{1}{5}, -\dfrac{1}{5}$ **29.** 5 **31.** -2 **33.** 2.739

35. 5.292 **37.** 1.744 **39.** 4.431
41. -8.062 **43.** No **45.** Yes **47.** 3
49. Not real **51.** $25|x|$ **53.** $-3x$
55. $13x^2$ **57.** $\pm 3, \pm 2, \pm 1, 0$
  Page 213. Class Exercises **1.** 4
3. $3\sqrt{2}$ **5.** 7 **7.** $4\sqrt{mn}$ **9.** $4\sqrt{5}$
11. $5\sqrt[3]{2}$
  Page 214. Exercises **1.** 5 **3.** 12
5. $4\sqrt{3}$ **7.** $7\sqrt{2}$ **9.** 4 **11.** $\sqrt[3]{-22}$
13. $2\sqrt{30}$ **15.** $3\sqrt[3]{3}$ **17.** $2|x|$
19. $3|x|\sqrt{2}$ **21.** $2\sqrt{11}$ **23.** $9\sqrt{3}$
25. $1.2\sqrt{2}$ **27.** $6\sqrt[3]{2}$ **29.** $4x^3$
31. $12t^5$ **33.** $2k^4\sqrt{3}$ **35.** $5vw^2\sqrt{2}$
37. -6 **39.** $5\sqrt[3]{5y}$ **41.** $3\sqrt[4]{3}$ **43.** $\sqrt{15st}$
45. $8\sqrt{mn}$ **47.** $4p\sqrt{3q}$ **49.** $12x$
51. $12w\sqrt{3w}$ **53.** $20x^2y\sqrt{11}$
55. 45 **57.** $-250x^4$ **59.** $9(2x + 1)$
61. $36x\sqrt[3]{10}$ **63.** $12x\sqrt[4]{4x^3}$ **65.** $x^n\sqrt{x}$

67. x^n **69.** $x^{3n}y^n$ **71.** $|2x - 3y|$
73. $(2x + 1)\sqrt{3x}$
  Page 217. Class Exercises **1.** $8\sqrt{3}$
3. $9\sqrt[3]{5}$ **5.** $7\sqrt{3}$ **7.** $30 + 18\sqrt{2}$
9. $27 + \sqrt{15}$
  Pages 217–218. Exercises **1.** $12\sqrt{2}$
3. $7\sqrt{7}$ **5.** $9\sqrt[4]{9}$ **7.** 18 **9.** $\sqrt{3}$ **11.** $4\sqrt{3}$
13. 0 **15.** $7\sqrt{2} - 2\sqrt{7}$ **17.** $30\sqrt{2}$
19. $2\sqrt[3]{4} + 2\sqrt[3]{5}$ **21.** $\sqrt[3]{2}$ **23.** $19|x|\sqrt{6}$
25. $6\sqrt{6} + 6\sqrt{3}$ **27.** -20
29. $7 + 2\sqrt{10}$ **31.** $37 - 20\sqrt{3}$
33. $41 + 12\sqrt{5}$ **35.** $25x - 9y$
37. $2x\sqrt{2} - y^2\sqrt{2}$ **39.** $3x - x\sqrt{6}$
41. $10x + 10\sqrt{6xy} + 15y$ **43.** $x - y$
45. $-\sqrt[3]{5}$ **47.** $29y\sqrt{2xy}$
49. $14xy^2\sqrt[3]{2}$ **51.** $x^3 + 2$
53. $x^2 + 2x\sqrt[3]{x} - x + \sqrt[3]{x^2}$

  Page 221. Class Exercises **1.** $\dfrac{2\sqrt[3]{2}}{5}$

3. $\dfrac{4\sqrt{5}}{5}$ **5.** $\dfrac{16\sqrt{3}}{15}$
  Page 222. Exercises **1.** $\dfrac{2}{3}$ **3.** $\dfrac{1}{7}$

5. $-\dfrac{5}{11}$ **7.** $\dfrac{\sqrt{2}}{6}$ **9.** $\dfrac{3\sqrt{3}}{10}$ **11.** $\dfrac{3\sqrt{2}}{11}$

13. $\dfrac{3\sqrt{2}}{14}$ **15.** $3\sqrt{3}$ **17.** 2 **19.** 3

21. $\dfrac{\sqrt{6}}{2}|x|$ **23.** $\dfrac{\sqrt{3}}{2}|x|$ **25.** $\sqrt{6}$

27. $\dfrac{3\sqrt{2}}{4}$ **29.** $3\sqrt{3}$ **31.** $2\sqrt{2}$ **33.** $-\dfrac{\sqrt[3]{x}}{4}$

35. 3 **37.** 3 **39.** $\dfrac{2\sqrt{6}}{3}$ **41.** $\dfrac{\sqrt{6x}}{2}$

43. $-\dfrac{\sqrt{10y}}{4}$ **45.** $\dfrac{\sqrt{30x}}{6x}$ **47.** $\dfrac{x\sqrt{14}}{10}$

49. $3x$ **51.** $\dfrac{x\sqrt[3]{2y}}{y}$ **53.** $\dfrac{y\sqrt[3]{5}}{5x}$ **55.** $\dfrac{2\sqrt[4]{x}}{x}$

57. $5(\sqrt{5} - \sqrt{3})$ **59.** $4 - \sqrt{15}$

61. $\dfrac{14 - 5\sqrt{3}}{11}$ **63.** $\dfrac{x^2 - 2x\sqrt{y} + y}{x^2 - y}$

65. $\dfrac{2\sqrt{15x}}{15x}$ **67.** $2\sqrt{3} + 4\sqrt{2}$

69. $\dfrac{x + \sqrt{x - y}\,\sqrt{x + y}}{y}$

ANSWERS TO SELECTED EXERCISES

PREREQUISITE SKILLS FOLLOW-UP

COMPUTER HANDBOOK

TABLES

GLOSSARY

ANSWERS TO CHECKPOINTS

ANSWERS TO SELECTED EXERCISES

INDEX

Page 225. Class Exercises **1.** $\sqrt{7}$

3. $\sqrt[3]{4}$ **5.** $\sqrt[3]{9x^2}$ **7.** $13^{\frac{1}{4}}$ **9.** $x^{\frac{4}{5}}$ **11.** 4

13. 216 **15.** 8

Pages 225–226. Exercises **1.** $\sqrt{19}$

3. $\sqrt[4]{6}$ **5.** $\sqrt[3]{2a}$ **7.** $\sqrt[4]{27}$ **9.** $2\sqrt[3]{x^2}$

11. $\dfrac{5}{\sqrt{x}}$ **13.** $\dfrac{1}{\sqrt[3]{49}}$ **15.** $\dfrac{1}{\sqrt[4]{27b^3}}$

17. $35^{\frac{1}{2}}$ **19.** $(-25)^{\frac{1}{3}}$ **21.** $-31^{\frac{1}{2}}$

23. $9^{\frac{2}{3}}$ **25.** $8^{\frac{3}{4}}$ **27.** $x^{\frac{2}{3}}$ **29.** $(2x)^{\frac{2}{3}}$

31. 9 **33.** 3 **35.** $\dfrac{1}{3}$ **37.** $\dfrac{1}{343}$ **39.** $\dfrac{1}{9}$

41. $\dfrac{1}{3}$ **43.** $\dfrac{4}{9}$ **45.** $\dfrac{1}{8}$ **47.** $\dfrac{1}{30}$ **49.** $\dfrac{25}{8}$

51. $\sqrt[3]{5}$ **53.** $\sqrt[6]{3}$ **55.** 2 **57.** $\sqrt[6]{2}$

59. $\dfrac{5}{6}; \dfrac{\sqrt[3]{35}}{6}; \dfrac{5}{6} \neq \dfrac{\sqrt[3]{35}}{6}$

61. $\dfrac{1}{4}$ **63.** $\dfrac{1}{5}$ **65.** $-2ab^2$ **67.** $8a^6b^3$

69. $\dfrac{b^4}{5a}$ **71.** $\dfrac{b^6}{16a^6}$ **73.** $\dfrac{1}{x}$ **75.** $\dfrac{y^4}{x^2}$

Page 228. Class Exercises **1.** 11 **3.** $\dfrac{9}{2}$

5. 4 **7.** 7 **9.** 8 **11.** 2

Pages 229–230. Exercises **1.** 7 **3.** 23

5. 49 **7.** 50 **9.** -1 **11.** 512 **13.** $\dfrac{1}{16}$

15. $-\dfrac{7}{8}$ **17.** -2 **19.** 2, -2 **21.** $-5, -6$

23. 6 **25.** 5 **27.** 4, 5 **29.** 4 **31.** 9

33. 8 **35.** 3 **37.** 5 **39.** $\dfrac{729}{49}$ **41.** -1

43. $2\sqrt{3}, -2\sqrt{3}$ **45.** 3 **47.** $A = \pi r^2$

49. $V = \dfrac{1}{3}\pi r^2 h$ **51.** $h = \dfrac{1}{\pi r}\sqrt{S^2 - \pi^2 r^4}$

Pages 232–234. Review Exercises

1. -3 **3.** Not real **5.** b **7.** 2 **9.** $2|x|$

11. ± 7 **13.** ± 8 **15.** $\pm\dfrac{4}{5}$ **17.** 4

19. 2.408 **21.** 9.381 **23.** -3.050

25. 1.547 **27.** -1.765 **29.** -4.179

31. 5.848 **33.** -9.967 **35.** 13 **37.** 10

39. $2\sqrt{10}$ **41.** $4\sqrt{6}$ **43.** $4\sqrt[3]{3}$

45. $7|y|\sqrt{y}$ **47.** $5\sqrt{3}$ **49.** $3\sqrt{17}$

51. $2xy\sqrt[3]{3y}$ **53.** $4\sqrt[3]{4}$ **55.** $4\sqrt{3}$

57. $6\sqrt[3]{10}$ **59.** $2\sqrt{5}$ **61.** $5\sqrt{7}$

63. $17\sqrt{3}$ **65.** $6\sqrt{2} + 12$ **67.** $\sqrt[3]{25} - 1$

69. $-1 - \sqrt{10}$ **71.** $9x - 3y^2$

73. $(5 - \sqrt{15})x$ **75.** -4 **77.** 4

79. $\sqrt{17}$ **81.** $16\sqrt{2}$ **83.** $3x$ **85.** $\dfrac{3\sqrt{2}}{17}$

87. $\dfrac{\sqrt{15}}{15}$ **89.** $-\dfrac{7 + 2\sqrt{10}}{3}$ **91.** $2 - \sqrt{2}$

93. $\sqrt{x} - \sqrt{y}$ **95.** $\dfrac{1 - 2\sqrt{x} + x}{1 - x}$

97. $\sqrt{13}$ **99.** $\sqrt[3]{9}$ **101.** $\sqrt[3]{-2}$

103. $\sqrt[4]{27x^3}$ **105.** $\sqrt[5]{-3c}$ **107.** $37^{\frac{1}{2}}$

109. $71^{\frac{1}{4}}$ **111.** $7^{\frac{2}{3}}$ **113.** $7^{-\frac{2}{3}}$ **115.** $(3x)^{\frac{2}{3}}$

117. 12 **119.** $-\dfrac{1}{5}$ **121.** $\dfrac{1}{512}$ **123.** $\dfrac{3}{2}$

125. $\dfrac{1}{200}$ **127.** 2 **129.** $\dfrac{1}{25}$ **131.** 21

133. $\dfrac{76}{3}$ **135.** $\dfrac{49}{5}$ **137.** 5 **139.** $-2, -3$

141. No solution **143.** 12

CHAPTER 7

Page 237. Prerequisite Skills Review
1. c **2.** b **3.** b **4.** a **5.** d **6.** d **7.** a
8. b **9.** c **10.** d

Page 240. Class Exercises **1.** 4;
$(x + 2)^2$ **3.** 16; $(x + 4)^2$ **5.** 25;

$(x + 5)^2$ **7.** $\dfrac{25}{4}; \left(x + \dfrac{5}{2}\right)^2$ **9.** $\dfrac{1}{4}; \left(x - \dfrac{1}{2}\right)^2$

11. $\dfrac{81}{4}; \left(x + \dfrac{9}{2}\right)^2$

Pages 240–241. Exercises
1. 9; $(x - 3)^2$

3. 1; $(x + 1)^2$ **5.** $\dfrac{25}{4}; \left(x - \dfrac{5}{2}\right)^2$ **7.** 0, -4

9. 1, -7 **11.** $-1 \pm \sqrt{7}$ **13.** $-2 \pm \sqrt{3}$

15. 1, 5 **17.** 3, 5 **19.** 1, -5

21. $3 \pm 2\sqrt{5}$ **23.** 3, $-\dfrac{1}{2}$ **25.** $\dfrac{2 \pm \sqrt{10}}{3}$

27. 1, $-\dfrac{5}{2}$ **29.** $\dfrac{-1 \pm \sqrt{41}}{10}$ **31.** $\dfrac{1 \pm \sqrt{39}}{2}$

33. $\dfrac{-5 \pm \sqrt{33}}{4}$ **35.** $1 \pm \sqrt{5}$

37. $3 \pm \sqrt{13}$ **39.** $2 \pm \sqrt{3}$

41. $3\sqrt{3} \pm 2\sqrt{7}$

Page 244. Class Exercises 1. 1; 5; 6;
$x = -3, -2$ **3.** 1; -10; 25; $x = 5$
5. -2; 3; 2 **7.** 1; 3; 5 **9.** 1; -1; -4

Page 244. Exercises 1. $-3, -4$

3. $-4, 3$ **5.** $-1, -5$ **7.** $-\dfrac{1}{2}, -1$

9. $2, -\dfrac{1}{2}$ **11.** $\dfrac{1}{4}, -\dfrac{5}{2}$ **13.** $\pm\dfrac{\sqrt{6}}{2}$

15. $\pm\dfrac{\sqrt{15}}{3}$ **17.** $\dfrac{2 \pm \sqrt{2}}{2}$

19. $\dfrac{-3 \pm \sqrt{33}}{2}$ **21.** $\dfrac{1 \pm \sqrt{3}}{2}$ **23.** 5

25. $2 \pm 2\sqrt{2}$ **27.** $\pm 1, \pm 2$ **29.** 1.19,
-1.69 **31.** 4.73, 1.27 **33.** 2.12, -0.79

35. $\dfrac{1 \pm \sqrt{1 + 8\sqrt{2}}}{4}$

37. $\dfrac{1 \pm \sqrt{1 + 24\sqrt{3}}}{6}$ **39.** $\pm\dfrac{1}{3}$ **41.** 1

43. All real values of k such that $k \leq 1$

Page 246. Class Exercises 1. -12
3. -16 **5.** Two

Page 247. Exercises 1. One **3.** Two
5. One **7.** One **9.** None **11.** None
13. Two **15.** Two **17.** None
19. $k = 6$ or $k = -6$ **21.** $k = 6$

23. $k = \dfrac{1}{4}$ **25.** $-2\sqrt{6} < k < 2\sqrt{6}$

Page 250. Class Exercises 1. -4; 4

3. 0; -9 **5.** $\dfrac{1}{6}$; $-\dfrac{1}{3}$ **7.** $-\dfrac{1}{4}$; 0

9. 4; -8

Page 250. Exercises 1. -2; -3

3. $-\dfrac{5}{2}$; $-\dfrac{3}{2}$ **5.** -1; -3 **7.** -4; 4

9. 0; -4 **11.** $x^2 + x - 6 = 0$
13. $x^2 + 15x + 50 = 0$
15. $x^2 + 5x - 50 = 0$
17. $2x^2 + 3x - 2 = 0$
19. $x^2 - 2x - 1 = 0$
21. $4x^2 - 4x - 1 = 0$

23. $x^2 - 3x + 1 = 0$ **25.** $k = 3$; $k = \dfrac{3}{2}$

27. $x^2 + 2x - 1 = 0$

Page 253. Class Exercises
1. $n + (n + 1)$, or $2n + 1$, where n is the smaller integer

3. $n + \dfrac{1}{n}$ **5.** $\dfrac{1}{2}n + 5$ **7.** $n^2 + (n + 1)^2$,
or $2n^2 + 2n + 1$, where n is the smaller
integer **9.** $n^2 - n$

Pages 253–254. Exercises
1. 15 and 16
3. 11 and 12 **5.** $\dfrac{2}{3}, \dfrac{3}{2}$ **7.** 5

9. $w = 5$ cm, $l = 11$ cm **11.** 13 cm

13. $\dfrac{12\sqrt{5}}{5}$ cm, $\dfrac{24\sqrt{5}}{5}$ cm **15.** 5 in.

Page 258. Class Exercises 1. d **3.** a
5. b

Page 259. Exercises

1.
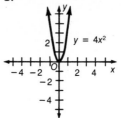

3.
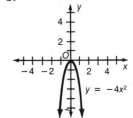

5.

7.
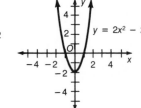

9.
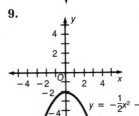

11.
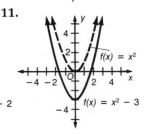

13. **15.**
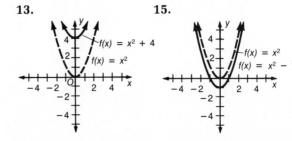

17. $(0, -5)$; $x = 0$; -5 min. **19.** $(0, -8)$; $x = 0$; -8 max. **21.** $(0, 2)$; $x = 0$; 2 max.
23. $a = 1$ **25.** $a = 1$; $c = -2$
27. $a = \dfrac{2}{3}$; $c = \dfrac{1}{3}$ **29.** D: all reals; R: nonnegative reals **31.** D: all reals; R: all reals less than or equal to 3

33. Yes

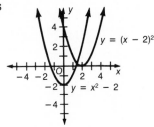

Page 262. Class Exercises **1.** b **3.** a
5. d

Pages 262–263. Exercises
1. $f(x) = (x + 4)^2 - 21$
3. $f(x) = (x - 1)^2 + 2$
5. $f(x) = (x + 2)^2$
7. $f(x) = \left(x - \dfrac{1}{2}\right)^2 + \dfrac{7}{4}$
9. $f(x) = 3(x + 1)^2 - 4$

11.

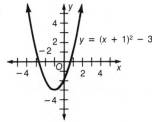

13. $y = (x + 3)^2$; $(-3, 0)$; $x = -3$; all reals; nonnegative reals

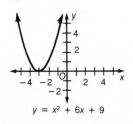

15. $y = (x - 1)^2 + 2$; $(-1, 2)$; $x = -1$; all reals; reals greater than or equal to 2

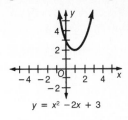

17. $y = -(x + 1)^2 + 6$; $(-1, 6)$; $x = -1$; all reals; reals less than or equal to 6

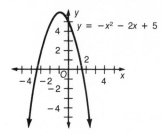

19. $y = -(x + 1)^2 + 4$; $(-1, 4)$; $x = -1$; all reals; reals less than or equal to 4

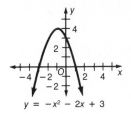

21. $y = -2(x - 1)^2 + 2$; $(1, 2)$; $x = 1$; all reals; reals less than or equal to 2

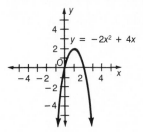

23. -11, min. **25.** 5, max. **27.** $-\dfrac{1}{2}$, max. **29.** $-\dfrac{7}{8}$, max.

ANSWERS TO SELECTED EXERCISES

PREREQUISITE SKILLS FOLLOW-UP

COMPUTER HANDBOOK

TABLES

GLOSSARY

ANSWERS TO CHECKPOINTS

ANSWERS TO SELECTED EXERCISES

INDEX

31.

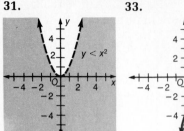

33.

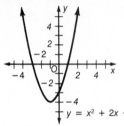

35. $5\sqrt{5}$ cm and $10\sqrt{5}$ cm

37.

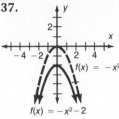

35. x-intercepts: $-3, 1$; $b^2 - 4ac = 16$; two x-intercepts when $b^2 - 4ac > 0$

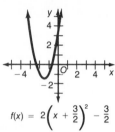

37. D: all reals; R: all reals ≥ 1; y-intercept: 3; No x-intercepts **39.** D: all reals; R: all reals ≤ -1; y-intercept: -3; No x-intercepts

Page 265. Class Exercises 1. $x = 2$; 1 (min.) **3.** $x = -3$; 10 (max.)
5. $x = -1$; -5 (min.)

Pages 265–266. Exercises 1. $x = -1$; 2 (max.) **3.** $x = 1$; 2 (min.) **5.** $x = -\frac{3}{2}$; $-4\frac{1}{4}$ (min.) **7.** $x = \frac{5}{2}$; $12\frac{1}{2}$ (max.)
9. $x = -4$; -11 (min.) **11.** 5 and 5
13. 10 and -10; -100 **15.** $\frac{n}{2}$ and $\frac{n}{2}$; no
17. 20 in. and 20 in. **19.** 8 sec

Pages 268–269. Review Exercises
1. 64; $(x + 8)^2$ **3.** $\frac{9}{4}$; $\left(x + \frac{3}{2}\right)^2$
5. $6, -2$ **7.** $3, 1$ **9.** $4, -\frac{1}{2}$
11. $\frac{3 \pm \sqrt{41}}{2}$ **13.** $\pm\frac{\sqrt{21}}{7}$ **15.** $\frac{4}{3}, -\frac{1}{2}$
17. two **19.** none **21.** $\pm 2\sqrt{6}$
23. $\frac{5}{2}; \frac{1}{2}$ **25.** $3; -5$ **27.** $-\frac{4}{5}; 0$
29. $x^2 + 5x - 24 = 0$
31. $x^2 - 6x + 7 = 0$ **33.** 12 and 6

39. $(0, -7)$; $x = 0$; max. -7 **41.** $a = 2$
43. $f(x) = 2\left(x + \frac{3}{2}\right)^2 - \frac{3}{2}$; $\left(-\frac{3}{2}, -\frac{3}{2}\right)$; $x = -\frac{3}{2}$

$f(x) = 2\left(x + \frac{3}{2}\right)^2 - \frac{3}{2}$

45. $x = -3$; min. -13 **47.** 25 ft by 25 ft

CHAPTER 8
Page 273. Prerequisite Skills Review
1. a **2.** d **3.** b **4.** b **5.** b **6.** b **7.** a
8. a **9.** c **10.** a
Page 276. Class Exercises 1. $x + 3$
3. $a - 3$ **5.** $-3x + 2$ **7.** $x + 2$ **9.** $-a$
11. $5 - \frac{1}{b}$ **13.** $2 - \frac{1}{2x}$ **15.** $1 + \frac{2x - 3}{x^2}$
Pages 276–277. Exercises 1. $x - 4$
3. $2h^2 - 4h + 6$ **5.** $-a$ **7.** $x + 3$
9. $2y + 1$ **11.** $x + 2y$ **13.** $2x + \frac{7}{2}$
15. $2x - 1 + \frac{7}{5x}$ **17.** $x - 7 + \frac{-3}{x - 3}$
19. $2x - 1 + \frac{2}{x + 5}$ **21.** $4x - 7 + \frac{10}{2x + 5}$
23. $5x - 9 + \frac{4}{x + 6}$ **25.** $4x - 5 + \frac{2}{2x + 3}$
27. $x^2 - 2x + 2 + \frac{-4x + 5}{x^2 + 2x}$
29. $3x - 4 + \frac{8}{x + 1}$

31. $x^2 - 3x - 5 + \dfrac{13}{x + 2}$ **33.** $x + 1$

35. $x^2 - x + 1 + \dfrac{-2}{x + 1}$

37. $x^4 - 2x^3 + 4x^2 - 8x + 16 + \dfrac{-64}{x + 2}$

39. $x^4 + 2x^3 + 4x^2 + 8x + 16 + \dfrac{64}{x - 2}$

41. $x^2 + 6x - 4 + \dfrac{10x - 4}{x^2 - 1}$ **43.** Is not a factor **45.** Is not a factor

Page 279. Class Exercises **1.** $c = 3$; 1, $-6, 9, 7$ **3.** $c = 5$; $-3, 8, 0, 1, 0, 12$
5. $c = 8$; 15, $-4, 9, -6$ **7.** $c = 4$; 1, 0, 0, -64

Pages 279–281. Exercises
1. $x^2 - 3x + 2$; 0 **3.** $x^3 - 2x^2 - x - 2$; -1 **5.** $-2x^2 + 5x - 8$; 13
7. $x^2 - 4x + 1$; -4 **9.** $3x^2 + x$; 1
11. $x^2 - x + 1$; 0 **13.** $2x^2 + x + 5$; 0
15. $4x^2 - x - 7$; 52 **17.** $x^2 + 4x + 4$; 22
19. $2x^2 - 4x + 17$; -54 **21.** $x^3 + 3$; 0
23. $x^3 + 2$; 2 **25.** $x^2 + 2x + 4$; 0
27. $x^2 + 3x + 9$; 0
29. $x^3 - 2x^2 + 4x - 8$; 0
31. $x^4 + 2x^3 + 4x^2 + 8x + 16$; 0

33. $x^2 + \dfrac{1}{2}x + \dfrac{1}{4}$; 0

35. $2x^3 - 4x^2 + 8x - \dfrac{9}{2}$; 2

37. $x^4 + 2x^3 + 4x^2 + 8x + 16$; 0
39. $n = 2$ **41.** $n = -4$
43. $n = -1$ **45.** $x^2 - 2$

47. $x^3 - 2x^2 + 3x + 2 + \dfrac{10}{3x - 2}$

49. $x^3 - 2$

Page 284. Class Exercises
1. remainder; 0 **3.** 100 **5.** 0; $x - 2$

Pages 284–285. Exercises **1.** 0 **3.** 6
5. 8 **7.** 0 **9.** 0 **11.** Is a factor **13.** Is not a factor **15.** Is not a factor **17.** Is not a factor **19.** $(x - 1)(x + 2)(x + 3)$
21. $(x + 2)(x - 3)^2$
23. $(x + 1)(2x - 7)(3x - 1)$
25. $(x - 3)(2x + 1)(x - 4)$
27. $(x - 1)(x - 3)(x^2 + 1)$
29. $(x + 2)(x - 4)(2x^2 + 1)$
31. $(x - 4)(x + 2)(x^2 - 2x + 4)$

33. $(x - 6)(x + 2)(x - 2)(x + 3)$
35. $d = 3$

Page 289. Class Exercises **1.** 3 is not a factor of 8. **3.** 6 is not a factor of 15.
5. 8 is not a factor of 5.

Pages 289–290. Exercises **1.** $\pm1, \pm2,$ $\pm3, \pm4, \pm6, \pm12; \pm1;$ $\pm1, \pm2, \pm3, \pm4,$ $\pm6, \pm12$ **3.** $\pm1, \pm2, \pm3, \pm6; \pm1, \pm3;$ $\pm1, \pm\dfrac{1}{3}, \pm2, \pm\dfrac{2}{3}, \pm3, \pm6$ **5.** $\pm1, \pm2, \pm4;$ $\pm1, \pm3, \pm9; \pm1, \pm\dfrac{1}{3}, \pm\dfrac{1}{9}, \pm2, \pm\dfrac{2}{3}, \pm\dfrac{2}{9},$ $\pm4, \pm\dfrac{4}{3}, \pm\dfrac{4}{9}$ **7.** 1, 2, 3 **9.** $-1, \dfrac{1}{2}, \dfrac{1}{3}$

11. $-\dfrac{1}{2}, 3, -4$ **13.** $-\dfrac{1}{2}, 4$ **15.** $\dfrac{1}{2}, \dfrac{1}{3}$

17. $(x - 2)^3$ **19.** $(x + 1)(x - 5)(x + 7)$
21. $(3x - 1)(2x - 5)(2x + 1)$
23. $w = 3$ in.; $l = 7$ in.; $h = 5$ in.

25. $l = 4\dfrac{1}{2}$ yd; $w = 3$ yd; $h = 2$ yd

27. $2, \dfrac{-1 + \sqrt{5}}{2}, \dfrac{-1 - \sqrt{5}}{2}$

29. $\dfrac{1}{2}, \dfrac{3 + \sqrt{17}}{4}, \dfrac{3 - \sqrt{17}}{4}$

31. Possible rational roots: ±1;
$(1)^4 + (1)^3 + (1)^2 + 1 + 1 = 5 \neq 0$;
$(-1)^4 + (-1)^3 + (-1)^2 + (-1) + 1 = 1 \neq 0$
Thus, neither number is a root.

Page 294. Class Exercises **1.** $7i$

3. $-64i$ **5.** $i\sqrt{5}$ **7.** $-\dfrac{9\sqrt{2}}{5}i$ **9.** -1

Pages 294–295. Exercises **1.** $i\sqrt{2}$
3. $5i$ **5.** $2i\sqrt{2}$ **7.** $-5i\sqrt{2}$ **9.** $9i$
11. $\dfrac{i\sqrt{3}}{3}$ **13.** $\dfrac{i\sqrt{2}}{4}$ **15.** $\dfrac{2i\sqrt{21}}{7}$
17. $-\dfrac{i\sqrt{6}}{3}$ **19.** $-\dfrac{9i\sqrt{2}}{4}$ **21.** i **23.** $-i$
25. i **27.** -1 **29.** $-i$ **31.** $6i$
33. $19i\sqrt{2}$ **35.** $\dfrac{8}{3}i$ **37.** -126
39. $-12\sqrt{3}$ **41.** $-\dfrac{\sqrt{30}}{12}$ **43.** 1 **45.** -6
47. $5i$ **49.** $i\sqrt{6}$ **51.** $\sqrt{rs} \neq \sqrt{r}\sqrt{s}$ when r and s are both negative. **53.** $7i$
55. $-\dfrac{1}{4}i$ **57.** $\dfrac{1}{2}i$ **59.** $\dfrac{1}{8}i$

PREREQUISITE SKILLS FOLLOW-UP

COMPUTER HANDBOOK

TABLES

GLOSSARY

ANSWERS TO CHECKPOINTS

ANSWERS TO SELECTED EXERCISES

INDEX

Page 298. Class Exercises 1. $a = 0$; $b = 3$ **3.** $a = 0$; $b = 0$ **5.** $a = 0$; $b = -1$ **7.** $a = 9$; $b = 2$ **9.** $a = -1$; $b = 1$ **11.** Not equal; $3 \neq 5$ and $-5 \neq -3$ **13.** Equal; $\frac{1}{2}(4) = 2$ and $\frac{1}{2}(6) = 3$

Pages 299–300. Exercises 1. $x = \frac{1}{4}$; $y = -9$ **3.** $x = -6$; $y = 8$ **5.** $11i$ **7.** $-5 - 2i$ **9.** $-11i$ **11.** 2 **13.** 0 **15.** $-3 - 5i$ **17.** 13 **19.** $75 + 43i$ **21.** $-1 + 12i$ **23.** 116 **25.** $\frac{3}{5} + \frac{4}{5}i$ **27.** $-1 - 2i$ **29.** $\frac{3}{4} + \frac{1}{4}i$ **31.** $7 - 21i$ **33.** 10 **35.** $-\frac{1}{2} - \frac{1}{2}i$ **37.** 11 **39.** 5 **41.** $-21 + 20i$ **43.** $6 + 10i$ **45.** $-\frac{1}{2} - \frac{19}{16}i$ **47.** $\frac{1}{3} + \frac{2\sqrt{2}}{3}i$ **49.** $\frac{7}{4} - \frac{7}{4}i$ **51.** $-\frac{10\sqrt{2}}{3}$ **53.** $6 + 10i$

55. $\dfrac{a + bi}{c + di} = \dfrac{a + bi}{c + di} \cdot \dfrac{c - di}{c - di}$

$\qquad = \dfrac{ac - adi + bci - bdi^2}{c^2 - d^2 i^2}$

$\qquad = \dfrac{ac + (bc - ad)i + bd}{c^2 + d^2}$

$\qquad = \dfrac{ac + bd}{c^2 + d^2} + \dfrac{bc - ad}{c^2 + d^2}i$

57. $\frac{13}{4} - \frac{9}{4}i$ **59.** $-\frac{1}{2}i$ **61.** $\frac{5}{26} - \frac{1}{26}i$ **63.** $\frac{2}{25} + \frac{3}{50}i$ **65.** $\dfrac{c}{c^2 + d^2} - \dfrac{d}{c^2 + d^2}i$ **67.** 0 **69.** $9 - 6i$ **73.** $3(x + 2i)(x - 2i)$ **75.** $(x - 5i)(x + 3i)$ **77.** $(x - 2i)^2$

Page 305. Class Exercises 1. Four **3.** Five **5.** $-2i$; one **7.** $2 - i$; $i\sqrt{3}$ **9.** -1; 2; $i\sqrt{2}$; $-1\sqrt{2}$

Pages 305–306. Exercises 1. $\pm 4i$ **3.** $\pm i\sqrt{2}$ **5.** $2 \pm 3i$ **7.** $-1 \pm i\sqrt{2}$ **9.** $-\frac{5}{2} \pm \frac{\sqrt{7}}{2}i$ **11.** $\pm\frac{3}{5}i$ **13.** $\frac{1}{2} \pm \frac{\sqrt{3}}{2}i$ **15.** $\frac{3}{4} \pm \frac{\sqrt{15}}{4}i$ **17.** $\frac{1}{3} \pm \frac{\sqrt{2}}{3}i$

19. $-\frac{1}{3} \pm \frac{\sqrt{14}}{3}i$ **21.** 0; $2i$; $-2i$ **23.** 0; $i\sqrt{5}$; $-i\sqrt{5}$ **25.** 0; $\frac{1}{6} + \frac{\sqrt{17}}{6}i$; $\frac{1}{6} - \frac{\sqrt{17}}{6}i$ **27.** i; $-\frac{2}{3}$ **29.** $4 + i$; $\frac{1}{2}$ **31.** $-i$; $\frac{3}{4}$; $-\frac{3}{4}$ **33.** $i\sqrt{3}$; $4i$; $-4i$ **35.** 1; i; $-i$ **37.** 1; $1 + i$; $1 - i$ **39.** $-\frac{2}{3}$; $i\sqrt{5}$; $-1\sqrt{5}$ **41.** 2; -2; $2i$; $-2i$ **43.** 0; -1; $\frac{1}{2} + \frac{\sqrt{3}}{2}i$; $\frac{1}{2} - \frac{\sqrt{3}}{2}i$ **45.** -4; $-\frac{1}{2}$; $2 + i$; $2 - i$ **47.** $(x + i)(x - i)[x - (1 + i)][x - (1 - i)] = x^4 - 2x^3 + 3x^2 - 2x + 2 = 0$

Pages 310–311. Review Exercises

1. $2 - \frac{12}{5}x$ **3.** $4x^2 - 2xy + 3y^2$ **5.** $x^3 - 4x^2 - 12x - 11 + \dfrac{-3x + 4}{x^2 - 3x}$ **7.** $x^4 + 2x^2 + 15 + \dfrac{150}{x^2 - 5}$ **9.** $x^3 - 2x^2 + 4x - 1$; 4 **11.** $4x^3 - 6x^2 - 8x - 3$; -1 **13.** 20 **15.** Is not a factor **17.** $\frac{3}{2}$ **19.** $3, -\frac{1}{3}, -\frac{2}{3}$ **21.** $-3, 4, \frac{1}{2}$ **23.** $-1, 3, \frac{1}{3}, -3$ **25.** $4i$ **27.** $14i\sqrt{3}$ **29.** $-20i\sqrt{3}$ **31.** $\frac{5\sqrt{10}}{2}i$ **33.** $\frac{3\sqrt{3}}{10}i$ **35.** $-i$ **37.** 1 **39.** $-i$ **41.** $19i$ **43.** $-\frac{2\sqrt{2}}{3}$ **45.** $31 - i$ **47.** $-\frac{2}{5} + \frac{11}{5}i$ **49.** $-\frac{21}{13} - \frac{1}{13}i$ **51.** $\pm\frac{1}{3}i$ **53.** $-i, -1$ **55.** $1 - 2i, 1$ **57.** $3, \pm 3i$

CHAPTER 9

Page 315. Prerequisite Skills Review
1. b **2.** d **3.** b **4.** d **5.** b **6.** b **7.** a **8.** c **9.** b **10.** c

Page 319. Class Exercises 1. 8 **3.** 6 **5.** 5 **7.** $(1, 2)$ **9.** $(4, 2)$ **11.** $(4, 6)$

Pages 319–321. 1. 4 **3.** 6 **5.** 12 **7.** 5 **9.** 17 **11.** $\sqrt{61}$ **13.** 24 **15.** 25 **17.** 48 **19.** $(10, 5)$ **21.** $\left(-3\frac{1}{2}, -4\right)$

23. $(0, 0)$ **25.** $\left(-5\frac{1}{2}, -\frac{1}{2}\right)$ **27.** $(4, -2)$

29. $2\sqrt{5}$ **31.** $\left(\frac{1}{2}, \frac{3}{4}\right)$ **33.** $\left(\frac{3c}{2}, 2d\right)$

35. $(4, -7)$ **37.** $(5.6, -3.7)$ **39.** $(2b, b)$
41. $(2d - f, 2e - g)$ **43.** $(-4, 6)$

45. $\left(6, -1\frac{1}{2}\right)$ and $\left(6, -8\frac{1}{2}\right)$ **47.** $A(5, 8)$;

$B(-7, -12)$ **49.** Not collinear;
$ED + DF = 3\sqrt{5} + 10 \neq \sqrt{277} = EF$
51. Right triangle   **53.** $10\sqrt{2}$

Page 324. Class Exercises   1. $(0, 0)$; 10

3. $(0, 0)$; $\frac{2}{5}$ **5.** $(2, 8)$; 8   **7.** $x^2 + y^2 = 16$
9. $x^2 + (y + 3)^2 = 36$
11. $(x + 5)^2 + (y + 6)^2 = 400$

Pages 324–325. Exercises   1. $(0, 0)$; 7

3. $(0, 0)$; 0.3   **5.** $(2, 0)$; 2   **7.** $(-3, 3)$; $\frac{3}{7}$
9. $x^2 + y^2 = 9$
11. $(x + 1)^2 + (y - 2)^2 = 36$
13. $(x + 3)^2 + (y + 7)^2 = 3$
15. $(0, 1)$; 1   **17.** $(-2, -2)$; 4

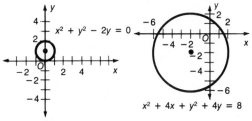

19. $(4, 10)$; 9

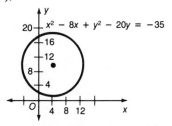

21. A circle cannot have a zero radius.
23. Writing the equation m, h, k form, we
get $(x + 1)^2 + y^2 = 0$. A circle cannot
have a zero radius.   **25.** $r = 13$;
$(x - 5)^2 + (y + 12)^2 = 169$
27. $(x + 5)^2 + y^2 = 25$; $(x - 5)^2 + y^2 = 25$
29. $(x - 4)^2 + y^2 = 4$
31. $(x + 2)^2 + (y - 9)^2 = 25$;
   $(x - 8)^2 + (y - 9)^2 = 25$;

$(x - 8)^2 + (y + 1)^2 = 25$;
$(x + 2)^2 + (y + 1)^2 = 25$
Page 329. Class Exercises   1. $(0, 0)$;
$x = 0$; upward   **3.** $(1, 0)$; $x = 1$; upward
5. $(0, -3)$; $x = 0$; upward   **7.** $(0, 0)$;
$y = 0$; right   **9.** $(2, 5)$; $y = 5$; right
Pages 329–330. Exercises   1. $(0, 0)$;
$x = 0$; upward   **3.** $(-2, 0)$; $x = -2$;
upward   **5.** $(1, 3)$; $x = 1$; upward
7. $(-1, -1)$; $x = -1$; downward
9. $(-3, -3)$; $x = -3$; downward

11. $(0, 1)$; $y = -1$ **13.** $\left(0, -\frac{1}{48}\right)$;

$y = \frac{1}{48}$ **15.** $\left(0, \frac{1}{2}\right)$; $y = -\frac{1}{2}$

17. $\left(-1, -\frac{1}{4}\right)$; $y = \frac{1}{4}$

19. 9; 4; 1; 0; 1; 4; 9

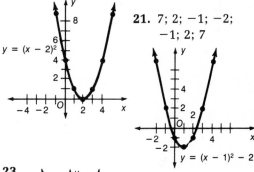

21. 7; 2; −1; −2;
   −1; 2; 7

23.

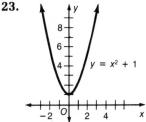

25.   **27.**

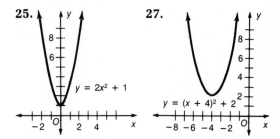

29. $y = 2$ **31.** $x = 0$

PREREQUISITE SKILLS FOLLOW-UP

COMPUTER HANDBOOK

TABLES

GLOSSARY

ANSWERS TO CHECKPOINTS

ANSWERS TO SELECTED EXERCISES

INDEX

33.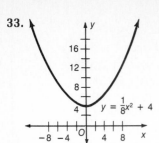

$y = \frac{1}{8}x^2 + 4$

35. $y = -\dfrac{3}{4}x^2$

37. $(-3, 0)$; $\left(-3, \dfrac{1}{4}\right)$; $x = -3$; $y = -\dfrac{1}{4}$

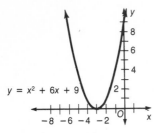

$y = x^2 + 6x + 9$

39. $(-4, 16)$; $\left(-4, 15\dfrac{3}{4}\right)$; $y = -4$;

$y = 16\dfrac{1}{4}$

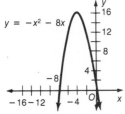

$y = -x^2 - 8x$

41. $\left(-\dfrac{1}{2}, -\dfrac{1}{4}\right)$; $\left(-\dfrac{1}{2}, 0\right)$; $x = -\dfrac{1}{2}$;

$y = -\dfrac{1}{2}$

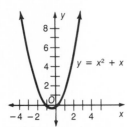

$y = x^2 + x$

43. $\left(\dfrac{3}{2}, \dfrac{1}{4}\right)$; $\left(\dfrac{3}{2}, 0\right)$; $x = \dfrac{3}{2}$; $y = \dfrac{1}{2}$

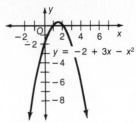

$y = -2 + 3x - x^2$

45. $\left(-\dfrac{1}{2}, 3\dfrac{1}{4}\right)$; $\left(-\dfrac{1}{2}, 3\right)$; $x = -\dfrac{1}{2}$; $y = 3\dfrac{1}{2}$

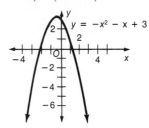

$y = -x^2 - x + 3$

47.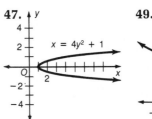

$x = 4y^2 + 1$

49.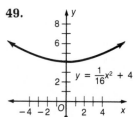

$y = \dfrac{1}{16}x^2 + 4$

51. $y = \dfrac{1}{8}x^2 - 4$ **53.** From Exercise 52,

$y = a\left(x + \dfrac{b}{2a}\right)^2 + \dfrac{4ac - b^2}{4a}$. Therefore,

$h = -\dfrac{b}{2a}$, and $k = \dfrac{4ac - b^2}{4a}$, and the ver-

tex is at $\left(-\dfrac{b}{2a}, \dfrac{4ac - b^2}{4a}\right)$.

Page 334. Class Exercises   1. 10

3. $(0, 0)$ **5.** $\dfrac{x^2}{100} + \dfrac{y^2}{36} = 1$ **7.** 30

Pages 334–335. Exercises   1. $(0, 5)$;

$(0, -5)$ **3.** 13   **5.** $(0, 0)$ **7.** $\dfrac{x^2}{169} + \dfrac{y^2}{25} = 1$

9.

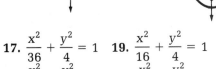

$F_1(-4, 0)$ $\dfrac{x^2}{25} + \dfrac{y^2}{9} = 1$ $F_2(4, 0)$

11.

$F_1(-5, 0)$ $\dfrac{x^2}{169} + \dfrac{y^2}{144} = 1$ $F_2(5, 0)$

13. Vertices: $(0, 6)$ and $(0, -6)$
Foci: $(0, 10)$ and $(0, -1)$

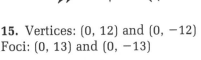

$\dfrac{x^2}{9} - \dfrac{y^2}{16} = 1$

13.

$F_1(-\sqrt{45}, 0)$ $\dfrac{x^2}{81} + \dfrac{y^2}{36} = 1$ $F_2(\sqrt{45}, 0)$

15.

$\dfrac{x^2}{9} + \dfrac{y^2}{25} = 1$ $F_1(0, 4)$ $F_2(0, -4)$

15. Vertices: $(0, 12)$ and $(0, -12)$
Foci: $(0, 13)$ and $(0, -13)$

$\dfrac{y^2}{144} - \dfrac{x^2}{25} = 1$

17. $\dfrac{x^2}{36} + \dfrac{y^2}{4} = 1$ **19.** $\dfrac{x^2}{16} + \dfrac{y^2}{4} = 1$

21. $\dfrac{x^2}{16} + \dfrac{y^2}{25} = 1$ **23.** $\dfrac{x^2}{36} + \dfrac{y^2}{11} = 1$

25. $\dfrac{x^2}{8} + \dfrac{y^2}{4} = 1$ **27.** $\dfrac{x^2}{24} + \dfrac{y^2}{49} = 1$;

$\dfrac{x^2}{74} + \dfrac{y^2}{49} = 1$ **29.** $\dfrac{x^2}{9} + \dfrac{y^2}{25} = 1$

31. $\dfrac{x^2}{100} + \dfrac{y^2}{51} = 1$

17. Vertices: $(0, 3)$ and $(0, -3)$
Foci: $(0, \sqrt{13})$ and $(0, -\sqrt{13})$

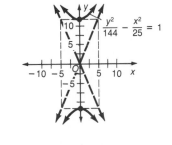

$\dfrac{y^2}{9} - \dfrac{x^2}{4} = 1$

35.

$\dfrac{(x - 2)^2}{25} + \dfrac{(y + 1)^2}{16} = 1$

19. $\dfrac{x^2}{36} - \dfrac{y^2}{64} = 1$ **21.** $\dfrac{y^2}{9} - \dfrac{x^2}{7} = 1$

23. $\dfrac{x^2}{9} - \dfrac{y^2}{16} = 1$

25. $\left(0, \dfrac{2\sqrt{13}}{3}\right)$ $9y^2 - 4x^2 = 16$ $\left(0, -\dfrac{2\sqrt{13}}{3}\right)$

Page 340. Class Exercises   1. $(0, 4)$, $(0, -4)$ **3.** $y = \pm 2x$

Pages 340–341. Exercises   1. x-axis; $(6, 0)$, $(-6, 0)$ **3.** x-axis; $(3, 0)$, $(-3, 0)$
5. x-axis; $(6, 0)$, $(-6, 0)$ **7.** $(5, 0)$, $(-5, 0)$
9. $(5, 0)$, $(-5, 0)$ **11.** $y = \pm \dfrac{5}{2}x$

PREREQUISITE SKILLS FOLLOW-UP

COMPUTER HANDBOOK

TABLES

GLOSSARY

ANSWERS TO CHECKPOINTS

ANSWERS TO SELECTED EXERCISES

INDEX

27.

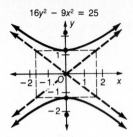

$16y^2 - 9x^2 = 25$

29.

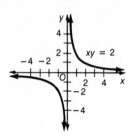

$xy = 2$

31. $y = \pm x$

33. $y = \pm\dfrac{\sqrt{6}}{2}x$ **35.** $\dfrac{y^2}{9} - \dfrac{x^2}{16} = 1$;

$\dfrac{x^2}{16} - \dfrac{y^2}{9} = 1$ **37.** $\dfrac{x^2}{4} - \dfrac{y^2}{3} = 1$

39. $(-6, 5)$; $(-18, 5)$; $(6, 5)$

41. $\dfrac{(x + 2)^2}{9} - (y - 1)^2 = 1$

Page 344. Class Exercises 1. Circle
3. Parabola **5.** Ellipse **7.** Circle **9.** Circle
Page 344. Exercises 1. Circle
3. Parabola **5.** Hyperbola **7.** Circle
9. Circle **11.** Ellipse **13.** Ellipse
15. Parabola **17.** Hyperbola **19.** Ellipse
21. Parabola **23.** $A \neq B \neq 0$ **25.** Either
$A > 0$ and $B < 0$ or $A < 0$ and $B > 0$
27. Circle **29.** Hyperbola **31.** Ellipse
Page 348. Class Exercises 1. $(0, 10)$
3. $(8, -6)$; $(-8, -6)$ **5.** $(6, 8)$; $(8, 6)$
7. $(1, 2)$; $(3, 2)$ **9.** $(4, 1)$; $(-4, -1)$
Pages 348–349. Exercises 1. $(1, -2)$
3. $(-2, 1)$; $(3, 6)$ **5.** $(-3, 6)$; $(1, -2)$
7. $(0, -5)$ **9.** $(-3, 4)$; $(3, 4)$ **11.** $(-3, 4)$;
$(4, -3)$ **13.** No points of intersection
15. $(-1, 0)$ **17.** $(3, 5)$; $(-3, -5)$
19. $(-5, -12)$; $(-12, -5)$ **21.** $(1, 1)$;
$(-1, -1)$ **23.** $(-5, 3)$ **25.** $(-1, 1)$;
$\left(-\dfrac{1}{2}, 2\right)$ **27.** $(2, 2)$ **29.** $(\sqrt{2}, 1)$;
$(-\sqrt{2}, 1)$

31. $(1, 5)$; $\left(-\dfrac{1}{2}, \dfrac{7}{2}\right)$

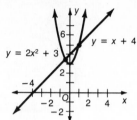

$y = 2x^2 + 3$ $y = x + 4$

33. $\left(\dfrac{-1 + \sqrt{17}}{2}, \dfrac{1 + \sqrt{17}}{2}\right)$;

$\left(\dfrac{-1 - \sqrt{17}}{2}, \dfrac{1 - \sqrt{17}}{2}\right)$

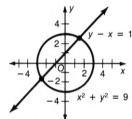

$y - x = 1$ $x^2 + y^2 = 9$

35. $r > 4$ or $r < -4$ **37.** $b = \pm 2$
39. No real values of m
Page 352. Class Exercises 1. $(2, 0)$;
$(-2, 0)$ **3.** $(0, 2)$ **5.** $(\sqrt{2}, \sqrt{2})$;
$(-\sqrt{2}, -\sqrt{2})$ **7.** $(3, 1)$; $(-3, -1)$
9. $(-2, 0)$; $(2, 0)$
Pages 352–353. Exercises 1. $(-1, 1)$
3. $(5, \pm3)$; $(-5, \pm3)$ **5.** $\left(3, \dfrac{1}{2}\right)$; $\left(-3, \dfrac{1}{2}\right)$;
$(\sqrt{6}, -1)$; $(-\sqrt{6}, -1)$ **7.** $(5, 2)$; $(-5, -2)$;
$(2, 5)$; $(-2, -5)$ **9.** $(2, -4)$; $(-2, -4)$
11. $(3, 4)$; $(-3, -4)$; $(4, 3)$; $(-4, -3)$

13.

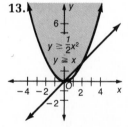

$y \geq \dfrac{1}{2}x^2$
$y \geq x$

15.

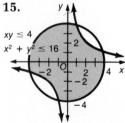

$xy \leq 4$
$x^2 + y^2 \leq 16$

17. None **19.** $\left(\dfrac{2}{3}, 6\right)$; $\left(-\dfrac{2}{3}, -6\right)$
21. $(2, \pm\sqrt{5})$; $(-2, \pm\sqrt{5})$

23.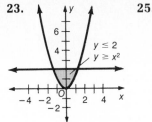

25.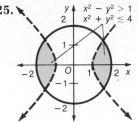

27.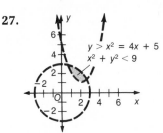

29. $(x - 2)^2 + y^2 = 4$; $x^2 + (y - 2)^2 = 4$

31. $x^2 + y^2 = \dfrac{1}{4}$; $x^2 + y^2 = \dfrac{1}{9}$

Page 355. Class Exercises 1. 9 and 13
Page 356. Exercises 1. 21 and 13
3. 6 and 19 **5.** 25 in. by 15 in. **7.** 6 and 4, or −20 and 30 **9.** 55 ft by 45 ft
11. 12 in. and 6 in. **13.** 20 ft

Pages 358–359. Review Exercises
1. 10; (−2, 3) **3.** $2\sqrt{13}$; (6, −10)
5. $\sqrt{41}$ **7.** 5 **9.** (−12, −16) **11.** (−10, 6) and (6, 6) **13.** (1, 0); $\sqrt{7}$ **15.** (2, −2); 1
17. $(x + 7)^2 + (y + 6)^2 = 2$
19. $(x + 2)^2 + (y - 8)^2 = 100$
21. Upward; (0, 0); $\left(0, \dfrac{1}{4}\right)$; x = 0; $y = -\dfrac{1}{4}$
23. Downward; (3, 0); $\left(3, -\dfrac{1}{4}\right)$; x = 3; $y = \dfrac{1}{4}$ **25.** Upward; (2, −3); $\left(2, -\dfrac{11}{4}\right)$; x = 2; $y = -\dfrac{13}{4}$ **27.** (3, 0); x = 3
29. (0, 0), (0, 8), (0, −8); 10; 6
31. $\dfrac{x^2}{9} - \dfrac{y^2}{5} = 1$ **33.** (0, 0); (3, 0), (−3, 0); (5, 0), (−5, 0); $y = \pm\dfrac{4}{3}x$ **35.** $\dfrac{x^2}{9} + \dfrac{y^2}{7}$
37. Ellipse **39.** Hyperbola **41.** (1, 0), (−1, 0) **43.** −6 < k < 6 **45.** ($\sqrt{2}$, 2), (−$\sqrt{2}$, 2), ($\sqrt{10}$, −6), (−$\sqrt{10}$, −6)
47. 4 and 12 **49.** 3 in. and 5 in.

CHAPTER 10
Page 363. Prerequisite Skills Review
1. b **2.** b **3.** c **4.** c **5.** c **6.** a **7.** d
8. b **9.** a **10.** a

Page 365. Class Exercises 1. Two
3. Four **5.** Two **7.** 3.7×10^{-4}
9. 8.09×10^0

Page 366. Exercises 1. Two **3.** Three
5. Two **7.** Four **9.** Five **11.** 1.4×10^4
13. 1.11×10^{-1} **15.** 5.11×10^0
17. 3.33×10^2 **19.** 5×10^5
21. 5.001×10^2 **23.** 2×10^{-6}
25. 2.40×10^{-1} **27.** 8,760,000,000
29. 0.00000066 **31.** 667,000 **33.** 0.00044
35. 0.00070 **37.** 260,000,000
39. 8.4×10^{-2} **41.** 5.7×10^3
43. 3.5×10^{-1} **45.** 3.8×10^1
47. 2.9×10^{-4} **49.** 7.1×10^1
51. 1.1×10^{-1} **53.** 2.7×10^{-1}
55. 1.2×10^{-3} **57.** 6×10^{-6}
59. 2×10^{-6} **61.** 4×10^8
63. 110,000,000, or 1.1×10^8 seconds

Page 370. Class Exercises 1. $7^{2\sqrt{3}}$, or $49^{\sqrt{3}}$ **3.** $15^{\sqrt{2}}$ **5.** 1 **7.** $\dfrac{5}{4}$ **9.** 2 **11.** 3

Page 371. Exercises 1. $12^{\sqrt{3}}$ **3.** $5^{2\sqrt{2}}$, or $25^{\sqrt{2}}$ **5.** $2^{2\sqrt{3}}$, or $4^{\sqrt{3}}$ **7.** 8 **9.** 1296
11. $6^{3\sqrt{2}}$, or $216^{\sqrt{2}}$ **13.** 1 **15.** 1
17. $\dfrac{5}{2}$ **19.** $\dfrac{4}{5}$ **21.** 16 **23.** 64 **25.** $12^{\sqrt[3]{10}}$
27. $4^{3\sqrt[3]{2}}$ or $64^{\sqrt[3]{2}}$ **29.** $x^{\sqrt{3}-\sqrt{2}}$ **31.** $9a^{2\sqrt{2}}$
33. b^4 **35.** $4m^{2+\sqrt{2}}$ **37.** $a^{3\sqrt{2}}$ **39.** a^6
41. $a^{2\sqrt{2}} + 2(ab)^{\sqrt{2}} + b^{2\sqrt{2}}$
43. $b^{2\sqrt{3}} - 2(bc)^{\sqrt{3}} + c^{2\sqrt{3}}$ **45.** 6 **47.** 5
49. 0 **51.** $\dfrac{20}{3}$ **53.** $\dfrac{1}{2}$ **55.** 2 **57.** −3
59. 6 **61.** $\dfrac{1}{2}$ **63.** 4 **65.** 1.41 **67.** 0.71
69. 5.33 **71.** 2, −2 **73.** 0, $\dfrac{1}{2}$ **75.** 8
77. 0, 4

Page 374. Class Exercises 1. Yes; no
3. No; no **5.** No

PREREQUISITE SKILLS FOLLOW-UP

COMPUTER HANDBOOK

TABLES

GLOSSARY

ANSWERS TO CHECKPOINTS

ANSWERS TO SELECTED EXERCISES

INDEX

Pages 374–375. Exercises 1. $27; \dfrac{1}{3}; \dfrac{1}{9};$
729 **3.** $100; 1,000,000; \dfrac{1}{10}; \dfrac{1}{1000}$ **5.** D:
all reals; R: negative reals; Decreasing

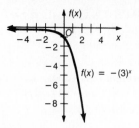

7. D: all reals; R: negative reals;
Increasing

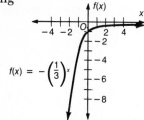

9. $y = 1$ **11.** $y = -\dfrac{3}{2}$ **13.** $x = -\dfrac{3}{2}$
15. D: all reals; R: negative reals

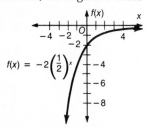

17. D: all reals; R: positive reals

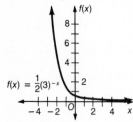

19. $y > \dfrac{1}{10}$ **21.** The graph does not cross
the x-axis. It crosses the y-axis at $\left(0, \dfrac{1}{10}\right)$.

23. 5,859,375 **25.** 234,375 **27.** All
$a > 0$ and $k < 0$ **29.** All $a > 1, k < 0$;
All $0 < a < 1, k > 0$ **31.** $y = \left(\dfrac{1}{4}\right)^{x}$
33. No point of intersection **35.** No
point of intersection **37.** (2, 9)

Page 381. Class Exercises
1. $\log_{10} 10,000 = 4$ **3.** $\log_{10} 100,000,000 = 8$
5. $\log_{10} 0.0001 = -4$ **7.** $10^2 = 100$
9. $10^{-5} = 0.00001$ **11.** -1 **13.** 0.1

Pages 381–382. Exercises 1. $\log_3 9 = 2$
3. $\log_3 \dfrac{1}{9} = -2$ **5.** $\log_5 \dfrac{1}{5} = -1$
7. $\log_9 \dfrac{1}{9} = -1$ **9.** $\log_9 \dfrac{1}{3} = -\dfrac{1}{2}$
11. $\log_{20} 0.05 = -1$ **13.** $4^3 = 64$
15. $4^{-\frac{1}{2}} = \dfrac{1}{2}$ **17.** $6^2 = 36$ **19.** $2^4 = 16$
21. $8^{\frac{4}{3}} = 16$ **23.** $0.1^{-1} = 10$ **25.** 4
27. 3 **29.** $\dfrac{1}{2}$ **31.** 1 **33.** -3 **35.** 2
37. $\dfrac{1}{9}; \dfrac{1}{3}; 1; 3; 9$

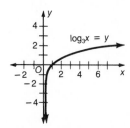

39. $a^2 = 3$ **41.** $4^c = 9$ **43.** -2 **45.** 3
47. -5 **49.** $\dfrac{3}{2}$ **51.** $y = 0.263$
53. $y = -0.322$

55.

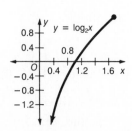

57. D: positive reals; R: all reals; Decreasing

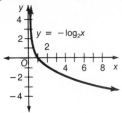

59. $y = -\log_{\frac{1}{2}}x$; x-axis **61.** $x = \dfrac{1}{10}$

63. $x = 32$ **65.** $b = 256$ **67.** $b = \dfrac{25}{8}$

69. $x > -3$

Page 386. Class Exercises 1. 3 **3.** 4
5. 1 **7.** -3 **9.** 4 **11.** -8

Pages 386–387. Exercises 1. 6 **3.** 4
5. 4 **7.** 10 **9.** 6 **11.** 12 **13.** 1.6826
15. 3.4130 **17.** 0.3413 **19.** 2.0000
21. 6.1918 **23.** 3.0000 **25.** -1.1918
27. 1.6021 **29.** 2.6021 **31.** -1.3979
33. 1.8063 **35.** 2.4084 **37.** -0.6021
39. 1.8063 **41.** 0.8011 **43.** 50
45. 50,000 **47.** 0.5
49. $\log_2 8 = \log_2(2^3) = 3 \log_2 2$
51. $\log_2 5 = \log_2(10 \div 2) =$
$\log_2 10 - \log_2 2 = \log_2 10 - 1$
53. 1.7782 **55.** 7 **57.** 200,000 **59.** $\dfrac{1}{6}$
61. 9.2876 **63.** 7.1700
65. 2.5647
67.

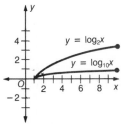

Page 390. Class Exercises 1. 0;
0.5866 **3.** 2; 0.7589 **5.** 1; 0.2355 **7.** 2;
0.9542 **9.** -2; 0.1818

Pages 390–391. Exercises 1. 2; 0.4065
3. 4; 0.2989 **5.** 0; 0.6532 **7.** 1; 0.4814
9. -2; 0.1139 **11.** 6; 0.5623 **13.** -4;
0.0934 **15.** 1; 0.9484 **17.** 0.3856
19. 2.3856 **21.** 0.8494 **23.** $0.8494 - 2$
25. 0.9031 **27.** $0.9031 - 4$ **29.** 4.8573

31. $0.8573 - 1$ **33.** 4.44 **35.** 444
37. 2.02 **39.** 0.0202 **41.** 9 **43.** 9,000,000
45. 0.8280 **47.** 2.9859 **49.** $0.6435 - 1$
51. $0.4654 - 3$ **53.** 3.8357 **55.** 5.5051
57. 3.45 **59.** 33.5 **61.** 0.563 **63.** 28,900
65. 0.0000235 **67.** 1000 **69.** 0.0000;
0.6021; 0.9542; 1.2041; 1.3979

Page 394. Class Exercises 1. 106,000
3. 0.000399 **5.** 74,800 **7.** 0.000000107
9. 11.9

Pages 394–396. Exercises 1. 59,400
3. 0.000270 **5.** 600 **7.** 346,000 **9.** 0.0590
11. 183 **13.** 30.5 **15.** 0.000000156
17. 119 **19.** 1320 **21.** 9.37 **23.** 531
25. 10.8 **27.** 0.199 **29.** 0.480 **31.** 0.0313
33. 95,600 **35.** 0.130 **37.** 1.17 **39.** 2910
41. 0.528 **43.** 631 **45.** 1430
47. 361,000,000,000 **49.** 361
51. 0.0000000000738 **53.** 13.3 **55.** 134
57. 3.14 **59.** 0.00203 **61.** 6370 **63.** 14
65. 0.707 **67.** 0.760 **69.** 3.77 **71.** $5740
73. $14,200 **75.** 987 cm^3

Page 401. Class Exercises 1. 4 **3.** $\dfrac{3}{2}$
5. 0.0001

Pages 401–402. Exercises 1. 3
3. 3; -1 **5.** 1 **7.** 100 **9.** 9 **11.** -1.99
13. 200 **15.** 0.5 **17.** 0.0792 **19.** 335
21. 7.73 **23.** 16.3 **25.** 2; 1 **27.** 0
29. 5 **31.** 1.26 **33.** 0.631 **35.** -4.82
37. 1.55 **39.** 0.111 **41.** $3370 **43.** 4%
45. 6400 **47.** 1.88 **49.** 8.42 m
51. 15.9 cm

Pages 404–405. Review Exercises
1. 2 **3.** 4 **5.** 2.3×10^4 **7.** 8×10^6
9. 460,000 **11.** 0.0000005 **13.** $15^{\sqrt{3}}$
15. 1 **17.** 1024 **19.** $a^{2\sqrt{3}}$ **21.** 2 **23.** $\dfrac{2}{3}$

25. $\dfrac{3}{4}$ **27.** 2 **29.** 32 **31.** 2048 **33.** $\dfrac{5}{8}$

35. D: all real numbers; R: positive reals

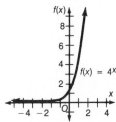

PREREQUISITE SKILLS FOLLOW-UP

COMPUTER HANDBOOK

TABLES

GLOSSARY

ANSWERS TO CHECKPOINTS

ANSWERS TO SELECTED EXERCISES

INDEX

37. $\log_3 81 = 4$ **39.** $\log_5 625 = 4$

41. $8^{\frac{1}{3}} = 2$ **43.** $10^{-1} = 0.1$ **45.** 3

47. -3

49.

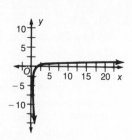

51. 3.3219 **53.** 6.6438 **55.** 1.6902
57. $9.6902 - 10$ **59.** 0.4969 **61.** 4.3345
63. 7.46 **65.** 5090 **67.** 175 **69.** 0.373
71. 4110 **73.** 3.07 **75.** 5 **77.** 0.01
79. 1.16

Pages 408–409. Cumulative Review

1. e **3.** d **5.** a **7.** b **9.** c **11.** a
13. b **15.** $x \le -1$ or $x \ge 5$ **17.** -3

19.

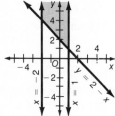

21. $\dfrac{x}{3(x - 3)}$ **23.** $\sqrt[3]{2}$

25. $\dfrac{9 + x + y - 6\sqrt{x + y}}{9 - x - y}$ **27.** $\pm 2\sqrt{2}$

29. $2x^2 - 3x - 2 = 0$ **31.** Min. -3

33. $\dfrac{\sqrt{2}}{3}i$ **35.** $\dfrac{\sqrt{6} + \sqrt{2} + (\sqrt{3} - 2)i}{3}$

37. $\pm 5; \pm 4; (\pm 3, 0)$

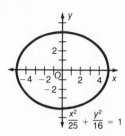

39. $\dfrac{1}{9}$ **41.** $9^c = 4$ **43.** 5.7589

CHAPTER 11

Page 411. Prerequisite Skills Review

1. c **2.** a **3.** d **4.** c **5.** d **6.** c **7.** b
8. b

Page 414. Class Exercises

1. I **3.** III
5. IV **7.** II **9.** I **11.** III **13.** IV **15.** I

Pages 414–415. Exercises

1.   **3.**

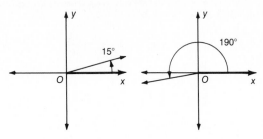

5.   **7.**

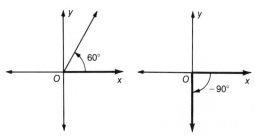

9.   **11.**

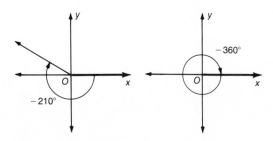

13.   **15.**

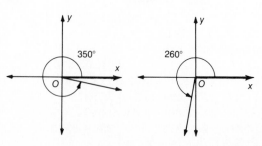

17. 180°   **19.** 230°

21.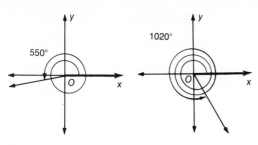

23.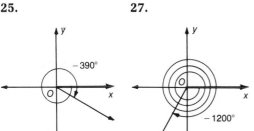

25.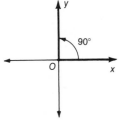

27.

29. −90°, −180°, −270°, −360°, −450°, −540°, −630°, −720°

31.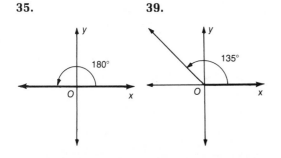

33.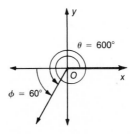

35.

39.

Page 418. Class Exercises   1. 32°
3. 60°   **5.** 20°   **7.** 5°   **9.** 50°   **11.** r = 13
13. y = −20

Page 419. Exercises

1.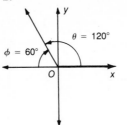

3.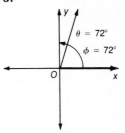

5.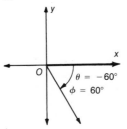

7.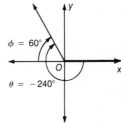

9.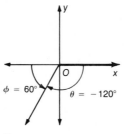

11.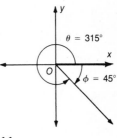

13.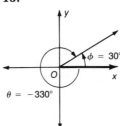

15.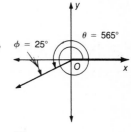

17.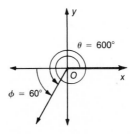

19.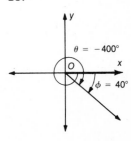

PREREQUISITE SKILLS FOLLOW-UP

COMPUTER HANDBOOK

TABLES

GLOSSARY

ANSWERS TO CHECKPOINTS

ANSWERS TO SELECTED EXERCISES

INDEX

21. $x = 4$ **23.** $y = -12$
25. 13   **27.** 25

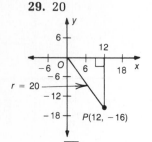

29. 20   **31.** 34

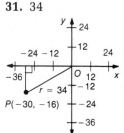

33. $\sqrt{13}$ **35.** $\phi = 45°$; $x = \sqrt{2}$; $y = \sqrt{2}$

37. $\phi = 45°$; $x = -\dfrac{\sqrt{2}}{2}$; $y = -\dfrac{\sqrt{2}}{2}$

Page 422. Class Exercises

1. $\sin \theta = -\dfrac{3}{5}$; $\cos \theta = \dfrac{4}{5}$; $\tan \theta = -\dfrac{3}{4}$;

$\csc \theta = -\dfrac{5}{3}$; $\sec \theta = \dfrac{5}{4}$; $\cot \theta = -\dfrac{4}{3}$

3. $\sin \theta = -\dfrac{2\sqrt{5}}{5}$; $\cos \theta = -\dfrac{\sqrt{5}}{5}$;

$\tan \theta = 2$; $\csc \theta = -\dfrac{\sqrt{5}}{2}$; $\sec \theta = -\sqrt{5}$;

$\cot \theta = \dfrac{1}{2}$ **5.** $x = -30$; $\sin \theta = \dfrac{4}{5}$,

$\cos \theta = -\dfrac{3}{5}$, $\tan \theta = -\dfrac{4}{3}$, $\cos \theta = \dfrac{5}{4}$,

$\sec \theta = -\dfrac{5}{3}$, $\cot \theta = -\dfrac{3}{4}$

Pages 423–424. Exercises

1. $\sin \theta = \dfrac{12}{3}$; $\cos \theta = -\dfrac{5}{13}$; $\tan \theta = -\dfrac{12}{5}$;

$\csc \theta = \dfrac{13}{12}$; $\sec \theta = -\dfrac{13}{5}$; $\cot \theta = -\dfrac{5}{12}$

3. $\sin \theta = -\dfrac{4}{5}$; $\cos \theta = \dfrac{3}{5}$; $\tan \theta = -\dfrac{4}{3}$;

$\csc \theta = -\dfrac{5}{4}$; $\sec \theta = \dfrac{5}{3}$; $\cot \theta = -\dfrac{3}{4}$

5. $\sin \theta = \dfrac{2\sqrt{5}}{5}$; $\cos \theta = \dfrac{\sqrt{5}}{5}$; $\tan \theta = 2$;

$\csc \theta = \dfrac{\sqrt{5}}{2}$; $\sec \theta = \sqrt{5}$; $\cot \theta = \dfrac{1}{2}$

7. $r = 15$; $\sin \theta = \dfrac{4}{5}$, $\cos \theta = \dfrac{3}{5}$, $\tan \theta = \dfrac{4}{3}$,

$\csc \theta = \dfrac{5}{4}$, $\sec \theta = \dfrac{5}{3}$, $\cot \theta = \dfrac{3}{4}$

9. $y = -24$; $\sin \theta = -\dfrac{24}{25}$, $\cos \theta = \dfrac{7}{25}$,

$\tan \theta = \dfrac{24}{7}$, $\csc \theta = -\dfrac{25}{24}$, $\sec \theta = \dfrac{25}{7}$,

$\cot \theta = \dfrac{7}{24}$ **11.** $y = -4$; $\sin \theta = -\dfrac{\sqrt{2}}{2}$,

$\cos \theta = -\dfrac{\sqrt{2}}{2}$, $\tan \theta = 1$, $\csc \theta = -\sqrt{2}$,

$\sec \theta = -\sqrt{2}$, $\cot \theta = 1$ **13.** $r = 8\sqrt{13}$;

$\sin \theta = \dfrac{3\sqrt{13}}{13}$, $\cos \theta = -\dfrac{2\sqrt{13}}{13}$,

$\tan \theta = -\dfrac{3}{2}$, $\csc \theta = \dfrac{\sqrt{13}}{3}$, $\sec \theta = -\dfrac{\sqrt{13}}{2}$,

$\cot \theta = -\dfrac{2}{3}$ **15.** $y = -2\sqrt{3}$;

$\sin \theta = -\dfrac{\sqrt{6}}{3}$, $\cos \theta = -\dfrac{\sqrt{3}}{3}$, $\tan \theta = \sqrt{2}$,

$\csc \theta = -\dfrac{\sqrt{6}}{2}$, $\sec \theta = -\sqrt{3}$, $\cot \theta = \dfrac{\sqrt{2}}{2}$

17. $\sin \theta = \dfrac{12}{13}$; $\cos \theta = -\dfrac{5}{13}$;

$\tan \theta = -\dfrac{12}{5}$; $\csc \theta = \dfrac{13}{12}$; $\sec \theta = -\dfrac{13}{5}$;

$\cot \theta = -\dfrac{5}{12}$ **19.** $\sin \theta = -\dfrac{4}{5}$;

$\cos \theta = \dfrac{3}{5}$; $\tan \theta = -\dfrac{4}{3}$; $\csc \theta = -\dfrac{5}{4}$;

$\sec \theta = \dfrac{5}{3}$; $\cot \theta = -\dfrac{3}{4}$ **21.** $\sin \theta = \dfrac{2\sqrt{5}}{5}$;

$\cos \theta = \dfrac{\sqrt{5}}{5}$; $\tan \theta = 2$; $\csc \theta = \dfrac{\sqrt{5}}{2}$;

$\sec \theta = \sqrt{5}$; $\cot \theta = \dfrac{1}{2}$ **23.** $\sin \theta = \dfrac{\sqrt{3}}{2}$;

$\cos \theta = \dfrac{1}{2}$; $\tan \theta = \sqrt{3}$; $\csc \theta = \dfrac{2\sqrt{3}}{3}$;

$\sec \theta = 2$; $\cot \theta = \dfrac{\sqrt{3}}{3}$ **25.** $\sin \theta = \dfrac{2\sqrt{13}}{13}$;

$\cos \theta = \dfrac{3\sqrt{13}}{13}$; $\csc \theta = \dfrac{\sqrt{13}}{2}$; $\cot \theta = \dfrac{3}{2}$

5. $\sin \theta = \dfrac{2\sqrt{5}}{5}$; $\cos \theta = \dfrac{\sqrt{5}}{5}$; $\tan \theta = 2$;

$\csc \theta = \dfrac{\sqrt{5}}{2}$; $\sec \theta = \sqrt{5}$; $\cot \theta = \dfrac{1}{2}$

27. $\sin \theta = -\dfrac{3\sqrt{10}}{10}$; $\cos \theta = -\dfrac{\sqrt{10}}{10}$;

$\sec \theta = -\sqrt{10}$; $\cot \theta = \dfrac{1}{3}$

29. $\cos \theta = -\dfrac{2\sqrt{2}}{3}$; $\tan \theta = -\dfrac{\sqrt{2}}{4}$;

$\csc \theta = 3$; $\sec \theta = -\dfrac{3\sqrt{2}}{4}$ **31.** $\sin \theta = \dfrac{12}{13}$;

$\cos \theta = -\dfrac{5}{13}$; $\tan \theta = -\dfrac{12}{5}$; $\csc \theta = \dfrac{13}{12}$;

$\sec \theta = -\dfrac{13}{5}$ **33.** $\sin \theta = -\dfrac{1}{2}$;

$\cos \theta = \dfrac{\sqrt{3}}{2}$; $\tan \theta = -\dfrac{\sqrt{3}}{3}$; $\sec \theta = \dfrac{2\sqrt{3}}{3}$;

$\cot \theta = -\sqrt{3}$

35. $\dfrac{\cos \theta}{\sin \theta} = \dfrac{\dfrac{x}{r}}{\dfrac{y}{r}} = \dfrac{x}{r} \cdot \dfrac{r}{y} = \dfrac{x}{y} = \cot \theta$

37. $(\sin \theta)^2 + (\cos \theta)^2 = \left(\dfrac{y}{r}\right)^2 + \left(\dfrac{x}{r}\right)^2$

$= \left(\dfrac{y}{\sqrt{x^2 + y^2}}\right)^2 + \left(\dfrac{x}{\sqrt{x^2 + y^2}}\right)^2$

$= \dfrac{y^2}{x^2 + y^2} + \dfrac{x^2}{x^2 + y^2}$

$= \dfrac{x^2 + y^2}{x^2 + y^2}$

$= 1$

Page 427. Class Exercises

1. $\sin \theta = \dfrac{\sqrt{3}}{2}$; $\cos \theta = \dfrac{1}{2}$; $\tan \theta = \sqrt{3}$;

$\csc \theta = \dfrac{2\sqrt{3}}{3}$, $\sec \theta = 2$; $\cot \theta = \dfrac{\sqrt{3}}{3}$

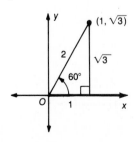

3. $\sin \theta = -\dfrac{1}{2}$; $\cos \theta = \dfrac{\sqrt{3}}{2}$; $\tan \theta = -\dfrac{\sqrt{3}}{3}$;

$\csc \theta = -2$; $\sec \theta = \dfrac{2\sqrt{3}}{3}$; $\cot \theta = -\sqrt{3}$

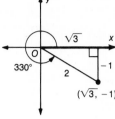

5. $\sin 120° = \dfrac{\sqrt{3}}{2}$ **7.** $\cos(-135°) = -\dfrac{\sqrt{2}}{2}$

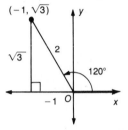

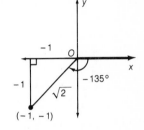

Pages 427–428. Exercises

1. $\sin \theta = -\dfrac{\sqrt{2}}{2}$; $\cos \theta = \dfrac{\sqrt{2}}{2}$; $\tan \theta = -1$;

$\csc \theta = -\sqrt{2}$; $\sec \theta = \sqrt{2}$; $\cot \theta = -1$

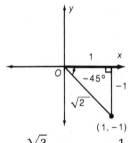

3. $\sin \theta = -\dfrac{\sqrt{3}}{2}$, $\cos \theta = -\dfrac{1}{2}$;

$\tan \theta = \sqrt{3}$; $\csc \theta = -\dfrac{2\sqrt{3}}{3}$; $\sec \theta = -2$;

$\cot \theta = \dfrac{\sqrt{3}}{3}$

PREREQUISITE SKILLS FOLLOW-UP

COMPUTER HANDBOOK

TABLES

GLOSSARY

ANSWERS TO CHECKPOINTS

ANSWERS TO SELECTED EXERCISES

INDEX

5. $\cos 120° = -\dfrac{1}{2}$ **7.** $\sec 240° = -2$

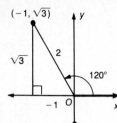

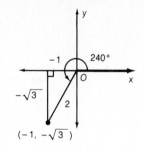

17. $\cot(-150°) = \sqrt{3}$

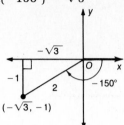

9. $\sin(-60°) = -\dfrac{\sqrt{3}}{2}$

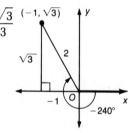

19. $\sin(-210°) = \dfrac{1}{2}$ **21.** $\tan 405° = 1$

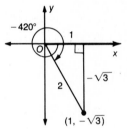
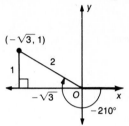

11. $\cos(-240°) = -\dfrac{\sqrt{3}}{3}$

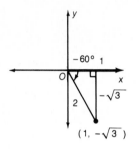

23. $\sec(-420°) = 2$ **25.** $\tan 495° = -1$

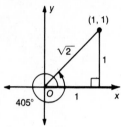
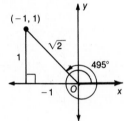

27. $\cot(-765°) = -1$

13. $\cos(-330°) = \dfrac{\sqrt{3}}{2}$

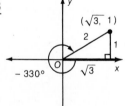

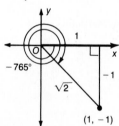

29. $\tan(-405°) = -1$

15. $\sec 210° = -\dfrac{2\sqrt{3}}{3}$

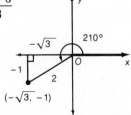

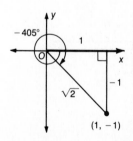

31. $\cos 390° = \dfrac{\sqrt{3}}{2}$

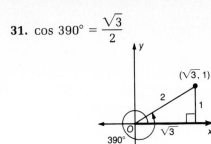

33. $\cot(-510°) = \sqrt{3}$

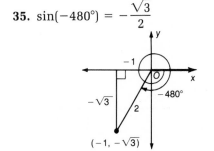

35. $\sin(-480°) = -\dfrac{\sqrt{3}}{2}$

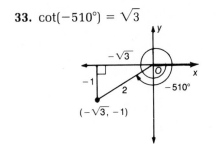

37. $\cos 870° = -\dfrac{\sqrt{3}}{2}$

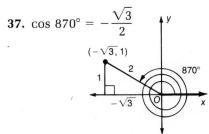

39. $\cos 660° = -\dfrac{2\sqrt{3}}{3}$

41. $\sec(-570°) = -\dfrac{2\sqrt{3}}{3}$

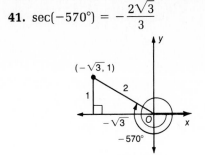

43. $\tan(-660°) = \sqrt{3}$

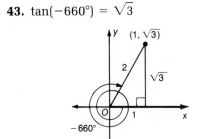

45. $\sin(-885°) = -\dfrac{\sqrt{2}}{2}$

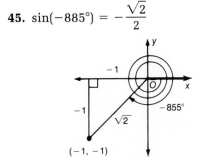

47. $\tan 840° = -\sqrt{3}$

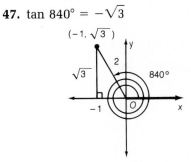

49. $x = \dfrac{5}{2}$, $y = \dfrac{5\sqrt{3}}{2}$; $\sin \theta = \dfrac{\sqrt{3}}{2}$, $\cos \theta = \dfrac{1}{2}$, $\tan \theta = \sqrt{3}$, $\csc \theta = \dfrac{2\sqrt{3}}{3}$, $\sec \theta = 2$, $\cot \theta = \dfrac{\sqrt{3}}{3}$ **51.** $x = -\sqrt{2}$,

PREREQUISITE SKILLS FOLLOW-UP

COMPUTER HANDBOOK

TABLES

GLOSSARY

ANSWERS TO CHECKPOINTS

ANSWERS TO SELECTED EXERCISES

INDEX

$y = \sqrt{2}$; $\sin\theta = \dfrac{\sqrt{2}}{2}$, $\cos\theta = -\dfrac{\sqrt{2}}{2}$,

$\tan\theta = -1$, $\csc\theta = \sqrt{2}$, $\sec\theta = -\sqrt{2}$,

$\cot\theta = -1$ **53.** $\theta_1 = 30°$, so $\sin\theta_1 = \dfrac{1}{2}$,

$\cos\theta_1 = \dfrac{\sqrt{3}}{2}$, $\tan\theta_1 = \dfrac{\sqrt{3}}{3}$, $\csc\theta_1 = 2$,

$\sec\theta_1 = \dfrac{2\sqrt{3}}{3}$, $\cot\theta_1 = \sqrt{3}$; $\theta_2 = -150°$,

so $\sin\theta_2 = -\dfrac{1}{2}$, $\cos\theta_2 = -\dfrac{\sqrt{3}}{2}$,

$\tan\theta_2 = \dfrac{\sqrt{3}}{3}$, $\cos\theta_2 = -2$,

$\sec\theta_2 = -\dfrac{2\sqrt{3}}{3}$, $\cot\theta_2 = \sqrt{3}$

Page 431. Class Exercises **1.** $\left(\dfrac{\sqrt{3}}{2}, \dfrac{1}{2}\right)$;

$\sin\theta = \dfrac{1}{2}$, $\cos\theta = \dfrac{\sqrt{3}}{2}$, $\tan\theta = \dfrac{\sqrt{3}}{3}$,

$\csc\theta = 2$, $\sec\theta = \dfrac{2\sqrt{3}}{3}$, $\cot\theta = \sqrt{3}$

3. $\left(-\dfrac{1}{2}, -\dfrac{\sqrt{3}}{2}\right)$; $\sin\theta = -\dfrac{\sqrt{3}}{2}$,

$\cos\theta = -\dfrac{1}{2}$, $\tan\theta = \sqrt{3}$, $\csc\theta = -\dfrac{2\sqrt{3}}{3}$,

$\sec\theta = -2$, $\cot\theta = \dfrac{\sqrt{3}}{3}$ **5.** $\sin 90° = 1$;

$\cos 90° = 0$; $\tan 90°$ is undefined;
$\csc 90° = 1$, $\sec 90°$ is undefined;
$\cot 90° = 0$
7. $\sin(-180°) = 0$; $\cos(-180°) = -1$;
$\tan(-180°) = 0$; $\csc(-180°)$ is undefined;
$\sec(-180°) = 1$; $\cot(-180°)$ is undefined

Pages 431–432. Exercises **1.** 0

3. Undefined **5.** $A\left(\dfrac{\sqrt{2}}{2}, \dfrac{\sqrt{2}}{2}\right)$;

$\sin 45° = \dfrac{\sqrt{2}}{2}$, $\cos 45° = \dfrac{\sqrt{2}}{2}$, $\tan 45° = 1$,

$\csc 45° = \sqrt{2}$, $\sec 45° = \sqrt{2}$, $\cot 45° = 1$

7. $C\left(-\dfrac{\sqrt{2}}{2}, -\dfrac{\sqrt{2}}{2}\right)$; $\sin 225° = -\dfrac{\sqrt{2}}{2}$,

$\cos 225° = -\dfrac{\sqrt{2}}{2}$, $\tan 225° = 1$,

$\csc 225° = -\sqrt{2}$, $\sec 225° = -\sqrt{2}$,

$\cot 225° = 1$ **9.** $-315°$; $-225°$; $-135°$;

$-45°$ **11.** $Q\left(-\dfrac{\sqrt{3}}{2}, \dfrac{1}{2}\right)$; $\sin 150° = \dfrac{1}{2}$,

$\cos 150° = -\dfrac{\sqrt{3}}{2}$, $\tan 150° = -\dfrac{\sqrt{3}}{3}$,

$\csc 150° = 2$, $\sec 150° = -\dfrac{2\sqrt{3}}{3}$,

$\cot 150° = -\sqrt{3}$ **13.** $S\left(\dfrac{\sqrt{3}}{2}, -\dfrac{1}{2}\right)$;

$\sin 330° = -\dfrac{1}{2}$, $\cos 330° = \dfrac{\sqrt{3}}{2}$,

$\tan 330° = -\dfrac{\sqrt{3}}{3}$, $\csc 330° = -2$,

$\sec 330° = \dfrac{2\sqrt{3}}{3}$, $\cot 330° = -\sqrt{3}$

15. $J\left(\dfrac{1}{2}, \dfrac{\sqrt{3}}{2}\right)$, $\sin 60° = \dfrac{\sqrt{3}}{2}$,

$\cos 60° = \dfrac{1}{2}$, $\tan 60° = \sqrt{3}$,

$\csc 60° = \dfrac{2\sqrt{3}}{3}$, $\sec 60° = 2$,

$\cot 60° = \dfrac{\sqrt{3}}{3}$; $K\left(-\dfrac{1}{2}, \dfrac{\sqrt{3}}{2}\right)$,

$\sin 120° = \dfrac{\sqrt{3}}{2}$, $\cos 120° = -\dfrac{1}{2}$,

$\tan 120° = -\sqrt{3}$, $\csc 120° = \dfrac{2\sqrt{3}}{3}$,

$\sec 120° = -2$, $\cot 120° = -\dfrac{\sqrt{3}}{3}$;

$L\left(-\dfrac{1}{2}, -\dfrac{\sqrt{3}}{2}\right)$; $\sin 240° = -\dfrac{\sqrt{3}}{2}$,

$\cos 240° = -\dfrac{1}{2}$, $\tan 240° = \sqrt{3}$,

$\csc 240° = -\dfrac{2\sqrt{3}}{3}$, $\sec 240° = -2$,

$\cot 240° = \dfrac{\sqrt{3}}{3}$; $M\left(\dfrac{1}{2}, -\dfrac{\sqrt{3}}{2}\right)$,

$\sin 300° = -\dfrac{\sqrt{3}}{2}$, $\cos 300° = \dfrac{1}{2}$,

$\tan 300° = -\sqrt{3}$, $\csc 300° = -\dfrac{2\sqrt{3}}{3}$,

$\sec 300° = 2$, $\cot 300° = -\dfrac{\sqrt{3}}{3}$

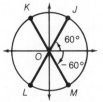

17. On the unit circle, $-1 \le x \le 1$, so $-1 \le \cos \theta \le 1$, since $x = \cos \theta$. **19.** 1
21. Undef. **23.** -1 **25.** 0 **27.** 0 **29.** 1
31. Undef. **33.** -1
35. $(\cos \theta)^2 + (\sin \theta)^2 = 1$

Page 435. Class Exercises
1. $\sin 15° = 0.2588$; $\cos 15° = 0.9659$; $\tan 15° = 0.2679$; $\cot 15° = 3.732$; $\sec 15° = 1.035$; $\csc 15° = 3.864$
3. $\sin 64° = 0.8988$; $\cos 64° = 0.4384$; $\tan 64° = 2.050$; $\cot 64° = 0.4877$; $\sec 64° = 2.281$; $\csc 64° = 1.113$
5. 0.9502 **7.** 1.000 **9.** 16° **11.** 43°40′

Pages 435–436. Exercises
1. $\sin 23°30′ = 0.3987$; $\cos 23°30′ = 0.9171$; $\tan 23°30′ = 0.4348$; $\cot 23°30′ = 2.300$; $\sec 23°30′ = 1.090$; $\csc 23°30′ = 2.508$ **3.** $\sin 45° = 0.7071$; $\cos 45° = 0.7071$; $\tan 45° = 1.000$; $\cot 45° = 1.000$; $\cos 45° = 1.414$; $\csc 45° = 1.414$ **5.** $\sin 81°40′ = 0.9894$; $\cos 81°40′ = 0.1449$; $\tan 81°40′ = 6.827$; $\cot 81°40′ = 0.1465$; $\sec 81°40′ = 6.900$; $\csc 81°40′ = 1.011$ **7.** $\sin 0° = 0.0000$; $\cos 0° = 0.0000$; $\tan 0° = 0.0000$; $\cot 0° = 0.0000$; $\sec 0° = 0.0000$; $\csc 0° = 0.0000$ **9.** 0.9998 **11.** 0.9998
13. 0.4566 **15.** 0.8541 **17.** 4.086
19. 0.9929 **21.** 1.970 **23.** 1.069
25. 0.1944 **27.** 0.3393 **29.** 12° **31.** 26°
33. 48° **35.** 76°40′ **37.** 38°50′ **39.** 20°30′
41. 36°20′ **43.** 54°40′ **45.** 18°40′
47. 81°30′ **49.** 76°10′ **51.** $\cot 37°30′$
53. $\sin 84°50′$ **55.** $\sec 48°20′$

Page 438. Class Exercises
1. $a = b \tan \alpha$ **3.** $c = b \sec \alpha$
5. $b = c \sin \beta$

Pages 439–440. Exercises **1.** $b = 3\sqrt{3}$
3. $b = \dfrac{8\sqrt{3}}{3}$ **5.** $\theta = 60°$ **7.** $\theta = 45°$
9. $s = 6$ **11.** $s = 6$ **13.** $s = 11$
15. $s = 42$ **17.** $b = 12$ **19.** $b = 25$
21. $\beta = 56°20′$ **23.** 114 m **25.** 1052 ft
27. 577 ft **29.** 20°20′ **31.** 137 in. each
33. 3179 ft

Page 444. Class Exercises **1.** 82°40′

3. 37°10′ **5.** 13°; III **7.** 63°; II
9. 26°10′; I **11.** 5°40′; II
Pages 444–445. Exercises **1.** I; 25°; 0.4226; 0.9063; 0.4663; 2.145; 1.103; 2.366 **3.** III; 25°; -0.4226; -0.9063; 0.4663; 2.145; -1.103; -2.366
5. I; 78°20′; 0.9793; 0.2022; 4.843; 0.2065; 4.945; 1.021 **7.** III; 78°20′; -0.9793; -0.2022; 4.843; 0.2065; -4.945; -1.021 **9.** $\sin 110° = 0.9397$; $\cos 110° = -0.3420$; $\tan 110° = -2.747$
11. $\sin 333°20′ = -0.4488$; $\cos 333°20′ = 0.8936$; $\tan 333°20′ = -0.5022$
13. $\sin(-161°) = -0.3256$; $\cos(-161°) = -0.9455$; $\tan(-161°) = 0.3443$
15. $\sin(-342°50′) = 0.2952$; $\cos(-343°50′) = 0.9555$; $\tan(-343°50′) = 0.3089$ **17.** 0.9848
19. 0.3249 **21.** 1.701 **23.** -0.9397
25. 0.9822 **27.** -1.159 **29.** 0.9100
31. 0.9993 **33.** 1.000 **35.** 0.9397
37. 12° **39.** 47°30′ **41.** 29°50′
43. 46°20′ **45.** 130°20′ **47.** 121°40′
49. 112°40′ **51.** 68°10′; 111°50′
53. 54°50′ **55.** 100°10′ **57.** 2°20′
59. 147° **61.** 87°10′; 267°10′
63. 177°10′; 357°10′ **65.** 210°; 330°

Page 448. Class Exercises
1. $b^2 + c^2 - 2bc \cos A$

3. $a^2 + b^2 - 2ab \cos C$ **5.** $\dfrac{a^2 + c^2 - b^2}{2ac}$

Pages 448–450. **1.** 5 **3.** 8 **5.** 60°
7. $b = 2.5$, $\alpha = 28°$ **9.** $\gamma = 90°$
11. $\alpha = \beta = \gamma = 60°$ **13.** $\beta = 41°20′$
15. $a = 7$; $\beta = 22°$; $\gamma = 98°$ **17.** $c = 2.4$; $\alpha = 17°$; $\beta = 118°$ **19.** $\alpha = 43°$; $\beta = 61°$; $\gamma = 76°$ **21.** $\beta = 2.2$; $\alpha = 31°$; $\gamma = 121°$
23. $\alpha = 20°$; $\beta = 35°$; $\gamma = 125°$
25. 300 m **27.** 35 in. **29.** 24 mi

31. $\cos A = \dfrac{x}{b}$, $\cos B = \dfrac{c - x}{a}$

$$a \cos B + b \cos A = a\left(\dfrac{c - x}{a}\right) + b\left(\dfrac{x}{b}\right)$$
$$= c - x + x$$
$$= c$$

PREREQUISITE SKILLS FOLLOW-UP

COMPUTER HANDBOOK

TABLES

GLOSSARY

ANSWERS TO CHECKPOINTS

ANSWERS TO SELECTED EXERCISES

INDEX

Page 454. Class Exercises **1.** $\dfrac{b \sin A}{\sin B}$

3. $\dfrac{a \sin B}{b}$ **5.** $10\sqrt{2}$ **7.** $60°$

Pages 455–456. Exercises **1.** $5\sqrt{2}, 7$
3. 100 **5.** $3\sqrt{6}, 7$ **7.** 20 **9.** $c = 30$;
$a = 28$ **11.** $\gamma = 71°10'$; $b = 63$; $c = 62$
13. $\alpha = 43°50'$; $b = 2093$; $a = 1756$
15. $\alpha = 39°50'$; $b = 32$; $c = 17$
17. 26 cm **19.** 100 **21.** 1540 m
23. $AB = 120$; $AD = 148$

Page 459. Class Exercises **1.** One
3. One **5.** One **7.** One **9.** None

Pages 459–460. Exercises **1.** None
3. None **5.** One **7.** $\gamma = 15°10'$
9. $\gamma_1 = 127°20'$; $\gamma_2 = 52°40'$
11. $\gamma = 14°50'$; $\beta = 35°10'$; $b = 11$
13. $\beta = 36°$; $\gamma = 108°$; $c = 19$
15. $\gamma = 34°10'$; $\beta = 35°20'$; $b = 3$
17. $\beta = 10°30'$; $\alpha = 152°50'$; $a = 70$
19. $y = 14°30'$, $\beta = 154°40'$, $b = 109.3$;
$\gamma = 165°30'$, $\beta = 3°40'$, $b = 16.3$
21. 90 cm

Pages 462–463. Review Exercises
1. $90°$ **3.** $280°$ **5.** $130°$

7.   **9.**

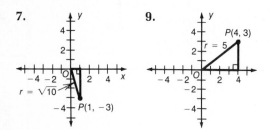

11. $\sin \theta = \dfrac{6\sqrt{37}}{37}$; $\cos \theta = -\dfrac{\sqrt{37}}{37}$;

$\tan \theta = -6$; $\csc \theta = \dfrac{\sqrt{37}}{6}$; $\sec \theta = -\sqrt{37}$;

$\cot \theta = -\dfrac{1}{6}$ **13.** $\sin \theta = -\dfrac{3\sqrt{13}}{13}$;

$\cos \theta = -\dfrac{2\sqrt{13}}{13}$; $\tan \theta = \dfrac{3}{2}$;

$\csc \theta = -\dfrac{\sqrt{13}}{3}$; $\sec \theta = -\dfrac{\sqrt{13}}{2}$;

$\cot \theta = \dfrac{2}{3}$

15. $\tan(-240°) = -\sqrt{3}$

17. $\sec 300° = 2$

19. $\left(-\dfrac{\sqrt{2}}{2}, \dfrac{\sqrt{2}}{2}\right)$; $\sin \theta = \dfrac{\sqrt{2}}{2}$,

$\cos \theta = -\dfrac{\sqrt{2}}{2}$, $\tan \theta = -1$, $\csc \theta = \sqrt{2}$,

$\sec \theta = -\sqrt{2}$, $\cot \theta = -1$ **21.** $(0, 1)$;
$\sin \theta = 1$, $\cos \theta = 0$, $\tan 90°$ is undefined,
$\csc \theta = 1$, $\sec 90°$ is undefined, $\cot \theta = 0$
23. 0.0175 **25.** 0.0175 **27.** $13°20'$
29. $51°10'$ **31.** About 572 m **33.** 3.018
35. $42°30'$ **37.** $97°50'$, $82°10'$
39. $a = 14$, $b = 14$, $\alpha = 30°$
41. No triangle is possible.

CHAPTER 12

Page 467. Prerequisite Skills Review
1. b **2.** c **3.** a **4.** c **5.** d **6.** d **7.** b
8. a

Page 470. Class Exercises **1.** $\sec \theta$
3. $\cos^2 \theta$ **5.** None **7.** $0°, 180°$ **9.** $0°, 180°$

Pages 470–471. Exercises **1.** $-\cos^2 \theta$
3. 1 **5.** $\sin \theta$ **7.** $0°, 180°$ **9.** $0°, 90°$,
$180°, 270°$ **11.** $\dfrac{1}{\cos \theta \sin \theta}$ **13.** $\dfrac{\cos \alpha + 1}{\sin \alpha}$

15. $-\sin x \cos x$ **17.** $\tan \theta = \dfrac{\sqrt{3}}{3}$ and

$\cot \theta = \sqrt{3}$, so $\tan \theta$ is not equal to $\cot \theta$
19. $45°, 60°, 90°$ **21.** 1 **23.** -1

25. $\dfrac{1}{1 - \cos^2 x}$ **27.** $\dfrac{\cos x}{1 - \cos^2 x} - 1$

29. $(\sin \theta)(\sec \theta)(\cot \theta)$

$= \sin \theta \cdot \dfrac{1}{\cos \theta} \cdot \dfrac{\cos \theta}{\sin \theta}$

$= \dfrac{\sin \theta}{\cos \theta} \cdot \dfrac{\cos \theta}{\sin \theta}$

$= 1$

31. $\csc \beta - \cos \beta \cot \beta$

$$= \frac{1}{\sin \beta} - \cos \beta \left(\frac{\cos \beta}{\sin \beta} \right)$$

$$= \frac{1}{\sin \beta} - \frac{\cos^2 \beta}{\sin \beta}$$

$$= \frac{1 - \cos^2 \beta}{\sin \beta}$$

$$= \frac{\sin^2 \beta}{\sin \beta} = \sin \beta$$

33. $(1 + \tan^2 \theta)(1 - \sin^2 \theta)$

$$= (\sec^2 \theta)(\cos^2 \theta)$$

$$= \frac{1}{(\cos^2 \theta)} (\cos^2 \theta) = 1$$

35. $\dfrac{1}{\sin \theta}$ **37.** $\pm \dfrac{\sqrt{1 - \sin^2 \theta}}{1 - \sin^2 \theta}$

Page 474. Class Exercises

1. Method I:

$$\cos \theta \cos \theta = \cos \theta \left(\frac{1}{\sin \theta} \right)$$

$$= \frac{\cos \theta}{\sin \theta} = \cot \theta$$

Method II:

$\cos \theta \csc \theta$	$\cot \theta$
$\cos \theta \left(\dfrac{1}{\sin \theta} \right)$	$\dfrac{\cos \theta}{\sin \theta}$
$\dfrac{\cos \theta}{\sin \theta}$	

Page 474. Exercises

1. $\sin^2 \theta - \cos^2 \theta$

$$= (1 - \cos^2 \theta) - \cos^2 \theta$$

$$= 1 - 2 \cos^2 \theta$$

3. $\sec^2 \alpha + 2 \tan \alpha$

$$= \tan^2 \alpha + 1 + 2 \tan \alpha$$

$$= \tan^2 \alpha + 2 \tan \alpha + 1 = (\tan \alpha + 1)^2$$

5. $\dfrac{\tan^2 \theta + 1}{\sec \theta \tan \theta} = \dfrac{\sec^2 \theta}{\sec \theta \tan \theta}$

$$= \frac{\sec \theta}{\tan \theta}$$

$$= \frac{\dfrac{1}{\cos \theta}}{\dfrac{\sin \theta}{\cos \theta}}$$

$$= \frac{1}{\cos \theta} \cdot \frac{\cos \theta}{\sin \theta}$$

$$= \frac{1}{\sin \theta} = \csc \theta$$

7. $\dfrac{\csc^2 \theta}{\csc^2 \theta - 1} = \dfrac{\dfrac{1}{\sin^2 \theta}}{\dfrac{1}{\sin^2 \theta} - 1}$

$$= \frac{1}{1 - \sin^2 \theta}$$

$$= \frac{1}{\cos^2 \theta}$$

$$= \sec^2 \theta$$

9. $2 \cos^2 \beta - 1 = 2(1 - \sin^2 \beta) - 1$

$$= 2 - 2 \sin^2 \beta - 1$$

$$= 1 - 2 \sin^2 \beta$$

11. $\dfrac{\cos \alpha + \cot \alpha}{1 + \csc \alpha} = \dfrac{\cos \alpha + \dfrac{\cos \alpha}{\sin \alpha}}{1 + \dfrac{1}{\sin \alpha}}$

$$= \frac{\cos \alpha \sin \alpha + \cos \alpha}{\sin \alpha + 1}$$

$$= \cos \alpha \left(\frac{\sin \alpha + 1}{\sin \alpha + 1} \right)$$

$$= \cos \alpha$$

13. $\dfrac{1 + \tan^2 \theta}{1 + \cot^2 \theta} = \dfrac{\sec^2 \theta}{\csc^2 \theta}$

$$= \frac{\dfrac{1}{\cos^2 \theta}}{\dfrac{1}{\sin^2 \theta}}$$

$$= \frac{\sin^2 \theta}{\cos^2 \theta}$$

$$= \tan^2 \theta$$

15. $\dfrac{\sin \theta \sec \theta}{\tan \theta \cot \theta} = \dfrac{\sin \theta \left(\dfrac{1}{\cos \theta} \right)}{\dfrac{\sin \theta}{\cos \theta} + \dfrac{\cos \theta}{\sin \theta}}$

$$= \frac{\dfrac{\sin^2 \theta}{\sin \theta \cos \theta}}{\dfrac{\sin^2 \theta + \cos^2 \theta}{\sin \theta \cos \theta}}$$

$$= \frac{\sin^2 \theta}{\sin^2 \theta + \cos^2 \theta}$$

$$= \frac{\sin^2 \theta}{1}$$

$$= \frac{1}{\csc^2 \theta}$$

(θ is not a quadrant angle.)

PREREQUISITE SKILLS FOLLOW-UP

COMPUTER HANDBOOK

TABLES

GLOSSARY

ANSWERS TO CHECKPOINTS

ANSWERS TO SELECTED EXERCISES

INDEX

17. $\dfrac{\cot x + 1}{\cot x - 1} = \dfrac{\dfrac{1}{\tan x} + 1}{\dfrac{1}{\tan x} - 1}$

$= \dfrac{\dfrac{1 + \tan x}{\tan x}}{\dfrac{1 - \tan x}{\tan x}}$

$= \dfrac{1 + \tan x}{1 - \tan x}$

(x is not a quadrantal angle, and is not coterminal with an angle of 45° or 225°.)

19. $\dfrac{\tan^2 y}{\sec y - 1} = \dfrac{\sec^2 y - 1}{\sec y - 1}$

$= \dfrac{(\sec y + 1)(\sec y - 1)}{\sec y - 1}$

$= \sec y + 1$

21. $\dfrac{1 - \sin A}{\cos A} + \dfrac{\cos A}{1 - \sin A}$

$= \dfrac{(1 - \sin A)^2 + \cos^2 A}{\cos A(1 - \sin A)}$

$= \dfrac{1 - 2 \sin A + \sin^2 A + (1 - \sin^2 A)}{\cos A(1 - \sin A)}$

$= \dfrac{2 - 2 \sin A}{\cos A(1 - \sin A)}$

$= \dfrac{2(1 - \sin A)}{\cos A(1 - \sin A)}$

$= \dfrac{2}{\cos A}$

$= 2 \sec A$

23. $\dfrac{\cos \theta}{1 - \sin \theta} = \dfrac{\cos \theta}{1 - \sin \theta} \cdot \dfrac{1 + \sin \theta}{1 + \sin \theta}$

$= \dfrac{\cos \theta(1 + \sin \theta)}{1 - \sin^2 \theta}$

$= \dfrac{\cos \theta(1 + \sin \theta)}{\cos^2 \theta}$

$= \dfrac{1 + \sin \theta}{\cos \theta}$

Page 477. Class Exercises 1. 30°, 150°, 210°, 330° **3.** 120°, 240° **5.** 30°, 150° **7.** 135°, 225° **9.** 60°, 120°

Pages 477–478. Exercises 1. 0°, 180° **3.** 120°, 300° **5.** 30°, 330° **7.** 45°, 135° **9.** 30°, 330° **11.** 90° **13.** 0°, 180° **15.** 60°, 120°, 240°, 300° **17.** 90°, 270°

19. 45°, 225° **21.** 45°, 135°, 225°, 315° **23.** 45°, 90°, 135°, 225°, 270°, 315° **25.** 0°, 180° **27.** 0°, 45°, 135°, 180°, 225°, 315° **29.** 0°, 45°, 180°, 315° **31.** 0° **33.** 0°, 60°, 300° **35.** 30°, 150°, 210°, 330° **37.** 0°, 120°, 240° **39.** 45°, 225° **41.** 63°30′ **43.** 14°30′, 90°0′, 165°30′ **45.** x = ±90°, ±270°, ±450°, . . . , or x = 90° + n(180°), where n is any integer **47.** x = 90° + n(360°) or x = 190°30′ + n(360°), where n is any integer **49.** r = 2, rn θ = 30°

Page 481. Class Exercises 1. 17 **3.** 30
5. $\sin 120° = \sin(60° + 60°)$
$= \sin 60° \cos 60° + \cos 60° \sin 60°$
$= \dfrac{\sqrt{3}}{2}\left(\dfrac{1}{2}\right) + \dfrac{1}{2}\left(\dfrac{\sqrt{3}}{2}\right) = \dfrac{\sqrt{3}}{2}$

Pages 482–483. Exercises 1. 81 **3.** 29
5. 16° **7.** 2x
9. $\sin 135°$
$= \sin(45° + 90°)$
$= \sin 45° \cos 90° + \cos 45° \sin 90°$
$= \dfrac{\sqrt{2}}{2}(0) + \dfrac{\sqrt{2}}{2}(1)$
$= \dfrac{\sqrt{2}}{2}$

11. $\sin 150°$
$= \sin(60° + 90°)$
$= \sin 60° \cos 90° + \cos 60° \sin 90°$
$= \dfrac{\sqrt{3}}{2}(0) + \dfrac{1}{2}(1)$
$= \dfrac{1}{2}$

13. $\sin(-225°)$
$= \sin(-270° + 45°)$
$= \sin(-270°) \cos 45° + \cos(-270°)$
$\quad \sin 45°$
$= 1\left(\dfrac{\sqrt{2}}{2}\right) + 0\left(\dfrac{\sqrt{2}}{2}\right)$
$= \dfrac{\sqrt{2}}{2}$

15. $\dfrac{1}{4}(\sqrt{2} + \sqrt{6})$ **17.** 81 **19.** 173

21. $\dfrac{1}{4}(\sqrt{2} - \sqrt{6})$ **23.** $-\dfrac{1}{4}(\sqrt{2} + \sqrt{6})$

25. $\dfrac{1}{4}(\sqrt{2} - \sqrt{6})$

27. $\sin 25° \cos 53° + \cos 25° \sin 53°$
$= (0.4226)(0.6018) + (0.9063)(0.7986)$
$= 0.9871$
$= \sin 78°$
$= \sin(25° + 53°)$

29. $\sin 62°10' \cos 74° 50' +$
$\cos 62°10' \sin 74°50'$
$= (0.8843)(0.2616) + (0.4669)(0.9652)$
$= 0.6820$
$= \sin 137°$
$= \sin(62°10' + 74°50')$

31. $\sin(45° + x)$
$= \sin 45° \cos x + \cos 45° \sin x$
$= \dfrac{\sqrt{2}}{2}(\cos x) + \dfrac{\sqrt{2}}{2}(\sin x)$
$= \dfrac{\sqrt{2}}{2}(\cos x + \sin x)$

33. $\sin(x + 356)$
$= \sin x \cos 360° + \cos x \sin 360°$
$= \sin x (1) + \cos x (0)$
$= \sin x$

35. $\sin(180° - \alpha) = \dfrac{h}{b}$, so $h =$
$b \sin(180° - \alpha)$; Area $\triangle ABC = \dfrac{1}{2}ch =$
$\dfrac{1}{2}c[b \sin(180° - \alpha)] = \dfrac{1}{2}bc \sin \alpha$ **37.** 835

Page 487. Class Exercises **1.** $45° + 30°$
3. $150° + 45°$ or $135° + 60°$ **5.** $45° - 30°$
7. $150° - 45°$ or $135° - 30°$

9. $\dfrac{1}{4}(\sqrt{6} + \sqrt{2})$

Pages 488–489. Exercises

1. $\dfrac{1}{4}(\sqrt{6} + \sqrt{2})$ **3.** $2 + \sqrt{3}$

5. $\dfrac{1}{4}(\sqrt{2} + \sqrt{6})$ **7.** $-\dfrac{1}{4}(\sqrt{6} + \sqrt{2})$

9. $2 - \sqrt{3}$; 0.268; 0.268; same

11. $-\dfrac{\sqrt{2}}{2}$; -0.707; -0.707; same **13.** $\dfrac{33}{65}$

15. $-\dfrac{63}{16}$ **17.** $-\dfrac{416}{425}$ **19.** $-\dfrac{156}{133}$

21. $-\dfrac{133}{205}$ **23.** $\cos 55° = 0.5736$,

$\cot 55° = 0.7002$, $\csc 55° = 1.2208$

25. $\cos(\theta + 90°)$
$= \cos \theta \cos 90° - \sin \theta \sin 90°$
$= \cos \theta (0) - \sin \theta (1)$
$= -\sin \theta$

27. $\tan(\theta - 135°) = \dfrac{\tan \theta - \tan 135°}{1 + \tan \theta \tan 135°}$
$= \dfrac{\tan \theta - (-1)}{1 + \tan \theta(-1)}$
$= \dfrac{\tan \theta + 1}{1 - \tan \theta}$

29. $\tan(-\theta) = \dfrac{\sin(-\theta)}{\cos(-\theta)}$
$= \dfrac{-\sin \theta}{\cos \theta}$
$= -\tan \theta$

Page 491. Class Exercises **1.** $\sin 60°$
3. $\cos 20°$ **5.** $\cos 20°$ **7.** $\tan 10°$
9. $\sin 4\theta$

Pages 492–493. Exercises

1. $\sin 2(90°)$ | $2 \sin(90°) \cos 90°$
$\sin 180°$ | $2(1)(0)$
0 | 0

5. $-\dfrac{\sqrt{3}}{2}$ **7.** $\dfrac{\sqrt{2}}{2}$ **9.** $\sqrt{2}$ **11.** $\dfrac{1}{3}$

13. $-\dfrac{120}{169}$; $-\dfrac{119}{169}$; $\dfrac{120}{119}$ **15.** $-\dfrac{720}{1681}$;

$-\dfrac{1519}{1681}$; $\dfrac{720}{1519}$

17. $\dfrac{\sec^2 \theta}{2 - \sec^2 \theta} = \dfrac{\dfrac{1}{\cos^2 \theta}}{2 - \dfrac{1}{\cos^2 \theta}}$

$= \dfrac{\dfrac{1}{\cos^2 \theta}}{2 - \dfrac{1}{\cos^2 \theta}} \cdot \dfrac{\cos^2 \theta}{\cos^2 \theta}$

$= \dfrac{1}{2 \cos^2 \theta - 1}$

$= \dfrac{1}{\cos 2\theta}$

$= \sec 2\theta$

19. $\dfrac{2 \cot \theta}{\csc^2 \theta} = \dfrac{\dfrac{2 \cos \theta}{\sin \theta}}{\dfrac{1}{\sin^2 \theta}}$

$= \dfrac{2 \cos \theta \sin \theta}{1}$

$= \sin 2\theta$

21. $\cos^4 \theta - \sin^4 \theta$
$= (\cos^2 \theta + \sin^2 \theta)(\cos^2 \theta - \sin^2 \theta)$
$= 1(\cos 2\theta)$
$= \cos 2\theta$

PREREQUISITE SKILLS FOLLOW-UP

COMPUTER HANDBOOK

TABLES

GLOSSARY

ANSWERS TO CHECKPOINTS

ANSWERS TO SELECTED EXERCISES

INDEX

23. $2 \sin x \csc 2x = \dfrac{2 \sin x}{\sin 2x}$

$$= \dfrac{2 \sin x}{2 \sin x \cos x}$$

$$= \dfrac{1}{\cos x}$$

$$= \sec x$$

25. $\dfrac{1 + \cos 2x}{1 - \cos 2x} = \dfrac{1 + (2 \cos^2 x - 1)}{1 - (1 - 2 \sin^2 x)}$

$$= \dfrac{2 \cos^2 x}{2 \sin^2 x}$$

$$= \cot^2 x$$

27. $\sin 3\theta$

$$= \sin(2\theta + \theta)$$

$$= \sin 2\theta \cos \theta + \cos 2\theta \sin \theta$$

$$= (2 \sin \theta \cos \theta) \cos \theta +$$

$$\quad (1 - 2 \sin^2 \theta) \sin \theta$$

$$= 2 \sin \theta \cos^2 \theta + \sin \theta - 2 \sin^3 \theta$$

$$= 2 \sin \theta (1 - \sin^2 \theta) +$$

$$\quad \sin \theta - 2 \sin^3 \theta$$

$$= 2 \sin \theta - 2 \sin^3 \theta +$$

$$\quad \sin \theta - 2 \sin^3 \theta$$

$$= 3 \sin \theta - 4 \sin^3 \theta$$

29. $d = 30$ **31.** $0°, 30°, 150°, 180°$

33. $0°, 180°$ **35.** $30°, 150°, 210°, 330°$

Page 495. Class Exercises 1. I **3.** II
5. III **7.** $\sin 10°$ **9.** $\cos 105°$
11. $\sin(-30°)$

Page 496. Exercises 1. $\dfrac{\sqrt{2}}{2}; \dfrac{\sqrt{2}}{2}; 1$

3. $\dfrac{\sqrt{2 - \sqrt{3}}}{2}$ **5.** $\dfrac{\sqrt{2 + \sqrt{3}}}{2}$

7. $-\dfrac{\sqrt{2 + \sqrt{2}}}{2}$ **9.** $\dfrac{\sqrt{10}}{10}; \dfrac{3\sqrt{10}}{10}; \dfrac{1}{3}$

11. $\dfrac{3}{5}; -\dfrac{4}{5}; -\dfrac{3}{4}$

13. $\sec^2 \dfrac{\theta}{2} = \dfrac{1}{\dfrac{\cos^2 \theta}{2}}$

$$= \dfrac{1}{\left(\pm\sqrt{\dfrac{1 + \cos \theta}{2}}\right)^2}$$

$$= \dfrac{1}{\dfrac{1 + \cos \theta}{2}}$$

$$= \dfrac{2}{1 + \cos \theta}$$

15. $\dfrac{\cos^2 \frac{x}{2} - \sin^2 \frac{x}{2}}{\cos^2 \frac{x}{2} + \sin^2 \frac{x}{2}} = \dfrac{\cos^2 \frac{x}{2} - \sin^2 \frac{x}{2}}{1}$

$$= \cos 2\left(\dfrac{x}{2}\right)$$

$$= \cos x$$

17. $\dfrac{\sin 2\alpha}{1 + \cos 2\alpha} = \dfrac{2 \sin \alpha \cos \alpha}{1 + (2 \cos^2 \theta - 1)}$

$$= \dfrac{2 \sin \alpha \cos \alpha}{2 \cos^2 \alpha}$$

$$= \dfrac{\sin \alpha}{\cos \alpha}$$

$$= \tan \alpha$$

19. $\alpha = \beta$, $\theta = \alpha + \beta = 2\alpha$, and $\alpha = \dfrac{\theta}{2}$

From the diagram: $\tan \alpha = \tan \dfrac{\theta}{2} =$

$\dfrac{y}{1 + x} = \dfrac{\sin \theta}{1 + \cos \theta}$

21. $120°$ **23.** $60°, 300°$

Pages 498–500. Review Exercises

1. $\csc x$ **3.** $2 \sin^2 x$ **5.** $\dfrac{\sin x - \cos^2 x}{\cos^2 x}$

7. $(1 + \cot^2 x)(1 - \cot^2 x)$

$$= \csc^2 x \ (\sin^2 x)$$

$$= \dfrac{1}{\sin^2 x} \cdot \sin^2 x$$

$$= 1$$

9. $(1 + \cos x)(1 - \cos x)$ $\quad\bigg| \quad \dfrac{1}{1 + \cot^2 x}$

$$1 - \cos^2 x \qquad\qquad\quad \dfrac{1}{\csc^2 x}$$

$$\sin^2 x \qquad\qquad\qquad\quad \sin^2 x$$

11. $\csc^2 x - 4 \cot^2 x$

$$= \csc^2 x - 4(\csc^2 x - 1)$$

$$= \csc^2 x - 4 \csc^2 x + 4$$

$$= 4 - 3 \csc^2 x$$

13. $120°, 240°$ **15.** $45°, 90°, 135°, 270°$
17. $30°, 150°, 210°, 330°$ **19.** 51 **21.** 43
23. $2 + \sqrt{3}$ **25.** $-\dfrac{\sqrt{3}}{2}$ **27.** $-\dfrac{1}{2}$
29. $\cos(\theta + 180°)$

$$= \cos \theta \cos 180° - \sin \theta \sin 180°$$

$$= \cos \theta(-1) - \sin \theta(0)$$

$$= -\cos \theta$$

31. $\dfrac{24}{25}$; $\dfrac{7}{25}$; $\dfrac{24}{7}$

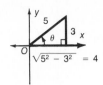

43. $\dfrac{7\sqrt{2}}{10}$; $\dfrac{\sqrt{2}}{10}$; 7

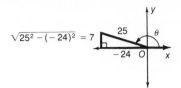

45. 90°, 270°

33. $\dfrac{336}{625}$; $-\dfrac{527}{625}$; $-\dfrac{336}{527}$

Page 503. Prerequisite Skills Review
1. c **2.** b **3.** a **4.** b **5.** a **6.** b
7. a **8.** d

Page 506. Class Exercises **1.** $\dfrac{\pi}{12}$

3. $-\dfrac{\pi}{6}$ **5.** $\dfrac{11\pi}{6}$ **7.** 135° **9.** −40°

11. 240°

Pages 507–508. Exercises **1.** $\dfrac{2\pi}{3}$

3. $\dfrac{5\pi}{4}$ **5.** $-\dfrac{4\pi}{3}$ **7.** 90° **9.** 12°

35.
$$\begin{aligned}
\dfrac{\csc 2x}{\sec x} &= \dfrac{\dfrac{1}{\sin 2x}}{\dfrac{1}{\cos x}}\\[4pt]
&= \dfrac{\cos x}{\sin 2x}\\[4pt]
&= \dfrac{\cos x}{2\sin x \cos x}\\[4pt]
&= \dfrac{1}{2\sin x}\\[4pt]
&= \dfrac{1}{2}\csc x
\end{aligned}$$

11. −225° **13.** $0° = 0$; $30° = \dfrac{\pi}{6}$;

$45° = \dfrac{\pi}{4}$; $60° = \dfrac{\pi}{3}$; $90° = \dfrac{\pi}{2}$; $135° = \dfrac{3\pi}{4}$;

$150° = \dfrac{5\pi}{6}$; $210° = \dfrac{7\pi}{6}$; $240° = \dfrac{4\pi}{3}$;

$270° = \dfrac{3\pi}{2}$; $300° = \dfrac{5\pi}{3}$; $315° = \dfrac{7\pi}{4}$

15. $\dfrac{\sqrt{2}}{2}$ **17.** $-\dfrac{\sqrt{3}}{3}$ **19.** −1 **21.** 1

23. Not defined **25.** 12°; 4.705
27. −10°; 0.9848 **29.** 2.18 **31.** 1.64
33. 7.85 **35.** 1.1868 **37.** 0.9163
39. 21°10′ **41.** 57°20′ **43.** 57°10′
45. 143°20′; −0.8021 **47.** 286°40′; 3.487

37.
$$\begin{aligned}
\dfrac{(\sin x + \cos x)^2}{(\sin x - \cos x)^2} &= \dfrac{\sin^2 x + 2\sin x \cos x + \cos^2 x}{\sin^2 x - 2\sin x \cos x + \cos^2 x}\\[4pt]
&= \dfrac{(\sin^2 x + \cos^2 x) + 2\sin x \cos x}{(\sin^2 x + \cos^2 x) - 2\sin x \cos x}\\[4pt]
&= \dfrac{1 + \sin 2x}{1 - \sin 2x}
\end{aligned}$$

49. $\dfrac{\sqrt{6}}{2}$ **51.** $\dfrac{\pi}{2}, \dfrac{3\pi}{2}$ **53.** $\dfrac{\pi}{6}, \dfrac{7\pi}{6}$ **55.** $0, \dfrac{\pi}{3}$,

$\pi, \dfrac{5\pi}{3}$ **57.** 2 **59.** $\sqrt{3 - 2\sqrt{2}}$, or $\sqrt{2} - 1$

39. 30°, 150°, 270°

Page 513. Class Exercises **1.** 2π; 1

3. $2\pi; \dfrac{1}{2}$ **5.** $0 < x < \pi$ **7.** $0 \le x < \pi$,

$\dfrac{3\pi}{2} < x \le 2\pi$

41. $\dfrac{\sqrt{5}}{2}$; $\dfrac{2\sqrt{5}}{5}$; $\dfrac{1}{2}$

PREREQUISITE SKILLS FOLLOW-UP

COMPUTER HANDBOOK

TABLES

GLOSSARY

ANSWERS TO CHECKPOINTS

ANSWERS TO SELECTED EXERCISES

INDEX

Pages 513–514. Exercises **1.** 2π; 3

3. 2π; 4 **5.** 2π; 1 **7.** $0 < x < \dfrac{\pi}{2}$

9. $\dfrac{3\pi}{2} < x < 2\pi$ **11.** sin x: 0; 0.4; 0.7;

0.9; 1; 0.9; 0.7; 0.4; 0 cos x: 1; 0.9; 0.7;
0.4; 0; −0.4; −0.7; −0.9; −1

13.

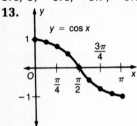

15. Increases from $x = -2\pi$ to $x = -\dfrac{3\pi}{2}$

and from $x = -\dfrac{\pi}{2}$ to $x = 0$; decreases

from $x = -\dfrac{3\pi}{2}$ to $x = -\dfrac{\pi}{2}$

17.

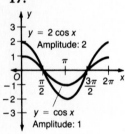

19.

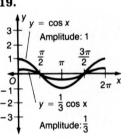

21.

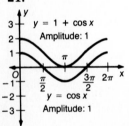

23.

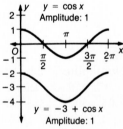

25.

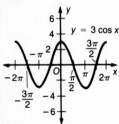

27.

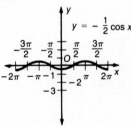

29.

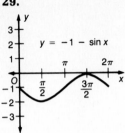

31.

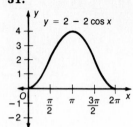

33.

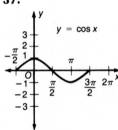

35.

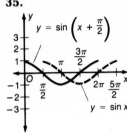

37.

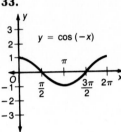

39. $\cos\left(\dfrac{x - \pi}{2}\right)$

$= \cos x \cos \dfrac{\pi}{2} + \sin x \sin \dfrac{\pi}{2}$

$= \cos x \, (0) + \sin x \, (1)$

$= \sin x$

41. sin x: 0.7; 1; 0.7; 0; −0.7; −1; −0.7; 0
cos x: 0.7; 0; −0.7; −1; −0.7; 0; 0.7;
1 sin x + cos x: 1.4; 1; 0; −1; −1.4; −1; 0; 1
a. and **b.**

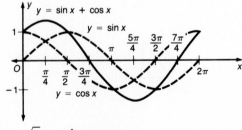

c. $\sqrt{2}$, or about 1.4

Page 517. Class Exercises 1. π; two; 1; 0, π; $\frac{\pi}{2}$; $\frac{\pi}{4}$, $\frac{3\pi}{4}$ **3.** $\frac{2\pi}{3}$; three; 1; $\frac{\pi}{2}$; $\frac{\pi}{6}$; 0, $\frac{\pi}{3}$, $\frac{2\pi}{3}$ **5.** 8π; one-fourth; $\frac{1}{3}$; 0, 8π; 4π; 2π, 6π

Page 518. Exercises 1. $\frac{\pi}{2}$; four; 1; $\frac{\pi}{8}$; $\frac{3\pi}{8}$; 0, $\frac{\pi}{4}$, $\frac{\pi}{2}$ **3.** 6π; one-third; 1; 0, 6π; 3π; $\frac{3\pi}{2}$, $\frac{9\pi}{2}$ **5.** 4π; one-half; 4; 0, 4π; 2π; π, 3π

7.

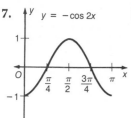

$y = -\cos 2x$

9.

$y = -\sin 8x$

11.

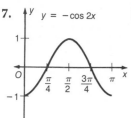

$y = -3\sin 3x$

13.

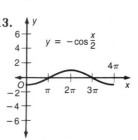

$y = -\cos \frac{x}{2}$

15.

$y = 2\sin 5x$

17.

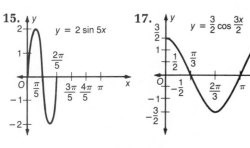

$y = \frac{3}{2}\cos\frac{3x}{2}$

19. $y = 2\sin\frac{x}{2}$ **21.** $y = \frac{1}{3}\cos\frac{x}{3}$

23.

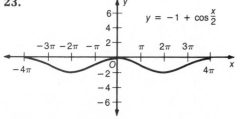

$y = -1 + \cos\frac{x}{2}$

25. One cycle of $y = a \sin x$ or $y = a \cos x$ is completed as x varies from 0 to 2π. So one cycle of $y = a \sin bx$ or $y = a \cos bx$ is completed as bx varies from 0 to 2π. Since $0 \le bx \le 2\pi$ is equivalent to $0 \le x \le \frac{2\pi}{b}$, the period of $y = a \sin bx$ or $y = a \cos bx$ is $\frac{2\pi}{b}$.

27. $y = 2 + \frac{3}{2}\cos\frac{2x}{5}$

Page 521. Class Exercises 1. $-\frac{3\pi}{2}$, $-\frac{\pi}{2}$, $\frac{\pi}{2}$, $\frac{3\pi}{2}$; $-\pi$, 0, $-\pi$ **3.** -2π, $-\pi$, 0, π, 2π; $-\frac{3\pi}{2}$, $-\frac{\pi}{2}$, $\frac{\pi}{2}$, $\frac{3\pi}{2}$

Pages 521–522. Exercises

1. $p = \frac{\pi}{3}$

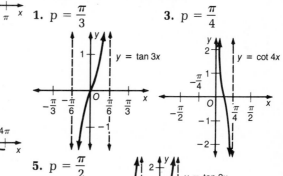

$y = \tan 3x$

3. $p = \frac{\pi}{4}$

$y = \cot 4x$

5. $p = \frac{\pi}{2}$

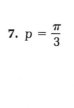

$y = \tan 2x$

7. $p = \frac{\pi}{3}$

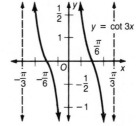

$y = \cot 3x$

9. $-\pi < x < -\frac{\pi}{2}$, $0 < x < \frac{\pi}{2}$

11. $-\pi < x < -\frac{\pi}{2}$, $0 < x < \frac{\pi}{2}$

13. Tan x increases over the intervals $-\pi \le x < -\frac{\pi}{2}$, $-\frac{\pi}{2} < x < \frac{\pi}{2}$, $\frac{\pi}{2} < x \le \pi$.

PREREQUISITE SKILLS FOLLOW-UP

COMPUTER HANDBOOK

TABLES

GLOSSARY

ANSWERS TO CHECKPOINTS

ANSWERS TO SELECTED EXERCISES

INDEX

15. $p = \pi$

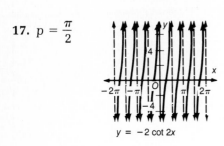

$y = -\tan x$

17. $p = \dfrac{\pi}{2}$

$y = -2 \cot 2x$

19. $p = 1$

$y = \tan \pi x$

21. $\operatorname{Tan}(x + \pi) = \dfrac{\tan x + \tan \pi}{1 - \tan x \tan \pi}$

$$= \dfrac{\tan x + 0}{1 - \tan x(0)}$$

$$= \dfrac{\tan x}{1}$$

$$= \tan x$$

23.   **25.**

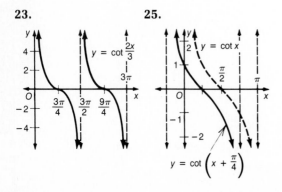

$y = \cot \dfrac{2x}{3}$

$y = \cot x$

$y = \cot\left(x + \dfrac{\pi}{4}\right)$

27.

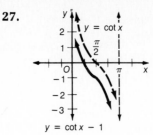

$y = \cot x$

$y = \cot x - 1$

29.

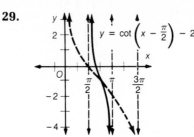

$y = \cot\left(x - \dfrac{\pi}{2}\right) - 2$

Page 524. Class Exercises

1. $p = \dfrac{\pi}{2}; \; x = \dfrac{\pi}{8}, \; x = \dfrac{3\pi}{8}$

$y = \sec 4x$

$y = \cos 4x$

3. $p = 2\pi; \; x = 0, \; x = \pi, \; x = 2\pi$

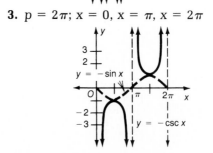

$y = -\sin x$

$y = -\csc x$

Pages 524–525. Exercises

1. $p = 4\pi$

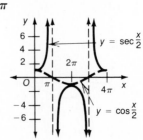

$y = \sec \dfrac{x}{2}$

$y = \cos \dfrac{x}{2}$

3. $p = 2\pi$

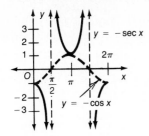

5. $p = 2\pi$

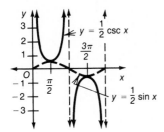

7. $-\dfrac{\pi}{2} < x < \dfrac{\pi}{2}$ **9.** $0 < x < \pi$

11. Increases over $0 < x < \dfrac{\pi}{2}$ and
$\dfrac{\pi}{2} < x < \pi$; decreases over
$-\dfrac{\pi}{2} < x < 0$ and $\pi < x < \dfrac{3\pi}{2}$

13. $p = \pi$

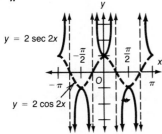

15. $p = \dfrac{2\pi}{3}$

17. $p = 3\pi$

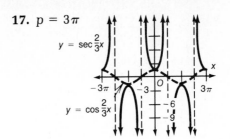

19. $p = 2$

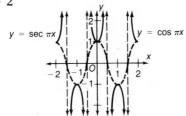

21.

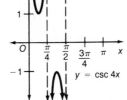

23. $x = 0,\ x = \dfrac{1}{2}p,\ x = p$

25.

27.

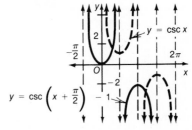

Page 528. Class Exercises   1. $-\dfrac{\pi}{2}$

3. 0 **5.** $\dfrac{\pi}{3}$ **7.** $-\dfrac{1}{2} \le x \le \dfrac{1}{2};\ -\dfrac{\pi}{2} \le y \le \dfrac{\pi}{2}$

9. $-2 \le x \le 2;\ -\dfrac{\pi}{4} \le y \le \dfrac{\pi}{4}$

PREREQUISITE SKILLS FOLLOW-UP

COMPUTER HANDBOOK

TABLES

GLOSSARY

ANSWERS TO CHECKPOINTS

ANSWERS TO SELECTED EXERCISES

INDEX

Exercises   1. $\dfrac{\pi}{6}$ **3.** $-\dfrac{\pi}{3}$

5. $-\pi$ **7.** $-1 \le x \le 1$; $-\dfrac{3\pi}{2} \le y \le \dfrac{3\pi}{2}$

9. $-\dfrac{1}{3} \le x \le \dfrac{1}{3}$; $-\dfrac{\pi}{2} \le y \le \dfrac{\pi}{2}$

11. $-\dfrac{1}{3} \le x \le \dfrac{1}{3}$; $-\dfrac{\pi}{4} \le y \le \dfrac{\pi}{4}$

13.   **15.**

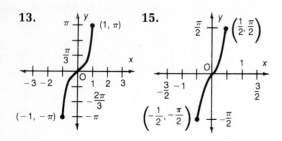

17.

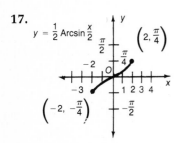

19. 0.3142; 18°   **21.** −0.1542; −8°50′

23. 1   **25.** $\dfrac{1}{2}$ **27.** $\dfrac{\pi}{4}$ **29.** $\dfrac{\pi}{2}$ **31.** $\dfrac{12}{5}$

33. $\dfrac{15}{17}$ **35.** $-\sqrt{3}$

37. $\sin 2\,\theta = 2\sin\theta\cos\theta$
$\sin(2\,\text{Arcsin } x) = 2\sin(\text{Arcsin } x)$
$\cos(\text{Arcsin } x)$
$\sin(2\,\text{Arcsin } x) = 2x\sqrt{1 - x^2}$

Page 532. Class Exercises   1. $\dfrac{\pi}{2}$ **3.** π

5. $-\dfrac{\pi}{3}$ **7.** $-\dfrac{1}{4} \le x \le \dfrac{1}{4}$; $0 \le y \le \pi$

9. All real numbers; $-\dfrac{\pi}{2} < y < \dfrac{\pi}{2}$

11. All real numbers; $-\pi < y < \pi$

Pages 532–533. Exercises   1. 0   **3.** $\dfrac{4\pi}{3}$

5. $\dfrac{\pi}{6}$ **7.** $-1 \le x \le 1$; $0 \le y < 2\pi$

9. $-\dfrac{1}{2} \le x \le \dfrac{1}{2}$; $0 \le y \le \pi$

11. $-2 \le x \le 2$; $0 \le y < \dfrac{\pi}{2}$

13.

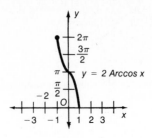

15.

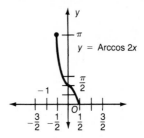

17.

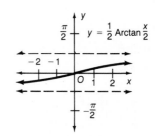

19. 1.1054; 63°20′   **21.** 0.2414; 13°50′

23. $\dfrac{\sqrt{2}}{2}$ **25.** $\dfrac{\sqrt{2}}{2}$ **27.** $\dfrac{\sqrt{3}}{3}$ **29.** $-\dfrac{12}{13}$

31. $\dfrac{1}{4}(\sqrt{2} + \sqrt{6})$ **33.** $-\dfrac{33}{65}$ **35.** $\dfrac{240}{289}$

37. From the diagram, $\theta = \text{Arccos } x$. By the Pythagorean theorem, $t = \sqrt{1 - x^2}$. Then $\tan x = \tan(\text{Arccos } x)$

$$= \dfrac{\sqrt{1 - x^2}}{x}$$

Pages 535–536. Class Exercises

1–6.

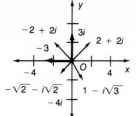

7. $2\sqrt{2}\left(\cos\dfrac{\pi}{4} + i\sin\dfrac{\pi}{4}\right)$

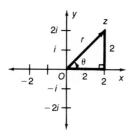

9. $3\left(\cos\dfrac{\pi}{2} + i\sin\dfrac{\pi}{2}\right)$

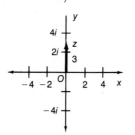

11. $3(\cos 180° + i\sin 180°)$

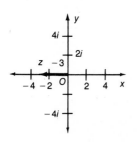

13. $1 + i\sqrt{3}$

Pages 536–537. Exercises

1.

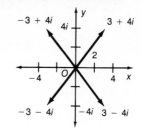

3. $2\left(\cos\dfrac{2\pi}{3} + i\sin\dfrac{2\pi}{3}\right)$

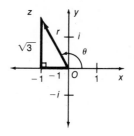

5. $\sqrt{2}\left(\cos\dfrac{5\pi}{4} + i\sin\dfrac{5\pi}{4}\right)$

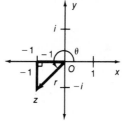

7. $2\left(\cos\dfrac{11\pi}{6} + i\sin\dfrac{11\pi}{6}\right)$

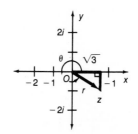

PREREQUISITE SKILLS FOLLOW-UP

COMPUTER HANDBOOK

TABLES

GLOSSARY

ANSWERS TO CHECKPOINTS

ANSWERS TO SELECTED EXERCISES

INDEX

9. $2\left(\cos \dfrac{\pi}{6} + i \sin \dfrac{\pi}{6}\right)$

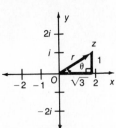

11. $2\left(\cos 135° + i \sin 135°\right)$

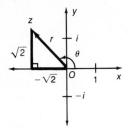

13. $2(\cos 330° + i \sin 330°)$

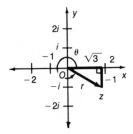

15. $\dfrac{\sqrt{2}}{2} + \dfrac{\sqrt{2}}{2}i$ **17.** $\dfrac{3\sqrt{3}}{2} + \dfrac{3}{2}i$

19. $-\dfrac{7\sqrt{3}}{2} + \dfrac{7}{2}i$ **21.** $2i$ **23.** $0.4540 +$
$0.8910i$ **25.** $-1.7208 - 2.4576i$

27. $\cos \dfrac{\pi}{6} + i \sin \dfrac{\pi}{6}$

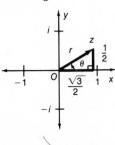

29. $\dfrac{2}{3}\left(\cos \dfrac{\pi}{4} + i \sin \dfrac{\pi}{4}\right)$ **31.** $4\left(\cos \dfrac{\pi}{6} + i \sin \dfrac{\pi}{6}\right)$

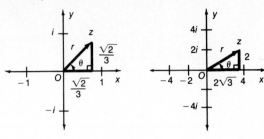

33. $7\left(\cos \dfrac{\pi}{2} + i \sin \dfrac{\pi}{2}\right)$ **35.** $5(\cos 36°50' +$
$i \sin 36°50')$

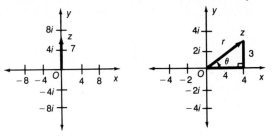

37. $13(\cos 157°20' + i \sin 157°20')$

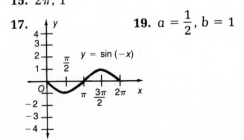

39. $4 - 4i\sqrt{3}$ **41.** -2

Pages 540–542. Review Exercises

1. $\dfrac{7\pi}{6}$ **3.** $-\dfrac{7\pi}{4}$ **5.** $-\dfrac{5\pi}{6}$ **7.** $15°$

9. $-150°$ **11.** $0, \dfrac{2\pi}{3}, \dfrac{4\pi}{3}$ **13.** $2\pi; 3$
15. $2\pi; 1$

17.

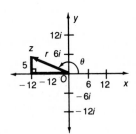

19. $a = \dfrac{1}{2}, b = 1$

21.

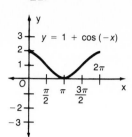

$y = 1 + \cos(-x)$

23.

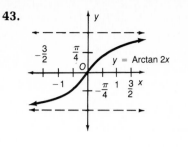

$y = 2 \sin \dfrac{x}{2}$

43.

$y = \text{Arctan } 2x$

25. $p = \dfrac{\pi}{2}$

27. $p = 4\pi$

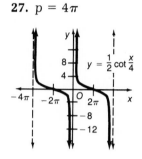

$y = -\cot x$

$y = \dfrac{1}{2}\cot \dfrac{x}{4}$

29. $p = \dfrac{2\pi}{3}$

$y = 4\cos 3x$

$y = 4\sec 3x$

45. $\dfrac{5}{3}$ **47.** $\dfrac{8}{15}$ **49.** $2\left(\cos \dfrac{5\pi}{4} + i \sin \dfrac{5\pi}{4}\right)$

51. $2\left(\cos \dfrac{5\pi}{6} + i \sin \dfrac{5\pi}{6}\right)$ **53.** $\sqrt{2} + i\sqrt{2}$

55. $-3i$ **57.** $-0.4360 + 4.9810i$

59. $8.192 - 5.736i$

Pages 544–545. Cumulative Review

1. e **3.** b **5.** d **7.** d **9.** e **11.** c

13. $y = -2x + 18$ **15.** $y = -\dfrac{3}{4}x + 8$

17. $(4, -4)$ **19.** $(11 + 7x)(11 - 7x)$

21. $2(5y - 1)(x - 2y)$ **23.** $-1 \pm \sqrt{3}$

25. $22 + 7i$ **27.** $\dfrac{3 + i}{5}$ **29.** Circle

31. $\dfrac{1}{36}$ **33.** $\sin \theta = -\dfrac{3}{5}$; $\cos \theta = -\dfrac{4}{5}$;

$\tan \theta = \dfrac{3}{4}$; $\csc \theta = -\dfrac{5}{3}$; $\sec \theta = -\dfrac{5}{4}$;

$\cot \theta = \dfrac{4}{3}$ **35.** $\sin \theta = -\dfrac{4}{5}$; $\cos \theta = \dfrac{3}{5}$;

$\tan \theta = -\dfrac{4}{3}$; $\csc \theta = -\dfrac{5}{4}$; $\sec \theta = \dfrac{5}{3}$;

$\cot \theta = -\dfrac{3}{4}$ **37.** $30°, 90°, 150°, 270°$

39. $p = 4\pi$

31. $-\dfrac{\pi}{4}$ **33.** $(-1, \pi), (1, -\pi)$

35. $\left(\dfrac{1}{2}, \dfrac{3\pi}{2}\right), \left(-\dfrac{1}{2}, -\dfrac{3\pi}{2}\right)$

37. -1 **39.** π **41.** $-\dfrac{2\pi}{3}$

41. No period **43.** $\dfrac{1}{2}$

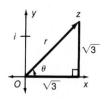

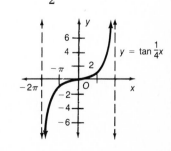

$y = \tan \dfrac{1}{4}x$

PREREQUISITE SKILLS FOLLOW-UP

COMPUTER HANDBOOK

TABLES

GLOSSARY

ANSWERS TO CHECKPOINTS

ANSWERS TO SELECTED EXERCISES

INDEX

CHAPTER 14

Page 547. Prerequisite Skills Review
1. a **2.** c **3.** d **4.** a **5.** c **6.** b **7.** a
8. b **9.** d

Page 549. Class Exercises 1. 4, 8, 12, 16 **3.** 2, 5, 8, 11 **5.** 1, 3, 7, 15 **7.** −2, 4, −8, 16 **9.** 5, 11, 17, 23 **11.** Finite; last term: 30; 7 terms **13.** Infinite

Page 550. Exercises 1. The first term is 3. Each term thereafter is 4 greater than the preceding term. Next three terms: 19, 23, 27 **3.** The first term is −7. Each term thereafter is 2 greater than the preceding term. Next three terms: 1, 3, 5 **5.** The first term is 4.

Each term thereafter is $\frac{1}{2}$ the preceding

term. Next three terms: $\frac{1}{4}, \frac{1}{8}, \frac{1}{16}$

7. Finite; last term: 25; 13 terms
9. Finite; last term: 107; 6 terms **11.** 3, 6, 9 **13.** 8, 9, 10 **15.** 0, 3, 8 **17.** 3, 5, 9
19. 0, 6, 24 **21.** $-\frac{1}{2}, \frac{1}{4}, -\frac{1}{8}$ **23.** 3, 7, 11

25. 1, 3, 7 **27.** $t_n = \frac{1}{n}$ **29.** $t_n = n + 2$

31. $t_n = 3^n$ **33.** $t_n = 1; t_{n+1} = t_n + 2$
35. $t_n = 1; t_{n+1} = t_n - 4$ **37.** $t_n = 5$;
$t_{n+1} = -2t_n$ **39.** 2, 4, 8, 16, 32. They are the same. **41.** The first term is 0. The terms thereafter increase by successive counting numbers, starting with 1. Next three terms: 15, 21, 28 **43.** The

first term is 1, or $\frac{1}{1}$. The numerator of

each term thereafter is 1 greater than that of the preceding term, and the denominator is 2 greater than that of the

preceding term. Next three terms: $\frac{6}{11}$,

$\frac{7}{13}, \frac{8}{15}$ **45.** The first term is $\frac{1}{2}$. The nu-

merators of the terms thereafter are squares of successive counting numbers, starting with 2^2, or 4. The denominator of each term is 1 greater than that of the preceding

term. Next three terms: $\frac{36}{7}, \frac{49}{8}, \frac{64}{9}$

Page 553. Class Exercises 1. Yes; 2; 2
3. No **5.** No **7.** 1, 9, 17 **9.** $-1, -\frac{1}{2}, 0$

Page 554. Exercises 1. Yes **3.** No
5. No **7.** Yes **9.** No **11.** −4, −7, −10
13. $-7\frac{1}{2}, -9, -10\frac{1}{2}$ **15.** $6 + 2i, 6 + 3i$,
$6 + 4i$ **17.** −7, −4, −1 **19.** 8, 4.5, 1
21. $-i, -1.5 - i, -3 - i$ **23.** 57 **25.** 25
27. $3 - i$ **29.** 12th **31.** 8th **33.** 8th
35. $-27 - 59i$ **37.** $-9a + \frac{29}{2}b$ **39.** $2\frac{1}{4}$,
$7\frac{1}{2}, 12\frac{3}{4}$ **41.** $9\frac{1}{2}, 14, 18\frac{1}{2}, 23$ **43.** −8
45. 22nd deposit

Page 557. Class Exercises 1. 140
3. 35 **5.** −180

Pages 557–558. Exercises 1. 234
3. 4950 **5.** 4410 **7.** $n = 17; S_n = 901$
9. $n = 11; S_n = 341$ **11.** $t_n = 85$;
$S_n = 558$ **13.** $t_n = 1475; S_n = 44{,}250$
15. 39 **17.** 3 **19.** 2325 **21.** 11,325
23. −615 **25.** −143 **27.** $647\frac{1}{2}$
29. \$19,625; \$190,950 **31.** 40

Page 562. Class Exercises 1. $r = 2$
3. $r = 1$ **5.** $r = 0.1$ **7.** $\frac{1}{54}, \frac{1}{162}, \frac{1}{486}$

Pages 562–563. Exercises 1. No
3. No **5.** Yes **7.** Yes **9.** Yes **11.** 6, −12, 24 **13.** $\frac{3}{8}, \frac{3}{2}, 6$ **15.** 8, 0.8, 0.08
17. $\sqrt{3}, 6, 12\sqrt{3}$ **19.** 56, 112, 224
21. $-5, \frac{5}{2}, -\frac{5}{4}$ **23.** $-\frac{4}{3}, -\frac{8}{3}, -\frac{16}{3}$
25. 80 **27.** −192 **29.** $\frac{3}{8}$ **31.** 0.000064
33. 12 **35.** −9 **37.** 18, 54 **39.** $45, \frac{5}{3}$
41. 4 or −4, 36 or −36 **43.** 1, 6 **45.** 6, 12, 24; −6, 12, −24 **47.** 4000; 64,000
49. 729 **51.** −8 **53.** 4th

Page 565. Class Exercises 1. 484
3. $\frac{91}{243}$ **5.** $20\frac{21}{25}$ **7.** $3\frac{49}{54}$

Page 566. Exercises **1.** $24 + 48 + 96$
3. $16 - 32 + 64$ **5.** $\dfrac{27}{64} - \dfrac{81}{512} + \dfrac{243}{4096}$
7. 315 **9.** -242 **11.** 1.1111 **13.** 364
15. -1 **17.** 62 **19.** 204 **21.** 3.3333333
23. $8\dfrac{1}{64}$ **25.** 979; neither **27.** 60; arithmetic **29.** $781\dfrac{6}{25}$ **31.** $6\dfrac{281}{1600}$
33. $\displaystyle\sum_{k-1}^{6}(-2)^{k-1}$ **35.** $\displaystyle\sum_{k-1}^{5} - (-4)^{4-k}$

Page 570. Class Exercises **1.** No
3. Yes; $1\dfrac{1}{9}$ **5.** Yes; 20 **7.** Yes; $-1\dfrac{5}{7}$
9. Yes; $40\dfrac{40}{99}$

Pages 571–572. Exercises **1.** No
3. No **5.** Yes; $\dfrac{3}{8}$ **7.** Yes; $4\dfrac{2}{3}$ **9.** No
11. Yes; 27 **13.** 4 **15.** -9 **17.** No fi-
nite sum, since $|r| = |-2| > 1$. **19.** $-2\dfrac{2}{7}$
21. No finite sum, since $|r| = |9| > 1$.
23. $8.\overline{8}$ **25.** $0.\overline{15}$ **27.** $0.\overline{125}$ **29.** $0.\overline{4}$
31. $S = \dfrac{20}{1 - \frac{1}{2}}$; 40 cm **33.** $S = \dfrac{50}{1 - 0.9}$;
500 cm **35.** 35 m **37.** $\dfrac{17}{99}$ **39.** $\dfrac{10}{9}$
41. $\dfrac{191}{37}$ **43.** $\dfrac{13}{55}$

Page 575. Class Exercises **1.** 14; 13
3. a^{10}; b^{10} **5.** $9xy^8$
Page 576. Exercises **1.** 5040 **3.** 240
5. 15 **7.** 1 **9.** $x^3 + 3x^2y + 3xy^2 + y^3$
11. $1 - 5y + 10y^2 - 10y^3 + 5y^4 - y^5$
13. $x^5 + 10x^4 + 40x^3 + 80x^2 + 80x + 32$
15. $x^7 - 7x^6y + 21x^5y^2 - 35x^4y^3 +$
$35x^3y^4 - 21x^2y^5 + 7xy^6 - y^7$
17. $8a^3 + 12ab + 6ab^2 + b^3$
19. $8a^3 + 36a^2b + 54ab^2 + 27b$
21. $792a^5b^7$ **23.** $3360x^6$ **25.** $15x^2y^4$
27. $495c^8$ **29.** $a^3 + 3a^2b^2 + 3ab^4 + b^6$
31. $a^5 + 10a^4b^2 + 40a^3b^4 + 80a^2b^6 +$
$80ab^8 + 32b^{10}$ **33.** 16 **35.** 1024
37. 4096; 4096

Pages 578–580. Review Exercises
1. $\dfrac{2}{3}, \dfrac{4}{3}, 2$ **3.** $-6, -5, -4$ **5.** $t_n = n + 6$
7. $t_n = 5 + \dfrac{1}{n}$ **9.** $t_1 = 23$; $t_{n+1} = t_n - 5$

11. Yes **13.** No **15.** 7, 10, 13 **17.** 5.9
19. $25 + 26\sqrt{2}$ **21.** 30; 1395 **23.** -102;
-630 **25.** No **27.** 3, 1, $\dfrac{1}{3}$ **29.** 3, -1, $\dfrac{1}{3}$
31. 1 **33.** -7.777 **35.** $1\dfrac{21}{64}$ **37.** 780
39. $\dfrac{156}{625}$ **41.** Sum: $\dfrac{2}{7}$ **43.** Sum: 14
45. Sum: 6 **47.** $65.\overline{65}$ **49.** $1 - 6x +$
$15x^2 - 20x^3 + 15x^4 - 6x^5 + x^6$
51. $18xy^8$ **53.** $715x^9$

CHAPTER 15
Page 583. Prerequisite Skills Review
1. b **2.** c **3.** a **4.** b **5.** d **6.** c **7.** c
8. b

Page 586. Class Exercises **1.** $\dfrac{1}{5}$ **3.** $\dfrac{3}{5}$
5. $\dfrac{3}{5}$ **7.** 0

Pages 587–588. Exercises **1.** $\dfrac{1}{6}$ **3.** $\dfrac{1}{2}$
5. $\dfrac{1}{3}$ **7.** $\dfrac{1}{3}$ **9.** $\dfrac{2}{3}$ **11.** 0 **13.** $\dfrac{1}{26}$ **15.** $\dfrac{25}{26}$
17. $\dfrac{3}{26}$ **19.** HHHH, HHHT, HHTH,
HTHH, THHH, HHTT, HTHT, HTTH,
THHT, THTH, TTHH, HTTT, THTT,
TTHT, TTTH, TTTT **21.** $\dfrac{1}{8}$ **23.** $\dfrac{11}{16}$
25.

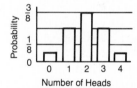

Number of Heads

27. 85%, or $\dfrac{17}{20}$ **29.** EEE, EEO, EOE,
OEE, EOO, OEO, OOE, OOO **31.** $\dfrac{1}{9}$
33. $\dfrac{1}{3}$ **35.** $\dfrac{1}{31}$ **37.** $\dfrac{14}{31}$ **39.** $\dfrac{4}{31}$ **41.** Not
mutually exclusive **43.** Not mutually
exclusive **45.** $\dfrac{3}{5}$ **47.** $\dfrac{1}{5}$ **49.** $\dfrac{3}{8}$ **51.** $\dfrac{34}{39}$
Page 591. Class Exercises **1.** 120
3. 120 **5.** $\dfrac{48}{120} = \dfrac{2}{5}$
Pages 591–592. Exercises **1.** $4 \times 4 =$
16 **3.** $2 \times 2 \times 2 \times 2 \times 2 = 2^5 = 32$
5. 6 **7.** 120 **9.** 10! **11.** 720 **13.** 720

PREREQUISITE SKILLS FOLLOW-UP

COMPUTER HANDBOOK

TABLES

GLOSSARY

ANSWERS TO CHECKPOINTS

ANSWERS TO SELECTED EXERCISES

INDEX

15. JU, JN, JI, JO, JR, UN, UI, UO, UR, UJ, NI, NO, NR, NJ, NU, IO IR, IJ, IU, IN, OR, OJ, OU, ON, OI, RJ, RU, RN, RI, RO
17. 20 **19.** 90 **21.** 1260 **23.** 1680
25. $\dfrac{1}{40,320}$ **27.** $\dfrac{6}{120}$ or $\dfrac{1}{20}$ **29.** 120

Page 595. Class Exercises 1. 10 **3.** 1
5. $\dfrac{2}{5}$

Pages 595–596. Exercises 1. 10 **3.** 15
5. 5 **7.** 56 **9.** 252 **11.** $\dfrac{26!}{9!\,17!}$
13. $\dfrac{26!}{26!\,0!} = 1$ **15.** True **17.** False **19.** 9
21. 45 **23.** 1, 5, 10, 10, 5, 1 **25.** 28
27. 120 **29.** $\dfrac{1}{3}$ **31.** 270,725
33. 2,598,960 **35.** $\dfrac{33}{16,660}$ **37.** $\dfrac{13}{90}$

Page 599. Class Exercises 1. $\dfrac{1}{5}$ **3.** $\dfrac{1}{30}$
5. $\dfrac{1}{2}$ **7.** $\dfrac{1}{15}$ **9.** $\dfrac{1}{5}$

Pages 599–600. Exercises 1. $\dfrac{1}{9}$ **3.** $\dfrac{4}{9}$
5. $\dfrac{1}{9}$ **7.** $\dfrac{2}{9}$ **9.** $\dfrac{1}{36}$ **11.** $\dfrac{1}{18}$ **13.** p^5
15. $1 - p^5$ **17.** $1 - [\,p^5 + (1 - p)^5\,]$
19. $\dfrac{64}{121}$ **21.** $\dfrac{64}{1331}$ **23.** $\dfrac{1}{55}$ **25.** $\dfrac{24}{55}$
27. $\dfrac{1}{4}$ **29.** $\dfrac{11}{850}$

Page 603. Class Exercises 1. $\dfrac{1}{6}$ **3.** 4
5. $\dfrac{625}{1296}$ **7.** $\dfrac{25}{216}$ **9.** $\dfrac{1295}{1296}$

Page 604. Exercises 1. (A, A), (A, B), (B, A), (B, B) **3.** 2 **5.** $\dfrac{9}{16} + \dfrac{6}{16} + \dfrac{1}{16}$
7. $\dfrac{3}{8}$ **9.** $\left(\dfrac{3}{4} + \dfrac{1}{4}\right)^3 = \dfrac{27}{64} + \dfrac{27}{64} + \dfrac{9}{64} + \dfrac{1}{64}$
11. $\dfrac{9}{64}$ **13.** $_9C_6\left(\dfrac{2}{3}\right)^6\left(\dfrac{1}{3}\right)^3$ **15.** $\dfrac{32}{625}$
17. $\dfrac{1}{36}$ **19.** $\dfrac{25}{216}$ **21.** 0.32805
23. 0.00856

Page 607. Class Exercises 1. 8 **3.** 10
Pages 608–609. Exercises 1. 6; 6
3. $1\dfrac{7}{8}$; $1\dfrac{1}{2}$ **5.** 16.88 **7.** 2.6 **9.** 64
11. 80 **13.** 8 **15.** 6; 3 **17.** 10; 2.55

19. 8; 3.61 **21.** 13.5; They are the same.
23. 2.49

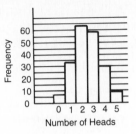

Page 612. Class Exercises 1. 0.68
3. 0.815 **5.** 0.84 **7.** 0.95
Page 613. Exercises 1. 1360 **3.** 16%
5. 8 **7.** 0.84 **9.** 34 **11.** 0.975
13. 0.6828 **15.** 0.0668 **17.** 0.0440

Pages 616–617. Review Exercises 1. $\dfrac{1}{12}$
3. $\dfrac{11}{12}$ **5.** $\dfrac{1}{4}$ **7.** 0 **9.** $\dfrac{5}{16}$ **11.** 1680
13. 30 **15.** 70 **17.** 35 **19.** $\dfrac{1}{8}$ **21.** $\dfrac{19}{27}$
23. $\dfrac{1}{5}$ **25.** $\dfrac{1}{4}$ **27.** 5 **29.** $\dfrac{270}{1024} = \dfrac{135}{512}$
31. $\dfrac{106}{1024} = \dfrac{53}{512}$ **33.** 132.5, 56, 20.3
35. 7 **37.** 0.16

CHAPTER 16
Page 621. Prerequisite Skills Review
1. c **2.** b **3.** d **4.** b **5.** a **6.** c
7. b **8.** d **9.** a
Page 624. Class Exercises
1. $\begin{bmatrix} 1 & -3 & \vdots & -1 \\ 3 & 2 & \vdots & 19 \end{bmatrix}$

3. $\begin{bmatrix} 2 & -2 & 1 & \vdots & 12 \\ 1 & 1 & 0 & \vdots & 5 \\ 1 & 0 & 3 & \vdots & 0 \end{bmatrix}$

5. $\begin{aligned} x - 2y + 3z &= 4 \\ y - 3z &= -3 \\ 2z &= 4 \end{aligned}$
$(4, 3, 2)$

Page 624. Exercises 1. $\left(-1, \dfrac{1}{2}\right)$
3. $\left(-2, 4, \dfrac{3}{2}\right)$ **5.** $(3, -2)$ **7.** $(4, 3)$
9. $(6, 4)$ **11.** $(6, -1, -2)$ **13.** $(2, -2, 1)$
15. $\left(\dfrac{1}{2}, -2, -4\right)$

17. The matrix given is equivalent to

$$\begin{bmatrix} 1 & 0 & -2 & \vdots & 6 \\ 0 & 3 & 4 & \vdots & 14 \\ 0 & 0 & 0 & \vdots & -18 \end{bmatrix}$$

The third row of this matrix represents the false equation $0 = -18$, so the system has no solution.

Page 627. Class Exercises

1. $\begin{bmatrix} 2 & 7 \\ -1 & 0 \end{bmatrix}$

3. These matrices cannot be added since they do not have the same number of rows and columns.

5. $\begin{bmatrix} 3 & -3 \\ 3 & -3 \end{bmatrix}$ **7.** $\begin{bmatrix} 7 & 2 \\ -6 & 5 \end{bmatrix}$

9. $\begin{bmatrix} 10 & -7 \\ 11 & 0 \\ -6 & 0 \end{bmatrix}$

Pages 627–628. Exercises

1. The addition is not possible since G and H do not have the same number of rows and columns.

3. $\begin{bmatrix} 2 & 0 & -1 \\ 1 & 0 & 3 \\ -3 & 1 & 4 \end{bmatrix}$ **5.** $\begin{bmatrix} 3 & -1 \\ 1 & -3 \end{bmatrix}$

7. $[-4]$ **9.** $\begin{bmatrix} -3 & 3 & -3 \\ -5 & 5 & -5 \end{bmatrix}$

11. $\begin{bmatrix} 12 \\ -13 \end{bmatrix}$ **13.** $\begin{bmatrix} 6 & 4 & 2 & 0 \\ 0 & 1 & 2 & 3 \\ -3 & -3 & -3 & -3 \\ 0 & 2 & 4 & 6 \end{bmatrix}$

15. $[11]$ **17.** $\begin{bmatrix} 0 & 0 & 0 \\ 0 & 0 & 0 \\ 0 & 0 & 0 \end{bmatrix}$

19. $\begin{bmatrix} -4 & 0 \\ 0 & -2 \\ 2 & 2 \\ 0 & -4 \end{bmatrix}$ **21.** $[0, \ 0, \ 0, \ 0]$

23. $\begin{bmatrix} -9 & 6 & -1 \\ 0 & 9 & 0 \end{bmatrix}$

25.
$$IK = \begin{bmatrix} a & b & c \\ d & e & f \\ g & h & i \end{bmatrix} = K, \text{ and}$$

$$KI = \begin{bmatrix} a & b & c \\ d & e & f \\ g & h & i \end{bmatrix} = K.$$

So $IK = KI = K$.

27. $A + B = \begin{bmatrix} 2 & 0 \\ 3 & -2 \end{bmatrix}$ and

$B + A = \begin{bmatrix} 2 & 0 \\ 3 & -2 \end{bmatrix}.$

So $A + B = B + A$.

29. $(B + C)A = \begin{bmatrix} 10 & 1 \\ 8 & 0 \end{bmatrix}$ and

$BA + CA = \begin{bmatrix} 10 & 1 \\ 8 & 0 \end{bmatrix}.$ So

$(B + C)A = BA + CA$.

31. $(AB)C = \begin{bmatrix} 15 & 6 \\ -68 & -16 \end{bmatrix}$ and

$A(BC) = \begin{bmatrix} 15 & 6 \\ -68 & -16 \end{bmatrix}.$ So

$(AB)C = A(BC)$.

33.
$$P^2 = \begin{bmatrix} 4 & 0 & 0 \\ 0 & 9 & 0 \\ 0 & 0 & 16 \end{bmatrix} \text{ and}$$

$$P^2 \cdot P = \begin{bmatrix} 0 & 0 & 0 \\ 0 & 27 & 0 \\ 0 & 0 & 64 \end{bmatrix} = P^3$$

Pages 632–633. Class Exercises

1. $\begin{bmatrix} 1 & -3 \\ 0 & 1 \end{bmatrix}$ **3.** $\begin{bmatrix} 1 & -1 \\ \frac{1}{2} & -1 \end{bmatrix}$

5. $\begin{bmatrix} 3 & 8 \\ -1 & 5 \end{bmatrix}\begin{bmatrix} x \\ y \end{bmatrix} = \begin{bmatrix} 4 \\ 1 \end{bmatrix}$

7. $x = -1, y = 29$

Pages 633. Exercises

1. $\begin{bmatrix} 1 & -3 \\ 0 & \frac{1}{2} \end{bmatrix}$ **3.** $\begin{bmatrix} -4 & \frac{5}{2} \\ 1 & -\frac{1}{2} \end{bmatrix}$

5. $(21, \ -3)$ **7.** $(-7, \ 2)$

9. $\begin{bmatrix} -1 & -2 & -1 \\ 0 & -2 & -1 \\ 0 & -1 & -1 \end{bmatrix}$

11. $\begin{bmatrix} -13 & 7 & -5 \\ 2 & -1 & 1 \\ 8 & -4 & 3 \end{bmatrix}$ **13.** $(34, 29, 20)$

PREREQUISITE SKILLS FOLLOW-UP

COMPUTER HANDBOOK

TABLES

GLOSSARY

ANSWERS TO CHECKPOINTS

ANSWERS TO SELECTED EXERCISES

INDEX

15.
$$(AB)^{-1} = \begin{bmatrix} 1 & 3 \\ -\frac{1}{2} & -1 \end{bmatrix},$$

$$B^{-1} = \begin{bmatrix} 1 & 1 \\ -\frac{1}{2} & 0 \end{bmatrix}, \text{ and}$$

$$A^{-1} = \begin{bmatrix} 1 & 2 \\ 0 & 1 \end{bmatrix}.$$

So, $B^{-1}A^{-1} = \begin{bmatrix} 1 & 3 \\ -\frac{1}{2} & -1 \end{bmatrix}$, and

$(AB)^{-1} = B^{-1}A^{-1}$.

Page 636. Class Exercises 1. 15 **3.** 23

5.
$$\begin{vmatrix} 3 & 1 \\ -1 & 2 \\ -2 & 5 \end{vmatrix} = 6 - 8 + 0 - 0 - 60 + 1$$
$$= -61$$

7. $3\begin{vmatrix} 2 & 4 \\ 5 & 1 \end{vmatrix} - 1\begin{vmatrix} -1 & 4 \\ -2 & 1 \end{vmatrix} + 0\begin{vmatrix} -1 & 2 \\ -2 & 5 \end{vmatrix}$
$= 3(-18) - 1(7) = -54 - 7 = -61$

Pages 636–637. Exercises 1. 16 **3.** −2

5.
$$\begin{vmatrix} 3 & 2 \\ -2 & -3 \\ 0 & 4 \end{vmatrix} = 9 + 0 - 8 - 0 - 0 - 4$$
$$= -3$$

7. $1\begin{vmatrix} -2 & -3 \\ 0 & 4 \end{vmatrix} - 0\begin{vmatrix} 3 & 2 \\ 0 & 4 \end{vmatrix} - 1\begin{vmatrix} 3 & 2 \\ -2 & -3 \end{vmatrix}$
$= 1(-8) - 1(-5) = -8 + 5 = -3$

9. $0\begin{vmatrix} 2 & 1 \\ -3 & 0 \end{vmatrix} - 4\begin{vmatrix} 3 & 1 \\ -2 & 0 \end{vmatrix} - 1\begin{vmatrix} 3 & 2 \\ -2 & -3 \end{vmatrix}$
$= -4(2) - 1(-5) = -8 + 5 = -3$

11. −1 **13.** −27 **15.** −6 **17.** 16 **19.** 2
21. −3

Page 640. Class Exercises 1. 34
3. −1 **5.** 2 **7.** −69 **9.** 23

Page 640. Exercises 1. (4, −2)

3. $\left(\dfrac{13}{2}, -5\right)$ **5.** $\left(-\dfrac{1}{2}, -7\right)$

7. (−3, −2, 4) **9.** (3, 2, 1)

11. $\left(\dfrac{1}{2}, -\dfrac{3}{2}, 1\right)$ **13.** (2, −4, 3)

15. (2, −4, 3)

Pages 642–644. Review Exercises

1. (2, −4) **3.** $\left(\dfrac{1}{3}, -1, 3\right)$ **5.** (4, 5)

7. (2, 3, 4) **9.** (3, 0, 5)

11. $\begin{bmatrix} 40 & -40 \\ -94 & 94 \\ 148 & -148 \end{bmatrix}$

13. $\begin{bmatrix} -160 & 76 \end{bmatrix}$

15. $\begin{bmatrix} 5 & 3 \\ 2 & 1 \end{bmatrix}$

17. No inverse

19. $\begin{bmatrix} -4 & 1 & 2 \\ -\frac{7}{2} & \frac{1}{2} & \frac{3}{2} \\ \frac{3}{2} & -\frac{1}{2} & -\frac{1}{2} \end{bmatrix}$

21. (34, 13) **23.** (0, −1, 3)
25. (0, 1, 1) **27.** 25 **29.** −37 **31.** 147

33. $-\dfrac{5}{2}$ **35.** 2 or −3 **37.** (1, 1)

39. (3, 3, 3) **41.** $\left(\dfrac{2}{3}, -1, 0\right)$

Pages 646–647. Cumulative Review
1. b **3.** a **5.** b **7.** c **9.** a **11.** (3, 11)
13. $2xy(1 + x)(2 - y^2)$ **15.** $-2 \pm \sqrt{3}$
17. Max. value: 3
19. 3; (0, −3)

$x^2 + 6y + y^2 = 0$

21. 6 **23.** $\cos \theta = -\dfrac{12}{13}$; $\tan \theta = -\dfrac{5}{12}$;

$\csc \theta = \dfrac{13}{5}$; $\sec \theta = -\dfrac{13}{12}$; $\cot \theta = -\dfrac{12}{5}$

25. 0°, 180° **27.** $\sqrt{3}$ **29.** −210

31. $\begin{bmatrix} 3 & -2 & 4 \\ 8 & -4 & 6 \\ -10 & 6 & -11 \end{bmatrix}$

INDEX

Abscissa, 48
Absolute value, 7, 39
    of a complex number, 534
    in equations, 38–40
    function, 73
    in equalities, 38–40
Addition properties, 6, 19, 30
Algebraic expression, 3
Amplitude, 511, 515–518
Analytic geometry, 321
Angle(s)
    central, 504
    complementary, 434, 486
    coterminal, 413
    of depression, 440
    of elevation, 438
    quadrantal, 412
    reference, 416, 442–445
    in standard position, 412
Angular speed, 539
Antilogarithm, 389
Applications
    Approximating Areas
        Under Curves, 267
    Astronomy, 577
    Depreciation, 403
    Distance from an
        Earthquake, 111
    Equivalent Resistances,
        201
    Gear Speeds, 309
    Linear and Angular
        Speeds, 539
    Logic Gates in Computers,
        41
    Navigation, 461
    Parabolic Reflectors, 357
    Present Value, 157
    Relating Skid Marks to
        Speed, 231
    Sampling, 615
    Statistical Data, 79
    Using Matrices for
        Problems in
        Manufacturing, 641
    Vectors, 497
Archimedes, 267
Area
    under a curve, 267

of a sector, 508
    of a triangle, 480, 484
Arithmetic mean, 553, 605
Arithmetic sequence, or
    progression, 551–554
Arithmetic series, 555–558
Associative properties, 13
Asymptotes, 337, 519, 523
Axis of symmetry, 256, 264, 328

BASIC. See Computer
    Activities; Computer
    Handbook.
Binomial, 122
    distribution, 601–604
    expansion, 573–576
    theorem, 574

Calculator activities. See
    Using the Calculator.
Cancellation rule, 166
Cardioid, 538
Challenges, 22, 134, 144, 200,
    230, 247, 291, 295, 336,
    415, 484, 489, 522
Characteristic, 388
Checkpoint
    Ch.1, 18, 37
    Ch.2, 60, 74
    Ch.3, 98, 106
    Ch.4, 128, 153
    Ch.5, 180, 196
    Ch.6, 218, 226
    Ch.7, 254, 263
    Ch.8, 281, 300
    Ch.9, 341, 353
    Ch.10, 375, 396
    Ch.11, 432, 445
    Ch.12, 478, 493
    Ch.13, 525, 533
    Ch.14, 558, 572
    Ch.15, 600, 608
    Ch.16, 628
Circle, 322–325, 343
Circular functions, 509–525.
    See also Trigonometric
    functions.
Closure properties, 13
Coefficient, 16, 287
Combinations, 593–596
Common logarithms,
    388–391

Commutative properties, 13
Completing the square,
    238–241, 261, 324, 328
Complex fractions, 177–180
Complex numbers, 296–301,
    534–537
    argument of, 535
    conjugates of, 297, 303
    graphs of, 301, 534
    modulus of, 301, 534
    operations on, 296–300
    polar representation of,
        538
    trigonometric form of, 534
Complex plane, 301, 534
Compound inequalities,
    34–37
Compound interest, 157, 400,
    407
Computer Activities
    Distance Between Two
        Points, 361
    Doubling Your Money, 407
    Equation of a Line, 83
    The Golden Ratio, 619
    Frequency Distribution,
        645
    Greatest Common Factor,
        161
    Inflation, 205
    Orbital Speed, 465
    Profit or loss, 271
    The Richter Scale, 501
    Simplifying a Radical, 581
    Speed of Sound, 45
    Square Root, 235
    System of Equations, 115
    Trigonometric Functions,
        543
    Zeros of a cubic function,
        313
Computer Handbook,
    656–667
Computer, logic gates in, 41
Conic sections, 342–344
Conjugate root theorem, 303
Consistent system, 87
Constant, 16
    of variation, 192–193
Coordinate plane, 48–50
Coordinates, 48, 538
Cosecant, 420, 429, 524

PREREQUISITE SKILLS FOLLOW-UP

COMPUTER HANDBOOK

TABLES

GLOSSARY

ANSWERS TO CHECKPOINTS

ANSWERS TO SELECTED EXERCISES

INDEX

PREREQUISITE SKILLS FOLLOW-UP

COMPUTER HANDBOOK

TABLES

GLOSSARY

ANSWERS TO CHECKPOINTS

ANSWERS TO SELECTED EXERCISES

INDEX

Simplified form
of algebraic expressions, 16
of complex fractions,
177–178
of polynomials, 122
of radicals, 220, 581
of rational expressions,
166–168
Sine, 420, 429, 509–518
Sine waves, 511
Sines, law of, 452–461
Slope of a line, 56–59
Slope-intercept form, 61–63, 83
Speed of sound, 45
Square roots, 208–211, 235
Standard deviation, 606
Standard form of equation(s)
conic sections, 343
linear, 51
quadratic, 145
Statistics, 79, 605–613
Straight-line prediction, 614
Strategies for Problem Solving
Ch.1, Searching for
Patterns, 29
Ch.2, Discovering a Rule, 75
Ch.3, Generalizing from
the Specific, 99
Ch.4, Draw a Diagram, 148
Ch.5, Estimating with
Graphs, 188
Ch.6, Trial and Error, 215
Ch.7, Organizing and
Interpreting Data, 255
Ch.8, Estimating Roots
Graphically, 286
Ch.9, Visualization, 345
Ch.10, Using Diagrams for
Rate Problems, 367
Ch.11, Quick Geometric
Checks, 451
Ch.12, Transforming
Equations into
Familiar Forms, 479
Ch.13, Changing the
Coordinate System, 538
Ch.14, Using Successive
Differences, 559
Ch.15, Straight-Line
Prediction, 614
Ch.16, Using Matrices to
Organize Data, 629

Substitution property of
equality, 20
Subtraction, definition, 7
Sum and difference
formulas, 487
Sum and product formulas,
248
Summation notation, Σ, 557,
565
Symmetric property of
equality, 20
Symmetry, axis of, 256, 328
Synthetic division, 278–281
Systems of equations
consistent, 87
dependent, 87
inconsistent, 88
independent, 87
linear, 86–103, 622–624,
632, 638–640
linear-quadratic, 346–349
quadratic, 350–353
solved by addition, 95–98
solved by Cramer's rule,
115, 638–640
solved by graphing, 86–89
solved by matrices,
622–624, 632
solved by substitution,
90–93
Systems of inequalities,
104–105

Table of squares and square
roots, 668
Table of cubes and cube
roots, 669
Table of common logarithms,
670–671
Table of trigonometric ratios,
672–676
Tangent, 420, 429, 519
Term, 16
Transitive property of
equality, 20
Tree diagram, 585
Triangle, area of a, 480, 484
Triangles, reference, 416–417
Triangles, solution of right
triangles, 437–440
by law of cosines, 446–450
by law of sines, 452–460

Trichotomy property, 30
Trigonometric equations,
475–479
Trigonometric formulas
area of triangle, 480, 484
double-angle, 490
half-angle, 494
sum and difference, 487
Trigonometric functions,
509–525, 543
inverse, 526–533
of quadrantal angles, 431
tangent, cotangent,
519–522
secant, cosecant, 523–525
sine, cosine, 509–518
of special angles, 426
Trigonometric identities
basic, 468–471
for complementary angles,
486
negative angle, 489
proving, 472–474
Trinomial, 122
Two-point form of a linear
equation, 68

Unit circle, 429–432, 522
Using the calculator, 25, 55, 94,
211, 241, 391, 508, 563

Variable, 3
Variation, 192–196
Vectors, 497
Vertex of a parabola, 256, 328

x-axis, 48
x-coordinate, 48
x-intercept, 52

y-axis, 48
y-coordinate, 48
y-intercept, 52

Zero
division by, 11
exponent, 197
matrix, 625
property of, in products,
145
Zeros of a function, 313

PREREQUISITE SKILLS FOLLOW-UP

COMPUTER HANDBOOK

TABLES

GLOSSARY

ANSWERS TO CHECKPOINTS

ANSWERS TO SELECTED EXERCISES

INDEX

PHOTO CREDITS

(t) = top   (b) = bottom